Sierra Nevada Ecosystem Project

FINAL REPORT TO CONGRESS

Status of the Sierra Nevada

VOLUME III

Assessments, Commissioned Reports, and Background Information

Wildland Resources Center Report No. 38

CENTERS FOR WATER AND WILDLAND RESOURCES
UNIVERSITY OF CALIFORNIA, DAVIS

June 1996

Sierra Nevada Ecosystem Project: Final Report to Congress
Volume III: *Assessments, Commissioned Reports, and Background Information*
Wildland Resources Center Report No. 38
ISBN 1-887673-02-4

Support for this research was provided by cooperative research agreement with the United States Forest Service Pacific Southwest Research Station and the University of California.

This publication is a continuation in the Wildland Resources Center Reports series. It is published and distributed by the Director's Office of the Centers for Water and Wildland Resources. The Centers sponsor projects in water and wildland resources and related research within the state of California with funds provided by various state and federal agencies and private industry. Copies of this and other reports published by the Centers may be obtained from:

Centers for Water and Wildland Resources
University of California
1323 Academic Surge
Davis, CA 95616-8750
916-752-8070

Copies of the Centers' publications may be examined at the Water Resources Center Archives at 410 O'Brien Hall, Berkeley Campus; 510-642-2666.

Please cite this volume as: *Sierra Nevada Ecosystem Project, Final Report to Congress*, vol. III, *Assessments, Commissioned Reports, and Background Information* (Davis: University of California, Centers for Water and Wildland Resources, 1996).

Cover and title page photographs by Dwight M. Collins.

VOLUME III *Table of Contents*

*Peer reviewed

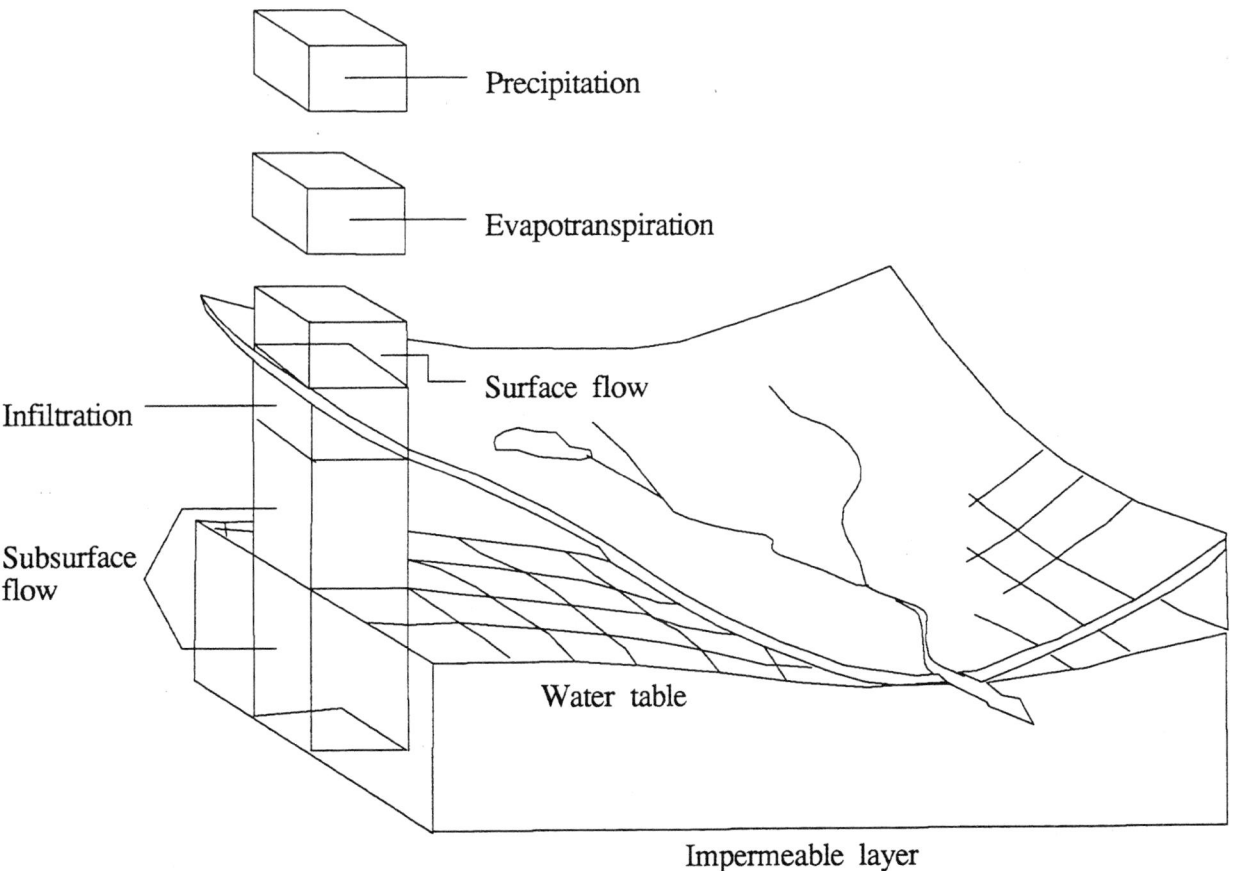

Precipitation

Evapotranspiration

Surface flow

Infiltration

Subsurface flow

Water table

Impermeable layer

Figure 2. Description of the model structure

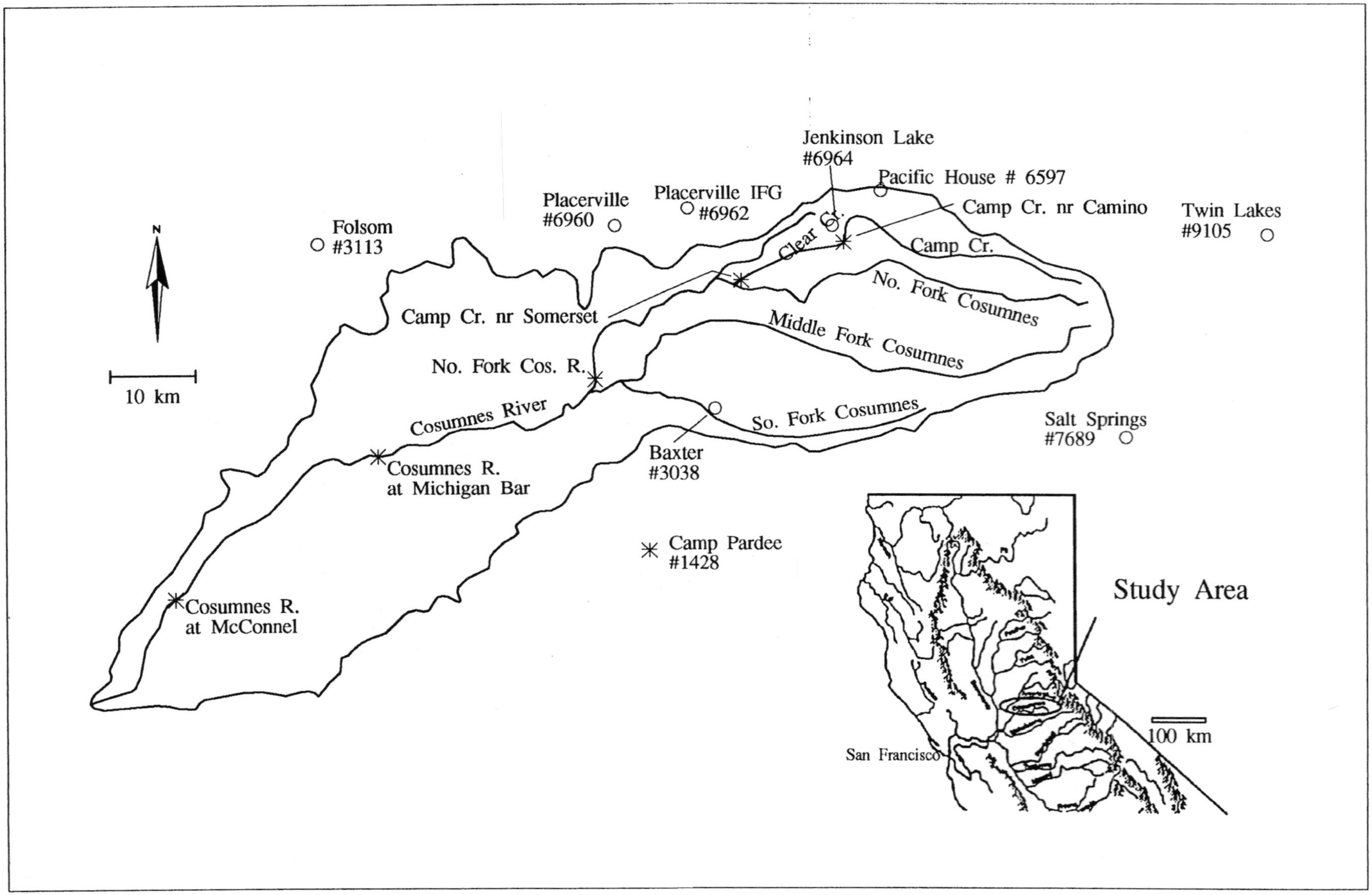

Figure 1. Location of study area and climate (O) and discharge stations (*) in the Cosumnes River basin, California

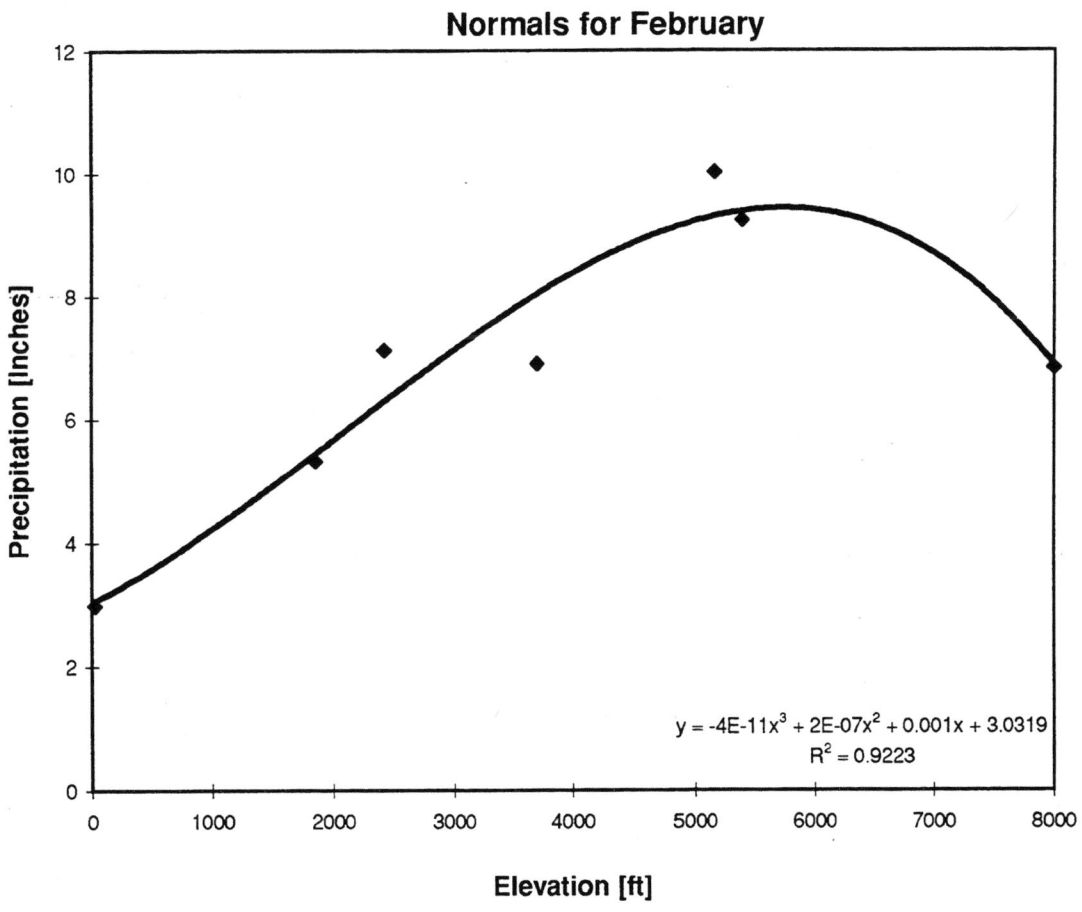

Normals for February

$$y = -4E-11x^3 + 2E-07x^2 + 0.001x + 3.0319$$
$$R^2 = 0.9223$$

Figure 6a. Long term 30 year means for precipitation in May

HYDROLOGY MODEL

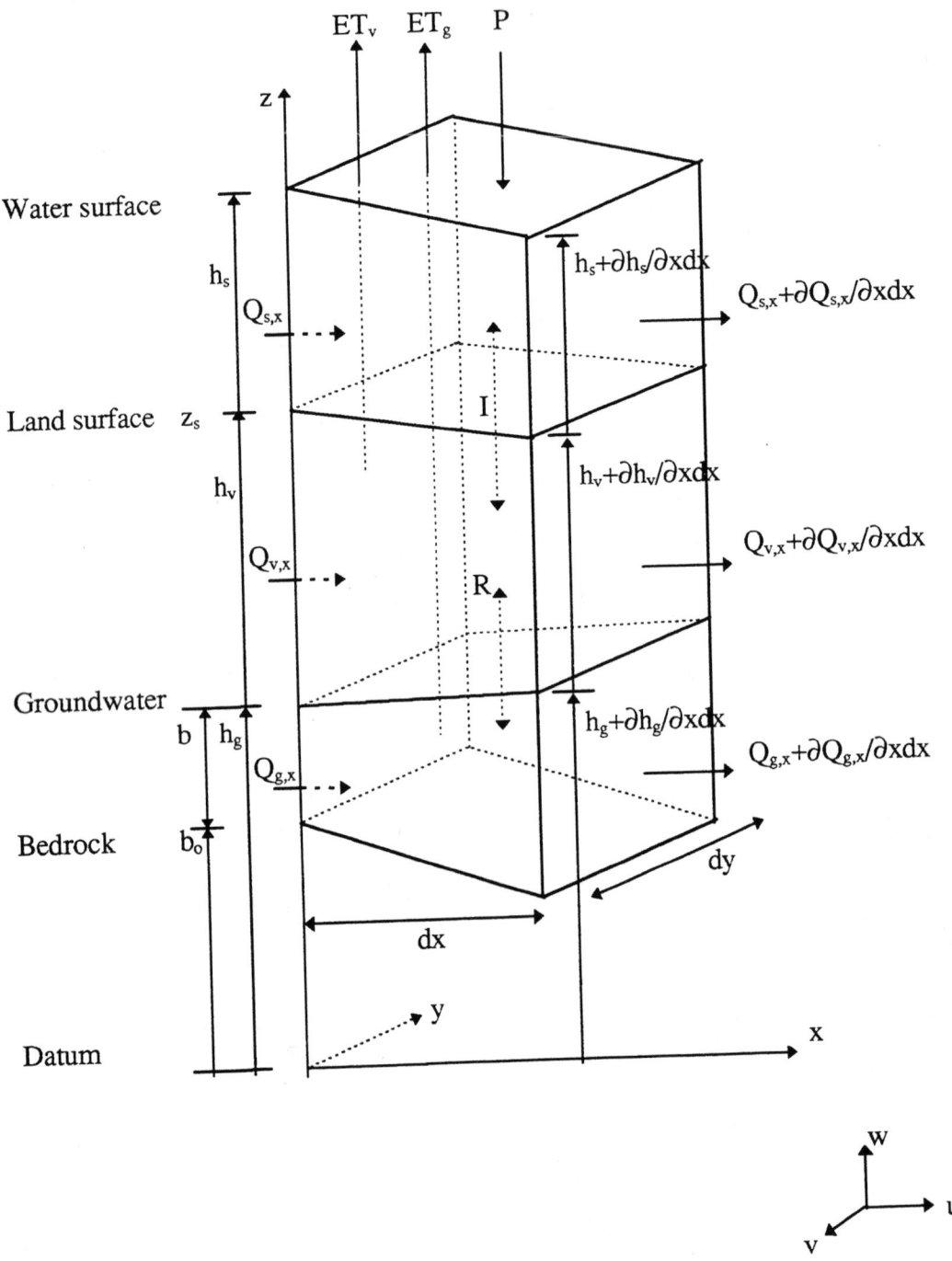

Figure 5. Schematic illustration of the fluxes of water from the atmosphere through the soil. Arrows indicate fluxes and directions of fluxes.

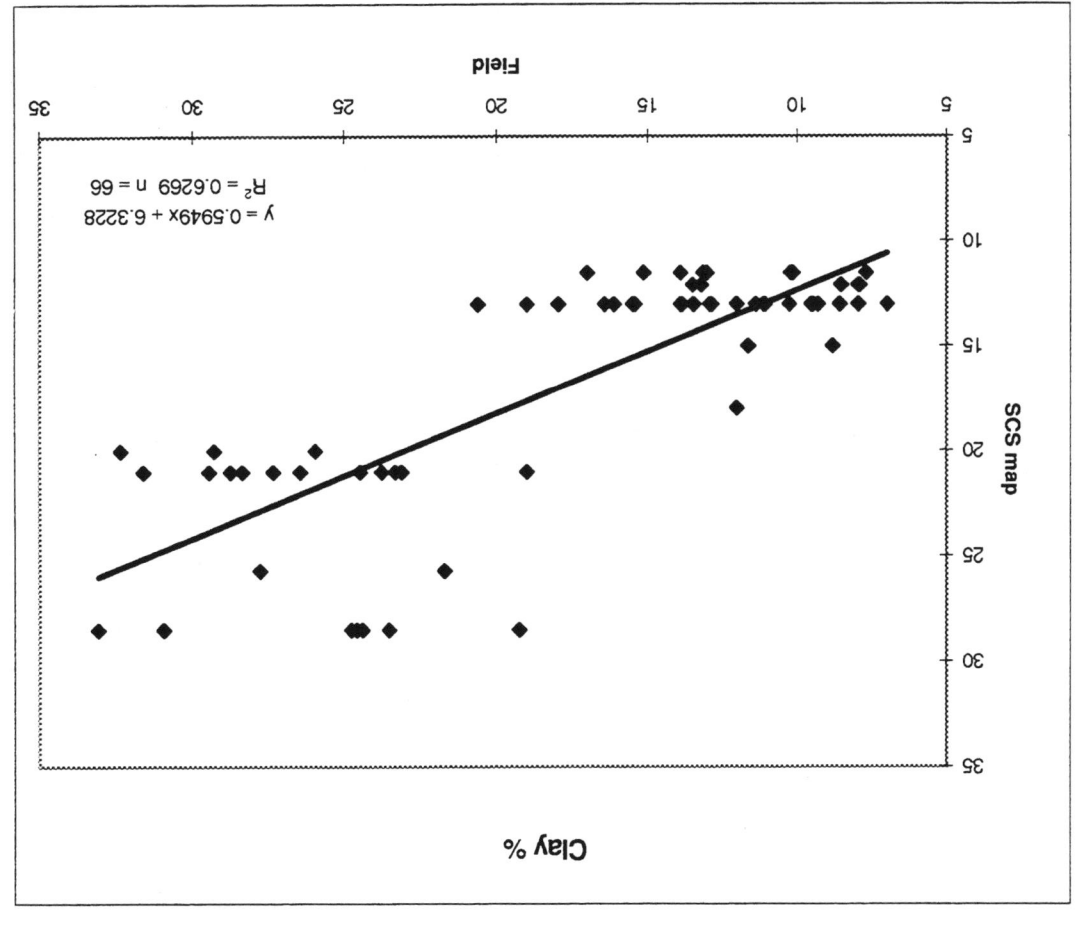

Figure 8a. Measured % clay content at Ecounit sites and predicted % clay estimated from SCS polygons.

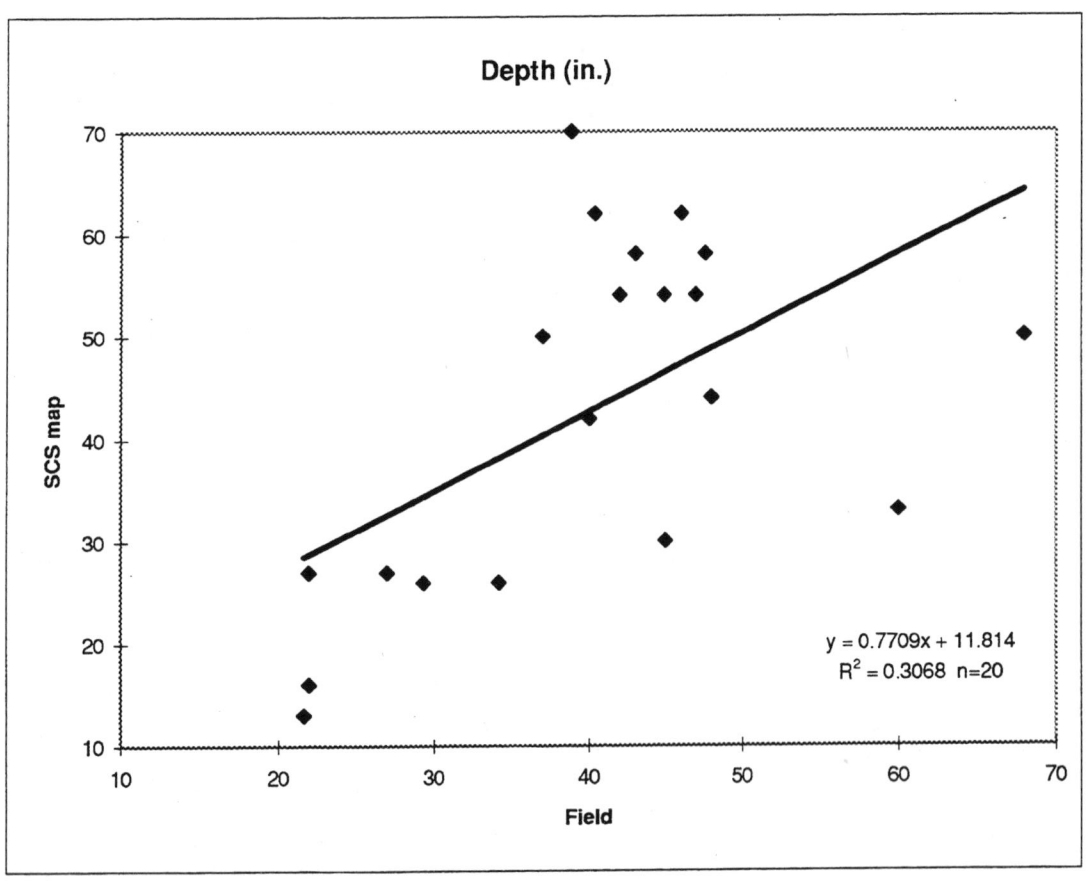

Figure 8b. Measured soil depth from Ecounit sites and estimated from SCS polygon

Subsurface Velocity

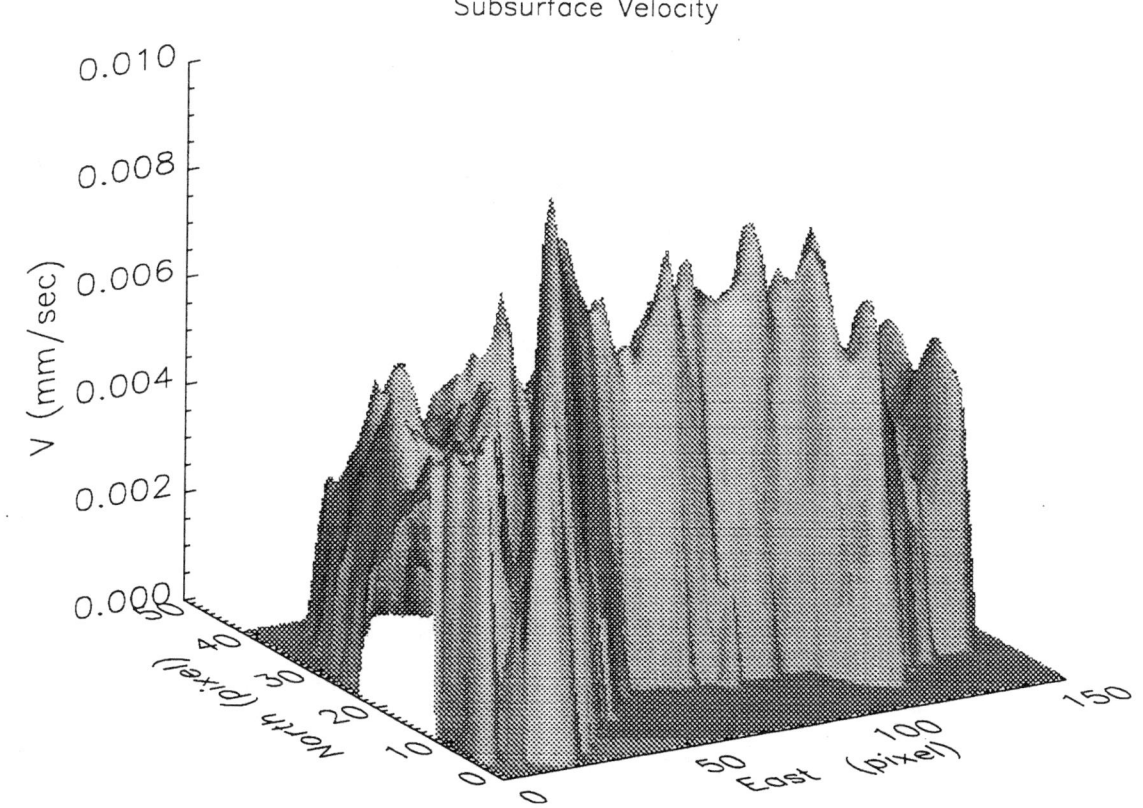

Figure 20.   Subsurface velocity

Soil Type

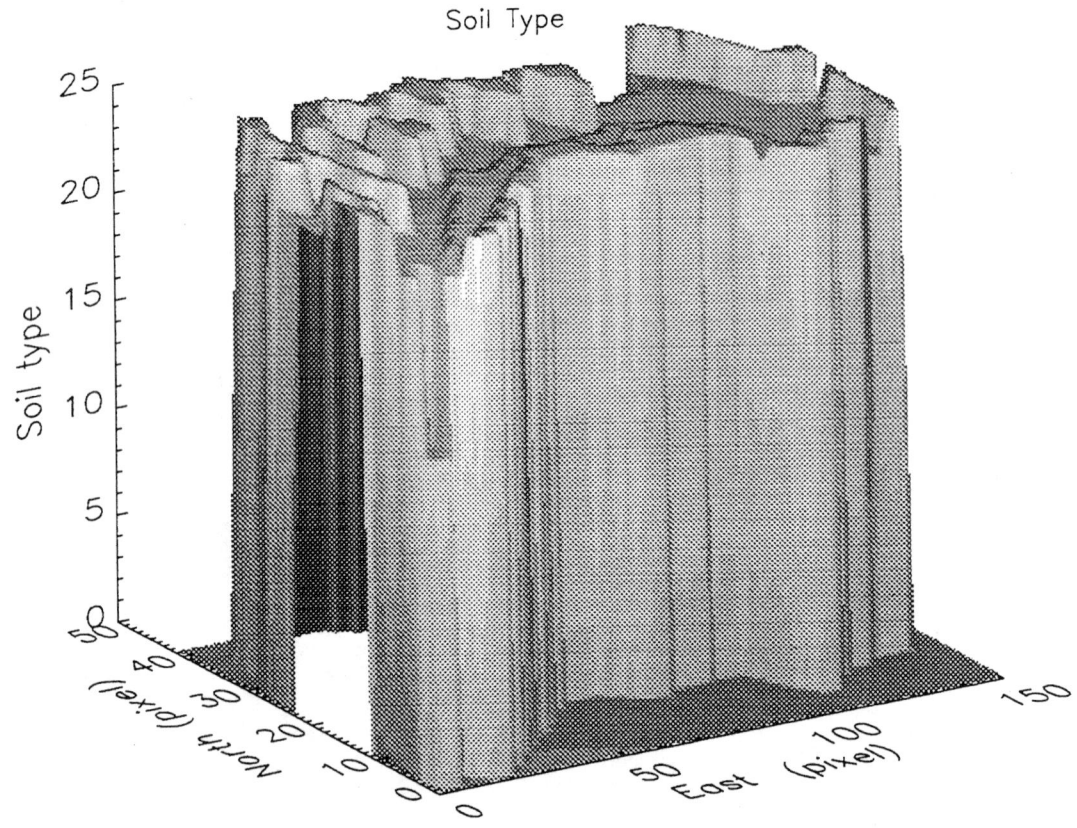

Figure 21. Soil type

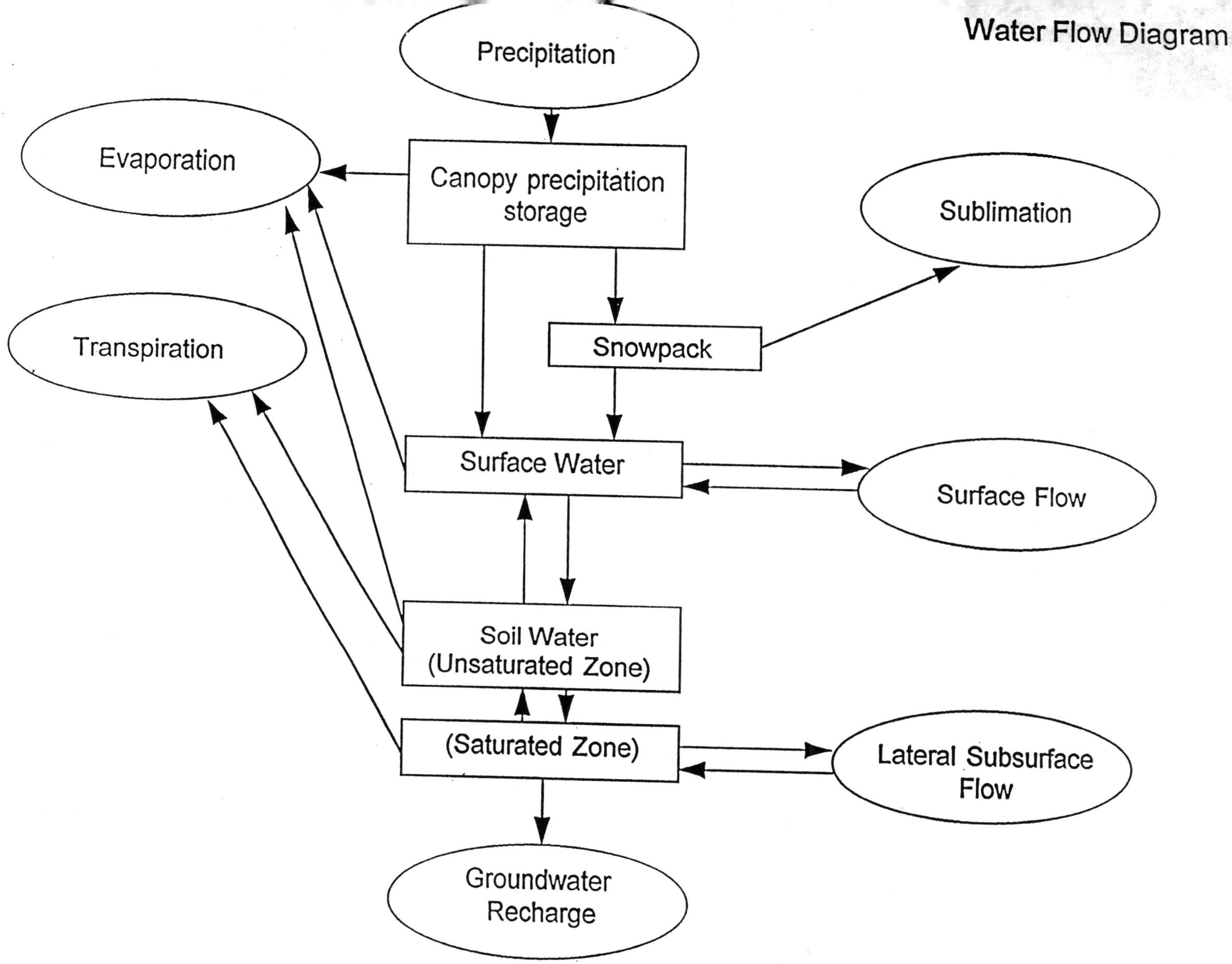

Water Flow Diagram

Figure 4. Diagrametric represtentaiton of the different sub-models within the Ecohydrologic Model.

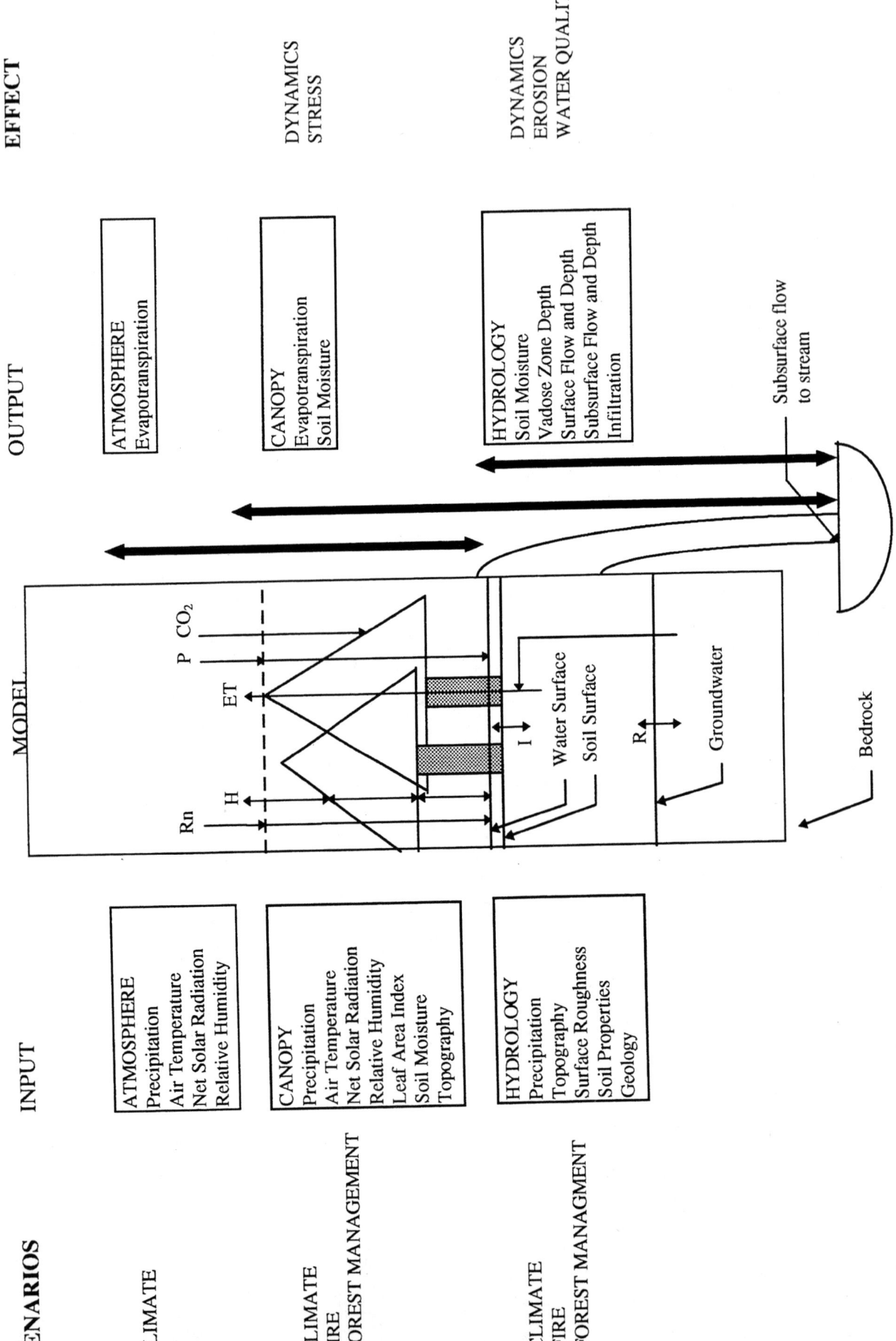

Figure 3. Schematic diagram showing the paths of water flow into and out of a cell with a description of input and output variables. Possible scenarios that could be used to drive the model are shown as are possible effects outputs.

Water Table

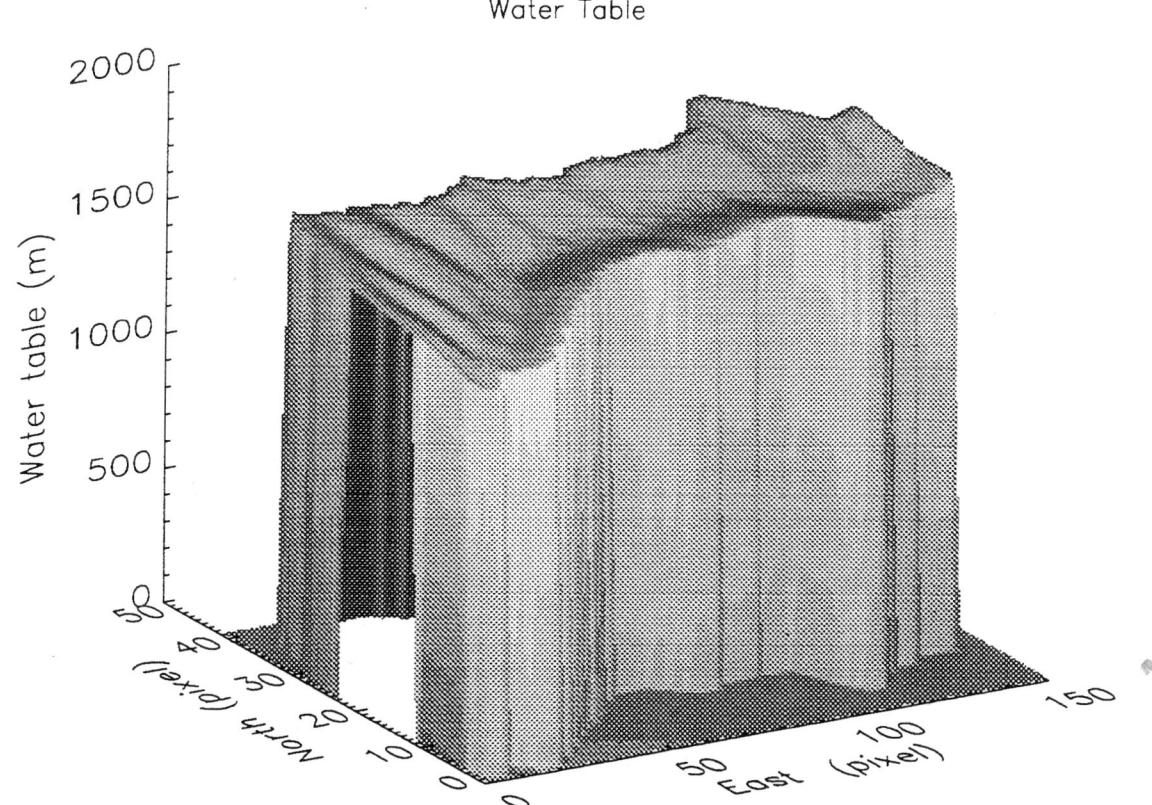

Figure 19.   Water table (with bedrock)

Surface Velocity

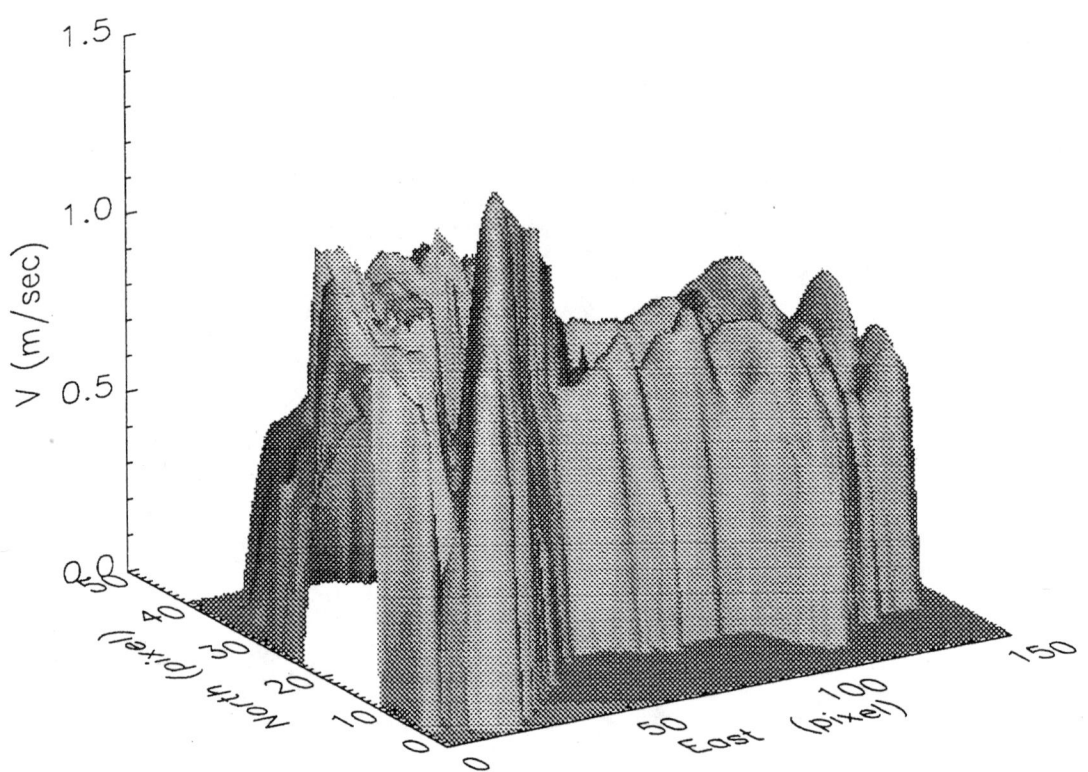

Figure 18.   Surface velocity

Surface Water Ponding Depth

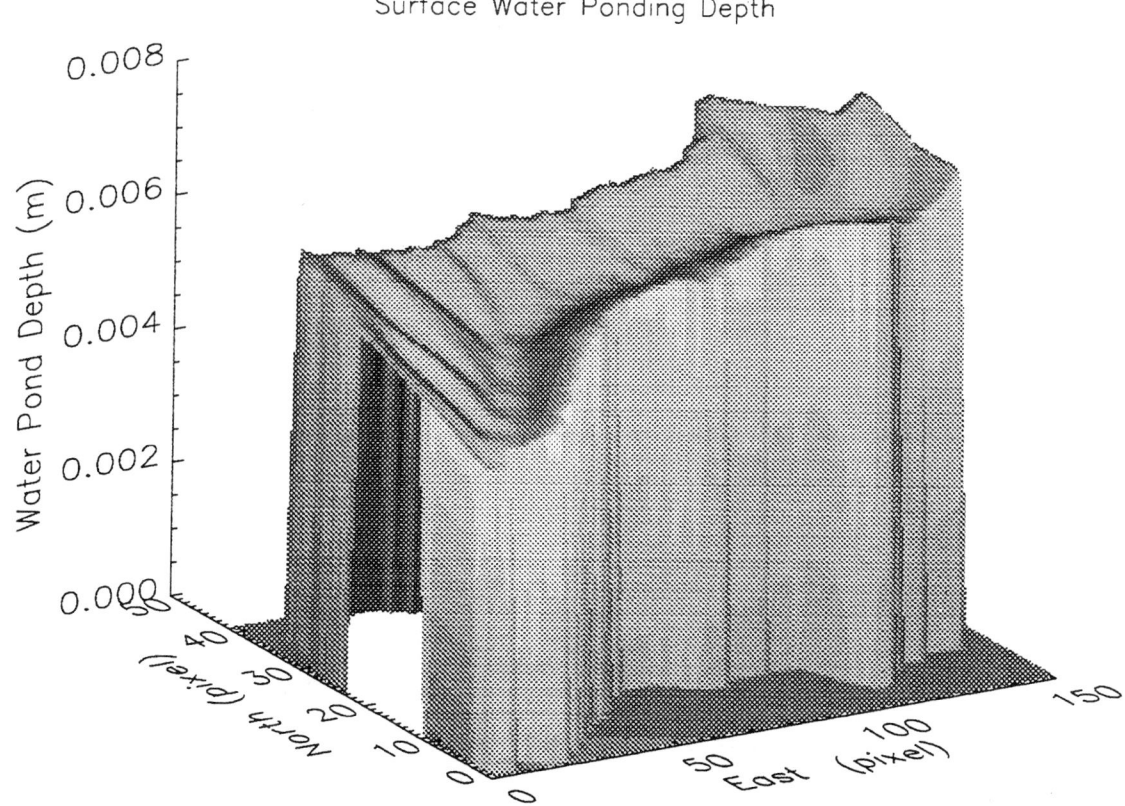

Figure 17.   Surface Water Ponding Depth

LAI
(Snow Creek, CA)

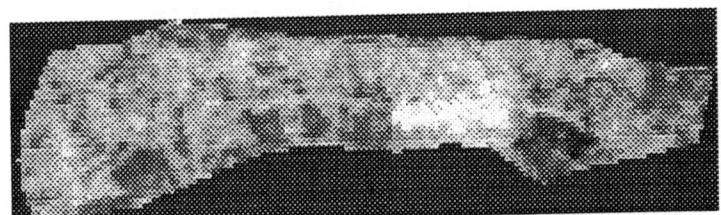

(Data derived from 1994 TM data)

Figure 16. Snow Creek LAI

Snow Creek

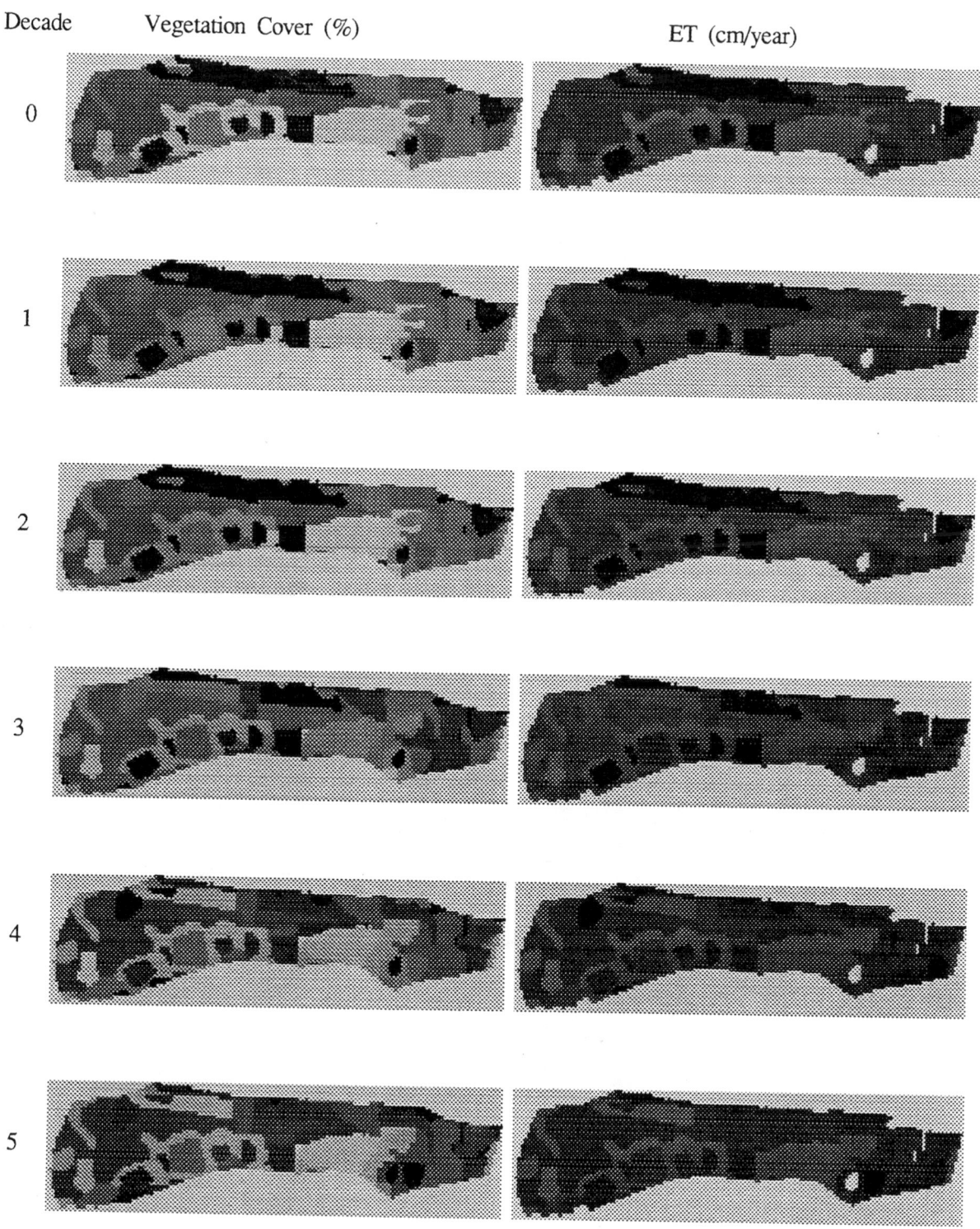

Figure 15. Current Vegetation Cover and Annual Evapotranspiration during the 1995 water year and projected forest growth under the Cal Owl Option A scenario as estimated from PROGNOSIS. Predicted annual evapotranspiration estimated from the ecohydrologic Model.

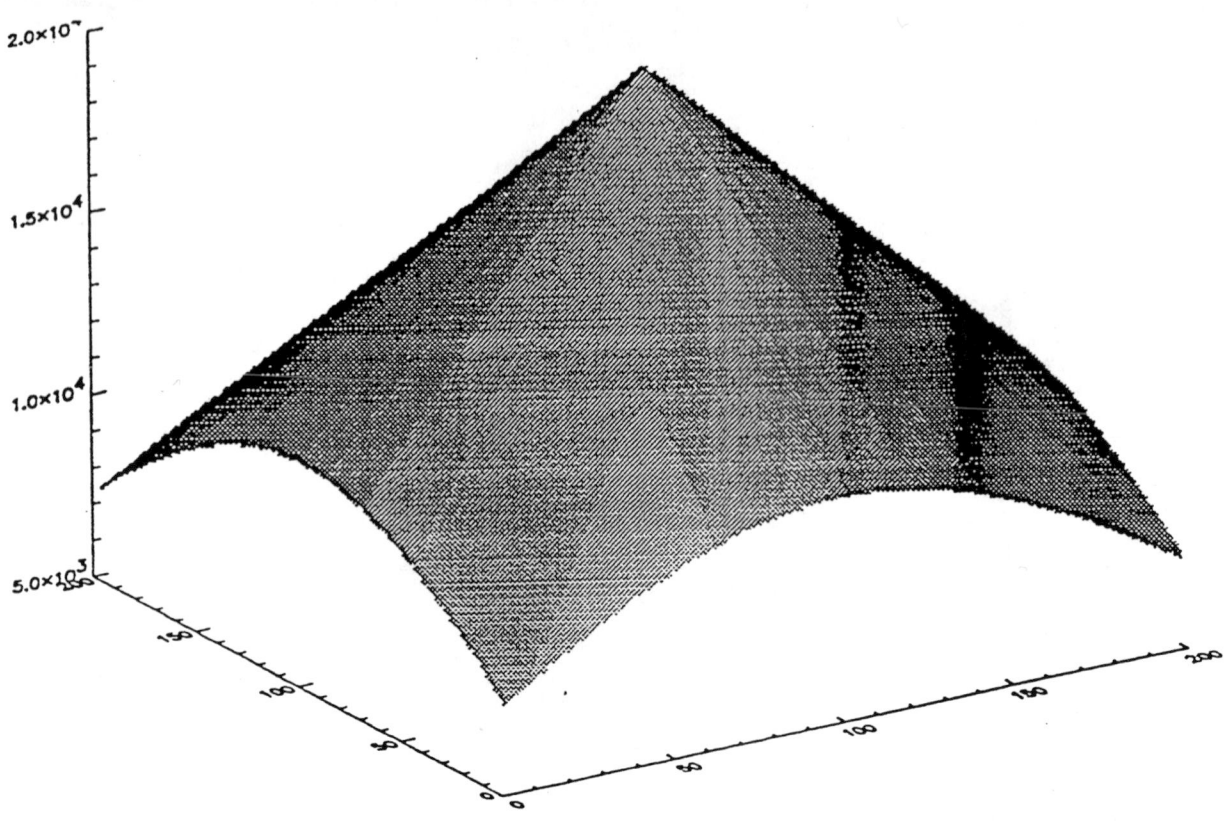

Figure 13.   Synthetic DEM created to test the hydrology runoff sub-models.

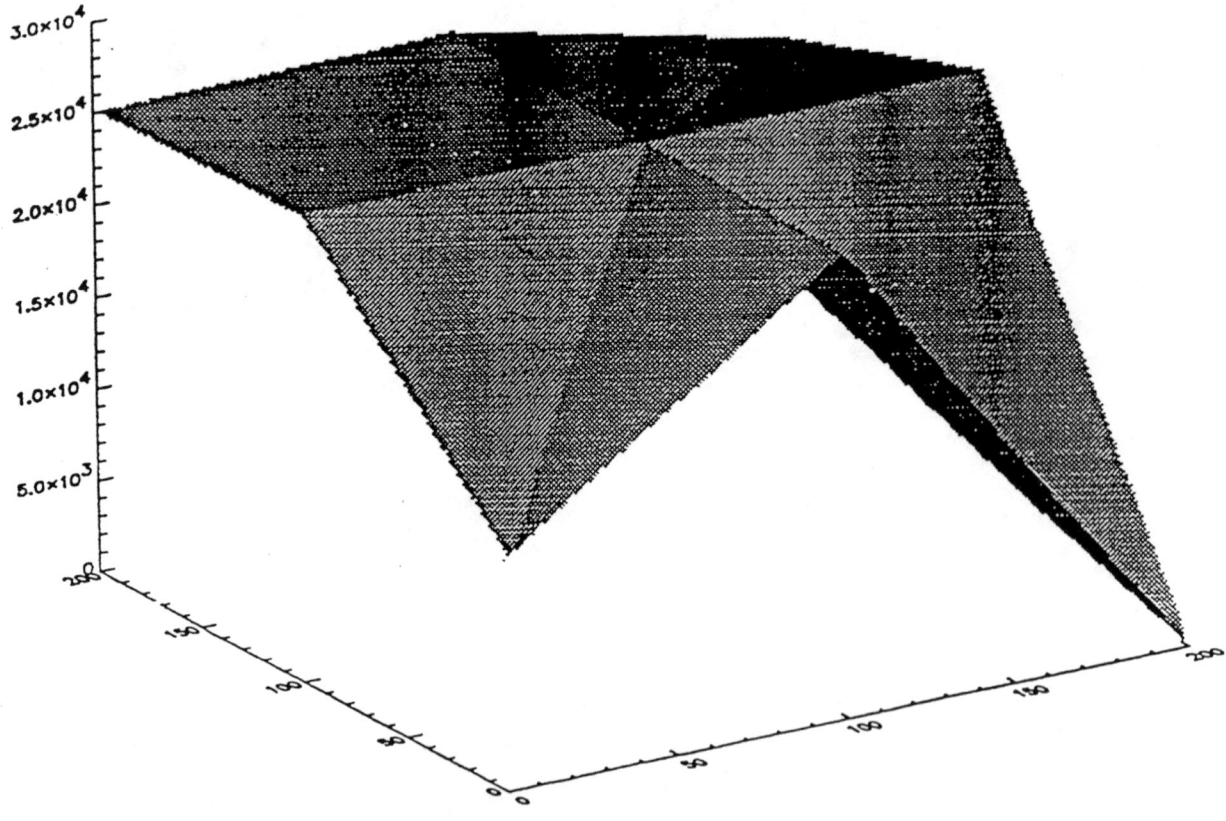

Figure 14.   Synthetic DEM to provide test of variable slopes and aspects.

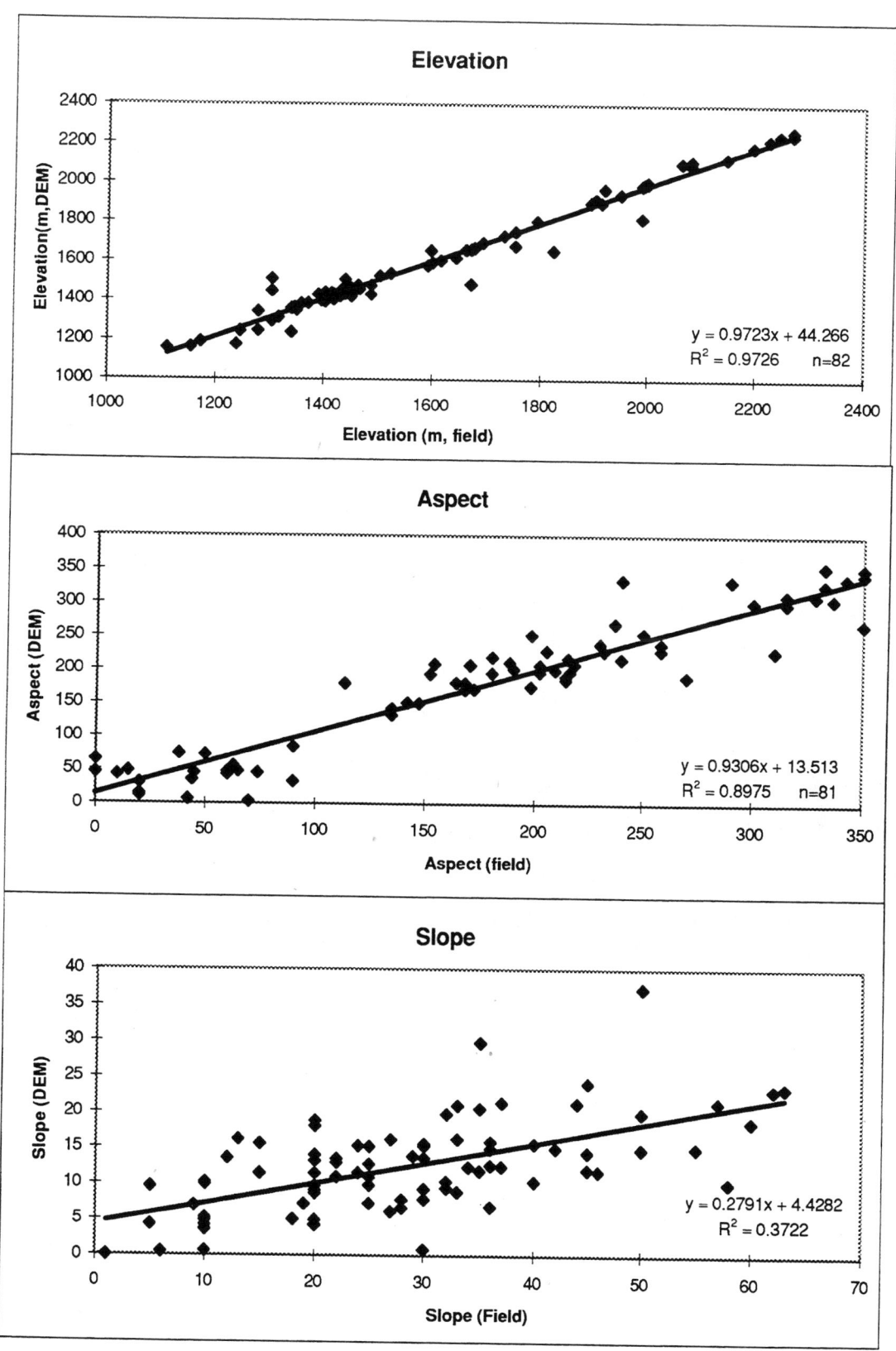

Figure 9. Test DEM, Aspect, and Slope

DEM

(Camp Creek, CA)

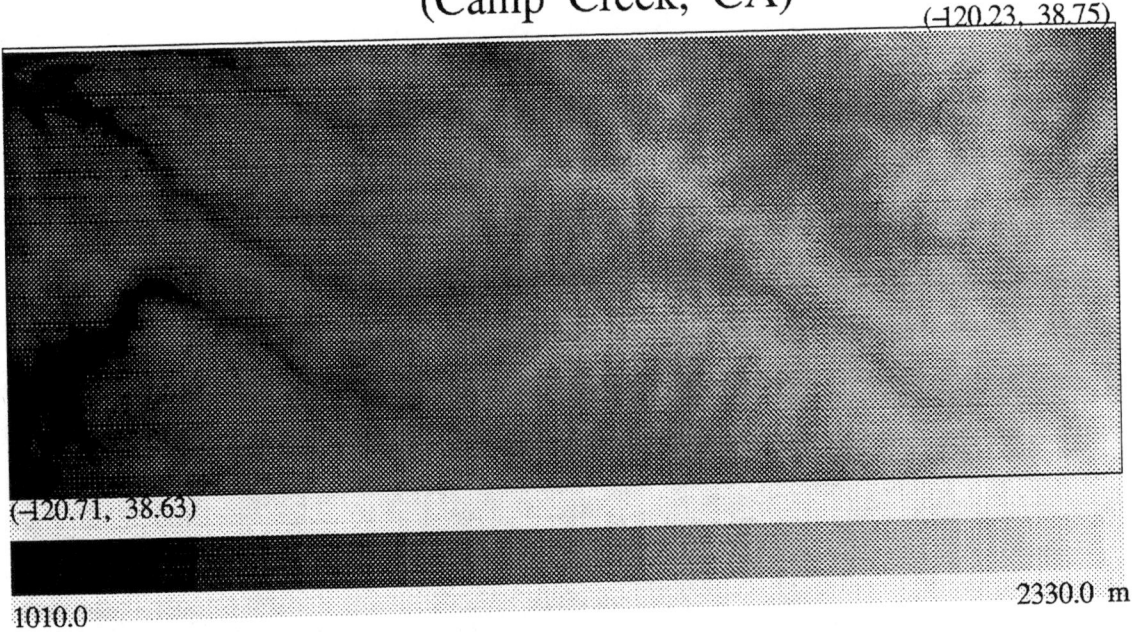

(−120.23, 38.75)

(−120.71, 38.63)

1010.0

2330.0 m

Figure 10. Camp Creek

DEM
(Snow Creek, CA)

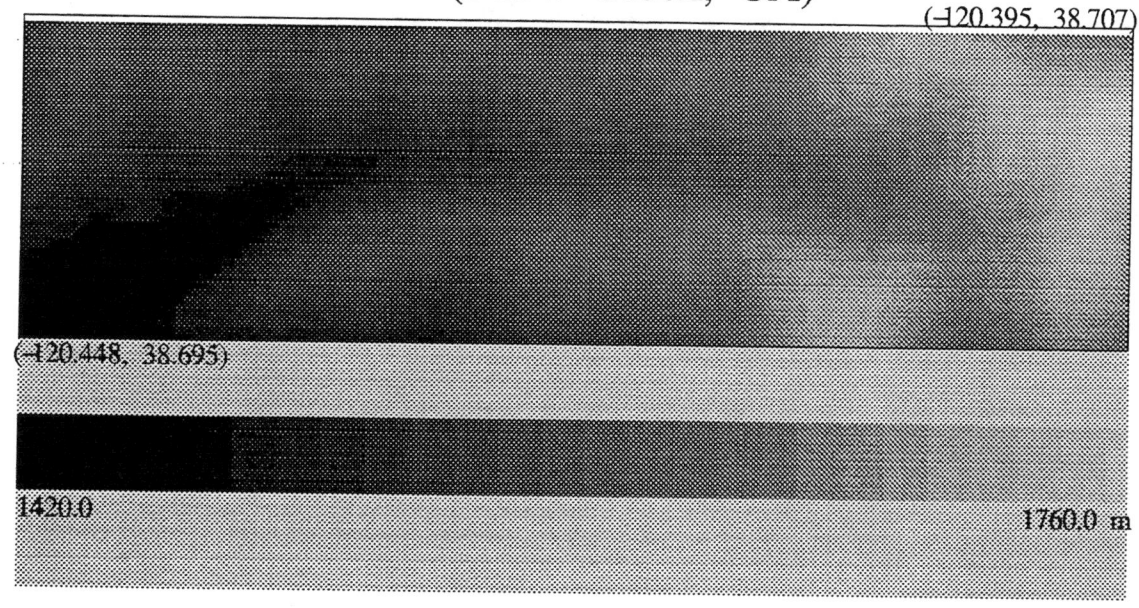

Figure 11. Snow Creek

DEM

(Pebble Creek, CA)

(-120.409, 38.700)

(-120.448, 38.688)

1420.0   1710.0 m

Figure 12.   Pebble Creek

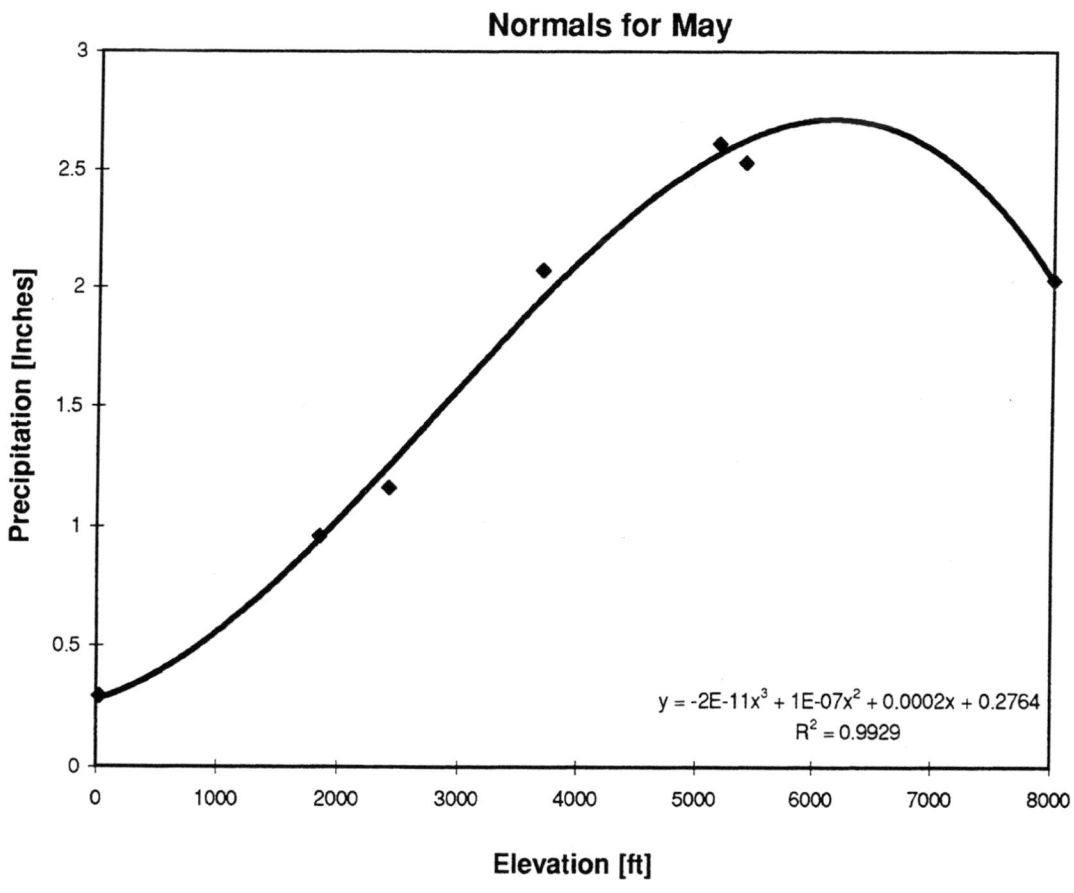

Figure 6b. Long term 30 year means for precipitation in May

Predicted Precipitation at El Camino

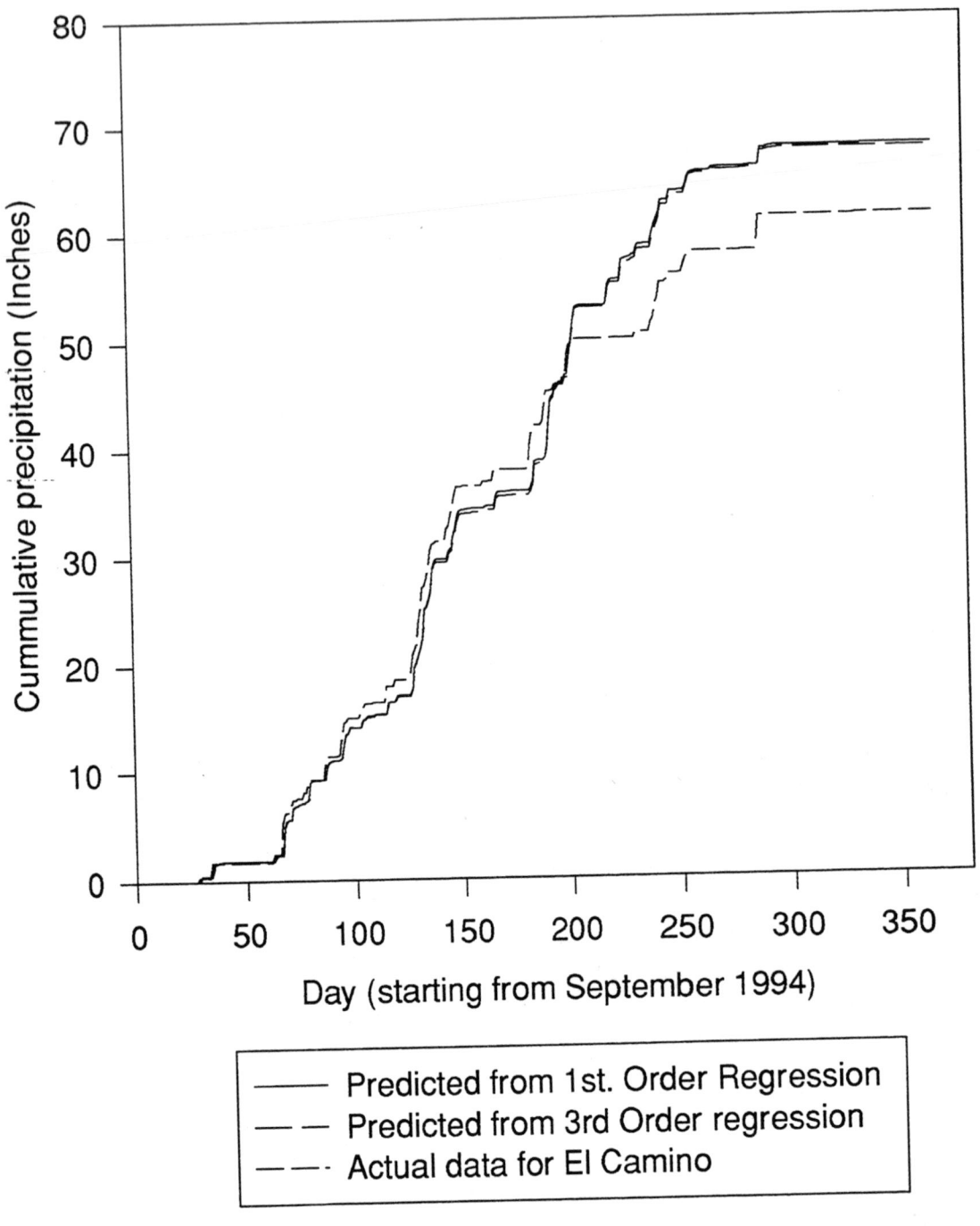

Figure 7. Rainfall predicted for El Camino site and actual cumulative rainfall measured in the 1995 rain year (Sept. 1,1994 - August 31,1995)

Preface

This volume contains the commissioned background reports, assessment chapters received too late to include in volume II, Science Team workshops, and other background materials for the Sierra Nevada Ecosystem Project (SNEP). Several of the reports have been peer reviewed and are so noted in the table of contents.

Three of the larger reports (Elliott-Fisk and colleagues; Ustin and colleagues) in this volume are special case studies. Part of the congressional guidance for the SNEP included direction to examine the mediated settlement agreement for giant sequoia groves (see preface, volume I). A review and assessment of the substantial body of information on giant sequoia and mapping of groves needed for the examination of the agreement is presented in this volume. Management implications and recommendations for giant sequoia ecosystems are summarized in volume I and ecology of giant sequoia is reported in volume II. Another major case study review included the Lake Tahoe ecosystem. This region is remarkable for the scope and duration of scientific research and policy development. Our case study could not cover adequately all of this enormous body of knowledge and experience but it does review some of the important lessons and information from this long-term attempt at ecosystem management.

Two other chapters in this volume represent major peer reviewed assessments that because of their scope and extensive data collection could not be completed until late in the process. These reports—economic conditions by Stewart and colleagues and rangeland conditions by Menke—bring together for the first time basic information on conditions and trends for the Sierra Nevada region.

The project also chose to examine a few areas in greater detail than elsewhere in the Sierra in order to develop and test improved models. The Camp Creek/Clear Creek basin, largely within the Eldorado National Forest, was selected as one of the areas. Several of the reports in volume II use this region, and a new generation ecohydrological model presented here in volume III by Ustin and colleagues used the spatial data from this watershed. This model can be used to simulate hydrologic processes at time intervals from seconds to days and at a spatial scale of 30 m by 30 m. Such modeling and resolution will become a new means of examining the possible consequences of alternative land use, vegetation modification, and climate change on hydrologic processes.

Other reports in volume III provide additional background for the aquatic sections of the project and for forest management. Here, too, extensive analyses of particular areas, such as the compilation of all known records of salmon distribution prior to major dams, the record of tree plantations on Sierran national forests, and the results of experimental forest management on the University of California Blodgett Experimental Forest are significant summaries.

The final section of this volume lists the topics and participants in our major workshops. These and many other less formal meetings and workgroups were essential to our work and contributed to our understanding of the system. Because of this substantial body of additional work, no single summary report can adequately cover the depth and richness of information developed by the contributors; we urge our readers to give these chapters and those in Volume II careful study.

DON C. ERMAN
Team Leader

PETER B. MOYLE
Department of Wildlife, Fish, and
  Conservation Biology
University of California
Davis, California

RICHARD KATTELMANN
Sierra Nevada Aquatic Research
  Laboratory
University of California
Mammoth Lakes, California

ROBERT ZOMER
Department of Land, Air and Water
University of California
Davis, California

PAUL J. RANDALL
Department of Wildlife, Fish, and
  Conservation Biology
University of California
Davis, California

1

Management of Riparian Areas in the Sierra Nevada

ABSTRACT

Because the ecological importance of riparian areas has long been recognized, many management schemes are in place or have been proposed to protect them. This report (1) reviews riparian management guidelines presently used or recommended for use in the Sierra Nevada, (2) summarizes general management goals for riparian areas presented in the literature, (3) presents some broad management prescriptions offering different levels of protection for riparian areas, for use until more site-specific prescriptions are in place,(4) provides a rating system for prioritizing riparian areas for management, and (5)provides suggestions for the development site-specific prescriptions for riparian protection and management. This report is designed to supplement other SNEP assessments of riparian resources (Kattelmann and Embury 1996; Kondolf et al. 1996 Menning et al. 1996).

INTRODUCTION

Riparian areas are usually defined as three-dimensional zones of direct interaction between terrestrial and aquatic ecosystems (Carlson et al., 1991, Gregory et al. 1991, Swanson et al. 1982, Kattelmann and Embury 1996). Riparian areas occur along all types of waterways, including streams, meadows, flood plains, peatlands, marshes, springs, and lake shores. Ecologically, each riparian area encompasses the aquatic ecosystem as well as adjacent terrestrial areas directly affecting the aquatic system (Carlson et al., 1991). The width of the riparian area varies with hydrology, geomorphology, vegetation, and upland conditions and processes (Cowardin et al. 1979; Ratliff 1982; Youngblood et al., 1985 a,b; Pierce and Johnson 1986: Hansen et al. 1987; Kovalchik 1987; Padgett et al. 1990; Kovalchik and Chitwood 1990, Belt et al. 1992), so that definitions for the purpose of management also vary (Appendix A). All natural riparian areas are highly sensitive to human-related disturbance, especially the portions closest to water. They often contain some of the most altered habitats in the Sierra Nevada and need special protection and management. Riparian areas also are among the most resilient habitats/ ecosystems in the range and they respond well to recovery programs (Kattelmann and Embury 1996; Kondolf et al. 1996).

Because riparian areas are so sensitive to disturbance, their management has to focus not only on the obvious zone of riparian vegetation immediately adjacent to the water body, but on a broader region that has direct influence on the water body. Erman et al (1996) suggest that this broader area can be viewed as having three overlapping zones; these zones are defined in relation to their influence on the adjacent aquatic ecosystem: (1) Community Influence Zone, (2) Energy Influence Zone, and (3) Land Use Influence Zone. The Community Influence Zone is the area usually recognized as clearly riparian, with its distinctive flora and fauna and with many organisms that use both terrestrial and aquatic habitats on a regular basis (e.g., aquatic insects, amphibians, waterfowl). The Energy Influence Zone includes all the riparian area that is likely to contribute energy and structure to the aquatic ecosystem. It usually encompasses the Community Influence Zone plus all the land as far from the stream as the tallest tree (if trees are present) that can contribute snags and leaves to the stream. The Land Use Influence Zone is the region along a stream in which human activity is likely to influence the aquatic ecosystem by increasing nutrient and sediment inputs and other factors. It includes both the other zones and may encompass much of a watershed, especially in smaller drainages. In general, the closer some human activity, such as road building, is to the aquatic ecosystem, the more restrictions have to be placed on that activity if the stream or lake is to continue to maintain its fish, amphibian, and invertebrate productivity and diversity. Likewise, the more such activity concentrates in or near the Community Influence Zone, the more it will alter both riparian and aquatic ecosystems.

Because the ecological importance of riparian areas has long been recognized, many management schemes are in place or have been proposed to protect them. The purpose of this report is to (1) review riparian management guidelines presently used or recommended for use in the Sierra Nevada, (2) present general management goals for riparian systems,(3) provide a rating system for prioritizing riparian areas for management, (4) present some broad management options that offer different levels of protection, and (5) provide suggestions for the development site-specific prescriptions for riparian protection and management.

3

RIPARIAN MANAGEMENT GUIDELINES

The purpose of this section is to review current policies on the use and management of streamside management zones in the Sierra Nevada Ecosystem Project area. In general, there seems to be a consensus among agencies concerned with riparian management that site-specific guidelines are required for best management but that interim guidelines are needed until site-specific assessments are completed (Appendix B). Interim guidelines are in place in National Forests in the SNEP area because few site-specific studies have been completed. Outside the forests, few guidelines exist, although there are numerous regulations that can be applied to riparian areas (Appendix C).

Present USDA Forest Service policy recognizes the importance and unique values of riparian ecosystems, as well as the importance of classification, inventory, and delineation of riparian ecosystems for land-management planning (Kovalchik and Chitwood 1990, McGuire 1977). Guidelines for establishing riparian and stream management zones emphasize the importance of delineating the zones based on functional characteristics. Generally, a zone or buffer strip based upon a set horizontal distance from the aquatic habitat has been instituted or proposed to define both interim riparian and streamside management zones. In most cases, riparian zones also include meadows, wetlands, seeps, and peatlands. Often the interim guidelines are based on studies of stream recovery rates for macroinvertebrate assemblages following logging. In particular, for small streams, the results of the studies by Erman et al (1977) and Erman and Mahoney (1983) that a 30 meter (minimum) buffer strip on each side was needed to protect the aquatic habitats is used as the basis for interim guidelines.

RIPARIAN MANAGEMENT GOALS

Management goals for riparian areas on national forest lands are imbedded in a complex set of legal directives and administrative procedures (FFRAP 1988), only a few of which can be mentioned here. Historically, national policy (as established by the Organic Act of 1897) caused forests to be managed primarily for timberland protection, despite provisions in the act for maintaining stream flow. The Multiple Use-Sustained Yield Act (1960), a cornerstone of Forest Service management, required federal lands be managed for long-term sustainable production and emphasized a multi-purpose management approach, including managing the forests for outdoor recreation, range, timber, watersheds, wilderness, wildlife and fish. The Wilderness Act of 1964 required that qualified lands be designated as wilderness areas with restrictions on use, although livestock grazing (which heavily impacts riparian areas) was allowed to continue. Under the National Environmental Policy Act (NEPA) of 1970, all federal agencies, including USFS, were required to formally consider the environmental impacts of their actions before decisions were made. A detailed environmental impact statement must be prepared if major environmental effects are anticipated.

The Forest and Rangeland Renewable Resources Planning Act (RPA) and the National Forest Management Act (NFMA), established the mid-1970's a three-level planning process.

Regulations issued under the NFMA required that fish and wildlife habitat should be managed to maintain "viable" populations of existing native and desired nonnative vertebrate species within planning areas (36 CFR Ch.II; 7-1-91 Edition, 219.19) Each national forest is required to prepare an individual forest plan based on the national and regional planning direction, legal requirements, and an assessment of forest conditions and demands. Included in these plans are basic inventory information, analyses of the forests's management environment, and an examination of management alternatives. NFMA regulations provide for public input on draft and final plans, and an appeals process with recourse to the courts.

In recent years, the shifts in public perceptions and expectations concerning resource management on federal lands have led to a gradual increase in protection of ecosystems and species, and to an increase in concern for riparian areas. Statutory requirements to protect water quality, wildlife habitat, and endangered species provide significant legislative restrictions on use. For example, states are required under Section 208 of the Federal Clean Water Act to prepare non-point source pollution treatment plans. The Porter-Cologne Water Quality Control Act designates the State Water Resources Control Board (SWRCB) as the state water pollution control agency. It is responsible for certification of the procedures outlined in the Forest Service water quality handbook as best management practices (BMP's).

The federal Endangered Species Act of 1973 initiates mechanisms which may supersede other planning processes as demonstrated by the Spotted Owl controversy in the Pacific Northwest and in California. Listing by the State of California of an animal or plant species as threatened or endangered requires USFS to provide protection even if the species is not included under the federal ESA. The ESA is especially important in relation to riparian habitat because so many endangered plants and animals are riparian-dependent.

As pressures to manage for environmental values grow, management activities increasingly require coordination between state and federal agencies, in order to address issues such as overlapping jurisdictions and mixed-ownerships. For instance, the California Department of Fish and Game (CDFG) retains the right to manage fish and wildlife game species across ownerships, including on federal and private lands.

Generally, USFS policies for management of riparian areas have become more protective in recent years (Appendix B). In particular, timber harvest has been increasingly limited near water courses and road engineering has improved. Grazing has been identified as a concern, but management changes have not been extensive (Menke 1996). Impacts from water development and recreation have received less attention. Water development and grazing have a greater direct effect on riparian resources than timber harvesting in the Sierra Nevada (Kattelmann and Embury 1996; Kondolf et al. 1996). Damage from impacts of the past have been identified, but restoration has been hampered by limited financial resources. Under minimum management requirements of the Forest Service manual:

"national direction is to manage the resources within riparian areas [defined as 100 feet on either side of perennial stream or lake edges] in a manner that is compatible with protection and maintenance of dependent resources, and give preferential treatment to dependent resources in cases of unresolved conflict."

Many more specific goals and management directives, applicable to the Sierra Nevada have appeared in the manuals and reports of various agencies (Appendix D). The goals have been combined and condensed into a single list (Table 1). They assume that self-sustaining riparian and aquatic systems dominated by native elements represent the ideal condition. Additional information about laws and regulations can be found in Menning et al (1996).

Table 1. Some general goals for management of riparian systems. Not listed in order of importance.

Goal 1. Identify and provide special protection for unusual/rare aquatic and riparian habitats and for rare, threatened, and endangered species that require riparian areas.

Goal 2. Maintain and restore wherever possible continuous corridors of riparian and upland habitat along streams for wildlife movement and migration.

Goal 3. Identify riparian areas that are in best condition (i.e., areas dominated by native species, with most natural ecosystem structure and processes intact) and give such areas the highest priority for formal protection and intense management.

Goal 4. Maintain water quality parameters (temperature, sediment load, pH, etc.) in associated water bodies within the natural range of variability for each water body.

Goal 5. Maintain or restore stream channel, pond, lake, and wetland ecological integrity and natural processes to within the natural range of conditions.

Goal 6. Maintain or restore stream channel or subsurface flows to levels that (1) support the natural riparian and aquatic biotic systems and that (2) maintain the natural functions of stream channels and aquifers.

Goal 7. Maintain or restore the natural elevation, size, and lateral extent of subsurface water in meadows and wetlands.

Goal 8. Maintain or restore the natural structure, diversity, and productivity of native riparian plant communities.

Goal 9. Maintain or restore stands of large riparian trees in order to provide large woody debris for instream habitat.

Goal 10. Maintain or restore riparian corridors to support well-distributed populations of plants and animals that depend on riparian and aquatic habitats for their movements and long-term survival.

A PRIORITY RATING SYSTEM FOR MANAGEMENT OF RIPARIAN AREAS

The goals listed in the previous section focus on natural riparian systems, assuming that complex structure and native species are a desirable attribute of riparian systems. Unfortunately, there are many areas where the riparian vegetation has been irreversibly altered or destroyed through major habitat alteration or through removal of the water from the associated aquatic system. Other riparian areas have been severely damaged but can be recovered through varying degrees of effort. Given the limited money and energy available for protection and recovery efforts, priorities must be set for action. The rating system presented below is designed to help set priorities for areas where the main goal is to restore and/or protect natural riparian systems. It may be necessary to develop somewhat different criteria for different riparian areas. Ideally, a more quantitative index of riparian integrity should also be developed for more precise (but still rapid) assessment, based on measurements of factors such as canopy cover, abundance of native species, and degree of disturbance.

Priority 1.

Highest priority for protection and management. Near-pristine and self-sustaining. Very uncommon. Found along waterways where natural hydrology is intact. Potential natural vegetation is present, e.g., full complement of native species expected for the seral stage present and exotic species rare. Human-related disturbance minimal although may have been extensive in past. Associated with healthy, natural aquatic systems. Part of a riparian corridor, although much of corridor may have lower ratings. Provides high level of ecosystem services (protection of water quality, stream bank stabilization, source of organic matter for aquatic system, habitat for wildlife, etc.).

Priority 2.

High quality riparian habitat associated with a fairly continuous corridor or otherwise part of a larger system. Self-sustaining. Potential natural vegetation dominant but some exotics present also, usually integrated into the native plant community. Human-related disturbance minimal in most areas and probably more extensive in past. Aquatic system typically in good condition. Provides high level of ecosystem services (as above).

Priority 3.

Adequate to moderately high quality riparian habitat, which is probably recoverable to the potential natural vegetation with major effort. Exotic species present, often significant part of community. Typically part of extensive riparian corridor which may be fragmented. Aquatic system appears to be functioning naturally, but likely to be altered (exotic species, modified flow regime, etc.). Provides moderately high level of ecosystem services but effects likely to be fairly localized. Shows effects of moderate to high levels of use by humans and livestock. Isolated patches of riparian habitat that would rate "1" or "2" if part of a larger system would be rated here, on the assumption such patches cannot persist without major recovery efforts focussed on associated riparian areas.

<u>Priority 4</u>.

Highly altered riparian systems with natural elements still present but probably not recoverable to potential natural vegetation, or only with tremendous effort. Exotic species major part of community, often dominant. Typically associated with highly altered aquatic system, with highly modified flow regime. Highly altered by use by humans and livestock (crumbling banks, roads, limited understory, etc.). Often in isolated fragments among even more degraded habitats but may be important as part of corridor associated with higher quality habitats. Can provide some ecosystem services, but potential very limited.

<u>Priority 5</u>.

Irreversibly altered riparian systems, in which riparian vegetation greatly restricted in quality and quantity, if present at all. Exotic species often dominate. Associated with highly altered aquatic systems. Typical example is channelized stream with road along one bank, railroad along another with dams diverting much of the flow of the stream. \

POTENTIAL INTERIM MANAGEMENT PRESCRIPTIONS

Ideally, riparian habitats and streamside zones should be managed on a highly individualistic basis, taking into account terrain, soils, plant communities, fish and wildlife requirements and other factors arising from intimate knowledge of the local situation. Because such site-specific knowledge of the structure and function of Sierra Nevada riparian and aquatic ecosystems is generally limited, broad management prescriptions are generally used until site-specific prescriptions can be developed. Ideally, these broad prescriptions should err on the side of protecting the resource, to make sure that no irreversibly detrimental management actions are taken. With such a constraint, the broad management prescriptions should be based on the following assumptions:

1. The need for riparian protection is just as strong, if not stronger, in intermittent, ephemeral, low order, fishless, and high-gradient streams as it is along other kinds of aquatic environments because such water courses are major sources of sediment, nutrients, and debris for lower stream reaches.
2. Continuous corridors of riparian vegetation are highly desirable for the protection of fish and wildlife.
3. Large woody debris is important in the functioning of most aquatic systems.
4. Many riparian areas are highly altered and are unlikely to be restored to anything approaching a natural condition because of urbanization, roads, and other factors. Nevertheless, riparian habitats in the Sierra Nevada have a remarkable capacity for recovery once destructive influences (roads, grazing, mining, etc.) are removed or reduced.

Working with these assumptions, we present three basic approaches to riparian management, recognizing that these approaches are highly generalized: (1) the low protection approach, (2) the moderate protection approach, and (3) the high protection approach. We recognize that under almost any circumstances, riparian management for the entire Sierra Nevada, or even for one watershed, is likely to be a mixture of the three approaches.

Low protection approach
Under this approach, the highest value of streamside regions is for direct use: housing, parks, transportation corridors, grazing, logging and other factors. A protection priority system, such as given above, is largely irrelevant. The approach does not recognize the uniqueness and importance of riparian ecosystems, except under special circumstances, and provides minimal recognition of riparian areas as transitional between upstream areas and the water course. Historically, this has been the principal approach to management and accounts for the poor condition of riparian areas along many streams, especially on private land or in areas where riparian areas have become transportation corridors. This approach requires no special, generalized management recommendations, except to recognize that upstream uses for grazing, roads, and recreation may conflict with downstream uses of the water through such factors as decrease in water quality or siltation of reservoirs. This approach is also highly individualistic because conflicts in use (e.g., fishing vs. grazing) have to be worked out on a stream-by-stream basis.

Moderate protection approach
This approach, used today mainly on some public lands, basically operates on the assumption that a 100 foot wide buffer strip on each side of permanent streams will offer adequate protection for riparian and aquatic resources. The buffer concept is usually not applied to intermittent or fishless streams, although occasionally 30 or 50 foot buffer strips may be recommended for them. The 100 foot buffer concept itself is derived from studies showing that effects of logging operations on aquatic invertebrates are minimized if no logging or roads are permitted within 100 feet of the stream. Priority 1 and 2 riparian areas may or may not receive special protection (usually not). The approach is well described in a number of the National Forest Plans with some additional prescriptions added (Appendix B). It is applied mainly to forested lands and not to grasslands or meadows. It also is not used in relation to grazing of livestock. If the 100 foot rule continues to be the main yardstick for protection, then it will continue to offer moderate protection to riparian habitats along permanent streams in forested areas. Presumably, other habitats (such as meadow systems) will continue to receive protection or special management only on an ad hoc basis, such as when an endangered trout species needs protection

High protection approach
The high protection approach greatly restricts human activity in riparian areas and encourages management activities aimed at maintaining and restoring as much of the biotic integrity (native organisms, natural processes) of riparian ecosystems as possible. It explicitly recognizes that riparian ecosystems are distinct entities with strong ties to both the associated water course and the associated upland areas, as outlined in Erman et al. (1996). This approach requires different management prescriptions for different types of streams; ideally such prescriptions should be fairly site specific or related to the aquatic habitat types of Moyle (1996). However, an interim

approach is give highest priority for management for Priority 1 and 2 riparian areas and to base management on the broad stream types of Rosgen (1994) because of their comparative simplicity. Rosgen stream types can often be determined by quick visual inspection or by viewing aerial photographs but when doubt exists a rapid assessment of gradient, sinuosity, substrates, and other factors may be necessary, using Rosgen's techniques. Under this approach, riparian systems associated with very steep or very unstable channels would receive the most protection.

DEVELOPING SITE-SPECIFIC MANAGEMENT OBJECTIVES

Under the moderate and high protection options, the basic goal of riparian management is to enhance/protect the ability of riparian and aquatic systems to provide ecosystem services to humans, including habitat for increasingly rare riparian-dependent plants and animals. Ideally, each forest or region should have in place a Riparian Management Team of scientists with different specialities to collect the needed information and design management strategies. This information should be collected for each EPA stream reach, as well as individual lakes, ponds, and wetlands. The information the team would need to collect would include:

1. Evaluation of overall condition of riparian and aquatic habitats
   a. Priority ranking for riparian systems (or similar subjective measure of "health" of biotic community).
   b. Index of biotic integrity for the aquatic community for stream reach (or if data not available, a subjective rating of "health.")
2. Basic inventory of plants and animals present or historically present
3. Riparian widths needed by riparian dependent animals, especially amphibians

4. Vegetation
   a. % canopy cover
   b. distribution and abundance of sensitive plant species
   c. plant communities/seral stages present
   d. trees
      1. site potential heights
      2. role as large woody debris in streams etc.
5. Connections to surrounding area
   a. width of 100 year flood plain
   b. continuity of corridor (patchiness)
   c. erodibility of watershed (condition of upland portions)
6. Physical variables
   a. channel gradient;
   b. adjacent hillslope gradient;
   c. pool frequency;
   d. Pfankuch stability rating;
   e. width/depth ratio;
   f. water temperature (range);
   g. riffle stability index;
   h. existing large woody debris;
   i. others
7. Aquatic habitats
   a. types present
   b. integrity/health of each type
8. Human impacts

a. number of stream crossings

b. length or percent of each bank that is rip-rapped, channelized, or otherwise severely altered.

c. Equivalent roaded area

d. Subjective or quantitative scales to rate impacts of following activities:

    1. mining

    2. dwellings/urbanization

    3. roads

    4. recreation

    5. grazing

    6. pollution

    7. logging

    8. others

REFERENCES

Anderson, D.B. 1984 The public trust and riparian systems: a case for preservation. Pp. 257-264. In: *California riparian systems: ecology, conservation, and productive management.* R. E. Warner and K.M. Hendrix, eds. Univ. of Calif. Press, Berkeley.

Belt, G. H., J. O'Laughlin, and T. Merrill. 1992. Design of forest riparian buffer strips for protection of water quality: analysis of scientific literature. Idaho Forest, Wildlife, and Range Experiment Station Report No. 8, University of Idaho.

California Office of Planning and Research. 1980. California permit handbook. California Office of Planning and Research, Sacramento. 270 pp.

Carlson, A., Chapel, M., Colborn, A., et al. 1991. Review of Literature Addressing Wildlife and Fish Habitat Relationships in Riparian and Stream Habitats. Tahoe National Forest, Old Forest and Riparian Habitat Planning Project. 27 pp.

Chapel, M., Craig, D, Reynolds, M., et al. 1991. Review of Literature Addressing Wildlife and Fish Habitat Relationships in Late-Seral-Stage Coniferous Forests. Tahoe National Forest, Old Forest and Riparian Habitat Planning Project. 22 pp.

Cowardin, L.M., Carter,V. Golet, F.C., and LaRoe, E.T. 1979. *Classification of wetlands and deep water habitats of the United States.* U.S. Department of Interior, Fish and Wildlife Service, Washington, DC, FWS/OBS-79/31. 103pp.

Doppelt, B., M. Scurlock, C. Frissell, and J. Karr. 1993. *Entering the Watershed: a new approach to save America's river ecosystems.* Island Press, Washington DC. 462 pp.

Eldorado National Forest. 1988. Eldorado National Forest: Land Resource Management Plan. Pacific Southwest Region USDA Forest Service.

Erman, D. C., J. D. Newbold, K. B. Roby. 1977. Evaluation of streamside buffer strips for protecting aquatic organisms.. *University of California Water Resources Center Contribution 165.*

Erman, D. C., and D. Mahoney. 1983. Recovery after logging in streams with and without bufferstrips in northern California. . *University of California Water Resources Center Contribution 186.* 50 pp.

Forest Ecosystem Management Team. 1993. Forest Ecosystem Management: An Ecological, Economic, and Social Assessment: Report of the Forest Ecosystem Management Assessment Team.

FRAPP. 1988. California's Forests and Rangelands: Growing Conflict Over Changing Uses. Forest and Rangeland Resources Assessment Program (FRRAP), Calif. Dept. of Forestry and Fire Protection.

Gebhardt, K., Leonard, S., Staidl, G. and D. Prichard. 1990. Riparian Area Management: Riparian and Wetland Classification Review. US Dept. of the Interior. Bureau of Land Management. Tech. Ref. 1737-5. 55 pp.

Gregory, S.V., F.J. Swanson, W.A. McKee, and K. Cummins. 1991. An ecosystem perspective of riparian zones. *BioScience*, 41:540-551.

Hansen, P.L., Chadde, S.W. and Pfister, R.D. 1987. Riparian dominance types of Montana. 1987. Montana Forest and Conservation Station, School of Forestry, University of Montana, Missoula, Miscellaneous Publication 49. 411p.

Harris, L.D. 1984. The Fragmented Forest. University of Chicago Press, Chicago. 211 pp.

International Conf. of Building Officials. 1979. Uniform Building Code. ICBO, Whittier, California. 734 pp.

Inyo National Forest. 1988. Inyo National Forest: Land Resource Management Plan. Pacific Southwest Region USDA Forest Service.

Johnson, K.N., J. F. Franklin., J. W. Thomas, J. Gordon. 1991. Alternatives for management of late-successional forests of the Pacific Northwest. A report to the Agriculture Committee and the Merchant Marine Committee of the U.S. House of Representatives. 59 pp.

Jones, B. 1983. A state mandate for riparian wetland system preservation. In: *California riparian systems: ecology, conservation, and productive management*. R. E. Warner and K.M. Hendrix, eds. Univ. of Calif. Press.

Kattelmann, R. and M. Embury. Riparian resources. Sierra Nevada Ecosystem project (in press).

Kovalchik, , B.L. 1987. Riparian zone associations of the Deschutes, Ochoco, Fremont and Winema National Forests, Portland, OR: USDA Forest Service, Pacific Northwest Region 6 R6 ECOL TP-279-87. 171 pp.

Kovalchik, B.L., and Chitwood, L.A. 1990. Uses of geomorphology in the classification of riparian plant associations in mountainous landscapes of central Oregon, U.S.A. Forest Ecology and Management 33/34: 405-418.

Lassen National Forest. 1988. Final Environmental Impact Statement Land Resource Management Plan: Lassen National Forest. Pacific Southwest Region USDA Forest Service.

Mahoney, D. and D. C. Erman. 1984. The role of streamside bufferstrips in the ecology of aquatic organisms. Pp. 168-176 In: R. E. Warner and K. W. Hendrix, eds. *California riparian systems: ecology, conservation, and productive management*. University of California Press, Berkeley.

Maser, C, R. F. Tarrant, J. M. Trappe, and J. F. Franklin, eds. 1988. From the forest to the sea: the story of fallen trees. Pacific Northwest Station, USDA Forest Service, General Technical Report PNW-GTR-229.

McQuire, J.R. 1977. Position paper: a riparian policy for changing times. Pp. 137-145 In: *Strategies for protection and management of floodplain wetlands and riparian ecosystems: a symposium,*. USDA Forest Service., Washington, D. C. General Technical Report 12.

Menning, K. M. , D. C. Erman, K. N. Johnson, and J. Sessions. 1996. Aquatic and riparian systems, assessments of cumulative watershed effects and limitations on watershed disturbance. Sierra Nevada Ecosystem Project (in press).

Mistch, W.J. and J.G. Gosselink. 1986. *Wetlands*. Van Nostrand Reinhold, New York. 539 pp.

Moyle, P. B. 1996. Status of aquatic habitats in the Sierra Nevada. Sierra Nevada Ecosystem Project (in press).

Osborne, L. L., and D. A. Kovacic. 1993. Riparian vegetated buffer strips in water quality restoration and stream management. *Freshwater Biology* 29: 243-258.

Pierce, J. and J. Johnson. 1986. Wetland community type classification for west-central Montana. USDA Forest Service, Northern Region I, Missoula, MT, Ecosystem Management Report.

Plumas National Forest. 1988. Plumas National Forest: Land Resource Management Plan. Pacific Southwest Region USDA Forest Service.

Ratliff, R.D. 1982. A meadow site classification for the Sierra Nevada, California.

Reeves, G.H., and J. R. Sedell. 1992. An ecosystem approach to the conservation and management of freshwater habitat for anadromous salmonids in the Pacific Northwest. *Proceedings of the 57th North American Wildlife and Natural Resources Conference:* 408-415.

Rosgen, D. L. 1994. A classification of natural rivers. *Catena* 22:169-199.

Sequoia National Forest. 1988. Final Environmental Impact Statement: Sequoia National Forest: Land Resource Management Plan. Pacific Southwest Region USDA Forest Service.

Smith, F.E. 1984. The Clean Water Act and the principles of the Public Trust Doctrine: a discussion. Pp. 265-288 In:R.E. Warner. and K.M. Hendrix, eds. *California Riparian Systems: Ecology, Conservation, and Productive Management.* University of California Press, Berkeley.

Sommarstrom, S. 1984. Riparian regulations: random, redundant, or rational? Pp. 274-280. In:R.E. Warner. and K.M. Hendrix, eds. *California Riparian Systems: Ecology, Conservation , and Productive Management.* University. of California Press, Berkeley.

Stevens, J. 1984. The state as a public trustee: neutral umpire or activist guardian? Pages 269-273. In: R.E. Warner. and K.M. Hendrix, eds. *California Riparian Systems: Ecology, Conservation , and Productive Management.* University. of California Press, Berkeley

Swanson, F.J., S.V. Gregory, J.R. Sedell, and A.G. Campbell. 1982. Land water interactions: the riparian zone. In: R.L. Edmunds, editor. *Analysis of Coniferous Forest Ecosystems in the Western United States.* US/IBP Synthesis series 14. Hutchinson Ross Publishing Co., Stroudsburg, PA. p. 267-291.

USDA Forest Service. 1988. Land and Resource Management Plan. Lake Tahoe Basin Management Unit. Pacific Southwest Region, USDA Forest Service.

USDA Forest Service. 1990. Tahoe National Forest: Land Resource Management Plan. Pacific Southwest Region, USDA Forest Service.

Thurow, C., Toner, W., and D. Erley. 1975. Streams and creeks. In: *Performance controls for sensitive lands; a practical guide for local administrators.* Planning Advisory Service Report Nos. 307, 308. American Society of Planning Officials, Chicago, Ill. 156 pp.

U.S. Army Corps of Engineers, 1987. Corps of Engineers wetlands delineation manual. Waterway Experiment Station Wetlands Research Program technical report Y-87-1.

Youngblood, A.P., W. G. Paget,. and A. H. Winward. 1985 Riparian community type classification for eastern Idaho-western Wyoming. USDA For. Serv. Intermount. For. Range Exp. Stn., Ogden, UT R4-ECOL-85-01, 78pp.

APPENDIX A: RIPARIAN ZONE DEFINITIONS

The following collection of definitions is not meant to be complete but only to give good sample of definitions that have been or can be applied to Sierra Nevada riparian and wetland habitats.

1. USDA Forest Service
"Geographically delineated areas, with distinctive resource values and characteristics, that area comprised of the aquatic and riparian ecosystems, flood plains, and wetlands. Includes all areas within a horizontal distance of 100 ft. from the edge of perennial streams and other water bodies . One-hundred year flood plains included in definition of riparian, include both wetland and irregularly flooded, drier sites. These drier sites generally do not meet the NWI definition of wetland." (Forest Service Manual 2526)

2. Inyo National Forest

"Geographically delineable areas with distinctive resource values and characteristics that are comprised of the aquatic and riparian ecosystems." (Inyo NF LRMP)

3. Stanislaus National Forest

"The transition between aquatic and terrestrial ecosystems, characterized by distinctive vegetation which requires free or unbound water." (Stanislaus NF LRMP).

4. Eldorado National Forest

"Riparian areas: consist of streamside ecosystems, aquatic ecosystems, wetlands and flood plains. Riparian encompasses all areas within a horizontal distance of 100 feet from both edges of perennial streams or other water bodies. Wet meadows are included in the riparian zone. Wetlands: included in total riparian area. Defined as: those areas inundated by surface or ground water with a frequency sufficient to support a prevalence of vegetation or aquatic life that requires saturated or seasonally saturated soil conditions for growth and reproduction. Includes marshes, wet meadows, alpine meadows, springs, seeps, potholes, river overflows and natural ponds, and may or may not be associated with Streamside Management Zone." (Eldorado NF LRMP)

4. Sequoia National Forest

"Riparian area: includes the aquatic ecosystem, riparian vegetation, 100-year floodplain and Streamside Management Zone (see Fig 3.4, p. 3-107). The extent of riparian areas is directly affected by the steepness of stream side slopes, with the steeper slopes having the narrower habitat. (Sequoia NF LRMP)

Aquatic ecosystem: extends to the normal bank high water mark.

Riparian vegetation: defined as vegetation communities that require free or unbound water.

100-year floodplain: "has a one percent chance of being flooded in any one year". This floodplain provides storage for flood flows, helps reduce the velocity and peak flow, moderates downstream flooding, reduces deposition of sediment in stream channels. The floodplain and the vegetation associated with it help reduce flood intensities." (Sequoia NF LRMP).

5. Tahoe National Forest

Riparian areas: "As a **minimum**, riparian areas are defined to be (1) areas a 100-foot horizontal distance from the edge of standing bodies of water; (2) areas a horizontal distance of 100 feet on each side of perennial stream channels; and (3) all wetlands." (emphasis added) (from PSW Planning Direction; also, direction in 36 CFR 219.27 (e) and in FSM 2526 3/86 AMEND 48).

Riparian vegetation: riparian vegetation includes the following characteristic species::

Acer macrophyllum	bigleaf maple
Alnus species	alders
Carex species	sedges
Deschampsia species	hairgrasses
Equisetum species	horsetails
Juncus species	rushes
Populus species	aspen, cottonwood, poplars
Salix species	wills
Taxus brevifolia	Pacific yew
Trifolium species	clovers
Veratrum californica	corn lily

Riparian-dependent resources - "Those natural, intrinsic resources directly dependent upon the riparian area for their existence, including: water, fish, certain wildlife species, riparian related aesthetics, and riparian related vegetation" (FSM 2526 11/86 R-5 SUPP 41)

Streamside management zones: These are administratively designated zones adjacent to perennial, intermittent, and in some cases ephemeral streams, and are designed to call attention to the need for special management practices aimed at the maintenance and/or improvement of watershed resources (e.g. water quality, channel stability). They may include wetlands, flood plains, riparian areas, inner gorges, perennial streams, intermittent streams, ephemeral streams, and the terrestrial ecosystem adjacent to these areas.

6. Forest Ecosystem Management Team (FEMAT)

"Riparian Zone: Refers to those areas where the vegetation complex and microclimate conditions are products of the combined presence and influence of perennial and/or intermittent water, associated high water tables, and soils that exhibit some wetness characteristics. The zone within which plants grow rooted in the water table of these rivers, streams, lakes, ponds, reservoirs, springs, marshes, seeps, bogs and wet meadow.

Riparian Reserves: Designated riparian areas intended to address the habitat requirements for fish and aquatic and riparian species."

APPENDIX B. RIPARIAN PROTECTION ON FEDERAL LANDS

The following is a survey of riparian management zone delineations for Federal lands

1. U.S. Fish and Wildlife Service

A report by Brinson (1981) recommended the following
widths of riparian buffer strips:

Protection function	Width
water quality	8 m + 0.6 m per 1% of slope
water quality in municipal ws	16 m + 1.2 m per 1% of slope
aquatic life	30 m
water quality and fish	25 m + riparian vegetation

2. HR6013: Sierra Nevada Forests Ecosystem Study Act of 1992:

2HR6013 (Congressional Record-House, Sept. 30, 1992) which is part of SNEP's genesis, included the following language for interim protection in Section 5 - C:

"No management practices causing detrimental changes in water temperature, chemical composition, blockages of water courses, or deposits of sediments, which would adversely affect water conditions or fish habitat, and no logging may be conducted within 100' of either side of all permanent streams and 50' on either side of all seasonally flowing and intermittent streams."

3. Forest Ecosystem Management Team

The Watershed/Fish Element (Reeves and Sedell 1992) of the FEMAT report (Johnson et al. 1991) recommended riparian management areas as:

> 300' on each side of fish-bearing streams;
> 150' on each side of non-fish bearing but perennial
> streams;
> 50' on each side of intermittent streams in unstable
> terrain; and
> 660' or 100-year floodplain on rivers draining > 30
> square miles.

The riparian portion of the FEMAT aquatic conservation strategy based interim (until locally established by watershed analyses and site-specific evaluations) widths of riparian reserves on height of site-potential trees (110-250') and distances along slopes. Several criteria were developed (see Table V-5 [pg V-37] in FEMAT report) for width on each side of active channel and can be summarized as follows:

Fish-bearing streams -- top of inner gorge, 100-year floodplain, perimeter of riparian vegetation, twice height of site-potential
trees, or 300' slope distance (whichever is greatest).

Nonfish-bearing, perennial -- as above except one tree height or 150'

Reservoirs and wetlands -- outer edges of riparian vegetation, extent of seasonally saturated soil or unstable areas, one tree height, or 150.

Lakes and natural ponds -- as above except two tree heights or 300'.

Intermittent, small wetlands -- outer edge of riparian vegetation, extent of unstable areas, top of inner gorge or 25 feet.

A detailed set of standards and guidelines is presented in Appendix V-F of the FEMAT report.

4. PACFISH Environmental Analysis

The PACFISH EA (March 1994) Alternative 4 (pages C-3 to C-17) uses essentially the same criteria for interim widths of Riparian Habitat Conservation Areas as FEMAT and nearly identical standards and guidelines as well. In rangelands, the interim riparian width is the 100-year floodplain for perennial streams.

5. CALOWL

Current CALOWL considerations for riparian zones distinguish the following habitats :
    seeps/springs
    ephemerals and intermittent streams
    small order perennials
    large order perennials
    bogs/fens/wetlands
    vernal pools
    wet meadows
    lakes
    ponds
    reservoirs

6. Pacific Rivers Council

The Pacific Rivers Council's aquatic conservation strategy (Doppelt et al. 1993) includes a similar list of habitats and the following criteria for interim width of riparian zones (from edge of active or braided channel):

> top of inner gorge
> 100-year floodplain
> outer edge of zone of control of stream microclimate
> outer edge of habitat areas of semi-aquatic, and riparian-dependent terrestrial or avian species
> adjacent unstable slopes

7. Eldorado National Forest

Riparian areas encompass all areas within a horizontal distance of 100 feet from both edges of perennial streams or other water bodies. Wet meadows are included in the riparian zone. (Eldorado NF LRMP EIS)

8. Inyo National Forest

Riparian areas consist of

(1) as a minimum, areas that are a 100-foot horizontal distance from the edge of standing bodies of water, lakes, and perennial streams, and

(2) all wetlands, including all ephemeral or intermittent streams which support riparian vegetation , wet meadows, springs, seeps, and bogs.

9. Tahoe National Forest

In the 1988 LRMP, identification and mapping of the stream environment zone includes determination of:

a). wetlands, meadows, and other areas of riparian vegetation;

b.) one-hundred year flood plain;

c.) ephemeral stream courses and soil areas associated with high runoff or high water tables:

d.) areas within 25 feet of first order stream, 50 feet of second order stream, and 100 feet of third order stream.

Chapel et al. (1992) recommended that Tahoe National Forest establish a minimum riparian width of one site-potential tree (125-200') on each side of the stream for combined old-growth and riparian reserves. Riparian zones include the 100-year floodplain, riparian vegetation, and upland areas influencing the stream environment.

10. Stanislaus National Forest

Riparian Areas:

> Perennial streams: approx. 100 feet on either side of the stream, plus an average of 25 feet for the water surface itself.

Standing bodies of water: includes 100 ft. from the shore, plus 25 ft. of the water surface.

Intermittent streams: within 50 ft. on each side of the channel.

11. Sequoia National Forest

Streamside Management Zones (SMZ's): Management zone width is determined on a individual project basis using "appropriate Standards and Guidelines", developed locally in consultation with CDFG. Average distance from the stream given special treatment is 100 feet. Timber equipment is prohibited from entering this zone except at designated stream crossings.

APPENDIX C. RIPARIAN REGULATIONS ON PRIVATE LANDS

Local, state, and federal governments have a variety of means of influencing conservation and development of privately-owned riparian lands. Overviews of various aspects of this regulatory legal framework are provided by Sommarstrom (1984), Stevens (1984), Anderson (1984), Smith (1984), Jones (1983) and Kramer (1983). Sommarstrom (1984), in a review of primary local, state and federal regulations points out that the term "riparian" need not be explicit for a law to include riparian areas. A wide range of activities and concerns associated with riparian areas are regulated according to (1) project location, (2) project activities, and (3) resources affected by the project (California Office of Planning and Research 1980, Table C-1).

Table C-1: Scope of riparian regulations (from Sommarstrom 1984)

Location

Navigable water	Coastal Zone
Wild and scenic rivers	Central Valley
Floodplain	

Project Activities:

Timber harvesting	Water diversion
Timberland conversion	Channelization
Dredging/filling	Grazing
Grading/excavating	Road construction
Gravel extraction	Road maintenance
Stream bed alteration	Dam construction
Vegetation removal	Subdivision
Stream crossing	bank alteration
Riprapping	Groundwater extraction

Affected Resources:

Endangered species	Commercial timber
Fish habitat	Vegetation
Wildlife habitat	Aesthetics
Water quality	Open space
Water supply	Land use
Stream flow	Land stability
Soils	Aquatic habitat

Local Regulations

Local governments have several mechanisms available which can be applied to streamside areas (Sommarstorm 1988). In most cases the planning agency is responsible for administering applicable ordinances. However, many cases also involve pubic works, building, flood control, or water departments. Zoning ordinances are the most common form of local land-use regulations influencing riparian zones. Each zoning district establishes a list of uses permitted on all private land within its borders, as well as listing prohibited uses and conditional procedures in conformity with general plan procedures. Floodplain regulations may be administered as a floodplain planning overlay zone. Grading ordinances are used to minimize or prevent disturbance of stream and riparian areas. Minimal excavation and grading regulations, established by Chapter 70 of the Uniform Building Code (International Conference of Building Officials 1979), have been adopted by most local governments. Some local governments have amended zoning or subdivision ordinances to minimize erosion or sedimentation from projects (Thurow et al. 1975). The California surface Mining and Reclamation Act of 1975 (SMARA - Section 2710-1793 Public Resources Code) required counties to adopt ordinances requiring reclamation of mining lands. Extraction of gravel is the most common mining operation potentially affecting riparian resources. The California Department of Fish and Game (1980) developed the "Model Riparian Ordinance" as an example watercourse or stream environment protection ordinance. Specifically designed to protect riparian vegetation, this site-specific regulation is not widely used.

State regulations

Several state agencies may require permits for projects affecting riparian resources (Sommarstrom 1984; Calif. Office of Planning and Research 1980), notably the Department of Fish and Game (CDFG), Department of Forestry (CDF), State Water Resources Control Board (SWRCB), regional water quality control boards, and agencies functioning under the California Environmental Quality Act.

A Stream Alteration Agreement is required by the CDFG Code Sections 1601-1603 for any work undertaken below the mean high water mark of a body of water containing or wildlife resources, or where the project will use material from the Stream bed. Specific conditions for mitigation of potential problems must be met by applicants.

CDF requires a Timber Harvest Plan conforming to the rules and regulations of the Board of Forestry, the Forest District, and the Z'berg-Nejedly Forest Practice Act of 1973 (as amended, Section 4511-4628 Public resources Code) to be approved before any harvesting of commercial timber species. Several riparian forest tress are included as "commercial species", such as red alder, white alder, pepperwood, and others. Minimum width for special protection measures are established in rules requiring a "Watercourse and Lake Protection Zone". Timber operations on less than 1.2 ha. (3 ac.) require no approval. A Timberland Conversion Permit is required for conversion of private commercial timberland to other uses.

Any person or public agency proposing to divert water from any surface stream for use on non-riparian land must obtain a Permit to Appropriate Water from SWRCB, according to the

California Water Code. Diversion of water under a riparian claim requires only an informational Statement of Water Diversion and Use to be filed. The SWRCB has a jurisdiction for subterranean water, limited to underground streams flowing through known and definite water channels and applied to non-overlying lands. Most groundwater use does not require this type of permit.

There are nine regional water quality control boards (RWQCB) that are delegated permit-issuing authority by the SWRCB for waste discharge into any surface waters or groundwater. Logging, construction, and other associated activities in riparian zones may be affected by regulations governing discharge of both point and non-point sources of pollution. Permits are issued based upon conformity with water quality standards adopted in the regional board's Basin Plan.

Under the California Environmental Quality Act (CEQU) referral process, agencies other than those mentioned above may be required to review proposed projects. It is the responsibility of the lead agency to determine significant effects on the environment, including riparian concerns. Minor alterations to land are exempted from CEQA requirements.

Federal Regulations

Federal law pertaining to riparian systems on private lands is generally administered at the state or local level. The US Army Corps of Engineers, however, under the authority of Section 404 of the Clean Water Act (as amended), may require a permit for projects involving the location of structures in or on, or the excavation or discharge of dredge or fill material in "navigable waters", including wetlands, rivers, and intermittent streams below the ordinary high-water mark. Although the riparian zone is not specifically included, certain activities affecting riparian resources are covered by the permit process (e.g. riprap, levees).

APPENDIX D. MANAGEMENT GOALS FOR RIPARIAN AREAS

The following is a representative selection of management goals extracted from various forest plans and other federal documents.

1. General management directives

Executive Order (E.O.) 11988 on Floodplain Management and E.O. 11990 on Protection of Wetlands: Directs government agencies to avoid adverse impacts on, protect, preserve and enhance wetlands and flood plains.

Rules implementing RPA and NFMA in 36 CFR 219.13 (e): "Special attention will be given to land and vegetation for approximately 100 feet from the edges of all perennial streams, lakes, and other bodies of water and will correspond to at least the recognizable area dominated by the riparian vegetation. No management practices causing detrimental changes in water temperature or chemical composition, blockages of water courses, and deposits of sediment will be permitted within these areas which seriously and adversely affect water conditions or fish habitat. Topography, vegetation type, soil, climatic conditions, management objectives and other factors will be considered in determining what management practices may be performed within these areas or the constraints to be placed upon their performance"

Public Law 92-500, Section 208: Required the Forest Service to develop Best Management Practices (BMP's) to protect water quality. BMP 1.8 (riparian areas) requires designation of Streamside Management Zones (SMZ's) along streams and wetlands to minimize the effects of nearby logging and related land disturbing activities.

2. Forest Ecosystem Management Team:

The FEMAT report recommends detailed standards and guidelines for riparian reserves, in their appendix V-F. In general, these standards and guidelines prohibit activities in Riparian Reserves that retard or prevent attainment of the Aquatic Conservation Strategy Objectives. Detailed guidance is delineated for the following management areas: timber, roads, grazing, recreation, minerals, fire/fuels, lands, general riparian area, watershed and habitat restoration, and fish and wildlife habitat. Timber harvest is prohibited in SMZ's, including firewood cutting. SMZ's are not included in the land base used to determine Allowable Sale Quantity, with some exceptions.

3. Sequoia National Forest

Forest-wide Standards and Guidelines, Riparian Areas (LRMP):

Delineate, manage, and monitor riparian areas using the "Riparian Standards and Guidelines for the Sequoia National Forest."

Prevent adverse riparian areas changes in water temperature, chemistry, and sedimentation; and maintain a balance of woody debris.

Give emphasis to riparian dependent resources.

4. Tahoe National Forest

Tahoe National Forest LRMP has the most complete guidelines for riparian management in the SNEP region. The general guidelines presented in the LTBMU Forest Plan (1988) and in Carlson et al. (1992) are presented here.

Lake Tahoe Basin Management U nit Forest Plan

Riparian Area Goal: Riparian areas area able to perform their natural function in the environment, such as providing habitat for dependent species and for watershed protection.

Predicted Condition: Riparian areas will be protected from new disturbance. Where new disturbance does occur, there will be off-setting mitigation to replace the loss. Damaged riparian areas will be restored through the watershed restoration program, adjustments in management practices, and natural rehabilitation over time.

Nonstructural Wildlife Habitat Management: protect or improve habitat through coordination with other management activities; require non-degradation of existing deciduous tree types, wetlands, and meadow habitat; increase the acreage in these riparian associations where opportunities are present.

Nonstructural Fish Habitat Management: obtain water availability assurance for instream flows sufficient to meet fisheries needs; remove of debris from streams in order to stabilize the channel in a manner to maximize improvement for fish habitat; maintain shaded conditions on rainbow trout streams by maintaining at least 50% of the stream bank site potential for herbaceous and shrub cover and at least 25% of the site potential for tree cover. Where natural tree cover is less than 20%, 80% of the potential should be retained. Thirty five to 70% of the stream should be shaded from 11:00 AM to 4:00 PM.

Water Quality: Manage existing naturally functioning stream environment zones (SEZ) lands in their natural hydrologic condition with few exceptions; Permit outdoor recreation facilities in SEZ where they are a part of long range development plans, where the nature of the activity must be so sited, where there is no feasible alternative, where it is fully mitigated, and where disturbed SEZ beyond allowed coverage is restored at 150% of the amount disturbed.

Tahoe National Forest

Primary goals for managing riparian areas: 1) provide high quality stream environments and 2) provide all the key structural elements of streamside areas that are important for wildlife and aquatic resources. The Tahoe NF LRMP presents detailed guidelines which are recommended for riparian zones. These prohibit management activities to occur within the stream management zone, except for activities which directly benefit riparian dependent resources.

5. Inyo National Forest

Forest-wide Standards and Guidelines: Riparian Areas:

Give emphasis to riparian-dependent resources in the management of riparian areas.

Protect streams, stream banks, shorelines, lakes, wetlands, and the plants and animals.

Prevent significant adverse riparian area changes in water temperature, chemistry, sedimentation , and channel blockages.

Use Allotment Management Plans as the vehicle for ensuring protection of riparian areas from unacceptable impacts from grazing. Institute positive measures such as salting, herding, water developments, fencing, rest rotation, deferred rotation, and other grazing systems as mitigation measures. If mitigation is unsuccessful in preventing unacceptable resource damage to the riparian habitat, as a last resort, livestock grazing will be reduced or eliminated in the affected areas.

Rehabilitate and/or fence riparian areas that consistently show resource damage from any cause if conflicts cannot be resolved.

Relocate existing roads, trails, and campsites outside riparian areas where necessary to eliminate or reduce unacceptable deterioration of riparian-dependent resources.

Allow new developments and surface disturbance in riparian areas only after on-site evaluations have determined that riparian-dependent resources are not adversely affected, or mitigation of adverse impacts is identified and incorporated in project design and implementation specifications.

Apply earth disturbance standards to each zone within each stream type. Earth disturbance is defined as complete removal of vegetation or a percentage of bare ground resulting for the disturbance.

Limit wildfire control methods and activities that would adversely affect the riparian zone. Avoid dozer-built lines in this zone where possible. Require the following water bar spacing on trails in riparian areas unless specifically determined otherwise by on-site project evaluations:

Trail Gradient (%)	Spacing (feet)
1-5	200
6-10	150
11-15	100
> 15	50

Prohibit new locations of equipment staging areas in riparian zones. Phase out existing staging areas that have adverse effects on these zones.

Maintain the integrity of desert springs to conserve plant and wildlife habitat.

Recognize the important and distinctive values of riparian areas when implementing management activities. Give preferential consideration to riparian-dependent resources when conflicts among land use activities occur.

Delineate and evaluate riparian areas before implementing any planned management activity.

Design range, fish and wildlife habitat improvement projects and/or silvicultural prescriptions to maintain or enhance riparian area dependent resources.

Give priority to the rehabilitation of riparian areas when planning range, wildlife habitat, and watershed improvement projects.

Move existing livestock watering locations out of riparian areas when and where feasible.

6. Lassen National Forest

<u>Forest-wide Standards and Guidelines Common to all EIS Alternatives:</u>

Aquatic and riparian areas:

Provide water of sufficient quality and quantity to meet current needs. Meet additional future demand where compatible with other resource needs.

Limit individual project impacts as needed to avoid significant, adverse cumulative effects on water quality and fisheries.

Comply with Federal, State, Regional and local water quality regulations, requirements, and standards.

Maintain or improve riparian-dependent resources in and around wetlands, stream corridors (including ephemeral and intermittent streams), lakes, seeps, springs, and wet meadows.

Evaluate riparian zones forest-wide and manage to reach natural or achievable site potential and desirable future conditions. Desired future conditions, where site potential exists, are late seral communities in good or better condition.

7. Plumas National Forest

General direction

Standards and guidelines

Riparian Areas

Favor riparian dependent resources and limit disturbance in all riparian are including riparian and aquatic ecosystems, wetlands, stream banks, and flood plains.

Favor riparian resources over other resources, except cultural resources in cases of conflict. Apply Rx-9, Riparian Areas Prescription. Also see standards and guidelines for "Water".

Streamside Management Zones (SMZ)

Limit disturbance in Streamside Management Zones.

Establish Streamside Management Zones (SMZ's) according to the guidelines shown in Appendix M, Guidelines for Width of Streamside Management Zones.

Prepare and adhere to a Streamside Management Zone plan for any activity within an SMZ. This plan shall establish site specific resource objective and include at least the following:

- objectives for vegetation management based upon the needs of riparian-dependent resources, and objectives to maintain or enhance water quality.
- manipulation practices and maximum amount of vegetation manipulation allowable to meet the stated objectives, while maintaining at least 75% effective organic ground cover. This cover includes humus, duff, litter, and vegetation in contact with the ground and at least 2" thick (or the existing thickness if less than 2" in the area), interwoven with sticks, branches, limbs, and logs.
- an analysis of project areas within the SMZ having over-steepened slopes (over 60%) with a very high erosion potential or a very high erosion potential or high instability, and procedures to limit soil disturbance to no more than 5% of these areas per decade. procedures for restoration of any deteriorated areas.
- prescription for roads, skid trails, landings, and other harvesting facilities.

31

<u>Plumas National Forest LRMP (Rx-9. Riparian Area Prescription)</u>

The purpose of this prescription is to manage riparian areas as unique ecosystems and to protect and improve them while implementing land and resource management activities. Riparian areas are to be managed in relation to various legal mandates, including those associated with flood plains, wetlands, rivers, and cultural resources. Emphasis will be given to protection and improvement of soil, water, vegetation, and riparian-dependent resources when conflicts occur among land use activities. Riparian areas consist of riparian ecosystems, aquatic ecosystems, and wetlands,. This prescription applies to approximately 45,000 acres scattered throughout the Forest. The Water Forestwide Standards and Guidelines are especially applicable to the riparian areas and provide an important supplement to this prescription.

General direction	Standards and guidelines

General direction

Standards and guidelines

Recreation

Protect riparian areas while providing developed facilities.

Locate any new developed recreation sites outside of riparian areas unless an analysis shows that overall impacts would be minimized by locating the site in a riparian area.

Wildlife and Fish

Assure adequate protection for wildlife and fish resources.

See Forestwide Standards and Guidelines.

Range

Improve ranges and implement grazing systems to protect riparian areas, and restore them where needed

Develop objectives and utilization standards in Allotment Management Plans for vegetation management based on the needs of riparian-dependent resources and water quality.

Select and implement grazing systems that allow for the maintenance of riparian vegetation now in good condition and the improvement of riparian vegetation in unsatisfactory condition. Favor riparian-dependent resources and water quality over livestock grazing when conflicts arise.

Monitor the condition and trend of streamside areas as an integral part of each allotment management plan.

Timber

Manage timber to ensure protection of
riparian areas.

Allow only vegetation removal within riparian
areas that benefits riparian-dependent
resources, controls insects and diseases,
protects public safety, or facilitates timber
harvest activities on adjacent land (i.e. cable
corridors or designated stream crossings).

Water

Assure an adequate water supply for
PNF and instream needs

Manage flows and/or reservoir storage to
maintain or enhance riparian plant
communities and habitat for all life stages of
fish. Cooperate with local, State, and other
Federal water management agencies.

34

Protect life and property from flooding and stream channel degradation where threat is moderate to high.	Preserve natural riparian flood control abilities. Remove only those log jams or major debris accumulations that have a high potential of causing channel damage, block fish passage, or could be transported down stream by high flows and cause loss of property.
	Through cooperation with the State Department of Fish & Game insure that stream alterations restore the original flow capacity while preserving the existing channel alignment.
	Comply with Executive Orders 11988, Floodplain Management, and 1190, Protection of Wetlands.
Protect riparian resources during storage and use of fuels and hazardous materials.	Prohibit the use, handling, or storage of any hazardous material within riparian areas unless no other alternative is available and suitable containment structures and spill cleanup contingency plans have been approved by the Forest Service.
Protect riparian resources from activities not directly related to Forest Service management activities.	Require riparian area protective measures in all applicable special use permits for non-PNF activities.

Minerals and Materials

Promote only mineral and common variety materials operations that protect riparian resources.

Ensure that Notices of Intent and Plans of Operations fully address riparian values.

Minimize adverse impacts to riparian resources through appropriate mitigation stipulations in operating plans, permits, and leases coordinated with applicable State and Federal agencies.

Energy

Facilitate hydroelectric development that provides protection of riparian resources.

Require proponents to coordinate with the PNF in analysis of in stream flow needs for all potentially affected riparian-dependent resources.

Lands

Assure protection of riparian areas during land exchanges.

Meet land exchange requirements of Executive Orders 11988, Floodplain Management, and 11990, Protection of Wetlands.

Facilities

Minimize the impact of roads on water quality and riparian areas.

Adjust road design and location, or use permanent or seasonal closures, to avoid or minimize impacts to riparian-dependent resources.

Manage roads at the standards necessary to provide riparian resource protection.

Provide for fish passage and maintain natural channel character at stream crossing. On Class I and II streams, use abridges, open bottom arches, and low water crossings unless an analysis shows that another structure is best.

Design cofferdams to minimize sedimentation to watercourses.

Take care during construction and removal of cribs, cofferdams, sheet pilings, etc. to minimize sedimentation to streams.

NEIL H. BERG
Pacific Southwest Research Station
USDA Forest Service
Albany, California

KEN B. ROBY
Plumas National Forest
USDA Forest Service
Quincy, California

BRUCE J. McGURK
Pacific Southwest Research Station
USDA Forest Service
Albany, California

Cumulative Watershed Effects: Applicability of Available Methodologies to the Sierra Nevada

Sierra Nevada Ecosystem Project: Final report to Congress, vol. III, *Assessments, Commissioned Reports, and Background Information.* Davis: University of California, Centers for Water and Wildland Resources, 1996.

Abstract: This project has two primary objectives: (1) to review and evaluate existing CWE analysis methodologies for their applicability to foothill and forested areas of the Sierra Nevada and (2) to identify and recommend one or several promising methodologies for further development or site-specific modification for use in the Sierra Nevada. A four-step approach was taken to address the objectives: (1) review and evaluate the literature on existing CWE methodologies, (2) obtain, review, and compare recent case studies of CWE analyses used (a) on national forests in the Sierra Nevada, and (b) by state and local officials for instream flow requirements and effects of multiple water diversions, (3) identify unique or critical biogeoclimatic and socio-economic elements of the Sierra Nevada pertinent to the applicability and use of specific CWE methods, and (4) interview experts in the development and application of CWE assessment procedures. Watershed Analysis methodology is recommended as being most suitable for adaptation and use in the Sierra Nevada.

The Sierra Nevada Ecosystem Project (SNEP) is an assessment of the economic, social, and ecological conditions of the Sierra Nevada ecoregion. Humans have been modifying the landscape in this region for over 150 years, and disturbances such as logging, fire, mining, water development, residential and road construction, and grazing have all occurred in various patterns and intensities across the region. In order to meet the SNEP mandate in terms of land disturbance, an assessment methodology had to be identified. Since the National Environmental Policy Act (NEPA) of 1969, cumulative effects analysis has been required, and state and federal agencies have developed a wide array of guidelines by which human disturbances in a landscape can be evaluated.

This project was designed to inventory and evaluate commonly used cumulative watershed effects (CWE) analysis methods so that SNEP staff would be aware of their strengths and weaknesses. Methods range in spatial scale from site-specific techniques for 100 mi^2 basins, such as Washington State Watershed Analysis approach (Washington Forest Practices Board 1993), to large-scale methods amenable to entire mountain ranges (Menning et al. 1996). This project focused on smaller-scale techniques because considerably more effort has been devoted to their development. This report was prepared early in the SNEP process, however, so the exact scale at which the CWE analysis was to be performed had not yet been established.

OBJECTIVES AND APPROACH

This project has two primary objectives: (1) to review and evaluate existing CWE analysis methodologies for their applicability to foothill and forested areas of the Sierra Nevada and (2) to identify and recommend one or several promising methodologies for further development or site-specific modification for use in the Sierra Nevada. The intent was not to develop a methodology, but rather to assess the currently available procedures for their applicability to the Sierra Nevada.

A four-step approach was taken to address the objectives. (1) Review and evaluate the literature on existing CWE methodologies. (2) Obtain, review, and compare recent case studies of CWE analyses used (a) on national forests in the Sierra Nevada, and (b) by state and local officials for in-stream flow requirements and effects of multiple water diversions. (3) Identify unique or critical biogeoclimatic and socio-economic elements of the Sierra Nevada pertinent to the applicability and use of specific CWE methods. (4) Interview experts in the development and application of CWE assessment procedures (appendixes 1 and 2). (Results from the interviews are integrated with information from the literature review and case studies as inputs to the final recommendations.)

This paper is the product of the above approach. In it we give a brief history and description of cumulative wateshed effects, describe the distinguishing characteristics of the Sierra Nevada, review current CWE methodologies, compare recent case studies, discuss water rights and adjudication as elements of CWE decisions, and assess the applicability of CWE methodologies to the Sierra Nevada and make recommendations to SNEP.

HISTORY OF CUMULATIVE WATERSHED EFFECTS ANALYSIS

Cumulative watershed effects are not a new phenomena. A classic example in California resulted from hydraulic mining in the foothills of the Sierra Nevada during the 1860s. Effects from this activity are still present more than 100 years after the banning of hydraulic mining. Massive amounts of coarse sediment were mobilized and moved downstream, and as a result, channels were filled in and this contributed to the flooding of lowland communities. In what may be the first comprehensive evaluation of CWE in California, Gilbert (1917, cited in Reid 1993) identified several combined effects leading to increased flooding of Central Valley towns and sand and silt bar development in San Francisco Bay. Flooding was caused by the combined effects of stream channel aggradation and the construction of levees to protect agricultural operations. "If these changes had been independent of those wrought by mining debris they would have resulted in the automatic deepening and widening of the channels" (Gilbert 1917, cited in Reid 1993). However, the combined effect caused channel flow capacities to decrease and downstream flooding to ensue.

Sand and silt bar development in San Francisco Bay, although related to incoming mining debris from the Sierra, was more substantially affected by tidal marsh reclamation. "... [E]very acre of reclaimed tide marsh implies a fractional reduction of the tidal current in the Golden Gate. For any individual acre the fraction is minute, but the acres of tide marsh are many, and if all shall be reclaimed, the effect at the Golden Gate will not be minute" (Gilbert 1917, cited in Reid 1993). Mining debris persists and continues to influence hydro-dynamics of the San Francisco Bay and its delta today.

This example illustrates many of the elements and complexities intrinsic to cumulative effects analysis:
- Spatial scales are larger than traditional project-level considerations; hydraulic mining affected approximately one-half of the foothill region on the western slope of the Sierra Nevada.
- Effects are felt off the site of the land-disturbing manipulation or activity; in this case hundreds of kilometers downstream from the hydraulic mining.
- Specific "beneficial uses" that are adversely affected are identifiable (e.g., a safe [non-flooding] and reliable water supply).
- Time scales can be great. Effects of mining persist today; the Sacramento River channel continues to be shallower than before the mining.
- The *combination* of mining effects and the construction of levees produced an effect that would not have resulted necessarily from each action singly.
- Incrementally small effects (e.g., of marsh reclamation) combine over time and space to produce significant repercussions.

Only recently has formalization of concerns gone beyond the effects of site-specific, single-impact land management. Gooselink and Lee (1989), however, point out that the roots of the issue can be viewed as a communal response to accumulating individual acts of environmental degradation, none particularly large or damaging, but when taken together sum to significant and potentially dramatic impacts. Hardin (1968) described this principle elegantly as the tragedy of the commons: the unrestricted use of a common resource by individuals to maximize individual profits, leads to a loss of the resource for both individuals and the public.

The first known published explicit definition of "cumulative effects" in a land management context stems from the National Environmental Policy Act of 1969. Associated with this Act, the federal Council on Environmental Quality (CEQ) defined cumulative impact as:

the impact on the environment which results from the incremental impact of the action when added to other past, present, and reasonably foreseeable future actions regardless of what agency (federal or non-federal) or person undertakes such other actions. Cumulative impacts can result from individually minor but collectively significant actions taking place over a period of time (Council on Environmental Quality 1971).

Additional published characterizations of cumulative effects include:

- "... environmental change resulting from the accumulation and interaction of the effects of one action with the effects of one or more other actions occurring on a common resource" (Stull et al. 1987).
- "The impacts of these multiple land uses on biota, soils, atmosphere, and aquatic systems, added together over a drainage basin and time... " (Sidle and Hornbeck 1991).
- "...two or more individual effects which, when considered together, are considerable or which compound or increase other environmental impacts" (State of California 1984).
- "The changes to the environment caused by the interaction of natural ecosystem processes with the effects of two or more forest practices" (Washington Forest Practices Board 1993).

Other regulatory actions add dimensions to the cumulative effects issue (Cobourn 1989a). Amendments in 1977 to the federal Clean Water Act "stipulated that water quality standards are determined by the highest 'beneficial uses' of the water in question [and] the Act specifically required 'a process to (i) identify, if appropriate, agriculturally and silviculturally related nonpoint sources of pollution including return flows from irrigated agriculture, *and their cumulative effects* [authors' italics], and (ii) set forth procedures and methods [including land use requirements] to control to the extent feasible such sources'" (U. S. Congress 1977). Beneficial uses of water (e.g., fish habitat, domestic water supply) are routinely specified as the focal point of CWE procedures and many of the procedures, provide a measure of the sensitivity of beneficial uses to management (NCASI 1992).

Although less comprehensive than the CEQ definition, the other definitions and regulatory statements share with the CEQ statement a focus on the combined results of multiple individual effects. Other, less obvious implications of the differences between traditional approaches to project-level impact assessment and cumulative effects assessments include:

- *Ecological complexity* — Because traditional approaches quickly lead to unmanageable complexities when extended to a cumulative effects framework, a challenge is to identify relevant ecosystem components as focal points for the cumulative analysis (e.g., identify the key links between physical and biological processes and potential management actions).
- *Incremental environmental change* — At the large temporal and spatial scales used in some cumulative impact analyses, project-scale activities may not be measurable. Changes at the project scale are real, but they may be undetectable with the analytical techniques needed for cumulative scale analyses. In a statistical sense, project-scale change is within the error term of the estimate. This factor further hampers the use of traditional project-level assessment techniques and procedures.
- *Patterns on the landscape* — Pattern is at least as relevant as total area of impact. 50,000 ha of forest in a single block, for instance, will support different wildlife dynamics than fifty separate 1,000 ha tracts. Relevant aspects of pattern from the cumulative effects perspective are patch size, continuity, and contiguity.
- *Boundaries* — Spatial scales of interest vary with the "beneficial uses." A watershed may be the best scale for hydrological problems like water quality and flood potential, but "wolf-sheds" or "bear-sheds" that cross watersheds may be more relevant for cumulative wildlife considerations. These boundary considerations imply that a variable geographical scale is probably desirable, but regulatory constraints may dictate the use of political boundaries or watersheds.

- *Time scales* — In many cases the time frame of induced impacts (e.g., timber harvest and stand regeneration) approximates one human generation. However, ecosystems processes are typically an order of magnitude longer (figure 1). Major hydrologic modifications by humans are essentially irreversible in human time scales. Cumulative impact regulation and analysis should consider these differences between human and ecosystem time frames, particularly in light of the effective irreversibility of some human impacts.
- *Fragmented jurisdiction* — In moving to larger spatial scales, the chance of multiple agency oversight increases. Project-scale impact assessment is typically within the jurisdiction of a single agency. Coherent regulatory approaches are more difficult to develop in a multi-institutional setting than within single-institution frameworks because of conflicting interests, regulatory criteria, and planning horizons, and because landowners may consider it not in their economic self-interest to divulge their future plans (Gooselink and Lee 1989).

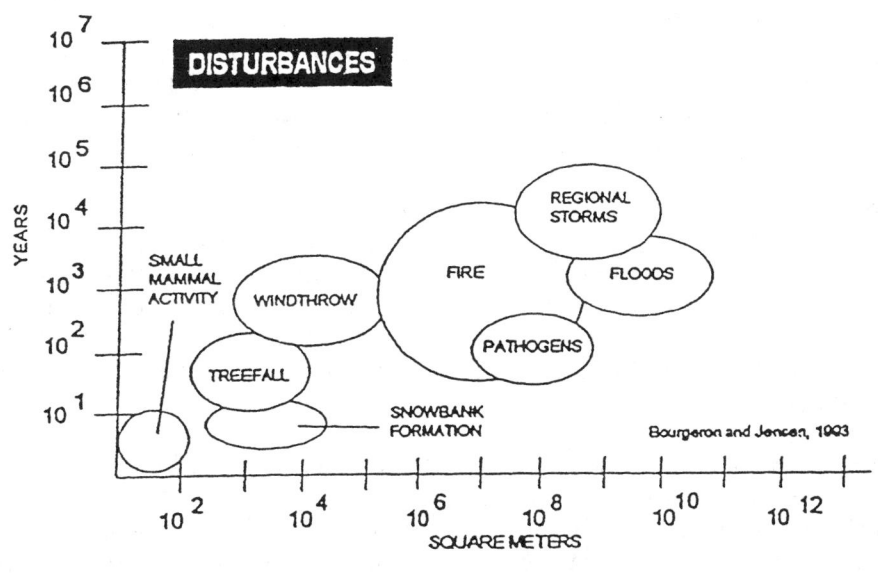

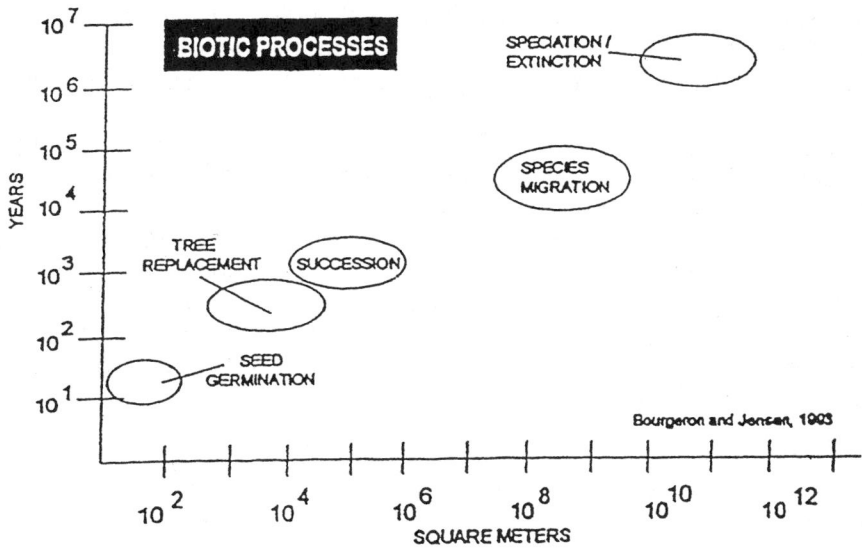

Figure 1. Disturbances and biotic responses occur in many forms and at various spatial and temporal scales (adapted from Bourgeron and Jensen 1993).

The context of cumulative effects issues is typically environmental damage or degradation. Positive cumulative impacts can, however, occur. Specific beneficial use characterizations are often the key to identifying positive impacts. Under arid conditions, increased stream flow— potentially resulting from the combined effects of timber harvest (which reduces evapotranspiration) and weather modification (to increase precipitation)—is a positive cumulative effect.

The potential for positive and negative cumulative effects, the relative difficulty in assessing cumulative effects, and in some situations the lack of agency initiative in analyzing potential cumulative effects has led to litigious determination of some cumulative effects issues. Relevant cases in California include:
1. A 1985 decision (*Environmental Protection Information Center v. Johnson* [1985 S. Ct. Sonoma County, CA 216 502]) requiring CWE to be considered in the approval of any timber harvest plan on state or private forests, and
2. A 1987 decision (*Environmental Protection Information Center v. Maxxam* [1987 S. Ct. Humboldt County, CA 79879) in which "the court agreed with EPIC that the Department of Forestry [California] failed to consider adequately the cumulative effects of stepped-up harvest operations by the Pacific Lumber Company after it was purchased by Maxxam Corporation" (Cobourn 1989a).
3. A 1993 decision (*East Bay Municipal Utility District v. California Department of Forestry and Fire Protection*) declared that the Department of Forestry's cumulative effects guidelines were adequately addressing cumulative effects associated with Timber Harvest Plans. The court did, however, direct the Department to stop using their cumulative effects evaluation guidelines as *de facto* forest practice rules unless they were approved as rules by the California Board of Forestry (Pete Cafferata, California Department of Forestry and Fire Protection, personal communication, January, 1996).

Taken to a logical conclusion, quantification of potential cumulative effects is a daunting exercise for numerous reasons. The spatial scale of cumulative effects is large relative to most individual site assessments, and partially because of this, ecological complexity is dramatically increased (Gooselink and Lee 1989). Also, watershed ecosystems involve a complex dynamic between many linked physical and biological processes operating at and across many spatial scales (figure 2). Scientific understanding of these processes is limited. The physical and biological elements of a watershed and its subareas reflect local geology, climate, vegetation, and other factors. Consequently, every watershed is unique, with its own distribution of these factors as well as effects due to the history of past natural or induced perturbations (Washington Forest Practices Board 1993).
It is clear that an exhaustive cumulative impact analysis following current regulatory procedures would be extremely complex and would cover incremental impacts to a host of environmental processes and organisms resulting from each human activity. In addition, the analysis would have to consider interactions among the activities and indirect impacts caused by them. Since the interactions increase as the square of the number of independent effects, the analysis would soon become entirely unmanageable. Thus, established procedures of environmental assessment may easily become data-limited or too cumbersome to be useful, if they are applied to cumulative assessment of the effects on the regional environment or over an extended period (Gooselink and Lee 1989:118).

Because of these complexities, Gooselink and Lee (1989:118) further argue that "[c]umulative impact assessment breaks new scientific, technical and regulatory ground...The required shift in focus is from species-oriented, linear, causal analysis based primarily on structural features of individual sites, to an ecosystem orientation where functional attributes of large-scale processes are emphasized." This is echoed by Horak et al. (1983) who state, "[t]he demand for cumulative impact assessment requires a complete restructuring of the problem itself; an articulation of the

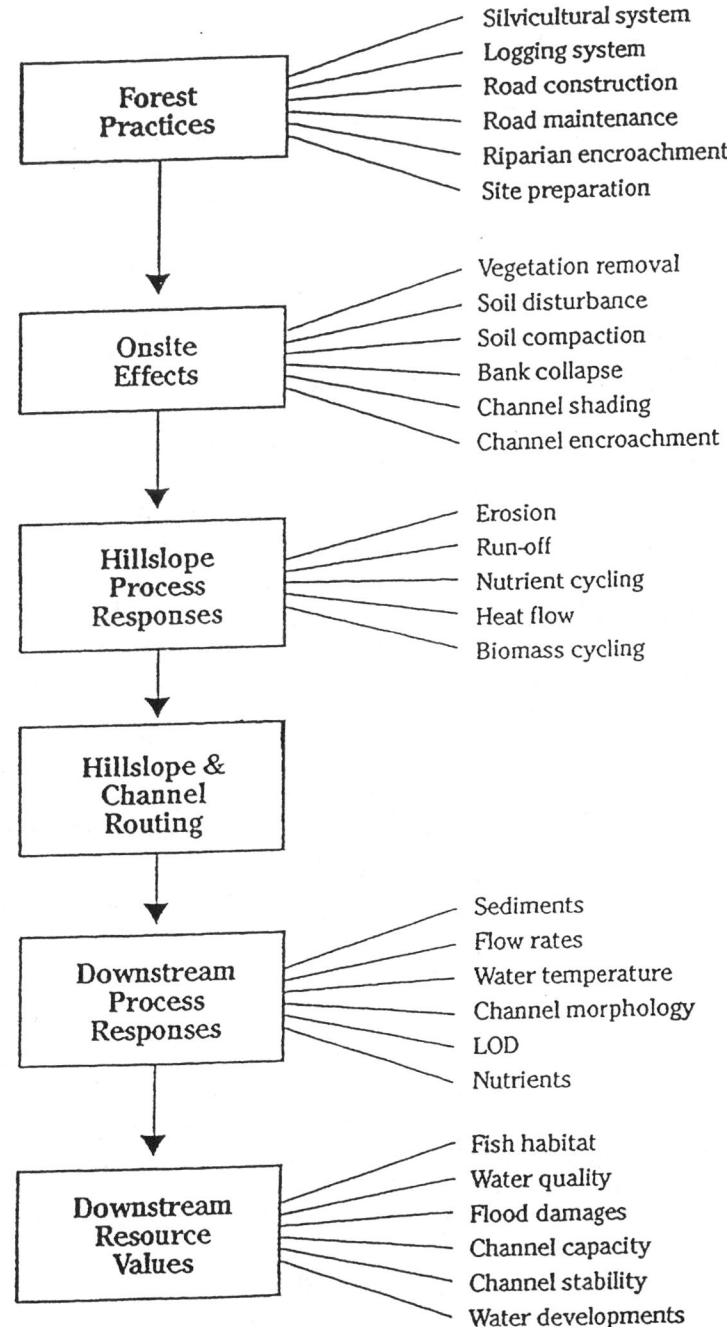

Figure 2. Links between forest management and water resources values. These links are for one type of management activity only, timber harvest. Similar sets of links could be diagrammed for grazing, mining, recreation, etc. (from NCASI 1992).

assumptions driving the assessment; new techniques and tools for aggregating diverse impacts; and a search for standards or criteria of significance in order to judge overall, long-range impacts."

Because of these challenges, comprehensive methods for assessing cumulative effects have been slow to develop. Although many methods follow the letter of the law, they are not based on the physical and biological processes that actually link management activities to cumulative effects. Emerging, "science-based" approaches, although more effectively addressing the actual cause and effect relationships driving cumulative effects, can be costly and time-consuming. Within this context, the need for an assessment of options for CWE evaluation was identified as an objective for SNEP.

This report focuses on cumulative *watershed* effects; not cumulative effects on other resources. The basic intent of NEPA and other legislation is, however, directed at all cumulative effects. And watershed effects are clearly related to and interwoven with other resource issues. Ultimately, cumulative effects analysis will encompass all of the major resource considerations.

DISTINGUISHING CHARACTERISTICS OF THE SIERRA NEVADA

None of the following characteristics is unique to the Sierra Nevada. However, taken together as a suite of attributes, they characterize the Sierra Nevada as a complex landscape in terms of physical and biological processes and socio-economic issues relevant to estimating and predicting CWE. In terms of CWE, these attributes are best considered in the context of their relevance to hydrological processes; no effort is made here to describe all of the ramifications of each attribute to issues related to land management in the Sierra Nevada.

On the scale of the mountain range as a whole, or at least its western slope, four primary influences overlay and interact with other factors: (1) Many areas are still recovering from hydraulic mining that took place in the 1800s. This continuing recovery is superimposed on (2) recovery from fires in some areas or (3) vegetation buildup in other areas resulting from fire suppression during the last sixty-eighty years, and (4) recovery from timber harvests of varying intensity and spatial scale. In the broad geographical sense, much of the mid-elevation zone of the west slope is a mosaic of conditions driven largely by these four influences. Five major factors characterize the Sierra Nevada:

Climate
The climate on the west slope is conditioned by maritime, temperate influences; on the eastside the continental-dominated climate results in greater extremes in precipitation and temperature. Rainfall onto the snowpack occurs over a wide elevational band, and the extent of the rain-on-snow zone changes appreciably from the northern to the southern part of the Sierra Nevada. Rain-on-snow can accelerate peak flows and increase erosion and sedimentation. Precipitation, air temperature, and other basic climatic attributes also vary widely from north to south and with elevation. Among the many implications of these gradients are the responses by biota that may be at the margin of their geographic range.

Geology/geomorphology
The preponderance of granitic parent material in the southern and eastern Sierra has implications for elevated levels of soil erosivity and sediment production. Sensitive inner gorge lands occur in middle- to lower-elevations on the west slope where the majority of precipitation falls as rain, and where streams are larger and stream power is highest. The inner gorges are found mainly in areas with granitic and metasedimentary rock, and are rare in areas with volcanic rock. Most of the mainstems of the river systems on the west slope were sized by major flood events and are in bedrock. This implies that channels will not change readily. In the upper-elevations, many channel segments are dominated by steep gradients, and consequently are energy-rich and supply-limited. Many of the lower gradient river sections in the foothills are dammed. The low-gradient,

alluvial reaches, with their buildup of herbaceous vegetation, become the most sensitive areas of management concern.

Biology
Over a hundred years of resource extraction and grazing have greatly changed many biological systems such that "natural" conditions often are not known. Dams, diversions, and fish stocking have severely affected natural aquatic populations. Although dams have largely eliminated anadromous fish above the foothills on the west slope of the range, anadromous fish issues must be considered in the lower ends of stream systems. Because the water quantity and quality of anadromous fisheries is driven largely by upstream processes, management activities at higher elevation are implicated in downstream anadromous and resident fish issues.

Hydrology
Surface-water flow regulation occurs at a wide range of scales. Impoundments range from major dams to small ponds, and flows are diverted for projects as small as irrigation of personal gardens or as large as domestic water supplies for millions. Hydroelectric power is produced on a range from massive turbines to run-of-the-river, small hydropower installations. Most of the mainstems of the major rivers are heavily regulated. At this broad river basin scale (e.g., the Stanislaus or the Tuolumne Rivers) development implications include:
   1. Little free-flowing water. Because water flows into massive reservoirs, activities that could otherwise affect flow magnitude and sediment transport are masked to the extent that suspected cumulative effects cannot be identified.
   2. A constancy of surface flows over what may have occurred naturally (e.g., downstream floods and dry periods are rare).
   3. Impediments to up- and down-stream fish movement are common.
In many situations these implications combine to implicate the hydropower project itself as *the issue* (e.g., as a potential cause of degraded anadromous fish habitat). These implications also have resulted in a focus of effort on the smaller tributary basins because identification of CWE is easier without the overriding effects of large-scale reservoirs.

Compared to many areas in the Pacific Northwest, the percentage of intermittent streams is high in the Sierra Nevada, and headwater streams (third order and smaller) are more common.

Socio-economic influences
There is a relatively high human population density in the urban-wildlife interface. This results in accelerated "people-related" influences on CWE (e.g., probably more fires, changes in hydrology due to [sub]urban development) and a high (and increasing) demand for high quality water).

The high level of mixed-ownership land, especially in the central Sierra Nevada, implies (1) the need to include numerous parties (both public and private) to effectively solve problems, (2) the high potential for gaps in information available for CWE analysis (e.g., some owners may be unwilling to supply data), (3) "inequities" can arise when management decisions by one owner (typically a public agency) must be constrained because of the potential heavy impact by other owners in a watershed, (4) difficulties in coordinating restoration efforts in problem watersheds, and (5) the potential lack of an impetus for some owners to mitigate for past actions.

Recreational use of forested lands is greater in the Sierra Nevada than in most other regions of the United States. This is compounded by the diversity of recreational uses and the increasing use of wildlands by users with non-traditional values.

The constituency for CWE issues is effectively statewide because of the high degree of water regulation via dams and diversions. Water fin conveyed rom the Sierra to the major metropolitan areas of California and to irrigated agricultural operations statewide. The values of the water users (e.g., urban dwellers and irrigators) may conflict, and the result is a lack of consensus on water policy, as seen today in California. A corollary harks back to the 1800s. Land-use actions in the Sierra Nevada have downstream implications. In the 1800s it was hydraulic mining during the Gold Rush; today salinization of the San Francisco Bay Delta and mortality of juvenile fish in the Delta are CWE issues driven largely by actions undertaken in the Sierra Nevada and the foothills.

SELECTED METHODS FOR PREDICTING AND ESTIMATING CUMULATIVE WATERSHED EFFECTS

Reid (1993) presents comprehensive documentation of major procedures used in California or the West for CWE prediction through 1991. Much of the following text on the Equivalent Clear-cut Area, Klock Watershed Cumulative Effects Analysis, Equivalent Roaded Area, R-1/R-4 Sediment-Fish Model, California Department of Forestry Questionnaire, Water Resources Evaluation of Non-point Silvicultural Sources, Limiting Factor Analysis, and Rational Approach is taken directly from Reid (1993).

Except for the Synoptic Approach, the methods listed here are directed to forested lands. A variety of approaches has been used. Some methods include development of disturbance indices for comparing sites or management alternatives; others address physical and biological processes. This distinction, between "science-based, cause and effect" approaches, and indexing methods is at the heart of the current debate over the future of CWE assessment procedures.

Equivalent Clear-cut Area (ECA)

One of the earliest CWE analysis procedures was developed by the U. S. Forest Service (USFS) for use in northern Idaho and Montana (U. S. Forest Service 1974; Galbraith 1975). The primary impact of concern was channel disruption, and this was assumed to be caused primarily by increased peak flows from reduced transpiration due to logging. Channel disruption was assumed to be an index of impacts on many beneficial uses, so specific impacts were not considered.

Application of the model first requires calibration for an area. The extent to which each management activity increases water yield is determined as a function of vegetation type, elevation, and age of the activity. Although these relationships could be defined for many land uses, only those related to timber management are usually included. Values for each land-type and land-use category are then compared to values for a clear-cut to calculate the area of clear-cut that would produce the same change, and this is used to calculate the equivalent clear-cut area (ECA) coefficients. The amount of monitoring data required for full calibration of model coefficients is usually prohibitive, so professional judgment is often used to define ECA coefficients.

Once the model is calibrated, application to particular sites requires measurement of the area of each land-use activity in each elevation zone and vegetation type. Areas are multiplied by ECA coefficients and summed to calculate total change in water yield, and altered water yield is assumed to be proportional to altered peak flows. Allowable thresholds for flow modifications are specified by law in northern Idaho, and calculated values are compared to the mandated thresholds. Allowable increases may be modified according to the perceived stability of channels in an area.

The ECA model is not presented as a complete CWE analysis method. Provisions are not made to evaluate the effects of other types of land use; other mechanisms of channel destabilization or peak-flow increase are not analyzed; other types of environmental changes are not considered; and specific impacts are not addressed. In effect, the estimated increase in water yield is used as an index of potential impact rather than as a predictor of impacts.

Because ECAs are calculated for a particular time, they do not account for past impacts that might interact with conditions at the evaluation time. Thus, the persistent effects of old landslides are not accounted for in an ECA analysis. Potential impact is assumed to be proportional to a year's transgression, and the recovery period for the impacted resources is implicitly assumed to be the same as that for water yield on a clear-cut. This means that the model does not apply to morphological changes that are cumulative through time. Figure 3 illustrates this problem. In this case, the driving variable (e.g., increased runoff, sediment input) has a relatively quick recovery period, but the impacted feature (e.g., channel width, volume of stored sediment, smolt mortality) takes considerably longer to recover from the effects of the temporary alteration in the driving variable (isolated activity). Even though the sequence of land-use activities is carried out in such a way that the driving variable has ample time to recover, the disturbance frequency is too high to allow recovery of the impacted feature between disturbances, and the impact accumulates through time (repeated activity). To assess a temporally cumulative impact, recovery periods of both impacts and driving variables would have to be considered.

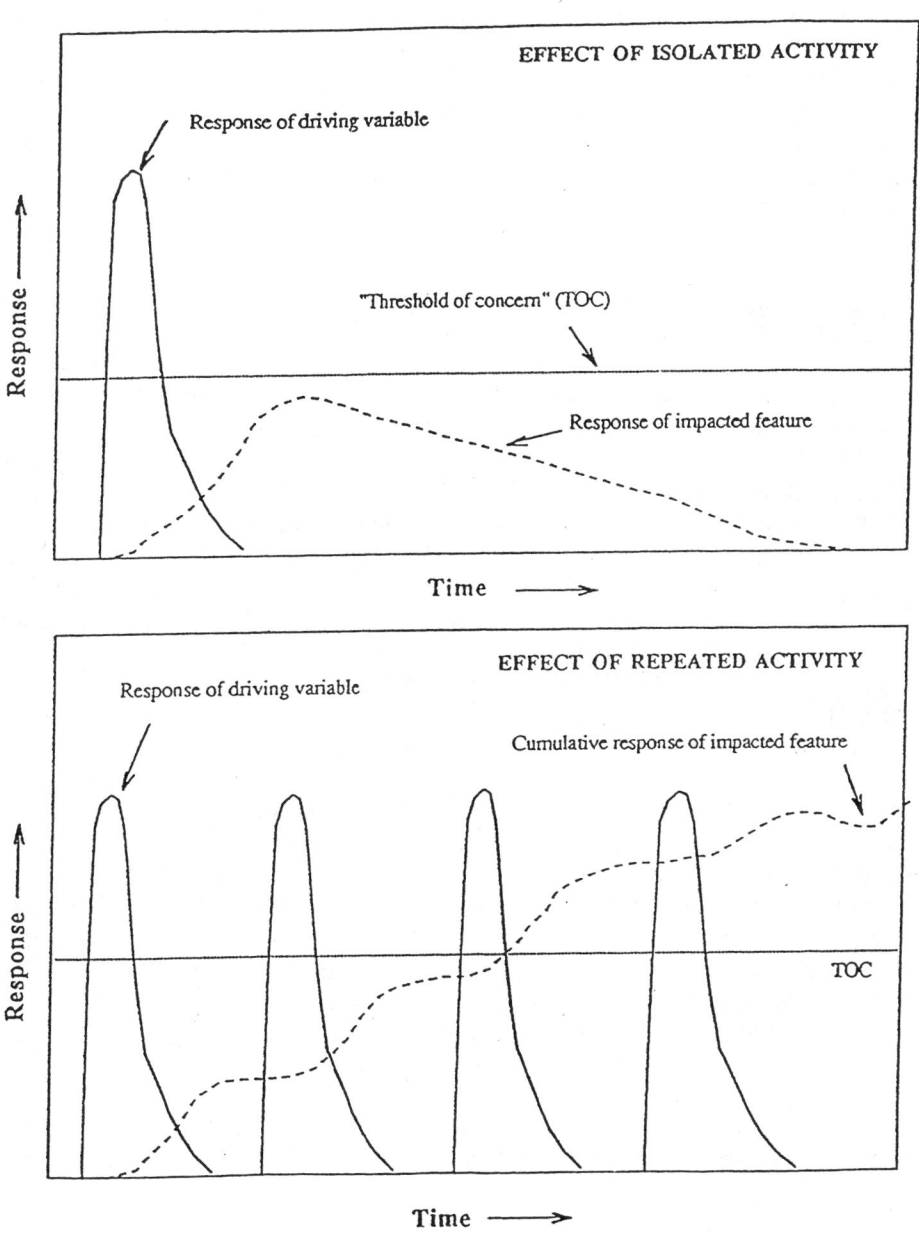

Figure 3. Cumulative effect of differing recovery times for a driving variable and an impact (after Reid 1993).

A model can be applied to a new site only if its assumptions are valid there. The ECA model assumes that (1) channel disruption is caused by increased peak flows, (2) increased peak flows are proportional to increased water yield, and (3) increased water yield is proportional to area logged. If these assumptions are valid for a particular area, then the model may be appropriate, but the assumptions must be tested carefully if the model is to be applied with confidence. Several studies have compared water-yield increases predicted by ECA with measured changes. King (1989) showed a 44% underestimate by ECA in basins smaller than those the model was designed for, and Belt (1980, quoted in King 1989) found a 38% underestimate in appropriately sized basins.

The theoretical foundation for the ECA method is weak. Logging is known to increase water yield by reducing transpiration, but this increase occurs primarily during the drier seasons and rarely affects the highest peak flows. However, peak flows may be significantly increased by logging in areas subject to rain-on-snow events, because more snow accumulates and then melts faster in cleared areas. This is likely to have a more significant effect on channel-modifying peaks than altered transpiration. An index of clear-cut area may fortuitously address both mechanisms of change, but numerical predictions are likely to be unfounded because the underlying processes are different.

Klock Watershed Cumulative Effects Analysis (KWCEA)

Klock (1985) adapted and combined elements from other CWE assessment methods into an equation to analyze CWE potential from timber management in the Washington Cascades. The impact of concern is again channel destabilization, but the driving mechanism is assumed to be increased sediment input. The KWCEA equation combines factors for local climate (the R-factor of the Universal Soil Loss Equation; Wischmeier and Smith 1978), susceptibility to surface erosion (the USLE K-factor adjusted by a disturbance index for logging practice and recovery through time), a landslide occurrence factor (a local landslide frequency adjusted by site recovery factors), a topographic factor that incorporates gradient and distance from a stream, and a hydrologic sensitivity factor that indexes increased evapotranspiration after logging. Model application thus requires information on soil characteristics, topography, landslide frequencies associated with logged sites and roads, land-use history, and areas of land-use types. Index values are calculated for each type of site in a watershed, normalized by watershed area, and summed to provide an index of potential impact. An index greater than 1.0 indicates a greater than 50% chance of "increased impact on the downstream aquatic ecosystem."

Unfortunately, no documentation was provided for the derivation of model components, and procedures for assigning relative weightings were not explained. Disturbance and recovery coefficients presumably reflect measurements from central Washington, so the equation must be recalibrated for regions where runoff and erosion processes interact with channels in different ways. But adjustment of component weights for new areas is an indeterminate problem because component indices do not represent physical quantities: there are too many adjustments to make and too little information to guide the adjustments. Klock (1985) did not indicate how impact probabilities were related to index values, the types of impacts considered, or if and how the model was tested. Other references to its application were not found.

The KWCEA model assumes a relatively narrow view of CWE. Only the effects of timber management and roads are considered, and the model is only relevant to those impacts that might be generated by altered sediment input. Because site-recovery functions are used to calculate each year's index, effects that accumulate through time are not addressed. This oversight is particularly relevant to sediment-related impacts, because introduced sediment may be stored for long periods and cause long-term lag effects.

Equivalent Roaded Area (ERA)

USFS Region 5 staff developed the ERA method to index CWE potential from timber management and roads. (For a more thorough treatment of the ERA method, see Menning et al. 1996 in SNEP Volume II). Although recent Region 5 direction (U. S. Forest Service 1988) for CWE assessment does not mandate the use of the ERA method, examples of the ERA approach are prominent in the directive, and most USFS practitioners in Region 5 use some form of the ERA method. A recent example implementing many aspects of the current direction is the Last Chance-Clarks Creek evaluation on the Plumas National Forest (see the Case Studies section of this report).

The original model assumed that channel destabilization is the impact of greatest concern in California, and that destabilization occurs primarily from increased peak flows due to soil compaction. The model has changed considerably since its initial release. The recent version (U. S. Forest Service 1988; Cobourn 1989b) extends the procedure to identify beneficial uses and to address downstream impacts generated by several mechanisms. Impact potential is indexed by relating the impacts expected from each activity to that expected from roads. The sum of indices for a watershed represents the percentage of basin in road surface that would produce the same effects as the existing or planned distribution of management activities. Indices for different planning options can then be compared to rank their potential for producing impacts.

Application of the method first requires identification of important downstream values and the criteria necessary to protect each. A land-use history is developed for the watershed, sensitive sites are identified, and ERAs are calculated for each activity with respect to the mechanism thought to be of greatest concern. Values are summed for the watershed and normalized by the area to calculate the total ERA percentage, and this is compared to the allowable threshold identified for the area. If the calculated ERA value is higher than the threshold, then the area may be singled out for further evaluation by other means.

Each national forest is expected to identify local concerns and mechanisms and calibrate coefficients for characteristic site types, and Haskins (1987) outlined this procedure for the Shasta-Trinity National Forest. Recent practices often cause less impact than older ones, so changes in land management procedures must be identified and accounted for, and recovery curves for various activities and site types must also be defined. Calibration ideally incorporates monitoring data for the identified impact mechanism from different land-use activities in that area, but the necessary data are rarely available, and calibration usually depends on professional judgment. Disturbances other than timber management and road construction can also be evaluated if their effects are appropriately quantified. Thresholds of concern (TOCs) are to be identified independently for each area and are to take into account inherent differences in sensitivity to impacts. TOCs are usually defined by calculating ERAs for areas showing different levels of impact. Users are expected to exercise judgment in modifying ERA coefficients and TOCs for particular sites.

In essence, the ERA method is an accounting procedure for assessing the instantaneous influence of past, present, and planned activities on the potential for environmental change. The method is designed to provide a screening tool for identifying areas of particularly intense use rather than to predict effects. As an index of use intensity, however, ERAs are likely to be grossly correlated with many types of impacts. The method also provides a framework for organizing local information on land-use impacts and mechanisms of change.

ERAs are not comparable between areas because the method is customized to address issues relevant to each implementation area. ERA coefficients defined for an area where landsliding is the major impact have little relation to those defined where the major concern is increased peak-flows from rain-on-snow events.

Management activities are usually planned to maintain a watershed's ERA below an identified TOC. If the threshold is approached or exceeded, then channel condition may be evaluated by an interdisciplinary team. Proposed activities may be reviewed to determine whether they should be modified or delayed, or whether existing conditions can be improved to lower the ERA values. A basin is assumed to be healthy again as soon as sub-threshold ERA values are reattained, but the recovery times actually required by impacted resources are not considered. The method cannot be used to identify sites where impacts persist from earlier disturbances, thus the method is incapable of addressing temporally accumulating effects: if recovery time for the impacted resource is longer than that for the driving variable, then impacts can continue to accumulate even though the driving variable does not (figure 3). Complementary effects are also excluded, because the method requires identification of a single impact mechanism. Monitoring programs are not yet in place to assess the success of the most recent ERA method in avoiding impacts, and earlier formulations of this method were not independently validated.

The early formulations of the ERA model used the results of a study in southern Oregon that showed peak flow increases in a basin with 12% roaded area (Harr et al. 1975) as the basis for identifying both the driving mechanism for change (increased peak flows) and the TOC (12% compacted area). However, these results are not transferable to California's geology and climate. Ziemer (1981), for example, demonstrated no significant change in peak flows in a California Coast Range watershed with 15% of its surface area compacted. In addition, because channels respond as readily to altered sediment inputs as to altered flows, selection of increased peak flows as the single driving mechanism does not fully address the problem. The most recent implementations of the ERA model avoid these problems by using ERA values primarily as an index of land-use intensity, so the hydrological basis of the original method is no longer important.

To assess the link between ERA and aquatic ecosytem response, McGurk and Fong (1995) compared time series of ERAs and diversity (measures of aquatic community health) for three forested areas with logging and roadbuilding in California. No relationship was found using the standard Region 5 method, but a significant, inverse relationship between ERA and diversity was found when the ERA calculations were limited to a 100-m strip on either side of the channel. Above a 5% no-effect threshold, as ERA increased, aquatic diversity declined. These results shows that an accounting and risk estimation procedure, when constrained, can predict aquatic response and condition.

R-1/R-4 Sediment-Fish Model

USFS researchers of the Intermountain Research Station, resource specialists and managers from USFS Regions 1 and 4, and university researchers worked together to develop a method for predicting fish survival as a function of sediment input in the Idaho Batholith. The procedure has two parts: first, sediment yields are estimated using a method described by Cline et al. (1981), and then the effects of increased yield on fish are calculated using relations presented by Stowell et al. (1983). The R-1/R-4 model addresses settings where deposition of fine sediment is the major impact on fish populations, and where sediment is eroded primarily by surface erosion on logged sites and roads. Components of the method are continually revised to incorporate new research results, and model coefficients are calibrated locally for each application area. Developers of the model stress that it is directly applicable only to the Idaho Batholith, and that results should be taken as broad estimates of trends and relative impacts rather than as precise predictions of change.

Sediment yield is predicted using relations developed from extensive research on erosion process rates as a function of land use in the Idaho Batholith. Average loss rates were calculated for roads, logged areas, and burned sites, and these are applied to the areas of each activity in a watershed to calculate on-site loss rates. A sediment delivery relation from WRENSS (Water Resources Evaluation of Non-point Silvicultural Sources, see later section; U. S. Forest Service 1980) is used to calculate input to streams, and a relation defined by Roehl (1962) allows estimation of delivery to critical stream reaches.

Gravel siltation, summer rearing habitat, and winter carrying capacity were identified as factors limiting salmonid survival. Results of studies in the Idaho Batholith were compiled to provide empirical correlations between substrate embeddedness and sediment yield, between habitat measures and substrate embeddedness, and between fish response and habitat quality. To apply the model, calculations are carried out for critical reaches downstream of a project area. If natural siltation levels are known and conditions prior to the project are measured, then the incremental effect of a planned project can be estimated.

As presented, the model applies only to the Idaho Batholith because its relationships depend strongly on runoff mode, runoff timing, climate, sediment character, erosion process, channel geometry, and species of fish. Use of the model in other areas requires remeasurement of each of the component relations.

This procedure is one of the few that relates land-use activities directly to a resource response, and is unique in its recognition that impact recovery rates cannot be indexed by recovery rates of the driving land use. Once a channel reach is modified, the new condition becomes the baseline for further changes, and effects that accumulate through time can therefore be predicted. The R-1/R-4 model is not a complete model for CWE evaluation because it addresses only one type of CWE from one mechanism, but it is well-founded on research results within the area for which it was developed.

California Department of Forestry Questionnaire

The California Department of Forestry and Fire Protection (CDF) has developed a procedure for use by Registered Professional Foresters to assess CWE potential from timber management (California Department of Forestry and Fire Protection 1994). This procedure differs from all others described in that it relies almost completely on the users' qualitative observations and professional judgment, and it provides only qualitative results. It also addresses a wider variety of uses and impacts than other procedures, and includes many that are not related to water quality, such as recreational, esthetic, biological, and traffic uses and values. It was designed to be used within the time and access constraints of timber harvest plan (THP) development, and a nonquantitative approach was adopted to avoid the complacency that accompanies a numeric, "right" answer.

For biological, recreational, esthetic, and vehicular traffic impact assessment, a four-step process is followed. The user is first asked to construct a resource inventory in the assessment area, and is then asked whether the planned timber operation is likely to produce changes on each of those uses. The third step identifies impacts of past or future projects, and includes projects either under the ownership or control of the timber/timberland owner or not under the control of the owner. Finally, the user is asked whether significant cumulative effects are likely from the proposed operation.

Analysis follows a slightly different procedure for watershed resources assessment. Onsite and downstream beneficial uses are listed. The analysis area for watershed assessments is an "area of manageable size relative to the THP (usually an order 3 or 4 watershed)" (California Department of Forestry and Fire Protection 1994). Existing channel conditions are first inventoried, and adverse impacts from past projects are identified. The user is then asked to rate the magnitude (e.g., "high," "medium," "low") of a variety of potential effects from the proposed project, from expected future projects, and from combined past, present, and future projects. When problems are identified, the assessment should be considered as an indicator of the need for further review by specialists.

The CDF procedure is essentially a checklist to ensure that the important issues have been considered. Although it provides descriptions of possible CWE, it does not specify how the likelihood of their occurrence is to be evaluated, and instead relies on the user's ability to make qualitative predictions based on observations of earlier projects in the area. Validity of the results rests completely on the user's expertise, experience, and professional judgment, so results are not necessarily reproducible. The specified spatial and temporal evaluation scales are based primarily on feasibility of evaluation, rather than on the nature of the potential CWE. This implicitly restricts the types of CWE that can be evaluated, although the procedure permits a larger scope where it is deemed by the user to be necessary.

The procedure's major strengths lie in its flexibility. This is the only CWE evaluation method that requires assessment of more than one type of impact from more than one type of mechanism. It is also one of the few procedures that allows evaluation of temporally accumulating impacts.

Water Resources Evaluation of Non-point Silvicultural Sources (WRENSS)

The most complete process-based approach to evaluating timber-management impacts is the series of procedures referred to as WRENSS (U. S. Forest Service 1980). This collection presents quantitative evaluation procedures for a variety of water-quality impacts, including altered flows, sediment, and temperature. Pollution by nutrients and chemicals is addressed qualitatively, as are changes in dissolved oxygen. Although not specifically intended to address CWE, WRENSS methods are applicable to CWE evaluations.

Application of WRENSS to a CWE analysis would require identification of likely environmental changes generated by a project, likely downstream impacts, and the mechanisms generating them. Appropriate WRENSS procedures would be selected to estimate the magnitude of expected impacts from a planned project, and these values would be added to those calculated for existing projects to estimate the total effect. Because the original focus for WRENSS was water quality, the procedures do not address impacts on other resources, and only the effects of timber management and roads are considered. Evaluation procedures are independent of one another, so modules can be replaced by improved methods as they become available.

The WRENSS procedure for evaluating hydrological change is based on computer simulation modeling of water budgets. The program PROSPER (Goldstein et al. 1974) was used to develop relationships for rain-dominated areas, and WATBAL (Leaf and Brink 1973a, 1973b) for areas with snow. Results are presented as graphs and tables that allow users to estimate changes in evapotranspiration, flow duration, and soil moisture for various logging plans. Stream temperature changes are assessed using the Brown model (Brown 1970).

Sediment modules include methods for estimating surface erosion, ditch erosion, landsliding, earthflow activity, sediment yield, and channel stability. Surface erosion is calculated using a modified Universal Soil Loss Equation (Wischmeier and Smith 1978) and sediment delivery relations, and ditch erosion is assessed by calculating permissible velocity. The landslide module is a step-by-step guide to performing a landslide inventory for an area: the area is subdivided into uniform subareas, hazard indices are calculated for each, and slides are inventoried in representative areas to determine characteristic volumes and delivery ratios as a function of hazard index and land use. Sediment yields are estimated using results of monitoring and process evaluations, and channel stability is indexed by changes in sediment and flow.

WRENSS is neither a CWE model nor an evaluation procedure, but is simply a collection of tools useful for impact evaluation. A CWE analysis using WRENSS would be flexible enough to handle a variety of impact mechanisms, but it would need to use additional methods to assess the effects of other land uses and to evaluate impacts on particular resources. Implementation of most of the procedures requires training in hydrology or geomorphology, and calculations are often complex and time-consuming. WRENSS is the only method described here that is capable of estimating the magnitudes of different types of watershed changes.

Each procedure presented in WRENSS was developed by researchers and resource specialists with relevant expertise, but procedures vary widely in sophistication, approach, and accuracy, and many have been superseded by more effective methods. Some of the methods have been intensively tested, while others have not been validated at all.

Limiting Factor Analysis (LFA)

Reeves et al. (1989) developed the LFA as a procedure for identifying factors that limit coho smolt production in coastal Oregon and Washington, and the procedure can be adapted for use in CWE analysis. Unlike the approaches described above, LFA is designed from the point of view of a particular impacted resource. Any procedure designed to predict CWE, rather than merely to assess their likelihood, must incorporate a component such as this.

The LFA model is in the form of a dichotomous key that leads users through computations to estimate smolt production from data on physical habitat in a watershed. Model application requires detailed surveys of fish populations and areas occupied by various habitat types in a watershed. The procedure is based on extensive fish and habitat surveys that were compiled to disclose patterns of habitat use in the Pacific Northwest. LFA can thus be applied only to sites with population-habitat relationships characteristic of the development area, but the model could be recalibrated for other areas if limiting factors are the same and appropriate relationships can be measured.

Because LFA sums smolt production from different habitat categories, the impacts of changes in habitat distribution can be calculated. Relations between cumulative habitat change and land-use activities would also be required for prediction of CWE, and these are produced in some form by most other models described here. A procedure capable of assessing impacts of timber management on fish would need to couple a trigger-based model such as ECA or ERA with an impact-based model like LFA.

Rational Approach (Grant)

Grant (1987) described a process-based procedure for establishing thresholds of concern for flow-related channel disruption. As was the case with LFA, this method is designed from the point of view of the impact rather than the activity.

Grant reasoned that channels can be disrupted only if their beds and banks are remolded, and this requires mobilization of bed sediment. If increased flows do not affect the frequency of sediment transport, then a river will remain stable. Grant presented equations to calculate flow thresholds for sediment transport as a function of particle size and channel geometry. Projected flow increases can then be compared to threshold discharges to evaluate their potential for altering a channel. The Rational Approach can also provide an index of channel stability.

The Rational Approach illustrates the potential use of process-based information for quantifying the potential effects of changing conditions, but it was not intended to provide a full CWE analysis. Use of the method to evaluate CWE would require its coupling with models that predict flow changes from land use, and with methods to analyze channel destabilization by other mechanisms, such as increased sediment input or riparian disruption.

The Synoptic Approach (EPA)

The Synoptic Approach was developed by the U. S. Environmental Protection Agency (EPA) (Leibowitz et al. 1992) for evaluation of cumulative impacts to wetlands for Section 404 (Clean Water Act) permit review. This method is not intended to provide a precise, quantitative assessment of cumulative impacts within an area. Rather, it provides a relative rating of cumulative impacts between areas. The major steps in the Synoptic Approach are:
    1. Define goal and criteria (including definition of the objectives and intended use of the assessment, accuracy needs, and assessment constraints).

2. Define synoptic index (including description of the natural setting, definition of the landscape boundary, function and values, identification of significant impacts, and definition of "combination rules").
3. Select landscape indicators (including surveying data and existing methods, assessing data adequacy, description of assumptions, and indicator selection).
4. Conduct of the assessment (including planning for quality assurance and control, map and data analysis, map production, and accuracy assessment).
5. Prepare final report.

The Synoptic Approach provides a framework for making comparisons between landscape subunits through the use of one or more landscape variables, or synoptic indices, for each subunit. Examples of possible subunits are counties, watersheds, and ecoregions. Key elements to the approach are determination of the synoptic indices, landscape indicators, and combination rules by an assessment team.

Four generic, synoptic indices relating to the function, value, functional loss, and replacement potential at the landscape level are defined. They are then replaced by individual indices relevant to the objectives of the analysis. These specific indices serve as the basis for comparing the characteristics of landscape subunits; they also represent the actual functions, values, and impacts of concern to the manager. For example, in an application concerned with nonpoint source nitrogen pollution within an agricultural region, the specific indices for capacity and landscape input might be the maximum denitrification rate and the nitrate loading rate, respectively. A specific synoptic index is typically a mathematical expression that includes several factors. The indices can represent single or combined factors. If a combination of factors is selected, a set of "combination rules" needs to be defined. These rules address issues such as how the factors will be combined (e.g., by addition, multiplication, or some other operation), whether the data will be normalized or whether weightings among factors are equal, and whether the same combination rules apply to all landscape types and across the entire range of conditions within the study area.

Quantifying the indices at the landscape scale would be difficult, if not impossible. Indicators of the actual functions are instead developed as first-order approximations of the particular index. For example, agricultural area could be used as the indicator for nonpoint source nitrate loading. This approximation process carries assumptions that must be described. Use of area as an indicator for landscape function assumes that function or capacity per unit area is similar for all landscape elements (e.g., wetlands) or, if it varies, that landscape units having different unit area response are similarly distributed between landscape subunits.

The Synoptic Approach is not meant to be used to assess the cumulative effects of specific impacts. It is meant to augment the site-specific review process and improve "best professional judgments" and is probably most effectively used at extremely large landscape scales (e.g., states).

Watershed Analysis
In the late 1980s, an interdisciplinary, interagency effort aimed at addressing concerns surrounding management of forested lands was initiated in the state of Washington. A consortium of individuals representing various organizations participates in a Timber/Fish/Wildlife (TFW) Agreement that continues today. TFW cooperators include state agencies (e.g., Washington Departments of Natural Resources, Fisheries, Wildlife, and Ecology), tribes, members of the forest products industry, small private landowners, and environmental groups. One product of the TFW Agreement is a "Watershed Analysis" manual sponsored by the Washington Forest Practices Board and initially published in 1992.

In 1993, President Clinton commissioned an interagency scientific team to develop a set of alternatives for management of forested ecosystems within the range of the northern spotted owl

(*Strix occiendtalis caurina*). This effort culminated in the report by the Forest Ecosystem Management Assessment Team (FEMAT) (1993) entitled *Forest Ecosystem Management: An Ecological, Economic, and Social Assessment*. A major product from FEMAT was the concept of "Watershed Analysis," an ecosystem management approach that shares many elements with the Washington State "Watershed Analysis" procedure. For purposes of clarity in this report, the FEMAT (federal) approach is labeled "FWA" and Washington State approach "WWA."

Both WWA and FWA are evolving, iterative processes that will be improved as experience and knowledge grow. There is formal recognition that both approaches will never be "complete" and that they will be upgraded as new techniques become available. Both approaches are modular so that specific methods can readily be modified or replaced in future editions. Several WWA projects have been completed and pilot FWA projects are underway. Because of the evolving nature of these programs, the following synopses should be viewed as snapshots in time that represent the current state-of-the-art. They should not be considered as descriptions of the ultimate FWA or WWA procedure.

Washington State Watershed Analysis (WWA) The WWA approach is aimed at developing forest plans for individual watersheds based on scientific understanding of significant links between physical and biological processes and management activities (Washington Forest Practices Board 1993). The method defines areas of sensitivity within each watershed and considers resource vulnerabilities based on potential specific impacts to public resources (specifically fish habitat, water quality, or public works) (figure 4). For this purpose, the state of Washington has been divided into approximately 400 watersheds ranging in size from 4,000 to 20,000 ha (10,000 to 50,000 acres). The process is collaborative involving resource scientists and managers representing landowners, agencies, tribes and other interested publics. Resource specialist and management teams conduct the assessment within a two- to five-month time frame. A detailed and specific policy structure encodes the steps, operating rules, key links, and decision requirements for the teams. Products can include area-specific management prescriptions, and monitoring to be implemented by landowners, agencies, tribes, and others to track the effectiveness of the prescriptions and the assessment on which they were based.

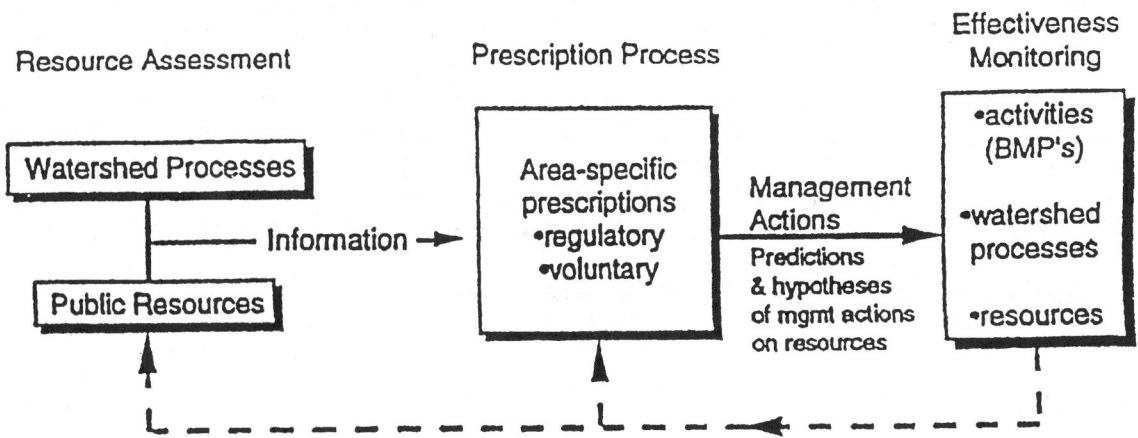

Figure 4. Components of the Washington Forest Practices Board Watershed Analysis methodology (from Washington Forest Practices Board 1993).

The approach incorporates a dual-level hierarchy. Watersheds are first screened by interdisciplinary teams of resource specialists to qualitatively assess their sensitivity to environmental change. If basins are found to be sensitive, they are evaluated by the appropriate experts to define more precisely the potential impacts and management alternatives. Version 2.0 of the Watershed Analysis manual (Washington Forest Practices Board 1993) incorporates resource assessment modules for mass wasting, surface erosion, hydrologic change, riparian function, stream channel assessment, fish habitat, water supply/public works, and routing through the fluvial system. Other modules (e.g., water quality) are planned or under development. Four specific steps are followed:

1. Startup: maps, photos, and data are collected; teams are formed and responsibilities defined.
2. Resource assessment: a trained and certified interdisciplinary team inventories watershed processes and resources following a structured approach to problem definition framed by a series of critical questions. Sensitive areas are located, mapped, and evaluated for potential or existing impacts and risks to public resources.
3. Prescription process: a trained and certified management team develops a tailored set of management prescriptions (potentially including required and voluntary components) that responds to the resource concerns identified by the resource specialists.
4. Wrap-up: the teams complete the report for public review prior to final acceptance of the plan.

Once the plan is accepted, further forestry activities in the watershed must be conducted within the provisions of the prescriptions for each sensitive area, unless an alternative plan is approved, with compliance regulated by the Washington Department of Natural Resources. Elements of WWA that differ from many traditional approaches include the "science-based" focus, a reliance upon diligent revision as monitoring provides feedback on whether resources are improving or degrading, a formalized structure, and a reliance on stakeholders within each watershed to make the process succeed.

A basic premise is that a change in erosion, hydrology, or riparian function resulting from forest practices is significant when it is sufficient to cause an adverse change in a public resource of fish habitat, water quality, or public works. Watershed processes (sources or causes) are linked to public resources by the flow of products including sediment, water, wood, and energy that shape and determine the stream environment. Since each watershed possesses distinct environmental conditions, resource characteristics and sensitivities, WWA is premised on the need to define locally active watershed processes that pose significant risks to public resources (e.g., reductions in large organic debris recruited to channels may result in fewer pools and unstable stream beds).

FEMAT Watershed Analysis (FWA) The intent of FWA is to develop and document a scientifically based understanding of the processes and interactions occurring within a watershed. This understanding focuses on specific issues, values, and uses within a watershed. Protecting beneficial uses is a fundamental aim of FWA. Because of the links between headwater areas, valley floors, and downstream users, FWA should encompass the entire watershed, including all owners. Application of FWA should result in reports describing the distribution pattern, types, and relative importance of resource values, altered environmental conditions, and mechanisms of environmental changes in watersheds (Furniss and McCammon n.d.).

Four analytic scales are included in the FWA approach. They are roughly analogous to geographical scales, and the scales are smaller than "river basins" (large, continuous land areas of hundreds to thousands of square miles) and larger than "sites" (a specific activity area within a watershed). The spatial scope of FWA is normally between 8 and 80 km^2 or 5,180 to 51,800 ha

(20 and 200 mi^2 or 12,800 to 128,000 acres). FWA suggests that ecosystem elements at the larger scale (e.g., region and river basin) be considered in order for FWA to be relevant.

FWA, somewhat contrary to WWA, is not a decision process in that it does not produce a formal decision notice or record of decision as required by NEPA. Ideally, FWA derives data and information from the larger-scale analyses and plans and provides information to smaller-scale site analyses, both of which are formal decision points under NEPA (Furniss and McCammon n.d.).

FWA is to be carried out by interdisciplinary/interagency teams of resource specialists who are professionally qualified to assess and interpret the structure, composition and function of the ecosystems within a given watershed. These teams incorporate public involvement to ensure that the full range of values, resource needs, and expectations associated with each analysis watershed are included in the analysis. The degree of public involvement varies based on the type and intensity of the issues involved, the availability of existing data and information, and the history of public participation within or adjacent to the subject watershed (Furniss and McCammon n.d.). Steps followed in FWA are:
*   identify issues, describe desired conditions, and formulate key questions
*   identify key processes, functions, and conditions
*   stratify the watershed
*   assemble analytic information needed to address key questions
*   describe past and current conditions
*   describe condition trends and predict effects of future land management
*   integrate, interpret, and present findings, and
*   manage information, monitor, and update the process.
Products from FWA should include:
*   a description of the watershed including its natural and cultural features
*   a description of the beneficial uses and values associated with the watershed, and, when supporting data allow, statements about compliance with water quality standards
*   a description of the distribution, type, and relative importance of environmental processes
*   a description of the watershed's present condition relative to its associated values and uses
*   a map of interim "Riparian Reserves"
*   a description of the mechanisms by which environmental changes have occurred and a description of the role of specific land-use activities in generating change
*   a description of likely future environmental conditions in the watershed, including a discussion of condition trends and of the potential future effects of past activities, and
*   interpretations and management recommendations: watershed processes and ecosystem concerns and interactions to be addressed at a project-planning-scale in different parts of the watershed (Furniss and McCammon n.d.).

FWA and WWA share many of the same objectives, goals, and philosophies. Nevertheless, differences do exist. WWA, for instance: uses scientist *and manager* teams—inclusion of managerial teams could expedite understanding of the results and recommendations and foster "buy-in"; has a strictly codified internal structure that forces decision-making—this could speed up the entire analysis process; is more formally codified in state regulations than FWA—WWA cannot order a land owner not to do something on her/his land, but WWA can direct the way an agreed-upon action is carried out; focuses on anadromous fish; and functions by implementing a set of prescriptive Best Management Practices.
On the other hand, FWA: has a wide latitude in prescriptive choices, largely because FWA focuses on federal lands; develops an "objective" (technical) understanding of how systems work in each analysis area—value-based socio-economic-cultural considerations on what is best for an area are not prominent; and encompasses a bigger land base for analysis (4,000-20,000 ha [10,000-50,000 acres] for WWA and 5,180-51,800 ha [12,800-128,000 acres] for FWA) that could potentially lead to different conclusions from a WWA conducted on the same land.

National Council of the Paper Industry for Air and Stream Improvement (NCASI)

The National Council of the Paper Industry for Air and Stream Improvement (NCASI) also advocates a hierarchical approach to CWE evaluation for application on timber-industry lands throughout the five western forested states. An initial screening procedure assesses watershed sensitivity, evaluates existing conditions, documents the existence of important downstream watershed values (beneficial uses), and defines how changes in hydrologic processes caused by forest management activities are linked to downstream watershed values. A second level of analysis is triggered when the initial screen predicts potentially unacceptable cumulative effects that cannot be controlled by management solutions (National Council of the Paper Industry for Air and Stream Improvement 1992).

This approach incorporates specific cause and effect links between hillslope management actions and in-channel fluvial responses. As a conceptual procedure, the method should be designed to meet the following objectives (National Council of the Paper Industry for Air and Stream Improvement 1992):

- Identify the important hydrologic and geomorphic processes of concern.
- Describe the relationships between environmental damage and beneficial uses by evaluating the physical processes linking on-site disturbances to downstream effects.
- Provide a measure of the sensitivity of beneficial uses to management.
- Describe effects of land management relative to background conditions (including natural variability and historic disturbance), and develop methods to assess recovery factors.
- Utilize methods that are understandable, reproducible and practical, and supported by available resource information.
- Provide evaluations of CWE that are based on measured physical or biological effects rather than indirect indicators of change (e.g., percent area cut), thus allowing assessment of accuracy in actively managed watersheds.
- Describe the uncertainty caused by gaps in technical knowledge.

The current focus of the NCASI CWE program is to fill in critical information gaps on the cause-effect links and to work with individual states to better define the process links (Walter Megahan, NCASI, personal communication, July 1994).

Idaho Forest Practices Method

In 1991 ,an inter-institutional task group was charged through an amendment to the Forest Practices Act of the State of Idaho to (1) review and evaluate existing tools for assessing CWE on beneficial uses and water quality, (2) develop processes and procedures for making assessments of CWE in any given watershed, and (3) formulate methods for controlling CWE and protecting water quality and beneficial uses, based on the results of these assessments. The process is designed to be systematic, structured, reproducible, defensible, and adaptive, thereby ensuring its technical and practical integrity. It is designed to give trained evaluators an understanding of: inherent hazards of the landscape within a watershed, and current conditions within a watershed relevant to hydrologic processes and to the disturbance history. A review draft of the proposed method became available for public comment in mid-1994 (Cumulative Effects Task Force n.d.).

The process consists of an assessment of fine sediment in stream bottoms, channel stability, sediment delivery, water temperature/stream shade, nutrients, and hydrology. A fisheries element is not included, and the process is limited to forest practices; effects of grazing, mining, recreation, or other nonforest practice activities are not addressed. The method provides keys to determine whether CWE exist for any of the factors assessed, along with guidance to help landowners design management practices to alleviate adverse conditions and prevent CWE problems from future forest practices.

Outcomes from the method include the following potential courses of action: allow forest practices to proceed using standard Best Management Practices; help resource managers redesign forest practices, and/or correct the identified watershed problems so that practices may proceed; or delay forest practices in those situations where technological solutions to adverse CWE are not available.

CASE STUDIES OF CWE ASSESSMENT PROCEDURES USED BY SELECTED NATIONAL FORESTS IN THE SIERRA NEVADA

A strong case can be made that historic attempts at cumulative effects analysis were, in many ways, the first attempts at practical landscape level analysis, in that generally watersheds larger than project areas were analyzed. Admittedly, nearly all of these analyses were functionally focused. Recent biodiversity and ecosystem health issues (e.g., Pacfish, FEMAT) have affirmed the need for integrated landscape analysis (i.e., integrated between resources, agencies and stakeholders, and geographic scales). In a sense, the objectives of CWE assessment have broadened.

In the past, CWE analyses were conducted to fulfill the NEPA requirement for assessment of cumulative effects. Analysis was project driven, rather than geographically based (e.g., a timber sale rather than a basin plan). Since about 1985, all timber sale project planning included cumulative effects analysis. The existing USFS Region 5 methodology recommends analysis of second or third order basins, and this was almost always the scale used for project assessments.

It is unfair to judge analyses of the past against a set of recently developed objectives, and that is not the intent of this review. The objective of this section is to review cases of CWE analysis for processes and components that will aid managers in addressing questions of ecosystem assessment in the Sierra Nevada. Four cases were selected for review:
1. The Meiss Allotment on the Lake Tahoe Basin Management Unit, as an example of a CWE analysis driven by the grazing issue.
2. The Last Chance-Clarks Creek evaluation on the Plumas National Forest, because a recent USFS Region 5 restoration review identified strengths in this analysis.
3. The Lower North Fork Cosumnes River watershed on the Eldorado National Forest, because the forest recently (June 1993) revised its CWE analysis process.
4. The Peppermint-Holby watersheds on the Sequoia National Forest, because this forest has a well-established CWE assessment procedure.
These cases represent a range of Sierran geography and management activities, but their representation of the quality and type of CWE assessments is not known.

No rating of the case studies was attempted. Instead, they were reviewed with numerous questions in mind. The factors considered are included in appendix 3. Essentially, the review centered on two questions: (1) How well is the situation (including watershed condition and risk of alternatives) explained to the decision maker and public? (2) How well does the analysis consider system function and process?

Case 1: Environmental Assessment of the Meiss Grazing Allotment (Lake Tahoe Basin Management Unit)
    Purpose of the Assessment Development of an Allotment Management Plan was the project objective. The analysis centered on stream and fish habitat conditions in the headwaters of the Upper Truckee River and Big Meadow Creek. There are approximately 4,000 ha (10,000 acres) within the analysis area, including 32 km (20 miles) of stream.

    Procedure and Findings The assessment procedure consisted of comparing the existing condition against desired conditions set forth as Forest Plan objectives, and assessing the impact of a variety of alternative range management strategies on those conditions. Fisheries habitat was identified as the key resource issue. Also discussed were downstream water quality issues, but the in-stream fish condition was selected for analysis, as it was thought to be most sensitive to management.

Streams within the planning area were stratified by geomorphic type, and streams types thought to be most sensitive to grazing were selected for further analysis. Indicators of habitat condition for each stream type were used to describe condition. These factors were stream shading, in-stream cover, residual pool volume, and percentage substrate as fines. The indicators were measured for selected stream reaches, and compared to standards for the stream types contained in the Forest Land Management Plan. Professional judgment was used to assess how each project alternative would effect current condition.

The project alternatives were evaluated against downstream water quality objectives (e.g., nutrients, turbidity) set with the aim of protecting Lake Tahoe. In this case, water quality sampling data indicated that Big Meadow Creek met Upper Truckee Basin water quality objectives. An unwritten assumption was that improvement of water quality (specifically temperature and sediment) within the allotment would meet downstream objectives in Big Meadow Creek and Lake Tahoe.

Review/Summary of Meiss Grazing Allotment Case The analysis focused on components of the stream system that were most sensitive to the management activities (streams were stratified). Assessment of condition was based on field measurement of indicators. The comparison of alternatives did not use models; the evaluation criterion was the probability (rated in subjective terms) of each alternative's chance of meeting the stated objectives. There were clearly defined resource objectives or "desired conditions" against which to compare existing conditions.

Case 2: Last Chance-Clarks Creek (Plumas National Forest)
Purpose of the Assessment Evaluate risk of proposed salvage timber harvest on subdrainages within this watershed. Chronic watershed and stream degradation within the watershed was recognized, and a method was needed to assess the relative condition of subwatersheds to both focus future inventories and to assess the risk of salvage logging in the subwatersheds.

Procedure and Findings A two-phase approach was followed, a large-basin analysis coupled with a ecosystem management project. The large-basin analysis followed the steps outlined in the Region 5 Cumulative Effects Handbook (U. S. Forest Service 1988). This included consideration of:
- Beneficial uses of water, with water quality protection criteria including no reduction in channel condition, and no reduction in streamside and riparian vegetation except for incidental situations such as road crossings or as necessary for structural stream restoration.
- Recovery objectives aimed at improving the trend for all channels rated poor, reducing daily maximum summer temperatures to 20°C (68°F) in all perennial streams, and increasing the abundance and diversity of riparian vegetation.
- Watershed history, including a description of the levels of both grazing (number of animal unit months) and timber harvest (board feet harvested) from the 1920s on.
- Mechanics for initiating CWE. Accelerated erosion was identified as the primary CWE process. Roads and stream bank erosion were named as primary sediment sources.
- Watershed sensitivity. Alluvial channels and meadows were identified as the most sensitive watershed components in the drainage.

The assessment divided a 40,470 ha (100,000 acre) eastside Sierra watershed into fifteen subwatersheds. Existing information was used to evaluate the condition of each of the smaller drainages using road density, road condition, channel stability, and the ERA procedure as input information. This evaluation was aided by a joint Soil Conservation Service-Forest Service evaluation of watershed, channel, and road conditions conducted in 1989.

Four criteria were used to rate relative levels of disturbance and condition in the watersheds. These were: ERA, miles of stream/mi^2 in fair or poor condition (Pfankuch rating), road density (miles/mi^2), and density of roads with severe erosion problems (miles/mi^2). No attempt was made to weight these criteria. Rather, subwatersheds were ranked for each, and a clear trend was apparent. Three of the watersheds (Clarks, Cottonwood, Granite) rated very high (poorest condition) for all criteria, indicating they had greatest need for additional analysis and treatment. Another four basins were classified in the next condition class.

Recommendations for management included increased use of appropriated funds targeted for restoration (versus KV [Knudsen-Vandenberg] funding, which is generated from timber sale receipts), road improvement planning and funding, accelerated revision of allotment management plans (AMP), linkage of AMP and salvage sale planning in these watersheds, revised approaches to post-wildfire treatments, and increased monitoring of poorly understood system components (e.g., vegetation recovery rates).

The information presented in the Last Chance Assessment served as an impetus for the second phase of the overall evaluation, the Clarks Creek Ecosystem Management Project. A desire to conduct salvage logging within the watershed was the primary project driver, but the larger scale Clarks assessment caused a different approach to be taken.

Site specific analysis of the basin revealed that both stream channels and riparian areas were far below potential condition. Stream bank erosion and sloughing rates were high. Riparian plant community diversity and vigor was low. Grazing and roads were identified as the two primary factors contributing to the poor condition.

As the project was planned, the following objectives were set: (1) increase upper bank and flood plain ground cover to 95% live vegetation, (2) increase tree-shrub layer riparian cover to 35% (low-flow period), (3) reduce ERA value to below 80% of the TOC (see ERA description), and (4) reduce road erosion by 50%.

Planning for timber sales, allotment management, and restoration were conducted concurrently. Management strategies were revised, roads were closed, and stream bank restoration undertaken.

Review/Summary of Last Chance-Clarks Creek Case The discussion of watershed history laid out plausible cause-response scenarios for causes of the current condition, and helped to identify key watershed processes and mechanisms. Existing data from a variety of sources were used effectively. The initial large-scale assessment identified issues and characteristics common to all subbasins, and provided a logical basis for addressing smaller-scale issues. The need for integration of planning across functional boundaries was a predictable outcome of the landscape-scale analysis, this in turn produced a link between management and restoration prescriptions. ERAs were essentially used as a screening tool (along with road density and channel condition) in the large-scale analysis. Though carried through as a condition criteria at the smaller (Clarks Creek) scale, other basin-specific criteria were added (e.g., miles of road and channel and riparian condition indicators).

Case 3: Lower North Fork Cosumnes River (Eldorado National Forest)
        Purpose of Assessment Evaluate susceptibility to adverse cumulative off-site watershed effects. The specific case reviewed was the Lower North Fork Cosumnes River CWE analysis.

Procedure and Findings The same steps outlined in the Last Chance-Clarks example were employed in this case. Forest planning watersheds (approximately 1,200-4,047 ha [3,000-10,000 acres]) were the unit of analysis. CWE susceptibility using ERA was based on a comparison of the calculated ERA value and the TOC for that watershed. Risk levels ran from low (<50% of TOC) to very high (>100% of TOC). This comparison served as an initial screening of condition, which was then modified by using watershed and stream condition information, a rating of the quality of information used in the screening (good data means higher confidence), and as needed, additional field survey of watershed and channel condition. Risk levels corresponded to different levels of resource protection during project implementation.

Watershed sensitivity rated very high, primarily due to a large proportion of inner gorge land, and soils with very high erosion hazard. The level of ERA disturbance was calculated at 5.2%, about one-half of the recommended TOC. An overall risk level of moderate was assigned to the watershed due to a lack of fishery habitat condition data, poor condition of the Upper North Fork watershed, and long-term drought conditions which may have delayed triggering of adverse effects.

Review/Summary of Lower Nork Fork Cosumnes River Case The results are tied to management prescriptions. Assessments take into account the availability and quality of data. The analysis addresses a larger scale. As disturbance levels increase (as measured by ERAs), the need for assessment of field conditions increases.

Case 4: Peppermint-Holby Watersheds (Sequoia National Forest)

Purpose of Assessment Objective of this evaluation was to assess the risk of a planned timber sale activity on two watersheds each approximately 1,200 ha (3,000 acres) in area.

Procedure and Findings A modified version of the ERA method was employed. Historic and planned activities were given disturbance values, to which a delivery coefficient was applied. The delivery coefficient was a product of six factors including slope, delivery distance, ground cover, and soil characteristics. Six other factors were used to derive a watershed sensitivity rating. These factors were soil, topography, climate, geology, vegetation, and channel type. A TOC was assigned to each watershed based on its sensitivity rating. Calculated ERA values were then compared to the TOC to evaluate the risk of adverse impacts. A monitoring plan was developed to track the response of in-channel variables to the management activity. Monitoring factors included fish habitat typing, macroinvertebrates, and turbidity.

Review/Summary of Peppermint-Holby Watersheds Case The need for monitoring was recognized and addressed. Watershed sensitivity was recognized and channel condition was used as a sensitivity component.

Lessons Learned from the Case Studies
NEPA promotes actions which will minimize environmental damage, and develop an understanding of the interrelationships of all components of the natural environment and the effects of human activities on the environment. It requires that direct, indirect, and cumulative effects be considered when conducting an environmental analysis.

The four cases reviewed had different objectives, but, as with any CWE analysis, they sought to provide the decision maker and the public with a clear picture of the condition of the resource, relevant issues, and possible consequences of alternative activities. In reviewing the case studies, some basic questions were asked. To what degree did the analysis reach these objectives? How well are the components and interrelationships understood? And, does the analysis help the decision maker take actions that minimize environmental damage?

64

The answers are somewhat nebulous, as might be expected from cases using different methods to assess different issues at different times and places. Each analysis presented information that could help a decision maker in assessing risk. Some of the analyses are quite clear while others require futher explanation for the decision maker and public to best put the information (and therefore the amount of acknowledged and unknown risk) in perspective. Condition (and analysis) indicators closest to the uses of concern (or the issue of concern) are probably best at clearly describing the condition. In other words, "temperature in degrees" is probably a better indicator than "percent shading," and certainly better than "amount of timber removed."

None of the analyses did an adequate job of describing the interrelationships between system components and processes. They can best be seen as indices rather than assessments of cause-effect relationships.

Integration The case studies showed very little evidence of public or interagency involvement. Such interaction is essential in identifying (or verifying) issues and beneficial uses, and in assembling the most accurate description of historic conditions, events, and patterns. (The one exception is the Sequoia example. The analysis procedures were developed as part of a mediated settlement that included extensive public involvement).

The degree of interdisciplinary assessment varied, but was generally low. The Meiss example centered on fisheries habitat, which was appropriate, but integration with watershed processes was not strong. Integration of resource functions in the other cases was weaker. In almost all cases the uses of concern are biological in nature, and the mechanisms are often physical; there is a need for improved integration between physical and biological specialists.

Watershed History and Disturbance Regimes The Last Chance case provided a good description of watershed and beneficial use history. The Meiss case did this to a lesser extent. Consideration of historic conditions (i.e., management history), with the intent of helping to explain how a particular watershed functions, is an important element that should receive more attention in CWE analysis.

With the exception of the Last Chance case, existing condition was not discussed in the context of historical trends. Discussion of the trends (some indicator of condition) relative to a desired condition or objective, and how alternatives might affect these trends is valuable but was generally lacking. In the simplest terms, discussion of conditions should describe what the conditions are, what they were in the past, and how alternative management activities might affect them in the future. The consideration of past conditions (especially as influenced by historical activities and disturbances) should greatly assist specialists in evaluating the potential impacts of alternatives on existing conditions.

In general, there was little discussion or inclusion of disturbance regimes (natural or induced) in the case studies. Disturbance regimes should be a component of historical reviews and should also be included in discussions of risk. In general, the ERA-based approaches (except for references to the effects of drought) seem to assume a static system in terms of natural influences. The Sequoia approach did include climate as a component of watershed sensitivity, but this approach probably diminishes the considerable influence that climatic variation plays in the response of most watersheds to land disturbance activities.

Spatial Scales Three of the four cases attempted, in various ways, to link the analysis of a relatively small watershed to a larger-scale area (i.e., effects farther downstream). Of the four cases, only the Last Chance analysis started at a larger scale and worked upstream to the smaller basins. Beginning with the larger-scale analysis seemed to produce several positive outcomes:

- The "importance" of the smaller drainage relative to larger scale effects was known.
- The large-scale processes, issues, and conditions were known.
- Broad-scale analysis established a priority for evaluation of the smaller drainages. Based on selected criteria, the highest priority areas are identified for further analysis, management, or other action.

Watershed Processes Important watershed processes were clearly identified only in the Last Chance case. The Eldorado and Sequoia cases considered these processes to some degree in their assessments of watershed sensitivity, but they focussed on structural landform sensitivity rather than on dynamic processes. The Meiss analysis addressed condition, and desired condition. The criteria selected for analysis indicated an understanding of stream and riparian processes, and the effects of the proposed management alternatives on those processes, though they were not specifically described. To some extent, key processes can be inferred from the selection of ERA as the measure of disturbance (e.g., in the Sequoia case, sediment is identified as the process of concern), but an explict discussion of watershed processes is recommended.

Watershed-Aquatic System Condition and Models All but one case used more than one criterion to characterize disturbance or condition. In at least one case, the channel criteria were not quantified. Two of the cases relied heavily on condition indicators (versus models or projections). We believe that, historically, USFS approaches have not stressed condition enough, and that future attempts at CWE assessment should place greater emphasis on condition assessment. Methods of assessing condition may vary, the interpretation of data may be difficult or even contentious, but given the error factor associated with nearly every predictive model, more discussion of existing condition (and implications for future management) is warranted. The ideal cumulative effects analysis would clearly distinguish indicators of disturbance (which carry a risk of affecting condition) and indicators of condition, which include the influence of past disturbance.

The Last Chance case, for example, benefitted by describing effects on beneficial uses (e.g., downstream reservoir sedimentation) to support the finding that the watersheds were in poor condition. This is in contrast to techniques which calculate a disturbance indicator, and use it to infer condition. The assessment of the Meiss Grazing Allotment essentially used no disturbance indicators; rather the analysis was of condition, and again (as with Last Chance) poor condition of channels was taken to mean that problems existed.

The recognition of the importance of sensitive lands affecting processes was generally lacking in all the cases. Perhaps this recognition is documented elsewhere (e.g., forest standards and guidelines) and is therefore implied in all analyses, but the analyses reviewed seemed to assume that impact of disturbance on beneficial uses is equal on all landforms and locations. The Sequoia example did account for sediment delivery by considering a variety of factors, including slope and soil texture and distance to streams, but the difference between response and delivery was not explained.

Assessment of Risk The Eldorado assessment included the preparer's level of confidence in the analysis. Because CWE analysis is essentially a risk assessment, it is important to clearly identify the limitations of the analysis, so this can be weighed against potential impacts. The other cases are mute on the level of confidence, though the Meiss and Last Chance cases infer a level of confidence in the explanation of the analysis procedures.

Monitoring Only the Sequoia example included monitoring aimed at validating assumptions made during the analysis. Both the Last Chance and Meiss cases include monitoring to see if conditions meet objectives. Given the present uncertainty in the veracity of currently-available predictive tools, and the uncertainty of assumptions made in more subjective evaluations, an increased level of monitoring is necessary.

WATER RIGHTS AND ADJUDICATION AS ELEMENTS OF CUMULATIVE WATERSHED EFFECTS DECISIONS

This section is not based upon extensive research on water rights or associated procedures. It is based on discussions with staff employees of the California Department of Fish and Game and the California State Water Resources Control Board (SWRCB).

Long before cumulative effects were recognized in the regulatory arena (e.g., NEPA, CEQ), issues that effectively were "cumulative" in nature were addressed through the water-rights system. This section presents two hypothetical illustrations of how California's water-rights systems relates to cumulative in-stream uses of water.

Example 1

An owner of property located on a watercourse observes in the summer of 1993 that the stream dries up. The owner, and other nearby owners of streamside property, expect inappropriate upstream diversions by a country club and mine as the cause. Analysis of historical flow records by staff of the SWRCB shows that although flows varied fifty-to-seventy years ago, the watercourse was seldom dry, or was dry for very short periods of time. More recently (ten-to-thirty years ago) the channel was often dry, and for long periods of time (sixty-to-ninety consecutive days). During the later period (from 1960-1980) development increased drastically relative to the earlier period. This suggests some sort of cumulative impact causing the reduced flows. This scenario quickly leads to a water-rights assessment. Primary players in this scenario are the SWRCB and the court system.

Although "riparian" and "appropriative" rights are typically the two primary rights in this type of situation, two additional types of rights, "pre-1914" and "Spanish land grant," may be involved. Spanish land grant rights are very old and are essentially untouchable by court action. A downstream holder of a Spanish land grant right can successfully adjudicate an upstream holder who does not have a Spanish land grant right.

Although the Board has full knowledge of pre-1914 rights, the actual authority on pre-1914 rights is not as clear. As an example, a legitimate pre-1914 right could take 100% of the flow on a hypothetical watercourse. However, if a state agency (e.g., Department of Fish and Game) cites a formal regulatory edict (e.g., to retain a healthy fishery) which conflicts with the 100% flow pre-1914 right, the SWRCB may be reluctant to step in; the Board may offer a recommendation, for instance to pass through additional flow to support the fishery, but often will not go beyond the recommendation stage.

Riparian rights allow the holder of property adjacent to a watercourse to use water directly; it cannot be stored for use in another season (e.g., cannot pump in winter for use in summer). Riparian-right holders are subject to SWRCB authority, but the SWRCB does not have jurisdiction over riparian rights and the process is not simple. Resolution of conflicts is typically accomplished through court action. Riparian-right holders are required to register their right with the SWRCB, but the SWRCB does not pursue this requirement aggressively and the extent of registration is not known. This means that the amount of diversion or water use is effectively unknown on non-adjudicated watercourses.

Holders of appropriative rights are subject to SWRCB jurisdiction and regulation. This type of right is for a given amount of water during a given season at a given location.

In disputes exemplified by the drying up of the watercourse, a basic intent of the SWRCB staff is to balance the interests of riparian- and appropriative-rights holders at the lowest possible level of conflict. Although riparian-right holders typically have the most fundamental water right, in this case, evaluation of the hydrologic flow data suggests that current water diversion is not the

67

cause of the cessation of flow; flow was intermittent during the 1960s, and possibly earlier. The cause is unknown but most likely is a combination of diversions, including uncontrolled riparian uses.

Options include the following: (1) develop an informal agreement among the parties, (2) issue a "finding" by the SWRCB (a report giving the staff's opinion on the solution of the dispute), (3) one party requests a hearing before the SWRCB to present evidence to convince the SWRCB of the validity of their claim, and (4) sue the SWRCB. In option (3), the adjudication will allocate all water in the basin, with the court deciding a fair and reasonable partition among all users. This action can result in losses of water to riparian-right holders and it effectively converts riparian rights to appropriative rights. One outcome of the adjudication is the establishment of a Water Master who administers the judgment of the court. Federal Water Masters are currently in place on the Truckee, Walker, and Carson Rivers.

An allied function of the SWRCB is the duty and obligation to review water rights in light of the public's use of water. The recent Mono Lake court decision exemplifies this "public trust" issue. Legitimate rights were held by Los Angeles for water from multiple watercourses influent to Mono Lake (i.e., a cumulative effect). In the Mono Lake ruling, the court broadened the previous scope of the public trust to include fisheries, recreation, and other activities and resources in finding that drying up the inflows to Mono Lake was damaging to the public trust. The watercourse referred to in Example 1 may well have been damaged with respect to the public trust. But the only way to make this determination would be court action bringing in all diverters and riparian users.

Example 2

If the town of Plymouth needs 10 cubic feet per second of water to meet projected growth demands, it will file an application with the SWRCB outlining needed facilities, places and type of water use, and other relevant information. As part of this process, Plymouth will eventually document its perspective on fishery concerns. The California Department of Fish and Game (CDFG) does not usually comment on this type of project until notice is made publicly of the project. SWRCB staff reviews Plymouth's documentation and responds with a list of actions needed to comply with the California Environmental Quality Act (CEQA), or to prepare a NEPA document, if appropriate. All issues relevant to CEQA (e.g., bypass flows, fisheries enhancement, wildlife areas, improvements to distribution facilities) must be addressed or mitigated foAfter receipt of this documentation, the SWRCB decides if a negative declaration is adequate or if a complete environmental impact report (EIR) is required. If Plymouth doesn't have the resources to prepare an EIR, the SWRCB may prepare its own EIR, requesting relevant information from Plymouth. The project is then reviewed by the appropriate state departments, and CDFG eventually recommends action on the project after determining in-stream flow needed, effects on riparian vegetation, and other relevant issues. Disagreement among the parties (i.e., CDFG and Plymouth) can go to a formal hearing with presentation of legal arguments. In this scenario, the SWRCB decides the final course of action.

SUMMARY AND RECOMMENDATIONS:
COMPARATIVE ASSESSMENT OF CWE METHODOLOGIES

The numerous approaches taken to CWE assessment offer a wide range of options for use in the Sierra Nevada. An area like the Sierra Nevada has a myriad of governmental, quasi-governmental, and private organizations and individuals that either own land or have an acute interest in land management. Agreement on the adaptation of a single (or even a small number of) CWE methodologies may be extremely difficult. Considerations are numerous and include cost of implementing the methodology, skill level and expertise needed, "defendability" of the procedure in a court situation, and availability of input data. Rather than make assumptions about these considerations, we list desirable attributes of a CWE methodology. The procedure(s) should:

- Be scientifically rigorous and specifically link natural or human-induced causes for system changes on the hillslope or in the channel with implications to downstream beneficial uses (e.g., fisheries, domestic water supply).
- Prescribe direct, specific management actions keyed to information collected in the affected basin.
- tie management prescriptions to conditions in the stream, causes for those conditions, and hazards in the watershed,
- include physical and/or biological measures that prompt change in management,
- include all major land uses (e.g., recreation, urbanization, mining, timber harvest, grazing),
- include a monitoring component to determine if prescriptions are implemented as specified,
- assess and track the temporal and spatial distribution of impacts from past actions,
- be structured so that results of the analysis are repeatable and readily verifiable,
- screen levels of disturbance so that the level of the analysis effort matches the severity of disturbances and/or condition of basin,
- incorporate a landscape scale (versus "project" scale), and
- involved all major stakeholders as full partners from the beginning of the process.

An underlying premise is the importance of specifically documenting the logic of all steps undertaken. In this sense, a CWE model or procedure should be seen as a tool, and should not be blindly applied without identification of relevant site-specific issues, processes, values, and concerns.

On a Sierra-wide scale, we believe a method is needed to screen for locations in particular need of a CWE assessment and to generate a priority listing of CWE assessment locations. This screening should include in-channel biological criteria because in-channel attributes often integrate the consequences of hillslope activities. In-channel processes, functions, and attributes also are generally less variable than hillslope attributes, and are consequently better indicators of ecosystem condition. We also see hillslope disturbance as a second important criterion for ranking of sites for CWE analysis.

Once a locality is chosen for CWE assessment, an area-specific screening is needed to identify (a) the socio-economic-cultural issues, values, and concerns which will be distinct to each locality, and (b) the intensity of analysis required. Input to these decisions, and subsequent derivations of watershed history and assessment of current ecosystem processes, require a broad interdisciplinary view of how the specific watershed works, and the involvement of all interested publics. Once the issues, values, and concerns are evaluated and documented, and the intensity of analysis determined, the analysis can move to a more technical phase traditionally conducted as part of many of the currently-available CWE methods.

The method that most closely matches these criteria, and the two-phase approach envisioned above, is Watershed Analysis. This approach, particularly the Washington state version of Watershed Analysis, appears to incorporate the best procedural steps to assure a high likelihood of success. The practitioners of WWA report positive results (e.g., as of August 22, 1994, every WWA had been carried to completion, with participation by all stakeholders [Kate Sullivan, Watershed Analysis Workshop, Portland Oregon, personal communication]). These initial successes imply that the procedure does work. The federal WA may work equally well, or better. Because federal WA projects were not completed at the time of the writing of this report, the veracity of the federal approach is still unknown.

From a procedural perspective, a major selling point of WWA is its codified structure with specific timelines and required results. Another advantage is the inclusion of a formal hand-off process between the scientist and manager. Major pluses of both FWA and WWA are their focus on science-based decisions and the link between causative processes and channel responses. In addition, WWA typically produces specific management prescriptions. The common occurrence of mixed ownerships in the Sierra Nevada is not dealt with well by procedures currently in use in the Sierra. WWA incorporates a codified process that appears to effectively address the mixed ownership dilemma.

WWA could not be transparently applied to the Sierra Nevada. Because the focus of WWA is anadromous fish, the approach would need to be modified for the Sierra. In this sense, FWA is more flexible. Other distinguishing features of the Sierra Nevada would also need to be incorporated into the procedure. Revisions of this type should not be inherently difficult. Both FWA and WWA are flexible procedures meant to be adapted to local conditions.

A comprehensive Watershed Analysis-type approach requires time and money. Agencies that can now produce an ERA analysis in a few weeks involving one or two staff members, may not be willing to accept the expense and time needed for completion of a Watershed Analysis. Watershed Analysis does not assure that all problems will be solved. Scientific unknowns still surround many process links. Understanding of these process links is central to assessing cumulative effects. We argue, however, that while a Watershed Analysis-like process may be relatively costly in dollars and expertise, investment is recouped over the long run, because the results of the process are agreed to by major stakeholders and management can then proceed with little fear of future appeal.

We further realize that regulatory constraints may inhibit Watershed Analysis-type management in the Sierra Nevada. Without FEMAT-based authorities, it is unclear how Watershed Analysis-type approaches could be integrated into the national forest planning process, or if exceptions to that process could be instituted. We believe, however, that a Watershed Analysis-type approach is an important advance worth pursuing.

To the extent that a science-based approach for CWE analysis compliments Ecosystem Management, and to the extent that other states (e.g., Washington) may be considered to be setting a standard by using Watershed Analysis, serious evaluation of Watershed Analysis, or a similar methodology, should be considered for the Sierra Nevada.

As a follow-up recommendation, we suggest that two workshops be convened. The first would involve practitioners and developers of Watershed Analysis-type approaches. It would be aimed at assessing and documenting the realistic opportunities for adapting a Watershed Analysis-type procedure to the Sierra Nevada. Participation by current users of Watershed Analysis, particularly USFS and Washington State department staff and industry representatives, and their counterparts in California, plus developers of Watershed Analysis from the federal and Washington state consortiums, should allow for a comprehensive and open discussion of the pros and cons of Watershed Analysis relative to the Sierra Nevada. Hopefully, in this scenario, potential concerns held by major stakeholders about adoption of a Watershed Analysis-type process would be voiced. This workshop should also address methods for ranking watersheds in the Sierra Nevada for priority CWE analysis. We believe that none of the currently-available methodologies do a good job of screening at this scale.

A second, follow-up workshop should involve managers and decision-makers. This group should have the wherewithal to assess the results of the first (technical) workshop in terms of the political and institutional realities of instituting a Watershed Analysis-type approach to the Sierra Nevada. For instance, are resources actually available to pursue a science-based Watershed Analysis-style approach? Do regulatory restrictions (e.g., requirements of the national forest planning process) limit opportunities for a Watershed Analysis-type approach, and if so, what options are available to deal with the restrictions?

ACKNOWLEDGMENTS

We thank the experts who responded to the survey questions. Their insights broadened the authors' perspective and provided up-to-date documentation of evolving methodologies. Special thanks are due to Dr. Leslie Reid, whose work we directly utilized and who provided excellent advice. Special thanks are also due to Maureen Davis, who incorporated internal SNEP review comments, extensively reformatted the paper to reflect SNEP style guidelines, and served as copyeditor and layout designer.

REFERENCES

Bourgeron, P. S. and M. E. Jensen. 1993. Ecosystem Management: principles and applications. In *An overview of ecological principles for Ecosystem Management in Eastside forest ecosystem health assessment*, vol. 2. U. S. Forest Service.

Brown, G. W. 1970. Predicting the effect of clear cutting on stream temperature. *Journal of Soil and Water Conservation* 25:11-13.

California Department of Forestry and Fire Protection. 1994. Guidelines for assessment of cumulative impacts. Sacramento: California Department of Forestry and Fire Protection.

Cline, R. G. Cole, W. Megahan, R. Patten, and J. Potyondy. 1981. Guide for predicting sediment yields from forested watersheds. Ogden, UT: U. S. Forest Service.

Cobourn, J. 1989a. Is cumulative water effects analysis coming of age? *Journal of Soil and Water Conservation* 44:267-70.

———. 1989b. An application of cumulative watershed effects (CWE) analysis on the Eldorado National Forest in California. In *Headwaters Hydrology*, 449-60. Bethesda, MD: American Water Resources Association.

Council on Environmental Quality. 1971. CEQ Guidelines, 40 CFR, Section 1,508.7. Washington, DC.

Cumulative Effects Task Force. n. d. A draft cumulative watershed effects process for Idaho. Boise, ID: Division of Forestry and Fire, Idaho Department of Lands.

Forest Ecosystem Management Assessment Team. 1993. Forest ecosystem management: An ecological, economic, and social assessment. Washington DC: U.S. Forest Service.

Furniss, M. and B. McCammon (compilers). n. d. A federal agency guide for pilot watershed analysis.

Galbraith, A. F. 1975. Method for predicting increases in water yield related to timber harvesting and site conditions. In *Water Management Symposium*, 169-84. Logan, UT: American Society of Civil Engineers.

Goldstein, R. A., J. B. Mankin, and R. J. Luxmore. 1974. *Documentation of PROSPER: A model of atmosphere-soil-plant water flow*. Environmental Science Division, Publication 579. Oak Ridge, TN: Oak Ridge National Laboratory.

Gooselink, J. G. and L. C. Lee. 1989. Cumulative impact assessment in bottomland hardwood forests. *Wetlands* 9:93-174.

Grant, G. 1987. Assessing effects of peak flow increases on stream channels: a rational approach. In *Proceedings of the California Watershed Management Conference*, Wildland Resources Center Report 11, edited by R. Z. Callaham and J. J. DeVries, 142-49. Berkeley: University of California, Wildland Resources Center.

Hardin, G. 1968. The tragedy of the commons. *Science* 162:1243-48.

Harr, R. D., W. C. Harper, J. T. Krygier, and F. S. Hsieh. 1975. Changes in storm hydrographs after roadbuilding and clearcutting in the Oregon Coast Range. *Water Resources Research* 11:436-44.

Haskins, D. M. 1987. A management model for evaluating cumulative watershed effects. In *Proceedings of the California Watershed Management Conference*, Wildland Resources Center Report 11, edited by R. Z. Callaham and J. J. DeVries, 125-30. Berkeley: University of California, Wildland Resources Center.

Horak, G. C., E. C. Vlachos, and E. W. Cline. 1983. Methodological guidance for assessing cumulative impacts on fish and wildlife. Unpublished report prepared for the Eastern Energy and Land Use Team, U. S. Department of Interior, Fish and Wildlife Service. Ft. Collins, CO: Dynamac Corporation.

King, J. G. 1989. *Streamflow responses to road building and harvesting: a comparison with the equivalent clearcut area procedure*. Research Paper INT-401. Ogden, UT: U. S. Forest Service.

Klock, G. O. 1985. Modeling the cumulative effects of forest practices on downstream aquatic ecosystems. *Journal of Soil and Water Conservation* 40:237-41.

Leaf, C. F. and G. E. Brink. 1973a. *Computer simulation of snowmelt within a Colorado subalpine watershed*. Research Paper RM-99. Fort Collins, CO: U. S. Forest Service.

—————. 1973b. *Hydrologic simulation model of Colorado subalpine forest*. Research Paper RM-107. Fort Collins, CO: U. S. Forest Service.

Leibowitz, S. G., B. Abbruzzese, P.R. Adamus, L.E. Hughes, and J.T. Irish. 1992. *A synoptic approach to cumulative impact assessment: A proposed methodology*. US EPA/600/R-92/167. Corvallis, Oregon: Environmental Protection Agency, Environmental Research Laboratory.

McGurk, B. J., and D. R. Fong. 1995. Equivalent roaded area as a measure of cumulative effect of logging. *Environmental Management* 19(4):609-21.

Menning, K. M., D. C. Erman, K. N. Johnson, and J. Sessions. 1996. Aquatic and riparian systems, cumulative watershed effects, and limitations to watershed disturbance. In *Sierra Nevada Ecosystem Project: Final Report to Congress*, vol. II. Davis: University of California, Centers for Water and Wildland Resources.

National Council of the Paper Industry for Air and Stream Improvement, Inc. (NCASI). 1992. Status of the NCASI cumulative watershed effects program and methodology. Tech. Bull. 634. New York: National Council of the Paper Industry for Air and Stream Improvement, Inc.

Reeves, G. H., F. H. Everest, and T. E. Nickelson. 1989. *Identification of physical habitats limiting the production of coho salmon in western Oregon and Washington*. General Technical Report PNW-245. Portland, OR: U. S. Forest Service

Reid, L. M. 1993. *Research and Cumulative Watershed Effects*. General Technical Report PSW-141. Berkeley: U. S. Forest Service

Roehl, J. W. 1962. *Sediment source area, delivery ratio, and influencing morphological factors*. International Association of Scientific Hydrology, Commission on Landscape Erosion. Publication 59:202-13. Wallingford, UK: International Association of Scientific Hydrology.

Sidle, R. C. and J. W. Hornbeck. 1991. Cumulative effects: A broader approach to water quality research. *Journal of Soil and Water Conservation* 46:268-71.

State of California. 1984. California Environmental Quality Act, Law and Guidelines. Sacramento.

Stowell, R., A. Espinosa, T. C. Bjornn, W. S. Platts, D. C. Burns, and J. S. Irving. 1983. Guide to predicting salmonid response to sediment yields in Idaho Batholith watersheds. U. S. Forest Service Regions 1 and 4.

Stull, E. A., M. B. Bain, J. S. Irving, K. E. LaGory, and G. Witmer. 1987. *Methodologies for assessing the cumulative environmental effects of hydroelectric development on fish and wildlife in the Columbia River basin, vol. I: Recommendations*. Argonne, IL: Argonne National Lab.

U. S. Congress. 1977. Clean Water Act, Amendments of 1977 [PL 95-217]. Washington DC.

U. S. Forest Service. 1974. *Forest hydrology part II—hydrologic effects of vegetation manipulation*. Missoula, MT: U. S. Forest Service.

————. 1980. *An approach to water resources evaluation of non-point silvicultural sources (a procedural handbook)*. EPA-600/8-80-012. Athens, GA: Environmental Research Lab.

————. 1988. Cumulative off-site watershed effects analysis. In: USFS Region 5 Soil and Water Conservation Handbook. FSH 2509.22. San Francisco: U. S. Forest Service.

Washington Forest Practices Board. 1993. Board manual: Standard methodology for conducting watershed analysis. Version 2.0. Olympia, WA: Washington Forest Practices Board.

Wischmeier, W. H. and D. D. Smith. 1978. *Predicting rainfall erosion losses—a guide to conservation planning*. Handbook 537. Washington, DC: U.S. Department of Agriculture.

Ziemer, R. R. 1981. Storm flow response to road building and partial cutting in small streams of northern California. *Water Resources Research* 17:907-17.

Appendix 1. CWE Methodology Questionnaire

Name: Date:

Position & affiliation:
Location:

Knowledge of emerging CWE methodologies not yet in print

Knowledge of unique or critical biogeoclimatic or socio-political elements of the Sierra Nevada relevant to CWE assessment

   Any distinctions between subregions within the Sierra (e.g., southern, central, northern, eastern) re: CWE (or perhaps more broadly re management impacts—not necessarily cumulative)

Recommendations on CWE methods (existing or emerging) for use in the Sierra Nevada

Recommendations on necessary qualities of a CWE method appropriate to the Sierra Nevada

Any general considerations about the utility, value, and applicability of specific CWE methodologies

Suggestions on knowledgeable individuals in the field or recently published (or draft) versions of manuscripts on CWE methodologies

Do you know of any court cases involving CWE? If so, any specific information (e.g., issues or names of contestants)?

Do you make CWE determinations?

Practitioners

   (i) what procedure do you currently use?

   (ii) why do you use it (e.g., mandated by agency? best known method?)?

   (iii) what product (specifically) is produced?

   (iv) how big are the basins (what geographic scale is addressed)?

   (v) what time frame is addressed (do you/how do you incorporate potential future activities, & if so how?)?

   (vi) What are the data requirements of the method you use (e.g., topographic quads, photos, land-use history, water quality info)?

   (vii) how do you handle mixed ownership situations (how successful [or what types of situations are more likely to yield success] in mixed ownership situation)?

      Do they get adequate info in mixed ownership situations?

      If so, how?

(viii) what types of management activities do they look at (harvest only? grazing, mining, recreation...?)

   If you deal with multiple activities, how do you link them?

(ix) If you had more data, resources, $$, or labor would you have done things differently--a fleshed out product (if so what?)

(x) How would results differ (if had more resources [$$, data, labor])?

(xi) Do you analyze actual watershed (geomorphic) processes? If so, how?

(xii) Do you deal with a range of beneficial uses? If so, what? If not, what is your beneficial use?

(xiii) Do you have any natural resource issues of concern (e.g., site productivity? sediment yields? channel condition? flood flows? fisheries? general water quality? water yield? water temperature? aquatic habitat? onsite vs. downstream? overland flow runoff?)

(xiii) What would you like a CWE methodology for the Sierra Nevada to do differently/better?

(xiv) Any other comments about CWE and CWE methodologies?

Non-Practitioners

How would you describe your function re CWE analysis (researcher? manager? ____?)

What would you like a CWE methodology for the Sierra Nevada to do differently/better?

Any other comments about CWE and CWE methodologies?

Appendix 2. Interviewees

Name	Position/Affiliation/Location
Ann Carlson	Forest Fish Biologist, Tahoe National Forest, Nevada City, CA
John Cobourn	Water Resources Specialist, University of Nevada Cooperative Extension, Incline Village, NV
Larry Costick	Post-graduate researcher, Sierra Nevada Ecosystem Project, University of California, Davis
Sally DeBecker	Technical and Ecological Services, Pacific Gas and Electric Company, San Ramon, CA
Jim Frazier	Forest Hydrologist, Stanislaus National Forest, Sonora, CA
Kass Green	President, Pacific Meridian Resources, Emeryville, CA
George Ice	Research Forest Hydrologist, National Council of the Paper Industry for Air and Stream Improvement, Inc., Corvallis, OR
Matt Kondolf	Associate Professor of Environmental Planning, Department of Landscape Architecture, Univeristy of California, Berkeley, CA
Stafford Lehr	Fish Biologist, California Department of Fish and Game, Pollock Pines, CA
Dale McGreer	President, Western Watershed Consultants, Lewiston, ID
Walter Megahan	Program Manager, National Council of the Paper Industry for Air and Stream Improvement, Inc., Pt. Townsend, WA
Chuck Mitchell	Forest Resource Officer, Eldorado National Forest, Placerville, CA
Louis Moeler	Associate Water Resources Control Engineer, Division of Water Rights, Complaints Unit, California State Water Resources Control Board, Sacramento, CA
John Munn	Project Leader, California Department of Forestry and Fire Protection, Sacramento, CA
Robert Nuzum	Director, Department of Natural Resources, East Bay Municipal Utility District, Oakland, CA
Leslie Reid	Research Geologist, Pacific Southwest Research Station, U. S. Forest Service, Arcata, CA
Winston Wiggins	Assistant Director, Forestry and Fire, Idaho Department of Lands, Boise, ID
Nick Wilcox	Environmental Specialist, California State Water Resources Control Board, Sacramento, CA

Appendix 3. Core Questions for Assessment of Case Studies

Review of the case studies, the steps outlined in the Federal Agency Guide for Pilot Watershed Analysis, and the attributes of a successful CWE methodology described by Reid (1993) contributed to this set of core questions through which the strengths of the case studies were evaluated:

Are the key CWE issues identified?

Are the key system functions and processes which influence those issues identified?

Are the mechanisms which affect function and process identified?

Is there analysis of landform sensitivity (i.e. do some landforms influence or react differently than others)?

Is there recognition of disturbance regimes that drive the processes?

Is there recognition of system component recovery rates (especially that cause and response components may recover at different rates)?

Is the analysis conducted at the appropriate scale, and linked to evaluations of other scales?

Is the procedure flexible enough to account for local conditions, and accept developing technologies?

Does the end product clearly define risk?

Are current conditions described? Are past conditions described? Is a plausible cause-response scenario described which supports the analysis used to predict future impacts?

Are trends defined?

Are analysis procedures technically sound?

Are limitations of the analysis made clear?

Are key questions monitored?

Does the process provide the decision maker with information so that a decision can be made with some degree of confidence?

Does the process tie (logically, clearly) to the issues and beneficial uses?

Are the procedures appropriate for the scale of the analysis? Is there a tie between scales?

Is there any accounting for time scales in assessment of process?

Are the results linked to management prescriptions?

Does the process use all appropriate available information?

What are the key large scale issues and watershed-aquatic processes?

What are the mechanisms important to these processes? Have the mechanisms been active in a time scale relevant to display effects (e.g., fire or 10-year storm)?

What are indicators of this process?

What is the condition as displayed by these indicators?

How will alternatives affect condition?
    In particular, what about sensitive lands?
    What is the time scale of the response-effect? When might the responses occur? How long will they last? How great is the risk (i.e., are we playing with a firecracker, a grenade, or a bomb?)?

Is the relative accuracy of the assessment made clear?

LARRY A. COSTICK
Department of Land, Air,
    and Water Resources
and
Sierra Nevada Ecosystem Project
University of California
Davis, California

3

Indexing Current Watershed Conditions Using Remote Sensing and GIS

Sierra Nevada Ecosystem Project: Final report to Congress, vol. III, *Assessments, Commissioned Reports, and Background Information.* Davis: University of California, Centers for Water and Wildland Resources, 1996.

ACKNOWLEDGMENTS

This study was supported by the Sierra Nevada Ecosystem Project as authorized by Congress (HR5503) through a cost-reimbursable agreement No. PSW-93-001-CRA between the U.S.DA Forest Service, Pacific Southwest Research Station and the Regents of the University of California, Wildland Resources Center.

Special thanks are given to the SNEP hydrology group for their counsel and support and to the SNEP GIS team particularly Lian Duan and Qingfu Xiao for their preparation of the maps and coverages. Sincere appreciation is extended to the Georgia Pacific Corporation Resources Group in Martell California for their generous donations of data upon which much of this analysis is based.

ABSTRACT

Two objectives of the Sierra Nevada Ecosystem Project (SNEP) were to evaluate the current condition of watersheds in the Sierra Nevada and to identify physical processes such as soil erosion that effect watershed health and sustainability. In response to this request for a resource inventory an indexing or screening model has been developed that produces both an Natural Erosion Potential (NEP) and Sedimentation Hazard Index (SHI) which are indicators of the "current cumulative condition" in watersheds of the Sierra Nevada.

The goal of the study undertaken here is to design and test a methodology using geographic information systems (GIS) and remote sensing to rank watersheds prone to soil erosion and locate specific sites where stream sedimentation is likely to occur. One hundred and thirty-four watersheds on the Eldorado National Forest (ENF) were analyzed and ranked using a method which selects the parameters of slope, cover, and soil detachability that were assumed to be the most significant contributors to soil erosion, given uniform climatic conditions. Threshold values established for these parameters provided the link to locations where there is a high probability of sediment reaching the watercourse.

Correlation with US Forest Service equivalent roaded acres (ERA) and cumulative watershed effects (CWE) work previously completed and in progress on the ENF was positive when compared to NEP and SHI rankings created by this model. Additional correlation opportunities yet to be implemented using change detection techniques with Landsat TM imagery, spectral mixture analysis (SMA) with high resolution AVIRIS imagery, and the identification of large rock outcrops are expected to improve results. The model described here gives the resource manager a tool which can be used to quickly screen proposed CWE assessment areas and focus both human and financial resources on potential "hot spots." Once located, the cumulative effects benefit of a specific mitigation opportunity may be evaluated as to its cost and to the watershed improvement that it provides.

Keywords: cumulative effects; erosion; watersheds; resource management; forest management; forest roads; erosion control mitigation.

EXECUTIVE SUMMARY

HR 5503 and HR 6013 both requested assessments and inventories, by an independent group of scientists, to evaluate the current condition, health and sustainability of the Sierra Nevada. In order to insure these ecosystems are healthy and sustainable both agency and private land owners must be able to exchange cumulative effects information about their individual activities accurately, quickly and in similar formats. The assumption that a readily available, standardized, data set capable of producing information for a diverse group of scientists was erroneous.

Watersheds represent distinct topographic units and the understanding of there health and condition cannot be limited by ownership. Current condition is the culmination of all cumulative past events and the ecosystems response to those events whether natural or management induced. Implementation of management strategies may be unique to ownership; however, in order to account for mitigation activities in mixed ownership watersheds, when assessing for CWE, all disturbance activities must be calculated. The accuracy of assessments of this nature are dependent on the quality of the data base being utilized, and the lack of a homogeneous soil layer for either the study region or any of the sub-regions has severely hindered the progress of this work. A standardizes soils and disturbance history data base is needed that will provide resource managers, both public and private, the information they need for economically and environmentally sound decision making.

Soil erosion is one of the processes specifically mentioned in HR 6013 for evaluation. The susceptibility of soils and their underlying geologic units to mass failure and rill and gully erosion are part of this process. A healthy watershed, as defined here is an area of land, having the structure and density of forest stands to support a diverse wildlife population. In addition it has the natural stability of geology and soils to maintain the contribution of eroded sediments, reaching streams, at a level where natural hydrologic processes, balances the ability of the system to both store and transport these sediments without degrading aquatic habitats.

The model constructed for this study identifies sites with high potential for producing sedimentation. The hypothesis is that risk of erosion is a function of slope, soil detachability and bare unprotected ground. The risk of erosion becoming sediment is increased as a function of road location in proximity to streams and decreases in the presence of riparian vegetation buffers near streams.

This model yields a relative ranking for each Cal-Water planning watersheds without the need of extensive field surveys. Information is generated which ranks watersheds: one, in order of their natural sensitivity or their inherent erosion potential and two, predicting the probable origins of sediment to be used as guides for future mitigation activity. Its results are: significantly less costly to produce, objectively generated, easily updated, responsive to changes in elevation and precipitation conditions and minimize data corruption. Predicting the potential for erosional of a given unit area of land is the objective of this methodology it is intended to index "current condition", or "watershed health", for individual planning watersheds relative to their neighbors and given similar climatic conditions. It has been designed as a primary screening tool and environmental accounting system which provides objectively generated data to decision makers.

Because this study is a screening process which attempts to focus the resource managers attention on the most acute problem areas, potential sedimentation is its' primary consideration. This tool allows the manager to optimize both environmental and economic investment strategies by locating those areas which have the greatest impact on cumulative watershed effects and selecting the mitigation which is most cost effective. Thinking of this as an environmental accounting system allocates resources to those projects which have the most immediate impact on cumulative effects.

INTRODUCTION

Congressional Authorization and Mandate

Although, The Sierra Nevada Ecosystem Study Act of 1992, HR 6013 was not passed because of House adjournment, the bill requested the inventory of watersheds to evaluate their condition and to identify physical processes that affect watershed health and sustainability. Soil erosion is one of the processes specifically mentioned for evaluation. In a January 19, 1993, House Committee on Natural Resources Chairman George Miller sent a letter to US Forest Service (USFS) Chief Dale Robertson, that further defined the intent of Congress after the passage of, The Conference Report for Interior and Related Agencies 1993 Appropriation Act, HR 5503. He said "In order for this (assessment) effort to succeed and be credible it is imperative that an independent panel of scientists with expertise in a variety of forest disciplines be appointed to work with the many knowledgeable experts within the USFS... As this study will be conducted in a relatively short time frame, we do not expect that the panel will be gathering data from the field, but will compile existing information from the number of agencies and organizations involved in forest research in the Sierra Nevada range." It is likely that this statement assumes a readily available data set at resolutions, formats, and in units capable of producing combined information for a diverse group of scientists. The letter further states, "This study should provide the Congress with the comprehensive data needed to make important policy decisions concerning future management of the Sierra Nevada forests. It is our hope ... we can identify management alternatives that will assure the long-term health and sustainability of these forest ecosystems." This statement implies that scientists similar to the science team involved in the Sierra Nevada Ecosystem Project (SNEP) will be successful in determining the current "health" of these forest ecosystems and, from this base of information, generate a variety of management scenarios that will ensure their sustainability.

In 1995 after the 192nd Congress revised Committee assignments, newly appointed USFS Chief Jack Ward Thomas received correspondence prioritizing the Committee's expectations of SNEP's efforts and restated some specific products that were anticipated. As in previous correspondence and legislation, lands systems inventories, watershed health condition assessments, and insights into processes were high priorities. Management scenarios are to be formulated based on the results of the SNEP assessments, once more stressing the importance of understanding current watershed condition.

Sustainability of forest ecosystems in both the eastern and western United States depends on understanding the "current cumulative condition." In order to gain this understanding at a regional scale one must have information on what resource elements are present and how are they distributed, regardless of ownership. Providing this information in a standard format or as a standard tool to all consumers is an appropriate role of government. Congressional authorization of matching funds for resource unit inventories regardless of land ownership, and incentives for public-private data collection and exchange programs are options that should stimulate the development of these tools. Resource managers need these tools to do their jobs and this is an opportunity to equitably share the costs of data preparation.

Regional Background

Years of grazing, mining, road building, home construction and logging disturbances as well as fire, land slides and plant disease in the California Sierra Nevada has modified forest ecosystems. Present remote sensing technology provides for understanding, monitoring and in some cases quantifying these natural and management induced perdition such as soil loss, changes in vegetative cover, and the consequences of habitat disturbance. There are, however, very few predictive ecosystem models that use spatial and temporal remote sensing data to infer current watershed condition or ecosystem health. Comparison of current condition on a watershed by watershed basis allows us to index ecosystems relative to each other. An accurate indexing methodology is a valuable tool when allocating resources for CWE mitigation or adjudicating disturbance rights among landowners in mixed ownership watersheds.

The methodology presented here assesses the ecosystem, as defined by watershed boundaries, for natural erosion potential and sedimentation hazards. It presents parameters for ecosystem assessment and an accounting system to track and recalculate a watershed condition index. Data on the amount of ground cover, bare soil, soil detachability or sensitivity to erosion as well as slope are used to quantify the ecosystem's sensitivity to accelerated erosion and sedimentation. Geographic information system (GIS) layers of slope, soil type, soil detachability and disturbance history data are integrated to spatially display current relative watershed condition and to focus attention on locations which may be at greater risk of producing sedimentation.

Both National and State environmental quality acts (NEPA and CEQA) require cumulative effects assessment for all projects on private, state, and federal land. Definitions of cumulative effects vary and there are no universally accepted techniques for their measurement or monitoring. Our inability to objectively quantify cumulative effects and the absence of standards for comparison has created difficulty for regulatory agencies. This model aids resource managers and their regulators in objectively analyzing ecosystem complexities with particular regard for cumulative and synergistic impacts of human activity and natural processes.

With the advent of GIS technology spatial analysis procedures are available to quantify both present and historic physical features and land use practices on a landscape basis. From the rates of change in these features, as determined by GIS interpretations of aerial and space imagery, habitat improvement or degradation and habitat potential may be inferred. This model includes several GIS layers that, when analyzed together, provide a more objective view of ecosystem condition.

METHODS

Model Description

In response to the request for resource inventory information by the House Committee on Natural Resources, an indexing or screening model has been developed that produces both an Natural Erosion Potential (NEP) and Sedimentation Hazard Index (SHI) which are indicators of the "current cumulative condition" in the watersheds of the Sierra Nevada. For the purposes of this study a healthy watershed is defined as an area of land, having the structure and density of vegetative stands to support a diverse wildlife population, and having the natural stability of geology and soils to maintain the contribution of eroded sediments reaching streams at a level where natural hydrologic processes balance the ability of the system both to store and transport these sediments without degrading aquatic habitats. In this paper, "erosion" is defined as the detachment and transport of soil particles and "sedimentation" is the deposition of soil particles into the aquatic habitat.

Figure 1 Sierra Nevada Ecosystem Project Study Area and Eldorado National Forest

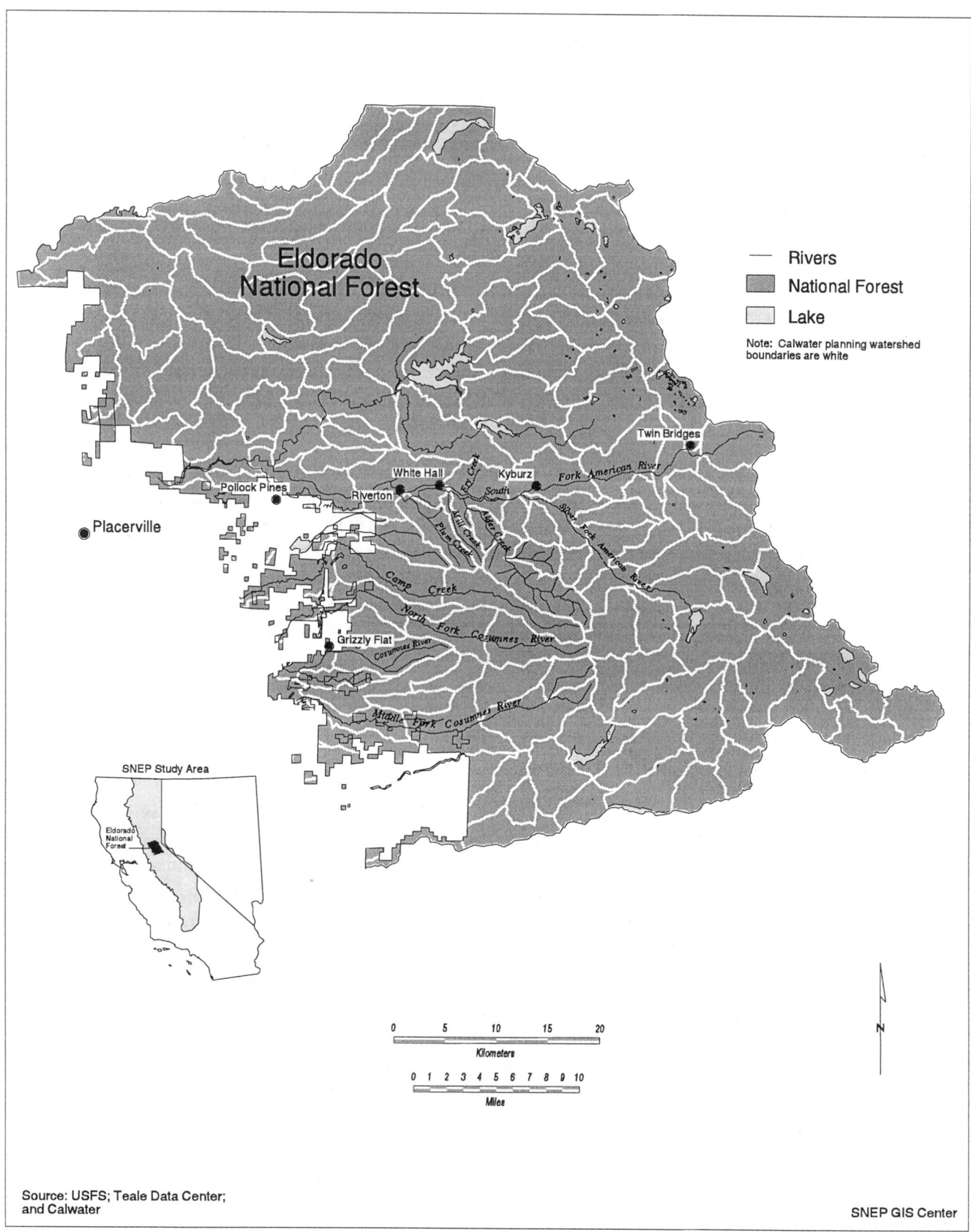

Source: USFS; Teale Data Center;
and Calwater

SNEP GIS Center

The methodology proposed herein is similar to USFS Region 5's current "equivalent roaded acres" (ERA) method of CWE analysis which has been evolving on the Eldorado National Forest (ENF) since the mid 1980s (Kuehn and Cobourn 1989) (Carlson and Christiansen 1993). However, results from early versions of ERA were considered subjective, difficult to reproduce, and expensive to develop. After two years of compiling data to run the ERA process, it was apparent that a screening model could be developed using remote sensing and GIS that could cut costs and give reliable, objective information.

Watershed characteristics that are used here to assess the relative health of watersheds include an estimate of their natural sensitivity to erosion, and an analysis of the location and number of roads, to allow prediction of probable origins of sediment. The model yields a relative ranking for each watershed without extensive field surveys and because it is spatially explicit it may be used to guide future mitigation activity. Advantages of the model include: lower dollar costs to produce, objective generation, capacity to be easily updated, responsiveness to changes in elevation and precipitation conditions, and less data corruption because minimal staff (one or two individuals) is required to process data.

Because this present model is a screening tool, it focuses on initial soil forming and erosional processes. The susceptibility of soils and geology to mass failure, and rill and gully erosion are part of this process. If the field resources manager is to have a practical tool for watershed assessments, that tool must be based on simple concepts and built around readily available or easily acquired information. The method proposed here requires the user to have access to Landsat imagery, and a limited knowledge of soils, geomorphology, and ecology. Doing hierarchical analysis, first using a screening tool, followed by more data intensive and quantitative procedures allows managers to identify and prioritize both analytical and restoration activities.

USLE and the Use of Erosion Risk Parameters

For this indexing methodology the slope, cover, and soil detachability parameters of the Universal Soil Loss Equation (USLE) (Wischmeier and Smith 1978) were chosen to characterize a watershed's natural susceptibility to erosion. These parameters were chosen because: the data needed to calculate USLE are generally available for large areas of the Sierra Nevada, and while not perfect, the USLE has been applied world wide. In the United States, the USLE has a record of predicting soil loss within $\pm 0.5 kg/m^2$ 84 % of the time (Wischmeier and Smith 1978). Only the Morgan et al. (1984) model has a better record but only when all the soil properties are based on local field measurements (Morgan 1986) thereby limiting its predictive capability when local data are not available. Morgan's model also uses the same basic parameters adopted here from USLE. USLE and Revised USLE (RUSLE) are erosion-prediction models that express the interrelationships among slope, slope length, cover, and soil detachability (McCool et al. 1987). RUSLE differs from USLE primarily in the algorithms used to generate the individual factors; in addition RUSLE has been adopted for computer use. The formula $A = R K L S C P$ remains the same, only the coefficients change: A is the   computed soil loss, R is the rainfall erosivity factor from runoff, K is the soils detachability or erodibility factor, L is the length of slope, S is the steepness or angle of slope factor, C is the farming or cover-management factor at or near the soil surface, and P is the supporting practice generally associated with farming or grazing (Renard et al. 1994). The USLE equation and the parameters that support it are based on the experience of thousands of field observations that can be arranged into four primary categories affecting erosion. They are: the effects of rainfall on erosion which in the equation are represented by R, the detachability of the soil unit represented by K, slope and topography represented by LS, and the land-use-management practices represented by CP.

Because surface and rill erosion are the primary erosional forces at work in the Central Sierra (Lewis and Rice, 1989) K, S, and C were selected as the three parameters to use in this study when calculating current watershed condition. Each of these parameters has a range of values across each watershed, K-factor for instance ranges from 0.10 to 0.46 for the ENF soils (USDA Forest Service 1985, USDA Forest Service 1991, USDA Soil Conservation Service 1961, USDA Soil Conservation Service 1974). Regardless of slope, soils with K-factor above 0.28 are observed to rill and gully more easily than soils at 0.24 and below (personal observations). The RUSLE does not set risk threshold values for these parameters; however other studies, which will be discussed at length later, on pages 13, 15, 20, and beyond suggest logical or intuitive points at which to begin setting threshold values. Thus the initial threshold values came from field experience, the literature, as well as current state and federal regulation.

While the contribution of mass failure to erosion and sedimentation are acknowledged to be significant problems in California's Coast Range, surface erosion and gullying, particularly related to road construction and road use, are the greatest contributors to sedimentation in the Sierra Nevada. Lewis and Rice in their 1989 Critical Sites Erosion Study reviewed 1104 timber harvest plans (THP's) looking for erosion problems. Of the 418 considered in the Sierra Nevada only eight had critical sites (an area of at least two acres where 200 cubic yard or more of erosion volume had been moved) This compared with the Coast Range where 33 sites were critical and 130 questionable out of 499 considered. They found road related problems to be the major contributor to sedimentation in both regions. After visiting 29646 acres in the Sierra Nevada compared to 24232 acres in the Coast Range the Sierra portion of the study was halted because the problems on the coast were more acute. While their study recognizes mass failures of all kinds to be the most significant problem for the Coast Range, surface and gully erosion were the problems most often encountered in the Sierra Nevada. This model points to locations where the potential for problems is high. The potential for mass failure and gullying is greater on soils with high detachabilities and increases as slope get steeper.

Inherent in the use of GIS and remote sensing is the ability to quickly modify your input parameters while seeking higher correlation's of one data set with another. Work done on the ENF by their hydrology and resource groups provided such an opportunity for comparison. This study used watershed boundaries mapped by the State of California's Department of Forestry and Fire Protection in a Data Dictionary project known as "Cal-Water". Cal-Water defines their smallest watershed unit as a Planning Watershed and give it the acronym (CWPWS) (Brandow 1995). The dates of several Landsat images provide points-in-time where conditions in the watershed may be assessed as confined by these CWPWS boundaries.

Interrill and Rill Erosion Processes

Hillslope erosion, a common process in land management, is broken into two segment's: interrill and rill. Each has different susceptibilities to physical and mechanical change. Interrill erosion can be generated by raindrop splash on unprotected soil, by overland flow and sheet wash (Morgan 1986). Rill erosion represents processes where the concentration of water on the slope creates a cutting force. Rills concentrate flow down slope and transport sediment from interrill and rill areas. Many erosion models describe soil detachment by the force of flowing water as a linear function of flow shear stress or energy typically called "critical shear" (Nearing et al. 1994). The Water Erosion Prediction Project (WEPP) model developed for use by the USDA-Natural Resources Conservation Service (NRCS) and the Bureau of Land Management on agricultural and range land uses the equations:

$$D_i = K_i \ I^2 \qquad\qquad (1)$$

for interrill processes: where D_i is the rate of interrill sediment delivery to rills, K_i is an interrill erodability parameter, and I^2 is the average rainfall intensity integrated over the duration of rainfall excess. And:

$$D_c = K_r(\tau - \tau_c) \qquad\qquad (2)$$

for rill and interrill detachment where D_c is the detachment capacity of clear water flow, K_r is the soil's rill erodibility, τ is the shear stress of the flow, and τ_c is the soil's critical hydraulic shear strength (Nearing et al. 1994). The first equation is an empirical relationship developed after intensive-rainfall simulations (Meyer 1981; Singer and Walker 1983). Kirkby and Morgan (1980) state that sediment yields from interrill areas are relatively low compared to rill erosion processes as described in the second equation. Each equation requires sequential analysis for detachment and transport phases. While WEPP does not yet support forest lands or road related erosion problems it is an event driven model and may provide the soil movement linkage to a Eco-hydrologic model currently being developed by Ustin and Wallendar (SNEP Rpt. 1995 Vol. III).

Model Use of GIS

The method employed here is similar to pre-GIS geographic map overlaying techniques where clear acetate sheets scribed with information at one spatial and temporal scale, such as the distribution of vegetation in the central Sierra Nevada in 1929, are overlain by other maps which have information from a different time period or a different spatial arrangement such as, a 1994 vegetation and land use map for the central Sierra Nevada. In this system both of these sheets are fixed to a base map which contains information, such as topography, streams, and soils common to both overlays. In order to see and begin to understand the relationships between the aggregate information, we analyze the composite, often assigning new values or classifications to the data in the form of similar clusters, which may be called polygons, or at a single point, which in this study is called a cell. Using a commercial GRID raster based GIS computer program all of our data is distributed over a matrix where the smallest block, the cell, approximately 0.22 acres has the dimensions of 30 meters on each side. This fine scale allows large numbers of attribute variables such as soil, slope, vegetation and so on, to be viewed individually or simultaneously in very rapid order for a single cell or a cluster of cells speeding the analysis process. Every major attribute, soil for instance may have dozens or hundreds of variables which describe the soil at a specific location. One data base or many may support our understanding of a fixed point on the ground. GIS provides a means of mathematically searching for relationships between data layers and their attribute's that might not be apparent to our eyes and may have been missed using earlier techniques.

Model Hypothesis

If a healthy watershed is determined by the degree to which physical processes and biological responses are at equilibrium, then excessive erosion and sedimentation suggest system instability and declining health. The hypothesis for this model is: risk of erosion is primarily a function of steep slopes, high soil detachability, and bare unprotected ground. Further, the risk of erosion becoming sedimentation increases where roads are close to streams and is decreased by the presence of a riparian vegetation buffer near stream banks. Using ARC/INFO GRID as well as available soil and topographic data, these four critical parameters are plotted from GIS and Landsat Thematic Mapper (TM) imagery. Slope, soil detachability or K-factor, ground cover, and proximity of roads to streams all become parameters of the model.

Literature Review for Selected Parameters

Slope

Wischmeier and Smith (1978) are generally credited with originating the USLE (Renard et al. 1994) while it was not created for use on steep forested slopes its principles do apply to the model being created here; i.e. soil loss increases much more rapidly than runoff as slopes get steeper. They also state that the logarithm of runoff from row crops was linearly and directly proportional to the percent slope. Further, neither good meadow sod nor smooth bare surfaces had any significant effect on this relationship. They did note, however, that as conditions became extremely wet the effect of slope on runoff was reduced (Wischmeier and Smith 1978). Their equation to evaluate their slope S is:

$$S = 65.41 \sin^2 \theta + 4.56 \sin \theta + 0.065 \tag{3}$$

where θ is the angle of the slope. They found that using the sine as opposed to the tangent of the slope gave the equation greater accuracy, especially as slopes became steeper than 20 % (Wischmeier and Smith 1978). Angle of slope in contrast to length of slope is a more important consideration when setting threshold parameters for erosion potential or measuring soil loss (Renard et al. 1994). As an example, a 10 % error in slope angle yields a 20 % error when computing soil loss with the USLE. The RUSLE, however, halves these errors as well as being sensitive to short slope interrill erosion and freeze-thaw phenomenon (Renard et al. 1994). While slope length is important in calculating runoff velocities and amounts of soil loss, it cannot be measured accurately with current GIS techniques and therefore has been justifiably omitted as a screening risk parameter at this time.

An important objective of this study was to provide a basic screening module for uses in other resource assessment models. The first iteration of this model set the slope threshold value at steeper than 50% gradient because it fell between the limits of tractor and cable yarding methods for logging permitted under California and Washington State Forest Practice Rules and was the standard used by McKittrick (1994). One project objective was to produce regional slope information from digital elevation models (DEMs) and to produce a GIS layer of slope distributions where a variety of slope classes could be tested. The DEMs available at the time through US Geological Survey (USGS) did not have fine enough vertical resolution for the needs of this model and the eco-hydrologic model being developed concurrently by Ustin and Wallendar (SNEP 1995 Vol. III). As an interim step Georgia Pacific Corporation provided digital 40 ft contour maps, developed from 200 foot DEMs, for the Camp Creek and Clear Creek study area.

In October of 1994, the combined efforts of the USFS and USGS finished the production of 30m DEMs for the SNEP study area. These DEMs are the basis for the slope maps and coverages used in this model and analysis.

Current USFS timber sale contracts require that cable yarding systems be utilized when slopes exceed 35%. Because of imprecise ways of measuring slope over large areas, the range of slopes from 35%-40% has been used as a general rule to separate areas of cable yarding from tractor operations and hence slopes greater than 40% became the threshold setting for the second model run (Christiansen 1995). The model is interactive with the parameter threshold selections so that alternative slope classes may be tested in the future.

Soil Detachability or K-Factor

There have been many attempts to develop simple indexes of erodibility using either soil properties determined in the laboratory or the response of soil to flowing water or wind (Morgan 1986). Bryan (1969) and Singer et al. (1978) argue for aggregate stability as the most efficient index of erodibility. However, those data depend heavily on information about soil chemistry. Soil detachability rating, or K-factor, is more easily obtained from existing soil surveys and therefore more likely to be used by resource managers because of availability. A K-factor indicates the susceptibility of soils to sheet and rill erosion and is calculated primarily on the basis of texture, structure, and permeability. Percent very fine sand, sand, silt, and organic matter are the key components modified by the percent of rock fragments. Values range from 0.2 to 0.69 with increasing susceptibility to erosion (Morgan 1986).

The effect of organic matter on K-factor rating, however, adding additional complexity should not be passed over lightly. Mitchell and Bubenzer's (1980) work in The effects of organic matter on K-factor, Table 1 shows how increases in percent organic matter change K-factor for a variety of soil textures. Increases in organic matter generally increase soil stability and reduce detachability. In that case, the K-factor is improved at an increasing rate as organic matter is increased. However, the addition of organic material has a decreasing effect as soil textures grade from light, sandy to heavy, clay. Table 1 from Mitchell and Bubenzer 1980 and is not for field use.

Table 1 The Effects of Organic Matter on K-Factor

Texture Class	K-factor <0.5% Org	K-factor 2% Org	% Change 75	K-factor 4% Org	%Change 50
Sand	0.05	0.03	40	0.02	33
Fine sand	0.16	0.14	13	0.1	29
Very fine sand	0.42	0.36	14	0.28	22
Loamy sand	0.12	0.1	17	0.08	20
Loamy fine sand	0.24	0.2	17	0.16	20
Loamy very fine sand	0.44	0.38	14	0.3	21
Sandy loam	0.27	0.24	11	0.19	21
Fine sandy loam	0.35	0.3	14	0.24	20
Very fine sandy loam	0.47	0.41	13	0.33	20
Loam	0.38	0.34	11	0.29	15
Silt loam	0.48	0.42	13	0.33	21
Silt	0.6	0.52	13	0.42	19
Sandy clay loam	0.27	0.25	7	0.21	16
Clay loam	0.28	0.25	11	0.21	16
Silty clay loam	0.37	0.32	14	0.26	19
Sandy clay	0.14	0.13	7	0.12	8
Silty clay	0.25	0.23	8	0.19	17
Clay		0.13-0.29			

An estimate for an unknown K value from soil properties can be calculated from the regression equation:

$$K = 2.8 * 10^{-7} M^{1.14} (12 - a) + 4.3 * 10^{-3} (b - 2) + 3.3 * 10^{-3} (c - 3) \quad (4)$$

where M, the particle size parameter, = % silt + % very fine sand * 100 - % clay; a is the percent organic matter; b is the soil structure code (very fine granular, = 1; fine granular, = 2; medium or coarse granular, = 3; blocky, platy, or massive, = 4); c is the profile permeability class (rapid, = 1; moderate to rapid, = 2; moderate, = 3; slow to moderate, = 4; slow, = 5; very slow, = 6) (Lal and Elliot 1994).

Calculating K in the field from the effects of running water is a more complex process but it is the basis of the mass of empirical K-value measurements taken from around the country over several decades (Wischmeier and Smith 1978). In the field, K is not only a function of texture, structure, and permeability but is highly influenced by S (slope gradient) and L (slope length). As an index of erodibility this complex inter-relationship is what makes the use of K-factor so promising. RUSLE provides for modeling complex slope and slope-length relationships (Renard et al. 1994). Topographic factors influence predicted erosion rate because longer, steeper, slopes yield greater volumes of soil during events of equal rainfall intensity (McCool et al. 1987; Wischmeier and Smith 1978). Lal and Elliot (1994) suggest that these differences are the result of increased rill erosion rates as runoff increases with longer slopes and the cutting force of water increases with increased gradients. To model this phenomenon, they propose:

$$L = \left[\frac{i}{22} \right]^m \qquad (5)$$

where L is the slope length factor; m the exponent, is 0.2 for slopes < 1%, 0.3 for 1% to <3%, 0.4 for 3.5% to <4.5% and 0.5 for slopes > 5%; and is the slope length in meters;

And, for slopes (S) less than 4 m long:

$$S = 3.0\,(\sin(\theta))^{0.8} + 0.56 \qquad (6)$$

For slopes greater than 4 meter long, and s < 9 %:

$$S = 10.8 \sin(\theta) + 0.03 \qquad (7)$$

For slope greater than 4 meter long, and s ≥ 9 %:

$$S = 16.8 \sin(\theta) - 0.50 \qquad (8)$$

where: θ is the field slope (= $\tan^{-1}$ (s/100). Equations of this nature provide for the creation of more dynamic threshold values for slope and K-factor as the accuracy and resolution of DEMs improve. Equation (3) will be used along with equation (4) in this study to generate an erosion hazard rating (EHR) on a cell by cell bases in the next iteration of the model. K-factor is currently being calculated for the Stanislaus National Forest (SNF) using equation (4). The current cell size used by the GIS, is 30x30 m with this course minimum resolution slope length for erosion prediction models cannot be measured accurately enough to adjust the K-factor by redefining the mapping unit boundaries.

K-factor information and a soils data base were acquired from the ENF and Georgia Pacific Corporation. Their data base included USFS very detailed 5 acre minimum mapping unit size Order 2 soil survey and a twenty acre unit size Order 3 as well as SCS Order 3 surveys for Eldorado and Amador Counties which were mapped at a 10 to 15 acre minimum map unit.

Watershed analysis using this model had to be limited to areas where complete digital soils data bases exist or could be quickly constructed. The time necessary to digitize soil maps and develop attribute tables for the entire SNEP study area limited the opportunity to expand this study.

Soil mapping units on the national forest are usually composed of several soil series having similar properties (USDA Forest Service 1985, USDA Forest Service 1991, USDA Soil Conservation Service 1961, USDA Soil Conservation Service 1974). Descriptions of physical, chemical, and engineering properties were entered into a data base and matched with the SCS versions for similar series. This information provided standard textures, permeability, and moisture-holding capacities so that the hydrologic flow and vegetation evapotranspiration models would have a consistent medium within soil mapping units and across soil-survey boundaries. The physical, chemical, and engineering properties and the unit name were taken from the series which made up the largest percentage of the combined unit. Effort would have been made to divide further the soil series by percentage contribution within the units but the component series were not spatially located. Since mapping units cross many cells and a unit may represent as many as six soil series, it was not appropriate to give each cell a fractional proportion of all soil-unit values. K-factor was taken from county and national forest Order 3 Surveys and where necessary, applied to the ENF's Order 2 mapping.

The threshold setting of 0.28 is in the range of K-factors selected to separate moderate and high erosion hazard ratings by the Washington State Board of Forestry in their Board Manual: Standard Methodology for Conducting Watershed Analysis (1993), results from the Boise National Forest (Megahan et al. 1981), and information obtained from personal observations. As an assumption for this model the attributes for the series occupying the largest area were entered into the data base. It was also assumed that if a series had a K-factor of 0.28 or greater for any horizon, that series would be considered over threshold. Likewise if any series within a unit had a K-factor in excess of 0.28, the entire unit was included in the high K-factor layer because significant sedimentation problems are often associated with relatively small areas especially where road construction exposes deeper and at times less well consolidated horizons (Rice 1993). Soil series with K-factors from 0.28 to 0.47 became the GIS high K-factor layer and each cell in the model exceeding 0.28 received a value of one. While the Washington State experience will vary from that the Sierra Nevada because of steepness of slope and climatic differences many of its watershed assessment methods are considered standards and are recommended for adoption by the California Division of Forestry and Fire Protection and others (Pete Cafferata personnel communication 1995)(Berg et al. 1995).

Cover

Bare ground, the most elusive parameter to measure, was identified and quantified in several ways using Landsat TM imagery. While Landsat imagery has been found acceptable for mapping vegetation and identifying bare ground at this scale (Roberts 1993), it must be recognized that all imagery and photography represent a single moment in time. Forest environments, at this latitude, typically regain vegetative cover sufficient to reduce erosion hazards within one or two seasons after disturbance (personal observation). Selective harvest methods, including small patch cuts, practiced by most commercial timber operators in mid-elevations of the central Sierra Nevada. These leave sufficient slash and understory vegetation after harvest to limit rain drop impact as a serious cause of soil detachment and transport (Euphrat 1992). Singer and Blackard (1978) working with rainfall simulators on Sierran foothill and forest soils, found that soil losses did not begin to decrease until mulching levels reached 50 % cover. However, reasonable protection was noted by Shaxson (1981) with 40 % cover. Contact cover, that which touches the soil, prevents soil loss from raindrop impact while micro diversions add roughness and reduce erosion by sheet flow. In earlier work, Wischmeier and Meyer (1973), Lal (1977), and Foster and Meyer (1975) found that the rate of soil loss decreased exponentially with increase in area covered by mulch. Laflen and Colvin (1981) expressed this with the equation:

$$MF = e^{-a.RC} \qquad (9)$$

where MF is defined as the ratio of soil loss with mulching to the loss without mulching, RC is the percentage residue or mulch cover, and a ranges in value from 0.03 to 0.07. Later Hussein and Laflen (1982) found that this exponential relationship worked only for rill erosion and that the rate of erosion on interrill areas decreased linearly with increasing cover. When multiplied by the C-factor of the USLE, the protective effects of mulching are included in its calculation (after Morgan 1986).

Clear-cuts and brushfield conversions may have as many as three separate disturbances prior to replanting. Each of these operations reduce cover until all natural protection has been eliminated (personal observation). For this reason it is useful to continue to monitor bare ground for short-term changes annually or bi-annually.

Calculation of Normalized Difference Vegetation Index

Landsat's TM imagery is made up of seven bands of spectral information. These bands register spectral reflectance from specific wavelengths of visible and near-infrared energy (Lillessand and Kiefer 1987). The wavelength band used here were selected because they are the most commonly used for identifying vegetation, soil and rock types, and are standard remote-sensing technology (Avery and Berlin 1992). Bands 3 and 4 are most widely used to distinguish various types of vegetation while band 5 in combination with band 4 is more widely used to enhance bare soil and rock features.

Ratios of these bands have been used to help separate vegetative from non-vegetative reflectance and to guide the classification of soil and geology. The Normalized Difference Vegetation Index (NDVI) is a ratio where the near-infrared (NIR) band (band 4) minus the red band (band 3) are divided by the sum of NIR + red. When displayed as a histogram the NDVI values for a scene allow separation of the non-green reflectance from green reflectance. Cells which have no vegetation green reflectance are assumed to be bare ground. The goal was to identify cells where more than 40% of the ground was bare and had neither an overstory for interception, nor litter for contact mulching. All cells below 20 on the NDVI ratio band 4/3 were classified as bare ground or rock as shown in NDVI/NDSI Ratio, Figure 1. Cells greater than 35 were considered completely vegetated and became background. Using the Normalized Difference Soil Index (NDSI) ratio band 5/4, cells below 20 were also considered bare soil or rock. When the two ratios are combined, the NDVI cells greater than 20 and the NDSI cells less than 25 equate to a transition where bare ground or rock is likely to have dry grass or logging slash present. These differences are given values and the resulting ARC/INFO coverage represents these values in different colors. With unique Universal Transverse Mercator (UTM) positions for the bare and part-bare cells, site visits were made by navigating to these locations via the GPS unit. Calculation of the actual amount of bare ground and litter at each site is continuing via step point transects.

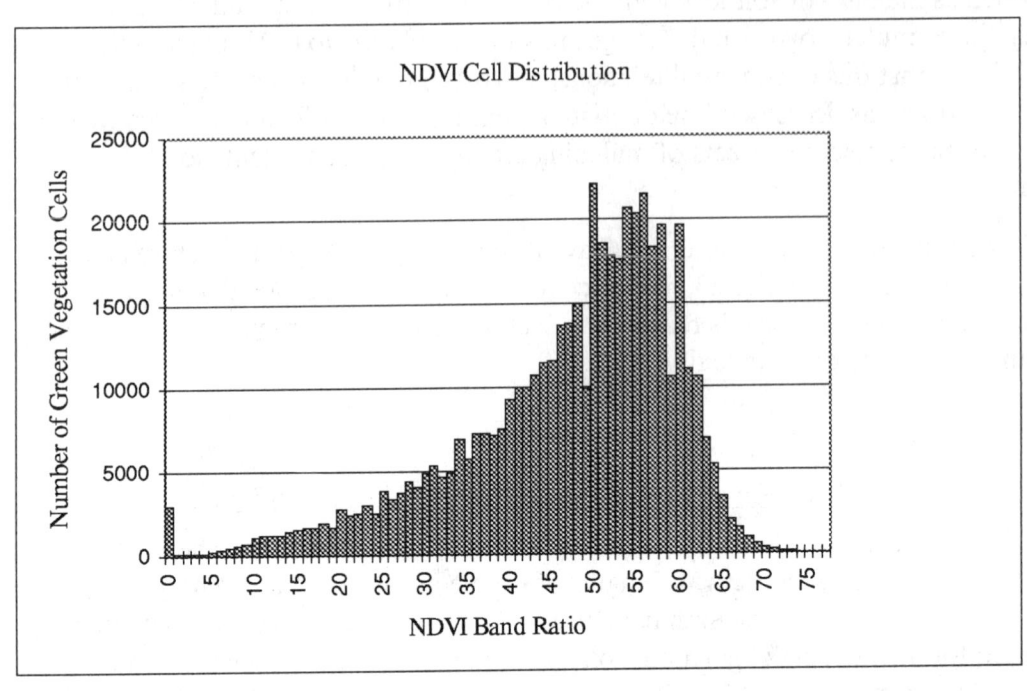

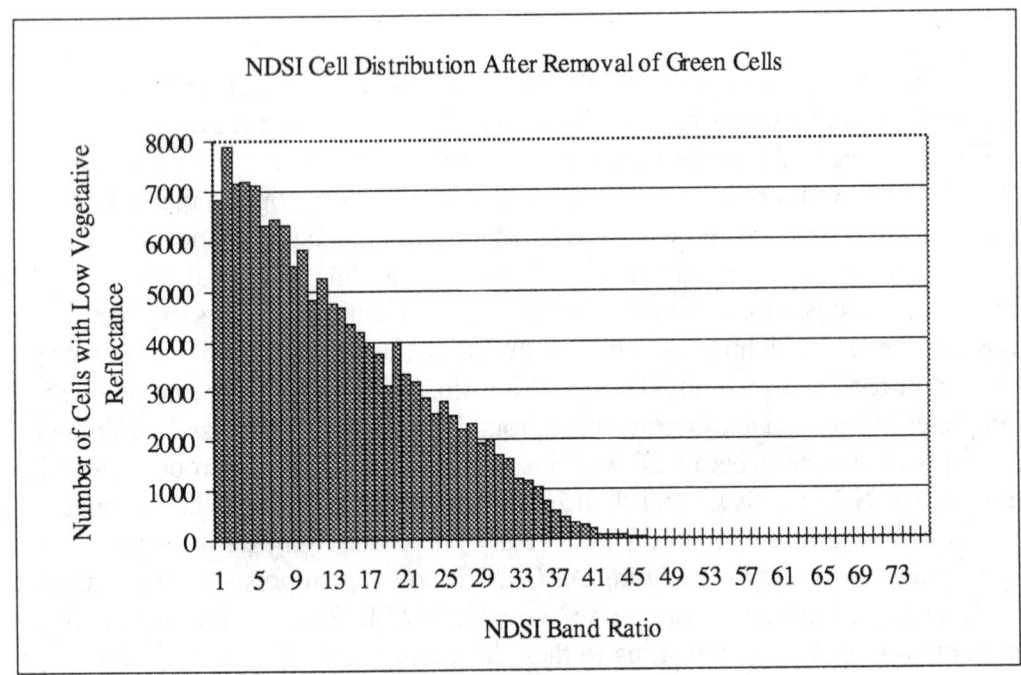

Figure 2 Support for Bare Ground Assumptions Using NDVI and NDSI Ratios From 1994
Landsat TM Image

Modified NDVI/NDSI ratios provide an array of spectral features and do not always identify the bare ground features correctly. In some cases what is classified as bare ground is soil exposed after logging, or an over-grazed meadow. In other cases it is bedrock such as granite outcrops, or volcanic lahar ridges common in many of the high elevation watersheds. When using TM imagery it is difficult to differentiate among the latter three conditions. At present this model does not distinguishing between bare soil and bare rock surfaces however this distinction is expected to be made easier with Airborne Visible and Infrared Imaging Spectrometer (AVIRIS) imagery, soon to be available for Camp and Clear Creeks (see Figure 1 and Plate 3). In the interim rock outcrops mapped as an attribute of the soil surveys provide a method for distinguishing rock out crops large enough to be mapped.

Large clear-cuts, two-to-three acre patch cuts, some log landings, borrow pit, mine spoil piles, and major natural disturbances, such as fires and landslides are easily distinguished using TM imagery. The current limitations on bare ground identification are image resolution and cells-value averaging. These limitations make the identification of bare areas less than 100 X 100 feet in size difficult. "Change detection," techniques such as those pioneered by Pacific Meridian Resources (Green et al. 1993), while confined by the same resolution restrictions, are able to detect disturbance from selective harvesting easily because the green bands of the spectrum are included and the changes in canopy closure suggests disturbance below. Change detection uses two registered Landsat TM images taken at different times. Color enhancement is added to those areas where the vegetation or surface cover has been altered (Green et al. 1993, Lachowski et al. 1994, Maus et al. 1992). Timber-harvest boundaries and property lines in particular become more easily detected.

Spectral Mixture Analysis Application to Bare Ground Predictions

Spectral Mixture Analysis (SMA) (Adams et al. 1986) is another image-analysis technique which was tested in this study on all the ENF watersheds to determine the location of bare ground or partially bare ground cells . The hypothesis was that SMA will improve the accuracy of identifying cells with mixed spectral features where a portion of the cell is more than 40% bare. If successful an SMA analysis would add to the amount of bare ground identified and help to improve the analysis limitations of the Landsat TM imagery with its 30m resolution.

Very few cells in any scene represent the pure spectra of a single feature such as a 100% vegetation or 100% bare ground. Most cells reflect a combination of spectral signatures. Mixing spectra of pure known features, called end members, until a simulation of the target cell spectra is achieved has been done by many others Smith (1990); Ustin et al. (1993); Ustin et al. (1995). Each cell in an image is broken down into its component pure spectra. It is assumed that the spectra for a cell which is 50 % tree and 50 % bare ground will appear as a linear addition of one-half the tree spectrum, plus one-half the soil spectrum (Ustin et al. 1995).

For this study, a number of end members were analyzed before three were chosen. Because of the unique contrast between volcanic-soil spectra and granitic or metasedimentary-soil spectra, I assumed that I could compensate for the changes in geology by adjusting the soil end member as elevation increased from west to east. In this area of the central Sierra Nevada, granitic rocks have been intruded into sediments forming metamorphic rocks. Volcanic mudflows from the Sierran crest have capped the granitic and metamorphic rocks. Subsequent glaciation and erosion have stripped away much of the volcanic rock leaving a mosaic of soil parent material at high elevations where volcanic flows and granite crop out. Mid-elevation rock outcrops are generally granitics and metamorphics in the stream channels and volcanics on the ridge tops with an occasional metasedimentary outcrop at mid-slope. (see theEldorado NF Geology of Soil Parent Material, Plate 1)

Using a granitic soil spectrum for stream channels and high elevation basins, volcanic soil spectrum for ridge tops in the mid-elevations, and metasediment soil spectrum for mid-slopes in the middle elevations an attempt was made to stratify the TM scene in order to identify more bare ground cells. Soil samples representing these three parent materials had been collected in the field, processed and analyzed for their spectral reflectance. While the soil spectra were distinct and easily distinguished from each other in laboratory samples the spectra for volcanic soils were not distinguishable from dry grass in the TM image. Grasses mature later in the season from low elevation to high elevation. Hence adjusting the soil end members for changes in elevation was not used in the last iteration of this analysis. The technique may still have some validity if attempted on an image acquired early in the season when all the grasses are green. SMA TM images with their limited number of spectral bands do not appear to have the same reliability separating soil, rock, and non-green vegetation in the near-infrared wavelengths as do AVIRIS images (Ustin 1995). The work of matching soil color to spectral signature and ultimately to soil parent material continues to engage many soil scientists and remote sensing specialists (Escadafal et al.1988, 1989, Fernandez 1987, Huete 1986, 1991, Melville and Atkinson 1985).

Initial Parameter Thresholds

In order to rank watersheds for comparison, erosion and sedimentation hazard risks are quantified. Each of the parameters described above is assigned a threshold value which becomes the bases for this quantification. These thresholds are pointers to potential erosion. Values for each watershed cell are assigned by the number of thresholds: slope, cover, and detachability, exceeded within that cell. Given normal precipitation conditions for the central Sierra Nevada, it is assumed that each parameter or risk factor has about the same probability of causing erosion. The GIS does not count the cell until the parameter value in that cell exceeds the established threshold. Each time a parameter threshold is exceed a "1" is tabulated for that cell. A cell value may be 0, 1, 2, or 3 as seen in Cell Value Calculation, Table 2 below where the seven possible combinations of parameters and their corresponding values are displayed.

Table 2 Cell Value Calculation

Possible combinations of parameters over threshold.

Parameter	Slope	K-factor	Cover	Slope+ K-factor	Cover+ K-factor	Slope+ Cover	Slope+ K-factor+ Cover
Value	1	1	1	2	2	2	3

Threshold Values

Here risk thresholds are defined as slopes in excess of 40 %, soils with K-factors (detachability ratings) higher than 0.28 and cells with more than 40 % bare soil no surface cover (Elwell and Stocking 1974). These threshold values were derived from the soil literature (Wischmeier and Smith 1978; Rose 1994; Stocking 1994), from current USFS limits for tractor and cable yarding, and from the California and Washington State Forest Practice Rules. Along with the intensity of precipitation, these three parameters are dynamically interactive, with each contributing to "critical shear," detachment as previously defined and transport of soil both individually and collectively. For example, bare, highly detachable soils are not as erodible at slopes of 0 % to 5 % as they are at 15% to 35 %; conversely, bare, steep slopes are not as erodible when soil textures have low detachability values such as clays, as they are when soils are highly detachable, like very fine sandy loams see Table 1 (Mitchell and Bubenzer 1980; Kirkby and Morgan 1980). As we gain more experience in using this model, the threshold values will be changed and further refined into a continuous scale, and the influences of other external factors such as climate and elevation will be added. Adding these factors allows us to predict the potential for rain-on-snow events thereby increasing the model's sensitivity to natural and management perturbations.

Parameters over threshold have been quantified and analyzed for each CWPWS to provide a comparative index which, when examined along with the proximity of roads to streams and total area of disturbance, ranks these watersheds by their percentage of area over threshold. The model calculates a current condition ranking on a "most-healthy to least-healthy" scale as judged by the percent of the watershed which exceeds each threshold or combination of thresholds. Examples of these combinations may be reviewed in Table 8, Results and Discussion.

Soils Data Base and Derived Map Products

This analysis draws from three primary sources of information: slope is derived from a 30 meter digital elevation model (DEM) produced by the US Geological Survey, bare ground is derived from a 1994 Landsat Thematic Mapper satellite image, and the soils information are found in four soil surveys form the ENF and the US Natural Resources Conservation Service (NRCS). The soils data base attributes in particular had to be constructed by gleaning information from the survey data such as engineering properties from one table and physical/chemical properties from another. A number of derived products have been crafted from this source including Eldorado NF Geology of Soil Parent Material, Plate 1. Here the soil parent material and particular geologic formations are used to group soils that have similar erosion characteristics. This map provides foresters and resource managers with a ready reference of spatial information by basic geologic group and soil series.

Eldorado NF Geology of Soil Parent Material

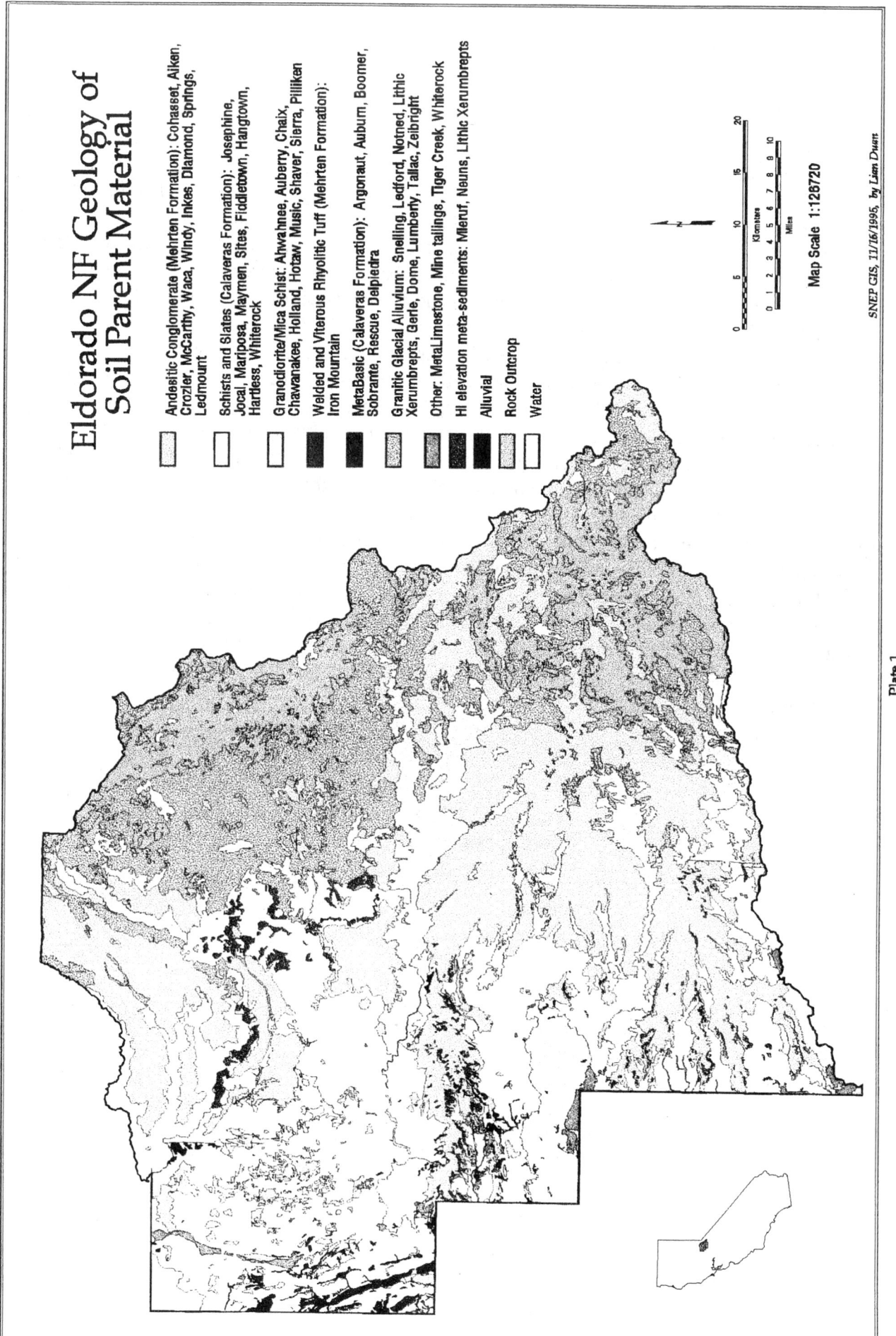

Andesitic Conglomerate (Mehrten Formation): Cohasset, Aiken, Crozier, McCarthy, Waca, Windy, Inkes, Diamond, Springs, Ledmount

Schists and Slates (Calaveras Formation): Josephine, Jocal, Mariposa, Maymen, Sites, Fiddletown, Hangtown, Hartless, Whiterock

Granodiorite/Mica Schist: Ahwahnee, Auberry, Chaix, Chawanakee, Holland, Hotaw, Music, Shaver, Sierra, Pilliken

Welded and Viterous Rhyolitic Tuff (Mehrten Formation): Iron Mountain

MetaBasic (Calaveras Formation): Argonaut, Auburn, Boomer, Sobrante, Rescue, Delpiedra

Granitic Glacial Alluvium: Snelling, Ledford, Notned, Lithic Xerumbrepts, Gerle, Dome, Lumberly, Tallac, Zeibright

Other: MetaLimestone, Mine tailings, Tiger Creek, Whiterock

Hi elevation meta-sediments: Mieruf, Neuns, Lithic Xerumbrepts

Alluvial

Rock Outcrop

Water

Map Scale 1:128720

SNEP GIS, 11/16/1995, by Lian Duan

Plate 1

Natural Erosion Potential Calculation

Natural erosion potential (NEP) is an index of stability or resilience, predicting an unmanaged watershed's ability to withstand erosion causing events. As seen in Eldorado NF Natural Erosion Potential, Plate 2 and in Lower Camp Creek Cells Over Threshold, Table 3 this model operates on Boolean logic: when a cell's value exceeds any threshold it is assigned a one; conversely, if the feature being assessed is less than the threshold, the cell value is assigned a zero. Cell value accuracy is a function of grid size. Using the best available information 30X30m DEMs in the case of slope means that the angle formed using one cell's centroid elevation when compared to the centroid value of its neighbors either does or does not exceed the threshold. Each parameter has its own data layer in the GIS. Again referring to Table 2 when two thresholds are exceeded for the same cell, each cells value remains one and the combination of those cells has a value of two. Likewise, for the combination of all three thresholds being exceeded in the same cell the value of that cell becomes three. In the worst case every cell could have a value of three. In order to calculate percent NEP multiply three times the number of cells in a watershed this becomes the maximum potential NEP watershed value. The present watershed value is generated by counting the total number of cells over threshold in the composite GIS layers. The total number of cells exceeding thresholds, divided by the maximum potential for the watershed, times 100, becomes the relative watershed score or %NEP. The NEP for the whole national forest, graphically projected is found on "Eldorado NF Natural Erosion Potential" Plate 2: where K-factor, Bare ground and Slope are column headings and the presence of a "1" indicates the parameter is over threshold. If a "1" is present in more than one column it is interpreted as an increased erosion risk up to a value of three (See Table 2 for further explanation).

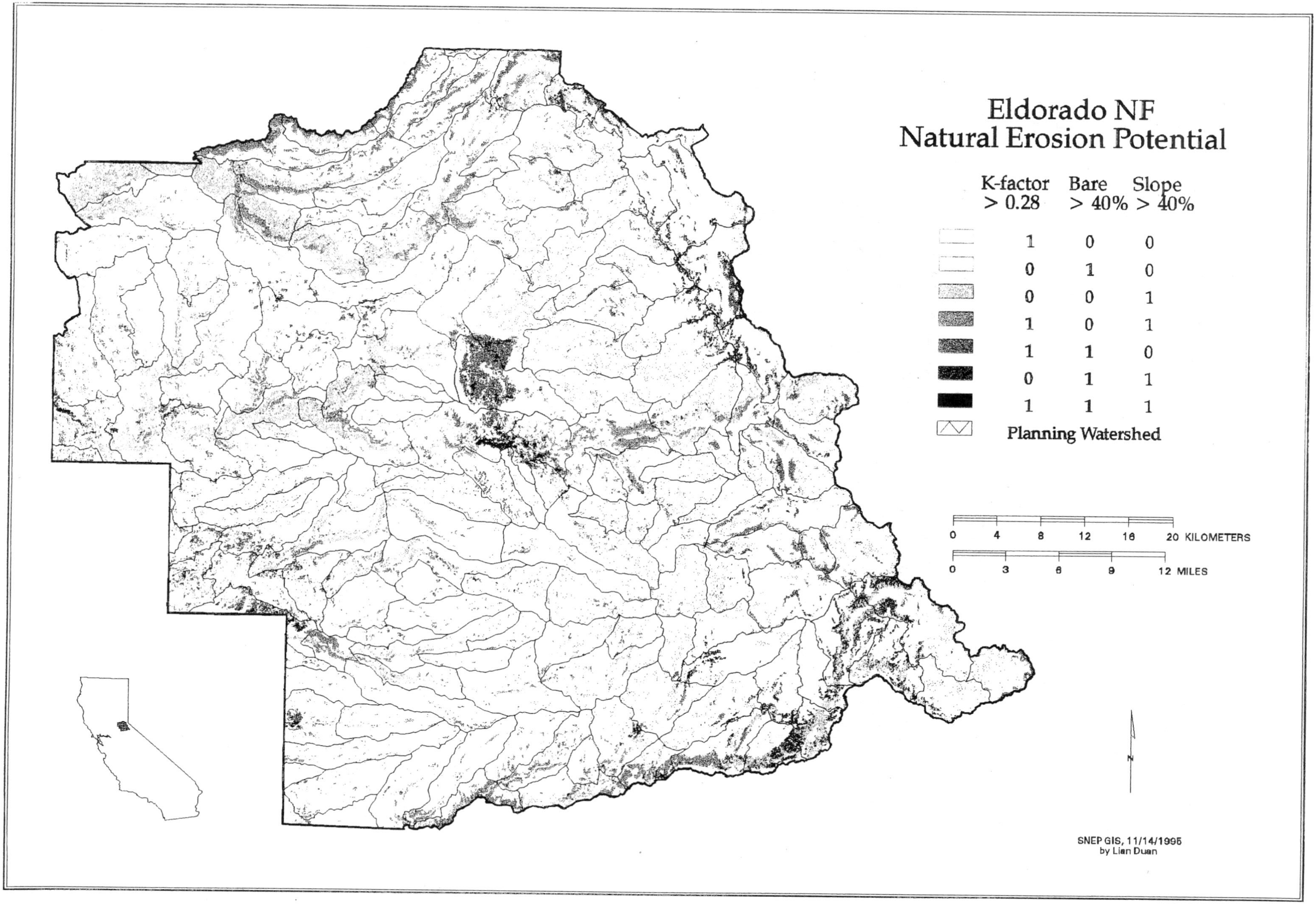
Eldorado NF
Natural Erosion Potential
K-factor > 0.28 | Bare > 40% | Slope > 40%
1 0 0
0 1 0
0 0 1
1 0 1
1 1 0
0 1 1
1 1 1
Planning Watershed
0 4 8 12 16 20 KILOMETERS
0 3 6 9 12 MILES
N
SNEP GIS, 11/14/1995
by Lian Duan

Plate 2

On a computer monitor Plate 2 can be blown-up so that individual 30 X 30m cells may be located and reviewed for soil, slope or bare ground attributes. Even at a very small scale this map provides sufficient spatially explicit information to make reasonable visual watershed comparisons and guide additional assessment work. Each watershed is given an attribute table which provides the user with specific information about the parameters being evaluated. These attribute tables on either a watershed or parameter bases may be accessed to add or edit data.

Camp Creek Area Natural Erosion Potential, Plate 3 is the type of map product that is used for field assessment work and is the basis for the tables used to calculate the ranking of every cell and aggregated up to planning watershed or river basin. Roads and stream buffers are shown so that areas of special concern, may be reviewed for possible mitigation opportunities e.g., the Fry Creek watershed, in red and in the upper center of Plate 3. Fry Creek Data Interpretation, Table 6 is an example of one of the data tables which is built for every watershed. The Interpretation column has been added for reader assistance. The digital version of ENF Watersheds with Acres Over Threshold, Table 9 provides acreage data on 21 separate combinations of parameters over threshold. Access to these data may be gained through computer programs such as Arc/View. Cells over threshold and their corresponding acreage's are summed at the bottom of the columns. Values are not duplicated when thresholds are combined. Maps similar to Plate 3 were used in the field to validate the parameter data. Both individual cells and clusters of cells were targeted and found for examination using global positioning equipment (GPS)

Camp Creek Area
Natural Erosion Potential

K-factor > 0.28	Bare > 40%	Slope > 40%
1	0	0
0	1	0
0	0	1
1	0	1
1	1	1
0	1	1
1	1	1

Road

Stream and lake buffer zone

Planning watershed

N

0	1	2	3	4	5 KILOMETERS

0	0.5	1	1.5	2	2.5	3 MILES

SNEP GIS Center, 12/03/95, by Lian Duan

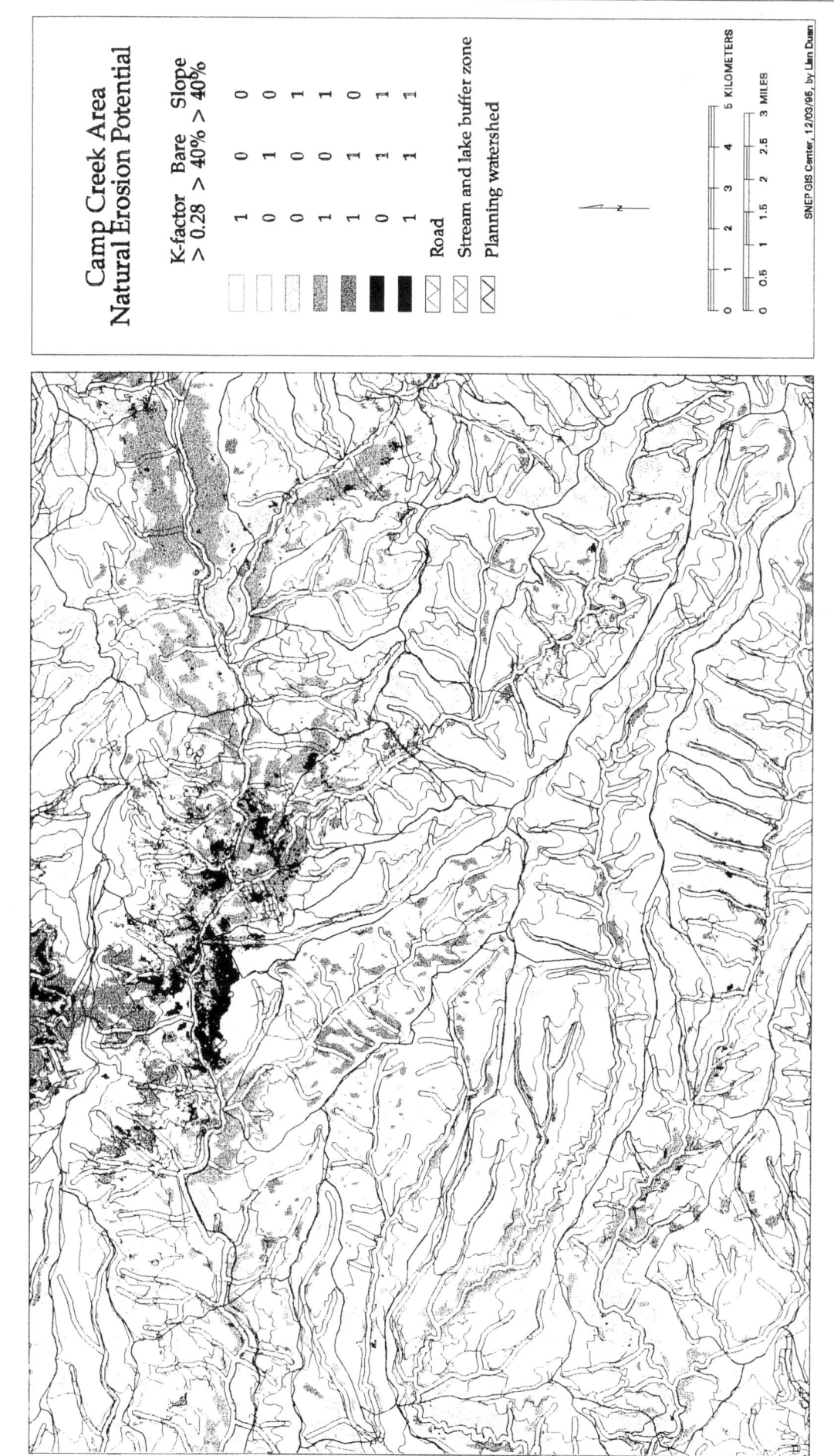

Plate 3

Percent Sedimentation Hazard Index Calculation

Although NEP reflects a watershed's natural stability, sedimentation hazard index (SHI) focuses on the potential to upset that stability through road construction and maintenance practices. Stream sedimentation is often the result of a very small erosional failure becoming a very large CWE disturbance (Megahan et al. 1991; Rice 1993). SHI seeks to micro-analyze a stream buffer zone by identifying areas at risk, predicting points most likely to fail, and reflecting reductions in its index numbers as road segments are abandoned, rocked or paved.

As defined earlier, a healthy watershed is one in which the natural stability of geology and soils maintains the contribution of sediments at a level where natural hydrologic processes balance the ability of a system to both store and transport these sediments without degrading aquatic habitats. If vegetation and debris in stream buffers trap and stabilize incoming sediments, how wide must these buffers be to protect habitat of aquatic and terrestrial species while permitting access to managed lands? Erman et al. (1977; 1983) looked at stream buffer widths and the impacts on benthic organisms. He found the population count and species diversity of these organisms was an indicator of the conditions of the habitat but only as it pertains to aquatic species. Buffers originally thought to be adequate to meet the needs of invertebrates and to prevent or minimize sedimentation may not be adequate to maintain stream organic inputs or provide for the needs of mammals and riparian species (Kattelmann, et al., 1996). Because this study is a screening process attempting to focus the resource manager's attention on the most acute problem areas, potential sedimentation is its primary consideration. In that regard, roads which fall within 60 m (197 feet) of a perennial stream become the target of GIS querying. Cells fully located in the buffer between a road and stream that exceed any of the thresholds are tagged. Where multiple thresholds are exceeded in the same cell, the magnitude of severity ensures that management attention will be focused on that location. Parameters exceeding thresholds for cells within a 60 m buffer zone along perennial streams and adjacent to roads are calculated in the same manner as for NEP except that the maximum potential SHI value becomes the total number of stream buffer cells where roads are present, times three. Actual SHI is made up of those cells over threshold, within the stream buffer where roads are present. Dividing the potential into the actual, yields the %SHI in the same manner as %NEP was generated (see Tables 4 and 5). These new values are the most critical of the process because they reflect the increased probability that sedimentation will occur at a location under specified conditions. The cells which potentially will cause problems are noted and are uniquely identifiable. Therefore, they can be monitored and/or mitigated. Maps of roads, stream buffers, watershed boundaries, and parameters over threshold are produced along with the tables so that graphical comparisons can be made and checked in the field. Camp Creek Area Sedimentation Hazard Index Plate 4 emphasizes the fact that the occurrence of cells over threshold inside stream buffers is limited. This limitation points to locations where increased sedimentation should be expected and to critical areas which should be monitored.

<u>NEP and SHI Analysis Applied to the Camp Creek Case Study Area</u>

NEP and SHI results for all CWPWS have been tabulated individually and are summarized in Appendix 1. Table 3 provides an example of watershed 532.23011 Lower Camp Creek Planning Watershed, which is a portion of the Camp and Clear Creeks case study (McGurk et al. 1995). The percent NEP and SHI are calculated from the cell totals; however, reading the values parameter by parameter yields additional information. The watershed area measured via GIS for the Camp Creek segment being analyzed is 46448 cells, (calculation not shown) at 0.22 acres per cell this portion of the watershed area is approximately 10330 acres. The maximum potential NEP for this example is 3 X 46448 or 139344. Assume that each combination of cells is unique and that cells are not counted twice: to interpret the last row where one cell is high K-factor, bare, and >40% slope we see that the cell is not in a stream buffer or beside a road because there are 1's in the first three columns and 0's in the last two. In the first row 10 bare ground cells were found inside the stream buffer with a road present. In the second row 444 cells where roads are inside the stream buffer and the soils there have K-factors above 0.28. In the third row 16 cells are bare with a high K-factor and adjacent to a roads. The calculations of NEP and SHI for this watershed are found in Tables 4 and 5.

Table 3 Lower Camp Creek Planning Watershed Cells Over Threshold

Cal-Water Planning Watershed ID	Number of cells over Threshold	Cells with K-factor > 0.28	Cells with > 40% bare ground	Cells with slopes >40%	Cells inside a 60m stream buffer	Cells inside a 60m stream buffer with a road
532.23011	602	0	0	0	1	1
532.23011	10	0	1	0	1	1
532.23011	444	1	0	0	1	1
532.23011	16	1	1	0	1	1
532.23011	2541	0	0	0	1	0
532.23011	917	0	0	1	0	0
532.23011	21	0	0	1	1	0
532.23011	398	0	1	0	0	0
532.23011	60	0	1	0	1	0
532.23011	19	0	1	1	0	0
532.23011	12663	1	0	0	0	0
532.23011	2618	1	0	0	1	0
532.23011	1988	1	0	1	0	0
532.23011	139	1	0	1	1	0
532.23011	64	1	1	0	0	0
532.23011	7	1	1	0	1	0
532.23011	1	1	1	1	0	0

Table 3 above is a typical ARC/INFO table where: Columns represent the data for each threshold parameter covered there is a 1 in the row if there is data, 0 if there is not. The number of cells exceeding each threshold or thresholds is found in the "Number of cells over threshold" column. A 1 in the "Cells inside a 60 m stream buffer column" indicates that the cells counted were also inside a stream buffer. If there is a 1 in the "Cells inside a 60 m stream buffer with a road" column it means the number of cells shown are over threshold and adjacent to roads. Each cell is identifiable and may be found using via GPS coordinates.

****

Table 4

Natural Erosion Potential (NEP) Calculations for Lower Camp Creek

Parameter	Total Cells Over Threshold
Bare Ground	468
Bare G + High K	87
High K-factor	15725
High K + Slopes	2127
Slopes over 40%	938
Bare G + Slopes	19
Bare G + Slopes + High K	1

Total cells over threshold = 19365

Lower Camp Creek NEP calculation 46448 WS cells * 3 = 139344 maximum potential NEP

19365/139344 X 100 = 13.9% NEP

Table 5 Sedimentation Hazard Index (SHI) Calculation for Lower Camp Creek

Only for cells inside the stream buffer and adjacent to roads.

Parameter	Total cells Over Threshold
Bare Ground	10
Hi K-factor	444
Bare G + High K	16
	470

1072 (total cells in stream buffers and adjacent to roads) * 3 = 3216 maximum potential SHI

470 / 3216 X 100 = 14.6% SHI

111

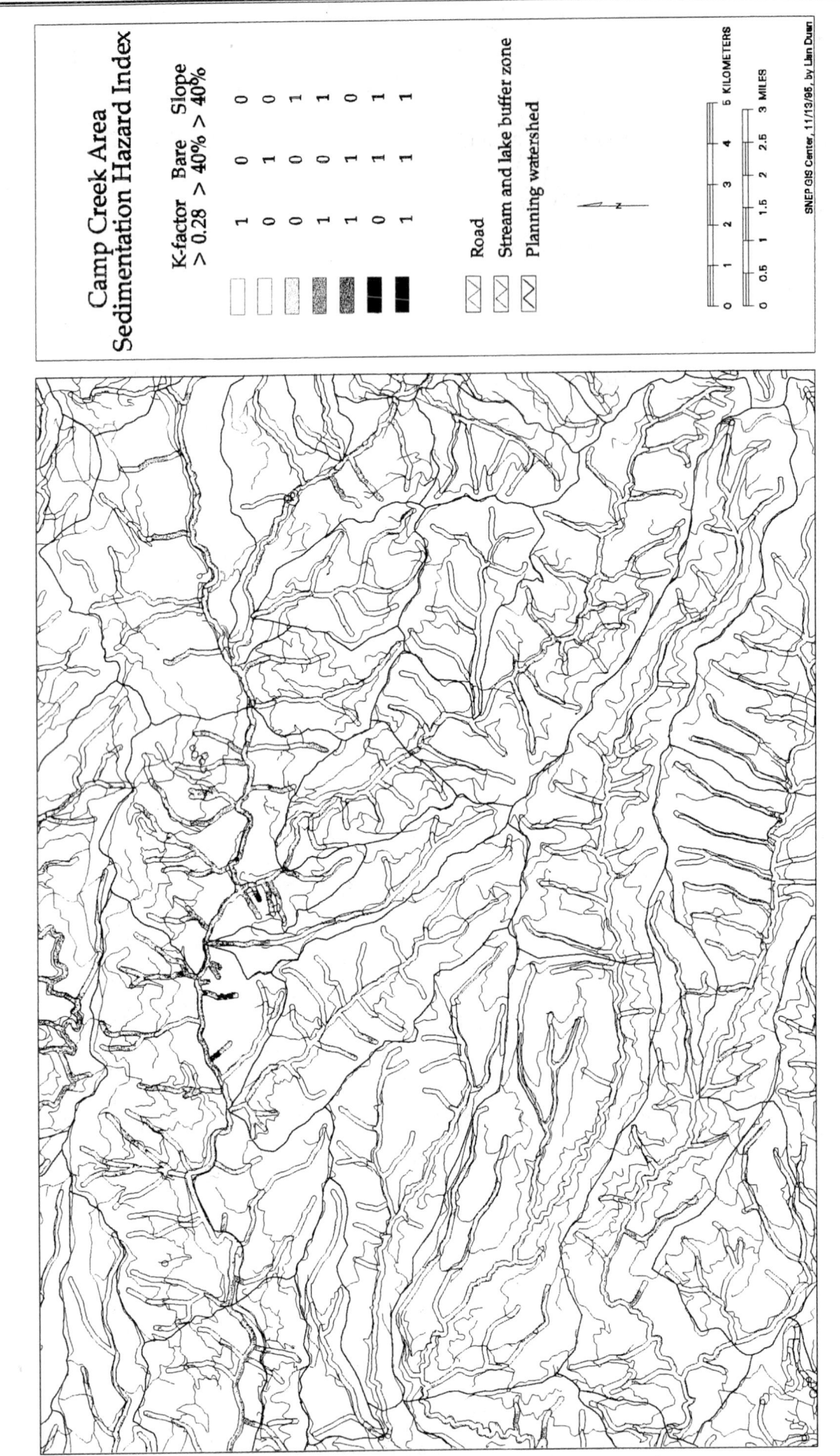

Camp Creek Area
Sedimentation Hazard Index

K-factor > 0.28	Bare > 40%	Slope > 40%
1	0	0
0	1	0
0	0	1
1	1	1
1	1	1
1	0	0
1	1	1
1	1	1

Road

Stream and lake buffer zone

Planning watershed

N

0 1 2 3 4 5 KILOMETERS

0 0.5 1 1.5 2 2.5 3 MILES

SNEP GIS Center, 11/13/95, by Lian Dunn

Plate 4

Table 6 Fry Creek Data Interpretation

Number of cells	Total Acres	% of Watershed	Soil K-factor >0.28	Bare Ground >40%	Steep Slopes >40%	Stream Buffer	Road in Steam Buffer	Interpretation
28535	6345	100	0*	0	0	1123 acs	134 acs	6345 acres is the watershed 1120 in stream buffers and 134 with roads in the buffer.
420	93	1.5	0	0	0	1	0	93 acres of stream buffer under threshold without roads.
81	18	0.3	0	0	0	1	1	18 acres of stream buffer under threshold with roads.
380	84	1.3	0	0	1*	0	0	84 acres of slopes >40% outside of stream buffers and without roads.
17	4	0.1	0	0	1	1	0	4 acres of slopes >40% in the stream buffer.
1363	303	4.8	0	1	0	0	0	303 acres of bare ground outside the stream buffer without roads.
14	3	0	0	1	0	1	0	3 acres of bare ground inside the stream buffer but without roads.
13	3	0	0	1	1	0	0	3 acres of bare, steep area outside the stream buffer and without roads.
8916	1982	31.2	1	0	0	0	0	1982 acres of high K-factor soils outside of stream buffers or roads.
2697	600	9.5	1	0	0	1	0	600 acres of Hi-K soils in stream buffers.
404	90	1.4	1	0	0	1	1	90 acres of Hi-K soils in stream buffers and beside roads.
5131	1141	18	1	0	1	0	0	1141 acres of Hi-K and steep lands outside of stream buffers or roads.
765	170	2.7	1	0	1	1	0	170 acres of Hi-K and steep lands inside stream buffers without roads.
18	4	0.1	1	0	1	1	1	4 acres of Hi-K and steep lands inside stream buffers with roads.
2334	519	8.2	1	1	0	0	0	519 acres of Hi-K and bare lands outside of stream buffers or roads.
420	93	1.5	1	1	0	1	0	93 acres of Hi-K and bare lands inside stream buffers without roads.
97	22	0.3	1	1	0	1	1	22 acres of Hi-K and bare lands inside stream buffers with roads.
1358	302	4.8	1	1	1	0	0	302 acres of Hi-K, bare and steep lands outside of stream buffers or roads.
112	25	0.4	1	1	1	1	0	25 acres of Hi-K, bare and steep lands inside of stream buffers without roads.
3	1	0	1	1	1	1	1	1 acre of Hi-K, bare and steep land inside of stream buffers with roads.
			4949 acs	1271 acs	1734 acs	1123 acs	134 acs	

* "0" Means no data in the "number of cells" column for this parameter. "1" means the number of cells shown in the "number of cells" column are the cells, acres, or percent over threshold for this parameter or combination of parameters.

<u>Watershed Assessment Terminology</u>

The application of the NEP and SHI methodology was limited to the Eldorado National Forest and to those CWPWS's that were completely within the national forest because of data limitations for areas beyond the national forest boundaries. Table 8, features 27 of 177 watersheds reviewed for this work. There were differences in watershed boundaries selected by the Forest Service and Cal-Water. These differences were reconciled by consolidating Cal-Water watersheds in some cases and Forest Service watersheds in others. The consolidating process yielded 120 watersheds with enough data to compare. Only 76 of the USFS watersheds had complete data which was directly compatible with the study model. However all 120 watersheds had the USFS generated Natural Sensitivity Index (NSI). Designed by Kuehn in 1989 for CWE analysis on the ENF this indexing system considers both hillslope and in-channel hydrologic and erosional processes. Soils, stream channel conditions, geomorphic instability, drainage density and precipitation regimes are all part of the NSI calculation. NSI is used to generate a watershed's Threshold of Concern or (TOC) (USDA-FS, 1987a). TOC relates to the percent of Equivalent Roaded Acres (ERA) which is a watershed ranking by the amount and type of land disturbance within a watershed. TOC for a watershed is determined by the NSI number where < 15 is very low and > 65 is very high. For watersheds with very low NSI numbers the TOC will range from 18 - 20% ERA. Meaning that 20% of the watershed may be disturbed before significant cumulative effect occurs. Likewise watersheds with very high NSI numbers have lower TOC's and as little as 10% ERA may trigger significant CWE.

Table 7 Relationship of Natural Sensitivity Index to Equivalent Roaded Acres and Threshold of Concern
(from Carlson and Christiansen 1993)

NSI	SENSITIVITY	TOC
<15	Very Low	18-20 % ERA
16-35	Low	16-18 % ERA
36-50	Moderate	14-16 % ERA
51-65	High	12-14 % ERA
>65	Very High	10-12 % ERA

RESULTS AND DISCUSSION

Watersheds represent distinct topographic units and the understanding of their health and condition cannot be limited by ownership. "Current condition" is the product of all past events and the ecosystems' response to those events, both natural and management induced. Implementation of management strategies may be unique to ownership, however, in order to account for mitigation activities in mixed ownership watersheds, when assessing CWE, all disturbances must be considered.

Standardization of Soil Data Collection and Data-Base Management

The accuracy of assessments of this nature is dependent on the quality of the data being used. The lack of a continuous and consistent digital soil map, standardized labeling and common physical descriptions, for the SNEP study area as well as adjacent national forests, has severely hindered progress of this work. The fact that there are no standardized mapping, labeling, analytical processing, or report formats between national forests from the same Region is further complicated in that soil surveys completed by the Soil Conservation Service (SCS) (a.k.a. Natural Resources Conservation Service NRCS) and the State of California Soil-Vegetation Survey are at different scales and have varying standards.

Given the emphases placed on accuracy of the assessment process and the proposed future needs for precise inter-agency and public-private monitoring protocols, standardized data-base resource information to support varied geographic information systems (GIS) is imperative. Watershed names, identification numbers and boundaries as well as soils and geology information should be collected, standardized, maintained and disseminated by a single agency to federal, state, local, and private consumers. Such an approach would be consistent with CWE issues of both the National Environmental Protection Act (NEPA) and the California Environmental Quality Act (CEQA).

Model Limitations

This model does not calculate soil movement it directs attention to those areas where management activity has a high likelihood of detaching soil particles and making them available for transport. Predicting soil loss with mathematical models continues to challenge soil scientists and engineers because of the vast number of variables and the wide range of data needs. Some models predict accurately for time steps of a few minutes but are confined by scale and cannot be applied to large areas (Morgan 1986). Screening models, while simple in concept, are designed to identify problem locations. Assessment models must predict with greater accuracy and thus are used to quantify severity of erosion under various land management options (Morgan 1986). McGurk and Berg (1995) applied the Water Yield and Sediment Model (WATSED) (USDA Forest Service 1991) model for determining sedimentation to Clear and Camp Creeks and found it both data and labor intensive. Doing hierarchical analysis, first using a screening tool, followed by more data intensive and quantitative procedures allows managers to identify and prioritize both analytical and restoration activities.

Determining rates of erosion and volumes of sediment moved requires sophisticated models and extensive amounts of empirical data. Models of that caliber typically require twenty to thirty years of data to test and validate. Although these models are reasonably successful in characterizing annual processes, they have difficulty in predicting erosion on a localized area from a single storm event. Scale also has a great influence on model selection and the accuracy of the output. Modeling large basins requires significantly different data demands than modeling a small field or the impact of a single raindrop. Although much theoretical work has focused on the latter, it is difficult to scale these findings up to a watershed or region (Nearing et al. 1994).

Model Comparison With USFS Outputs

One of the highest Forest Service NSI and TOC rankings is that of Fry Creek (see Table 8). Fry Creek is a tributary of the South Fork of the American River its ground cover was burned in the 1993 Cleveland Fire. It has steep slopes and highly detachable soils. This model calculated Fry Creek as one of its highest risk watersheds with NEP and SHI ratings of 41.7% and 35.5 % respectively. Fry Creek is approximately 6346 acres in area its NSI and %TOC are 183 and 138%. A TOC of 138% indicates that this watershed is significantly over the US threshold and that further unmitigated disturbance may result in considerable harm to the ecosystem. The erosion hazard rating (EHR) Risk Nr for this watershed, as seen in the seventh column of Table 8, is 5: extreme. Table 8 is one example of the type of data that may be extracted from the model. Here using percent allows for relative scaling when comparing a 2,000 acre watershed with a 13,000 acre watershed. Table 9 uses the same base cell data generated from ARC/INFO to compare the acres over threshold in these same watersheds.

Table 8 Twenty-Seven Eldorado National Forest Watersheds with the Highest Sedimentation Hazard Index and Their Corresponding Natural Sensitivity Index and Threshold of Concern Rankings

CPWS ID Nr Cal-Water Planning watershed ID number	Cal-Water watershed Name	CPWS Acs Cal-Water planning watershed acres	NSI Natural Sensitivity Index	% TOC Threshold of concern	% ERA Equivalent roaded acres	EHR RiskNr Erosion Hazard Rating Nr	%NEP Natural Erosion Potential	%SHI Sedimentation Hazard Index	% Rd acs Roaded acres	%SB/Rd Roaded acres inside stream buffers
514.33021	Peavine Creek	11,510	60	125.0	15	5	40.9	38.6	10.5	11.4
514.35021	Fry Creek	6,346	183	138.0	13.8	5	41.7	35.5	9.1	11.9
514.32010	Gaddis Creek	8,684	81	106.0	10.6	5	35.2	34.6	8.2	9
532.60051	Beaver Creek	2,464	95	100.0	10	5	31.7	34.6	8.2	9.5
514.33035	Camp Seven	4,248	291	70.0	7	3	32.4	34.4	6.1	5.3
514.32012	Brush Creek	5,132	37	36.4	5.1	2	36.6	34.0	10.2	7.7
532.23043	Clear Creek	2,896	34	61.3	9.8	3	28.1	32.2	10.3	14.1
514.33030	Little Silver Creek	8,604	28	68.1	10.9	3	30.6	32.0	9.6	11.3
514.35050	Twenty-five Mile Cyn	10,972	138	129.0	12.9	5	33.6	31.6	9.6	10.8
532.60061	W Panther Creek	5,853	79	104.0	10.4	5	26.1	30.2	11.3	9.9
532.23042	Middle Butte	2,925	160	53.0	5.3	2	31.1	29.8	6.2	3.2
514.36033	Middle Creek	4,735	119	50.0	5	3	24.5	29.8	7.0	6.9
514.32022	Whaler Creek	10,209	91.3	62.0	6.2	3	29.7	29.4	11.5	11
532.23033	North Canyon	3,541	25	23.1	3.7	1	29.5	28.8	10.0	15.3
514.32011	Slab Creek	5,493	114	43.0	4.3	2	32.3	27.9	11.0	8.6
532.23062	Clear Creek	6,840	28	50.0	8	2	28.0	27.7	13.1	14.5
514.32031	Bear Creek	5,358	59	68.3	8.2	3	28.1	27.4	12.6	16
514.32013	Slab Creek Res	5,723	174	51.0	5.1	2	28.7	26.8	9.8	6.1
514.35022	Mill Creek	2,178	61	117.5	14.1	5	11.5	24.9	8.6	8.1
514.35051	Grays Canyon	8,308	173	51.0	5.1	2	31.2	24.6	9.0	5.7
514.43033	Zero Spring	8,212	220	30.0	3	2	34.8	24.5	6.0	4.2
514.32015	Iowa Canyon	5,107	41	95.0	13.3	4	18.2	24.5	14.2	10.9

Cal-Water ID	Name	Total Acres								
514.32021A	AWS1	13,502	94	34.0	3.7	25.1	2	24.4	10.3	0
532.24012	Cat Creek	5,655	93	138.0	13.8	14.4	5	23.9	10.7	13.8
532.23032	Van Horn Creek	7,516	77	64.0	6.4	26.5	3	23.8	10.2	12.3
514.35052	Soldier Creek	3,414	52	103.3	12.4	17.6	5	23.5	9.3	13.4
532.23051	Camp Creek	10,140	92	66.0	6.6	29.9	3	23.3	7.4	3.9

See Eldorado National Forest Watershed Statistics, Appendix 1 for a complete listing.

Table 9 ENF Watersheds Ranked by Acres Over Threshold

Cal-Water Planning Watershed ID Nr	Cal-Water Planning Watershed Name	Cal-Water Planning Watershed Total Acres	Slope >40% No Stream Buffer No Road Acs	Slope >40% in Stm Buff With Rd Acs	>40% Bare Gd In Stm Buff No Rd Acs	>40% Bare Gd In Stm Buff With Rd Acres	Hi-K Soil No Stm Buff No Rd Acres	Hi-K Soil In Stm Buff With Rd Acres	Hi-K+Steep In Stm Buff No Rd Acres	Hi-K+Bare In Stm Buff No Rd Acs
514.33021	Peavine Ck	11510	40.9	2.2	311.1	27.6	1423.3	44.9	0.2	547.2
514.35050	Twentyfive Mile Cyn	10972	366.9	3.1	67.4	8	2754.9	115.2	40	154.1
514.34031	Union Valley Res	11288	34.5	0.2	975	8.4	1632.9	26.7	0.7	134.3
532.23062	Clear Ck	6840	59.6	0	13.8	1.8	2709.8	96.7	6.2	97.8
514.35021	Fry Ck	6346	84.5	0	3.1	0	1982.5	89.8	170.1	93.4
514.32030	Traverse Ck	9378	184.1	0	60.5	9.8	4634.4	137.4	0	86.5
514.32024	Redbird Ck	8228	696.8	4.2	18.5	2.4	4345.6	149	8.2	78.5
532.24041	Lower Perry Ck	4801	144.5	2.2	6.7	1.3	1478.8	25.6	8	68
532.23070	Long Ravine	4952	214.6	0	49.1	0	2340.9	61.6	17.8	55.6
514.35030	Upper Alder Ck	9233	91.6	0	76.7	18.2	778	38.2	1.3	55.4
514.43040	Upper Pilot Ck	9543	21.3	0	33.4	1.3	5385.3	56.7	7.8	52.5
532.23072	Squaw Hollow Ck	2414	0	0	0.2	0.2	1165.1	54.5	0	47.4
514.33032	Onion Ck	3358	31.8	0	0	0	2155	15.3	5.1	45.1
514.32040	Big Sailor Ck	9835	70.7	0	94.7	9.6	2593	74.7	1.6	43.4

532.23031	Mid-Upr. NF Cos. R	6247	73.2	0	43.8	6.7	745.3	36.9	6	39.1
514.44021	Lower SF Rubicon R	6676	606.6	0	28	4.2	607.7	8.7	16.2	36.2
514.32041	Kelsey Cyn	6687	1043.7	1.3	115.2	10.2	1264.9	45.4	12	35.6
514.32032	White Rock Ck	10831	2143	8	44.2	4.9	2854.1	88.9	34.5	35.6
532.23061	Jackass Ck	6047	150.3	0	13.3	3.6	2497	28	3.8	34.5
514.32010	Gaddis Ck	8684	0.4	0	2.2	0	6411	117.6	25.3	32.7
514.32031	Bear Ck	5358	73.4	0	6	1.3	3468	123.8	0.4	31.8
514.31022	Cold Springs Ck	1480	0	0	6.9	0.7	693.7	19.6	0	29.8
514.36030	Bark Shanty Cyn	5371	14.2	0	28.9	2.4	1802.1	31.4	12	29.1
532.23050	Jenkinson Lake	3057	2.4	0	81.4	0	595.9	12.9	0	29.1
514.33030	Little Silver Ck	8604	93.8	6	37.4	3.8	5499.4	136.5	8.4	26.7
532.23051	Camp Ck	10140	1771	0	15.1	1.1	4409.4	31.4	30.5	21.6
514.35022	Mill Ck	2178	18.5	0	6	0	223.5	16	7.1	21.1
532.23043	Clear Ck	2896	0	0	0	0	1770.1	52.5	0	20.7
532.23060	Butte Ck	5420	123.8	1.1	4.7	0.2	3433.5	46.9	1.3	20.5

See Eldorado National Forest Watershed Statistics, Appendix for a complete listing.

<u>Frequency distribution results of the models watershed ranking</u>

In Natural Erosion Potential rankings of the top twenty-seven watersheds, Figure 3, histograms for each index suggest that the NEP/SHI data are more evenly distributed across all the watersheds than the USFS comparisons. There was a concern that the effects of the various parameters selected to determine watershed sensitivity might not be evenly distributed across the study watersheds. In order to review that possibility the 40 watersheds having the highest NEP scores were selected, and their parameters graphed in Frequency distributions of watershed ranking in method comparison, Figure 3 to examine the distributions. While high K-factor and Steep Slopes have the greatest influence on NEP, bare ground is dominant in several cases leading to the conclusion that one factor does not overshadow all others.

Distribution of Cells Over Threshold for 27 ENF Watersheds with the Highest %NEP

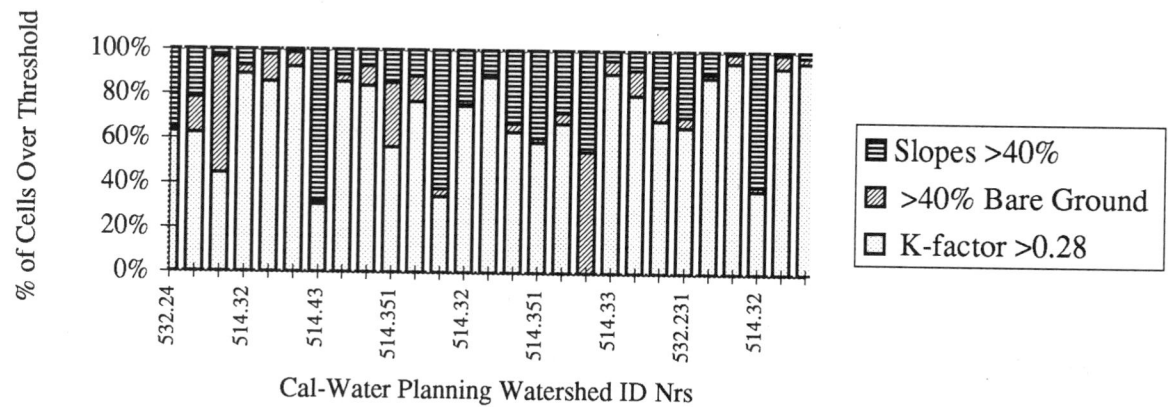

Figure 3 Distribution of Cells Over Threshold for 27 ENF Watersheds with the Highest %NEP

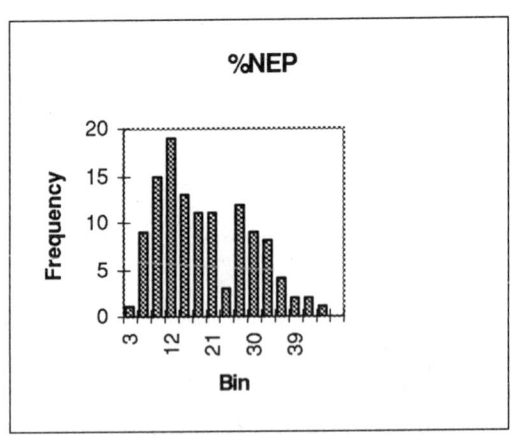

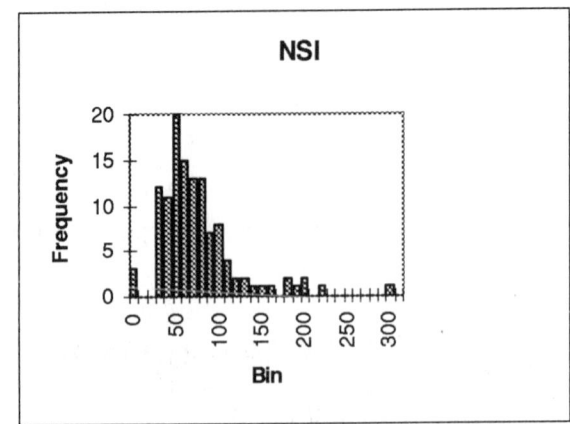

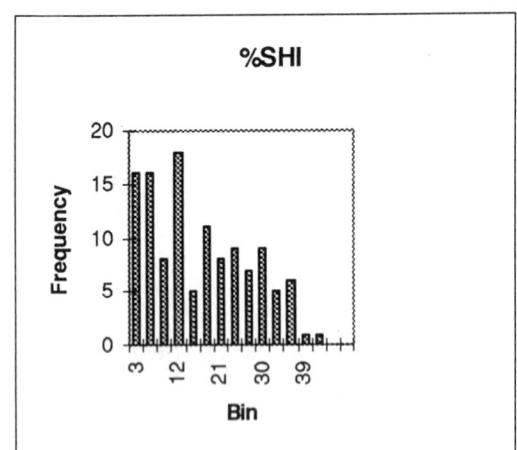

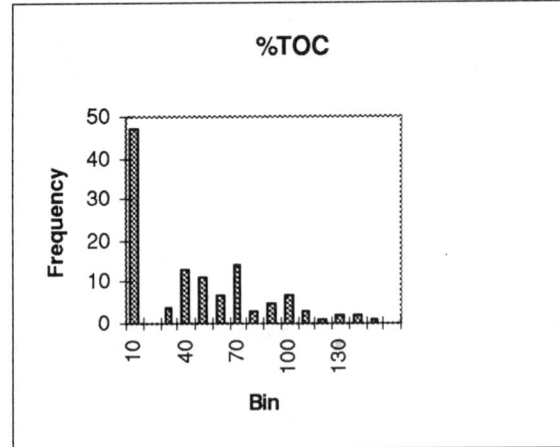

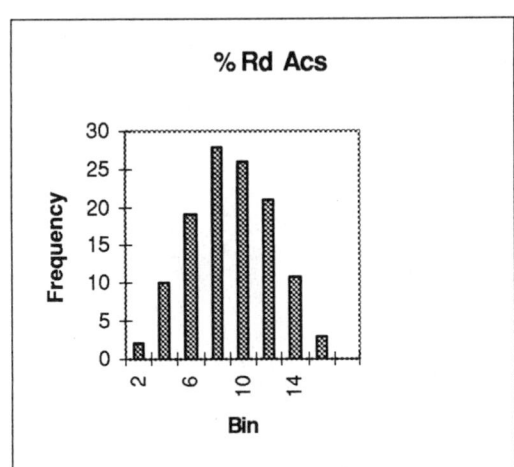

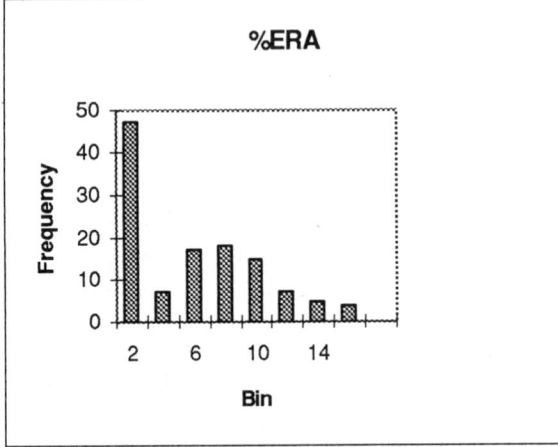

Figure 4 Frequency Distribution of ENF Watershed Rankings

Model Construction Time and Proposed Uses

After the soil data base was constructed, 177 CWPWS were reviewed and 134 analyzed for natural erosion potential and sedimentation hazards using approximately 10 days of GIS and analysis time. Positive correlation with the Eldorado National Forest's natural sensitivity index and equivalent roaded acres methodology provides significant encouragement to continue refining this model and expanding its application to other portions of the Sierra Nevada Ecosystem Project study area. NEP and SHI rankings may be modified by testing mitigation alternatives which include the surfacing and abandonment of road segments in areas over erosion parameter threshold. While this model is relatively easy to apply, and cost effective, it is a screening tool and is proposed for use in the allocation of human resources. Pre-assessment screening with NEP and SHI provide resources managers with information to guide selection of watersheds for more focused CWE analysis. Modeling the NEP and SHI response to various mitigation options allows the optimization of mitigation budgets.

Correlation Comparisons

The correlation coefficients, r are positive for the four major indexes: USFS's NSI, ERA, and this model's NEP and SHI. The correlation between NEP and NSI is 0.54. Between SHI and TOC it is 0.44 and between SHI and ERA it is 0.34. The model has been run once, hence ground truthing to calibrate its prediction will continue. Finding that 54% of the variation in NSI ranking is explained by the variation in NEP is encouraging considering the difference in these methodologies, and with limited field validation. Calibration for large areas of exposed bedrock as in high elevation watersheds, precipitation isohyets and their influence on areas of high rain-on-snow potential, as well as change detection analysis will further improve the correlation between these two NEP and ERA watershed assessment methods. The ERA method of analysis is likewise an evolving technique requiring large commitments of personnel time in both the field and disturbance history research. Because of frequent opportunity for human bias the objectivity of the ERA method is often questioned.

Table 10 Correlation Coefficients, r, for the NEP and SHI Model Output

	NSI	ERA	TOC
NEP	0.54	0.19	0.33
SHI	0.43	0.34	0.44
RdAcs	-0.12	0.47	0.42
StBufAc	-0.29	0.37	0.24

	NSI	TOC	ERA
NSI		0.1865*	0.0698*
TOC	0.1978*		
ERA	0.0617*	0.9220*	

	NEP	SHI	RdAcs
NEP		0.8948	0.1491
SHI			0.3724
RdAcs		0.3724	
StBufAc	-0.1159	0.0405	0.6276

Where: NEP is the natural erosion potential, SHI is the sedimentation hazard index, RdAcs are this models roaded acres, StBufAc are acres within the stream buffer. NSI is the USFS natural sensitivity index, ERA is the USFS equivalent roaded acres, and TOC is the USFS threshold of concern. * = USFS data available only for comparison of 77 watersheds, all others had data from 120 watersheds.

Correlation using watershed improvement needs reports

Several validation methods were conceived and applied to the NEP and SHI data to analyze better the results of the watershed ranking. Thorough sampling continued into the Fall of 1995 and other data sets that were used in previous or concurrent assessments are being actively sought.

Both the ENF and Georgia Pacific Corporation collect and maintain reports of Watershed Improvement Needs (WIN) where opportunities to improve CWEs through mitigation are recorded. Reviewing 333 of these reports for the watersheds being studied yielded a correlation coefficient of 0.2 when total WINs for 114 watersheds were compared to the percent of the stream buffer that is roaded. While this fact has limited statistical significance, no other significant correlationís were observed. Attempts to correlate NSI, %ERA, %TOC, %NEP, and % RdAcs were all negative. The assumption that WINs represented randomly gathered data that were distributed evenly across all watersheds was false (Christiansen 1995). As a matter of practice, both industry and USFS road crews routinely repair problem spots eliminating the need for work requests or WIN reports. Table 10 contains the WIN report data reviewed. Each group of data collectors focused its attention primarily on lands belonging to or managed by their separate entities.

Table 11 Tabulation of Watershed Improvement Needs (WIN) Forms for the 24 ENF Watersheds Receiving the Most Reports

ENF Watershed ID Nr	Cal-Water planning watershed Nr	Cal-Water planning watershed name	USFS watershed improvement rpts	GP watershed improvement rpts	Total watershed improvement rpts
2236	532.23031A	AWS6	37	0	37
2176	532.2301	Camp Cr	30	0	30
4013	514.43032	Big Grizzly Cyn	19	0	19
1121	532.6006	E Panther Creek	7	7	14
1011	532.60063	Little Tiger Creek	0	12	12
1001	532.60064	Mill Creek	0	11	11
1211	532.60051	Beaver Creek	3	7	10
2471	532.24012	Cat Creek	9	0	9
3325	514.3505	Twentyfive Mile Cyn	6	3	9
2246	532.23032	Van Horn	7	0	7
3143	514.3202	Brass Cr	7	0	7
3355	514.35021	Fry Creek	7	0	7
2136	532.23021	Sly Park Creek	1	5	6
2456	532.2402	McKinney Creek	6	0	6
3336	514.3504	Plum Creek	5	1	6
3736	514.3603	Bark Shanty Cyn	5	1	6
3916	514.35017(A)	AWS3	6	0	6
1111	532.60061	W Panther Creek	0	5	5
3116	514.32015	Iowa Canyon	5	0	5
3133	514.32022	Whaler Creek	5	0	5
3386	514.3503	Upper Alder Creek	3	2	5
4123	514.4301	S F Long Canyon	5	0	5
4123+4143A	514.4301	S F Long Canyon	5	0	5

Pending correlation with other erosion potential assessments

The work of McKittrick (1994) using a GIS model to classify the erosion potential of private forested watersheds in northern California is currently being reviewed for additional comparisons. Integrating McKittrick's use of precipitation and geology will improve the NEP/SHI model. Other SNEP science team members are currently completing sensitive watershed assessments which will eventually be compared to the NEP/SHI results. Change detection analysis mentioned earlier (Maus et al. 1992, Green et al. 1993, Lachowski et al. 1994) allows more precise measurements of moderate cumulate disturbance such as selective timber harvesting and road construction. Using this technique to calculate the bare ground parameter requires the calibration and analysis of several images registered to the same location. Using change detection is expected to improve the indexing correlation with that of the ERA method this work will take place as Post-SNEP research.

Results of Cover Typing and Location Validation

In order to validate the TM band ratio and SMA techniques used here, selected bare ground sites were visited in the field. A Trimble Pathfinder Pro-exel Global Positioning System (GPS) was used in the field to locate the bare ground cells defined in the image, and to fix the position of additional data-collection points. Post-SNEP research will continue to evaluate the ease of use and accuracy of the various methods of bare-ground identification. This assessment has demonstrated that features as small as log landings 30 to 40 meters square (10,000 to 15,000 ft^2) are identifiable when their locations coincide with the matrix of the TM image.

In addition, the thresholds set to estimate vegetative crown closure appear effective. In the areas where field work has been conducted, young plantations with sparse weeds and some bare ground between the trees were easily distinguished. However, other plantations, along Darlington Creek, a tributary of Camp Creek, for example where broad leaf shrubs dominate the area between trees, did not appear on the coverage because their green reflectance was over the threshold. This suggests that the bare ground threshold is reasonable and distinct.

Field checking has revealed that many logging landings, one-quarter to one-half acre in size, used for storage and loading of logs, are easily identified as bare ground. Others, however, which are equal in size, aspect, and surrounding vegetation are not visible in the TM data. One explanation is cell registration. The resolution of Landsat imagery is about 30 m on a side. Values within a cell are averaged across the surface and, in the case of spectral reflectance, the averaged spectrum is reported. When cell boundaries directly register or match with the boundary of a feature on the ground, such as a landing, bare ground is easily detected. However, if the cell boundary falls across the middle of a landing and captures an equal amount of green vegetation, it is likely that the average spectral value will be considered green and not bare.

Other opportunities to influence the NEP/SHI are available through planting or seeding and mulching of bare areas. The Fry Creek watershed has 5614 cells or 1248 acres that could be considered for treatment. This number includes all those cells or combinations of cells that are bare and exceed other thresholds. It includes many areas already planted in trees which are not yet tall enough to provide a closed canopy. Bare rock outcrops and heavily grazed meadows also give the spectral signature of bare ground or bare ground covered with non-green vegetation. Many of these conditions cannot be mitigated. When they can be, however, those cells so mitigated are deducted from the number of cells over threshold and the NEP and SHI indexes are re-calculated. This system allows resource managers to optimize both environmental and economic-investment strategies by locating those areas which have the greatest impact on CWE and selecting the mitigation which is most cost effective. Thinking of this as an environmental accounting system permits one to allocate resources to those projects which have the most immediate impact on the net reduction of cumulative effects.

Model Directed Mitigation

After reviewing the results of the screening analysis and making an on-the-ground inspection of potential hazards, one of the first questions to be asked is, "what are the mitigation opportunities here?" It is not possible to change a soil's K-factor but one can consider abandoning or surfacing roads when they are located adjacent to streams and on soils that are highly detachable or combined with, steep slopes, and bare ground. In the Fry Creek example Table 6 (read down column 8, Road in Stream Buffer, where there is a 1 read across to column 1, Number of cells, and sum the cell numbers), 603 cells, 134 acres or 61 hectors of roads within stream buffers represent opportunities for possible CWE mitigation and each cell can be located by its coordinates. Finding these cells, via GPS, portable computer, and GIS programs provides for immediate optimization of mitigation alternatives based on the recalculation of SHI. Some high risk cells will become candidates for road abandonment, road surfacing, culvert replacement or fill-slope ripraping. The current cumulative condition of the watershed can be evaluated and improved as soon as steps are taken to reduce these risks. Abandoning a portion of road within a stream buffer, on steep bare ground, and where the soils are highly detachable reduces the denominator in the formula thereby reducing the percent SHI. It will also reduce the percentage of the watershed exceeding thresholds and, if it does not improve the watershed's ranking relative to others, it will at least allow for additional management to take place without excessive risk.

Other opportunities to influence the NEP or SHI are available through planting or seeding and mulching of bare areas. The Fry Creek watershed has 5716 cells, 1271 acres or 578 hectors that could be considered for this treatment. The number includes all those cells or combinations of cells that are bare and exceed other thresholds. It includes many areas already planted in trees which are not yet tall enough to provide a closed canopy. Bare rock outcrops and heavily grazed meadows also give the spectral signature of bare ground or bare ground covered with non-green vegetation such as logging slash or litter. Some of these conditions cannot be mitigated or may not need treatment. When they can be, however, those cells so mitigated are deducted and the NEP and SHI indexes are re-calculated. This system allows resource managers to optimize both environmental and economic-investment strategies by locating those areas which have the greatest impact on CWE and selecting the mitigation which is most cost an environmentally effective. Thinking of this as an environmental accounting system permits one to allocate resources to those projects which have the most immediate impact on the net reduction of cumulative effects.

Camp Creek Case Study and Cumulative Watershed Effects Comparison

In order to develop and test hydrologic process tools for CWE analysis models the SNEP Science Team and the Hydrology Working Group selected Camp Creek and Clear Creek in Eldorado County as sites for intensive case studies. Two teams worked on the study. One team built the traditional conceptual hydrologic model using locally available data and air photo analysis (McGurk and Berg 1995). The other team built a spatially-explicit eco-hydrologic model using 30-m DEMs, Landsat imagery, and an extensive ecological unit inventory data base (Ustin et al. 1995). The two teams are working to predict the hydrologic responses to land use changes in a forested and an urbanized watershed. Their tools will also be used to model several land-use scenarios being developed by the Science Team.

The development of the NEP and SHI screening methodology began in Camp and Clear Creeks because of the availability of data for that area. Early review of the screening-technique's output suggested that a thorough evaluation of this technique needed to be attempted on a much larger area. The ENF was selected also because of data availability and the fact that the soils data base, created to aid the eco-hydrologic modeling efforts, could easily be expanded to cover the rest of the ENF.

A Cumulative Effects Analysis of Upper Camp Creek

An existing study for the area titled "A Cumulative Off-site Watershed Effects Analysis for the Upper Camp Creek Watershed USFS #2176" (Carlson and Christiansen 1993) was completed in June of 1993 by the ENF staff using ERA and it found 9.3 % of the watershed to be disturbed. The Threshold Of Concern (TOC) range for this portion of the watershed had been set at 12 to 14 % ERA. This means that when cumulative disturbance of exceeds 14 % of the watershed area, there could be adverse CWE to the aquatic resources in this portion of Camp Creek. If management activities such as timber harvesting proceeded without sufficient mitigation, significant environmental damage could result.

Some Analytical Limitations of this Model and Remote Sensing and GIS Tools

Based on the NEP/SHI scores from Tables 3, 4, and 5, Camp Creek does not appear to be in a sensitive condition; a finding which is consistent with Forest Service calculations for NSI and ERA found in Table 8. One of the advantages of using a data format like that in Cell Counts for Parameters Over Threshold Lower Camp Creek, Table 3 is that it is a practical guide to management opportunities for mitigation of problems affecting the watersheds "current cumulative condition," or "health," as seen from a sedimentation or erosion control point of view. While steep slopes and high K-factor soils cannot be changed managing the use of these areas can become more sensitive. Mitigation of these conditions takes place through road surfacing, relocation or abandonment along with continuous seeding and mulching after operations. The Cal-Water Project, has divided Camp Creek into three segments two inside the ENF and the most westerly segment outside the Forest. The two most easterly segments have been named Lower and Upper Camp Creek by the ENF but the 1993 CWE analysis refers to the entire area as Upper Camp Creek which has lead to some confusion.

As an example of how the NSI, ERA, NEP, and SHI ranking methods may miss important findings the following anecdote is offered. During several trips into the watershed, with Science Team members and other experts on the SNEP staff the validity of the ENF CWE analysis was questioned because the watershed from the ground appears to be a healthy ecosystem. Many of the major logging haul roads in the watershed are paved or rocked and the areas of steep slopes and highly detachable soils are limited in comparison to neighboring basins. Large areas of old-growth forest in the center of the watershed, well-stocked plantations that were previously harvested clear-cuts, and nearly closed canopy in areas that had been selectively logged, all suggest a healthy condition. Appearances indicate that if this basin is near TOC, elements other than those normally measured by ERA might be making significant contributions to watershed sensitivity.

Access to the heart of Upper Camp Creek is provided by paved road directly from Highway 50 via Sly Park Reservoir and Iron Mountain Road, which connects with another trans-Sierra Nevada highway, Route 88. Water, that features numerous gentle stretches along Camp Creek and its tributaries, as well as no prohibition to stream-side camping, attract many visitors and their off road vehicles (ORVs) to this area every weekend (Richardson, 1994 SNEP Vol. III). Intense use has created tens of miles of ORV trails. These trails which lack drainage or erosion controls have made a significant contribution of sediment to Camp Creek. NEP and SHI techniques may detect disturbance from ORV use, however if these trails are under a closed forest canopy and in the riparian zone they may have overwhelming impacts on aquatic habitat without triggering the screening indices. Only an expensive and time consuming stream channel survey will identify these kinds of watershed impacts. Both Camp Creek and Rock Creek have sustained similar riparian degradation form heavy ORV use (Swanson et al. 1993, USDA Forest Service 1995). Public policy concerning recreational access to, and use of, riparian zones needs to be examined.

CONCLUSIONS

After the soil data base was constructed 177 CWPWS were reviewed and 134 analyzed for NEP and SHI using approximately 10 days of GIS and analysis time. There were positive correlation with the ENF's NSI and ERA methodology which are not objective scientifically based assessments. With an emerging field of study such as CWE even a low r square value suggests that the results are not random and therefore provides significant encouragement to continue refining this model and expanding its application to other portions of the SNEP study area (Berg et al. 1995, Mening 1995, SNEP Vol III). NEP and SHI rankings may be modified by testing mitigation alternatives which include the surfacing and abandonment of road segments in areas over erosion parameter threshold. While this model is relatively easy to apply, and cost effective, it is a screening tool and is proposed for use in the allocation of human resources. Pre-assessment screening with NEP and SHI provide the resources managers with information to guide selection of watersheds for more focused CWE analysis. Modeling the NEP and SHI response to various mitigation options allows the optimization of mitigation budgets.

Need for Public-Private Cooperation

The structure of SNEP provided for many work groups with specific interests, one of the most important conclusions of the Hydrology Group is the extreme need for standardized digital tools such as a soils data base and disturbance histories. These will help to provide resource managers, both public and private, the information they need for economically and environmentally sound decision making. To do accurate CWE analysis which will contribute to making the Sierra Nevada ecosystem sustainable, both public and private land owners must be able to exchange information about their individual activities accurately, quickly, and in similar formats. Data base programs like ORACLE may be the type of mechanism to provide data, but it will require a commitment of Congress to fund the building of a data-base. As an example, recent revisions of the California Forest Practice Act mandated the development of Sustained Yield Plans by September 1996. These plans must address CWE's. However, currently there is no digital source of information which identifies and locates previous timber harvest activity on federal land. Furthermore, a standardized digital soils layer which covers entire watersheds on both sides of the national forest boundary does not exist. This kind of information is critical for accurate CWE assessments and monitoring of outcomes of any management scenarios. Sustainability of forest ecosystems in both the eastern and western United States depends on understanding the "current cumulative condition." In order to gain this understanding at a regional scale one must have information on what resource elements are present and how are they distributed, regardless of ownership.

The most productive elevation range in the Sierra Nevada for the west side Ponderosa Pine dominated mixed conifer forests is between 3000 and 6000 feet. Historically these lands have been in private ownership. Generally, there are large blocks of commercially owned timberland in this range and there is a steady encroachment of residential uses advancing west to east as well as both north and south of all major access routes. Because the drainage of the western Sierra Nevada is east to west most, major watersheds have their headwaters at elevations above 6000 feet, where Federal ownership predominates. Watershed analysis, especially for cumulative effect, must consider natural and management disturbances along a continuum of private residential, commercial timberland, and national forest lands.

Thirty-six percent of the nearly twenty-nine million acres in the SNEP study area are privately owned. These private lands are relatively evenly dispersed in "mixed ownership watersheds." The natural boundaries of many mixed ownership watersheds often cross the administrative boundaries of the national forests and divide a watershed for analysis purposes. As an example, there might be one-third of a watershed inside the national forest, and two-thirds outside, half of which is held by large land owners and half held in small lots for residential use or investment. While each land-holding group may have extremely different management plans, all agencies and private operators need a standardized data base in order to calculate the combined impacts of their land use histories and from which to project their combined future activities.

Re-establishing National Forest Boundaries

National forest boundaries were established many decades ago prior to ecosystem management and watershed analysis. Today's GIS analytical environment operates more effectively when boundaries are defined along major drainage divides. Currently the Tahoe National Forest (TNF), ENF, and SNF are divided along the channels of sub-basins. Therefore, the SNF shares the North Fork of the Mokelumne River with the ENF and the ENF shares the Middle Fork of the American River with the TNF. Inter-forest and forest-industry watershed management could be made more efficient if national forest boundaries were moved to the ridges dividing these major basins.

As public and private resource managers move toward ecosystem management and watershed analysis, the location of boundaries between national forests must be called into question. Ridge tops are now the division between analysis units and should become administrative boundaries. When each national forest is allowed to adopt its own naming and numbering conventions, and boundary lines for watersheds, and soil mapping units, chaos follows when cross-agency and inter-agency assessments are required. With multiple agencies and private landowners needing to share data for CWE studies, delays caused by differences in naming conventions and formats are expensive and unnecessary.

Model Expansion and Improvement

As standardized and integrated soils data bases are completed for other portions of the Sierra Nevada and as DEMs of higher resolution become available, a Sierra Nevada regional NEP and SHI analysis could be run and re-run periodically to evaluate the impacts of residential development, fire, timber harvest, and other regionally important phenomenon that can be observed from space. Although this model will continue to be evaluated and validated, effects of additional elements such as climate, rain-on-snow, and geology will be tested to improve model performance. High-elevation basins are important and sensitive even if unmanaged; however, their contribution to the sediment load is not potentially as high as lower-elevation areas that are heavily managed. Therefore the problem of separating bare rock outcrops from bare exposed soil will be an important element of future NEP models.

Adjudication of "Disturbance Rights" in CWE Limited Watersheds

An accurate indexing methodology is a valuable tool when allocating resources for watershed improvement or adjudicating "disturbance rights" between landowners. Predicting the erosional potential for a given unit area of land is the objective of this methodology; it is intended to index current cumulative condition for individual planning watersheds relative to their neighbors given similar climatic conditions. It was designed as a primary screening tool and environmental accounting system that provides objective information for decision makers.

The adjudication of logging rights has not yet been implemented in mixed ownership watersheds but when watersheds become, "cumulative effects limited" or over TOC, to the extent that management operation must be modified. My model provides the basis for the selection of mitigation projects that will improve the cumulative condition of the watershed as well as locating those areas which should be avoided or managed with informed sensitivity.

With these tools, decisions about road location and abandonment, skid trail layout, as well as recreation and grazing practices may be reviewed on local or regional scales and provide information for use when attempting to balance ecosystem health and cumulative watershed effects with human need in order to maintain all systems in sustainable condition.

LIST OF ACRONYMS

ARC/INFO	A geographic information system developed Environmental Systems Research Institute, Inc. ESRI. Primarily for workstation use.
ARC/INFO GRID	A geographic information system tool used to analysis spatially distributed data in a matrix or raster format.
Arc/View	A geographic information system program used to display coverage's developed on either ARC/INFO or ARC/INFO GRID. Primarily for PC use.
AVIRIS	Airborne Visible and Infrared Imaging Spectrometer a NASA research tool which collects 220 bands of spectral data simultaneously.
AWSI	Associated USFS watershed assembled to match CWPWS boundaries.
BLM	Bureau of Land Management
CDF	California Division of Forestry and Fire Protection
CEQA	California Environmental Quality Act
Change Detection	A technique using images taken at different times registered to the same location. Color enhancement differentiates areas on the ground that have changed form areas that have not changed.
COUNT	An ARC/INFO term which related to the sum of the cell in a particular query.
CWE	Cumulative watershed effects the total impact of past, present, and foreseeable activities in a watershed.
CWPWS	Cal-Water planning watersheds the boundaries defined by the California Department of Forestry and Fire Protection.
DEM	Digital elevation model a matrix draped over a landscape which reflects the topography of the surface.
EHR	Erosion Hazard Rating an index of a soils susceptibility to disturbance.
ENF	Eldorado National Forest
ERA	Equivalent Roaded Acres one method of calculating CWE for a watershed. It equates all disturbance to acres of roaded surface.
FSWSID	Forest Service watershed identification numbers are not the same as the Cal-Water numbers nor are the boundaries
GIS	Geographic Information System a method of organizing and analyzing information about a landscape both spatially and temporally.
GP	Georgia Pacific Corporation
GPS	Global Positioning System an instrument used to find or fix the users location on the ground.
GPWIN	Georgia Pacific Corporation watershed improvement needs forms used to inventory and monitor potential problems on Company lands.
ID	Identification
Interrill	An area between rills normally susceptible to sheet or surface erosion.
K-factor	K is the soils detachability or erodibility factor
Landsat TM	Thematic Mapper images taken by satellites and used for many resource based monitoring functions.

NDSI	Normalized Difference Soil Index a method of ratio satellite reflectance date to enhance our identification of soils versus vegetation.
NDVI	Normalized Difference Vegetation Index a measure of the greenness of vegetation.
NEP	Natural Erosion Potential a product of this study which indexes a watersheds natural stability based on the amounts of bare, steep and highly erodible soils present.
NEPA	National Environmental Protection Act
NIR	near-infrared a portion of the electromagnetic spectrum used to identify vegetation.
NRCS	Natural Resources Conservation Service. Agenciy name changed from Soil Conservation Service (SCS).
NSI	USFS Natural Sensitivity Index derived from soil, stream channel, and climate assessment used to define a watersheds natural stability.
ORACLE	A data base management program.
ORV	Off Road Vehicle
Rill	A linear void caused by erosion having less than 1 square foot of crossection, when it exceed 1sq/ft it becomes a gully.
RUSLE	Revised Universal Soil Loss Equation a method of calculating erosion losses. Used mainly on mid-western agricultural soils.
SB	Stream Buffers any distance one wishes to set on either side of a stream.
SCS	Soil Conservation Service (USDA) currently Natural Resources Conservation Service (NRCS).
SHI	Sedimentation Hazard Index a product of this study which indexes the impact of management and road systems adjacent to flowing streams.
SMA	Spectral Mixture Analysis a statistical method of using spectral reflectance of selected features to suggest how much of each feature is contained in mixed cell or pixel.
SNEP	Sierra Nevada Ecosystem Project
SNF	Stanislaus National Forest

The following are acronyms used frequently in this paper:

TNF	Tahoe National Forest
TOC	USFS Threshold Of Concern based on NSI and normally falling between 10 and 20 % ERA.
USDA	United States Department of Agriculture
USDA-FS	United States Department of Agriculture Forest Service
USDA-NRCS	United States Department of Agriculture Natural Resources Conservation Service formerly the Soil Conservation Service
USDA-SCS	United States Department of Agriculture Soil Conservation Service
USFS	US Forest Service
USGS	US Geological Survey
USLE	Universal Soil Loss Equation a method of calculating erosion losses. Used mainly on mid-western agricultural soils.

USWIN	USFS Watershed Improvement Needs watershed improvement needs forms used to inventory and monitor potential problems on federal lands.
UTM	Universal Transverse Mercator
WATSED	Water Yield and Sediment Model a model which predicts amounts of soil loss in forest and range watershed of Montana. A CWE model for use in mixed ownership's.
WEPP	Water Erosion Prediction Project is a distributed parameter, continuous simulation, erosion prediction model developed by several federal agencies for use in watersheds of moderate slope steepness.

REFERENCES

Adams, J.B., M.O. Smith, and P.E. Johnson. 1986. Spectral mixture modeling: A new analysis of rock and soil types at the Viking Lander 1 site. *J. Geophys. Res.* 91: 8098-8112.

Avery, T.E., and G.L. Berlin. 1992. *Fundamentals of Remote Sensing and Airphoto Interpretation.* Fifth ed. New York: Macmillian Publishing Co.

Berg, Neil , Ken Roby, and Bruce McGurk. 1995. Cumulative watershed effects: applicability of available methodologies to the Sierra Nevada: 1. Pacific Southwest Research Station, Albany, CA 2. Plumas National Forest, Quincy, CA

Brandow, Clay. 1995. Calwater 1.0 - California planning watersheds data dictionary: California Department of Forestry and Fire Protection, Sacramento.

Bryan, R.B. 1969. The relative erodibility of soils developed in the Peak District of Derbyshire. *Geografiska Ann.* 51-A: 145-159.

Cafferata, Peter. 1995. Conversation with State CFD Hydrologist, California Department of Forestry and Fire Protection, Sacramento, July.

Carlson, Joan, and Christine Christiansen. 1993. Eldorado National Forest cumulative off-site watershed effects (CWE) analysis process: USDA, Forest Service, Eldorado National Forest, Placerville, California.

Christiansen, Christine. 1995. Conversation with Forest Hydrologist, USDA Forest Service, Placerville, California, July 1994.

Christiansen, Christine. 1995. CWE meeting for USDA Forest Service, Region 5, UC Davis, Davis California, June 27.

DaCosta, L M. 1979. *Surface soil color and reflectance as related to physio-chemical and mineralogical soil properties.* Columbia: University of Missouri.

Elvidge, C D, and Portigal F P. 1990. Change detection in vegetation using 1989 AVIRIS data. In *Proc SPIE Imaging Spectroscopy of the Terrestrial Environment, Apr16-17, 1990*, edited by G. V. ed. Orlando FL.

Elvidge, C D. 1990. Visible and near infrared reflectance characteristics of dry plant materials. *Int J Remote Sens* 11:: 1775-1795. Int J Remote Sens.

Elwell, H.A., and M.A. Stocking. 1974. Rainfall parameters and a cover model to predict runoff and soil loss from grazing trials in the rhodesian sandveld. *Proceedings of the Grassland Society of South Africa* 9: 157-164.

Elwell, H.A., and M.A. Stocking. 1976. Vegetal cover to estimate soil erosion hazard in Rhodesia. *Geoderma* 15 (1): 61-70.

Erman, Don C., and Donald Mahoney. 1983. Recovery after logging in streams with and without bufferstrips in northern California. University of California, Water Resources Center, Davis, California.

Erman, Don C., J. Denis Newbold, and Kenneth B. Roby. 1977. Evalutaion of streamside bufferstrips for protection aquatic organisms: University of Californiam, Berkeley Department of Forestry and Conservation.

Escadafal, R , M C Giard, and D Courault. 1988. Modeling the relationships between Munsell soil color and soil spectral properties. *Int Agrophysics* 4:: 249-261. Int Agrophysics.

Escadafal, R , M C Giard, and D Courault. 1989. Munsell color and soil reflectance in the visible spectral bands of Landsat MSS and TM data. *Rem Sens Environ* 27:: 37-46. Rem Sens Environ.

Euphrat, F.D. 1992. *Cumulative impact assessment and mitigation for the middle fork of the mokelumne river, calaveras county, california*. Ph.D. dissertation, Department of Forestry, Wildland Resource Science, University of California at Berkeley.

Fernandez, R N , and D G Schultze. 1987. Calculation of soil color from reflectance spectra. *Soil Sci Soc Am J* 51:: 1277-1282. Soil Sci Soc Am J.

Foster, G.R., and L.D. Meyer. 1975. Mathematical simulation of upland erosion by fundamental erosion mechanics, in Present and prospective technology for predicting sediment yeilds and sources: USDA Agr. Res. Serv. Pub.

Green, R. O., J. E. Conel, and D. A. Roberts. 1993. Estimation of aerosol optical depth and calculation of apparent surface reflectance from radiance measured by the Airborne Visible-Infrared Imaging Spectrometer (AVIRIS) using MODTRAN2 SPIE 1937. In *Imaging Spectrometry of the Terrestrial Environment in press*.

Huete, A. R. , and R. Escadafal. 1991. Assessment of biophysical soil properties through spectral decomposition techniques. *Remote Sens Environ* 35:: 149-159. Remote Sens Environ.

Huete, A. R. 1986. Seperation of soil-plant spectral mixtures by factor analysis. *Remote Sens Environ* 19: 237-251. Remote Sens Environ.

Hussein, M. H., and J. M. Laflen. 1982. Effects of crop canopy and residue on rill and interrill soil erosion. *Trans. Am. Soc. Agric. Engnrs.* 25: 1310-1315.

Judd, D. B. , and G. Wyszecki. 1975. *Color in business science and industry*. New York: John Wiley and Sons.

Kattelmann, R. 1996. Hydrology and water resources. In <u>Sierra Nevada Ecosystem Project: Final report to Congress,</u> vol. II, chap. 33. Davis: University of California, Centers for Water and Wildland Resources.

Kirkby, M.J., and R.P.C. Morgan, ed. 1980. *Soil Erosion*. Edited by M. J. Kirkby, *Modelling water erosion processes*. Chichester, England: John Wiley and Sons.

Kuehn, M.H. and J. Cobourn. 1989. Summary report for the 1988 cumulative watershed effects anaylses on the Eldorado National Forest. USDA Forest Service, Placverville, California.

Lachowski, H.M., T. Wirth, P. Maus and P. Avers. 1994. Remote sensing and GIS: their role in ecosystem management. *Journal of Forestry* 92(8):39-40

Laflen, J.M., and T.S. Colvin. 1981. Effects of crop residue on soil loss from continous row cropping. *Trans. Am. Soc. Agric. Engnrs.* 24: 605-609.

Lal, R., and W. Elliot. 1994. Erodibility and erosivity. In *Soil Erosion Research Methods*, edited by R. Lal. Delray Beach, Florida: St. Lucie Press.

Lal, R., ed. 1977. *Soil-conserving versus soil-degrading crops and soil management for erosion control*. Edited by D. J. G. a. R. Lal, *Soil conservation and management in the numid tropics*: Wiley.

Lewis, J., and R. M. Rice. 1989. Critical Sites Erosion Study Vol II Site conditions related to erosion on private timber lands in northern California. In Final report submitted to the Calif Department of Forestry and Fire Protection May 1989.

Maus, P., V. Landrum, J. Johnson, M. Schanta, and B. Platt. 1992. Utilizing satellite data and gis to map land cover change. *GIS '92 Proceedings*. Vancouver, B.C., Canada.

McCool, D.K., L.C. Brown, G.R.Foster, C.K. Mutchler, and L.D. Meyer. 1987. Revised slope steepness factor for the universal soil loss equation. *Transactions, American Society of Agricultural Engineers* 30: 1387-1396.

McGurk, Bruce J., Neil H. Berg, and Maureen L. Davis. 1995. Predicted sediment yield from forest management and residential development: camp and clear creek basins, eldorado county california: Pacific Southwest Research Station, USDA Forest Service, Sierra Nevada Ecosystem Project, Vol. III.

McGurk, Bruce, and Maureen Davis. 1995. A 50 year history of logging, road building, and urban development in Camp and Clear Creeks, Eldorado County, California: Pacific Southwest Research Station, USDA Forest Service, Albany, California.

McKittrick, Mary Anne. 1994. Erosion potential in private forested watersheds of northern california: A GIS model: Prepared for the California Division of Forestry, by California Department of Mines and Geolology and US Geologic Survey.

Megahan, W. F., S. B. Monsen, and M. D. Wilson. 1991. Probability of sediment yields from surface erosion on granitic roadfills in Idaho. *J of Envirn Quality* 20 ((1)): 53-60. J of Envirn Quality.

Megahan, Walt, R. Cline, G. Cole, R. Patten, and J. Potyondy. 1981. Guide for predicting sediment yields form forested watersheds: U.S. Forest Service Northern Region Intermountain Region, Salt Lake City.

Melville, M. D., and G. Atkinson. 1985. Soil colour: its measurement and its designation in models of uniform colour space. *J Soil Sci* 36:: 495-512. J Soil Sci.

Meyer, L.S. 1981. How rain intensity affects interrill erosion. *Trans. Am. Soc. Agric. Engnrs.* 24: 1472-1475.

Mitchell, J.K., and G.D. Bubenzer. 1980. Soil loss estimation. In *Soil Erosion*, edited by M. J. Kirkby and R. P. C. Morgan. Chichester, England: John Wiley & Sons.

Morgan, R P C. 1986. *Soil Erosion and Conservation*, edited by D. D. A. Essex, England: Longman Scientific & Technical Copub. John Wiley & Sons, Inc New York.

Morgan, R.P.C., D.D.V. Morgan, and H.J. Finney. 1984. A predictive model for the assessment of soil erosion risk. *J. Agric. Engng. Res* 30: 245-253.

Nearing, M.A., L.J. Lane, and V.L. Lopes. 1994. Modeling Soil Erosion. In *Soil Erosion Research Methods*, edited by L. R. Delray Beach, Florida: St. Lucie Press.

Renard, K. G., J.M. Laflen, G.R. Foster, and D.K. McCool. 1994. The Revised Universal Soil Loss Equation. In *Soil Erosion Research Methods*, edited by R. Lal. Delray Beach, Florida: St. Lucie Press.

Reneau, S. L., W. E. Dietrich, M. Ruben, D. J. Donahue, and A. J. T. Jull. 1989. Analysis of hillslope erosion rates using dated colluvial deposits. *Jour of Geology* 97: 45-63. Jour of Geology.

Rice, R M, and P D Gradek. 1984. Limits on the usefulness of erosion-hazard ratings: experiences in northwestern California. *Can J For Res* 14: 559-564. Can J For Res.

Rice, R.M. 1993. A guide to data collection and analysis in support of an appraisal of cumulative watershed effects in california forests: Special Report for the Georgia Pacific Corporation, Martell California.

Richardson, Becky. 1994. Conversation with SNEP team collegue concerning personal observations, UC Davis, Davis, California, August.

Roberts, D. , J. B. Adams, and M. O. Smith. 1993. Discriminating green vegetation non-photosynthectic vegetation and soils in AVIRIS data. *Remote Sens Environ* 44: 1-25. Remote Sens Environ.

Roberts, D. 1991. *Separating spectral mixtures of vegetation and soils*. Ph.D. dissertation, Department of Geology, University of Washington, Seattle.

Rose, C.W. 1994. Research progress on soil erosion processes and a basis for soil conservation practices. In *Soil Erosion Research Methods*, edited by R. Lal. Delray Beach, Florida: St. Lucie Press.

Shaxson, T.F., ed. 1981. *Reconciling social and technical needs in conservation work on village farmlands*. Edited by R. P. C. Morgan, *Soil conservation: problems and prosopects*: Wiley.

Shields, J. A. , E. A. Paul, R. J. St Arnaud, and W. K. Head. 1968. Spectrophotometric measurement of soil color and its relationship to moisture and organic matter. *Can. J. Soil. Sci.* 48: 271-280. Can. J. Soil. Sci.

Singer, M.J. , and P.H. Walker. 1983. Rainfall-runoff in soil erosion with simulated rainfall, overland flow and cover. *Austrailian Journal of Soil Research* 21: 109-122.

Singer, M.J., and J. Blackard. 1978. Effects of mulching on sediment in runoff from simulated rainfall. *Soil Science Society of America Journal* 42: 481-486.

Singer, M.J., John Blackard, Kandiah Arulanandan, and Ernest Gillogley. 1978. Engineering and pedological properties of soils as they affect soil erodibility: California Water Resources Center, University of California, Davis.

Smith, M. O. , J. B. Adams, S. L. Ustin, and D. A. Roberts. 1992. Using endmembers in AVIRIS images to estimate changes in vegetative biomass. *In Summaries of the Third Annual JPL Airborne Geoscience Workshop* Vol 1 (92-14): 69-71. In Summaries of the Third Annual JPL Airborne Geoscience Workshop.

Smith, M. O., and A. R. Gillespie. 1990. A mixing model strategy for analyzing and interpreting hyperspectral images. In *Remote Geochemical Analysis: Elemental and Mineralological Composition*, edited by C. M. Pieters and P. E. (.): LPI and Cambridge Univ Press.

Stocking, M.A. 1994. Assessing vegetative cover and management effects. In *Soil Erosion Research Methods*, edited by R. Lal. Soil Erosion Research Methods: Soil Erosion Research Methods.

Swanson, F. J., and C. T. Dyrness. 1975. Impact of clearcutting and road construction on soil erosion and landslids in the West Cascade Range, Oregon. *Geology* 3: 393-396.

Swanson, M., B. Emery, D. de Clercq, and J. Vollmar, and E. Bianci. 1993. Upper Camp Creek watershed restoration and monitoring plan. Draft Final prepared for the Eldorado National Forest. USDA Forest Service. Placerville, California.

USDA, Forest Service. 1993b. National Center of Forest Health Management strategic plan. USDA Forest Service, at Morgantown, West Virginia.

USDA, Forest Service. 1991. *WATSED, Water Yield and Sediment.* USDA Forest Service, Region 1, Missula, Montana

USDA, Forest Service. 1995. *Rock Creek OHV Area Sediment Delivery Analysis.* Unpublished data, Supervisor's Office, Eldorado National Forest, Placerville, California.

USDA, Forest Service. 1985. *Soil Survey Eldorado National Forest California.* USDA Forest Service, Eldorado National Forest, Placerville, California.

USDA, Forest Service. 1991. *Soil SurveyReport 1991 Ecological Unit Inventory Camp Creek Watershed Eldorado National Forest.* USDA Forest Service, Eldorado National Forest, Placerville, California.

USDA, Soil Conservation Service. 1974. *Soil Survey of Eldorado Area, California.* USDA Soil Conservation Service in cooperation with University of California Agricultural Experimental Station, Placerville, California.

USDA, Soil Conservation Service. 1965. *Soil Survey of Amador Area, California.* USDA Soil Conservation Service in cooperation with University of California Agricultural Experimential Station, Series 1961, No. 26, Jackson, California.

Ustin, S. L., M. O. Smith, and J. B. Adams. 1993. Remote Sens of Ecological Processes: A strategy for developing and testing ecological models using spectral mixture analysis. In *Scaling Physiological Processes: Leaf to Globe*, edited by J. Ehlringer and C. Field. New York: Acad Press.

Ustin, Susan L., Quinn J. Hart, George J. Scheer, and Lian Duan. 1995. Herbaceous Biomass on Hardwood Rangelands in California: University of California, Davis Department of Land Air and Water Resources.

Ustin, S.L. and W.W. Wallendar. 1996. *Modeling Terrestrial and Acquatic EcosystemsResponces to Hydrologic Regime in a California Watershed*: Sierra Nevada Ecosystem Project: Final report to Congress, vol. III, chap. 33. Davis: University of California, Centers forWater and Wildland Resources.

Washington Forest Practices Board. 1993. Board manual: Standard methodology for conducting watershed analysis: Version 2.0. Olympia, WA: Washington Forest Practice Board.

Wischmeier, W.H., and D.D. Smith. 1978. *Predicting Rainfall Erosion Losses-a Guide to Conservation Planning*. No. 537 vols. Vol. Agricultural Handbook. Washington, D.C.: U.S.Dept. of Agriculture.

Wischmeier, W.H., and L.D. Meyer. 1973. Soil erodibility on construction areas.: National Academy of Science, Highway Research Board.

Wright, K A. 1985. *Changes in storm hydrographs after roadbuilding and logging on a coastal watershed in northern California*. Arcata, California: Humboldt State University.

Appendix 1 Eldorado National Forest Watershed Statistics

Eldorado National Forest 120 Watershed Comparisons of NSI, ERA, TOC, NEP, and SHI

Natural Sensivity and Natural Erosion Potential Comaprison for 120 Eldorado National Forest Watersheds

CPWS ID Nr Cal-Water Planning watershed ID number	Cal-Water watershed Name	CPWS Acs Cal-Water planning watershed acres	NSI Natural Sensitivity Index	% TOC Threshold of concern	% ERA Equivalent roaded acres	EHR RiskNr Erosion Hazard Rating Nr	%NEP Natural Erosion Potential	%SHI Sediment ation Hazard Index	% Rd Roaded acres	%SB/Rd Roaded acres inside stream buffers
514.31010	N F Webber Creek	6376	44	0.0	0	0	15.6	9.6	12.2	10.5
514.31011	S F Webber Creek	4916	30	0.0	0	0	12.3	14.9	20.1	17.3
514.32010	Gaddis Creek	8684	81	106.0	10.6	5	8.2	35.2	34.6	9
514.32011	Slab Creek	5493	114	43.0	4.3	2	11.0	32.3	27.9	8.6
514.32012	Brush Creek	5132	37	36.4	5.1	2	10.2	36.6	34.0	7.7
514.32013	Slab Creek Res	5723	174	51.0	5.1	2	9.8	28.7	26.8	6.1
514.32014	Long Canyon	2876	69	149.0	14.9	5	14.3	20.5	19.2	5.7
514.32015	Iowa Canyon	5107	41	95.0	13.3	4	14.2	18.2	24.5	10.9
514.32022	Whaler Creek	10209	90	62.0	6.2	3	11.5	29.7	29.4	11
514.32023	One Eye Creek	4521	66	75.0	7.5	3	12.4	26.8	21.6	12.4
514.32030	Traverse Creek	9378	36	0.0	0	0	12.3	25.7	27.1	12.3
514.32031	Bear Creek	5358	59	68.3	8.2	3	12.6	28.1	27.4	16
514.33010	Lyons Creek	11306	42	49.3	6.9	2	5.0	13.5	8.8	7.4
514.33020	Ice House Res	6175	49	0.0	0	0	6.7	7.5	7.3	3.6
514.33021	Peavine Creek	11510	60	125.0	15	5	10.5	40.9	38.6	11.4
514.33030	Little Silver Creek	8604	28	68.1	10.9	3	9.6	30.6	32.0	11.3
514.33031	Sugar Pine Creek	10713	103	87.0	8.7	4	5.0	26.0	17.3	6.4
514.33032	Onion Creek	3358	27	0.0	0	0	5.7	36.0	39.3	3.5
514.33033	Jay Bird Canyon	1643	50	58.6	8.2	2	11.3	6.7	3.2	17.6
514.33034	Round Tent Canyon	2403	61	60.8	7.3	3	6.9	10.8	6.8	16.3
514.33035	Camp Seven	4248	291	70.0	7	3	6.1	32.4	34.4	5.3

514.34010	Jones Silver Creek	6150	65	7.5	0.9	1	3.4	14.6	10.5	2.5
514.34011	Table Rock	10084	41	39.3	5.5	2	8.4	5.2	4.9	7.8
514.34020	Lawrence Lake	5234	60	4.2	0.5	1	1.6	14.2	2.7	1.9
514.34021	Bassi F Silver Creek	8290	50	29.3	4.1	1	3.5	8.4	3.4	5.1
514.34022	Big Siver Creek	6725	59	39.2	4.7	2	4.7	6.2	1.2	5.9
514.34030	Tells Creek	5899	30	41.9	6.7	2	6.8	4.3	4.7	9
514.34031	Union Valley Res	11288	57	80.8	9.7	4	8.8	18.9	18.2	2.9
514.35010	Pyramid Creek	6051	91	0.0	0	0	2.6	26.8	15.8	2.7
514.35012	Aspen Creek	6675	44	0.0	0	0	5.9	14.4	2.5	11.3
514.35013	Sayles Canyon	4237	62	0.0	0	0	4.1	11.3	2.2	8.5
514.35014	Strawberry Creek	7418	54	33.3	4	2	5.1	11.1	2.8	5.5
514.35016	Cody Creek	2437	46	0.0	0	0	5.9	6.9	2.2	10.6
514.35018	Station Creek	2275	43	0.0	0	0	7.0	7.1	0.5	5.2
514.35020	Carpenter Creek	9215	79	0.0	0	0	7.9	31.5	25.2	8.4
514.35021	Fry Creek	6346	183	138.0	13.8	5	9.1	41.7	35.5	11.9
514.35022	Mill Creek	2178	61	117.5	14.1	5	8.6	11.5	24.9	8.1
514.35030	Upper Alder Creek	9233	45	72.9	10.2	3	10.2	10.0	11.6	15.3
514.35031	North Creek	2717	55	0.0	0	0	6.6	3.9	1.5	8.9
514.35032	Lower Alder Creek	2209	192	100.0	9	5	11.1	30.2	20.3	7.8
514.35040	Plum Creek	5466	69	94.0	9.4	4	6.5	11.0	9.2	7.6
514.35050	Twentyfive Mile Cyn	10972	138	129.0	12.9	5	9.6	33.6	31.6	10.8
514.35051	Grays Canyon	8308	173	51.0	5.1	2	9.0	31.2	24.6	5.7
514.35052	Soldier Creek	3414	52	103.3	12.4	5	9.3	17.6	23.5	13.4
514.36010	Emigrant Creek	8742	72	0.0	0	0	4.9	10.7	5.6	6
514.36011	Kirkwood Creek	2306	90	0.0	0	0	6.0	14.8	10.4	7.5
514.36012	Caples Creek	9212	67	0.0	0	0	4.0	13.2	5.0	6.2
514.36013	Silver Lake	9691	87	0.0	0	0	4.7	13.9	6.4	5.6
514.36014	Oyster Creek	5400	83	0.0	0	0	3.2	10.4	1.1	4.9
514.36020	North Tragedy Creek	4781	38	47.9	6.7	2	1.9	12.4	8.0	1.9
514.36021	Sherman Canyon	6262	142	0.0	0	0	7.6	4.5	3.9	9.8
514.36022	Mule Canyon	3505	54	49.2	5.9	2	8.9	9.7	9.7	12.2
514.36023	Matin Creek	3253	72	38.0	6	2	7.2	5.6	4.9	8.4

514.36030	Bark Shanty Cyn	5371	94	80.0	9.9	4	8.8	19.9	15.1	9.9
514.36031	Girard Creek	2067	58	91.7	11	4	10.0	10.9	11.0	18.5
514.36032	Long Canyon	3597	45	0.0	0	0	6.3	9.1	3.6	8.2
514.36033	Middle Creek	4735	119	50.0	5	3	7.0	24.5	29.8	6.9
514.36034	Beanville Creek	2343	123	0.0	0	0	7.7	25.8	21.1	7.6
514.41020	Missouri Canyon	11451	109	44.0	4.4	2	9.6	18.8	11.9	6.5
514.41030	Canyon Creek	8807	51	52.5	6.3	2	12.5	21.5	19.3	11.6
514.43010	S F Long Canyon	6375	39	0.0	0	0	7.8	5.7	1.3	7.1
514.43011	N F Long Canyon	4244	49	0.0	0	0	7.9	7.1	1.0	9.6
514.43012	Long Canyon	11700	110	82.0	8.2	4	6.4	19.0	9.3	3.7
514.43013	Wallace Canyon	8347	44	59.3	8.3	2	9.4	10.1	7.9	10.6
514.43020	Stony Creek	11933	72	34.0	3.4	2	7.7	18.7	10.8	6.2
514.43021	Little Deer Creek	2727	45	0.0	0	0	13.9	6.7	4.5	22.4
514.43032	Big Grizzly Cyn	4321	64	95.8	11.5	4	9.3	17.8	19.1	9.6
514.43033	Zero Spring	8212	220	30.0	3	2	6.0	34.8	24.5	4.2
514.43040	Upper Pilot Creek	9543	22	92.5	14.8	4	6.7	26.8	21.3	5.6
514.43041	Lower Pilot Creek	9818	73	0.0	0	0	8.9	34.6	30.0	5.3
514.44010	Gerle Creek	7943	38	35.7	5	2	6.6	7.1	7.7	8.1
514.44011	Rocky Basin Creek	6584	47	37.9	5.3	2	6.0	6.3	3.8	4.7
514.44012	Loon Lake	5141	38	5.0	0.7	1	4.8	6.8	10.7	2.7
514.44020	Up S F Rubicon R	10127	28	38.8	6.2	2	6.5	6.1	1.5	4.6
514.44021	Lwr S F Rubicon R	6676	90	62.0	6.2	3	9.7	15.2	6.6	9
514.45022	Rockbound Lake	4434	102	0.0	0	0	4.4	18.3	13.3	5.9
514.45023	Phipps Creek	11722	0	0.0	0	0	2.7	19.5	13.5	5.6
514.45024	Lake Schmidell	8249	0	0.0	0	0	3.5	22.7	10.7	6
532.23010	Upper Camp Creek	8716	51.4	65.0	7.6	3	12.4	2.6	1.9	13.6
532.23011	Lower Camp Creek	10330	41.3	27.9	3.9	1	11.2	15.5	15.1	16.6
532.23021	Sly Park Creek	6275	42	0.0	0	0	7.7	11.0	9.6	11.1
532.23022	Hazel Creek	1755	33	0.0	0	0	7.7	8.5	10.9	4.3
532.23032	Van Horn Creek	7516	77	64.0	6.4	3	10.2	26.5	23.8	12.3
532.23033	North Canyon	3541	25	23.1	3.7	1	10.0	29.5	28.8	15.3
532.23040	North Steely Creek	6857	28	46.3	7.4	2	11.7	14.2	16.5	16.7
532.23041	String Canyon	6964	73	0.0	0	0	12.2	27.5	23.3	8.6
532.23042	Middle Butte	2925	160	53.0	5.3	2	6.2	31.1	29.8	3.2

532.23043	Clear Creek	2896	34	61.3	9.8	3	10.3	28.1	32.2	14.1
532.23050	Jenkinson Lake	3057	36	0.0	0	0	9.6	10.1	11.2	4.4
532.23051	Camp Creek	10140	92	66.0	6.6	3	7.4	29.9	23.3	3.9
532.23062	Clear Creek	6840	28	50.0	8	2	13.1	28.0	27.7	14.5
532.24010	Anderson Canyon	3252	72	64.0	6.4	3	7.3	10.3	16.2	3.1
532.24011	Prothro Creek	9263	83	0.0	0	0	11.7	16.7	17.2	13.2
532.24012	Cat Creek	5655	93	138.0	13.8	5	10.7	14.4	23.9	13.8
532.24013	Shingle Mill Creek	9609	60	83.3	10	4	11.7	9.5	9.6	10.8
532.24014	Crystal Mine	4493	92	47.0	4.7	2	9.9	16.3	18.6	7.2
532.24020	McKinney Creek	3005	29	39.4	6.3	2	8.6	4.6	3.4	18.6
532.24021	Dogtown Creek	6799	63	50.0	6	2	8.3	17.1	15.7	7.2
532.24022	Middle Dry Creek	3383	33	54.4	8.7	2	13.6	3.8	1.7	24.5
532.24030	Sopiago Creek	7699	43	85.0	11.9	4	12.7	9.8	11.6	11.7
532.24040	OConnor Gulch	2623	193	0.0	0	0	7.8	42.2	34.4	1.8
532.24060	Oregon Gulch	5742	22	62.5	10	3	11.1	13.2	12.4	9.4
532.60040	Bear River	7838	80	0.0	0	0	2.9	15.2	4.8	3.3
532.60041	Tragedy Creek	4736	78	0.0	0	0	2.8	13.3	0.0	1.4
532.60042	Corral Flat	3633	58	0.0	0	0	4.2	5.5	0.6	4.6
532.60043	Bear River Res	7659	32	31.9	5.1	2	8.1	6.2	3.3	4.7
532.60050	Rattlesnake Creek	6639	93	0.0	0	0	7.0	16.4	5.9	9.7
532.60051	Beaver Creek	2464	95	100.0	10	5	8.2	31.7	34.6	9.5
532.60060	E Panther Creek	5463	47	68.6	9.6	3	9.2	24.8	18.1	11.4
532.60061	W Panther Creek	5853	79	104.0	10.4	5	11.3	26.1	30.2	9.9
532.60063	Little Tiger Creek	7394	24	0.0	0	0	10.1	17.3	17.7	11.4
532.60064	Mill Creek	8005	61	0.0	0	0	8.3	16.5	15.4	11.4
514.32021A	AWS1	13502	94	34.0	3.7	2	10.3	25.1	24.4	0
514.32032(A)	AWS2	19057	71	0.0	0	0	11.6	28.9	29.2	0
514.35017(A)	AWS3	13698	63	0.0	0	0	5.7	18.1	9.7	0
514.43031A	AWS4	14221	123	32.0	3.2	2	5.1	23.9	22.2	0
514.45024A	AWS5	19971	0	0.0	0	0	3.0	20.8	12.3	0
532.23031A	AWS6	13728	53	62.5	7.5	3	8.5	8.4	9.9	0
532.60017A	AWS7	21307	74	0.0	0	ukn	2.9	24.4	17.7	0
532.60031A	AWS8	13760	69	0.0	0	0	4.2	11.9	3.6	0

Eldorado National Forest Watersheds with Acres Over Threshold

Cal-Water Planning Watershed ID Nr	Cal-Water Planning Watershed Name	Cal-Water Planning Watershed Total Acres	Slope >40% No Stream Buffer No Road Acs	Slope >40% in Strm Buff With Rd Acs	>40% Bare Ground No Stm Buff No Rd Acs	>40% Bare Gd In Stm Buff No Rd Acs	>40% Bare Gd In Stm Buff With Rd Acres	>40% Bare + Steep Gd No Stm Buff No Rd Acs	Hi-K Soil No Stm Buff No Rd Acres	Hi-K Soil In Stm Buff No Rd Acs	Hi-K Soil In Stm Buff With Rd Acres
514.31010	NF Webber Ck	6376	203.9	0.2	231.5	11.6	0.7	8.7	947	231	38.9
514.31011	SF Webber Ck	4916	64.3	0.2	266.4	14.5	2.4	0.2	1308.3	132.7	52.5
514.31012	China Ck	4562	28	0.9	168.1	12.2	1.1	0	1990.9	329.5	39.6
514.31020	Ringold Ck	1061	6.4	0	33.4	5.1	0.7	0	555	54	17.6
514.31021	Hangtown Ck	418	4.2	0	43.8	2.2	0	1.6	82.7	5.1	3.6
514.31022	Cold Springs Ck	1480	0	0	108.5	6.9	0.7	0	693.7	141.6	19.6
514.32010	Gaddis Ck	8684	0.4	0	4	2.2	0	0	6411	1170.7	117.6
514.32011	Slab Ck	5493	389.3	1.6	6.7	0.9	0	5.6	2373.8	656.2	70.7
514.32012	Brush Ck	5132	42.5	1.1	0	2	0.2	0	3659.7	720.2	55.8
514.32013	Slab Ck Res	5723	2186.6	24.9	7.6	42	0.4	16.9	1214.5	217	31.1
514.32014	Long Cyn	2876	286.2	0	13.8	3.1	0.2	0.2	1080	97.8	14.2
514.32015	Iowa Cyn	5107	185.2	0.2	28.5	3.6	0	0	1654.3	280.2	59.1
514.32020	Brass Ck	6089	72.9	0	20.5	0.7	0	0	2539.5	627.7	79.4
514.32021	Bald Mtn Cyn	7413	495.2	0.9	17.8	0.7	0	3.1	3529.1	869.6	60.9
514.32022	Whaler Ck	10209	438.9	2.4	15.6	0.4	0	3.1	6177.3	1039	138.7
514.32023	One Eye	4521	222.6	1.6	22	0.7	0	1.3	2262.9	495	65.8
514.32024	Redbird Ck	8228	696.8	4.2	54	18.5	2.4	2.9	4345.6	836.3	149
514.32030	Traverse Ck	9378	184.1	0	154.5	60.5	9.8	0.7	4634.4	791.6	137.4
514.32031	Bear Ck	5358	73.4	0	5.3	6	1.3	5.8	3468	581.9	123.8
514.32032	White Rock Ck	10831	2143	8	201.4	44.2	4.9	109.4	2854.1	494.5	88.9
514.32040	Big Sailor Ck	9835	70.7	0	965	94.7	9.6	18.7	2593	504.7	74.7

514.32041	Kelsey Cyn	1043.7	1.3	308.4	115.2	10.2	236.4	1264.9	236.1	45.4
514.32050	Georgetown Ck	0	0	0.7	0	0	0	17.3	0.4	0.2
514.33010	Lyons Ck	649	1.8	2177.9	309.7	28.2	670.2	0.4	0	0
514.33020	Ice House Res	100.9	0.4	884.3	147.2	9.6	13.6	138.1	34	1.1
514.33021	Peavine Ck	40.9	2.2	2464.5	311.1	27.6	99.4	1423.3	308	44.9
514.33030	Little Silver Ck	93.8	6	75.8	37.4	3.8	36	5499.4	971.7	136.5
514.33031	Sugar Pine Ck	1561.6	6.7	635	114.5	14.2	73.2	4071.5	684.2	37.1
514.33032	Onion Ck	31.8	0	7.1	0	0	0.4	2155	447.1	15.3
514.33033	Jay Bird Cyn	10.5	0.2	19.1	1.6	0	0	160.1	58.7	3.3
514.33034	Round Tent Cyn	140.3	0	127.4	1.3	0.2	2.9	317.7	67.1	7.8
514.33035	Camp Seven	2036.5	0.9	2.9	16.7	0	57.1	1004.1	129	33.1
514.34010	Jones Fk Silver Ck	299.7	0	1549.1	221.5	6.9	307.5	0	0	0
514.34011	Table Rock	158.1	0	987.7	96.7	12	18.5	143.4	22.2	6.4
514.34020	Lawrence Lake	196.8	0	1372.6	237.9	1.3	207	0	0	0
514.34021	Bassi Fk Silver Ck	718.4	0	908.1	115.8	4.9	171.9	0.2	0	0
514.34022	Big Siver Ck	312	0	649.5	50	2	65.8	76.3	0	0
514.34030	Tells Ck	63.1	0.2	607.7	59.1	11.8	0.4	2.4	0	0
514.34031	Union Valley Res	34.5	0.2	557.7	975	8.4	3.6	1632.9	204.3	26.7
514.35010	Pyramid Ck	825.6	0	1603.4	758.2	22.7	777.3	0	0	0
514.35012	Aspen Ck	1377	0	878.7	72.9	9.3	196.8	0	0	0
514.35013	Sayles Cyn	384.9	0	640.6	38.9	2.9	183.4	0	0	0
514.35014	Strawberry Ck	1500.9	0.7	674.4	17.1	3.6	92.3	0	0	0
514.35015	Rocky Cyn	945.2	0	409.8	16.5	5.8	63.8	54	4.7	0.9
514.35016	Cody Ck	100.1	0	343.3	16.2	2.7	14	0	0	0
514.35017	Forni Ck	1254.3	0	1047.5	46.9	2.4	107.6	967.2	229.9	20
514.35018	Station Ck	234.8	0	191.2	3.3	0.2	0.9	17.8	15.8	0
514.35020	Carpenter Ck	499.8	0.4	173.4	10.2	0.9	8.9	2482.1	529.2	48.2
514.35021	Fry Ck	84.5	0	303.1	3.1	0	2.9	1982.5	599.7	89.8
514.35022	Mill Ck	18.5	0	129.4	6	0	9.1	223.5	112.7	16
514.35030	Upper Alder Ck	91.6	0	753.1	76.7	18.2	9.8	778	312	38.2
514.35031	North Ck	80.3	0	211.5	30	1.8	0.2	0	0	0

ID	Name										
514.35032	Lower Alder Ck	2209	2.7	0	70.5	6	1.8	0	0	181.7	12.9
514.35040	Plum Ck	5466	587.9	0.2	66	2.4	0.4	4	662.4	181.7	13.1
514.35050	Twentyfive Mile Cyn	10972	366.9	3.1	1202.5	67.4	8	150.5	562.3	851.4	115.2
514.35051	Grays Cyn	8308	1685.9	1.3	30.9	21.1	0.2	16.7	2754.9	416.7	38.9
514.35052	Soldier Ck	3414	20.9	0.4	49.6	2.7	0.4	3.1	2885.7	204.8	40
514.36010	Emigrant Ck	8742	750	0.9	1328.1	197	18.2	226.6	1368.3	0	0
514.36011	Kirkwood Ck	2306	625	0	189.4	30	6.2	80.9	0	0	0
514.36012	Caples Ck	9212	1301.9	1.1	1654.7	289.3	12	179	0	0	0
514.36013	Silver Lake	9691	612.8	0	2466.8	347.1	20.5	285.9	0	0	0
514.36014	Oyster Ck	5400	623.5	0	758.4	81.2	1.1	94.5	0	0	0
514.36020	North Tragedy Ck	4781	173.9	0	1182.9	206.6	3.8	103.8	0	0	0
514.36021	Sherman Ck	6262	92.3	0	656.6	59.1	10.9	4.2	0	0	0
514.36022	Mule Cyn	3505	20.9	0	172.5	11.3	3.6	0	533.9	105.8	9.6
514.36023	Matin Ck	3253	40.7	0	119.6	12.2	0.9	10.9	173.9	61.4	3.3
514.36030	Bark Shanty Cyn	5371	14.2	0	212.3	28.9	2.4	0	1802.1	356.6	31.4
514.36031	Girard Ck	2067	25.8	0	166.3	18.5	7.8	0.2	268.6	52.3	11.6
514.36032	Long Cyn	3597	41.4	0	318.6	17.1	2.4	1.1	468.9	91.6	1.8
514.36033	Middle Ck	4735	293.1	0	57.6	10	0	9.1	1275.2	219.2	27.8
514.36034	Beanville Ck	2343	8.7	0	30.7	0.9	1.3	0	1035.9	250.1	8.9
514.41010	Mad Cyn	1282	849.4	3.8	0	1.3	0	0	105.6	0	0
514.41012	Dardanelles Ck	6372	3147.8	2.2	32.2	40.5	0.4	11.3	528.7	40.2	1.1
514.41020	Missouri Cyn	11451	2017.8	8	53.4	3.6	0	10.9	3447.3	289.5	36.5
514.41030	Cyn Ck	8807	78.7	1.6	48.9	4.2	0.9	0	4075.7	856.7	101.2
514.41040	New Orleans Gulch	1597	5.8	0	0	0	0	0	8.9	0	0
514.41041	Gas Cyn	569	0	0	0.4	0	0	0	0	0	0
514.42012	French Meadow Res	647	115	0	12.5	0.4	0	1.1	0	0	0
514.42013	Chipmunk Ck	4456	841.4	1.1	77.2	6.4	1.8	2	29.8	15.1	0.2
514.42030	Big Mosquito Ck	3768	1200	4.2	59.4	4	0.2	11.8	102.7	46	0
514.42031	Brushy Cyn	6455	510.1	0.7	187.4	14.9	0.4	0.7	772.7	176.1	8.4
514.43010	SF Long Cyn	6375	879.6	0.9	145.9	20.2	1.6	3.6	0	0	0
514.43011	NF Long Cyn	4244	731.3	0	119	10.2	1.8	13.1	0	0	0

514.43012	Long Cyn	11700	2669.1	2	127.6	15.1	2.4	80.7	911.6	212.1	10.7
514.43013	Wallace Cyn	8347	515.4	0	397.6	26.2	6.7	7.1	825.8	222.4	18.5
514.43020	Stony Ck	11933	1888.4	5.1	129	46.9	0.4	48.5	1522.7	338	15.6
514.43021	Little Deer Ck	2727	147.9	0.2	206.8	10.2	4.9	0.7	90.7	34.9	7.3
514.43030	Lawyer Trail	7149	1919.5	2.9	28.5	14.7	0.2	15.3	1081.7	227.9	10.7
514.43031	Little Grizzly Cyn	7072	2382.5	0	51.1	10.5	0	28.7	1141.5	113	0.4
514.43032	Big Grizzly Cyn	4321	256.1	0	205	6.9	2	1.1	1139.8	189.7	21.3
514.43033	Zero Spring	8212	3932.5	24.2	5.6	8.2	0.9	45.8	1118.6	180.5	7.3
514.43040	Upper Pilot Ck	9543	21.3	0	133	33.4	1.3	3.1	5385.3	974.1	56.7
514.43041	Lower Pilot Ck	9818	440.5	0	0.2	1.8	0	0	6651.6	1015.7	60
514.44010	Gerle Ck	7943	279.9	0	1249.8	96.7	20.9	30.5	0	0	0
514.44011	Rocky Basin Ck	6584	288.6	0	481.2	76.3	4	66.3	129.9	6.4	0
514.44012	Loon Lake	5141	155.4	0.9	631.5	165.9	12.5	40	0	0	0
514.44020	Upper SF Rubicon R	10127	411.3	0	1077.7	112.3	2.4	107.8	9.6	0.4	0
514.44021	Lower SF Rubicon R	6676	606.6	0	228.8	28	4.2	2.2	607.7	191.2	8.7
514.45013	Hell Hole Res	7156	1746.8	4.9	322.4	342.4	7.3	156.3	156.3	57.8	2.4
514.45020	Barker Ck	3232	1011.2	1.1	340.9	54.9	3.6	513.2	0	0	0
514.45021	Miller Ck	4403	351.5	0	1087.5	210.6	3.6	255.3	0	0	0
514.45022	Rockbound Lake	4434	232.8	0	1669	222.4	17.3	152.1	0	0	0
514.45023	Phipps Ck	11722	675.1	0.7	4265.6	508.7	30.9	654.2	0	0	0
514.45024	Lake Schmidell	8249	1144.4	1.8	2104.5	247.3	17.6	1007.9	0	0	0
532.23010	Upper Camp Ck	8716	205.9	0.7	396.9	56.3	8.2	3.1	2.4	0	0
532.23011	Lower Camp Ck	10330	203.9	0	88.5	13.3	2.2	4.2	2815.6	582.1	98.7
532.23021	Sly Park Ck	6275	207	0	150.1	2.9	0.2	8.7	1027.7	311.5	27.3
532.23022	Hazel Ck	1755	40	0	67.6	8.2	0	0.7	207	56.9	3.6
532.23030	Leek Spring Valley	7481	113	0	641	44	6.4	8.2	193	130.3	15.1
532.23031	Mid-Upper NF Cosumnes	6247	73.2	0	472.5	43.8	6.7	16.7	745.3	329.7	36.9
532.23032	Van Horn Ck	7516	712.9	0.2	140.5	3.3	0.4	6.9	2962.1	541.9	81.8
532.23033	North Cyn	3541	0	0	21.6	0	0.2	0	2340.9	402	69.4
532.23040	North Steely Ck	6857	84.3	1.3	32.5	2.9	0.4	0	2013.8	455.2	74.7

532.23041	String Cyn	6964	13.1	0	23.3	0.7	0	0	4331.4	596.6	57.8
532.23042	Middle Butte	2925	540.8	0.4	7.1	4.4	0	9.3	1351.2	181	7.8
532.23043	Clear Ck	2896	0	0	6.9	0	0	0	1770.1	263.5	52.5
532.23050	Jenkinson Lake	3057	2.4	0	51.4	81.4	0	0	595.9	88.5	12.9
532.23051	Camp Ck	10140	1771	1.1	60.5	15.1	1.1	20.2	4409.4	488.3	31.4
532.23060	Butte Ck	5420	123.8	0	8.7	4.7	0.2	0	3433.5	448.7	46.9
532.23061	Jackass Ck	6047	150.3	0	130.5	13.3	3.6	9.8	2497	336.2	28
532.23062	Clear Ck	6840	59.6	0	292.2	13.8	1.8	6	2709.8	626.6	96.7
532.23070	Long Ravine	4952	214.6	0	77.8	49.1	0	32.2	2340.9	490.3	61.6
532.23072	Squaw Hollow Ck	2414	0	0	73.4	0.2	0.2	0	1165.1	188.8	54.5
532.24010	Anderson Cyn	3252	82.5	0	294.8	31.4	1.1	14.5	369.3	87.2	3.3
532.24011	Prothro Ck	9263	309.1	1.1	457.6	26.2	5.1	5.3	2528.6	483.4	72.9
532.24012	Cat Ck	5655	2.9	0	279.7	8.2	0.7	0	1259.4	382.7	73.8
532.24013	Shingle Mill Ck	9609	91.2	1.1	143.2	13.8	1.8	0.9	1303.9	486.5	39.4
532.24014	Crystal Mine	4493	726.4	0.4	31.6	6.9	0.4	13.8	664.8	197.9	24
532.24020	McKinney Ck	3005	85.4	0	97.4	13.8	2.9	3.1	96.7	77.6	5.3
532.24021	Dogtown Ck	6799	377.6	0.4	139.4	12.7	1.6	1.6	1743	406.5	29.4
532.24022	Middle Dry Ck	3383	23.3	0.4	81.4	8	0.7	0	164.1	55.8	5.3
532.24030	Sopiago Ck	7699	272.4	1.1	37.4	2.9	2.4	0	1372.6	372.2	41.6
532.24040	OConnor Gulch	2623	222.1	0	4.7	5.3	0	8.2	949.4	198.3	6.4
532.24041	Lower Perry Ck	4801	144.5	2.2	199.2	6.7	1.3	19.6	1478.8	178.1	25.6
532.24042	Upper Perry Ck	1243	0	0	33.6	0	0	0	786.9	118.3	2.7
532.24060	Oregon Gulch	5742	178.1	0	66.9	1.8	0.2	0	1424.8	358	27.1
532.24061	Farnham Ck+C118	5887	2.4	0	131.2	13.1	2.7	0	2901.9	467.6	66.9
532.24062	Cedar Ck	4572	9.3	0.7	86.9	2.4	0.4	0.2	1220	333.3	26.2
532.24063	John Schell Mine	7590	164.5	0	186.8	7.6	0.7	2	2669.8	452	40.2
532.40010	Ashland Ck	8229	2	0	127.9	27.1	0	0	4427.2	733.5	5.1
532.40011	Pioneer Ck	3531	0.7	0	23.8	7.1	0.7	0	2334.5	320	15.6
532.40020	SF Dry Ck	1389	3.1	0	17.8	0	0	0	511.2	35.1	2.9
532.60012	Upper Deer Ck	5183	342.2	0	593.7	89.6	6.9	84.3	0	0	0
532.60013	Lower Deer Ck	5624	236.8	0	1175.8	177.9	2	156.3	0	0	0

ID	Name										
532.60014	Deadwood Cyn	6411	1371.5	0	1862	311.3	1.8	787.6	0	0	0
532.60016	Upper Summit Ck	12557	1382.8	0.2	2428.1	499.4	19.1	1461.5	0	0	0
532.60017	Lower Summit Ck	8750	1879.3	0.4	2335.3	359.5	16.5	1607.8	0	0	0
532.60020	Ladeux Meadow	4960	468	3.8	1983.4	245.9	5.6	269.9	0	0	0
532.60021	Fourth of July Cyn	3923	1535.8	0	379.3	78.5	0.2	694.4	0	0	0
532.60022	Jelmini Ck	4360	775.6	0	481.8	22.5	0	849.6	0	0	0
532.60023	Tanglefoot Cyn	6643	1001.5	4.9	508.3	138.1	4.9	277.7	169.9	34.2	13.8
532.60030	Upper Cole Ck	5828	385.1	0	1429.5	259.5	1.6	438.5	0	0	0
532.60031	Middle Cole Ck	7932	295.7	0	1039.9	192.3	7.6	155.6	33.6	2.2	0
532.60032	Lower Cole Ck	3498	166.1	0	107.6	10.7	2	116.3	888.1	249.9	20
532.60040	Bear R	7838	207.7	0	2214.6	395.8	6.2	365.1	0	0	0
532.60041	Tragedy	4736	54.3	0	1517.3	205.7	0	63.1	0	0	0
532.60042	Corral Flat	3633	62.7	0	436.3	54.3	0.4	24.7	0	0	0
532.60043	Bear R Res	7659	229.7	0.4	681.7	250.1	7.6	52	107.4	8.4	0
532.60050	Rattlesnake Ck	6639	334.4	2.2	372.4	56	7.3	145.2	912.1	270.4	5.1
532.60051	Beaver Ck	2464	8.7	0	10.2	0.2	0	0	1528.2	236.1	24.2
532.60052	Camp Ck	5087	713.1	0.4	35.8	5.1	0	9.3	1742.8	239	18.2
532.60060	East Panther Ck	5463	260.6	0.2	56.7	6.4	1.1	4.7	1671.4	313.3	32.9
532.60061	West Panther Ck	5853	152.8	0	71.4	0.7	0	0.9	2904.3	609	69.4
532.60062	Panther Ck	4137	284.8	0	6.4	4.4	0	2.2	1127.5	337.7	21.3
532.60063	Little Tiger Ck	7394	145.9	2.4	34.2	1.8	0.2	1.6	1976.5	446.5	63.1
532.60064	Mill Ck	8005	36.9	0.2	86.3	2.7	0.9	1.1	2296.9	539	51.8

SARAH MARVIN
Department of Environmental Science,
    Policy, and Management
University of California
Berkeley, California

4

Possible Changes in Water Yield and Peak Flows in Response to Forest Management

Sierra Nevada Ecosystem Project: Final report to Congress, vol. III, *Assessments, Commissioned Reports, and Background Information.* Davis: University of California, Centers for Water and Wildland Resources, 1996.

ABSTRACT

This chapter is composed of two sections relating to potential hydrologic effects of forest management. The first part concerns total water yield, and the second is about peak flows.

The water-yield section describes a simple method of estimating the trend and magnitude of annual runoff response to changes in amount of forest cover in the Sierra Nevada. The use of this method is strictly limited to reconnaissance level assessments of the potential effects of broad-scale forest management scenarios. A model relating annual runoff response to timber harvest was developed from a simple linear regression of 31 catchment experiment results from the western United States. Correlations of runoff response following timber harvest with mean annual precipitation, mean annual runoff, and the ratio of mean annual runoff to mean annual precipitation indicated that the model would benefit from stratification by one or more of these variables. Because mean annual precipitation data are generally easier to obtain, a model was developed by stratifying the data set to a mean annual precipitation range representative of the Sierra Nevada conifer forest zone.

The simple linear regression indicates that a ten percent increase in timber harvest distributed evenly across the Sierra Nevada conifer forest zone may result in a 0 to 26-mm increase in mean annual runoff. Stratification of the data set to regions of above and below average mean annual precipitation indicated that a ten percent reduction in forest may result in a 10 to 52-mm and a -1 to 18-mm increase in annual runoff, respectively. Furthermore, these results indicate that trend and magnitude of changes in runoff following forest reduction are much more difficult to predict in drier regions. Further analyses were conducted to compare the results obtained from more complex multiple regressions. For the purpose of estimating trend and magnitude of runoff response, the multiple regressions produced results nearly identical to the simple runoff versus forest reduction regression.

The results of the stratified regressions were applied in two examples of projected changes in forest, one forest-wide and one Sierra Nevada-wide. The results indicate that annual runoff would be minimally affected by projected trends in forest reduction alone. However, these results do not include further effects from logging road construction, skid trails, or any other aspect of multiple-use management. Furthermore, the models and results herein are limited to annual runoff, only.

A paired catchment technique was used to assess historical trends in channel-forming peak flows in response to long-term watershed conversion to a logging-based ecosystem in the southern Sierra Nevada. The "treated" watershed, the South Fork Tule River, was subject to cumulative logging and road construction from approximately 1950 to 1989. By 1984, 58% of the forested area and 21% of the entire watershed had been logged. Double-mass plots of the treated and control watersheds over the period 1940-1989 indicated that an inflection point occurred at water years 1967-1969, about the same time as a significant increase in the land-conversion. Separation of the data set at 1967 produced a post-conversion slope twice as steep as the pre-conversion period, implying that channel-forming peak flows increased in response to cumulative canopy reduction and road construction. One possible cause of the increase in peak flows is an increase in snowpack and exposure to latent and sensible heat flux in clearcuts. Two hypothetical scenarios were developed to assess the increase in water available for runoff from the clearcut watershed. Increases of 15% and 11% were found for the forested area and the whole watershed, respectively.

Vegetation-Runoff Relationships for Predicting Water Yield Change

INTRODUCTION

One of the goals of the Sierra Nevada Ecosystem Project is to determine how broad-scale planning scenarios resulting in changes in vegetation cover or density may affect annual runoff from Sierra Nevada watersheds. Complex models have been used to predict changes in runoff from changes in vegetation at the individual watershed level (e.g., McGurk and Davis 1996). These models require watershed specific data for a number of components that affect the water balance. When a region, rather than an individual watershed, is the study area and the desired information is a determination of trend or magnitude, researchers have resorted to simple models based only on percentage of vegetation removed (Bosch and Hewlett 1982; Hibbert 1983; Harr 1983). These models are developed from relationships established by linear regression of multiple paired catchment experiments.

Around the world, hundreds of experiments have been conducted to determine the effect of removing or planting vegetation on streamflow. The primary purpose of these studies has been to determine whether and by how much water supplies can be augmented by removing vegetation from watersheds. These studies usually follow the typical "catchment experiment" design, wherein the mean annual water yield of two similar forested catchments, or small watersheds (10-200-ha) are calibrated to each other (typically 5-10 years). Following calibration, the vegetation on one of the catchments is partly or completely removed by mechanical means, burning, or herbicide application (or a combination of the three) while the second catchment is left untreated as a control. Annual precipitation and streamflow measurements are typically recorded for one to ten years following treatment. Comparisons are then made between the predicted streamflow from the calibrated relationship and the observed, post-treatment streamflow. Statistical analyses are usually employed to determine the significance of measured changes. A common use of the results of these individual experiments is to predict water yield increases from vegetation treatments in other watersheds.

Bosch and Hewlett (1982) used a world-wide sample of catchment experiments to develop a simple linear regression equation between the percentage of forest cover removed and the maximum increase in water yield recorded in the first five years following the treatment. The regressions were stratified by conifer, hardwood, and shrubland vegetation types. The authors estimated a 40 mm increase in runoff per 10 percent reduction in cover for the conifer forest. The equation explained 42% of the variability in water yield change.

The purpose of this study is threefold: 1) to develop a simple model that could be used to determine general trend and magnitude of runoff response across the Sierra Nevada to broad-scale planning scenarios resulting in change in forest density; 2) to compare this relationship to Bosch and Hewlett's (1982) world-wide estimate; and 3) to estimate trend in runoff by applying the models developed in this study to proposed broad-scale scenarios in the Sierra Nevada. An extensive review of the literature is included to explain the concepts involved in predicting changes in runoff from vegetation treatments. Other components of the water balance that have a greater effect on stream ecology and geomorphology as well as on water supply are also affected by vegetation changes. An assessment of annual runoff is only the first step of a watershed analysis. This analysis is restricted to annual runoff, because the effects of change in vegetation on peak and low flows are far more complex.

REVIEW OF WATER YIELD LITERATURE

Due to the fact that most of the experimental studies involve reductions rather than increases in forest cover, the following discussion is necessarily limited to this scenario. The catchment experiments show that, all other hydrologic factors remaining equal and favorable to runoff, water yield may be increased by removing vegetation. The premise of this statement is that vegetation intercepts and evapotranspires precipitation that might otherwise become runoff. 'All factors remaining equal' refers to the fact that there are many environmental factors that complicate this simple premise, some of which are not favorable for increasing water yield.

Many researchers group all runoff factors into three variables:

runoff = precipitation - (evapotranspiration + deep seepage).

Since runoff and precipitation are easy to measure and evapotranspiration is not, this simple relationship is often used to predict evapotranspiration, by substituting runoff and precipitation values and dropping the unmeasurable, but presumed insignificant deep seepage factor:

evapotranspiration = precipitation - runoff.

This simplification is a tempting method to determine evapotranspiration rates that can then be used to predict runoff from removing all or parts of the source of evapotranspiration. While the basic relationship is valid, back-calculating reductions in evapotranspiration this way frequently results in overestimating water yield change from vegetation removal. Furthermore, the method transfers errors in both precipitation and runoff measurements to the evapotranspiration term.

Direction and magnitude of runoff response to changes in vegetation is not always predictable, because the relationship depends on the interaction of physical and biological factors present in the individual watershed. For example, five studies conducted in Arizona on a ponderosa pine forest found varying increases in runoff in response to clearcutting and thinning (U.S. Environmental Protection Agency 1980). The difference between the predicted and measured yields ranged from 16-222%. However, the differences do not correlate well with the percentage of cover reduction. The 100% clearcut watershed increased yield by 35% (~51 mm); the 75% thinned watershed yielded a 222% (~43 mm) increase; and the 50% clearcut and thinned watershed yielded a 103% (~142 mm) increase. Similarly, the results from logging eleven drainages within a Virginia river basin failed to produce a reliable or accurate model to predict hydrologic response to vegetation manipulation within the 148-ha area. The following is a discussion of factors that affect the magnitude of runoff response to vegetation treatment, including the ways in which each may confound the ability to predict amount or direction of water yield change from vegetation treatment.

Climate

The review of catchment studies supports previous findings that the greatest initial water yield increases occur on watersheds with the highest mean annual precipitation (MAP) (Bosch and Hewlett 1982; Ziemer 1986). However, the duration of an increase in runoff may be shorter in regions with high MAP, because revegetation occurs at a faster rate. The magnitude of the increase in runoff varies with annual and seasonal precipitation. Wet years produce higher increases than dry years, which may produce no increase at all (David et al. 1994). Wet seasons produce higher absolute increases than dry seasons. In Mediterranean climates where most precipitation occurs in the dormant season, transpirational draft may not be greatly affected by reducing vegetation.

Detectable increases in runoff are unlikely from watersheds with MAP less than 18 inches (Bosch and Hewlett 1982), and the potential for increasing runoff remains low for watersheds with MAP below 27-31 inches (MacDonald 1985 cited in Kattelmann 1987). Shallow-rooted grasslands can transpire as much as some forested sites when a water deficit exists and soils are shallow (Eagleson and Segarra 1985; MacDonald 1991), or when clearing results in an increase in evaporation that is not counteracted by a decrease in transpiration (Calder 1993).

Vegetation

The amount of vegetation existing prior to treatment may be more important to changes in water yield than the amount of vegetation that is removed. For example, much of subalpine zone in California is already at or close to maximum water yield efficiency (Kattelmann 1987). This efficiency is attributed to the open vegetation cover which optimizes snow retention, evapotranspiration, and runoff to produce the highest water yields. Kattelmann (1987) concludes that vegetation cover below forty percent cannot be effectively managed for increased water yields.

Transpiration varies with differences in vegetation species, vigor, density, and environmental constraints (availability of water and energy). Interception of rain and snow and subsequent ablation also vary by vegetation type (deciduous versus evergreen), canopy cover, and leaf size and shape. The disposition of these factors in both vegetation removed and the remaining or succeeding vegetation affect runoff response. For example, Kauffman et. al. (1987) found that remaining understory vegetation offset expected evapotranspirational savings from clearing an aspen overstory. The remaining understory had no such effect on savings from removal of a spruce-fir overstory.

Location

The effect of evapotranspiration on water yield may be influenced more by the location of the vegetation treatment within the watershed than by any other factor. One study in Arizona found an average increase of 16 mm (40%) when channel-side shrubs on 15% of the chaparral-dominated watershed were chemically treated. A further reduction in cover of 20% on the upper slopes produced no additional increase (Hibbert et al. 1983). Similar results were found in several studies conducted in climates where a soil moisture deficit exists during the growing season (Calder 1993; Greenwood et al. 1985; Hornbeck 1975; Whitehead and Calder 1993). The amount of increased runoff that actually reaches the stream channel is partly determined by potential uptake by other vegetation between the origin of the runoff and the channel (Kattelmann et al. 1984; Eagleson and Segarra 1985). If a goal of management is to increase runoff, location of the treatment is especially important on watersheds that cannot be completely clearcut or that must retain a riparian buffer zone, such as streams in the National Forests.

Topography

Slope aspect and gradient may influence the effectiveness of vegetation removal on runoff, in both amount and timing. Southern exposure, especially combined with steep slope gradient, will increase solar radiation to any snowpack present and accelerate snowmelt. Even nearby rocks and vegetation not covered with snow absorb energy which is re-radiated to the snowpack.

The greater solar radiation received by south-facing slopes often limits vegetation to more drought-tolerant species that use so little water that changes in cover do not significantly affect runoff. Slope may also be important in that steep slopes are less capable of retaining excess soil moisture on site or delaying its movement downhill.

Silvicultural Method

Vegetation cover reduced by a given percentage after thinning may produce a smaller (or non-detectable) yield than the same percentage reduction through clearcutting (depending on the location of the treatments). Most studies have failed to detect changes in runoff from vegetation treatments of less than 20-35% (Bosch and Hewlett 1982; Turner 1993). This is especially true of watersheds with low MAP. It is not known whether this lack of detectable response is due solely to the inability of stream gauges to detect small changes in runoff or if typical watershed characteristics prevent small increases in runoff from reaching the channel.

Several studies have shown that net snow water equivalent (SWE) may be increased by harvesting a watershed in strips or patches through reduced snow interception and subsequent ablation (Troendle and King 1985, Kauffman et al. 1987). The change in SWE is dependent upon the height of the neighboring forest stand and the size and shape of the cut. Maximum SWE frequently fails to translate to maximum annual runoff. Much of the increased runoff may be used by the surrounding forest stand (MacDonald 1989) unless it is melted by warm rain storms before the growing season begins.

Soils

Soil permeability and soil moisture capacity are critical factors that affect both the ability to increase annual water yield and the timing of runoff. Deep soils have been found to produce some of the greatest water yield increases, while shallow soils (especially in Mediterranean climates) produce the smallest yields (Bosch and Hewlett 1982; Kattelmann 1987). Furthermore, shallow soil combined with a steep slope may already efficiently transport runoff to stream channels. Removing vegetation from such sites will have nominal effects on runoff.

Infiltration and runoff rates for a given soil type change with land-use impacts and reduction in cover. Soil compaction from logging equipment and from mineral soil exposure to the force of raindrops decreases infiltration and increases overland flow, which may result in greater annual runoff (Harr 1975; Reid 1993).

Land Use/Cover

The current and historic uses of a watershed may determine whether any increase in water yield is possible. The Mokelumne River basin has undergone logging, grazing, road construction, and development since the 1850's. Euphrat (1992) analyzed stream and precipitation gage data for two branches of the Mokelumne River from 1941 to 1990 and compared runoff to an earlier study covering the period up to 1949. Euphrat concluded that annual water yield had increased at the onset of logging activities and peaked by 1949. Apparently, from 1949 to 1990, the detected peak remained constant, even as the cumulative watershed area affected by logging, grazing, and settlement increased. There may be a point in road-based logging ecosystems at which water yield is maximized, regardless of increasing harvest. Over a large landscape, a balance between reforestation and deforestation, watershed rehabilitation and destruction, and road construction and obliteration may keep long-term mean annual runoff relatively constant. This balance of

158

activities may have the opposite effect on annual runoff in individual years. The Mokelumne River study reported a trend in streams "producing both more water in wet years, and less water in dry years" beginning around 1971 (Euphrat 1992).

In summary, magnitude and in some cases trend, of runoff response to vegetation change may be less related to the amount of vegetation change than another environmental factor. The literature points to the role of climate particularly in the form of seasonal precipitation.

The following analysis attempts to produce general runoff-vegetation treatment relationships tailored to the average range of environmental conditions in the Sierra Nevada conifer forests. As stated previously, the goal of developing these relationships is to provide a method of first approximation of trend and magnitude of runoff response to broad-scale planning scenarios.

RUNOFF-TREATMENT RELATIONSHIPS FOR THE SIERRA NEVADA

Methods

To develop runoff-treatment relationships for the Sierra Nevada region I compiled a database of water yield studies that were similar to Sierra Nevada conditions. Since there are very few studies specific to the Sierra Nevada itself, I started with all studies in the western United States mountain ranges, excluding the coast ranges. While this eliminated the confounding effects of the different precipitation-growing season relationship of the eastern United States, I could not eliminate similar climatic differences existing in western study sites controlled more by a continental than by a marine climate regime. Reducing the study to only marine-influenced climates would have drastically reduced the sample size and biased the results towards a higher range in mean annual precipitation.

Tables 1 and 2 document the attributes of 31 catchment studies, all of which have coniferous forests. The data set includes studies from Arizona, Colorado, Oregon, Washington, and California. Mean annual precipitation ranges from 400 mm in Colorado to 2840 mm in Oregon, mean annual runoff (MAF) ranges from 18 mm in Arizona to 2710 mm in Oregon, mid-area elevation ranges from 500 m in Oregon to 3200 m in Colorado, and drainage area ranges from 9 to 563-ha.

The two main variables used in the following regressions are: the independent variable 'treat', which is the area of the watershed treated (by logging or clearing vegetation), in percent; and the dependent variable 'Qdyr5', which is the corresponding average annual change in water yield (in millimeters) for the first five years following vegetation removal. Most catchment studies reported cover treated as percent of watershed. However, some mixed percent basal area with percent watershed area. This may be a source of error in the following regressions, as the two methods are not equivalent.

The basic question is whether there is a statistically significant, positive relationship between the area of a watershed treated and change in runoff. The null hypothesis is that there is no relationship between these variables (slope = 0) at the 90 percent confidence level (p=.10). If a positive, statistically significant slope results, the trend for water yield to increase with vegetation removal will be valid for the data set. Depending on the ability of the regression equation to explain the variability in water yield change, the slope will indicate the magnitude of change that may be expected from a given percentage of watershed area treated.

This first approximation of runoff response to vegetation change is followed by attempts to account for differences from other significant independent variables: mean annual precipitation, vegetation type, and slope aspect. Mean annual runoff is so strongly correlated with mean annual precipitation that inclusion in a model is redundant. The usefulness of these variables is tested in stratified linear regressions and multiple-regressions. The results are compared to the simple runoff versus percent treatment model.

Results and Discussion

Simple Runoff versus Treatment Regression Figure 1 shows the results of the first regression: increase in runoff versus reduction in forest cover for all western U.S. studies in the data set (see table 3 for a complete comparison of model results from this study). The plot shows a non-zero slope, which is statistically significant at the 90% level of probability (p-value=.042; the probability that the estimated change in water yield could be due solely to random variability instead of percent treatment is 4.2%). Presumably, the water yield change due to a 0% change in vegetation would be zero. However, due to a lack of data points at 0% watershed treatment and non-normal data, the equation gives a mean intercept of 12 mm (0 mm falls well within the confidence interval).

To more accurately reflect the variability in the mean runoff-treatment relationships, I report the range in response as the 95% confidence limits. The estimated mean water yield increase associated with a ten percent change in cover for this data set is 12 mm, within a range of 0 to 24-mm. The regression coefficient is extremely low (r^2=0.14), indicating that area treated fails to explain most of the variability in water yield change. For comparison, Bosch and Hewlett's (1982) regression (covering a greater range in climate) produced an r^2 of 0.42. The greatest variation about the regression line is for treatments of 100%. Both the highest (positive) and lowest (negative) residuals occur at 100% treatment. The rest of the data points are fairly well distributed. The lack of a normal distribution for this data can be partly accounted for by two major factors. The first is the variability inherent in the way experiments were conducted and the data were collected by the individual researchers of each sample point. The second is the influence of more dominant independent variables that is magnified as percentage of watershed area treated increases.

Stratification by Mean Annual Precipitation Ideally, the data set used to develop a runoff-treatment equation representative of the forest zone of the Sierra Nevada would consist of results from dormant season precipitation, because 80-90% of precipitation in this zone occurs from October to April. All of the studies included in the data set have a winter precipitation period. However, too few catchment studies reported the differences in seasonal changes in runoff. In addition, to be representative of the Sierra Nevada the data set should correspond to a pattern of high MAP being dominated by snow and lower MAP being dominated by rainfall. Unfortunately, study watersheds with the highest MAPs are located in the Oregon Cascades where precipitation is a mix of rain and snow and the lowest MAPs are located in the snow zones of Arizona. Due to the limited availability of catchment study results, MAP is used as a surrogate for the more complex relationship between precipitation and runoff.

A comparison of correlation coefficients between percent cover treated (r = .38), MAP (r = .82), and MAF (r = .84) shows that both MAP and MAF individually explain a far greater amount of the variability in streamflow change following treatment than does the amount of treatment. The potential for changes in vegetation to affect mean annual runoff is so dependent upon the water available to the system that the vegetation change itself is almost insignificant in comparison. These results suggest that a better runoff-treatment relationship should be possible by stratifying the data set by ranges in MAP.

The first stratification by MAP was made by limiting the data set to a range typical of the Sierra Nevada's MAP: 500 mm to 2400 mm (Schoenherr 1992). The goal was to retain sample points while reducing the variability in MAP. Three points below 500 mm and two points above 2400 mm were dropped, leaving 26 sample points. The goodness-of-fit for the new model was unchanged ($r^2 = .14$) while the regression slope was slightly less significant (p-value=.58). The only difference between the two runoff-treatment models was the elimination of three studies that reported no increase in water yield from treatments of 25% and 100%. The elimination of these points increased the estimated mean change in runoff associated with a ten percent increase in treatment from 12 mm to 13 mm (figure 2). However, the increase is not statistically significant. Because the purpose of developing the runoff-treatment relationships is to determine trend and magnitude, the models are considered identical: a mean increase on the order of 10 mm per 10 percent reduction in forested area may be expected from the average watershed in an average year (average as defined by the data set). An additional assumption is that the treated area is located on an "average site" within the watershed.

Conditions across the Sierra Nevada forest zone are not average. In particular, MAP ranges from relatively low in the southern Sierra to moderate in the northern Sierra to extremely high in the central Sierra. To determine trend and magnitude of annual runoff response in broad regions that are not represented by average MAP, I stratified the data set to these three general regions. Rather than improve the model, further stratification of the data set into high, medium, and low MAP eliminated the statistical significance of the regression for the nine sample points within MAP 400 mm to 610 mm (roughly corresponding to the foothill woodland community in the Sierra Nevada. However, the 400 mm point is for a spruce forest in Colorado). The slope was not statistically significant ($r^2=0.14$; p-value=0.33), indicating that runoff response to change in vegetation in this low MAP range is considerably less than for the whole data set. This interpretation supports previous findings that regions of lower precipitation are associated with smaller changes in runoff following timber harvest.

The middle MAP range stratification of 630 mm to 960 mm (roughly equal to the mixed conifer forest in the Sierra Nevada) also failed to produce a significant relationship between treatment and runoff ($r^2=0.09$; p-value=0.37). A significant relationship only emerged when the MAP reached a range of 950 mm to 2400 mm (roughly equal to the Sierra Nevada lodgepole pine - red fir community, but the sample is dominated by Douglas fir). The results of the high MAP regression indicate that a 10 percent increase in treatment may be associated with a 31 mm mean increase in runoff, within a range of 10 to 52-mm. The goodness-of-fit is also relatively high ($r^2 =0.64$), with treatment explaining 64% of the variation in water yield increase.

The results from stratifying the data set by MAP range show that the simple treatment-runoff model may explain up to 64% of the change in runoff for regions with the highest MAP. For watersheds with MAP falling within the range 400 mm to 1000 mm, percent watershed treatment is a very poor indicator of changes in runoff. Stratification within this range failed to produce any significant relationship. The results of the lower MAP range also indicate that during periods of low precipitation, watershed treatments throughout the Sierra Nevada are unlikely to affect runoff. Similarly, the higher MAP range illustrates that a greater response to treatment will occur in high precipitation years. Watersheds with MAP falling between 900 mm and 1000 mm are in a transition zone. If stratified into the higher MAP range, use of the model would probably result in overestimates of runoff associated with percent treatment, as was the case with the southern Sierra Nevada sample point (study number 104).

Stratification by Aspect Aspect is most important in the lower elevations where plant communities may be defined by north and south facing slopes. In higher elevations, aspect will determine the locations and densities of individual tree species. In addition to plant distribution, aspect may be a useful indicator of stomatal activity between and within plant species.

The following treatment-runoff models were derived from the Sierra Nevada MAP data described above. Ten south and one west aspect were grouped into the south-facing data set; nine north and three east aspects were grouped into the north-facing data set. Neither data set benefited from further stratifying into south only and north only groups.

The regression for south-facing slopes produced no significant relationship between treatment and runoff. (r^2=0.07; p-value=0.38). The regression for north-facing slopes produced a higher regression coefficient (r^2=0.28), but the model still explains a small fraction of the variability of runoff response to watershed treatment. The treatment-runoff relationship is statistically significant at the 90% level of confidence (p-value = 0.076). The main difference between the data sets for north and south facing slopes (besides aspect) is the mean treatment, which is 76% for south-facing slopes and 56% for north-facing slopes. MAP and mean change in runoff are virtually equal between the data sets. Stratification by aspect supports the trends revealed by the stratification by MAP: runoff response to vegetation removal is dependent upon greater availability of moisture, whether by higher precipitation or by lower solar radiation.

Stratification by Plant Community In addition to representing broad climatic conditions, stratification by plant community may also substitute for broad differences in edaphic conditions. The data set was stratified into three associations determined by the dominant tree species: mixed conifer (dominated by ponderosa pine); lodgepole pine-spruce-fir; and Douglas fir.

The only statistically significant regression by plant community is for the Douglas fir. The r^2 is 0.56, which is similar to the highest MAP stratified model because both data sets include many of the same sample points. The model indicates that a ten percent reduction in vegetation may be associated with a mean increase in runoff of 27 mm, within a range of 3 to 51 mm.

Stratification by vegetation type is almost the same as stratification by MAP. The Douglas fir data set (8 points, all of which occur in the Oregon Cascades) corresponds to a mean MAP of 1887 mm. Mixed conifer (12 data points, primarily in Arizona) corresponds to a mean MAP of 705 mm. The lodgepole pine - spruce - fir (6 data points, primarily in Colorado) corresponds to MAP 633 mm. The lodgepole pine-spruce-fir subset is not representative of the environment of these species in the Sierra Nevada. A more appropriate surrogate for the Sierra Nevada red and white fir forests would be the Douglas fir type. The problem with this substitution is the precipitation type: the Sierra Nevada red and white fir zones are characterized by deep snowpack, which is not the case of the Douglas fir in the Oregon Cascades.

Multiple Regression The purpose of the following multiple regression analysis is to determine the differences between estimating trend and magnitude of runoff response from the simple runoff-treatment model (with or without stratification) and a more complex model requiring basin-specific characteristics. The data set used is the set of 26 samples fitting the Sierra Nevada MAP range.

The independent variables tested were percent treatment, MAP, MAF, and the ratio of MAF to MAP. The regression with all four variables results in an r^2 of 0.81 and the relationships for all the variables except MAF are significant at the 90% level. Even though the correlation between runoff response and MAF is strongly positive, there is no statistical significance of MAF in the multiple regression the relationship. Despite this result, the model has a better fit with MAF retained. The multiple regression equation is:

$$Y_{fit} = -217 + 1.15X_1 + 0.24X_2 + 323X_3 - 0.25X_4,$$

where X_1 is percent cover reduction, X_2 is MAP, X_3 is MAF/MAP ratio, and X_4 is MAF.

For this data set, holding all other factors equal, a 10% increase in treatment is associated with an 12 mm mean increase in runoff, within a range of 4 mm to 19 mm. As anticipated from the literature review, runoff response to vegetation removal is greater for watersheds with higher MAP, higher MAF/MAP ratio. In terms of trend and magnitude, the change in runoff from change in treatment produced by the multiple regression is virtually identical to the results from the simple runoff-treatment model.

Stratification into south- and north-facing slopes significantly improves the goodness-of-fit for both aspects, but not the significance of the independent variables. For the first time, a model explains most of the variability in runoff response for drier watersheds. For the south-facing aspect, the r^2 is 0.90. However, only the MAF/MAP ratio was significant at the 90% level.

For north-facing slopes, the fit is slightly lower, with an r^2 of 0.87. Treatment is the only variable significant at the 90% level. Holding all other variables equal, a ten percent treatment is associated with an 18 mm mean increase in runoff, within a range of 3 to 32-mm. The multiple-regression resulted in a slight reduction in the effect of treatment.

Stratification by plant community produces the highest fit of any previous model, but the results are inconsistent. The drawback of using the stratification with the multiple regressions is the loss of degrees of freedom. This flaw in methodology is apparent in the failure of two of the models to produce statistically significant relationships between runoff response and all the independent variables.

In the previous analysis of the simple treatment-runoff model, stratification by plant community produced only a weak relationship for the 'mixed conifer' and 'lodgepole pine-spruce-fir' forests (r^2 of 0.18 and 0.01, respectively). With the multiple regression, these two forest types produced r^2 values of 0.58 and 1.0, respectively. Despite the improvement in fit for the models, the relationship between treatment and runoff is not significant at the 90% level. The Douglas fir data set indicates a positive treatment-runoff relationship at the 90% level (p-value=0.075).

To summarize, multiple regression, in this case, does not significantly improve or change the results from the simple runoff-treatment regressions. The primary limitation to using multiple regression on this data set is the small sample size that reduces the power of the analysis. The trends and magnitudes in runoff response to vegetation treatment are the same: greater response to vegetation treatment will occur in wetter environments and no trend can safely be predicted for driest environments. Inclusion of MAP, MAF, and the ratio of the two did not change the magnitude of potential change in runoff from treatment in an average watershed, which is approximately a 0 to 20-mm increase in runoff per 10 percent change in watershed area treated. The multiple regression did increase the statistical significance of this estimated value.

In terms of magnitude, combined with the indications from stratifying by MAP, it may be concluded that treatment of watersheds in drier regions of the Sierra Nevada will probably result in less than 10 mm (as low as 0 mm) change in runoff per 10 percent change in treatment. Regions wetter than the average conditions of this data set may result in a greater than 10 mm change (up to 50 mm for extreme conditions).

APPLICATION OF RUNOFF-TREATMENT MODELS

The following is an application of the runoff-treatment models developed above to broad, generalized areas whose average site characteristics fall within the sample averages. As discussed in the previous section, the tremendous variability in actual watershed conditions render the following examples suitable only for comparisons of runoff response to broad-scale scenarios applied evenly across the range of watershed conditions represented by the data set used to develop the particular model.

The purpose of the following applications is twofold: 1) to compare the results of the models developed in this study to results produced by other methods in the same region; and 2) to assess the maximum potential runoff change from realistic, broad-scale, forest treatments. The proposed forest treatments are projections made in U.S. Forest Service (USFS) and California Department of Forest and Fire Protection (CDF) planning documents.

Methods

The following calculations purposely err on the high side of potential runoff response. In the following applications, a period of fifty years (the period of the typical U.S. Forest Service Land and Resource Management Plan [LRMP]) is used to estimate the maximum cumulative change in runoff that could be produced from projected changes in forest cover or volume. The USFS and the CDF project changes in standing volume rather than changes in forest area. Annual rates of change in forest volume were calculated as the difference between projected rates of regrowth and timber harvest. In order to compare results to USFS estimates of water yield, the long-term annual change in runoff over the entire period had to be calculated as the cumulative sum of each net annual change in runoff, divided by the study period: annual change in runoff x 1275/50. For practical purposes, the resulting "annual change in runoff" is meaningless, because change in runoff will be minimal in the first few years and much greater at the end of the 50 year period. A projected annual net reduction in forest volume of one percent would equal a 50 percent reduction in volume by year 50.

Results and Discussion

Forest-scale Scenario The first example is a comparison of the runoff-treatment equation developed in this study to the USFS estimated water yield from increased timber harvest in the Sequoia National Forest (SQF). The average SQF forest environment is characterized by relatively low precipitation and runoff, shallow soils, sparse forest cover, and a low percentage of forest type associated with high water yields from treatment (Douglas and red fir). Forest-wide mean annual precipitation is 762 mm (U.S. Forest Service 1988). Over 75% of SQF land is composed of rock-outcrop dominated soils. The standing timber strata is dominated by mixed conifer (70%). Based on data provided in the LRMP, 291,320 acre-feet of runoff come from the

364,000 acres of total timber strata.[1] Therefore, unit-area annual runoff from the conifer forest averages 244 mm.

The LRMP projected an average annual decrease in forest volume of 11.5 million board feet (mmbf).[2] Standing volume is 8100 mmbf, therefore the annual reduction in standing timber volume is 0.14%. I stratified the data set for the SQF conifer forest MAP range of 510 to 1230-mm. I used an upper MAP limit that is greater than the actual upper limit for the SQF to make the model average MAP (772 mm) similar to the SQF average MAP (762 mm). The SQF model estimates a mean increase in runoff of 8 mm per 10 percent reduction in forest ($r2=.14$; p-value=.077). Using 95% confidence limits, the range in mean response is -1 to 18-mm. Applying the stratified runoff-treatment model to the projected change in timber volume produced a mean total increase of 143 mm over 50 years, or an annual average increase of 3 mm. The range as defined by the 95% confidence limits is a 0 - 6 mm average annual increase for 50 years. In terms of percentage of existing runoff, the increase is 0 - 1%. The upper estimate is one-third to one-half of the USFS estimate for the same scenario (U.S. Forest Service 1988).

Sierra Nevada Scenario To determine the potential range of runoff response to realistic projections of change in forest standing-volume, I applied the stratified runoff-versus-treatment models to the Forest and Range Resource Assessment Program's (FRRAP) projections (California Department of Forestry and Fire Protection 1993). The FRRAP estimates of both standing timber volume and projected logging volume are lower than the USFS estimates in sample LRMPs. For the three FRRAP regions and the Sierra Nevada as a unit I calculated the possible range in mean change in runoff using the Sierra Nevada runoff-treatment model developed in this study.

The results of the projected changes in timber volume and runoff response are displayed in tables 4 and 5, respectively. The projected change in the rate of forest reduction for the central Sierra Nevada is the greatest, producing 2 to 11-mm of additional annual runoff. Projected change is so low in the southern Sierra Nevada that no detectable change in annual runoff would occur. The northern Sierra Nevada falls in the middle with a projected increase in annual runoff of 1 to 4-mm. The "Sierra Total" is the FRRAP estimate for change across the Sierra Nevada as a whole. The resulting increase in annual runoff is 1 to 6-mm.

Kattelmann et al. (1983), using completely different methods, concluded that water yield could be augmented by one half to two percent from the Sierra Nevada National Forests, or an average increase of 0.6 cm. This estimate is based on a scenario of intensive forest management within the constraints of existing environmental and multiple-use regulations. The authors proposed cutting 25% of well-suited watersheds every 25 years. In terms of total area treated, this would be similar to cutting 1% of the selected watersheds per year for 25 years. It is unknown what percentage of the total National Forest area could be treated in this way, however it is reasonable to assume that the increase in treatment would be well under 1%. If this is the case, Kattelmann et al.'s estimate falls within the 95% confidence interval (1 to 6-mm) generated by the "Sierra Nevada MAP" model, for the 50 year period.

---

[1] Acres from Table 3.11 (US Forest Service 1988, p. 3-53) were multiplied by water yield coefficients for existing timber species from the SQF water yield method (US Forest Service 1984, p. 2).

[2] Annual logging rate increases from 97 mmbf to 102 mmbf, while regrowth rate decreases from 104 mmbf to 97.5 mmbf, an increase in vegetation loss of 11.5 mmbf (US Forest Service 1988).

DISCUSSION

General Trends in Annual Runoff Response to Forest Treatment

The results of the bivariate and multiple regressions are supported by trends found in the water yield literature. Regional variation in precipitation is the greatest determinant of potential for runoff change from vegetation removal. Across the United States, both total mean annual precipitation and seasonal distribution determine the magnitude of runoff response: catchment studies from the high mean annual precipitation regions of the Pacific Northwest and the eastern states are consistently associated with the greatest increases in runoff resulting from timber harvest. These catchments also recover the most rapidly from timber harvest. High increases in runoff also occur in regions that receive significant precipitation in the growing season.

The Sierra Nevada has a Mediterranean climate: on average, eighty percent of precipitation occurs outside of the growing season, from December through April. Primarily because of its seasonal distribution of precipitation, most regions of the Sierra Nevada (certainly those most in need of augmented streamflow) do not fit Bosch and Hewlett's 1982 estimates of runoff for a percentage reduction in cover. Runoff potential from Sierra Nevada watersheds with exceptionally high MAP and dense forest cover may be comparable to Bosch and Hewlett's estimates, however very little of the increase would occur during the growing season, when additional runoff is most needed. Value of streamflow augmentation is temptingly great in dry regions of the Sierra Nevada, but the most drastic, permanent reductions in forest cover would be required to convert a significant proportion of precipitation to runoff in these areas. As in the rest of the Sierra Nevada, most of the increase would occur in winter or spring snowmelt peaks, when the monetary (which is greatest for hydroelectric power) and ecological values are lowest.

Unless timber harvest is specifically designed to increase water yield (e.g., clear-cutting significant areas near stream channels and treating densely forested sites), total annual runoff is unlikely to change noticeably. Large-scale increases that would be detectable in major rivers will not occur and local changes will not occur when and where they are needed. A significant cumulative change in forest cover and associated roads and landings over the long term (a total ecosystem conversion), as has occurred in parts of the Sierra Nevada since the post-World War II years, may (and probably has) increase total annual runoff. In other parts of the Sierra Nevada, increase in biomass and canopy cover from fire suppression may counteract or bring about the reverse effect on flow.

Application of Treatment Versus Runoff Models

A simple treatment versus runoff relationship stratified to region-wide average conditions appears to be a useful tool for estimating potential trend and magnitude of annual runoff response to very general planning scenarios. Application of the models in a reconnaissance level assessment suggests that the minor increases in rates of timber harvest projected by the USFS and the CDF are unlikely to affect annual runoff in the short term. Over the fifty year planning period, an increase in annual runoff would peak in the last decade, when the greatest amount of forest would have been removed and the evapotranspiration rate of regrowth would not have reached that of mature forest.

For National Forest planning purposes, the biggest source of error in using the treatment versus runoff models will be in extending the use of the model below the 25% treatment limit.

166

Changes in the rates of vegetation removal on National Forest lands are of a minute magnitude, on the order of 0.1% per year, or 5% total over fifty years. At this level of change, it is arguable whether any change in runoff would occur. Two catchment studies in the Sierra each reported watershed treatments of 25%. The southern Sierra watershed produced no change in runoff (McCammon 1977); the central Sierra watershed produced a first year increase of 40 mm (Rick - please insert cite). Lack of runoff response at low levels of treatment may be due to an inability to detect a real change with available equipment, a change in runoff that falls within the error term (e.g. for USGS gauges, data accuracy ranges from 5-15%), or the existence of a minimum threshold of forest treatment before excess runoff is generated. In any case, extreme caution must be used in applying the models to treatments under 25%.

The model does not predict timing and use of water yield. For water value, timing will determine the cost or benefit of any change in runoff. The drier the location, year, or season, the more valuable the water and the smaller the probability that an increase in water yield will result from treatment. Other potential effects of timber harvest activities include changes in peak and low flows, sediment yield, channel configuration, and related cumulative and secondary effects. These models do not address any effects of vegetation removal other than annual runoff within the first five years of treatment.

Mean values should not be applied to any planning use requiring a specific value of runoff, such as cost benefit analyses and statements of forest outputs. An appropriate use of the models in these types of analyses might be to use the 95% confidence limits, and report all results as a range of possible mean values. Incorporation of the confidence limits is crucial, because they indicate that the mean increase could fall anywhere within that interval.

CONCLUSIONS

The results of linear regression analyses of 31 western United States catchment experiments produced a simple method of estimating the trend and order of magnitude of annual runoff response to changes in amount of forest cover for regions of the Sierra Nevada conifer forest zone. Further multiple regressions produced results nearly identical to the simpler model. However, the multiple regressions were hampered by the small sample size. Because of the strong correlations of runoff response following timber harvest with mean annual precipitation, mean annual runoff, and the ratio of mean annual runoff to mean annual precipitation the models developed herein were stratified to match regional characteristics. Mean annual precipitation data are generally easier to obtain, hence models targeted for Sierra Nevada-wide, above, and below average moisture conditions were developed by stratifying the data set to the appropriate mean annual precipitation ranges. The use of this method is strictly limited to reconnaissance level assessments of the potential effects of broad-scale forest management scenarios.

The regression results indicate that a ten percent increase in timber harvest distributed evenly across the Sierra Nevada conifer forest zone may result in a 0 to 26-mm increase in mean annual runoff. Results targeted for regions of above and below average mean annual precipitation suggest that a ten percent reduction in forest may result in a 10 to 52-mm and a -1 to 18-mm increase in annual runoff, respectively. Thus, runoff response in regions of low mean annual precipitation cannot be expected to produce detectable changes in annual runoff from moderate changes in forest cover or density. Furthermore, these results indicate that trend and magnitude of changes in runoff following forest reduction are much more difficult to predict in drier regions. These findings are supported by the water yield literature which indicates that significant changes in annual runoff are common in wet regions and in wet years, but not in dry regions or dry years.

The stratified models were applied to two scenarios of projected changes in forest, one forest-wide and one Sierra Nevada-wide. The forest-wide scenario, based on U.S. Forest Service projections for the Sequoia National Forest, resulted in a 0 to 6-mm mean increase in annual runoff averaged over a period of 50 years. The Sierra Nevada-wide scenario, based on California Department of Forestry and Fire Protection projections, resulted in a 1 to 6-mm mean increase in annual runoff averaged over a period of 50 years. Thus, the results indicate that annual runoff would probably be minimally affected by projected trends in forest reduction alone. However, these results do not include further effects from logging road construction, skid trails, or any other aspect of multiple-use management. Furthermore, the models and results herein are limited to annual runoff, only. Timing of runoff, peak flows, baseflow and sediment yield may all be affected by the scenarios used in this study.

Peak Flow Changes with Watershed Conversion to a Logging-based Ecosystem

INTRODUCTION

The purpose of this study was to determine if a change in channel-forming peak flows could be detected from the gradual, long-term conversion of a Sierra Nevada watershed to a logged, multiple-use ecosystem. An increase in channel-forming and larger size peak flows may lead to detrimental effects to many beneficial uses of the watershed, such as fish habitat, riparian vegetation, and reservoir space. A significant increase in peak flows may cause bed scour, channel incision (leading to a lowered water table), downstream aggradation, and bank erosion among other channel changes (see Reid 1994; Meehan 1991; and MacDonald et al. 1991 for thorough reviews of these processes).

There is a paucity of knowledge of the effects of timber harvest activities (vegetation removal, skid trails, road construction and use, and site-preparation) on peak flows in Sierra Nevada streams. Most watersheds in the Sierra timber zone have been altered by multiple-use management since at least the 1940s. Some of these watersheds, such as the National Parks, have been primarily affected by recreational use, fire-suppression policy, and grazing. Others have been altered more by timber harvest. It is this latter category that has the potential to increase peak flow size through reduction of evapotranspiration, decreased infiltration (to deep soils or groundwater), and increased exposure of snowpack to warm rain-dominated storms. In this study, I evaluate the significance of timber harvest activities on channel-forming peak flows in the Sierra Nevada by: 1) assessing the literature from other regions to determine what principles of timber harvest and peak flows may be most relevant to the Sierra Nevada; and 2) applying those principles to a watershed analysis of peak flow response to long-term conversion to a logged, multiple-use ecosystem in the Tule River basin.

BACKGROUND

Channel-Forming Peak Flows

Channel-forming peak flows are those peaks that occur frequently enough to dominate channel geometry and grain size (Dunne and Leopold 1978) or are large enough to cause a sudden but long-lasting change in channel geometry and bed load (Lisle 1981). There is relatively little information on what recurrence interval is the channel-forming flow for different streams (the recurrence interval is the average rate of recurrence of a given annual peak discharge over the period of record). The "bankfull discharge" is generally accepted as the channel-forming flow for most streams (Dunne and Leopold 1978), and tends to correspond to a 1.5- to 2-year (Q1.5 to Q2) recurrence interval. However, this may be an over-generalization when applied to steep mountain drainages, where the 5-year event may be the more significant flow (Washington Forest Practices Board 1994). An increase in the frequency of the Q2 to Q5 flow (depending on the stream) or a volume increase sufficient to raise the Q2 size flow to a Q5 size may have a detrimental effect on the stream ecosystem as the channel adjusts to a new hydrologic regime. Some watershed managers use a rule-of-thumb of a 20% increase to determine whether the Q2 has increased to a Q5 flow (Washington Forest Practices Board 1994). However, it is important to note that bed load mobilization may be predicted for flow size, but this determination is not a substitute for depth of scour (Washington Forest Practices Board 1994). The literature search for this report did not uncover published research on channel-forming flows for Sierra Nevada streams.

Most paired catchment experiments testing the effects of timber harvest on peak flows failed to address the relevance of peak flow size to long-term channel stability and consequent long-term changes to aquatic habitat and other sensitive beneficial uses. This is partly because the typical post-harvest study period was from 1 to 8 years. While there are exceptions, these are too few to extrapolate results to Sierra Nevada watersheds without long-term monitoring of peak flows in representative watersheds. The necessary monitoring is just beginning in some regions such as the Sequoia National Forest, under the 1990 Land Management Plan Mediated Settlement Agreement. The most valuable monitoring resource is the USGS stream gauge program. Unfortunately, very few Sierran watersheds have continuous records and many long-term gauges are being terminated (e.g., the South Fork Tule gauge was terminated in 1989).

Flood Flows

The flood-sized peak flows are vivid in the minds of most Californians. One of the significant debates over the establishment of the U.S. Forest Service under the Organic Act was initiated by California legislators who wanted to ensure that the flood-dampening effects of the forests were preserved (Bassman 1974; Steen 1976). The storm events in most western slope Sierra watersheds that cause major downstream flooding tend to occur with a frequency of one in ten years (Kattelmann et al. 1991). The majority of these floods are generated by mid-winter rain-on-snowpack storms. The major storms and flows are capable of mobilizing and carrying massive amounts of sediment from hillslope erosion and channel scour (Dean 1972). Part of the sediment load is transported into reservoirs, resulting in a decrease in storage capacity. Sediment exceeding flow capacity or capability is deposited instream to aggrade the channel. Such aggradation can put the river in a state of disequilibrium for a long time, especially in Mediterranean climates where precipitation is highly variable (Lisle 1981).

Potential Effects of Timber Harvest Activities on Peak Flows

Although there is variability in the effects of timber harvest activities on peak flows, researchers have identified several processes by which peak flows may be altered. Processes that may produce increases in peak flow size include: 1) soil disturbance that results in compaction or in concentration of drainage resulting in decreased infiltration at the site of disturbance; 2) reduced transpiration resulting in increased antecedent soil moisture; 3) reduced canopy interception of precipitation resulting in increased antecedent soil moisture and increased snowpack; 4) increased exposure of the snowpack to sensible and latent heat flux. A process that may increase or decrease peak flows from snowmelt is the downstream desynchronization or synchronization of peak flows from different tributaries due to advancing the peak flow date of harvested watersheds. The effects on peak flows are more complex and variable than the following summary can convey. Furthermore, due to the diverse methods that can activate a long-term change in peak flows, the associated impacts on beneficial uses will vary.

Soil Disturbance The creation of impervious surfaces by soil compaction or fire-caused hydrophobic soils results in decreased infiltration, increased overland flow, and more efficient delivery to the stream. These effects are limited to the area of the watershed disturbance. In the

Kings River, timber harvest activities (mainly skid trails) caused as much as 19% compaction (G. M. Kondolf, University of California, Berkeley, conversation with the author, October 30, 1995). Infiltration is also decreased by loss of detention storage (leaf litter and depressions in the soil that retain runoff and facilitate infiltration). The magnitude of the effect on peak flow size depends upon the amount of area no longer capable of infiltration and the amount of precipitation rerouted. The literature on peak flows is dominated by this consideration. However, unless a significant percentage of the watershed is burned or compacted, the potential increase in peak flow size is not as large as for other mechanisms.

Studies in the Idaho Batholith (Gray and Megahan 1981; Megahan and Molitor 1975) and Washington (Helvey 1980) on the effects of clear-cutting before and after fire demonstrate that the effects of fire on sediment yield are significantly greater with clear-cutting. Unfortunately, these studies did not measure peak flows. However, antecedent soil moisture and increased overland flow were controlling factors in the Idaho and Washington studies, respectively.

Reduced Transpiration A reduction in transpirational draft that increases antecedent soil moisture may increase peak flows generated by summer thunderstorms or by the first fall rains. In order for there to be antecedent soil moisture at the end of the growing season the soil must either be deep enough so that no herbaceous vegetation could tap all the moisture or there must be no vegetative layer whatsoever. In Mediterranean climates, where summers are virtually dry, soil with just herbaceous cover may be as dry as soil with deep-rooted vegetation. In those forests with deep, moisture retaining soils, a clear-cut plot may retain antecedent soil moisture over the growing season. In this case, the clear-cut site will reach saturation earlier than the equivalent forested site and will generate Hortonian or saturation overland flow more readily. The antecedent soil moisture will then augment stormflow. However, the greater stormflow from the clear-cut site will only last as long as it takes the depleted soil beneath the forest canopy to reach saturation. Therefore, antecedent soil moisture is considered significant only in increasing the size of fairly small peak flows, and only for a short time following the growing season.

Reduced Canopy Interception A portion of canopy-intercepted rainfall may be evaporated. The effect of preventing this small amount of rainfall from reaching the ground is also considered minor in its effect on channel-forming peak flows. Canopy interception plays a larger role where precipitation falls as snow. Snowpacks in the highest elevations (coldest winters) of the Sierra Nevada cause the largest peak flows to occur in the springtime, when the longer days increase air temperature. Increased snowpacks in clear-cut patches augment springtime and early summer peak flows (Troendle and King 1987). Increases of 21% to 59% in annual peak flows from spring snowmelt were documented in Colorado, Alberta, and British Columbia (Cheng 1989). Clear-cuts that are small enough to be shaded by nearby forest (1 to 3 tree heights) will melt later and may not contribute to streamflow at all (MacDonald 1989).

Increased Exposure of Snowpack Most paired catchment studies to date conclude that channel-forming peak flows are unaffected by *carefully implemented* timber harvest (Harr et al. 1982; Harr and McCorison 1979; Hibbert and Gottfried 1987; Wright et al. 1990; Ziemer 1981). In the western United States, these conclusions are being revised in light of evidence from studies conducted in watersheds subject to rain-on-snow storms (Berris and Harr 1987; Christner and Harr 1982). The influence of timber harvest on the size and frequency of rain-on-snow events is complex and fairly unpredictable. Researchers generally agree that timber harvest in small clear-cut patches increases snowpack (Troendle and King 1987; MacDonald 1989; Kattelmann 1982) and that, in regions subject to warm winter or spring rainstorms while snow is still on the ground, these increased snowpacks are subject to greater latent and sensible heat flux from warm storms (Berris and Harr 1987; MacDonald and Hoffman 1995). On the other hand, MacDonald and Hoffman (1995) were unable to detect a correlation between size of rain-on-snow generated peak flows and timber harvest. Harr and McCorison (1979) actually detected decreases in rain-on-snow peak flows for one year following timber harvest due to a lack of large warm storms.

Relevance of Peak Flow Change to Sierra Nevada

All the peak flow generating processes described above may be augmented from timber harvest activities in the Sierra Nevada, however I located only two Sierra studies of these effects. One paired catchment experiment studied the effect of timber harvest activities on annual May peak flows in the Kern Plateau (Sequoia National Forest). McCammon (1977) found no effects from timber harvest on May snowmelt peak flows, but he did not monitor the potential effects on winter peak flows. The post-treatment monitoring period lasted only three years. The second study was conducted on the Mokelumne River in the central Sierra Nevada (Euphrat 1992). The results of Euphrat's (1992) study of the Middle and South Forks of the Mokelumne River reflect the reality of long-term multiple-use management dominated by logging on a basin scale. The problem with this study is that effects from vegetation removal cannot be separated from roads, skid trails, or fire. Using USGS stream gauge data , Euphrat detected a statistically significant increase in ten-inch and greater storm residuals (from a regression of rainfall against runoff) that track with time for the period 1960-1990. Furthermore, Euphrat found no similar tracking between climate, and time. The only apparent cause of the increase in storm residuals was the effect of cumulative logging activities.

The role of soil disturbance in the Sierra Nevada is still unknown and should also be researched. Although the greater potential to affect large peak flows appears to be through increased rain-on-snow generated peaks, increases in large peak flows without rain-on-snow have been documented (see examples in Cheng 1989). Research should focus on the combined effects of soil disturbance, roads and landings, and different intensities of fire (e.g., intensities of broadcast burning, prescribed fire, and wildfire).

Virtually no published research has been conducted to determine specifically how peak flows in Sierra Nevada watersheds are affected by timber harvest. Given the magnitude of peak flow increases due to rain-on-snow storms and the fact that much of the Sierra Nevada timber zone is subject to these conditions, it is crucial to develop monitoring specifically to determine the effects of vegetation management on rain-on-snow peak flows. In the absence of this monitoring, historical trend analyses can increase our understanding of how we have affected and may continue to affect peak flows through multiple-use management. The following is such a study for the South Fork Tule River.

STUDY WATERSHED DESCRIPTIONS

The Tule River basin is located on the western slope of southern Sierra Nevada. The South Fork gauge is located at latitude 36° 02' 33", longitude 118° 51' 24", at an elevation of 235 m (770 ft). The North-Middle Fork gauge is located at latitude 36° 10' 29", longitude 118° 41' 41" at an elevation of 890 m (2,920 ft). Drainage areas are 282 km^2 and 102 km^2 (109 mi^2 and

39.3 mi^2) for the South Fork and North-Middle Fork, respectively. The South Fork drains to the west with timbered slopes facing north, west, and south. The North-Middle Fork drains primarily south, with timbered slopes facing east and west. The South Fork varies in elevation from 235 m (770 ft) at the stream gauge to 2835 m (9300 ft); the North-Middle Fork varies from 890 m (2,920 ft) at the stream gauge to 2926 m (9600 ft) at the headwaters.

Mixed conifer, ponderosa pine, and giant sequoia forest types (including cut-over area) cover the upper one-third of the South Fork (approximately 8,539 ha; 21,100 ac); dense oak stands (2,224 ha; 5,495 ac), rangeland (13,485 ha; 33,322 ac), and grassland (963 ha; 2,380 ac) cover the lower elevations (Tule River Planning Commission 1973). The North-Middle Fork has a similar vegetation distribution, but with a greater percentage of area in mixed conifer, red fir, and giant sequoia forest types. Three-quarters of the South Fork is part of the Tule River Indian Reservation (TRIR), but almost half of the timbered area is owned by the USFS. The TRIR is rural with two, approximately 1 km (0.6 mi) long, sparsely developed, narrow strips along the river. The timbered area is criss-crossed with logging roads. The North-Middle Fork is technically designated as an "unroaded" area; however, a limited amount of recreational development, similar in extent to the TRIR, exists in the lower part of the watershed (see Results Section for more detail).

Precipitation occurs as rain, snow, and rain-on-snow in both watersheds. Mean annual precipitation (MAP) ranges from 460 mm to 1,140+ mm (18 in to 45+ in) on the South Fork; and 760 mm to 1,270+ mm (30 in to 50+ in) on the North-Middle Fork. The higher MAP range in the North-Middle Fork produces a greater annual runoff than on the South Fork, even though the South Fork is a larger watershed. However, except for the two highest recorded peaks, annual peak flows tend to be greater on the South Fork. Snow falls as low as 1520 m (5000 ft), but average snow line elevation is 1980 m (6500 ft). Warm mid-winter storms produce rain as high as 2740 m (9000 ft) in the Tule River basin (California Department of Water Resources 1960). The majority of annual peak flows occur during mid-winter rain-on-snow storms in both watersheds. Smaller annual peaks occur during the spring snowmelt.

Bedrock of the Tule River basin is predominantly Mesozoic granitic intrusives with some pre-Cretaceous metamorphic bedrock in the lower South Fork. Soils are moderately developed granitics, coarse-textured and well-drained (CH2M Hill 1974).

METHODS

Determination of Land-Cover Change

To determine the relationship between peak flow trend and long-term multiple-use management I estimated relative changes in land-cover over the period 1916 to 1989. I documented growth of the road network from maps and aerial photographs; chaparral clearing and permanent woodland thinning from aerial photographs and rangeland management documents; and timber removal from land-use planning and forest management documents. Aerial photographs were available for years 1970 and 1979. Maps spanned the period from 1916 to 1989, in several different scales. Consulted maps were produced by the USGS (7.5 minute quadrangle maps) and the USFS.

Analysis of Peak Flow Data

The purpose of this analysis was to determine whether cumulative changes in land-cover may have produced detectable changes in channel-forming and larger peak flows in a Sierra Nevada watershed. Following traditional practice, the channel-forming peak flow is assumed to be the Q2 flow ("bankfull"). Most similar analyses look for changes sufficient to increase the Q2 flow to Q5 size. Since little is known about effects of long-term changes in peak flows on beneficial uses in the Sierra Nevada, I do not employ any minimum threshold of concern. The purpose is to determine whether or not peak flows have changed detectably.

To control for changes in climate over the study period, I selected two similar watersheds that have been subjected to the same peak flow generating events. Problems with finding appropriate watersheds were the lack of continuous gauge data, both peak flow and precipitation, and the existence of a nearby gauged control watershed that had not already been significantly affected by land-use change or whose records were not affected by flow diversions. I could locate only one pair of watersheds that did not completely violate these conditions: the South Fork Tule River (South Fork) and the North Fork of the Middle Fork Tule River (North-Middle Fork). Only annual peak flows could be included in the analysis, because the records for the North-Middle Fork do not include partial duration flows (all flows above a baseflow). Peak flows were gauged on the South Fork at USGS station South Fork Tule River near Success (no. 11204500) and on the North-Middle Fork at North Fork of Middle Fork Tule River near Springville (no. 11202000).

I determined the Q2 flow by constructing a flood frequency curve from the entire data set available for the South Fork, 1932 through 1989 (water years 1955 and 1956 were missing from the records; 1956 was a major flood for both watersheds). Notwithstanding the data inconsistencies, the Q2 was 22 cms (780 cfs). I matched peak flow events by comparing dates of annual peak flows from the North-Middle Fork and corresponding partial peak flows from the South Fork. If the peaks occurred within one day of each other, I considered them a pair. Use of South Fork partial peaks occurred in only two pairs (i.e. all but two pairs represent the annual peak on both watersheds). I could not use precipitation data to assist the pairing, because the only nearby gauge (Springville Ranger Station) does not cover the necessary period of record. Furthermore, because of the lack of continuous and representative precipitation data, I could not test for peak flow trends with precipitation. I did not stratify the data between rainfall, rain-on-snow, and spring snowmelt generated peaks for two reasons: 1) without climate data, I could not be certain of the distinction between events; and 2) a separation may have resulted in too few data points for analysis.

There were three major limitations to the data from these watersheds. First, the "control" watershed is only relatively unaffected by land-cover change (see results section). However, the change in land-cover in the timber zone of the South Fork is significant enough relative to the North-Middle Fork to make comparisons. Second, the more problematic limitation is the lack of a continuous record of instantaneous peak flows for either watershed. The common period of record begins in 1940 and ends in 1989. Fortunately, this period does contain significant changes in land-cover on the South Fork. Several years of data are missing from both records and when years of non-similar peak flow events are dropped, the data set drops to only thirty pairs. The third problem is that the North-Middle Fork peak flows are affected by diversions for a hydroelectric facility. The maximum average daily diversion is 2 cms (66 cfs) (Woodward-Clyde Consultants 1985). A comparison of mean annual maximum flow between the combined river and conduit and river only indicates that the larger peak flows are not diverted. However, as flow size decreases, the influence of the diversion increases. To reduce the effect of the diversion to an acceptable level, I eliminated all flows for which more than five percent of the annual daily mean flow was diverted. This eliminated seven peak flow pairs, leaving a total of twelve (table 6). The South Fork is also diverted, but the 0.3 cms (10 cfs) (CH2M Hill 1974) is a minuscule percentage of the peak daily flows.

I analyzed the peak flow data by producing double-mass plots in which the cumulative values of peak flows in both watersheds were plotted against each other. From this plot, I looked for inflection points in the slope and compared dates of these to the dates of significant cumulative land-cover change. I separated the data set at a point that was both the most prominent break in slope and corresponded to a period of significant cumulative land-cover change from what had existed in previous years. I conducted linear regressions (least-squares method) of the South Fork (dependent variable) and the North-Middle Fork (independent variable) cumulative values for the two slopes to determine if there was a statistically significant difference between the two periods.

As a second phase of the analysis I conducted a pre- and post-ecosystem conversion analysis of the annual (i.e., not cumulative) peak flow values, based on the break in slope identified in the first analysis. I developed a linear regression for the pre-treatment period (considered the calibration period, even though land-cover change had already begun) and used this to predict South Fork peak flows from North-Middle Fork peak flows. I then plotted South Fork peak flow values with the regression line and visually compared the difference. I did not determine the statistical significance of actual South Fork peak flows compared to the predicted values, because I did not expect to find significance for individual years. The purpose of the study was to detect a change in trend rather than in individual years.

Determination of Change in Water Available for Runoff

The purpose of this assessment was to determine whether the changes in canopy cover were sufficient to increase the size of peak flows from rain-on-snow storms. Again, due to a lack of site specific data, this part of the analysis is only appropriate as an indicator of the potential for long term multiple-use management to affect rain-on-snow peak flows. The major assumptions of this analysis were: 1) the difference in snow water equivalence (SWE) before and after timber harvest equals additional water available for runoff; and 2) seasonal precipitation patterns in the Tule River watershed are similar to those in the Kings and American River watersheds (in terms of the percentage of annual precipitation delivered by a given date).

Only the first assumption is potentially problematic. The method for determining change in water available for runoff (WAR) was drawn from the watershed analysis guidelines used by the state of Washington (Washington Forest Practices Board 1994; hereafter referred to as the Board) and research conducted by Brunengo et al. (1992) in which available water is based upon varying levels of canopy cover. However, WAR only represents the increase in effective precipitation, not the increase in runoff, which is dependent upon soil properties and flow paths. Therefore, the results of this analysis will only indicate the potential change in water available for runoff in rain-on-snow storms.

Brunengo (1992) determined (empirically) that new clear-cuts retain three times as much snow on the ground as mature forest and that the difference in water available for runoff is the same ratio. The Board modified these values, assigning the difference in water available for runoff between a mature stand and a fully stocked young stand a ratio of 2. The ratio of a mature stand to an intermediate stand is 1.5. Smith and Berg (1982) presented ratios of SWE under three different canopy covers to SWE in open adjacent plots at the Central Sierra Snow Lab. For the months of January and February, the ratios for red fir averaged 0.65, meaning the open areas accumulated 1.5 times more SWE than under fir canopy. Based on these results, I assigned WAR modifiers of 0.65 for forested cover and 0.98 for logged areas (to account for minimal regrowth). These ratios reflect percentage of precipitation intercepted by canopy. I divided the watershed into hydrologic units based upon elevation and mean annual precipitation (MAP). Elevations above 1524 m (5000 ft), approximately one-third of the watershed, were demarcated as subject to rain-on-snow peaks. These elevations also coincide with most of the timber stand. WAR from the remaining watershed area was considered unchanged. The rain-on-snow zone includes four hydrologic zones ranging in MAP from 762 mm to >1,143 mm (30 in to 45 in). These zones are based on an isohyetal map produced by CH2M Hill (1974). Table 7 lists hydrologic units and associated changes in forested area.

To estimate the potential magnitude of changes in WAR from long-term logging in the upper watershed I developed two plausible scenarios of snowpack and snowmelt. Snowpack, precipitation, and temperature data were not available for the South Fork Tule watershed, so I constructed scenarios based on observations of the South Fork Tule combined with normal conditions in other Sierra Nevada watersheds within the rain-on-snow zone. I determined the potential SWE for each month based on monthly distributions of MAP in the Kings (G. M. Kondolf, University of California, Berkeley, conversation with the author, October 30, 1995) and American River watersheds (Smith and Berg 1982). For both watersheds, in an average year 25% of seasonal precipitation has fallen by mid-December. However, the 25% mark may occur as early as late-October and as late as mid-February. The average date for 50% of precipitation is late-January, with extremes of early-December and mid-March (Smith and Berg 1982). The significance of these dates is that warm rainstorms throughout the Sierra are most frequent November through January (McGurk et al. 1993) and there is a greater chance of snowpack for melting later in the season. The potential for a significant change in WAR from a rain-on-snow storm will be greatest after canopy-intercepted snow has melted and accumulation of snow in openings is greatest.

I developed a rain-on-snow scenario based on reasonable SWE values for the Tule River watershed. I determined change in WAR for each hydrologic unit and calculated a weighted total for the forest zone and for the whole watershed (table 8). The scenario assumes that the maximum SWE available for runoff equals the maximum amount of SWE that could be melted by an average, 2-year 24-hour rainstorm, which is approximately 5 cm (R.C. Kattelmann, written communication, 19 December 1995). SWE amounts for before and after logging periods were adjusted by the appropriate canopy cover ratios. I did not construct a maximum potential change in WAR scenario, because there were too many unknown variables for this watershed.

RESULTS

Land-Cover History of the South Fork Tule River Watershed

The South Fork Tule has undergone a continuous increase in cumulative land-cover change in three general spurts, all primarily within the timber zone: 1950, pre-1966, and pre-1972.

Maps and historical documents indicate that the South Fork was virtually undeveloped and unlogged from the turn-of-the-century until approximately 1950, shortly after a lumber mill was constructed on the TRIR. Conversion of the conifer forest to a logged ecosystem began at this time. Over the period 1950 to 1972, ~140 million board feet (mmbf) were logged from 4,000 ha, 46 percent of the conifer forest (Tule River Planning Commission 1973). Also by 1970, at least 540 ha of dense oak woodland had been converted to grassland. Between 1952 and 1966 area in roads more than doubled, all in the conifer forest. By 1972, there were 165 ha of roadways on the TRIR (Tule River Planning Commission 1973), primarily improved dirt and jeep trails, judging from map designations. An additional 20 to 25-km of improved roads on USFS land appear on maps between 1972 and 1984. Assuming road widths and surfaces based on USFS classifications, the 1972-1984 additional area in roads equals 13 ha.

Records of logging in the USFS section of the South Fork begin in 1961, with pieces of larger salvage cuts on neighboring watersheds occurring in 1961 and 1962. Light timber harvest continued through 1972. Between 1984 and 1989, 550 ha were clear-cut. A second boom in road construction in the conifer forest occurred between 1972 and 1984, when logging increased on the USFS land (between 1972 and 1984, these timber stands changed ownership from private inholdings to USFS). Apparently, a modest amount of timber (12 mmbf) was thinned from TRIR land from 1977 to 1987. Aerial photographs show that woodland area converted to grassland doubled by 1979. A range management plan called for a continuation of type conversion, but with an emphasis on thinning rather than clearing. By 1984, 12 to 34 years of regeneration had occurred on timber stands that had been harvested between 1950 and 1972. Not all stands had regenerated successfully (U.S. Soil Conservation Service 1979).

A conservative estimate of timber harvest over the period 1950 to 1972 is 146 mmbf on 4,210 ha, or ~50% of the conifer forest. From 1972 to 1989, approximately 18 mmbf of additional timber was harvested on 590 ha, for a total of ~56% of the forest. Road area in the entire watershed increased at minimum 170 ha between 1950 and 1984. Most of the road construction occurred in the upper watershed. This brings the altered area to ~58% of the forest zone and ~21% of the entire watershed (see table 7). These estimates do not include landings and only include roads that have been recorded on published maps.

Range reports state that the primary grazing sites were overgrazed and compaction occurred at watering sites. There is no indication as to whether grazing area and intensity increased significantly over the period of study. The oak woodland thinning and chaparral conversion that were recommended in range documents were intended to alleviate existing grazing problems and perhaps increase the herd. Compared to the harvest of over half of the timber zone, hydrologic changes from this scale of grazing management are expected to be minimal. A similar conclusion applies to rural development within the TRIR. The sources used here indicate that no significant expansion took place between 1940 and 1988.

Due to the diversity of the data sources and the patchy coverage over the study period, the estimates of land cover change are approximate. Percentages should be viewed as the magnitude of change rather than precise values. The greatest uncertainty lies in the rate of logging that occurred between 1950 and 1970. This point is important in determining the amount and age of regrowth that occurred by the end of the study period.

Peak Flows

The double-mass plot of cumulative peak flow showed a definite break in slope occurring sometime after 1950 (figure 3). The points for years 1967 and 1969 fall where the break in slope begins and could go with either slope. Because the land-cover change was cumulative, it is likely that the change became significant enough to affect a detectable change in peak flows by 1967, around seventeen years after timber harvest began. By 1966, road area in the timber zone had doubled. Hence, I separated the pre- and post-periods at water year 1967: the period before significant land-cover change is 1940 to 1963 (5 flows); the significantly altered land-cover period is 1967 to 1988 (7 flows) (see table 6 for Q2 and larger size flows in each period).

The results of the linear regressions for South Fork versus North-Middle Fork cumulative peak flows for each period are shown in figure 4. The slope of the double-mass plots for the before and after periods are 0.62 and 1.25, respectively. The fit is very high for both slopes, with the North-Middle Fork explaining 98% and 99% of variation in the South Fork for the before and after periods, respectively. Most importantly, there is no overlap in slope between the two periods (the 95% confidence intervals for each slope do not overlap with each other), indicating a statistically significant difference in trend between the two periods.

A second method of viewing the results was to generate a pre-conversion relationship of individual peak flows (i.e. non-cumulative), predict the post-conversion South Fork values, and plot the calibration slope with the observed values. Figure 5 shows that five of the seven post-conversion peak flows fall above the regression line, meaning that the pre-conversion relationship underestimates these post-change peak flows. No statistical significance is implied from this plot.

Change in Water Available for Runoff (WAR) in Rain-on-Snow Zone

The hypothetical SWE and storms produced only slight increases in WAR between the pre- and post-logging periods (table 8). Increases of 10% or more were only produced on the headwaters. The lack of change in the lower part of the watershed masked the increases in WAR from the upper watershed. The scenario resulted in increases of WAR of 6 to 15-mm , with the highest increase generated from the hydrologic unit with the highest precipitation and greatest area logged. The area-weighted increase in WAR was 9 mm (5%) across the forest zone and 3 mm (5%) for the whole watershed. Although I did not determine a test for the statistical significance of the changes in WAR, these values would be within the margin of error of USGS stream gauge data.

DISCUSSION

Peak Flows

These results indicate the primary factors altering conditions in the South Fork Tule watershed are timber harvest and road construction. Although the effects of each factor cannot be conclusively separated, the more drastic factor in terms of watershed area is the amount of forest removed from logging. Results also suggest that logging dominated multiple-use management may be associated with increased peak flows on the South Fork Tule River. The effects of fire-suppression in the North-Middle Fork may also reduce peak flows in that watershed, accounting for the perceived increase in the South Fork. However, the 40% of the

South Fork timber zone that was not logged has also been managed under a fire-suppression policy since the 1900s. It is unlikely that the forest canopy of the North-Middle Fork could have increased nearly as much as forest canopy has been reduced on the South Fork. Competition for water, light, and soil nutrients would put a limit on the amount increased density, even without fire.

The hypothetical WAR results indicate that the amount of timber harvest documented for the South Fork may be sufficient to increase WAR, hence peak flows. However, the method used to estimate changes in WAR from timber harvest probably underestimates potential increases. The method accounts for reduced canopy interception from clear-cutting, but does not incorporate the greater potential for snowmelt in the openings. Because I did not develop a relationship between increase in WAR and increase in peak flow (primarily due to the fact that WAR is more a factor of wind speed than storm size), I cannot conclude the magnitude of an increase in peak flows, nor can I determine the recurrence interval in question. If the watershed soils were previously saturated from prior snowmelt one could assume that any increase in WAR (especially from a cleared area) would translate to stormflow. This assumption would also be valid due to the extremely permeable soils underlain by unfractured bedrock. If one assumes that the 2-year storm typically generates a 2-year peak flow, a rough analysis of the effect of increased WAR on a potential channel-forming flow may be made. Under these conditions, the increase in WAR of 5% across the watershed would not increase the Q2 flow to Q5 size for this hypothetical example. Increases in peak flows could still be significant to channel geomorphology in headwater streams within the forested zone. Furthermore, without monitoring of streamflow and beneficial uses specific to this and similar Sierra watersheds, one cannot conclude that no negative effects will occur from these increases in peak flow.

A weakness of this study is the small data set. Although the period of record covers years 1940 to 1989 (with a few missing years), only twelve pairs of Q2 and larger annual peak flows could be matched. Since climate data were not readily available for the two watersheds, I could not completely rule out the possibility that climate change has affected the records of either watershed. Some researchers have documented a decrease in April to July runoff relative to total annual runoff from Sierran watersheds (Roos 1991). This trend may instead be viewed as an increase in total annual runoff concentrated in winter runoff (Wahl 1991). This trend would indicate an increase in rain-dominated winter storms or in winter and early spring snowmelt due to increasing temperatures (Pupacko 1993). If there has been a change in climate exposing snowpack to warm storms, the effect on peak flows would be greater in a watershed that had been extensively logged.

The Roles of Historical Trend Studies and Controlled Experiments in Determining the Effects of Multiple-use

The only non-modeling investigations of the long-term effects of "ecosystem conversion" on peak flows in the Sierra Nevada are post-watershed change assessments. Because these studies are conducted after land-use and land-cover change have occurred and do not conform to the requirements of a controlled catchment experiment, many researchers are reluctant to accept the results. However, these studies provide information that the controlled catchment experiments are incapable of providing: a case study of watershed management conducted with the complexities and problems of multiple-use policies. Controlled experiments are essential to tease out the hydrological effects of specific actions, such as removing vegetation, while holding all other factors equal. However, the typical short-term controlled experiment cannot capture the hydrological effects of long-term interacting changes in natural factors such as climate, fire, and insect populations. Nor can controlled experiments simulate the individual and cumulative effects of a commercial timber harvest conducted under a variety of constraints; residential development patterns; or political and economic pressure to protect or exploit a variety of natural resources within the watershed. The results of controlled experiments may be used to develop comprehensive models, calibrated by real data, capable of simulating past or future hydrologic change, but the accuracy of the results and conclusions are dependent upon the factors used to develop the model. Calibration does not make up for missing components or gaps in theory.

Post-treatment research is invaluable in that it checks the assumptions and results of controlled experiments and modeling simulations. Vegetation management in actual practice will rarely approximate the "treatment watershed" in a controlled experiment. Typically, there will be other practices occurring upstream or downstream in the watershed, prescribed Best Management Practices (BMPs) will have to be altered to fit the budget of the project, as will "programmed" watershed restoration projects. The effects of past management choices will unexpectedly crop up (e.g. sediment wedges accumulating behind rotting culverts). Also, hydrological theory is not completely developed, and modeling simulations may fit a data set while masking effects. For example, a study on the effects of timber harvest on peak flows in an Oregon watershed concluded that peaks were unaffected by harvest. Although the test was statistically correct, the experiment method masked the changes in peak flows caused by rain-on-snow storms (Harr 1986).

Long-term monitoring of land-cover change and hydrologic response would both demonstrate the usefulness of controlled experiments for predicting the important consequences of land-use choices and call attention to the potential gaps in theory. USGS gauge data is a potential source of this long-term monitoring. Preferably, USGS monitoring would have been conducted with ecological assessments in mind, from implementation of gauges, through changes in land use, to the present. However, historical reconstructions are possible and wherever continuous gauge data exists, there is a potential to discover what really happens to a hydrologic system when its watershed is progressively converted to a full-fledged human ecosystem. Then, supplemented with findings from controlled experiments and modeling, the complex webs of cause and effect may be unraveled.

CONCLUSIONS

Analyses of land-cover change, potential increase in water available for runoff, and channel-forming (annual series) peak flows were conducted to determine the long-term effects of watershed conversion to a logged ecosystem. Over the period 1940 to 1989, land-cover had changed significantly on the South Fork Tule, primarily in the form of timber harvest and new road construction. Beginning around 1950, cumulative land-conversion progressed slowly until sometime prior to 1966, at which point the rate of conversion increased. The forest zone canopy was reduced by at least 58%. Across the watershed, the forest and woodland was reduced by at least 21%.

The significant cumulative change in land-cover corresponded to an inflection point found in a double-mass plot of South Fork (dependent variable) and North-Middle Fork (independent variable) peak flows. Separation of the slope at the inflection point, between water years 1963 and 1967, produced two slopes without overlapping confidence intervals (95%). The slope of the post-conversion period peaks was double the slope of the pre-conversion period. Thus, the increase in peak flows tracked with time and cumulative logging and road construction. The analysis did not determine the size of the increase.

Two hypothetical rain-on-snow storms with varying amounts of snowpack indicated that the decrease in canopy cover resulting in increased snowpack subject to latent and sensible heat flux may be responsible for at least part of the increased peak flows. The hypothetical snowpack and storm scenarios were insufficient to increase the Q2 to the Q5 peak flow size.

REFERENCES

Alexander, P. R., and R. K. Watkins. 1977. The Fraser experimental forest, Colorado. General Technical Report RM-40. Fort Collins, CO: U.S. Forest Service, Rocky Mountain Forest and Range Experiment Station.

Bassman, R. 1974. The 1897 Organic Act: a historical perspective. Natural Resources Lawyer 7(3): 503-20.

Bates, C. G., and A. J. Henry. 1928. Forest and streamflow experiments at Wagon Wheel Gap, Colorado. U.S. Weather Bureau, Monthly Weather Review, Supplement. No. 30.

Batini, F. E., R. E. Black, J. Byrne, and P. J. Clifford. 1980. An examination of the effects of changes in catchment condition on water yield in the Wungong catchment, Western Australia. Australian Forestry Research 10:29-38.

Berris, S. N., and R. D. Harr. 1987. Comparative snow accumulation and melt during rainfall in forested and clear-cut plots in the western Cascades of Oregon. Water Resources Research 23(1): 135-42.

Bjornn, T. C., and D. W. Reiser. 1991. Habitat requirements of salmonids in streams. In Influences of forest and rangeland management on salmonid fishes and their habitats, edited by W. R. Meehan, 83-138. Bethesda, MD: American Fisheries Society.

Bochkov, A. P. 1970. Review of the catchment experiment to determine water yield. In Proceedings: Joint U.N. Food and Agriculture Organization - U.S.S.R. international symposium on forest influences and watershed management, 93-108. Rome: Food and Agriculture Organization.

Bosch, J. M. 1979. Treatment effects on annual and dry period streamflow at Cathedral Peak. South African Forestry Journal 108: 29-38.

Bosch, J. M., and J. D. Hewlett. 1982. A review of catchment experiments to determine the effect of vegetation changes on water yield and evapotranspiration. Journal of Hydrology 55(1/4): 3-23.

Brown, H. E. 1971. Evaluating watershed management alternatives. Journal of Irrigation and Drainage, 97(IR1): 93-108.

Brunengo, M. J., S. D. Smith, and S. C. Bernath. 1992. A GIS-based method of modeling water input from rain-on-snow storms, for management and regulation of clearcut forest harvest. Proceedings of the Western Snow Conference 60: 125-28.

Burgy, R. H., and A. G. Papazafiriou. 1971. Vegetation management and water yield relationships. In 3rd International Seminar on the Hydrologic Profession. Lafayette, IN: Purdue University.

Bush, R. D., and I. L. Sealander. 1970. An assessment of the resources and grazing management problems on the Tule River Indian Reservation. Visalia, CA: U.S. Soil Conservation Service.

Calder, I. R. 1993. The Balquhidder catchment balance and process experiment results in context -- What do they reveal? Journal of Hydrology 145: 467-80.

California Department of Forestry and Fire Protection. 1988. California's forests and rangelands: Growing conflict over changing uses; an assessment. Sacramento: California Department of Forestry and Fire Protection, Forest and Rangeland Resources Assessment Program.

California Department of Water Resources. 1960. Upper Tule River reconnaissance investigation. Bulletin no. 82. Sacramento: California Department of Water Resources, Division of Resources Planning.

California Department of Water Resources. 1964. Land and water use in Tule River hydrographic unit. Bulletin no. 94-1. Sacramento: California Department of Water Resources.

Callaham, R. Z. 1990. Case studies and catalog of watershed projects in western provinces and states. Report 22. Berkeley: University of California, Wildland Resources Center.

CH2M Hill. 1974. Water resources inventory, Tule River Indian Reservation, Tulare County. Sacramento: Tribal Council and Bureau of Indian Affairs.

Chamberlin, T. W., R. D. Harr, and F. H. Everest. 1991. Timber harvesting, silviculture, and watershed processes. In Influences of forest and rangeland management on salmonid fishes and their habitats, edited by W. R. Meehan, 181-206. Bethesda, MD: American Fisheries Society.

Cheng, J. D. 1989. Streamflow changes after clear-cut logging of a pine beetle-infested watershed in southern British Columbia, Canada. Water Resources Research 25(3): 449-56.

Christner, J., and R. D. Harr. 1982. Peak streamflows from the transient snow zone, western Cascades, Oregon. Proceedings of the Western Snow Conference 50: 27-38.

Clary, W. P., M. B. Baker Jr., P. F. O'Connell, T. N. Johnsen Jr., and R. E. Campbell. 1974. Effects of pinyon-juniper removal on natural resource products and uses in Arizona. Research Paper RM-128. Fort Collins, CO: U.S. Forest Service, Rocky Mountain Forest and Range Experiment Station.

Coats, R. N., and T. O. Miller. 1981. Cumulative silvicultural impacts on watersheds: A hydrologic and regulatory dilemma. Environmental Management 5(2): 147-60.

David, J. S., M. O. Henriques, T. S. David, J. Tomé, and D. C. Ledger. 1994. Clear-cutting effects on streamflow in coppiced Eucalyptus globulus stands in Portugal. Journal of Hydrology 162: 143-54.

Dean, W. W. 1972. Flood of December 1966 in the Kern-Kaweah Area, Kern and Tulare Counties, California. Water-supply Paper 1870-C. Menlo Park, CA: U.S. Geological Survey.

Douglass, J. E. and W. T. Swank. 1976. Multiple use in southern Appalachian hardwoods - a ten year case history. Proceedings: 16th International Union of Forest Resources Organization (I.U.F.R.O.) world congress, 425-36. Oslo: I.U.F.R.O.

Dunne, T., and L. B. Leopold. 1978. Water in environmental planning. San Francisco: W. H. Freeman.

Eagleson, P. S., and R. I. Segarra. 1985. Water limited equilibrium of savanna vegetation systems. Water Resources Research 21(10): 1483-93.

Eschner, A. R. 1965. Forest protection and streamflow from an Adirondack watershed. Ph.D. dissertation, State College of Forestry, Syracuse, NY.

Euphrat, F. D. 1992. Cumulative impact assessment and mitigation for the middle fork of the Mokelumne River, Calaveras County. Ph.D. dissertation, University of California, Berkeley, Wildland Resource Science.

Furniss, M. J., T. D. Roelofs, and C. S. Yee. 1991. Road construction and maintenance. In Influences of forest and rangeland management on salmonid fishes and their habitats, edited by W. R. Meehan, 297-324. Bethesda, MD: American Fisheries Society.

Goldstein, R. A., J. B. Manken, and R. J. Luxmoore. 1974. Documentation of PROSPER: A model of atmosphere-soil-water flow. Environmental Science Division, Publ. No. 579.

Gottfried, G, J. 1991. Moderate timber harvesting increases water yields from an Arizona mixed conifer watershed. Water Resources Bulletin. 27(3): 537-47.

Gray, D. H., and W. F. Megahan. 1981. Forest vegetation removal and slope stability in the Idaho Batholith. Research Paper INT-271. Logan, UT: U.S. Forest Service, Intermountain Forest and Range Experiment Station.

Greenwood, E. A., L. Klein, J. D. Beresford, G. D. Watson, and K. D. Wright. 1985. Evaporation from the understorey of the Jarrah Forest, SW Australia. Journal of Hydrology 80: 337-49.

Harr, R. D. 1975. Changes in storm hydrographs after road building and clear-cutting in the Oregon Coast Range. Water Resources Research 11(3):436-44.

___. 1976. Forest practices and streamflow in western Oregon. General Technical Report PNW-49. Corvallis, OR: U.S. Forest Service,

___. 1980. Streamflow after patch logging in small drainages within the Bull Run municipal watershed, Oregon. Research Paper PNW-268. Corvallis, OR: U.S. Forest Service, Pacific Northwest Forest and Range Experiment Station.

___. 1981. Some characteristics and consequences of melt from shallow snowpacks during rainfall in western Oregon. Journal of Hydrology 53: 277-304.

182

___. 1983. Potential for augmenting water yield through forest practices in western Washington and western Oregon. <u>Water Resources Bulletin</u> 19(3): 383-93.

___. 1986. Effects of clear-cutting on rain-on-snow runoff in western Oregon: A new look at old studies. <u>Water Resources Research</u> 22(7): 1095-1100.

Harr, R. D., and R. L. Fredriksen. 1988. Water quality after logging small watersheds within the Bull Run watershed, Oregon. <u>Water Resources Bulletin</u> 24(5): 1103-12.

Harr, R. D., R. L. Fredriksen, and J. Rothacher. 1979. <u>Changes in streamflow following timber harvest in southwestern Oregon.</u> Research Paper PNW-249. Corvallis, OR: U.S. Forest Service, Pacific Northwest Forest and Range Experiment Station.

Harr, R. D., A. Levno, and R. Mersereau. 1982. Changes in streamflow after logging 130-year-old Douglas-fir in two small watersheds in western Oregon. <u>Water Resources Research</u> 18(3): 637-44.

Harr, R. D., and F. M. McCorison. 1979. Initial effects of clearcut logging on size and timing of peak flows in a small watershed in western Oregon. <u>Water Resources Research</u> 15(1): 90-94.

Harris, D. D. 1973. Hydrologic changes after clear-cut logging in a small Oregon coastal watershed. <u>U.S. Geological Survey Journal of Research</u> 1(4): 487-91.

___. 1977. <u>Hydrologic changes after logging in two small Oregon coastal watersheds.</u> Water-Supply Paper 2037. Menlo Park, CA: U.S. Geological Survey.

Heede, B. H., and R. M. King. 1990. State-of-the-art timber harvest in an Arizona mixed conifer forest has minimal effect on overland flow and erosion. <u>Hydrological Sciences</u> 35(6): 623-35.

Helvey, J. D. 1973. Watershed behavior after forest fire in Washington. In <u>Proceedings of the ASCE, Irrigation and Drainage Division, Special Conference</u>, 402-22. New York: American Society of Civil Engineers.

___. 1980. Effect of a north-central Washington wild-fire on runoff and sediment production. <u>Water Resources Bulletin</u> 16(4):625-34.

Hewlett, J. D. 1970. Review of the catchment experiment to determine water yield. In <u>Proceedings. Joint U.N. Food and Agriculture Organization - U.S.S.R. international symposium on forest influences and watershed management</u>, 145-55. Rome: Food and Agriculture Organization.

___. 1979. <u>Forest water quality: an experiment in harvesting and regenerating piedmont forest.</u> Research Paper. Athens, GA: University of Georgia, School of Forestry Resources.

Hewlett, J. D. and J. E. Douglass. 1968. Blending forest uses. <u>U.S. Forest Service Research Paper</u>, SE-37.

Hewlett, J. D., and A. R. Hibbert. 1961. Increases in water yield after several types of forest cutting. <u>International Association of Scientific Hydrology Bulletin</u> 6(3): 5-17.

Hibbert, A. R. 1967. Forest treatment effects on water yield. In <u>Forest Hydrology</u>, edited by W. E. Sopper and H. E. Lull. New York: Pergamon Press.

___ 1979. <u>Managing vegetation to increase flow in the Colorado River basin.</u> General Technical Report RM-66. Fort Collins, CO: U.S. Forest Service, Rocky Mountain Forest and Range Experiment Station.

___ 1983. Water yield improvement potential by vegetation management on western rangelands. <u>Water Resources Bulletin</u> 19(3): 375-81.

Hibbert, A. R., and G. J. Gottfried. 1987. Stormflow responses to forest treatments on two Arizona mixed conifer watersheds. In <u>Management of subalpine forests: Building on 50 years of research,</u> 189-94. General Technical Report RM-149. Fort Collins, CO: U.S. Forest Service, Rocky Mountain Forest and Range Experiment Station.

Hibbert, A. R., O. D. Knipe, and E. A. Davis. 1986. Streamflow response to control of chaparral shrubs along channels and upper slopes. In <u>Proceedings of the chaparral ecosystems conference, Santa Barbara</u>, edited by J. DeVries, 95-103. Report 62. Davis: University of California, Water Resources Center.

Hicks, J. H., R. L. Beschta, and R. D. Harr. 1991. Long-term changes in streamflow following logging in western Oregon and associated fisheries implications. <u>Water Resources Bulletin</u> 27(2): 217-26.

Hornbeck, J. W. 1975. Streamflow response to forest cutting and vegetation. <u>Water Resources Research</u> 11: 1257-60.

Ingebo, P. A., and A. R. Hibbert. 1974. <u>Runoff and erosion after brush suppression on the natural drainage watersheds in central Arizona.</u> Research Note RM-275. Fort Collins, CO: U.S. Forest Service, Rocky Mountain Forest and Range Experiment Station.

Johnson, M. G., and R. L. Beschta. 1980. Logging, infiltration capacity, and surface erodibility in western Oregon. <u>Journal of Forestry</u> 78(6): 334-37.

Kattelmann, R. C. 1982. Water yield improvement in the Sierra Nevada snow zone: 1912-1982. Proceedings of the Western Snow Conference 50: 39-48.

___. 1987. Feasibility of more water from Sierra Nevada forests. Report No. 16. Berkeley: University of California Wildland Resources Center.

Kattelmann, R., N. Berg, and B. McGurk. 1991. A history of rain-on-snow floods in the Sierra Nevada. In Proceedings of the Western Snow Conference 59: 138-41.

Kattelmann, R. C., N. H. Berg, and J. Rector. 1983. The potential for increasing streamflow from Sierra Nevada watersheds. Water Resources Bulletin 19(3): 395-402.

Kattelmann, R. C., N. H. Berg, and J. Rector. 1984. Reply to discussion by K. M. Turner. Water Resources Bulletin 20(3): 455-56.

Kaufmann, M. R., C. A. Troendle, M. G. Ryan, and H. T. Mowrer. 1987. Trees--the link between silviculture and hydrology. 54-60. General Technical Report RM-149. Fort Collins, CO: U.S. Forest Service, Rocky Mountain Forest and Range Experiment Station

Knoerr, K. R. 1960. Exponential depletion of soil moisture in the Sierra Nevada. Ph.D. dissertation, Yale University, New Haven, CN.

Lewis, D. C. 1968. Annual hydrologic response to watershed conversion from oak woodland to annual grassland. Water Resources Research 4(1): 59-72.

Lisle, T. E. 1981. The recovery of aggraded stream channels at gauging stations in northern California and southern Oregon. In Erosion and sediment transport in Pacific Rim steep lands, 188-211. Publication 132. Wallingford, England: International Association of Hydrological Sciences.

Love, L. D. 1955. The effect on streamflow of the killing of spruce and pine by the Engelmann spruce beetle. Transactions American Geophysical Union 36(1): 113-18.

MacDonald, L. H. 1989. Snowmelt and streamflow in the central Sierra Nevada: effects of forest harvest and cloud seeding. Ph.D. Dissertation, Department of Forestry, University of California, Berkeley.

MacDonald, L. H. and J. A. Hoffman. 1995. Causes of peak flows in northwestern Montana and northeastern Idaho. Water Resources Bulletin 31(1): 79-95.

MacDonald, L. H., A. W. Smart, and R. L. Wissmar. 1991. Monitoring guidelines to evaluate effects of forestry activities on streams in the Pacific Northwest and Alaska. Report EPA/910/9-91-001. Seattle: U.S. Environmental Protection Agency.

Martin, I. L. and E. R. Tinney. 1962. Logging in west coast watershed shows no effects on the area's water yield. Timberman May: 46-48.

McCammon, B. 1977. Salmon Creek administrative study. Unpublished report, U.S. Forest Service, Sequoia National Forest, Porterville, CA.

McGurk, B. J., and M. L. Davis. 1996. Camp and Clear Creeks, El Dorado County: Chronology and hydrologic effects of land-use change. In Sierra Nevada Ecosystem Project: Final report to Congress, vol. II, chapter 55. Davis: University of California, Centers for Water and Wildland Resources.

McGurk, B. J., N. H. Berg, and R. C. Kattelmann. 1993. Identification and regional/spatial extent of rain-dominated winter storms in California's Sierra Nevada. Proceedings of the Western Snow Conference 61: 67-74.

Meehan, W. R., ed. 1991. Influences of forest and rangeland management on salmonid fishes and their habitats. Special Publication 19. Bethesda, MD: American Fisheries Society.

Megahan, W. F. and D. C. Molitor. 1975. Erosional effects of wildfire and logging in Idaho. In Watershed Management Symposium, 423-44. New York: American Society of Civil Engineers.

Pupacko, A. 1993. Variations in northern Sierra Nevada streamflow: Implications of climate change. Water Resources Bulletin 29(2): 283-90.

Reid, L. M. 1993. Research and cumulative watershed effects. General Technical Report PSW-GTR-141. Albany, CA: U.S. Forest Service, Pacific Southwest Research Station.

Rice, R. M., and J. R. Wallis. 1962. How a logging operation can affect streamflow. Forest Industries 89(11): 38-40.

Rich, L. R. 1968. Preliminary water yields after timber harvest on Castle Creek, Arizona watersheds. In Proceedings of the Arizona Watershed Symposium, 12: 9-12.

___. 1972. Managing a ponderosa pine forest to increase water yield. Water Resources. Research 8(2): 422-28.

Rich, L. R., and G. J. Gottfried. 1976. Water yields resulting from treatments on the Workman Creek experimental watersheds in central Arizona. Water Resources Research 12(5): 1053-60.

Rich, L. R., H. G. Reynolds, and J. A. West. 1961. The Workman Creek experimental watershed. Research Paper RM-65. Fort Collins, CO: U.S. Forest Service, Rocky Mountain Forest and Range Experiment Station.

Rich, L. R., and J. R. Thompson. 1974. Watershed management in Arizona's mixed conifer forests: The status of our knowledge. Research Paper RM-130. Fort Collins, CO: U.S. Forest Service, Rocky Mountain Forest and Range Experiment Station.

Romm, J. M., and A. Ewing. 1987. The economic value of water in national forest management. In Proceedings of the California watershed management conference, edited by R. Z. Callaham and J. J. DeVries, 89-102. Report No. 11. Berkeley: University of California, Wildland Resources Center.

Romm, J. M., R. Z. Callaham, and R. C. Kattelmann. 1988. Toward managing Sierra Nevada forests for water supply. Report No. 17. Berkeley: University of California, Wildland Resources Center.

Roos, M. 1991. A trend of decreasing snowmelt runoff in northern California. Proceedings of the Western Snow Conference 59: 29-36.

Rothacher, J. 1970. Increases in water yield following clear-cut logging in the Pacific Northwest. Water Resources. Research 6(2): 653-58.

Rowe, P. B. 1963. Streamflow increases after removing woodland riparian vegetation from a southern California watershed. Journal of Forestry 61: 365-70.

Schneider, J., and G. R. Ayer. 1961. Effect of reforestation on streamflow in central New York. Water-Supply Paper 1602. Reston, VA: U.S. Geological Survey.

Smith, J. L., and N. H. Berg. 1982. The Sierra ecology project, Volume III. Berkeley: U.S. Forest Service, Pacific Southwest Forest and Range Experiment Station.

Smith, J. L., and H. G. Halverson. 1969. Hydrology of snow profiles obtained with the profiling snow gage. In Proceedings of the Western Snow Conference 37: 41-48.

Sopper, W. E. 1971. Water supply augmentation by watershed management in wildland areas. Report NWC71-008. Washington, DC: U.S. National Water Commission.

Stabler, F. 1985. Increasing summer flow in small streams through management of riparian areas and adjacent vegetation: A synthesis. 201-10. General Technical Report RM-120. Fort Collins, CO: U.S. Forest Service, Rocky Mountain Forest and Range Experiment Station

Steen, H. K. 1976. The U.S. Forest Service: A history. Seattle: University of Washington Press.

Subbotin, A. I. 1970. Review of the catchment experiment to determine water yield. In Proceedings. Joint U.N. Food and Agriculture Organization - U.S.S.R. international symposium on forest influences and watershed management, 156-62. Rome: Food and Agriculture Organization.

Swank, W. T., and J. E. Douglass. 1974. Streamflow greatly reduced by converting deciduous hardwood stands to pine. Science 185: 857-59.

Swank, W. T., and J. D. Helvey. 1970. Reduction of streamflow increases following regrowth of clear-cut hardwood forests. In Symposium on results of research on representative and experimental basins, 346-360. Publication no. 96. Wallingford, England: International Association of Hydrologic Sciences.

Swank, W. T., and N. H. Miner. 1968. Conversion of hardwood-covered watersheds to white pine reduces water yield. Water Resources Research 4(5): 947-54.

Swanston, D. N. 1991. Natural processes. In Influences of forest and rangeland management on salmonid fishes and their habitats, edited by W. R. Meehan, 139-179. Bethesda, MD: American Fisheries Society.

Troendle, C. A., 1983. The potential for water yield augmentation from forest management in the Rocky Mountain region. Water Resources Bulletin 19: 359-73.

Troendle, C. A., and R. M. King. 1985. The effect of timber harvest on the Fool Creek watershed, 30 years later. Water Resources Research 21(12): 1915-22.

____. 1987. The effect of partial and clearcutting on streamflow at Deadhorse Creek, Colorado. Journal of Hydrology 90: 145-57.

Tule River Planning Commission. 1973. Comprehensive development plan, Tule River Indian Reservation. Porterville, CA.: Tule River Planning Commission, Tribal Office.

Turner, K. M. 1987. Vegetation management for water supply augmentation. In Proceedings of the California watershed management conference, edited by R. Z. Callaham and J. J. DeVries, 65-67. Report No. 11. Berkeley: University of California, Wildland Resources Center.

___. 1991. Water salvage from Mediterranean-type ecosystems. In Water supply and water reuse: 1991 and beyond, 83-90. Bethesda, MD: American Water Resources Association.

___. 1993. Water harvesting/salvage: coming of age, unpublished paper presented at Weeds and people, putting weed management in perspective, 45th annual weed conference. Costa Mesa, CA.

U.S. Environmental Protection Agency. 1980. An approach to water resources evaluation of non-point silvicultural sources (A procedural handbook). Publication EPA-600/8-/80-012.

U.S. Forest Service. 1984. Determining water yields and values for the Sequoia National Forest Planning Area. Unpublished report. Porterville, CA: U.S. Forest Service, Sequoia National Forest.

___. 1988. Sequoia National Forest land and resource management plan and environmental impact statement. San Francisco: U. S. Forest Service, Pacific Southwest Region.

___. 1990. Tahoe National Forest land and resource management plan and final environmental impact statement. San Francisco: U.S. Forest Service, Pacific Southwest Region.

U.S. Soil Conservation Service. 1979. Tule River Indian Reservation range conservation plan. Visalia, CA: Tulare County Range Conservation District.

Wahl, K. L. 1991. Is April to July runoff really decreasing in the western United States? In Proceedings of the Western Snow Conference 59: 67-78.

Washington Forest Practices Board 1994. Board manual: Standard methodology for conducting watershed analysis, Version 2.1. Seattle: Washington Forest Practices Board.

Whitehead, P. H., and I. R. Calder, eds. 1993. The Balquhidder experimental catchments. Journal of Hydrology 145: 215-480.

Woodward-Clyde Consultants. 1985. Tule River Project (FERC 1333) fisheries technical report. San Ramon, CA: Pacific Gas and Electric Company, Department of Engineering Research.

Wright, K. A., K. H. Sendek, R. M. Rice, and R. B. Thomas. 1990. Logging effects on streamflow: storm runoff at Caspar Creek in northwestern California. Water Resources Research 26(7): 1657-67.

Ziemer, R. R. 1981. Streamflow response to road building and partial cutting in small streams of northern California. Water Resources Research 17(4): 907-17.

Ziemer, R. R. 1986. Water yields from forests: An agnostic view. In Proceedings of the California watershed management conference, edited by R. Z. Callaham and J. J. DeVries. Report No. 11. Berkeley: University of California, Wildland Resources Center.

Table 1. Western United States water yield experiments used in regression analysis

Location	Study site	Type of study	Percentage of watershed treated	Mean Annual Precipitation MAP (mm)	Mean Annual Flow MAF (mm)	MAF/MAP Ratio	Increase in Flow (mm)	References	Study No.
Beaver Creek, AZ	WS 1	paired catchment	100%	457	20	0.04	0	Brown (1971); Clary et al. (1974); Hibbert (1979)	10
Beaver Creek, AZ	WS 3	paired catchment	83%	457	18	0.04	11.4	Brown (1971); Clary et al. (1974); Hibbert (1979)	11
Beaver Creek, AZ	WS 6	paired catchment	100%	508	67	0.13	11.3	Brown (1971); Clary et al. (1974)	12
Beaver Creek, AZ	WS 12	paired catchment	100%	621	152	0.24	68.7	Brown (1971)	13
Beaver Creek, AZ	WS 9	paired catchment	33%	686	172	0.25	72.9	Brown (1971)	15
Castle Creek, AZ	West Fork	paired catchment	100%	639	71	0.11	16.5	Rich (1968, 1972); Rich and Thompson (1974)	16
Coyote Creek, OR	1	paired catchment	50%	1229	627	0.51	60	Harr (1976, 1983); Harr et al. (1979)	40
Coyote Creek, OR	2	paired catchment	30%	1229	643	0.52	90	Harr (1976, 1983); Harr et al. (1979)	41
Coyote Creek, OR	3	paired catchment	100%	1229	674	0.55	290	Harr (1976, 1983); Harr et al. (1979)	42
Deadhorse Creek, CO	North Fork	paired catchment	36%	648	147	0.23	75	Alexander and Watkins (1977); Troendle (1983); Troendle and King (1987)	43
Entiat, WA	McCree	uncontrolled for climate	100%	579	112	0.19	91	Helvey (1973, 1980)	45
Entiat, WA	Burns	uncontrolled for climate	100%	597	155	0.26	74	Helvey (1973, 1980)	46
Entiat, WA	Fox	uncontrolled for climate	100%	-	175	-	112	Helvey (1973, 1980)	47
Fox Creek, OR	FC-1	paired catchment	25%	2790	2710	.97	0	Harr (1976, 1980); Harr and Fredriksen (1988)	60
Fox Creek, OR	FC-3	paired catchment	25%	2840	2350	0.83	0	Harr (1976, 1980); Harr and Fredriksen (1988)	61
Frazer, CO	Fool Creek	paired catchment	40%	762	283	0.37	115	Alexander and Watkins (1977); Troendle and King (1985)	62
H.J. Andrews, OR	WS 1	paired catchment	100%	2388	1376	0.58	418	Rothacher (1970, 1973); Harr (1976, 1986); Harr et al. (1979) Hicks, Beschta, and Harr (1991)	64

187

Table 1 (Continued)

Location	Study site	Type of study	Percentage of watershed treated	Mean annual precipitation MAP (mm)	Mean annual flow MAF (mm)	MAF/MAP ratio	Increase in flow (mm)	References	Study No.
H.J. Andrews, OR	WS 3	paired catchment	25%	2388	1346	0.56	218	Rothacher (1970); Harr (1976, 1986); Harr et al. (1979); Hicks, Beschta, and Harr (1991)	65
H.J. Andrews, OR	WS 6	paired catchment	100%	2150	1290	0.60	322	Rothacher (1970); Harr (1976); Harr et al. (1979)	66
H.J. Andrews, OR	WS 7	paired catchment	60%	2150	1290	0.60	176	Rothacher (1970); Harr (1976); Harr et al. (1979)	67
H.J. Andrews, OR	WS 10	paired catchment	100%	2330	1650	0.71	243	Rothacher (1970); Harr (1976, 1986); Harr et al. (1979)	68
Meeker, CO	White River	uncontrolled for climate	30%	400	261	0.65	39	Love (1955)	92
Salmon Creek, CA	Burton	paired catchment	25%	953	157	0.16	0	McCammon (1977)	104
Sierra Ancha, AZ	North Fork, Workman Creek (a)	paired catchment	32%	813	86	0.11	31.4	Rich et al. (1961); Ingebo and Hibbert (1974); Rich and Gottfried (1976); Hibbert (1979)	108
Sierra Ancha, AZ	North Fork, Workman Creek (b)	paired catchment	73%	813	86	0.11	76.6	Rich et al. (1961); Rich and Gottfried (1976); Hibbert (1979)	109
Sierra Ancha, AZ	South Fork, Workman Creek (a)	paired catchment	45%	813	87	0.11	0	Rich et al. (1961); Rich and Gottfried (1976); Hibbert (1979)	111
Sierra Ancha, AZ	South Fork, Workman Creek (b)	paired catchment	83%	813	87	0.11	93	Rich et al. (1961); Ingebo and Hibbert (1974); Rich and Gottfried (1976); Hibbert (1979)	300
Wagon Wheel Gap, CO	B	paired catchment	100%	536	157	0.30	28.2	Bates and Henry (1928); Reinhart et al. (1963); Van Haveren (1981)	123
Deadhorse Creek, CO	Inter-basin area	paired catchment	28%	-	-	-	0	Alexander and Watkins (1977); Troendle (1983); Troendle and King (1987)	210
Deadhorse Creek, CO	North Slope (8)	paired catchment	40%	-	-	-	0	Alexander and Watkins (1977); Troendle (1983); Troendle and King (1987)	211
Thomas Creek, AZ	South Fork	paired catchment	34%	768	82	0.11	44	Gottfried (1991)	301

Table 2. Site features of water yield experiments used in regression analysis

Location	Study Site	Drainage Area (ha)	Mid-area Elevation (m)	Aspect	Percent Slope	Vegetation	Soils	Soil Depth (cm)	Treatment	Study No.
Beaver Creek, AZ	WS 1	124	1700	W	21%	Utah juniper-pinyon forest	volcanic rock, soils stoney clay	<60	cleared by cabling and burning	10
Beaver Creek, AZ	WS 3	146	1600	W	7%	Utah juniper-pinyon forest	volcanic rock, soils stoney clay	<60	herbicide application to overstory, no vegetation removal	11
Beaver Creek, AZ	WS 6	42	1977	SW	5%	alligator and Utah juniper-ponderosa pine forest	silty clay	<76	clear-cut	12
Beaver Creek, AZ	WS 12	184	2157	SW	7%	ponderosa pine, gambel oak, alligator juniper	silty clay	<60	clear-cut	13
Beaver Creek, AZ	WS 9	452	2246	W	6%	ponderosa pine and gambel oak	silty clay loam	<60	clear-cut in strips	15
Castle Creek, AZ	West Fork	364	2500	SE	-	ponderosa pine	igneous origin	-	clear-cut and thinned	16
Coyote Creek, OR	1	69	900	NE	23-36% average	Douglas fir, mixed conifer	well-drained gravelly loam, altered volcaniclistic parent material	50-150	shelterwood cut by tractor	40
Coyote Creek, OR	2	68	900	NE	23-36% average	Douglas fir, mixed conifer	well-drained gravelly loam, altered volcaniclistic parent material	50-150	patch-cut; 14% by tractor, 16% by high-lead	41
Coyote Creek, OR	3	50	900	NE	23-36% average	Douglas fir, mixed conifer	well-drained gravelly loam, altered volcaniclistic parent material	50-150	clear-cut; 23% by tractor, 77% by high lead	42
Deadhorse Creek, CO	North Fork	41	-	S	~40%	old-growth lodgepole pine	angular gravel and stone derived from schist and gneiss rocks	-	commercial clear-cut (2450 cu m or 168 cu m/ha) downhill skidding	43
Entiat, WA	McCree	514	1348	SE	-	Ponderosa pine and Douglas fir	sandy loam	-	burned	45
Entiat, WA	Burns	563	1403	-	-	Ponderosa pine and Douglas fir	sandy loam	-	burned	46
Entiat, WA	Fox	473	1495	-	-	Ponderosa pine and Douglas fir	sandy loam	-	burned	47

189

Table 2 (Continued)

Study No.	Treatment	Soil Depth (cm)	Soils	Vegetation	Percent Slope	Aspect	Mid-area Elevation (m)	Drainage Area (ha)	Study Site	Location
60	clear-cut by high-lead (1969)	100-300	silt loams or stony, cobbly loams	Pacific silver fir, overmature western hemlock and Douglas-fir	5-9% average	WNW	895	59	FC-1	Fox Creek, OR
61	clear-cut by tractor (6%) and high-lead (19%) (1971-1972)	100-300	silt loams or stony, cobbly loams	Douglas fir, western hemlock	5-9% average	W	920	71	FC-3	Fox Creek, OR
62	commercial cut in strips perpendicular to contour	-	angular gravel and stone derived from schist and gneiss rocks	77% subalpine forest (lodgepole pine, spruce-fir); 23% alpine forest	-	N	3200	289	Fool Creek	Frazer, CO
64	commercial clear-cut by skyline suspension	-	gravely loams and clay loams, altered volcaniclistic parent material	Douglas-fir, western hemlock	53-63%	NW	700	96	WS 1	H.J. Andrews, OR
65	patch-cut by high-lead cable	-	gravely loams and clay loams, altered volcaniclistic parent material	Douglas-fir, western hemlock	53-63%	NW	760	101	WS 3	H.J. Andrews, OR
66	clear-cut, 93% by high-lead cable, 7% by tractor	-	relatively unaltered volcaniclastic parent material	Douglas-fir	27-31%	S	900	13	WS 6	H.J. Andrews, OR
67	shelterwood cut, 40% by high-lead cable, 60% by tractor	-	relatively unaltered volcaniclastic parent material	Douglas-fir	27-31%	S	900	21	WS 7	H.J. Andrews, OR
68	clear-cut by high-lead cable	-	altered volcaniclastic parent material	Douglas-fir, western hemlock spruce	65-70%	SW	500	9	WS 10	H.J. Andrews, OR
92	80% killed by insect infestation	-			-	-	-	308	White River	Meeker, CO
104	commercial selection harvest	-	gravely sandy loam to loamy sand	montane chaparral and ponderosa pine-red fir forest	30-50%	N	2490	119	Burton	Salmon Creek, CA
108	moist site cleared	up to 5	clay loam	ponderosa pine	-	SW	2225	100	North Fork, Workman Creek (a)	Sierra Ancha, AZ
109	dry site cleared	up to 5	clay loam	ponderosa pine	-	SW	2225	100	North Fork, Workman Creek (b)	Sierra Ancha, AZ

Table 2 (Continued)

Location	Study Site	Drainage Area (ha)	Mid-area Elevation (m)	Aspect	Percent Slope	Vegetation	Soils	Soil Depth (cm)	Treatment	Study No.
Sierra Ancha, AZ	South Fork, Workman Creek (a)	129	2165	NW	-	ponderosa pine	clay loam	up to 5	clear-cut and thinned	111
Sierra Ancha, AZ	South Fork, Workman Creek (b)	78	~2250	E	~40%	spruce-fir, lodgepole pine	angular gravel and stone derived from schist and gneiss rocks	-	Partial cut	300
Wagon Wheel Gap, CO	B	81	3110	NE	-	84% aspen and conifer	augite, quartzite, rocky clay loam	-	clear-cut	123
Deadhorse Creek, CO	Inter-basin area	141	~3200	E	~40%	lodgepole pine-spruce-fir	angular gravel and stone derived from schist and gneiss rocks	-	treatment of North Fork (15 ha) and North Slope (24 ha)	210
Deadhorse Creek, CO	North Slope (8)	41	-	N	~40%	spruce-fir	angular gravel and stone derived from schist and gneiss rocks	-	selection cut	211
Thomas Creek, AZ	South Fork	227	2667	N and S	22%	old-growth southwestern mixed conifer	loamy-skeletal Alfisols formed from basalt material and alluvial deposits	51-102+	patch clear-cutting, group selection, and single-tree selection	301

Table 3. Summary of runoff versus treatment results

Model Description	Mean runoff per 10% change in treatment	95% confidence limits	R^2	Statistical level of confidence	N	Reference
World-wide, treatment-runoff	~40 mm	not reported	0.42	not reported	94	Bosch and Hewlett, 1982
Western U.S. mountains, treatment-runoff	12 mm	0-24 mm	0.14	95%	31	this paper
Sierra MAP range (500-2400 mm), treatment-runoff	13 mm	0-26 mm	0.14	90%	26	this paper
MAP 400 - 610 mm, treatment-runoff	4 mm	-5-12 mm	0.14	not significant (67%)	9	this paper
MAP 630 - 960 mm, treatment-runoff	5 mm	-6-15 mm	0.09	not significant (63%)	11	this paper
MAP 950 - 2400 mm, treatment-runoff	31 mm	10-52 mm	0.64	95%	9	this paper
Sequoia National Forest MAP range (510-1230 mm), treatment-runoff	8 mm	-1-18 mm	0.16	90%	20	this paper
Southern aspect, MAP 500-2400 mm, treatment-runoff	9 mm	-15-32 mm	0.07	not significant (56%)	11	this paper
Northern aspect, MAP 500-2400 mm, treatment-runoff	23 mm	-3-49 mm	0.28	90%	12	this paper
Mixed conifer, treatment-runoff	5 mm	-2-12 mm	0.18	not significant (83%)	12	this paper
Lodgepole pine-spruce-fir, treatment-runoff	2 mm	-21-25 mm	0.01	not significant (18%)	6	this paper
Douglas fir, treatment-runoff	27 mm	3-51 mm	0.56	95%	8	this paper
Western U.S. mountains, multiple regression (see text)	14 mm	8-20 mm	0.80	99%	31	this paper
MAP 500-2400 mm, multiple regression	12 mm	4-19 mm	0.81	95%	26	this paper
MAP 400 - 610 mm, multiple regression	6 mm	-5-17 mm	0.78	not significant (80%)	9	this paper
MAP 630 - 960 mm, multiple regression	7 mm	-3-16 mm	0.68	not significant (86%)	11	this paper
MAP 950 - 2400 mm, multiple regression	30 mm	12-48 mm	0.93	99%	9	this paper
Sequoia National Forest MAP range (510-1230 mm), multiple regression	8 mm	0-16 mm	0.57	95%	20	this paper
Southern aspect, MAP 500-2400 mm, multiple regression	8 mm	-5-21 mm	0.90	not significant (80%)	11	this paper
Northern aspect, MAP 500-2400 mm, multiple regression	18 mm	3-32 mm	0.87	95%	12	this paper
Mixed conifer, multiple regression	3 mm	-8-14 mm	0.58	not significant (43%)	12	this paper
Lodgepole pine-spruce-fir, multiple regression	-5 mm	-22-13 mm	1.00	not significant (83%)	6	this paper
Douglas fir, multiple regression	27 mm	-5-59 mm	0.91	90%	8	this paper

Table 4. Projected change in forest cover by Sierra Nevada region

FRRAP Region	Productive Available Timberland (acres)	1980-1990 Inventory (mbf)	1980-1990 Average Annual Harvest (mbf)	(%)	1990-2000 Average Annual Harvest (mbf)	(%)	Average Annual Change in Harvest (mbf)	(%)	1980-1990 Average Annual Growth (mbf)	1990-2000 Average Annual Growth (mbf)	Average Annual Change in Growth (mbf)	(%)
Sacramento (Northern Sierra)	1,778,000	29,587,200	394,476	1.33%	430,214	1.45%	35,738	0.12%	393,850	406,308	12,458	0.04%
Central Sierra	1,211,000	30,296,320	469,295	1.55%	496,233	1.64%	26,938	0.09%	441,069	402,401	-38,668	-0.13%
San Joaquin (Southern Sierra)	948,000	9,013,802	99,951	1.11%	112,382	1.25%	12,431	0.14%	105,929	117,207	11,278	0.13%
Sierra Total	3,937,000	68,897,322	963,722	1.40%	1,038,829	1.51%	75,107	0.11%	940,848	925,916	-14,932	-0.02%

Table 5. Range in annual runoff increases from projected changes in forest cover

FRRAP Region	Average Annual Change in Timber Volume (mbf)	(%)	Average Annual 50 yr Min. (mm)	Average Annual 50 yr Max. (mm)
Sacramento (Northern Sierra)	-23,280	-0.08%	1	4
Central Sierra	-65,606	-0.22%	2	11
San Joaquin (Southern Sierra)	- 1,153	-0.01%	0	0
Sierra Total	-90,039	-0.13%	1	6

Table 6. Peak flow pairs used in analysis.

year	month	South Fork (cms)	North-Middle Fork (cms)
1943	3	176	62
1945	2	55	34
1951	11	201	311
1957	5	32	53
1963	2	50	155
1967	12	405	478
1969	1	149	144
1970	1	96	69
1980	1	186	178
1982	4	114	73
1983	12	59	26
1984	11	66	38

Table 7. Hydrologic units in the South Fork Tule Watershed

Forest Zone

Hydrologic Unit	Mean Annual Precipitation (mm)	Pre-logging vegetated area (ha)	Area logged (ha)	Percentage logged (%)	Post-logging vegetated area (ha)	Post-logging vegetated area (%)
A	>1143	1253	1183	94	70	6
B	1016 - 1143	2723	1062	39	1661	61
C	889 - 1015	2334	715	31	1619	69
D	762 - 888	2230	2006	90	224	10
total forest zone		**8540**	**4966**	**58**	**3574**	**42**

Woodland, Chaparral, and Grassland Zone

E	457 - 761	19660	1000	5	18660	95
total watershed area		**28200**	**5966**	**21**	**22234**	**79**

Table 8. Water available for runoff

Hydrologic Unit	Pre-logging SWE (mm)	Post-logging SWE (mm)	Change in SWE (mm)	Estimated 2-yr, 24-hr rainfall (mm)*	Pre-logging WAR (mm)	Post-logging WAR (mm)	Percentage change in WAR
A	33	48	15	102	135	150	11%
B	33	39	6	89	122	128	5%
C	26	32	6	76	102	108	6%
D	26	38	12	64	90	102	13%
Total Forest						9	**5%**
E	0	0	0	38	38	38	0%
Total Watershed						3	**5%**

*Adapted from Dunne and Leopold 1978.

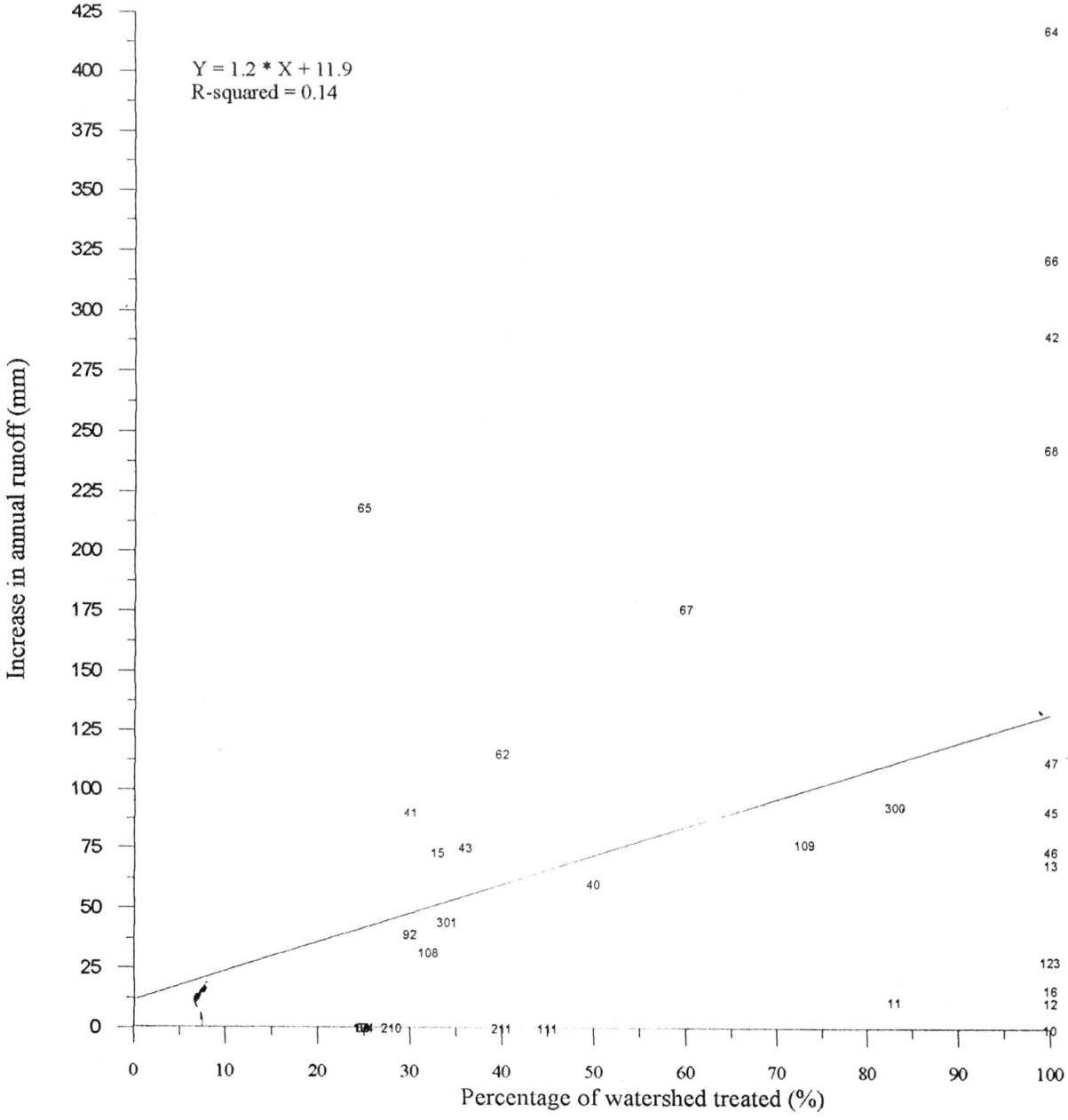

Figure 1. Regression results of increase in runoff versus percentage of watershed treated for the western United States data set. Symbols correspond to study numbers in tables 1 and 2.

195

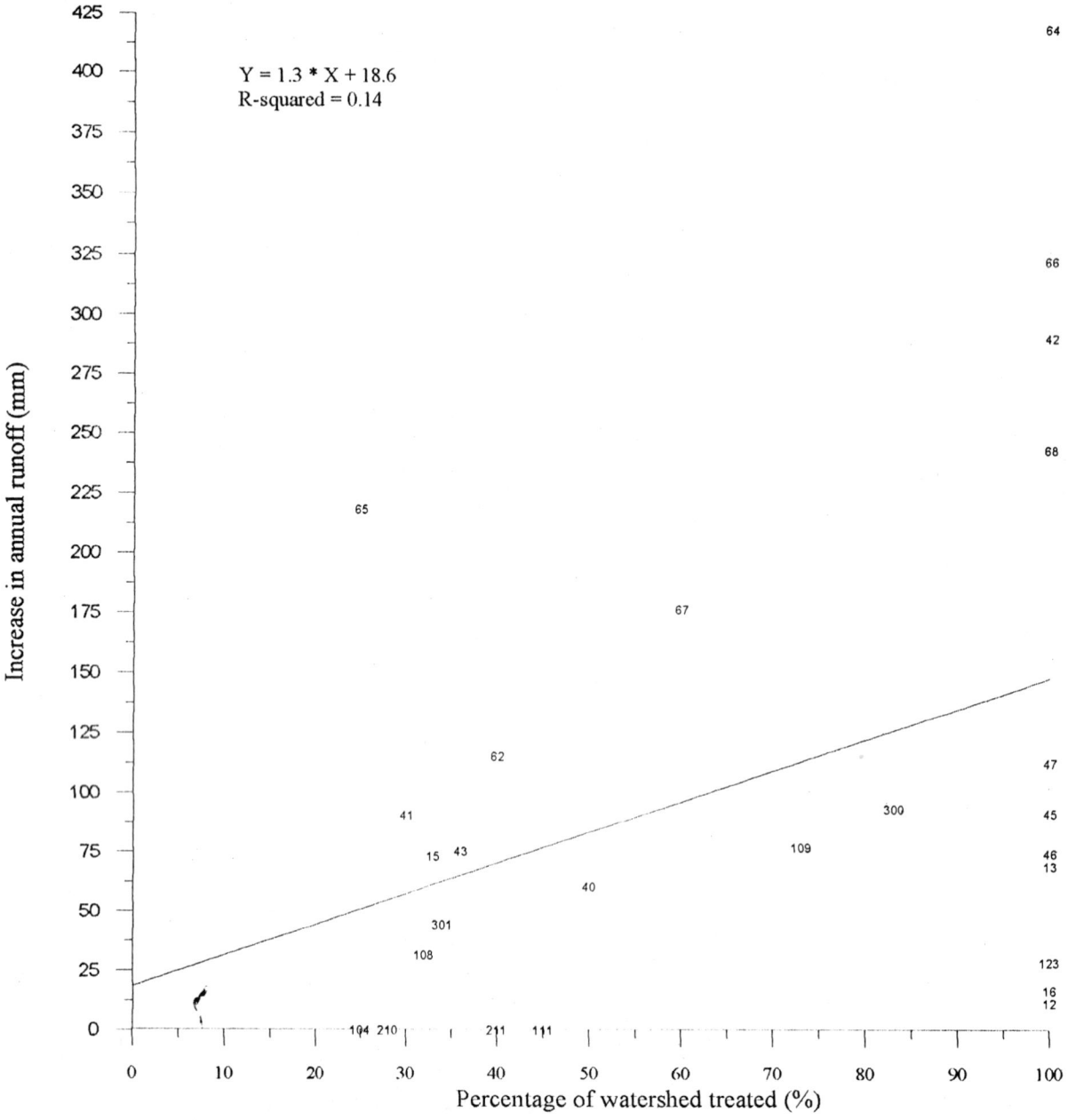

Figure 2. Regression results of increase in runoff versus percentage of watershed treated after restricting mean annual precipitation to a range typical of the Sierra Nevada. Symbols correspond to study numbers in tables 1 and 2.

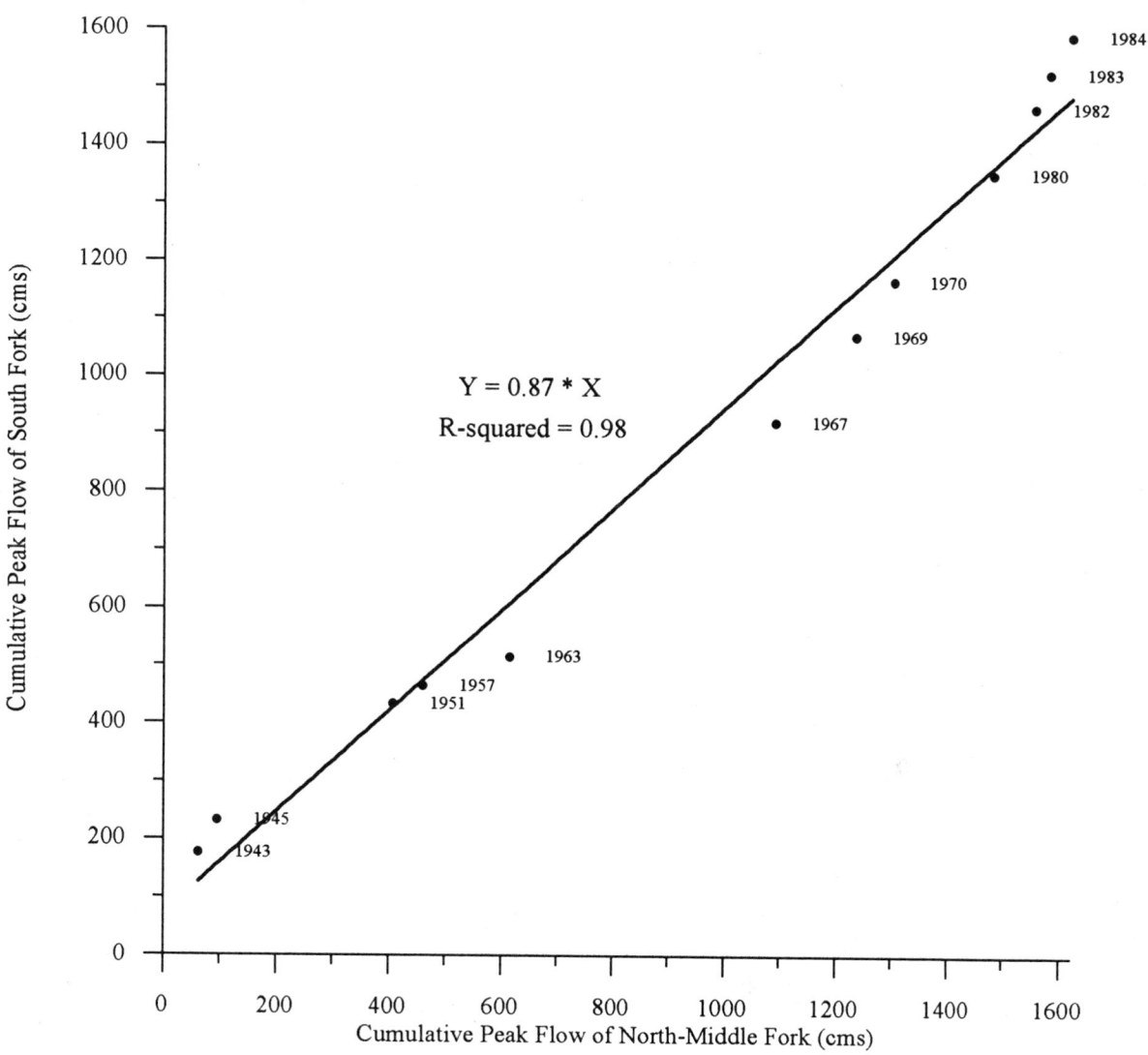

Figure . Double-mass plot of cumulative peak flows of the South Fork and North-Middle Fork Tule River. Curve was fitted by least-squares regression.

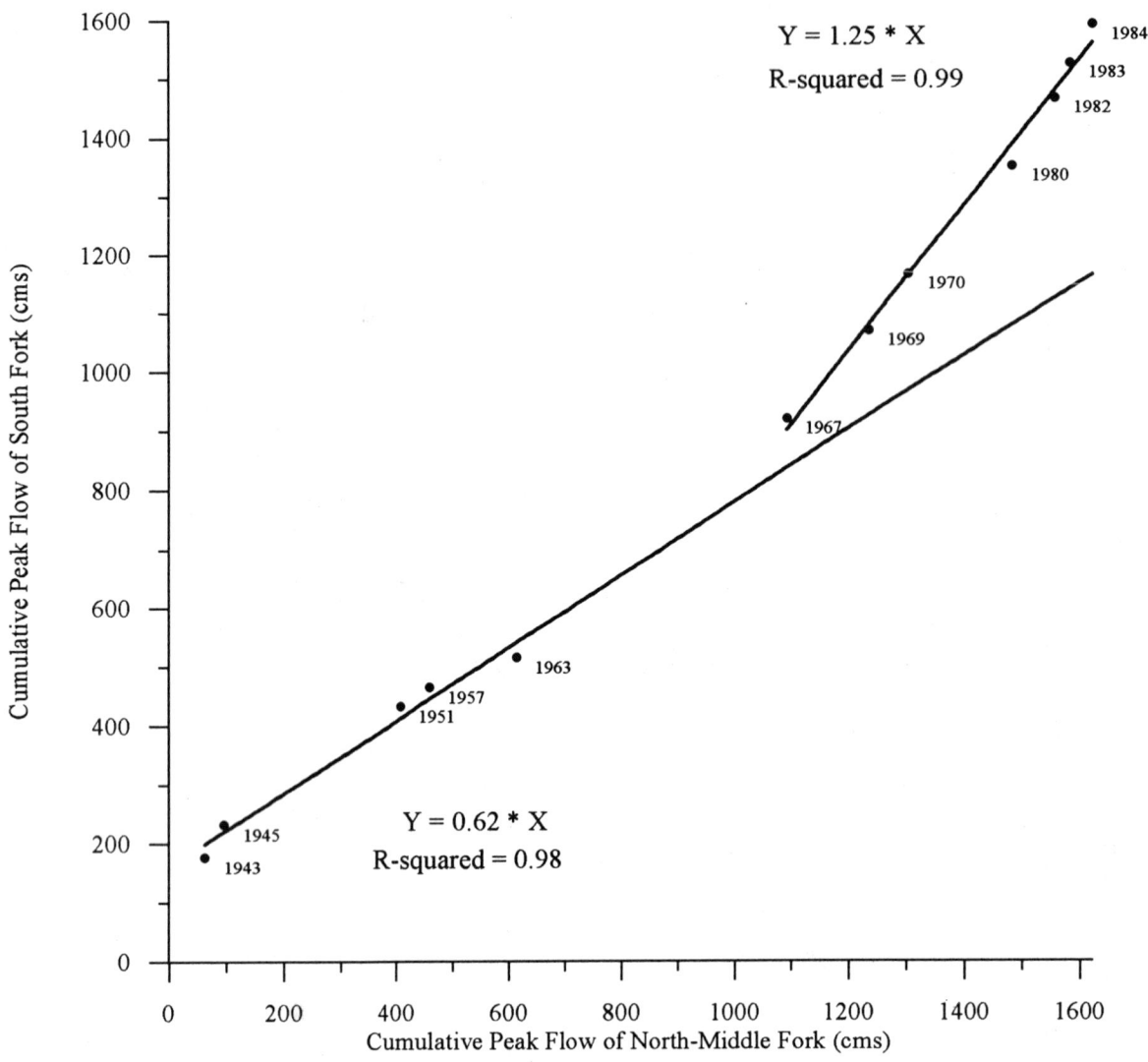

Figure   . Double-mass plot of cumulative peak flows of the South Fork and North-Middle Fork Tule River for periods 1943-1963 and 1967-1984. Curves were fitted by least-squares regression.

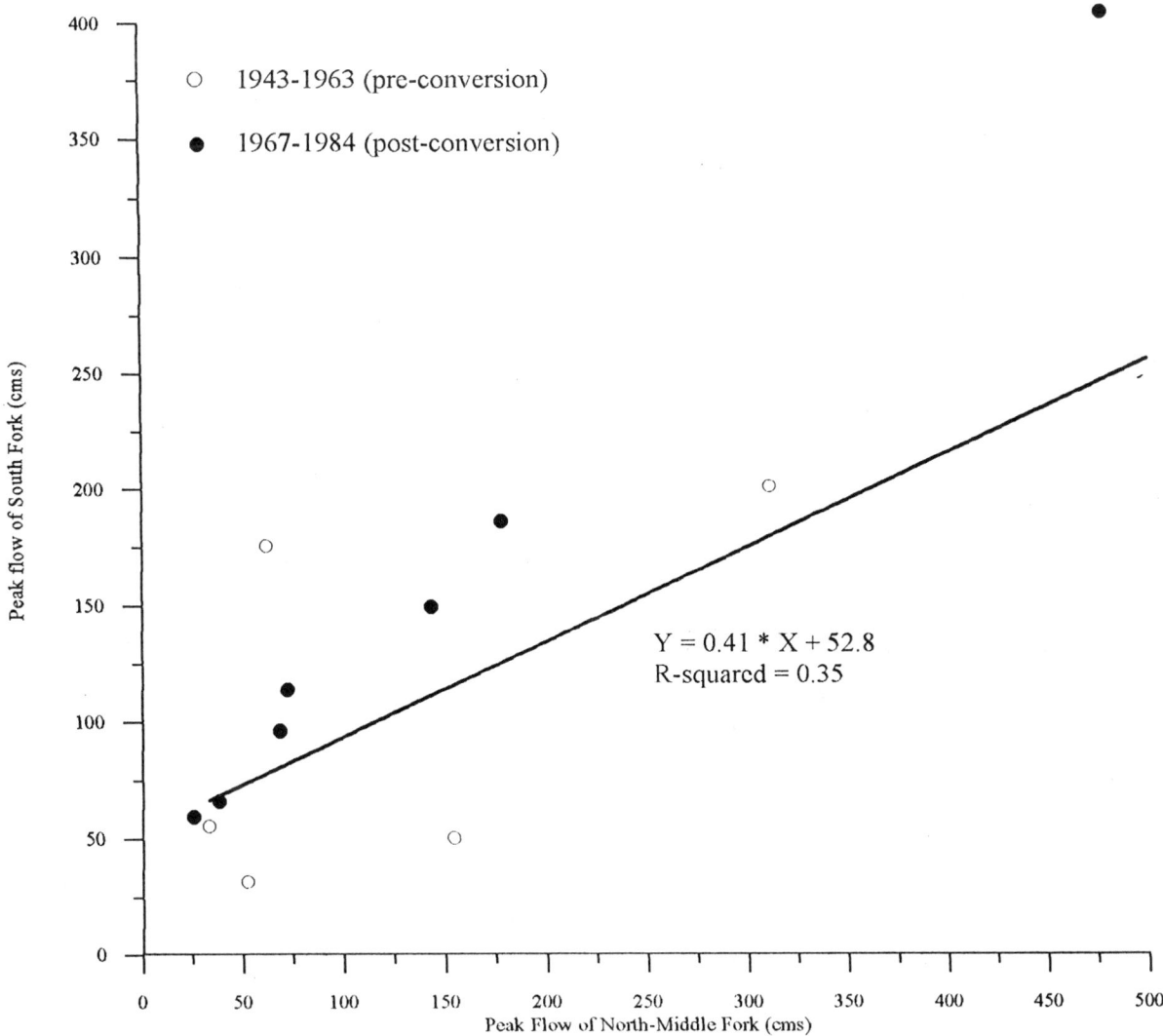

Figure . Relationship between annual peak flows on the South Fork and
North-Middle Fork Tule River during the pre- and post-conversion periods.
See text for explanation.

RICHARD KATTELMANN
Sierra Nevada Aquatic Research Lab
University of California
Mammoth Lakes, California

MICHAEL EMBURY
Sierra Nevada Aquatic Research Lab
University of California
Mammoth Lakes, California

Appendix on Management and Land Use
  Buffers by Don C. Erman,
  Nancy A. Erman, Larry Costick and
  Steve Beckwitt

5

Riparian Areas and Wetlands

Sierra Nevada Ecosystem Project: Final report to Congress, vol. III, Assessments and scientific basis for management options. Davis: University of California, Centers for Water and Wildland Resources, 1996.

CONTENTS

ABSTRACT

Riparian areas are the focal point of many resource conflicts in the Sierra Nevada because they are a critical ecological link between land and water. Although scarcity of quantitative information and unaltered reference sites currently limit the development of quantitative conclusions about riparian health across the entire Sierra Nevada, a few generalities emerged from this assessment. Riparian areas have been changed by human activities to varying degrees throughout much of the range. The basic functions of riparian systems, such as providing shade, stability, and organic matter to streams and habitat for avian and terrestrial wildlife, still remain in most places although often in impaired form. These functions have been largely lost in thousands of localities. The loss of functions is particularly evident in mountain meadows throughout the Sierra Nevada. A survey of riparian cover from aerial photographs showed that fragmentation is common along most riparian corridors. Riparian areas lacking vegetation cover identified in the aerial photograph analysis were usually associated with vehicular access. Roads and urban development have converted riparian areas to impermeable surfaces and channelized streams. Stream crossings by roads impact riparian areas at thousands of places and are the main current impact associated with timber harvesting. Many, if not most, of the broad valleys with formerly extensive riparian areas have been developed or inundated. About 1,000 km (600 miles) of riparian corridors have been submerged under reservoirs throughout the Sierra Nevada. These reservoirs and other gaps break the continuity of the riparian corridors and impair wildlife migration. Overgrazing has altered riparian communities throughout much of the Sierra Nevada. Impacts from overgrazing vary from subtle changes in plant vigor to conversion of wet meadows into sparsely vegetated and eroding landscapes. Besides these continuing impacts, future risks to riparian areas include accelerated urban development and additional water development. There are thousands of opportunities for restoration of locally degraded riparian areas. Streamside vegetation has remarkable ability to recover from disturbance, but artificial disturbances need to be removed or relaxed to give the natural recovery processes a chance.

PREFACE: SCOPE AND TERMINOLOGY

Although riparian areas are an integral part of stream ecosystems (e.g., National Research Council 1992; California State Lands Commission 1993), our separation of riparian from aquatic systems is artificial and merely for the purpose of report preparation. In this report, we are examining the riparian subsystem of riverine-riparian ecosystems (Jensen and Platts 1989). These subsystems are mutually interdependent in terms of ecological processes and consequences of impacts. For example, artificial regulation of streamflow alters the availability of water in riparian areas, and changes in riparian vegetation can alter physical and biological characteristics of streams. Assessments of other aspects of water resources and aquatic ecology are discussed in several chapters of the SNEP report (Erman 1996; Jennings 1996; Kattelmann 1996a; Knapp 1996; Moyle 1996a; Moyle 1996b; Moyle et al. 1996a). Further treatment of riparian areas is found in Kondolf et al. 1996; Menke et al. 1996; and Moyle et al. 1996b. Assessments of terrestrial vegetation and wildlife that have some association with riparian areas are found in additional chapters (Davis et al. 1996; Franklin and Fites-Kaufmann 1996; Graber 1996; McDonald and Tappeiner 1996; Schwartz et al. 1996; Shevock 1996). We have attempted to discuss riparian systems in the context of the entire Sierra Nevada, which is admittedly awkward because riparian properties, processes, and problems are local in nature.

In this report, we will use the terms riparian area and streamside area interchangeably to refer to the transition between the upslope terrestrial ecosystem and the adjacent aquatic ecosystem. We will use the term riparian corridor to refer to the land on either side of the stream and including the stream. The term riparian (or streamside) management zone has been used by agencies in a management or protection context to include some upland areas that may influence or buffer the riparian corridor. In our context, watersheds are units of land that potentially contribute water to a given point along a stream. Although our perspective in this riparian report is biased toward streams, we are not excluding those associated with lakes, reservoirs, springs, seeps, etc. Definitions of riparian terms are discussed by Warner and Hendrix (1984: xxv-xxvi), Anderson (1987), DeBano and Schmidt (1989), and Gregory et al. (1989). In this report, the terms grazing and overgrazing will be used in reference to commercial grazing of domestic livestock.

A brief assessment of wetlands has been included in this report. Because many wetlands are found in riparian corridors, much of the general discussion in this report applies to wetlands. However, wetlands have distinct characteristics and management problems and therefore receive some additional discussion.

INTRODUCTION AND BACKGROUND

Riparian areas are water-dependent lands along streams and lakes where transitions occur between terrestrial and aquatic parts of a watershed. They may be best described as the zone of direct interaction between land and water (Swanson et al 1982; Gregory et al. 1991; Cummins 1992). Riparian corridors connect the headwaters to the valley and facilitate transfer of materials (Gregory et al. 1991). Water, energy, and organic matter move downstream through a continuum of changing ecological processes along each stream (Vannote et al. 1980). The continuity of riparian areas is one of their critical characteristics, which is readily disrupted by human activities.

Riparian areas do not have precise boundaries because of temporal fluctuations of stream levels and intermixed vegetation types on the upland side. During most of the year, riparian areas are clearly separate from (though intimately connected to) their adjacent stream. However, during periods of high water, the topographically-lower sections of a riparian area that constitute a floodplain become part of the stream. Riparian communities usually contain a gradient in soil moisture from the stream through the floodplain and sometimes up into the terraces, depending on geomorphology and hydrology of the particular site. Typical riparian vegetation requires the high soil moisture usually found along streams, and some can even tolerate saturated soils and occasional inundation.

Riparian systems are distinct in mountain areas because they traverse broad vegetation belts that are arranged largely by elevation. They connect all the major life zones and are often dramatically different in vegetation composition and microclimate from the lands they cross. At variable distances away from the stream, riparian vegetation grades into upland vegetation. In some cases, there is little obvious difference in the composition of vegetation between the streamside area and the adjacent hillslopes. Elsewhere, there are marked contrasts between deciduous species in the riparian area and conifers or chaparral on the hillsides. In the lower margins of the east side of the Sierra Nevada, riparian areas appear oasis-like in comparison to the surrounding sagebrush scrub. In all cases, the vegetation near streams has profound influences on the aquatic system.

The thin, linear nature of riparian areas in the Sierra Nevada limits their total area to a small fraction of any watershed. Because habitat elements associated with riparian areas are relatively rare compared to the entire landscape, modification of even small areas has a proportionally greater impact in riparian areas than elsewhere in the watershed (Graber 1996). Depending on criteria used for delineation, estimates of the riparian fraction of total area in different river basins of the Sierra Nevada range from 0.1 to 1 percent (Langley 1984; Federal Energy Regulatory Commission 1986; Kondolf et al. 1987). National Forests use definitions of Streamside Management Zones that are different than typical biophysical delineations and consider that about 3-4 percent of the area of their Forests is "riparian" (e.g., Plumas National Forest 1988; Stanislaus National Forest 1988). The total amount of land in the Sierra Nevada classified as the Holland type *riparian forest* by Davis et al. (1996) is quite limited: 58 km^2 plus 119 km^2 of riparian scrub.

In general, streamside areas are the most productive and diverse parts of the landscape (e.g., Meehan et al. 1977; Naiman et al. 1992b; Risser 1995). Microclimates and soil moisture regimes found along streams are highly favorable for plant growth to be sustained for longer periods of each year than in other geographic locations. The frequent disturbance by floods and variety of physical habitats promotes much greater diversity of species than on more uniform hillslopes (Odum 1978; Gregory et al. 1991). Under natural flow regimes, frequent disturbance by various levels and durations of flooding results in riparian vegetation with a patchy distribution of species and ages (Swanson et al. 1990). The diversity of species and habitat structure may be reduced by human impacts that tend to simplify ecological processes and components.

Plant species of the riparian area are usually different from those found upslope. The plants considered typical of riparian areas (Appendix 1) generally share a set of distinct ecological characteristics: broad-leaved; winter-deciduous; fast-growing; often short-lived; requirement for high soil-moisture to support high rates of transpiration; ability to tolerate seasonal flooding and low-oxygen root environments that are often saturated; and ability to produce sprouts, suckers, and new root systems (California State Lands Commission 1993). Among riparian plants, there are substantial differences in their tolerance for flooding, which stratifies different species at different elevations along the floodplain and terraces.

Hydrologic and Geomorphic Controls on Development of Riparian Areas

Riparian vegetation at a particular location and time results from interactions between the physical conditions created by geomorphic and hydrologic processes in the stream channel and responses by the plants (California State Lands Commission 1993). The development of riparian communities is also influenced by hydrologic conditions in adjacent uplands, such as infiltration capacity and subsurface water movement (LaFayette and DeBano 1990). In turn, physical and biological processes in the riparian area can modify water and its constituents enroute from upland hillslopes to a stream as well as from upstream to downstream areas (Karr and Schlosser 1978). Some of the physical factors that influence the structure of riparian communities include channel pattern, slope, and morphology; flood frequency and magnitude; timing and duration of flooding; sediment transport and deposition; and streamflow-groundwater interactions (Leopold 1994; Grant and Swanson 1995). Channel pattern and valley shape are important to vegetation by providing the substrate for vegetation establishment adjacent to the stream. These influences shift over time, and some are episodic. In response, riparian areas are highly dynamic.

Many stream reaches in the Sierra Nevada are confined within relatively narrow canyons. However, in deep glacial valleys (e.g., Kings Canyon and Yosemite Valley), broad flats (e.g., Sierra Valley and Kern Plateau), and scattered meadows (e.g., Hope Valley and Tuolumne Meadows), channels may meander and form multiple channels across a broad area. In these relatively flat valleys and meadows, there is ample opportunity for an extensive riparian community to develop. Unfortunately, these wider valleys have also been attractive areas for various human activities, with corresponding loss of some of the best riparian habitat. Braided conditions can also develop on the alluvial fans of the eastern slope. Sierra Nevada streams tend to have confined reaches of steep gradients alternating with those of low gradient and a wider floodplain (Janda 1966).

Flood events influence riparian vegetation directly through inundation, mechanical damage, and indirectly through changes in channel morphology. Floods in Sierra Nevada streams are produced by a variety of mechanisms depending on geographic location (Kattelmann 1990, 1992, 1996b). The period of saturation of the root zone during high water can result in a stratification of plant species along a microtopographic gradient up the floodplain (Walters et al. 1980). If the plants are dormant at the time of flooding, there may be little effect (Jones and Stokes Associates 1983). Most of the physical damage during floods results from the mechanical stress on the plant leading to uprooting or impacts from debris and bedload. Erosion of streambanks during floods also carries away the vegetation. Conversely, the vegetation dramatically increases the resistance of the streambanks to erosion (Zimmerman et al. 1967). The removal or death of some plants during peak flows creates opportunities for other plants to grow, ensuring regeneration and contributing to a structurally diverse canopy. Sediment deposition can bury and damage some plants that may be able to resprout above the new surface and provide fresh substrate for other plants that thrive where competition has been reduced (Sigafoos 1964).

Sediment deposition occurs both as channel bars, which add new substrate for colonization, and layers on the floodplain during overbank flows. If the bars continue to grow vertically, they become more suitable for continued growth. As plants grow on the new substrate, they can minimize loss of the early deposits by reinforcement with their roots and enhance additional deposition by slowing the current and physically trapping materials. As bars and the floodplain aggrade, soil moisture may become limiting to shallow-rooted plants as the surface height above the stream increases (Jones and Stokes Associates 1983).

Soil moisture along the floodplain and its relation to streamflow depend on the hydraulic gradient in the riparian area. Water moving down from adjacent hillslopes often saturates the floodplain area, maintains high soil moisture, and contributes to streamflow (Hewlett and Hibbert 1967; Dunne et al. 1981). In other situations, such as streams on alluvial fans, water may flow out of the stream into the bed and banks. The water that circulates between the stream and its bed and banks also promotes nutrient exchange and provides important habitat for some macroinvertebrates and microbes (Stanford and Ward 1988, 1993; Hakencamp et al. 1993). During periods of high runoff, water can spread over the floodplain and infiltrate or flow into the upper portions of streambanks, thereby raising the local water table. Some of this bank storage may return to the channel as streamflow declines. Streams in intact meadows are often supplied with water through this mechanism during the summer. If meadow streams become incised and water tables fail to rise during wet periods, the source of low-season streamflow is lost. Similarly, if the natural delivery of water and sediment is disrupted by human activities, the normal disturbance and development of riparian areas are also disrupted (Faber and Holland 1988).

Riparian-Dependent Animals

The diversity and structural complexity of riparian vegetation creates a wide variety of habitats for animals (e.g., Zeiner et al. 1988, 1990a, 1990b). More species and greater numbers of wildlife are found in riparian environments than any other habitat type (Sands and Howe 1977; Thomas et al. 1979; Brinson et al. 1981; Kauffman and Krueger 1984). Many species are completely dependent on riparian and adjoining aquatic environments. Of about 400 species of terrestrial vertebrates found in the Sierra Nevada, about one-fifth (84 species) are dependent on riparian areas (Graber 1996). On the Stanislaus National Forest, the number of wildlife species associated with riparian areas numbered 177 below 900 m (3,000 ft), 165 between 900 and 1,800 m (3,000 and 6,000 ft), and 77 above 1,800 m (6,000 ft) (Stanislaus National Forest 1988). In the well-studied Sagehen Creek basin, which is a tributary of the Little Truckee River, almost 40 percent of the vertebrates are strongly dependent on riparian habitat (Morrison et al. 1985). All of the 6 amphibians, 5 of 12 reptiles, 17 of 54 mammals, and 46 of 120 birds found in the Sagehen Creek basin are believed to depend on riparian areas. General habitat relationships for two amphibians, one snake, six mammals, and eleven birds strongly associated with streamside areas are reviewed by Carlson et al. (1991).

Although riparian environments are often considered as a single unit, they are usually composed of a mosaic of habitats and microhabitats with distinctive characteristics and organisms. The typical riparian microclimate of cool temperatures, high humidity, shade, and relatively constant air movement is favorable for many species. Additionally, many wide-ranging wildlife species spend time in the riparian area seeking water, food, or cooler temperatures. The linear nature of riparian areas gives them a high edge to area ratio, which seems to be desirable to some species. Relatively mature riparian communities tend to be well-stratified, which increases diversity and edge-effect (Thomas et al. 1979). Their configuration as natural corridors promotes their use as migratory routes for animals and aids in plant dispersal.

The vegetation of riparian areas supports complex habitats and abundant food resources for insects and other herbivores, which in turn, support a wide variety of vertebrates. Emerging aquatic insects contribute to the great abundance of invertebrates in riparian areas (Erman 1996). Aquatic invertebrates are a critical food supply for fish, amphibians, mammals, and birds. The density and diversity of birds, in particular, tends to be much greater in riparian areas than in adjacent uplands (e.g., Miller 1951; Small 1974; Gaines 1977). The variety of plant canopies at different heights that are common in riparian areas provides many ecological opportunities for individual species and coexistence among species (Krzysik 1990). Deciduous vegetation provides two seasonally contrasting structural conditions (Reynolds et al. 1993). The presence of open water and associated edge effects, abundant food resources of terrestrial and aquatic invertebrates, and diversity of vegetation contribute to the desirability of riparian areas for birds (Carlson et al. 1991). Riparian habitat is important for both breeding birds and migratory species. Numbers of migratory birds found in riparian areas can be more than ten times greater than in adjacent uplands (Stevens et al. 1977).

Changes in riparian areas along Sierra Nevada rivers has been associated with decreases in bird populations (e.g, Klebenow and Oakleaf 1984; Ohmart 1994; Manley and Davidson 1995). Among the birds thought to be declining in riparian habitats of the Sierra Nevada, the Willow Flycatcher has received considerable study and may be suggestive of the plight of other species. Willow Flycatchers depend on dense thickets of riparian vegetation for breeding and foraging. The geographic range and numbers of Willow Flycatchers have shrunk dramatically in recent decades (Harris et al. 1987). A few small remaining populations inhabit isolated meadows of the Sierra Nevada, such as along the Little Truckee River (Flett and Sanders 1987). Overgrazing of meadows has been suggested as a major cause of the decline of Willow Flycatchers (Ohmart 1994). Cattle can directly disturb Willow Flycatchers and other birds nesting in montane meadows by knocking over nests in willows or crushing eggs on the ground (Sanders and Flett 1989). Parasitic brown-headed cowbirds lay their eggs in the Willow Flycatcher nests at lower elevations and occasionally at higher elevations where the breeding seasons have less overlap (Airola 1986). Opportunities for nest parasitism are increased by thinning or clearing riparian vegetation (Laymon 1987). The extirpation of Bell's vireo from the Sierra Nevada was associated with the spread of brown-headed cowbirds. Destruction of willow-dominated riparian areas also contributed to the decline of Bell's vireo (Graber 1996).

Mammals also take full advantage of riparian habitats because of the availability of water, food (vegetation, invertebrates, fish, other mammals, and carrion), cover, shelter, and a favorable microclimate (Cross 1988; Raedeke et al. 1988). Deer, beaver, raccoons, ringtail, skunks, shrews, and wood rats are relatively common in riparian areas. Although fur-bearing animals such as weasels, ermine, pine marten, and fishers are commonly associated with riparian areas, only mink and beaver are truly dependent on riparian habitat (Graber 1996). The role of beaver in riparian systems of the Sierra nevada has been debated for decades (e.g., Hall 1960) and is yet to be resolved. Several species of bats are an important component of the riparian community and feed on the abundant insects. Because bats use lower elevations for part of the year, loss of high-quality riparian habitat in the foothills and eastern part of the Central Valley may be a factor in the decline of some species (Graber 1996). Many mammals depend on riparian habitats seasonally in summer when uplands have dried out. Riparian areas serve as something of an oasis for wildlife during the hot, dry summer. Streamside areas also provide access to food, water and a favorable microclimate during winter. The obvious travel and migration corridors provided by riparian areas are becoming even more important as uplands are also modified by human activities (Nelson et al. 1994).

Riparian areas are also prime habitat for reptiles and amphibians (Jennings 1995), but relatively little is known about their ecological relationships (Reynolds et al. 1993). Many species of turtles, lizards, and snakes occupy or travel through riparian areas. Several types of lizards tend to stay very close to the water's edge to maximize feeding opportunities (Krzysik 1990). The presence of open water, damp soils, and a cool, moist microclimate make riparian areas particularly important for amphibians (Brode and Bury 1984; Jennings 1995). Almost all the 21 species of salamanders and 9 species of frogs and toads native to the Sierra Nevada spend significant portions of their life cycles in riparian areas (Jennings 1995). Riparian areas offer the damp soil necessary for lungless salamanders. Dense vegetation provides the cover and microclimate needed by many amphibians, especially frogs. For example, mountain yellow-legged frogs (Rana muscosa) require perennial water and, before their sudden decline, were abundant in dense herbaceous vegetation along streams (Mullally and Cunningham 1956). Amphibians going to the water to breed and juveniles emerging from the water, at least travel through riparian areas (Jennings 1995). The linear connectivity of riparian corridors has contributed to genetic continuity of reptiles and amphibians (Brode and Bury 1984; Carlson et al. 1991). Dramatic declines in amphibian populations are often related to deterioration and fragmentation of riparian habitat (Jennings 1995).

Several endangered species are associated with riparian areas in the Sierra Nevada. About one-quarter of the species dependent on riparian habitat are at risk of extinction (Graber 1996). The fact that these species are in severe decline is suggestive that their habitat has been seriously degraded. A list of threatened and endangered species dependent on riparian habitat is included in Appendix 2

Influences on Streams

Besides their ecological value for terrestrial biota, riparian areas provide critical functions for the adjacent stream (Meehan et al. 1977). Riparian vegetation both limits radiant energy reaching streams by shading (affecting temperature and primary productivity within the stream) and adds chemical energy and nitrogen compounds through plant materials and insects that fall into the stream (Cummins et al. 1989). In headwaters, these organic materials from outside the stream provide most of the base of the aquatic food chain (e.g., Knight and Bottorff 1984; Cummins 1992). Aquatic insects depend on this food source and the riparian habitat for parts of their life cycles (Erman 1984, 1996). Riparian vegetation provides habitat for both prey and predators of aquatic organisms (California State Lands Commission 1993). Streamside soils and vegetation regulate the entry of groundwater, surface runoff, nutrients, sediments and other particulates, and fine and coarse organic matter to streams. During floods, plant roots and fallen trees help stabilize the soil and streambanks. Vegetation and organic debris slow the movement of flood waters and dissipate stream energy, allowing deposition of sediments on the floodplain. Vegetative protection of streambanks against erosion effectively reduces sediment delivery to downstream reaches. Fallen trees and large branches that enter streams strongly influence channel pattern and structure and velocity distribution. Riparian areas also moderate the adverse effects of increased movement of water, sediments, and nutrients generated from upslope disturbances (Schlosser and Karr 1981). This role as a buffer and filter is often relied upon to limit stream degradation from land use activities in the uplands. Riparian soils and vegetation can capture a large fraction of the nutrient load entering from upslope and prevent its release to streams. Even the large inputs of nutrients from agricultural fields can be controlled with an adjacent healthy riparian forest (Peterjohn and Correll 1984; Pinay and Decamps 1988).

Streambank vegetation, especially dense overhanging rootwads, sod, bushes, and undercut banks, provides cover for fish. Submerged vegetation and dead wood contribute to the structural complexity of underwater habitat. Even intermittent streams can offer spawning habitat for trout (Erman and Hawthorne 1976) and cannot be ignored in consideration of riparian areas. For many years, removal of vegetative cover and related physical damage to streambanks by livestock has been considered one of the main impacts causing the decline of trout in upland streams of western states (Behnke and Zarn 1976; Platts 1991). The most obvious impacts to fish habitat from degradation of the riparian area are reduction of shade and cover with consequent changes in water temperature, sediment delivery, and channel morphology (Platts 1979; Baltz and Moyle 1984).

The degree of influence on a stream and the width of the zone of greatest interactions depend largely on the size of the stream, the shape and size of the valley, soil conditions, and the local surface and subsurface hydrology (Bilby 1988; Gregory et al. 1991). Streams with steeper gradients and steeper side slopes tend to have narrower riparian areas than streams of shallow gradient in broad valleys. Bedrock and boulder substrates offer little opportunity for establishing higher riparian vegetation but are colonized by mosses and lichens.

Riparian vegetation probably exerts the greatest influence on streams of small to moderate size, where local groundwater discharge and overland flow contribute a biologically significant fraction of the water and dissolved load of the stream, primary food sources are external to the stream, shading by trees is effective, and the vegetation affects geomorphic processes (Swanson et al. 1982; Knight and Bottorff 1984). In headwater areas, the riparian area usually provides water, sediment, nutrients, and energy to the stream, whereas the direction of these influences is often reversed in larger river-floodplain systems (Swanson and Sparks 1990). As the size of the stream increases, riparian vegetation provides less shade and primary food to the stream and has less influence on geomorphic processes. Nevertheless, upstream interactions still influence downstream conditions through the net transfer of water, energy, and organic matter downstream through a continuum of changing communities and ecological processes along the stream (Vannote et al. 1980). Energy, water, and nutrient balances of larger rivers are more affected by the mixing of their tributaries than by local riparian influences.

210

Other Riparian Studies in the Sierra Nevada

Until about 30 years ago, riparian areas were barely recognized as places of special ecological significance, except by ornithologists. Some books on natural history of the Sierra Nevada do not even mention the word riparian. There was remarkably little scientific literature on riparian areas anywhere in North America until the 1970s, when riparian areas became widely recognized as critical bird habitat. Throughout the country, there has been comparatively little research on riparian systems in mountain areas (Kauffman 1988). Although there has been widespread interest and concern about riparian areas in California, the bulk of research work presented at a series of conferences has concerned riparian systems in the Central Valley and Coast Range (Sands 1977; Warner and Hendrix 1984; Abell 1989). Most papers in these three proceedings relevant to the Sierra Nevada contributed to and are cited in this report. Much of the research on riparian areas of the Sierra Nevada has been associated with hydroelectric projects and was largely sponsored by the Pacific Gas and Electric Company and Southern California Edison (e.g., Harris et al. 1987; Patten 1986; Jones and Stokes Associates 1989).

Several other assessments of riparian conditions are in progress in different parts of the Sierra Nevada. Refinements of the National Wetland Inventory continue under the auspices of the U.S. Fish and Wildlife Service (now incorporated largely within the new biological division of the Geological Survey). Local jurisdictions, such as Mono County, are also mapping wetlands at a finer scale (Robert Curry, personal communication 1995). The Bureau of Land Management continues to assess riparian conditions on the lands they administer (Gradek et al. 1989; Myers 1989). Detailed riparian assessments are performed during hydroelectric relicensing procedures. Considerable activity is in progress in relation to riparian restoration projects on streams tributary to Mono Lake (e.g., Los Angeles Department of Water and Power 1995).

A variety of riparian evaluation and monitoring programs are in progress on National Forest lands. Most Forests have ongoing stream survey projects, both systematic and project-driven. Unfortunately, little of this data was collected or archived in a consistent format in the past. A new procedure, currently called Stream Condition Inventory, may see wide application throughout the National Forests of California (U.S. Forest Service 1994). On the Sequoia National Forest, field surveys of riparian areas are generating assessments of riparian conditions (Hot Springs Ranger District 1994). In this procedure, riparian ecotypes are identified on the basis of channel type and plant community. A stability value of each stream reach is determined by evaluation of vegetative bank protection and channel morphology (Kaplan-Henry et al. 1995). A monitoring program of effects of hydroelectric operation on riparian systems, involving periodic measurement of a suite of physical and vegetative attributes, is underway on the Inyo National Forest (Hicks 1995). Two intensive riparian studies are in progress in the Lake Tahoe Basin Management Unit that are funded by the California Tahoe Conservancy. In one project, high-resolution remotely sensed images from helicopters are being analyzed to evaluate health of riparian vegetation. The other project is studying indicators of biodiversity in riparian areas with detailed field surveys performed by a ten-person team. In this program, data collection is structured to allow examination of the effects of data at different resolutions on optimal sampling strategy (Manley 1995). A major effort at classifying riparian vegetation is underway on the southern portion of the west slope of the Sierra Nevada between the Mokelumne and Kern Rivers. Almost 300 riparian sites were sampled in 1995. A report on this work is expected to be issued by the Ecology Program of the Region 5 office of the U.S. Forest Service in 1997 (Don Potter, Stanislaus National Forest, personal communication, 1996).

Threats to Riparian Systems of the Sierra Nevada

There are a variety of threats to the natural integrity of riparian areas because they are valuable in economic as well as ecological terms. Floodplains and terraces held vast quantities of gold 150 years ago and are still important sources of sand and gravel. Reservoirs, roads, and urban areas break up the continuity of riparian corridors, one of their critical ecological attributes. Dams inundate riparian corridors and their included streams. Storage, controlled release, and diversion of water alter the flow regime and, consequently, affect plant establishment, growth, reproduction, and removal. Some streamside forests have been logged where trees were accessible and of high quality for lumber. Roads, railways, and flumes near streams can eliminate the valuable ecological functions of the riparian area from a substantial fraction of their original area. The broader valleys are desirable for conversion to pastures and agriculture. Construction may remove vegetation, expose and compact soils, decrease infiltration capacity, convert some areas to impervious surfaces, and alter channel morphology. Fire can damage the entire community for several years. Increased peak flows following intense and widespread fire can scour stream channels and alter the land base for re-establishment of riparian communities. Virtually all the Sierra Nevada has been grazed at some time (Kinney 1996; Menke et al. 1996). Livestock consume plants that hold the streambanks and soil together; mechanically alter the form, structure, and porosity of soils; and change the composition of the plant community. While all these disturbances occur throughout much of the Sierra Nevada and have changed the form, composition, and continuity of riparian areas, the extent of such changes has not been quantified. Except for grazing, the immediate scope of these threats is usually local, but they often have other downstream consequences. These different on-site and downstream impacts can take a cumulative toll on riparian systems.

METHODS

Three approaches were taken to assessing the current status of riparian systems in the Sierra Nevada: literature review, examination of video tapes of river corridors, and analysis of conventional aerial photography. Literature sources included studies that were part of the Pacific Gas and Electric and Southern California Edison research program of the 1980s, a few independent scientific studies, reports made for hydropower relicensing requirements and applications for proposed projects, and various reports of the Forest Service and Bureau of Land Management. Stream surveys, reports for evaluation of cumulative watershed effects, project environmental assessments, and miscellaneous documents of these agencies provided information about selected stream reaches. The geographic coverage of the available material was scattered throughout the range. The region with the most complete coverage from a variety of sources was the Mono Lake and Owens River basins. Otherwise, project reports covered a few parts of some river basins, while no information was found for other regions. The most detailed information was available for the vicinity of a few hydroelectric projects that have recently prepared environmental documentation for relicensing procedures. The literature review provides our primary information about changes that are short of total destruction of the riparian community. This information is limited and localized. The available literature (and this assessment) do not provide a comprehensive evaluation of riparian health.

A fundamental disturbance of riparian ecosystems is removal of vegetation. Elimination of riparian vegetation as a result of other land uses is the principal impact discussed in general literature on riparian systems (e.g., Johnson 1971; Bakker 1972; Smith 1977; Katibah et al. 1984). Therefore, the task we focused on was to determine the presence or absence of tree overstory along streams of the Sierra Nevada. Even such basic information about riparian areas has not been previously developed on a large scale for the Sierra Nevada (Nelson et al. 1994).

Video tapes of river and riparian conditions were recorded from helicopters flying through the canyons of many of the principal rivers and their tributaries of the Sierra Nevada in 1979, 1981, and 1987. This work was done by the National Park Service as part of an evaluation of the suitability of different rivers for inclusion in the National Wild and Scenic River system. Twenty-four of these tapes were available from the Water Resources Center Archives at the University of California at Berkeley. The tapes were used in our assessment to identify areas lacking streamside vegetation and describe possible causes of those gaps. Additional changes may be assumed to have occurred since the tapes were recorded.

Our attempt at assessing the extent of large-scale removal of riparian vegetation relied on interpretation of aerial photos. Aerial photography is commonly used for evaluations of riparian conditions (e.g., Nelson and Nelson 1984; Cuplin 1985; Cuplin et al. 1985; Walsh et al. 1987; Batson et al. 1987; Grant 1988; California Rivers Assessment 1995). Aerial photography is also being used to assess riparian vegetation in the current Interior Columbia River Basin Project.

The procedure we used was only suitable for identifying obvious gaps in an otherwise continuous riparian forest of large trees. It was not suitable for identifying changes in meadows, headwater areas, small tributaries, community composition or local disturbance below a canopy, except in extreme cases. Because of the length of all watercourses in the Sierra Nevada, only a sample could be examined. Nevertheless, more than 9,500 km (5,900 mi) of streams were examined in about 130 watersheds out of a total of 694 in the SNEP core study area. Riparian areas in each of the 24 major river basins of the Sierra Nevada were studied. Sequoia/Kings Canyon and Yosemite National Parks were not examined to allow us to focus on areas with greater potential impacts.

The geographic units of analysis were watersheds of 40 to 80 km^2 (10,000 to 20,000 ac) that are delineated and called Super Planning Watersheds (SPW) in the Calwater system of the California Resources Agency. The SPW were stratified into three broad elevation categories (high, medium, and low) in each river basin, and approximately one-quarter of the SPW in each elevation category were randomly selected as samples for photo analysis.

Maps of the SPW boundaries prepared by the SNEP GIS staff were used to transfer the boundaries to 1:100,000 scale maps. Aerial photographs at 1:12,000 or 1:15,840 scales from 1991, 1992, or 1993 were available for all national forests in the Sierra Nevada except for portions of the Inyo and wilderness portions of the Sierra National Forest. Photographs of the lower-elevation portions of the range were available from the Bureau of Land Management at 1:12,000 scale and at a 1:24,000 scale from the California Department of Forestry and Fire Protection. Photography was unavailable for a few areas originally selected, and those areas were not sampled.

Stereo images of stream reaches designated on the 1:100,000 scale maps within the selected SPW were examined to visually identify areas with apparently unnatural discontinuities in riparian vegetation. There were many more streams visible on the photos that were not marked on the maps. Those smaller streams were not explicitly studied, but major impacts to such areas were noted separately. The ecological importance of small streams is not to be overlooked; however, practical difficulties in examining unmapped tributaries prevented a detailed analysis. Reaches of 1 to 4 km in length were examined at one time. The approximate percentage of each reach that was obviously impacted or artificially void of vegetation was recorded. The threshold for deciding when an area was sufficiently affected to score it as impacted was based on subjective interpretation of the image. In most cases, the decision was easy: vegetation was present and fairly dense or nearly absent. Areas naturally devoid of riparian vegetation (such as bedrock stream channels) were readily distinguished most of the time from those that had been disturbed. In cases where the reason for absence of vegetation was uncertain (such as intermittent streams at low elevation or high-elevation meadows), the reaches were not included in either the percent-void estimates or the total. Inundated areas were not included in these totals, but were handled separately for the entire range. The first few SPW to be examined were later redone to ensure consistency throughout the study area.

The principal problems and uncertainties of this approach were inability to determine reason for absence of vegetation in all cases, inability to rate partial impairment of the riparian vegetation, inability to identify changes in species composition, inability to see below tree tops, and a lack of field verification. We were unable to compare changes in vegetation over time. Impacts to upper headwaters and small streams were not assessed by this method. Only impacts that removed riparian canopy were discernible. Such a technique tells us nothing about the finer-scale impacts and changes. These less dramatic, though ecologically critical changes could not be studied over any appreciable fraction of the mountain range within the scope of this project. However, the method did allow an assessment of complete removal of riparian vegetation throughout the Sierra Nevada with a sampling strategy that included more than 9,500 km (5,900 mi) of riparian corridors out of about 72,000 km (45,000 mi) of streams mapped at a scale of 1:100,000. Although this large-scale analysis with aerial photography is only suggestive about the presence or absence of riparian trees and possible causes of any decline, outside reviewers found the method to be inadequate to quantify the extent of riparian degradation. Therefore, only qualitative observations are reported in this document.

HISTORICAL IMPACTS TO RIPARIAN AREAS

Different aspects of the history of impacts to riparian areas in the Sierra Nevada are described in several chapters (Beesley 1996; Kattelmann 1996; Kinney 1996; Larson 1996). The following is a brief overview based on those chapters of the SNEP report. Prior to Euro-American exploration and settlement, Native Americans made considerable use of riparian areas where food and other resources were available (Anderson and Moratto 1996). The overwhelming majority of prehistoric sites in the foothills are located along streams. Wet meadows were horticulturally managed for food plants and game habitat (Anderson and Moratto 1996). On the east side of the Sierra Nevada, the Paiute built dams and irrigation canals to irrigate areas exceeding 5 km² (2 mi²) in the bottomlands of the Owens Valley to enhance the growth of native vegetation (Steward 1934; Lawton et al. 1976).

The discovery of gold in 1848 had swift and dramatic consequences to streams and rivers of the Sierra Nevada, especially in the central portion of the western slope. Streams were dammed, diverted, dewatered, excavated, polluted, and filled with debris of enormous hydraulic mines. Virtually all streams on the central western slope were prospected (Averill 1946; Clark 1970). These excavations destabilized channel beds and banks and devastated riparian vegetation over a vast area. Mining debris was redeposited throughout the channels, but often formed tailings dams at confluences where channel gradients lessened (James 1994). Temporary reservoirs formed behind these debris accumulations, which occasionally failed catastrophically, releasing large volumes of sediment and further scouring and burying riparian areas. Dredging was an important source of gold within the riparian area of the lower reaches of the main rivers where the Sierra Nevada meets the Central Valley (Aubury 1910).

Acquisition of water for hydraulic mines developed engineering technology and physical works that have had lasting impacts on California's water distribution system and riparian areas. Generation of power for mines and mills led to one of the world's most extensive hydroelectric networks. Irrigated agriculture in the foothills initially occurred in or near riparian areas with frequent drainage of wetlands. Continued water development for hydropower, irrigation, flood control, and municipal supply installed hundreds of dams, large and small, throughout riparian areas of the Sierra Nevada.

Grazing was a nearly ubiquitous impact as cattle and sheep were driven virtually everywhere in the Sierra Nevada that forage was available (Kinney 1996; Menke et al. 1996). Anecdotal accounts describe vast herds and severe overgrazing (Sudworth 1900; Leiberg 1902). Overgrazing has been blamed for accelerated erosion beginning in the late 1800s and massive gullying of meadows in the decades that followed (Wagoner 1886; Hughes 1934). Widespread deterioration of meadows led to efforts by the Forest Service to reduce the degradation (Kraebel and Pillsbury 1934). However, continuing presence of large herds did not allow riparian vegetation to recover enough to reduce erosion of streambanks.

Timber harvesting in the 19th century impacted local streams, but perhaps mainly because of its typical location: near streams. We can assume that riparian and near-channel forests were targeted during the mining era because they grew on gold-bearing stream deposits and wood was needed where most of the activity was: along streams. Rivers were also used for log transport. Railroads facilitated log removal and were often located within riparian areas for efficiency of construction and routing. Meadows were drained for railway and road placement, as well as for homes and agriculture. Most of the bridges and stream crossings for roads that currently fragment riparian areas were built between 1945 and 1975 (Nelson et al. 1994).

CONTINUING IMPACTS TO RIPARIAN RESOURCES

Cumulative Interactions of Impacts

The great variety of impacts to riparian areas outlined below often work in combination to further degrade a particular site or an extended length of the riparian corridor and downstream aquatic systems. Some impacts are chronic or persistent like water diversions or roads. Other

215

effects are short-term or periodic, such as fire or timber harvest. The different impacts usually result in a simplified system of fewer species or individuals or reduced habitat diversity. Multiple impacts generally increase the fragmentation of habitat. A couple of short breaks in the continuity of a riparian area (small bridges, for example) may not be too important, but several road crossings and reservoirs produce a highly fragmented riparian system. Present uses are superimposed on the legacy of placer and hydraulic mining. Streamflow regulation by dams alters channel conditions on all downstream reaches that may also have local impacts, such as logging or grazing. The possible combinations of effects from cows in campgrounds to off-road vehicle use of logging roads are manifold. Nevertheless, pieces of the riparian area are affected by all the different uses, influences, and impacts that occur at a particular site. In addition, downstream areas are affected by degradation of upstream sites through changes in water or sediment delivery; changes in water temperature; lack of leaves, logs, or seeds; etc. With streams, the concept of everything being connected to everything else is easy to visualize, especially in the downstream direction.

Dams and Water Management

Water-resource development activities necessarily take place in stream channels and riparian corridors. Construction of a dam and filling of a reservoir eliminate riparian habitat directly. Downstream of a dam or diversion, riparian conditions are affected by project-induced changes in water availability, substrate, and flood frequency and magnitude. Most water projects alter the natural hydrograph and create a different regime of seasonal water availability for riparian plants. The most common change in streamflow is substantial reduction of peak flows -- often an order of magnitude or more. Plant species that require high flows for seed dispersal and moist soil for germination may decline where peak flows are controlled. However, plant establishment and growth can also be enhanced by reductions in flood frequency and magnitude (Harris et al. 1987). Changes in sediment delivery and the capability to move sediments downstream of dams further influence riparian communities.

Some common effects of construction and operation of dams on riparian vegetation include:
- breaking the continuity of riparian habitat and its wildlife migration routes;
- loss of vegetation to roads, penstocks, canals, transmission lines, dams, and other facilities;
- temporary loss of vegetation during construction activities;
- non-native plants may encroach on areas cleared of native vegetation;
- loss of upstream vegetation under continual or seasonal inundation;
- where peak flows are reduced, riparian cover can increase (except on very steep or flat reaches);
- reduced flooding allows formerly flood-suppressed plants (often non-native) to flourish;
- colonization of the formerly active channel can stabilize sediments there and constrict the channel;
- during very large events, flood levels may be increased by the decline in channel capacity;
- lack of routine floods can reduce seed dispersal and germination of many native plants;
- when discharge during low flow periods is reduced, there is less recharge of floodplain aquifers;
- when less water is available, moisture stress can decrease riparian cover, esp. on uphill edges;
- in such cases, the riparian area will contract toward the channel;
- more xeric plant species may move into the outer margin of the formerly wet soils;
- when water availability is limited, deep-rooted trees are favored over shallow-rooted species;
- channel incision caused by stream rerouting during construction may lower ground water levels;
- delivery of sediment from upstream is reduced, and fine-grained substrate may be lost eventually;

216

(Williams and Wolman 1984; Federal Energy Regulatory Commission 1986; Harris et al. 1987; Jones and Stokes Associates 1989; Kondolf and Matthews 1993; Mount 1995).

Because broad valleys with wide riparian areas were often optimum reservoir sites, much of the best former riparian habitat in the Sierra Nevada is now under water. The extent of inundation across the range becomes apparent when one realizes that virtually all flatwater on the western slope of the Sierra Nevada below 1,500 m (5,000 ft) is artificial.

The many possible combinations of environmental conditions and flow regimes have resulted in a variety of vegetation responses to water management throughout the Sierra Nevada (Harris et al. 1987; Smith et al. 1991; Stromberg and Patten 1992). More than a century of excessive diversion combined with other impacts on the Little Truckee River has resulted in a wide unstable channel unprotected by riparian vegetation (Erman 1992). Riparian width has decreased dramatically in many eastern Sierra Nevada streams on alluvial fans (Taylor 1982). Riparian communities along stream reaches that lose water through seepage into their bed or banks are at particular risk from diversions (Jones and Stokes Associates 1989; Kondolf 1989). About one-third of all stream reaches in Inyo and Mono counties have been dewatered with severe consequences for riparian environments (Taylor 1983). Riparian vegetation has essentially disappeared where no water is permitted to flow in the natural channel (e.g., segments of Rush Creek in the Mono basin [Stine 1991]). In channels depleted of riparian vegetation, floods have caused severe bank erosion, channel migration, and road failures (Vorster and Kondolf 1989). The loss of riparian vegetation contributed substantially to the instability of the channels (Vorster and Kondolf 1989). Where peak flows have been reduced, both width of the riparian area and species richness on some diverted segments of Bishop Creek were significantly greater than on some undiverted reaches (Harris et al. 1987). The loss of daily fluctuations in streamflow during the snowmelt season below dams has probably altered ecological processes in the floodplain that was wetted on a daily basis, but these effects are not known to have been studied. Reduced flow in the lower Owens River allowed exotics to invade and native vegetation to move into the former channel (Brothers 1984). Augmentation of flows at the receiving end of trans-basin diversion has widened channels and has pushed back riparian vegetation, as in the case of the upper Owens River (Stromberg and Patten 1991). Below many dams, streamflow during summer and autumn is usually many times greater than the natural inflow to the reservoir because the high flows of winter and spring captured by the dam are gradually released from storage to meet water demands not synchronized with the Mediterrenean climate. These managed flows further alter the development of riparian communities.

Encroachment of vegetation into river channels has been noted below many dams and diversions on the west slope of the Sierra Nevada such as below Tulloch, Don Pedro, La Grange, and McClure reservoirs (Pelzman 1973), but it is not a universal response. Canopy cover increased and vegetation encroached upon the formerly active channel below a diversion on the North Fork of the Kings River (Taylor and Davilla 1985). In the same river basin and same study, no change was noted on Black Rock Creek below a partial diversion, but little vegetation remained in a tributary where all summer streamflow was diverted. Where peak flows were reduced on upper forks of Willow Creek, canopy cover apparently increased from about 78 percent above diversions to about 94 percent below, although other confounding factors may have been involved (Taylor and Davilla 1986). Farther downstream on Willow Creek, where most flow is diverted, riparian vegetation was substantially depleted. On Cherry Creek, aerial photographs indicated an increase in woody riparian vegetation after reservoir completion (Federal Energy Regulatory Commission 1994). As these examples illustrate, vegetation responds differently to river management depending on site conditions and the nature of regulation (Jones and Stokes Associates 1989). Variability in channel morphology, groundwater regime, and flow conditions confounds generalization about the extent of change of riparian vegetation in response to water management (Harris et al. 1987).

Creation of a reservoir with fluctuating water level eliminates the original riparian area and prevents establishment of a new one. Therefore, most dams destroy the continuity of riparian corridors. The lengths of these gaps along streams range from tens of meters to tens of kilometers. More than 150 riparian gaps greater than 0.5 km (0.3 mi) in length were found by inspecting maps of water developments. More than 20 reservoirs with pools greater than 0.5 km (0.3 mi) in length occur in highly developed river basins such as the Feather and American Rivers. This large-scale fragmentation is worst in the northern river basins of the west slope and numerically limited in the three southern basins (Kaweah, Tule, and Kern), which have one major reservoir apiece. Crude measurements from maps assuming straight-line channels in the absence of knowledge of the route of original river courses under the reservoirs provided a total estimate of 900 to 1,200 km (550 to 750 mi) of inundated riparian corridors throughout the Sierra Nevada. In addition, hundreds of small stockponds seasonally inundating intermittent stream channels at elevations below 1,000 m (3,300 ft.) were observed on the aerial photographs.

The artificial waterways created by the miners and their successors have also created riparian areas where they would not otherwise exist. Acquisition and delivery of water to mines was to become a huge industry that was probably more profitable than mining. In the 1860s, more than 8500 km (5300 mi) of main canals and about 1280 km (800 mi) of branch ditches had been constructed (Browne 1868; Logan 1948; McPhee 1993). Many of these old ditches and canals still supply water for hydroelectric generation, municipal use, or irrigation and have become a secondary channel system. Leakage is a significant and persistent difficulty with many of these waterways. In a 160 km (100 mile) long canal network in El Dorado County, about half of the initial water plus any gains enroute are lost to seepage (Soil Conservation Service 1984). However, the leakage has been found to benefit wildlife habitat by creating artificial riparian areas. This application of water may have acquired some legal status that prevents the ditch owner from converting to a pipe and drying up the leaks. A decision is pending on such a case involving the Crawford Ditch of the El Dorado Irrigation District (Borcalli and Associates 1993). Another aspect of water management that affects riparian vegetation is groundwater pumping. In a few areas of the Sierra Nevada, such as the Owens Valley, the water table has been artificially lowered by pumping, thereby reducing the availability of water to plants and changing the composition of riparian communities (Perkins et al. 1984; Groeneveld and Or 1994).

Grazing

A much more comprehensive assessment of range conditions and grazing in the Sierra Nevada is available in Menke et al. (1996). Impacts of overgrazing are considered second only to dams and river regulation as causing degradation of riparian areas in the Sierra Nevada foothills (Nelson et al. 1994). Grazing by sheep and cattle is widely believed to have been virtually ubiquitous throughout the Sierra Nevada before 1930 (Vankat and Major 1978; McKelvey and Johnston 1992; Kinney 1996), and almost all accessible riparian areas were impacted (Dudley and

218

Embury 1995). Historical analysis of grazing allotment records found persistent patterns of overstocking in many areas (Menke et al. 1996). This period of overgrazing may have had dramatic impacts on stream systems. If these historical inferences are correct, current riparian conditions reflect that history of use and impact on the vast majority of streams in the Sierra Nevada. Therefore, we are unsure of exactly what constitutes natural riparian vegetation in most parts of the range. A reasonable approximation of natural riparian conditions may exist along many streams that have been grazed only lightly or have been rested for many years. Riparian areas in the national parks have been rested from commercial grazing since about 1930, although pack stock continue to be used for recreational and administrative purposes. Pack stock are now the primary impact in some high-elevation meadows, but there is little monitoring of their effects (Menke et al. 1996). Only those rare areas that were physically inaccessible or offered insignificant forage were not affected by grazing. Anecdotally, those ungrazed reference sites tend to have much denser vegetation. Some highly altered systems may be perceived as natural. Because livestock grazing has been such an extensive activity over the past 150 years, many people today have never seen an ungrazed stream and assume that present conditions are natural (Elmore and Beschta 1987). In some places, streams that are shallow and wide with a minimal amount of riparian vegetation have existed for so long that those situations are often regarded as normal.

The interrelated impacts commonly attributed to overgrazing include:
- reduction in vegetative cover,
- changes in species composition,
- introduction of exotics,
- reduction or elimination of regeneration,
- compaction and cutting of meadow sod,
- depletion or elimination of deeply rooted vegetation that strengthens banks,
- loss of litter and soil organic matter,
- erosion of stream banks, beds, and flood plains,
- loss of overhanging streambanks,
- destabilization of alluvial channels and transformation to wide shallow channels,
- initiation of gullies and headcuts,
- channel incision and consequent lowering of water tables,
- desiccation of meadows,
- increased water temperature during summer due to reduction of shade,
- increased freezing in winter from reduction of insulation and snow trapping efficiency,
- siltation of streams,
- bacterial and nutrient pollution,
- and decline of summer streamflow

(e.g., Platts 1984; Blackburn 1984; Kauffman and Krueger 1984; Skovlin 1984; Elmore and Beschta 1987; Armour et al. 1991; Platts 1991; Chaney et al. 1993).

Impacts to riparian areas are now widely recognized as a principal issue in range management (U.S. General Accounting Office 1988; National Research Council 1994). Riparian conditions were the only key range elements not found to be recovering in the national Range Reform '94 report (U.S. Bureau of Land Management 1994). Adequate methods to quantitatively assess impacts of overgrazing in evaluations of cumulative watershed effects are yet to be developed (e.g., U.S. Environmental Protection Agency 1993).

Riparian areas often suffer from overgrazing because their vegetation tends to be grazed more heavily than upland vegetation because of consumption preference and availability of water and shade. Fenced exclosures along streams illustrate vegetation recovery after grazing, which has been dramatic in some areas. Although geomorphic recovery can take decades longer than vegetative recovery (Kondolf 1993), there can be some response after plants are sufficiently re-established to provide bank stability and sediment trapping (Elmore and Beschta 1987). For example, after only five years of rest within a fenced exclosure, bank stability and bank undercut were greater on rested reaches of Silver King Creek and Coyote Valley Creek (tributaries to the Carson River) than on grazed reaches (Overton et al. 1994). Channels in the rested areas were also deeper and narrower than channels in nearby grazed areas (Overton et al. 1994). However, on the Kern Plateau, stream morphology has not recovered after 12 years of exclosure (Dudley and Dietrich 1995). A recent study of channel characteristics between pairs of currently grazed areas on National Forests and long-rested areas in National Parks in the Sierra Nevada found significant differences in bank angle, unstable banks, undercut banks, bed particle size, and pool frequency (U.S. Forest Service 1995b). Significant differences in undercut banks and unstable banks were also observed between grazed areas and adjacent fenced exclosures with a few years of rest. A recent evaluation of a sample of 24 locations throughout the Sierra Nevada found 13 to be at risk of loss of critical functions and 4 to be not functioning (Menke et al. 1996). That evaluation also found a strong association between the condition of meadow vegetation and the condition of adjacent streams.

Healthy riparian vegetation is critical to the maintenance of channels in alluvium. Vegetation deflects the erosive power of flowing water and shields the soil. Roots add substantial structural strength to the soil. Floodplain vegetation also enhances deposition of sediments above the active channel. The North Fork Feather River provides an example of severe streambank degradation from overgrazing. The Plumas National Forest was heavily grazed from the 1860s into the early 20th century and began to show signs of degradation by 1920 (e.g., Hughes 1934; Clifton 1992). Severe gullying was already in progress by 1900 (Leiberg 1902). Soil losses from overgrazed meadows in the North Fork Feather River basin have been estimated as 15-30 cm (6-12 in) since grazing began (Soil Conservation Service 1989). Alluvial channels without vegetation protection along their banks have increased in width severalfold and downcut as well. About 60 percent of the sediment delivered down a major tributary to the North Fork Feather River has been attributed to bank erosion where vegetation has been eliminated (Soil Conservation Service 1989). A major program of channel stabilization and vegetation re-establishment has been started on tributaries to the North Fork Feather River (Wills and Sheehan 1994).

Combination of lack of vegetative cover, increased channel width, absence of undercut banks, increased sedimentation, decreased streamflow in summer, and higher water temperatures can dramatically decrease fish production in grazed streams (Behnke and Raleigh 1979). Many studies throughout the western United States have demonstrated impairment of fisheries in streams with overgrazed riparian areas (e.g., various papers in Menke 1977; Elmore 1989; Platts 1991; Armour et al. 1991). The more open vegetation resulting from grazing may expose amphibians to predation and desiccation. Direct trampling by livestock may be an important cause of amphibian mortality (Jennings 1995). Effects on benthic invertebrate communities are currently being investigated on streams of the eastern Sierra Nevada (Herbst and Knapp 1995).

Riparian areas with dense vegetation are sometimes credited with enhancing late-season streamflow. In the absence of gullying, this assertion is probably only true when surface conditions are greatly altered. Removal of vegetation and compaction of soils by cattle can decrease infiltration and consequently increase surface runoff and augment local peak flows (Behnke and Raleigh 1979; Platts 1984). Natural riparian vegetation and undisturbed soils allow more infiltration than compacted soils (e.g., Dudley and Dietrich 1995). Therefore, soil moisture and bank storage would be greater and could contribute more water to the adjacent stream than if water were not allowed to enter the soil in the first place. However, transpiration by riparian vegetation also depletes soil moisture. Therefore, base flow amounts depend on a balance between additions to soil moisture through high infiltration and depletion through transpiration.

Riparian vegetation also protects streambanks against erosion and the vicious cycle of degradation that leads to a deeply incised channel and a lowered water table. When the water table drops as a result of channel incision, streamflow in the summer and autumn can be drastically reduced. Avoidance of gullying and resultant drops of the water table can more than compensate for evapotranspiration depletion of potential releases of water to streams from adjacent alluvial aquifers (Elmore and Beschta 1987).

Riparian vegetation degraded by overgrazing generally recovers within a decade once grazing pressure is removed (e.g., Platts and Nelson 1985; Chaney et al. 1993; Nelson et al. 1994). As long as gullying has not lowered the water table, riparian and meadow plants will regrow in a few years if not consumed (Odion et al. 1990). However, there are many potential successional pathways, and some systems do not necessarily recover to pre-disturbance states (Menke et al. 1996). Channel morphology responds to the cessation of the disturbance much more slowly (Kondolf 1993). Decades to centuries may be required. Rates of recovery tend to be highly variable between locations and depend on ability of riparian vegetation to trap sediment and build streambanks. A variety of structures have been installed in channels throughout the Sierra Nevada in attempts to halt gully progression (Kraebel and Pillsbury 1934; Hagberg 1995). By locally raising the water table, check dams can also increase bank storage and baseflow (Ponce and Lindquist 1990). Among land managers, a trend is beginning away from instream structures and toward patience with allowing vegetative recovery and geomorphic processes to rebuild damaged meadows and streams (e.g., Elmore and Beschta 1989). The structural approach has involved substantial expenditure of public funds to repair damage caused in pursuit of private profits and has avoided or delayed making changes in grazing practices. Small check dams and other in-channel structures often fail in dynamic alluvial systems (Elmore and Beschta 1989; Odion et al. 1990). Allotment management plans are now under review or revision on several national forests of the Sierra Nevada following a legal decision in 1994 that the grazing program of the Sierra National Forest was in violation of regulations relating to the National Environmental Policy Act. Throughout the Sierra Nevada, riparian conditions may continue to decline if current practices are not improved (U.S. Bureau of Land Management 1994). There is tremendous potential for improvements in both ecosystem functions and forage production through more careful range management (Menke et al. 1996).

Roads

When roads are located in riparian areas, the ecological impacts are often severe. Generally, roads are intended to last for decades, at least. Roads are a true conversion in land cover with little hope of natural recovery unless they are abandoned. Early roads were often located near streams simply to take advantage of the flat ground of the valleys. Such roads running parallel to streams can replace a large fraction of the riparian area with an unvegetated impermeable surface. Bridges, culverts, revetments to protect roads, and other engineering works associated with roads near streams impact riparian vegetation directly and indirectly. Direct effects include removal or burial during construction and compaction of adjacent soil. Indirect effects include alterations in surface and subsurface hydrologic flow paths and erosion and redeposition within the riparian area (Furniss et al. 1991). With each new road crossing, a piece of riparian habitat is lost directly, and the riparian corridor is further fragmented. Secondary effects of the construction may extend upstream and downstream, as well.

The availability of digital maps of roads and streams allowed the SNEP GIS group to calculate how often roads are found near streams. The analysis was based on a grid of one-hectare (100 x 100 m) [2.47 ac; 328 x 328 ft] cells. Sources of digital road information were the U.S. Forest Service road layer of so-called "system roads" and a road layer at 1:100, 000 scale provided by the Teale Data Center for areas outside the proclaimed boundaries of the National Forests. At the resolution of these maps, if a road touched any part of a cell, that cell was designated a road and similarly for streams. Although the analysis at this resolution is somewhat awkward, it provides a basis for comparing the proximity of roads and streams between river basins. The quantity of interest was the number of cells containing both a road and a stream expressed as a percentage of the cells containing a stream. For the 24 river basins in the SNEP study area, the values ranged between 3 and 11 percent. Basins with the lowest values (3-4 %) were the Kings, Kern, Kaweah, Carson, Mono, Tuolumne, Merced, and San Joaquin. Basins with the highest values (8-11 %) were the Cosumnes, Walker, Truckee, Yuba, and Mokelumne. Smaller analysis areas would be expected to have a much wider range (no roads to roads following most streams in a small watershed). Results for 141 Calwater (California Department of Forestry and Fire Protection 1996) "hydrologic subareas" from the same analysis are reported in Kondolf et al. 1996. The equivalent values ranged from 2 to 33% with a median of 14%.

A study of logging impacts on stream invertebrates showed that the worst effects occurred below failures of roads and culverts (Erman et al. 1977). Road construction activities seemed to affect the aquatic communities much less than did the repeated failure of poorly designed and constructed roads. Riparian corridors along major rivers affected by highways for long distances include the Feather, North Yuba, South Yuba, Truckee, South Fork of the American, Merced, Kaweah, Tule, and Kern Rivers. In several cases, what remains of the riparian corridor is sandwiched between a highway and a railway or secondary road on the opposite bank. Along the Truckee River, additional riparian vegetation has been replaced by a large flume.

Timber Harvest and Buffer Strips

During the Gold Rush, riparian areas were intentionally denuded to allow access to stream gravels or to relocate the stream in a flume for riverbed mining. When most mining activity was located along streams, trees in the riparian areas were also more accessible than those farther upslope. In some cases, such as the Truckee and Little Truckee Rivers (Erman 1992), water courses were used to transport logs downstream. Where riparian forests were not harvested during the mining era, subsequent timber operations obtained high-quality trees from the productive soils of valley flats. Apparently, little thought was given to consequences of near-stream logging until after World War II, and serious concern did not develop until the 1960s. Removal of trees from the riparian area continued through the 1970s when "best management practices" and "streamside management zones" were adopted. Forest practices of the past 25 years have become progressively more cautious near riparian areas (Adams et al. 1988). Today, clearcut harvesting near streams is rare in the Sierra Nevada, though not absent. Our aerial photograph survey revealed a substantial number of harvested units that included riparian areas, but their age could not be determined. On national forests, streamside management zones have been removed from the timber base of scheduled harvest, but may be entered for salvage logging, thinning, and special management needs. The timber base, lands where scheduled harvesting may occur, still includes the smallest channels that may not support fish or carry water all year. California's Forest Practice Rules (California Department of Forestry and Fire Protection 1994) set goals for maintaining buffer strips in streamside areas on private timberlands and set some limits on timber removal and heavy-equipment operations near water courses.

The riparian area has been identified as a critical area for minimizing sediment input into streams (e.g., Brown 1980; Megahan and King 1985). Under current forest practices, riparian areas on fish-bearing streams are usually partially protected by standards and guidelines that affect management activities in streamside management zones between the stream and timber harvest activities. Buffer strips have benefits for both the adjacent stream environment as well as that downstream by reducing pulses of sediment (Mahoney and Erman 1984). In a study of several streams in the northern Sierra Nevada, effects of logging on invertebrates were not noticed in streams with wide bufferstrips (Erman et al. 1977; Newbold et al. 1980). Streams with narrow buffer strips (less than 30 m) had impacted invertebrate communities to about the same extent as streams without any residual forest (Erman et al. 1977) and did not recover more quickly than those without buffer strips (Erman and Mahoney 1983).

Maintaining the effectiveness of streamside buffer strips requires careful consideration of their design and the influence of other management activities. Concern exists about the potential for wind damage to narrow strips of trees formerly surrounded by a dense forest. Susceptibility of buffer strips to windthrow should be carefully evaluated prior to harvesting adjacent timber. Denser streamside stands may have shallower roots reflecting a mutual dependency in dissipating wind forces (Steinblums et al. 1984; Brown 1980). Herbicide use near buffer strips can potentially cause severe damage to the riparian vegetation. Similarly, grazing in streamside areas seems counterproductive to the intended functions of buffer strips for timber management but occurs throughout most of the Sierra Nevada.

Considerable uncertainty exists about whether buffer strips act as a filter for upslope effects or simply avoid disturbance in the zone that is most likely to contribute water, sediment, nutrients, or introduced chemicals to the stream (Brown 1980). Although reduction of undesirable inputs to an adjacent stream occur in either case, improved understanding of the processes is needed. One of the presumed actions of riparian buffer strips is their ability to reduce the speed of overland flow and cause some of the stormwater's sediment to be deposited before reaching the stream (e.g., Adams 1993; Nelson et al. 1994). Comparisons have been made between slopes with and without buffer strips, and those without riparian vegetation usually produce far more sediment than those with streamside vegetation (e.g., Heede 1990). However, the mechanisms of erosion, sediment transport, and sediment deposition are rarely studied directly. Although riparian vegetation can function in a sediment trapping mode, conditions for sediment delivery in sheet wash are probably rare in the Sierra Nevada except occasionally on agricultural fields, construction sites, and roads. Any sediment in motion on a hillslope that has not been redeposited within a few meters of its starting point is probably in channelized flow (Brown 1980). Channels are likely to pass through riparian areas unhindered because the streamside land usually has high soil moisture and may be generating saturated overland flow itself during a storm. An alternative hypothesis to explain the lower sediment yield commonly observed below buffer strips is that the riparian area itself is not producing any sediment that would be available for immediate delivery to the stream. When riparian vegetation is cleared, conditions favorable for sediment production and delivery are established (e.g., Megahan and King 1985). This streamside erosion is likely to overwhelm any contributions from upslope under typical conditions of climate and logging in the Sierra Nevada.

Stream Temperature The temperature of streams has several direct and indirect effects on fish and other aquatic organisms. The metabolic activity of fish is most efficient within a limited range of temperatures. Water temperature partially determines how much oxygen is contained in the water and available to fish. The amount of a gas dissolved in a liquid is inversely proportional to its temperature. Therefore, streams at higher water temperatures contain less dissolved oxygen. Many aquatic bacteria thrive in warm water, and some of these bacteria are pathogenic to fish. Increased light penetration to streams stimulates growth of aquatic plants and increases overall productivity. However, the resulting higher water temperatures (above 20 to 24°C [68 to 75°F]) can be lethal to salmonids.

The temperature of small forest streams depends primarily on availability of solar energy. Sunlight striking the water surface and exposed rocks that can reradiate and conduct energy to the stream warms the water. Water temperature follows a sinusoidal pattern on a daily and seasonal basis associated with radiant energy received by the stream. Creeks exposed to sunlight have much more dynamic temperature patterns than those receiving little direct solar radiation. Little heat is exchanged with most streams by convection, conduction, or evaporation (Brown 1969). Therefore, shading provided by riparian vegetation is critical to the energy balance of small streams. When shade is removed, maximum stream temperatures can increase by several degrees (Brown 1970; Brown and Krygier 1970; McGurk 1989). Average daily maximum temperatures for the warmest ten-day period of each year of a stream draining a 325 km² (125 mi²) watershed in Oregon increased 6°C (11°F) between 1955 to 1984, apparently in response to timber harvesting (Beschta and Taylor 1988). Stream temperature is also influenced by the initial temperature of the sources of water, volume of water to be heated (small streams warm faster than large streams with the same energy input), surface area (wide, shallow streams warm faster than narrow, deep streams), and bed and bank materials (dark rock will absorb and retain more heat than will light-colored fine sediments). Larger rivers have more thermal inertia, and their temperature depends more on the temperature of tributary waters than on their surface energy balance. Releases from reservoirs can dramatically alter downstream water temperatures, depending on whether water is discharged from deep cold layers or warm near-surface layers. Groundwater inputs can also affect stream temperatures, especially near hot springs!

Stream temperature can be affected by changing stream shading. By maintaining the integrity of riparian vegetation, natural levels of sunlight will reach the stream. The orientation of the stream in different reaches will determine the optimum location of riparian vegetation for maximum shading. Canopy closure above and to the south of the stream is perhaps the best overall measure of shading efficiency. Avoidance of undesired warming along all reaches is necessary because once the stream gains extra heat, it does not readily cool. Even by flowing through long distances of well-shaded channel in mid-summer, little heat is lost. In rangeland streams, maintenance of riparian vegetation is critical even though canopy closure is rarely attained even on ungrazed streams. Loss of riparian vegetation and undercut banks from overgrazing removes whatever shade might be available and may lead to stream widening as well. Riparian vegetation also reduces the radiational loss of heat from streams during cold periods and can reduce freezing. During winter in the snow zone, riparian vegetation may help to trap more snow over the channels and reduce the depth of ice formation by insulating the stream. Simple models of temperature response to energy input are available to predict impacts of altering shade (Brown, 1969; Brown 1980; Beschta 1984).

Large Woody Debris Fallen trees and branches in stream channels influence movement of sediment and water through channels, dissipate energy of flowing water, create pools, provide micro-habitat for some organisms, and act as substrates for microbes and invertebrates (Harmon et al. 1986; Naiman et al. 1992a). The presence of large woody debris in channels can dramatically alter channel morphology and sediment storage (Keller and Swanson 1979; Nakamura and Swanson 1993; Keller and MacDonald 1995). Large wood can provide a stepped profile, which dissipates potential energy from the stream and stores large quantities of sediment (Marston 1982). For example, more than 70 percent of the potential energy of forested streams in a Colorado study area was dissipated in vertical falls over logs (Heede 1972). Woody debris can be an important means of forming pool habitat and variability in depth and velocity (Sedell 1984; Bilby and Ward 1989). Wood can be a reliable source of food for decomposers when leaves and other fine organic matter are unavailable (Maser and Sedell 1994) as well as a physical habitat for invertebrates (Erman 1996). Because of the slow decay processes and episodic movement, consideration of wood in streams requires a time perspective of decades to centuries. Changes in the composition and size of trees in riparian areas affect the potential delivery of wood to streams (Robinson and Beschta 1990). Large woody debris from logging tends to be less stable than natural snags because of the lack of rootwads and limbs on logging waste (Ralph et al. 1994).

In the past, large woody debris was often removed from streams because it was thought to be a problem with respect to fisheries and flooding (Maser and Sedell 1994). Wood was removed from the Merced River in Yosemite Valley until 1989 because it could be a hazard to recreationists (Madej et al. 1994). Wood continues to be removed from streams by the highway departments and local flood control agencies. Removal of wood from channels can dramatically alter the morphology of channels and reduce the diversity of micro-habitats for aquatic organisms (Keller and MacDonald 1995).

Only a few studies have measured large woody debris in streams of the Sierra Nevada. Accumulations of woody debris were not found to be significantly different between logged and control reaches of a couple of streams in the northern Sierra Nevada because logging waste compensated for the decrease in natural supply (O'Connor 1986). The abundance of wood accumulations in streams might be expected to decrease downstream of riparian harvests after the first pulse of logging waste is flushed out of the channel. Data on large wood were collected on 93 plots on 17 streams of the Stanislaus National Forest between 1,100 m (3,600 ft) and 2300 m (7,500 ft) (Ruediger 1991). Plots that reflected either unlogged or light salvage logging contained about the three times the volume of wood per unit area that was contained on plots that had been logged a few decades ago (152 m^3 ha^{-1} unlogged vs. 52 m^3 ha^{-1} logged). On 18 of the plots, the volume of large woody debris exceeded 200 m^3 ha^{-1} and was as high as 1,175 m^3 ha^{-1}, values that are more typical of the Pacific Northwest (Ruediger 1991). On unlogged plots, both the volume per unit area and number of pieces per 100 m decreased with large stream size. On the average, the number of stable pieces (those that had at least one end buried and were storing sediment) per 100 m were 11, 6, 4, and 3 on 2nd, 3rd, 4th, and 5th order streams, respectively (Ruediger 1991). A study of wood in headwater streams on the Tahoe National Forest suggests that although wood improves fish habitat and can protect streambanks, it has little influence on current deflection or pool formation in the reaches examined (Carlson et al. 1995). Data collected on 29 channel reaches in the Sierra Nevada including harvested areas during a comprehensive study (Hawkins et al. 1994) found about 8 pieces of large wood (more than 0.3 m by 3 m) per 100 m of channel on the average in small streams of the forest zone of the Sierra Nevada. The number of pieces per 100 m ranged from 1 to 16. Woody debris is often a problem for reservoir managers in the Sierra Nevada after peak flows move large quantities of logs and branches out of the channels and into reservoirs.

Fire

Catastrophic fire can produce intensive and extensive changes in watershed conditions. Riparian areas that would not be harvested under current forest practices may be burned in intense fires. As with other impacts, the proportion of a catchment that is modified by fire and the location of the burned area with respect to the channel largely determine the effects on streams. Fire intensity is often highly variable over the landscape, and patches of unburned or lightly burned vegetation (especially near streams) can reduce the adverse effects of upslope areas that were intensely burned. Recovery of riparian vegetation usually occurs within a few years after a fire.

Fire suppression during this century in combination with logging and grazing has created forests with much greater density of vegetation than in the past (Skinner and Chang 1996). The dense vegetation also increases the opportunity for intense conflagrations (Skinner and Chang 1996) that could produce major increases in water and sediment yields.

Wildfires often burn less intensely in riparian areas than in upland areas because of the generally moist conditions near streams (Nelson et al. 1994; Toth et al. 1994). Riparian areas may serve as effective barriers to the spread of low severity fires across the landscape (Skinner and Chang 1996). Narrower riparian areas are at greater risk of burning than wider areas, and riparian sites with less water are more likely to burn than wetter sites (Agee 1993). Although riparian areas tend to burn less frequently and less severely than adjacent uplands, they can burn under more intense fire conditions. For example, riparian vegetation was killed on 72 km (45 mi) of perennial streams and partially burned on another 86 km (54 mi) of streams within the Stanislaus Complex burn of 1987 (Stanislaus National Forest 1988). The 1992 Cleveland fire on the Eldorado National Forest and the 1994 Cottonwood/Crystal fire on the east side of the Tahoe National Forest also thoroughly burned many kilometers of riparian corridors. Greater lengths of stream channel escaped serious burning than were actually burned during these fires. Some fires burn relatively little riparian vegetation, such as the Silver Fire Complex in southern Oregon, which occurred at the same time as the Stanislaus Complex fire (Amaranthus et al. 1988). Even light fires can be damaging to susceptible streamside vegetation. Fire is another disturbance factor that contributes to the diverse mosaic of riparian vegetation. Riparian areas are often the first areas to resprout following catastrophic wildfires, and therefore, are usually the first areas to be reoccupied by wildlife.

In general, sediment yields increase markedly after fires, particularly where slopes are steep, fire intensity was severe, and riparian vegetation was burned. Most of the sediment response seems to be from the channels and adjacent areas. In the absence of streamside vegetation, soil particles move into the channels and the banks become less stable. Increases in total discharge and peak flows result in channel erosion. Debris torrents may scour streams if extreme climatic events follow the fire (Helvey 1980; Kuehn 1987). If the fire is particularly hot, woody debris which helped stabilize the channel may be destroyed. Until revegetation occurs following a fire, many riparian functions are seriously impaired. The water table usually raises after a fire in the absence of transpiration demand, leading to increased streamflows against banks with diminished vegetative protection. Dramatic increases in flow of a small spring and a creek in the Sierra Nevada were observed following burning of riparian vegetation (Biswell 1989). Without vegetation and leaf litter as ground cover, erosion can be severe in the saturated near-stream areas. Food supplies for the stream are greatly reduced. Mobile wildlife will seek other unburned riparian areas.

Even when fires are limited to upslope areas, the loss of ground cover on the hillsides can increase water and sediment delivery to the riparian area. Downslope runoff may increase with the reduced transpiration and decreased infiltration where the fire produces hydrophobic conditions. Surface erosion will increase without the vegetative cover and leaf-litter layer. Landslides into the riparian area may increase after roots of dead trees decay.

Studies of the aquatic effects of a fire on the Plumas National Forest demonstrate how both physical and biological features of the stream change over time (Roby 1988; Roby and Azuma 1995). The lower two-thirds of this catchment including riparian vegetation were thoroughly burned. Initially, the channel widened in response to presumed higher flows of water and sediment. However, as vegetation became established and the watershed recovered, the cross sections of the channel returned to their pre-fire areas within six years of the burn. Partial recovery of the invertebrate community seemed to have occurred relatively quickly. No differences in community similarity were noted between burned and unburned reaches one year after the fire, and density and taxa richness were comparable within three years. However, significant (though declining) differences in species diversity between the burned and unburned reaches remained throughout eleven years of monitoring (Roby and Azuma 1995). Aquatic recovery following the 1988 Yellowstone fires in areas that were severely burned is expected to take decades with subtle changes in response to vegetation succession in the riparian area and uplands (Minshall et al. 1989).

Following fires, there is usually a strong desire by land owners, agencies, and the public to do something. Allowing natural recovery processes to function may often be the best policy (Beschta et al. 1995). Salvage logging after a fire is often proposed to recover some financial return from the burnt timber. However, logging operations disturb soils when they are particularly sensitive to erosion in the absence of cover and organic matter. Significant ground disturbance during a salvage sale of the Clark Burn in the Last Chance Creek watershed of Plumas County led to severe erosion during a thunderstorm (Cawley 1991).

The principal objectives of post-fire rehabilitation work should be to avoid making things worse, repair potential problems from fire-fighting activities (bulldozed fire breaks), enhance establishment of native vegetation to provide soil cover and organic matter and streambank stability and shade as quickly as possible, attempt to stabilize channels by non-structural means, minimize adverse effects from the existing road network, schedule operations to minimize exposure of bare soil, and allow natural processes to heal the landscape. Although we have created forests that carry a high risk of damage to aquatic resources, pursuit of quick fixes in an atmosphere of crisis carry substantial risks as well (Beschta et al. 1995).

Exotics

Non-native species have invaded many riparian areas, particularly in the foothills and Owens Valley (Schwartz et al. 1996). Replacement of many native perennials with annuals in meadows (Burcham 1970) may have been facilitated by regulation of streamflow and overgrazing (Nelson et al. 1994). Excessive grazing reduces plant density and increases availability of bare ground for invasion of exotic species if they are present in the area. Kentucky bluegrass is the primary invader of montane meadows throughout the Sierra Nevada (Menke et al. 1996). Salt cedar (Tamarisk) is a major problem (Robinson 1965) along some streams of the eastern Sierra Nevada. The extent of salt cedar along the Owens River has expanded markedly over just the past eight years (Inyo County Water Department 1995). Salt cedar has competitive advantages over cottonwood and other natives in the absence of floods (Krzysik 1990). Salt cedar produces seed over a longer period of the year and is relatively drought tolerant. Dense thickets of salt cedar prevent growth of seedlings of other species. The thickets tend to support fewer insects than other riparian vegetation and are not conducive to foraging by birds (Krzysik 1990). Elimination of native riparian vegetation in the lower Owens River allowed salt cedar and russian olive to invade (Brothers 1984). Attempts at eradication of salt cedar have been made along the Owens River. Both salt cedar and Russian olive have proved to be very difficult to eradicate once established (Schwartz et al. 1996). A few common weedy plants, such as bull thistle, Canadian thistle, scotch broom, and medusa head, have invaded disturbed riparian areas in the Sierra Nevada (Dudley and Collins 1995). Himalayan blackberry and Tree-of-heaven have been able to outcompete native riparian plants. Some exotic aquatic plants have also made their way into Sierra Nevada streams, but growth rates seem to be slow, so eradication is possible if they are discovered before expanding too far (Dudley and Collins 1995).

Alien animals, such as Brown-headed cowbirds, that have invaded riparian areas of the Sierra Nevada have had significant impacts on native riparian species (Graber 1996). Introduced bullfrogs have become widely distributed in ponds and slow-moving streams in the foothills of the Sierra Nevada and are regarded as an important factor in the rapid decline of native frog species and the western pond turtle (Graber 1996). Bullfrogs have largely replaced red-legged frogs and foothill yellow-legged frogs in many locations.

228

Drainage Programs

Wetlands in the Sierra Nevada have been drained since the earliest settlers attempted to "reclaim" meadows and other seasonally wet areas. Mountain meadows were commonly drained with the intent of improving forage conditions and to permit agriculture (Hughes 1934). Galen Clark, the fabled Guardian of Yosemite Valley, dynamited a moraine to drain the El Capitan meadow in 1879 to open more land for grazing and eliminate mosquito breeding areas (Greene 1987). This action of lowering the base level caused the Merced River to downcut several feet. Vegetation near the river was probably altered as a result. Drainage activities have continued until recent times. The Soil Conservation Service and Plumas County removed a natural control on Indian Creek near Crescent Mills in the North Fork Feather River basin during the 1950s and set in motion progressive channel degradation in Indian Creek and Wolf Creek (Greenville Ranger District 1985). Drainage activities on small lots progressively reduce the total amount of wetlands. Road construction in or near meadows often involves drainage measures to stabilize the roadbed.

Phreatophyte Control

Riparian vegetation can account for a disproportionate fraction of total transpiration in small watersheds because it has access to almost unlimited water and favorable conditions for an extended growing season. Phreatophytes (plants with roots extending below the water table) are particularly thirsty. Reductions in this water loss have long been sought by downstream water users, especially in arid regions (Dunford and Fletcher 1947). Although most of these phreatophyte-control projects were in Arizona and New Mexico (e.g., Hibbert 1983), some were also carried out in the Sierra Nevada (e.g., Biswell 1989). Such programs were soon realized to involve some serious environmental consequences (Campbell 1970) and have been largely discontinued. The use of non-destructive chemicals to inhibit transpiration has been studied (e.g., Davenport 1977), but operational programs in the Sierra Nevada are not known.

Residential Development

Development of individual parcels and large subdivisions continues to damage and fragment riparian areas. Areas around streams are aesthetically attractive to people, and riparian areas become preferred locations for our facilities, homes, roads, trails, etc. Obvious effects of residential development on riparian areas include removal of riparian vegetation and construction of roads and structures near streams. Wetlands are routinely drained or filled to make room for structures. However, just the proximity of dwellings to streams leads to a variety of secondary effects. Frequent travel within the riparian area disturbs wildlife. Domestic pets and farm animals interfere with native wildlife. Alien plants from farms and gardens compete with natural flora. Wood is removed from the riparian forest floor and standing trees and snags for fuel. Much of our waste ends up in the riparian corridor. Development of local water supplies for even small communities can significantly reduce streamflow, especially during low flow periods (medina 1990). For example, Sierra City on the North Yuba River, with only a hundred service connections, uses about 185,000 m^3 (20 AF) of water annually, with most of that use during the summer (Don Erman, University of California at Davis, personal communication 1995).

Hydrologic effects of residential development alter riparian areas by changing the streamflow regime that influences riparian plants and animals. Vegetation both near and away from streams is commonly removed in the process of development. Loss of its interception and transpiration functions results in higher soil moisture levels and a tendency toward more rapid runoff. Construction of roads, driveways, gutters, and roofs increases the impervious surface area of a catchment, which leads to more water arriving in channels in less time from even modest rainfall than under natural conditions (Leopold 1968). More frequent floods of larger magnitude can lead to channel enlargement and removal of riparian vegetation (Dunne and Leopold 1978; Booth 1990). If the total area of limited infiltration is a significant fraction of a catchment, ground water levels will decline. Riparian vegetation in many areas depends on subsurface water that is enroute from uplands to streams and may suffer if ground water is less available. Streamflow during non-storm periods that was formerly generated by this mechanism will also decline. Ground water pumping for domestic and irrigation supply can exacerbate the problems of restricted recharge. In some cases, irrigation return flows may augment summer streamflow.

Despite the initial attraction of streams, people are often not satisfied with the location of streams and their tendency to flood on occasion. Therefore, urban and suburban streams are often rebuilt in an attempt to exercise some control over them. Riparian areas suffers both from the construction activities and the artificial waterway in the long term. Around roads and towns, the usual objective of channelization is to get water away from a place where it was not wanted. Creeks of all types and sizes have been relocated, smoothed and straightened to get water away from roads and homes as quickly as possible. These ditches, canals, and storm sewers enhance the flood-producing effects of general land conversion by routing the extra runoff away from the town or road much more quickly than under natural conditions. Peak flows are augmented downstream, but that is typically beyond the concern of the local channelization project. Flooding in Roseville during January 1995 was a classic example of this phenomenon.

Changes in runoff are closely related to declines in water quality associated with urban development. Enhanced runoff washes various contaminants off of roofs, streets, parking lots, gutters, horse corrals, and golf courses and into streams. Diminished baseflow increases the concentration of residual pollution entering after the floods. Urban pollutants include soil particles, nutrients, heavy metals, toxic organic chemicals including pesticides, oil and grease, fertilizers, oxygen-demanding materials such as yard waste, and bacteria and other pathogens (Terrene Institute 1994). Development of riparian areas limits opportunities for filtering, uptake, and assimilation of contaminants. The combined effects of changes in runoff regime, water quality, and channel structure resulting from urbanization has profound effects on aquatic and riparian organisms. Eliminating infiltration on as little as a tenth of the catchment area led to declines in population of fish and amphibians near Seattle (Booth and Reinelt 1993). Residential development requires water supplies that are sometimes developed from local surface water. Creation of reservoirs and diversion structures directly damage riparian areas, and reduced streamflow reduces water availability to the aquatic and riparian communities. Excessive water withdrawals from local streams can threaten recreational fisheries that form part of the economic base supporting the communities seeking the extra water for more development (Kattelmann and Dawson 1994). Development of additional water supplies is likely to become increasingly costly in both financial and environmental terms. The projected demand for additional water in the foothills in the next few decades is staggering (Duane 1996). For example, the Georgetown Divide Public Utilities District expects a 50 percent increase in water use in the next 30 years, and the El Dorado Irrigation District anticipates demand to double in the same period (Borcalli and Associates 1993).

Recreation

Many recreationists have a strong affinity for water, both for visual and direct-contact enjoyment. This desire to be close to streams and lakes has resulted in the riparian location of roads, vacation cabins, campgrounds, trails, and other facilities. River-based recreation can have substantial impacts on riparian vegetation (e.g., Martin 1984). Off-road vehicle tracks were occasionally noted in the river video tapes. Widespread vehicle impacts were found in the South Fork of the Kern River basin. Use of old skid trails and stream fords by off-road vehicles was a frequently noted impact to riparian areas in notes on stream surveys of the Tahoe National Forest. Repeated trampling by hikers eventually kills low plants and compacts the soil (Liddle 1975). Foot traffic has destroyed riparian vegetation and accelerated streambank erosion in Yosemite Valley (Madej et al. 1994). Bank erosion and channel widening were found to be more common around areas of concentrated use, such as campgrounds (Madej et al. 1994). A simple count from USFS maps indicated that more than 75 percent of the National Forest campgrounds in the Sierra Nevada are located within a riparian area or in close proximity. Soil compaction, chemical and bacterial pollution, litter, vegetation damage, wildlife disturbance, and fire ignition are impacts associated with recreational sites in riparian areas (Nelson et al. 1994). Gathering of firewood from riparian areas around campgrounds can also eliminate much of the potential wood supply to streams (Madej et al. 1994).

Mining

Placer and hydraulic mining in the 19th century devastated many of the riparian corridors on the western slope of the Sierra Nevada. As discussed in Kattelmann 1996a, gold mining in the creeks and rivers totally destabilized their riparian systems. Affected streams and hillslopes have been recovering ever since (e.g., James 1994). In most cases, the degree of recovery is remarkable. Much of the region appears to have partially healed over the past century. Some form of riparian vegetation has become re-established, and there has been partial return of aquatic biota to the streams (e.g., Marchetti 1994). Nevertheless, there are still many localities lacking soil and vegetation. One may assume that the present form of the riverine-riparian ecosystems is simplified compared to the pre-Gold Rush situation, but we really do not know what the west slope of the Sierra Nevada might have looked like had gold not existed in the range.

The legacy of gold mining continues to influence riparian ecology. Hydraulic mine pits are slowly becoming revegetated, but continue to release unnaturally high volumes of sediment as their walls continue to collapse until a stable slope angle is attained (Senter 1987). The unnaturally high sediment loads continue to affect aquatic biota (Marchetti 1994). Massive riverbed dredging operations at the lower margins of the foothills persisted until 1967 (Clark 1970). The spoil piles may remain as a peculiar landscape feature for centuries. Rapid drainage and minimal soil development limit opportunities for vegetation establishment on the dredging debris. Some modern mines adversely affect the localities of the mines and their access routes.

Small-scale suction dredging continues in many streams of the Gold Country. This activity has become widespread wherever there is easy access to the streams (McCleneghan and Johnson

231

1983). Powerful vacuums mounted on rafts remove stream gravels from the bed for separation of any gold particles, and the waste slurry is returned to the river where the plume of sediment stratifies in the flowing stream. Some characteristics of small tributaries, such as bed particle size, armoring, microtopography, streambanks, woody debris, and channel plan form, can be dramatically altered by suction dredging (Harvey 1986; Harvey et al. 1995). Where streambanks are excavated, the potential for damage is much greater. A study of effects of suction dredging on benthic macroinvertebrates showed local declines in abundances and species richness, but biota rapidly recolonized the disturbed sites after dredging stopped (Harvey 1986).

California's Surface Mining and Reclamation Act of 1975 and amendments should prevent future disasters (Pomby 1987), but remediation of past problems requires massive investments. Scores of small mines have been established under the terms of the antiquated 1872 Mining Act. In many cases, the properties are sources of sediment and toxic chemicals. Reform of portions of the Mining Act could finally alleviate some major land and water management problems associated with mining. Conversely, legislation has been introduced in California to weaken the state's regulations regarding reclamation of mined land.

Sand and gravel are the most economically important non-fuel minerals mined in California. The $560 million value of sand and gravel produced in California in 1992 far surpassed the combined total value of all metallic minerals mined in the state (McWilliams and Goldman 1994). More aggregate is used per capita in California than in any other state, and the State Department of Transportation is the largest single consumer (California State Lands Commission 1993). Excavation within stream channels will obviously have direct effects on the fluvial system (Sandecki 1989; Kondolf and Matthews 1993). Removal of part of the streambed alters the hydraulic characteristics of the channel and interrupts the natural transport of bedload through the stream. Where deeper channels form, they can lower the local water table and kill riparian vegetation as the former floodplain dries out. Loss of the vegetation in turn makes the banks more susceptible to erosion. Incision of the channel limits the opportunity for overbank flooding to deposit sediments on the floodplain. These combined effects can result in dramatic changes in the overall form and structure of the channel and dependent aquatic and riparian habitat (Collins and Dunne 1990; Kondolf and Matthews 1993). Human structures in the channel such as bridges, culverts, pipelines, and revetments may be damaged by the geomorphic changes. Gravel is also mined from streams by skimming a shallow layer off of gravel bars. Depending on the flow regime, distribution of particle sizes, and opportunities for establishment of riparian vegetation, a variety of complex channel and vegetation responses may occur (Kondolf and Matthews 1993).

RESTORATION OF RIPARIAN SYSTEMS

The various impacts to riparian areas outlined above have been recognized by some agencies, groups, and individuals for many years. This recognition of impaired streamside areas has led to a variety of attempts to restore some of the functions of some damaged riparian areas (National Research Council 1992). Much of this work has been called watershed restoration but has usually focused on riparian areas. Rehabilitation efforts began in the Sierra Nevada during the 1930s (e.g., Kraebel and Pillsbury 1934). Fish habitat improvement also began in the 1930s in the Kaweah River (Ehlers 1956) and has been a strong tradition in many parts of the Sierra Nevada (e.g., Gard 1972). Fisheries continue to be a primary justification for watershed restoration work.

The California Wildlife Conservation Board has funded more than 70 watershed and aquatic habitat improvement projects in the Sierra Nevada in the past decade under the Fish and Wildlife Habitat Enhancement Act of 1984 (Schulenburg 1994). Restoration projects have been initiated throughout the Sierra Nevada for a host of other reasons as well (Pawley and Quinn 1995). Projects lumped together as riparian restoration include augmentation of flows impaired by diversion; re-establishment of willows, cottonwoods, and other riparian vegetation; road closures and obliteration; long-term rest from grazing; fenced exclosures and riparian pastures; channel realignment; excavation of pools and side channels; installation of rock or log sills and check dams; bank protection with plantings, geotextiles, woody debris, and/or rock; addition of boulders or logs for altering microhabitats; prescribed fire; seeding; etc. (Elmore and Beschta 1989; Lindquist and Bowie 1989; Hunter 1991; National Research Council 1992; Kondolf 1995a).

Many projects have been undertaken to treat symptoms and results of poor land-use practices instead of the causative factors. Although this approach has been long recognized as inefficient and often futile (VanHaveren and Jackson 1986; Elmore and Beschta 1989), some land managers are finally paying more attention to the causes of degradation and relying more on natural recovery after the disturbance is halted (Kauffman et al. 1995). A holistic watershed approach is usually needed to identify all the causes of aquatic and riparian degradation and investigate comprehensive solutions rather than just treating a few isolated sites (Hunter 1991).

In many impaired streams, the fundamental problem is providing adequate water to the channel and riparian area. Where excessive diversions have damaged riparian systems, carefully-planned release of additional water can allow rapid recovery of riparian vegetation (Stromberg and Patten 1989, 1992; Ridenhour et al. 1995). Some shifts back toward a natural hydrograph, such as seasonally fluctuating flows, occasional flushing flows, maintenance of adequate (and non-constant) low flows, or whatever is appropriate in a particular situation will be beneficial to the ecological health of the stream. Simply maintaining constant minimum flows is rarely sufficient. Stream habitat conditions and aquatic biota have developed in response to a highly variable natural flow regime. Restoring some aspects of that variability in managed streams should have ecological benefits in most cases. Adequate channel-maintenance flows that allow streams to behave in a dynamic manner usually meet the needs of riparian plants as well (Troendle 1993; Ridenhour et al. 1995). The critical factor is often raising riparian ground water levels into the root zone of streamside plants. Where that can be accomplished, the growth of suppressed vegetation is usually quite rapid (e.g., Odion et al. 1990; Kauffman et al. 1995).

Depression of the local water table because of channel incision is a common problem in heavily-grazed areas and is difficult to repair. Check dams of various construction have been used for decades in attempts to retain sediment and raise the bed of incised channels (Kraebel and Pillsbury 1934; Lindquist and Bowie 1989). However, such structures routinely wash out and create problems elsewhere in the channel (Beschta and Platts 1986; Swanson 1989). Re-establishment of vegetation within gullies and incised channels can eventually allow aggradation to raise the local water table, but may take decades (Elmore and Beschta 1989; Swanson 1989; Kondolf 1993). Removal of the disturbance that led to the incision is essential to allowing the natural resilience of riparian vegetation to restore damaged channels (VanHaveren and Jackson 1986; U.S. General Accounting Office 1988; Kauffman et al. 1995).

Perhaps the most widespread riparian restoration work in the Sierra Nevada has been attempted by the U. S. Forest Service. National Forest engineering and watershed staffs have been attempting to reduce the sediment yield produced by roads and stabilize gullies on a piecemeal basis where problems are identified in "watershed improvement needs inventories" (e.g., Myers 1992). Although techniques for retiring roads and limiting their impacts are continuing to improve (e.g., Furniss et al. 1991; Costick 1993; Harr and Nichols 1993), actual progress has been slow. For example, a few years ago, restoration projects were being implemented on about 40 acres per year by the Inyo National Forest (1988). Most of those projects involved structural headcut and gully control, with mixed results. Meadow restoration and gully stabilization on one just district of the Sierra National Forest has cost more than $100,000 in each of the past few years (Hagberg 1995). At the same time, funds for such work appear to be declining. Decreases in the timber receipts that partially financed road maintenance and obliteration and rehabilitation of other consequences of the timber program have not been compensated by rebudgeting.

Several riparian restoration campaigns with tighter geographic focus exist around the Sierra Nevada. The Lake Tahoe basin probably has the greatest array of watershed rehabilitation efforts in California and Nevada (e.g., Todd 1989). With sediment yields perhaps up to twenty times natural background rates (Goldman 1993), extraordinary efforts have been taken to slow the rate of cultural eutrophication of Lake Tahoe. The level of investment aimed at slowing deterioration of the aquatic system of the basin is unique in the West with more than $250 million dollars spent on acquisition of private property, stormwater management, slope stabilization, wetland restoration, and revegetation. Restoration of riparian areas as a means of improving water quality has been a primary emphasis of the combined programs, but work has been much slower than planned (Tahoe Regional Planning Agency 1988; Hill 1994). Another example of interagency and private cooperation on riparian rehabilitation is the pilot program of channel stabilization and vegetation re-establishment along tributaries to the North Fork Feather River (Lindquist and Bowie 1989; Wills and Sheehan 1992; Wills and Schramel 1994). Along the South Fork Kern River, the Nature Conservancy has been extensively planting cottonwoods and willows and studying site conditions in relation to survival and growth of the plants to assist future restoration efforts (Tiller and Tollefson 1992). In the Kings River basin, catastrophic failure of a large pipeline between two reservoirs devastated the canyon downstream and led to some novel revegetation efforts that appear to be highly successful (Chan 1993).

Recent legal developments regarding water management in the eastern Sierra Nevada have led to the restoration of several stream segments that have been dewatered for decades. In 1994, the State Water Resources Control Board amended the water rights licenses on streams tributary to Mono Lake to increase flows and require restoration of the channels and associated habitat (Los Angeles Department of Water and Power 1995). Restoration work completed between 1991 and 1995 focused on physical habitat improvements for fish and reestablishing riparian vegetation (e.g., Trihey and English 1991; Stine 1994). The next phase of restoration proposes to return large flows to the channels and allow natural stream dynamics to control the redevelopment of these long-dry channels (Ridenhour et al. 1995). Re-establishment of riparian vegetation would also be part of the continuing program, but considerable controversy surrounds the potential role of channel maintenance and flushing flows (Los Angeles Department of Water and Power 1995). Failure of a penstock and accidental release of water into the Owens Gorge in 1991 led to the rewatering of this section of the Owens River, which had been dry for about four decades. Saturation of the river bed took several months, but since then, riparian vegetation under active management has been thriving and the fishery is being restored.

Restoration of riparian areas and streams is still an emerging field with relatively little theory or experience to guide restoration work. Careful monitoring and evaluation of results, and especially failures, is critical to advancing our collective knowledge (Beschta and Platts 1986; Hunter 1991; National Research Council 1992; Kondolf 1995b; Kondolf and Micheli 1995). Elimination of the disturbance mechanisms is usually the most important step in riparian restoration. Economic and ecological analyses of the tradeoffs involved in removing or modifying disturbances and rehabilitating damaged areas would be instructive to managers. Evaluations should include determination of what activities are essential, desirable, convenient, or irrelevant to locate in riparian areas. In most cases, avoidance of riparian damage will be found to be far less expensive than eventual mitigation or restoration.

WETLANDS AND MEADOWS

Wetlands are of wide public concern because of the tremendous loss of wetlands throughout the United States and the relatively recent acknowledgment of their ecological importance (National Research Council 1995). Drainage and destruction of wetlands continued to be an accepted and often encouraged practice across the country until the mid-1970s. A perception of wetlands as more valuable to nature and society in general than to individuals and landowners has led to conflicts over their use and development. The greatest fractional loss of wetland area of all states has occurred in California, where only 9 percent or about 183,700 ha (454,000 ac) remains of an estimated unimpaired wetland area of about 2 million ha (5 million ac) (National Research Council 1992). They are characterized by presence of the water table at or near the surface, which may result in a periodic cover of shallow water. A common characteristic of wetlands is oxygen-deficient conditions in the root zone during some substantial fraction of the year resulting from seasonal saturation. The low-oxygen conditions result in distinctive soils and plant associations.

The most widely valued function of wetlands is providing habitat for invertebrates, fish, birds, and other wildlife. Riparian wetlands have been considered the most important habitat type in California for mammals (Reynolds et al. 1993). Wetlands also provide several hydrologic and water quality functions or ecological services. Floodplain wetlands allow flood waters to spread over a large area, thereby providing additional conveyance capacity and detention storage that can decrease peak flows downstream. Some wetlands provide source areas for streams while others contribute to recharge of ground water, depending on local hydraulic gradients (Carter 1986). Sediment moving from adjacent uplands or borne in flood waters can be deposited in wetlands where flow velocities are reduced by vegetation and as water spreads out. Rapid vegetation growth stabilizes deposited sediments. Nutrients can also be retained or transformed by wetlands, leading to lower nutrient loads downstream (e.g., Johnston 1991, 1993). A variety of biochemical processes in wetlands can precipitate or volatilize assorted compounds and ions from detained water. Accumulation of organic peat can act as a long-term sink for many substances (Mitsch and Gosselink 1986). Wetlands that accumulate peat have a wide range of conditions from fens that are alkaline and supported by emerging groundwater to bogs that are acidic, maintained mostly by precipitation, and largely vegetated by sphangum moss. These different types of peatlands support diverse communities of invertebrates (Erman 1973, 1976; Erman and Erman 1975).

Wetlands in mountain areas have received much less attention than their counterparts in lowlands and coastal areas. Much of the research and applications work in mountain wetlands has been done in the Lake Tahoe basin in efforts to improve the quality of water entering the lake (e.g., Rhodes et al. 1985; Whitall and Champion 1989). Water in Squaw Creek is depleted of the excess nitrate load acquired from Squaw Valley developments as is passes through a meadow reach (Woyshner and Hecht 1989). Detailed investigations of wetlands in Mono County began in 1991 with a study of the Bridgeport Valley (Curry 1992). Mono County and the Lahontan Regional Water Quality Control Board continue to advance wetland mapping and planning with another field effort in 1995 by Curry and his associates. Initial results include discovery of a variety of unusual types of wetlands and their associated floras. One particular wetland in southern Mono County, Fish Slough, has attracted attention for at least 40 years because of its value as a refuge for rare fish and plants (Pister and Kerbavaz 1984; Odion et al. 1992; Mary DeDecker, botanist, Indepenedence, personal communication, 1995). Water diversions and groundwater development have reduced wetlands in much of the Owens Valley (e.g., Perkins et al. 1984; Groeneveld and Or 1994). Loss of springs, seeps, and remnant marshes around Owens Lake has reduced important habitat for resident and migratory bird populations (Kohen et al. 1994). Physical modification (i.e., draining, dredging, or filling) on a piecemeal basis has steadily contributed to the loss of wetland functions throughout the Sierra Nevada.

Montane meadows are a distinct type of riparian community comprised of relatively low vegetation usually dominated by sedges. Some sedges have extraordinarily long and dense root and rhizome networks that produce a sod inherently resistant to erosion. Other meadow plants include rushes, grasses, and broad-leaved forbs. Meadows of the Sierra Nevada range in size from a few square meters to several square kilometers (Allen 1987). Most meadows are found in glaciated basins of the subalpine zone, but scattered meadows occur down to about 1,200 m (4,000 ft) in the northern part of the range and 1,800 m (6,000 ft) in the southern Sierra Nevada (Whitney 1979). All meadow types are characterized by high ground water levels that limit suitability of the site for most plant species. In most cases, depth to the water table is the sole distinction between the presence of conifers or meadow vegetation (Wood 1975). Soil and drainage characteristics differentiate three prominent types of montane meadows. Poorly drained sites with organic, oxygen-deficient soils create wet meadows that often have standing water for most of the summer. Moist meadows occur on well-drained loam soils that are saturated only briefly during the final part of the snowmelt season. Dry meadows are found on rapidly drained coarse soils that are often dry and dormant by August and are typified by Tuolumne Meadows (Whitney 1979). So-called stringer meadows are narrow features along streams (Allen 1987).

Mountain meadows are particularly important habitats for birds in the Sierra Nevada. Besides the species that are limited to meadows, population densities of many species of birds that live within the forest are greatest along the forested edges of montane meadows (Graber 1996). During summer, montane meadows may be the single most important habitat in the Sierra Nevada for birds that breed elsewhere (Graber 1996).

Conversion of meadows to dry flat areas with an incised channel as a result of overgrazing is a widespread concern in the Sierra Nevada (e.g., DeBenedetti and Parsons 1979; Ratliff 1985; Hagberg 1995). The large meadows of the upper South Fork of the Kern River provide dramatic examples of deep channel incision (Odion et al. 1990). Meadow restoration and gully stabilization on the Kings River Ranger District of the Sierra National Forest alone has cost more than $100,000 in each of the past few years (Hagberg 1995). Until about 1900, meadows in the Sierra

236

Nevada had been aggrading (building up) for the past 10,000 years (Wood 1975). Overgrazing in the late 1800s seems to have reversed that trend. One hypothesis suggests that as meadows were compacted and depleted of vegetation near the main channel in the meadow, streams began to cut a deeper channel progressively upstream. As streams got deeper, the local water table dropped below the root zone of the original meadow vegetation. The native grasses and other plants could no longer survive. Plants better adapted to low soil moisture conditions colonized the former meadows, but usually did not provide complete ground cover. Exposure of bare soil can accelerate erosion by sheetwash, rill formation, gullying, and wind erosion. The gullying itself moves large quantities of soil. At higher elevations, oversnow flow may be another important erosion process in disturbed meadows (Kattelmann 1989). Recent studies suggest that destruction of sod even over limited areas may be sufficient to initiate gully erosion in montane meadows (Wood 1975; Hagberg 1995). Progressive headward cutting tends to be episodic and associated with large flood events when plunge pool erosion (progressive upstream collapse as the head of the gully is undermined by excavation of a pool at its base) is the principal mechanism (Hagberg 1995).

In natural meadows, runoff tends to spread out through a network of small channels. Meadows act as wide floodplains, capable of detaining large volumes of water, thereby reducing peak flows downstream. By slowing and spreading streamflow, meadows allow sediment to be deposited where it adds mass and nutrients. Meadows have been heavily used for forage and agriculture since the Gold Rush, and many have been greatly altered over the past century and a half, still remaining in poor condition (Ratliff 1985). Following the intense overgrazing of the 19th century, meadows in the east side of the Feather River basin began to erode during the wet years of 1890-1920 (Clifton 1994). Some small meadows washed out and were lost completely during this period (LeBoa et al. 1994). The legacy of the loss of meadow sod and other bank-stabilizing vegetation is that instead of being sites of sediment deposition and storage, many meadows are now sources of sediment (LeBoa et al. 1994). Broken meadow sod, trampled streambanks, and widened streambeds are commonly documented in Sierra Nevada meadows under excessive grazing pressure (e.g., Allen 1989; Hagberg 1995; Range Watch 1995). An example is found in Nichols Meadow on the Sierra National Forest where gully dimensions have reached 6 m (20 ft) in depth, 18-27 m (60-90 ft) in width, and 105 m (350 ft) in length (Myers 1993). Given the historical pattern of abuse, severely degraded conditions could be much more widespread if not for the resilience of meadows where the sod remains intact (Hagberg 1995). Meadows are more responsive to management and rest than any other type of range ecosystem (Menke et al. 1996). Removal of commercial livestock and decreasing use of pack stock in Sequoia, Kings Canyon and Yosemite National Parks have led to significant recovery of mountain meadows in the parks (DeBenedetti and Parsons 1979; Holmes 1979). Poor trail location and off-trail hiking continue to cause local problems in some high-elevation meadows (Lemons 1979). An inventory of wet meadows by the Inyo National Forest (1988) indicated that 90% were damaged or threatened with damage by accelerated erosion.

RIPARIAN CONDITIONS FROM AERIAL PHOTOGRAPHY AND VIDEOGRAPHY

Examination of aerial photography of more than 9,500 km (5,900 mi) of streams throughout the Sierra Nevada showed that riparian corridors are depleted of vegetation in thousands of individual locations. Although the total distance of these gaps in riparian continuity is a limited fraction of the entire stream length of the Sierra Nevada, this fragmentation was common to almost all watersheds examined. The complete removal of riparian vegetation documented in this analysis represents only the worst case of loss of riparian vegetation. Areas of partial impairment of riparian vegetation can be assumed to be much more extensive than these sites of total loss.

Riparian vegetation removal was especially common between about 100 and 1,000 m (330 and 3,300 ft) elevation. Even on the smallest scale photographs (1:24,000), streams that traversed pastures had dramatically less riparian vegetation than on adjacent lands that were fenced and not grazed. Local water development and diversion on to pastures appeared to dewater downstream reaches enough to impair growth of riparian plants in combination with other grazing impacts. Roads and residential development were the next most-often observed causes of riparian impairment. Impacts of roads were localized but often had secondary effects contributing to a broader zone of impact than the road itself. Streams in urban areas, such as Jackson and Sonora, were obviously channelized and devoid of vegetation in spots. Riparian vegetation was commonly removed from individual lots as well.

Areas of impact in the forest zone identified from the aerial photograph analysis were localized and were usually associated with roads. Obvious exceptions to these local impacts were the extensive development of the broader valleys and widespread overgrazing (which was not discernible from the aerial photograph analysis). The larger and more obvious impacts of mining and logging in the riparian area were found on private land. The intensity and extent of impacts tended to decrease with increasing elevation. Overall, there were fewer major gaps in riparian canopy on public lands than on private lands. Wilderness areas had the least visible impacts. Again, fine-scale impacts and changes, as in meadows and small tributaries, could not be discerned with this approach.

The degree of impact varied greatly between watersheds. A few watersheds had no observed impacts at all while others were substantially affected. The smaller watersheds tended to have higher fractions affected, simply because a single impact could occupy a greater proportion of the total stream length.

The video tapes of the main (e.g., Yuba) river channels and their primary tributaries provided qualitative impressions of the extent, intensity, and types of impacts. In general, there were few obvious impacts along the main rivers except where roads crossed or paralleled the river. In those cases, riparian vegetation was largely destroyed.

One of the few other pieces of regional information about riparian conditions was an aggregate of riparian canopy density measurements from 13 unlogged first and second order streams in the northern Sierra Nevada (Erman et al. 1977). This survey in 1975 found that angular canopy density over streams that had not been logged ranged from 50 to 100 percent with a mean of 75 percent.

INTERPRETATIONS

Historical Development and Current Status

As is the case with hydrology, the most significant impacts to the riparian systems of the Sierra Nevada started with the Gold Rush. The effects of riverbed and hydraulic mining were devastating to the rivers of the western slope. Regrowth of riparian vegetation has provided the appearance of natural rivers, but the aquatic and riparian systems may remain quite simplified compared to the pre-1848 conditions. However, we will never know if recovery proceeded along a different trajectory than if riparian areas of the west slope had not been shredded in pursuit of gold among the stream gravels. Along streams not laden with gold, domestic livestock may have transformed riparian areas into their present form. Because grazing seems to have occurred virtually everywhere in the Sierra Nevada there was accessible forage, we do not know what riparian communities would look like had they never been grazed. Areas long devoid of substantial riparian vegetation, such as in the eastern part of the Feather River basin, are accepted by many people as the normal, natural condition.

This assessment focused on obvious, dramatic changes in riparian areas. We may assume that there are a variety of more subtle changes in riparian areas that require field inspection at the least, and possibly rigorous scientific investigation to discern. Such studies could not even be contemplated in the context of a range-wide evaluation. Instead, we chose to search for large-scale impacts that are easily recognized and have caused dramatic changes in the riparian areas. Throughout the Sierra Nevada, riparian areas have been altered to varying degrees by human activities. The basic functions (providing shade, organic matter, root stability, habitat, etc.) of riparian areas appear to have been maintained at least in part where vegetation has not been obliterated. However, fragmentation was found to be common in every river basin during our aerial photography analyses. Although we lack any quantitative measures of its extent, meadow degradation is another widespread problem that we have observed and that is frequently mentioned by resource managers. Severe alterations have occurred in meadows that have become incised and have suffered a consequent drop in the water table. In those cases, the original meadow vegetation has been replaced by xeric species such as sagebrush.

Water development has impacted a considerable amount of the riparian areas of the mountain range. About 1,000 km of riparian areas are inundated under artificial reservoirs. Many of these reservoirs destroyed some of the best riparian areas in the Sierra Nevada. Almost every water project results in a break in the continuity of the riparian vegetation. The overall effects of this fragmentation are unknown. Regulation and diversion of streamflow have markedly altered riparian vegetation over thousands of kilometers. Where streams have been totally or seasonally dewatered, such as lower Rush and Parker Creeks in the Mono Basin until a few years ago, riparian vegetation died out. In streams with diminished volumes, the riparian area becomes thinner as groundwater recharge from the stream is not as great as before diversion. In streams below dams that reduce flood peaks, the riparian vegetation usually encroaches upon the channel.

Roads and urban development have converted riparian areas to impermeable surfaces and channelized streams. Concrete replaced soil, grasses, and trees. Although these impacts are particularly severe, they do not cover vast areas. Riparian corridors along some major rivers are impacted by highways for long distances. Stream crossings by roads adversely affect riparian areas at thousands of places and are the main current impact associated with timber harvesting.

Although forest practices of the past often removed nearly all trees in some riparian areas and exposed the stream, logging in streamside areas is less common and is subject to a variety of controls. The effectiveness of such controls is often debated (Moyle et al. 1996). Salvage logging can still occur within riparian areas and poses a threat to the integrity of riparian forests.

Trends in the condition of riparian systems in the Sierra Nevada are mixed. Recovery continues from the wholesale destruction of the gold mining era, short-term construction projects, and streamside timber harvests. Although various geomorphic and biological adjustments continue in response to permanent structures (e.g., dams, canals, roads, and houses) in the riparian area, such changes are not necessarily recovery toward a former condition. Persistent or recurring disturbance, such as grazing and off-road vehicle traffic usually impedes or prevents recovery from perhaps more intensive disturbances of the past. Few major mining and water projects are expected in the next couple of decades. Compared to the road-building boom of the 1960s and 1970s, relatively little additional road construction is anticipated with tightly constrained budgets. In the past few years, forest practices have improved with respect to reducing negative impacts in riparian areas. Grazing practices on public lands are finally under environmental review, as required by the 1969 National Environmental Policy Act. This process could eventually result in improved range management and long-term rest for unsuitable lands. If road building is indeed restricted, if timber harvests are precluded from streamside management areas, if grazing pressures on riparian areas are reduced, and if all existing laws and regulations that are intended to minimize resource damage are implemented and enforced, then there could be a trend of substantial recovery in riparian corridors of the Sierra Nevada. However, urban development may accelerate rapidly in the foothills (Duane 1996) and could present the greatest risk of large-scale destruction of riparian areas.

Some Implications

Growing public awareness of riparian areas should help slow and perhaps reverse degradation. For example, the NEPA process for review of grazing practices on public lands allows a major opportunity for public involvement. The vast majority of identified impacts to riparian areas other than grazing were associated with roads. Although these impaired areas may expand somewhat, new foci of riparian damage should be limited in the absence of new roads. Where access is not available, major impacts aside from grazing should be few. Some of the adverse effects of the existing road network can be reduced by relocation and reconstruction of roads and stream crossings that are known to be damaging to the stream environment. Hundreds of such sites have already identified by National Forest staffs in their "watershed improvement needs inventories". However, new sources of funding must be identified for road maintenance, realignment, and obliteration. So far, the costs of extensive environmental improvements in the road system have not been included in budgets of the entire National Forest system or individual timber sales. Many county roads and state and federal highways located in riparian areas could also be re-engineered to reduce their impacts to riparian resources. Depending on the value that society puts on riparian areas, there is no shortage of individual sites in need of rehabilitation or restoration. Prioritization of such needs to maximize the effectiveness of limited funding requires agreement between riparian ecologists, engineers, and the public. Declines in resource and recreation management and road maintenance budgets imply fewer funds available to maintain facilities, mitigate damage, and control use.

Direct effects of urban and exurban development and associated gravel mining are likely sources of additional riparian degradation. The extent and severity of these potential impacts is somewhat controllable through rigorous enforcement of existing laws and regulations. However, citizens must insist upon such enforcement. Improved planning and zoning and acquisition of conservation easements could reduce the pressure for development of riparian lands.

Catastrophic fire involving unnaturally large fuel loads represents a risk to some riparian areas even when burned areas are confined to upslope areas. Any fuels management program (Weatherspoon and Skinner 1996) for upland forest and chaparral will have strong implications for the riparian area as well. Reductions in upland stand density and ground cover could increase runoff and sediment delivery to streams unless carefully designed. As part of the investment in fuels management programs, a team of aquatic ecologists, soil scientists, and hydrologists must be actively involved to minimize damage to the riparian area. Although the artificial build-up of fuels throughout the Sierra Nevada seems to have created the potential for severe fires (Weatherspoon and Skinner 1996), society's response must not ignore the potential consequences of any fuels treatment program (Beschta et al. 1995).

There is tremendous potential for rehabilitation of degraded riparian areas. Some riparian vegetation tends to become reestablished rapidly once a chronic disturbance is removed, provided adequate water is available. Often, the chronic disturbance simply is the lack of water below a diversion. Even where streams have been completely dewatered for decades, resumption of streamflow rapidly returns life to the riparian area. Rewatering of long-diverted streams in the Mono Basin and the Owens Gorge below Crowley Lake have had dramatic results in just a few years. Geomorphic and wildlife recovery will require decades, but the re-establishment of a basic vegetation canopy is a fundamental step to ecosystem recovery.

Time-Significance

Halting the decline of riparian-dependent endangered species (e.g., Kern Canyon Slender Salamander, Yosemite Toad, and Willow Flycatcher) is the most urgent priority of riparian-area management. Protection and enhancement of critical riparian habitat for those species at risk must happen as soon as possible to reduce the possibility of their extinction. For example, the refuges for foothill yellow-legged frogs seem to be small perennial streams with well-developed riparian canopies and intact understory vegetation (Jennings 1996). Besides the threat to particular species, which may have some regional implications, the riparian system at the scale of the entire mountain range does not seem to be breaking down as in the case of the Central Valley. Nevertheless, there are thousands of local problems needing attention with various degrees of urgency. These localized issues, which may have far-reaching cumulative effects, require site-specific solutions. These problems must be addressed through a watershed by watershed approach.

The relative urgency of particular problems depends on the resources at risk and whether the impact can be discontinued or reduced. In general, riparian vegetation tends to begin to re-establish itself within a few years to a decade if given the opportunity and appropriate hydrologic conditions (e.g., Nelson et al. 1994). A prime problem with respect to grazing is that areas degraded in past decades have never had a chance to recover, even though grazing intensity may have greatly diminished. Such areas have to be rested for at least a few years if recovery is to begin. The sooner that rest begins, the sooner the riparian areas will heal. As mentioned by

Kattelmann (1996a), reducing streambank erosion in the North Fork Feather River is clearly an important goal. As long as serious action is delayed, productive alluvial land will continue to be lost, streams will continue to carry high sediment loads, and downstream reservoirs will continue to fill with sediment at unnaturally high rates. Allowing riparian vegetation to become re-established would significantly slow the rate of streambank erosion.

Gaps in Knowledge

The aerial photography analysis only examined the most severe impacts where riparian cover has been completely lost. We know little about the real health of riparian areas, even where vegetative cover seems to be continuous. Our knowledge is especially limited in the foothills where impacts and threats appear to be extensive. A thorough assessment is needed that can progress beyond the anecdotes and inferences presented here.

Although there are dozens of examples of seriously degraded meadows with deeply incised channels, we have not inventoried the extent of such damage. Examples of severe degradation on the Kern Plateau and in the North Fork Feather River basin stand out, but we do not know whether situations of similar severity are common. Extensive field investigations are necessary to advance our knowledge. For example, a widespread field reconnaissance could sample a large number of stream reaches in areas of concern. A procedure proposed by Terry Hicks of the Inyo National Forest (personal communication 1995) would establish a functional ranking for riparian corridors based on observations of surface erosion, channel downcutting, bank stability, potential vegetation, and habitat quality. This approach would also identify factors affecting function, human uses, sensitive areas, potential for improvement, means for achieving potential and improving functions, and mitigation possibilities. More comprehensive surveys of physical habitat, fish populations, and aquatic invertebrates would help identify problem areas and critical ecological processes (e.g., Rinne 1990; Herbst and Knapp 1995).

Ecosystem Sustainability and Management

Riparian vegetation seems to recover relatively fast after damage because of favorable conditions for plant growth along streams and its rapid recolonization and growth in response to natural flooding (Nelson et al. 1994). A critical condition for recovery is that the disruption of natural processes must be halted. Persistent impacts such as seasonal grazing never provide the opportunity for recovery to really get started. Recovery of other ecosystem properties and processes following an impact requires more time and possibly some management to accelerate the schedule if desired. In particular, channel morphology and aquatic organisms may require several decades to recover following vegetative re-establishment.

Riparian communities that are reestablished after cessation of some human-induced disturbances may be quite simplified in composition and structure compared to community development under fully natural conditions. Unfortunately, we lack many undisturbed reference areas for comparison, and the high degree of inherent variability between sites can confound any understanding of natural recovery trajectories. In light of limited understanding of natural processes and conditions and specific habitat relationships, setting broad goals may be the best strategy for now. Maintaining the obvious elements of sound riparian areas, such as natural streamflow regimes and unaltered soils, should allow other processes and interactions to recover from impacts and reestablish fully functioning communities. If basic ecological conditions can be maintained or rehabilitated, then wildlife should respond in a positive manner (e.g., Carlson et al. 1991).

Complex ownership patterns and organizational jurisdictions in the riparian area will complicate efforts to perform integrated watershed-scale management and planning (Nelson et al. 1994). Institutional evolution does not seem to keep pace with shifting notions of ecosystem management and conservation biology. Even the intuitively powerful concept of adaptive management is frustrated by our administrative inability to initiate and maintain adequate monitoring programs. One initial step path toward conservation of riparian resources is simply for society to recognize the ecological importance of riparian corridors. Public education about natural resources has had some profound effects in changing social values and, despite current political setbacks, will hopefully continue to promote more effective policies and management.

Remaining Questions

One fundamental question regarding the status of riparian areas in the Sierra Nevada is the degree to which they have been altered in their composition and structure. Our analysis of aerial photography merely dealt with extent of severely damaged riparian areas. We may assume that even where riparian vegetation appears to be healthy, it may be quite different from that existing 150 years ago. We do not know how different it might be in various parts of the range or the ecological importance of those differences to various species and processes. The absence of reference conditions from areas unmodified over the past 150 years is a difficult problem for ecosystem management in general (Kaufmann et al. 1994).

Another set of important unknowns are the ecological consequences of fragmentation of the riparian corridors. We have observed a lot of longitudinal discontinuities in riparian areas, but we do not know how those breaks affect the ecosystem beyond generalities from studies in other regions.

As efforts to rehabilitate damaged riparian areas (hopefully) become more common, we need better measures of ecological success. Although every restoration effort is something of an uncontrolled experiment, adequate pre- and post- project monitoring is usually lacking (Kondolf 1995b). Therefore, the collective learning process is stifled, and there is little additional information available for designing the next project.

An ambitious research initiative has recently been proposed as a basis for enlightened management of water resources (Naiman et al. 1995). The entire package as proposed would potentially provide a greatly improved foundation for management of land and water resources. Among the dozens of lines of suggested research are several that would improve conservation of riparian resources: hydrologic processes in the riparian area, especially ground water - surface water interactions; nutrient cycling; mechanisms of filtering functions and water quality protection in wetlands; sediment - vegetation interactions; and sensitivity to land use change (Naiman et al. 1995). Several important research questions relating to riparian areas have also been identified by the Sierra Nevada Research Planning Team (Parrish and Erman 1994).

CONCLUSIONS

The health of Sierra Nevada watersheds depends on the ecological integrity of riparian areas. These lands along water courses influence the entry of water, energy, sediment, nutrients, and pollutants into streams. Fully-functioning riparian areas are critical to aquatic biodiversity and good water quality.

Riparian areas in the Sierra Nevada have been degraded by a long history of placer mining, dam construction, streamflow regulation, overgrazing, logging, road construction, urban development, recreation, and other impacts. Although most of these effects are initially local in extent, riparian systems suffer from combinations of multiple impacts over time and influences from upstream. Chronic impacts, such as roads and water diversions, do not allow opportunities for recovery, while riparian communities usually become re-established after short-term disturbances such as fire or timber harvest. Streamside areas have been sufficiently impaired to place several riparian-dependent species in danger of extinction. Many of the best riparian areas that once existed along the wide floodplains of the relatively few broad valleys in the Sierra Nevada has been lost to reservoirs and conversion to pastures, farms, highways, and towns.

Despite the variety of impacts, some canopy cover is still in place or has partially recovered in most riparian areas of the Sierra Nevada. However, the continuity of this vegetation has been lost, and the canopy structure has been simplified in a large, though unquantified, fraction of riparian corridors. Although fragmented and simplified, current riparian vegetation still appears to provide some level of shade, stability, and organic matter to streams and habitat for avian and terrestrial wildlife along most streams. Compared to pre-Gold-Rush conditions, these and other functions have been impaired to varying degrees on a site-specific basis. Widespread changes in riparian vegetation are believed to have occurred as a result of overgrazing, but their nature and extent have not been quantified. Persistent grazing often prevents the re-establishment of riparian plants that could retard erosion of devegetated streambanks. If meadows and other riparian areas could be rested from grazing and restored to their full productivity, livestock could be reintroduced to far more resilient and vigorous pastures than exist under current conditions. Although there has been considerable vegetative recovery in some areas of past river mining and overgrazing, geomorphic and hydrologic recovery has proceeded more slowly, especially in former wetlands. There is great potential for active restoration of riparian elements and processes to augment and accelerate natural recovery processes.

Water development has damaged riparian systems in all river basins of the Sierra Nevada. More than 1,000 km (600 mi) of riparian corridors have been submerged under reservoirs throughout the range. These reservoirs and other large gaps break the continuity of the riparian corridors and impair wildlife migration. Below dams, the usual response of riparian vegetation has been to encroach upon the formerly active channel because high flows that once scoured the channel have been almost eliminated. In cases where little or no water has been left in the natural channel below a diversion, the riparian area has narrowed and even disappeared in totally dewatered channels. Wetlands have been drained, filled or submerged throughout the Sierra Nevada.

The lower foothills seem to have suffered widespread impacts. At elevations below about 1,000 m (3,300 ft), riparian vegetation continues to be a casualty of overgrazing and both large and small water development projects. With the loss of the original riparian habitat in the Central

Valley, riparian areas in the lower foothills may be critical to several riparian-dependent species with low populations (Graber 1996). Major losses of riparian areas have occurred in the Kern and Feather River basins, particularly in their broad alluvial valleys. Meadows have been greatly altered throughout the Sierra Nevada, with many of them converted to dry terraces above a deeply incised stream.

With minimal research information available about baseline or current conditions, we focused on the most fundamental issue: whether or not riparian canopy still exists. A survey of riparian vegetation cover from aerial photographs showed vegetation has been removed at thousands of locations that seriously fragment the continuity of riparian vegetation. The majority of these sites where riparian vegetation has been converted to other land uses are associated with roads. Vehicular access is generally necessary to generate impacts besides grazing. Roads and urban development have converted riparian areas to impermeable surfaces and channelized streams. Continued development will undoubtedly damage additional areas. Riparian corridors along several major rivers are impacted by major highways for long distances. Stream crossings by roads impact riparian areas at thousands of places and are currently the main impact associated with timber harvesting. Although forest practices of the past often removed riparian trees and exposed the stream, logging in riparian areas is now somewhat restricted compared to past abuses. Nevertheless, examples of riparian harvesting were still evident on recent aerial photographs.

The future health of riparian areas in the Sierra Nevada will depend on interactions between recovery from past degradation by natural processes and restoration efforts, reduction of ongoing chronic disturbances, and new impacts. Some fuels management proposals could create considerable disturbance and must be weighed against the risk of fire damage to watersheds and riparian areas. An accelerated salvage logging program with little oversight could pose a serious threat. Other potential risks to riparian areas include catastrophic fire where fuel loads are unnaturally high, persistent grazing of riparian vegetation, accelerated residential development, and new water projects.

Riparian areas are likely to remain a critical environmental issue for the foreseeable future. Because of their broad ecological values, riparian areas should be a high priority in any type of watershed analysis, project planning, land management or construction activity, and restoration work. Riparian areas are influenced by almost any environmental change because of their position in the landscape, their value to most plants and animals, and their regulation of interactions between land and water. Conservation of riparian areas is central to sound watershed management.

MANAGEMENT IMPLICATIONS

Improved management of riparian areas is needed to halt and ultimately reverse the degradation of streams and areas that influence them. Simply pulling back from streams and out of riparian areas should be a guiding philosophy to allow natural recovery processes to repair damaged functions of streamside areas. Although location of land disturbing activities in riparian areas has often been more convenient or slightly more economical than location upslope, close proximity to water is rarely necessary for many of our activities that degrade riparian areas. Any further modification of riparian areas should be done with careful deliberation and full understanding of the potential consequences. Much of the damage to streamside areas of the Sierra Nevada has been done in ignorance and without any evaluation of alternative locations.

Conservation of aquatic and riparian resources will require better protection and management of streamside lands. A strategy for identifying the areas of influence along streams is described in Appendix 3 by Erman and others. Ideally, the management alternatives for such lands should be evaluated on a local basis (Sullivan 1994). Several protective strategies for riparian areas have recently been proposed (e.g., Association of Forest Service Employees for Environmental Ethics 1995; Doppelt et al. 1993; Pacific Rivers Council 1995; Palmer 1994; Sedell et al. 1994). The applicability of such concepts to streams of the Sierra Nevada need to be evaluated in detail. On federal lands, establishment of a riparian management team with adequate funding on each national forest and BLM district should be considered. On private lands, financial incentives and technical assistance from the state along with better coordination and enforcement of existing laws and regulations could improve riparian conditions and functions. The Resources Agency should designate a lead agency for riparian zone management and coordination of watershed management activities. Instream flow conditions need to be evaluated for the riparian community as well as minimum fish survival and should be considered in a cumulative context for entire watersheds. Relicensing of hydroelectric projects provides an opportunity for improving flow conditions below many dams and diversions.

Where riparian functions are impaired, rehabilitation options need to be explored. Removal of the source of disturbance is usually the critical management decision. Once the disturbance is halted, natural recovery processes are often sufficient to largely restore the site. Cessation of disturbance is particularly important with respect to overgrazing. Long-term rest of riparian areas should usually result in a much more resilient and productive pasture that could support carefully managed grazing in the future. However, these areas must be allowed to recover first. Potential benefits of relocation of incompatible land-uses, such as roads, campgrounds, residential and commercial development, should be weighed against the costs of rehabilitating the site. Such costs will generally be quite high, as will public purchase of land title and conservation easements. A potential mechanism for raising revenue for a watershed management and restoration trust fund would be a tax on water diversions. The most obvious human beneficiaries of watershed and stream improvement are downstream water users. Reinvesting a small proportion of the economic value of water in the watersheds that produce it seems worthy of public support.

A primary goal of future riparian management should be to reduce the direct and indirect impacts of roads on riparian and aquatic systems. A thorough evaluation of road effects should be conducted on a watershed by watershed basis. In most cases, better road maintenance and minor modifications to culverts, ditches, and drains along with revegetation of cut and fill slopes would greatly reduce accelerated sediment delivery associated with roads. Elsewhere, seasonal and long-term road closures will be appropriate. A piecemeal approach after identification of problems may be more politically acceptable than comprehensive closure programs (e.g., Inyo National Forests 1993). Where particularly serious impacts exist, road obliteration and relocation (if necessary) should be undertaken. All road maintenance, re-engineering, and obliteration activities will be very expensive. Declines in timber receipts on national forests are already limiting road maintenance budgets. New sources of funds for rehabilitating roads must be identified. In addition to a possible tax on water diversion for general watershed improvement needs, a gas tax should be considered as a connected funding source to reduce the negative impacts of roads.

246

ACKNOWLEDGMENTS

Several members of the SNEP team took an unusual interest in this particular chapter and helped improve the product. The assistance of Peter Moyle, Don Erman, Nancy Erman, and Dave Graber is particularly appreciated. Matt Kondolf was added to the team late in the game to write a more acceptable riparian report for volume 2 after an early version of this document was found wanting in the review process. Discussions with Matt were very helpful in upgrading this report. Apologies go to the anonymous reviewers and key contacts who were burdened with a very premature draft, and no thanks go to whoever scheduled it for release at that time. Detailed comments by Lynn Decker and Diana Jacobs on later drafts were most helpful even though we disagreed on a few issues. Discussions with most of the SNEP team on matters relating to riparian areas over the past two years were very useful in refining some of the ideas presented here. In particular, we wish to acknowledge Michael Barbour, Larry Costick, Frank Davis, Mike Diggles, Tim Duane, Hap Dunning, Debbie Elliott-Fisk, Jerry Franklin, Bill Kinney, Roland Knapp, Jonathan Kusel, Doug Leisz, Dennis Machida, Bruce McGurk, John Menke, Kurt Menning, Connie Millar, Rowan Rowntree, Jim Shevock, Bill Stewart, and Susan Ustin.

We appreciate the help of Sarah Marvin and the staff of the Water Resources Center Archives at U.C. Berkeley in obtaining and analyzing the National Park Service video tapes of selected rivers. The staff of the Geometronics Division of the Engineering Department of the Region 5 office of the U.S. Forest Service in San Francisco were extraordinarily helpful on an almost daily basis for several months in 1995. Without their assistance, guidance, and access to photographs and equipment, the aerial photography analysis would not have been possible. Critical aerial photographs and assistance were also provided by the Toiyabe National Forest; offices of the Bureau of Land Management in Folsom, Bakersfield, and Bishop; and the California Department of Forestry and Fire Protection. The California Department of Fish and Game in Bishop provided a wealth of information and documents.

Other folks who provided data, information, ideas, and reviews included Jane Baxter, Clay Brandow, Caroline Christian, Christine Christiansen, Bob Curry, Gayle Dana, Dan Dawson, Mary DeDecker, Brett Emery, Jim Frazier, Gary Freeman, Anna Halford, Terry Hicks, Terry Kaplan-Henry, Brett Matzke, Luci McKee, Sally Miller, Mike Prather, Ken Roby, Terry Russi, and Darrell Wong.

The assistance of Steve Beckwitt, Mary Cunha, Lian Duan, Sue Enos, Erin Fleming, John Gabriel, Karen Gabriel, Russ Jones, Jen Lucas, Mike Oliver, Paul Randall, Cindy Seaman, and Robert Zomer with various analytical, graphical, communications, and logistical matters is gratefully acknowledged. Mignon Moskowitz is warmly thanked for her invaluable help with the mass (and mess) of references.

REFERENCES

Abell, D. L. ed. 1989. <u>Proceedings of the California riparian systems conference: Protection, management, and restoration for the 1990's</u>. General Technical Report PSW-110. Berkeley: U.S. Forest Service, Pac.fic Southwest Forest and Range Experiment Station.

Adams, M. B. 1993. Movement of sediment and nutrients through riparian areas. In <u>Proceedings technical workshop on sediments</u>, 41-44. Washington, DC: Terrene Institute.

Adams, P. W. , R. L. Beschta, and H. A. Froehlich. 1988. Mountain logging near streams: Opportunities and challenges. In <u>Proceedings, international mountain logging and Pacific Northwest skyline symposium</u>, 153-62. Corvallis, OR: Oregon State University, College of Forestry.

Agee, J. K. 1993. <u>Fire ecology of Pacific Northwest forests</u>. Washington, DC: Island Press.

Airola, D. A. 1986. Brown-headed cowbird parasitism and habitat disturbance in the Sierra Nevada. <u>Journal of Wildlife Management</u> 50(4): 571-75.

Allen, B. H. 1987. Forest and meadow ecosystems in California. <u>Rangelands</u> 9(3): 125-28.

_____. 1989. Ten years of change in Sierran stringer meadows: An evaluation of range condition models. In <u>Proceedings of the California riparian systems conference: Protection, management, and restoration for the 1990's</u>, edited by D. L. Abell, 102-108. General Technical Report PSW-110. Berkeley: U.S. Forest Service, Pacific Southwest Forest and Range Experiment Station.

Amaranthus, M., H. Jubas, and D. Arthur. 1988. Stream shading, summer streamflow and maximum water temperature following intense wildfire in headwater streams. In <u>Proceedings of the symposium on fire and watershed management</u>, edited by N. H. Berg, 75-78. Berkeley: U.S. Forest Service, Pacific Southwest Forest and Range Experiment Station.

Anderson, E. W. 1987. Riparian area definition--a viewpoint. <u>Rangelands</u> 9: 70.

Anderson, M. K., and M. J. Moratto. 1996. Native American land-use practices and ecological impacts. In <u>Sierra Nevada Ecosystem Project: Final report to Congress</u>, vol. II, chapter 9. Davis: University of California, Centers for Water and Wildland Resources.

Armour, C. L., D. A. Duff, and W. Elmore. 1991. The effects of livestock grazing on riparian and stream ecosystems. <u>Fisheries</u> 16(1): 7-11.

Association of Forest Service Employees for Environmental Ethics. 1995. The AFSEEE-sponsored ecosystem management alternative for the Interior Columbia River Basin. Eugene, OR: Association of Forest Service Employees for Environmental Ethics

Aubury, L. E. 1910. <u>Gold dredging in California</u>. Bulletin 57. San Francisco: California State Mining Bureau.

Averill, C. V. 1946. <u>Placer mining for gold in California</u>. Bulletin 135. San Francisco: California Division of Mines.

Bakker, E. S. 1972. <u>An island called California</u>. Berkeley: University of California Press.

Baltz, D. M., and P. B. Moyle. 1984. The influence of riparian vegetation on stream fish communities of California. In <u>California riparian systems: Ecology, conservation, and productive management</u>, edited by R. E. Warner and K. M. Hendrix, 183-87. Berkeley: University of California Press.

Batson, F. T., P. E. Cuplin, and W. A. Crisco. 1987. <u>Riparian area management: The use of aerial photography to inventory and monitor riparian areas</u>. Technical Reference 1732-2. Denver: U.S. Bureau of Land Management.

Beesley, D. 1996. Reconstructing the Sierra Nevada landscape: An environmental history, 1820-1960. In Sierra Nevada Ecosystem Project: Final report to Congress, vol. II, chapter 1. Davis: University of California, Centers for Water and Wildland Resources.

Behnke, R. J., and R. F. Raleigh. 1979. Grazing and the riparian zone: Impact and management perspectives. General Technical Report WO-12. Washington, DC: U.S. Forest Service.

Behnke, R. J., and M. Zarn. 1976. Biology and management of threatened and endangered western trouts. General Technical Report RM-28. Fort Collins, CO: U.S. Forest Service, Rocky Mountain Forest and Range Experiment Station.

Benedict, N. B. 1982. Mountain meadows: Stability and change. Madrono 29(3): 148-53.

_____. 1984. Classification and dynamics of subalpine meadow ecosystems in the southern Sierra Nevada. In California riparian systems: Ecology, conservation, and productive management, edited by R. E. Warner and K. M. Hendrix, 92-95. Berkeley: University of California Press.

Beschta, R. L. 1984. TEMP84: A computer model for predicting stream temperatures resulting from the management of streamside vegetation. Report WSDG-AD-00009. Fort Collins, CO: U.S. Forest Service, Watershed Systems Development Group.

_____. 1990. Effects of fire on water quantity and quality. In Natural and prescribed fire in Pacific Northwest forests, edited by J. D. Walsted, S. R. Radosevich, and D. V. Sandberg, 219-32. Corvallis: Oregon State University Press.

Beschta, R. L., and W. S. Platts. 1986. Morphological features of small streams: Significance and function. Water Resources Bulletin 22(3): 369-79.

Beschta, R. L., and R. L. Taylor. 1988. Stream temperature increases and land use in a forested Oregon watershed. Water Resources Bulletin 24(1): 19-24.

Beschta, R. L. et. al. 1995. Wildfire and salvage logging: Recommendations for ecologically sound post-fire salvage logging and other post-fire treatment on federal lands in the west. Corvallis: Oregon State University.

Bilby, R. E. 1988. Interactions between aquatic and terrestrial systems. Journal of Forestry 82: 609-13.

Bilby, R. E., and J. W. Ward. 1989. Changes in characteristics and function of woody debris with increasing size of streams in western Washington. Transactions of the American Fisheries Society 118: 368-78.

Biswell, H. H. 1989. Prescribed burning in California wildlands vegetation management. Berkeley: University of California Press.

Blackburn, W. H. 1984. Impacts of grazing intensity and specialized grazing systems on watershed characteristics and response. In Developing strategies for rangeland management, 927-83. Boulder: Westview Press / National Research Council.

Booth, D. B. 1990. Stream-channel incision following drainage-basin urbanization. Water Resources Bulletin 26: 407-17.

Booth, D. B., and L. E. Reinelt. 1993. Consequences of urbanization on aquatic systems- measured effects, degradation thresholds, and corrective strategies. In Watershed '93: A national conference on watershed management, 545-50. Report EPA 840-R-94-002. Washington, DC: U.S. Environmental Protection Agency.

Borcalli and Associates. 1993. Draft county water resources development and management plan. Placerville, CA: El Dorado County Water Agency.

Brinson, M. M., B. L. Swift, R. C. Plantico, and J. S. Barclay. 1981. Riparian ecosystems: Their ecology and status. FWS/OBS-81/17. Washington, DC: U.S. Fish and Wildlife Service.

Brode, J. M., and R. B. Bury. 1984. The importance of riparian systems to amphibians and reptiles. In California riparian systems: Ecology, conservation, and productive management, edited by R. E. Warner and K. M. Hendrix, 30-36. Berkeley: University of California Press.

Brothers, T. S. 1984. Historical vegetation change in the Owens River riparian woodland. In <u>California riparian systems: Ecology, conservation, and productive management</u>, edited by R. E. Warner and K. M. Hendrix, 75-84. Berkeley: University of California Press.

Brown, G. W. 1969. Predicting temperatures on small streams. <u>Water Resources Research</u> 5: 68-75.

————. 1970. Predicting the effect of clear-cutting on stream temperatures. <u>Journal of Soil and Water Conservation</u> 25: 11-13.

————. 1980. <u>Forestry and water quality</u>. Corvallis: OSU Book Stores.

Brown, G. W. and J. T. Krygier. 1970. Effects of clear-cutting on stream temperature. <u>Water Resources Research</u> 6(4): 1133-40.

Browne, J. R. 1868. <u>Mineral resources of the West</u>. cited by Coleman 1952.

Bull, W. B. and K. M. Scott. 1974. Impact of gravel mining from urban streambeds in the southwestern United States. <u>Geology</u> 2: 171-78.

Burcham, L. T. 1970. Ecological significance of alien plants in California grasslands. <u>Proceedings of the Association of California Geographers</u> 11: 36-39.

California Department of Forestry and Fire Protection. 1994. <u>California forest practice rules. Title 14, California code of regulations</u>. Sacramento: California Department of Forestry and Fire Protection.

————. 1996. Calwater database online. Sacramento: California Environmental Resource Evaluation System. Available from http://resources.agency.ca.gov

California Rivers Assessment. 1995. <u>Rivers assessment progress report</u>. Davis: University of California.

California State Lands Commission. 1993. <u>California's rivers: A public trust report</u>. Sacramento: California State Lands Commission.

Campbell, C. J. 1970. Ecological implications of riparian vegetation management. <u>Journal of Soil and Water Conservation</u> 25: 49-52.

Carlson, A. et. al. 1991. <u>Review of literature addressing wildlife and fish habitat relationships in riparian and stream habitats</u>. Nevada City, CA: U.S. Forest Service, Tahoe National Forest.

Carlson, A., N. Berg, and D. Azuma. 1995. <u>Function and dynamics of woody debris in stream reaches in the central Sierra Nevada</u>. Manuscript in review. Albany, CA: U.S. Forest Service, Pacific Southwest Research Station.

Carter, V. 1986. An overview of the hydrologic concerns related to wetlands in the United States. <u>Canadian Journal of Botany</u> 64: 364-74.

Cawley, K. 1991. <u>Cumulative watershed effects in the Last Chance Creek watershed</u>. Milford, CA: U.S. Forest Service, Plumas National Forest, Milford Ranger District.

Chan, F. J. 1993. Response of revegetation on a severely disturbed decomposed granite site. In <u>Proceedings of the conference on decomposed granite soils: Problems and solutions</u>, edited by S. Sommarstrom, 140-51. Davis: University of California Extension.

Chaney, E., W. Elmore, and W. S. Platts. 1993. <u>Livestock grazing on western riparian areas</u>. Eagle, ID: Information Center, Inc.

Chapel, M., A. Carlson, D. Craig, T. Flaherty, C. Marshall, M. Reynolds, D. Pratt, L. Pyshora, S. Tanguay, and W. Thompson. 1992. <u>Recommendations for managing late-seral-stage forest and riparian habitats on the Tahoe National Forest</u>. Nevada City, CA: U.S. Forest Service, Tahoe National Forest.

Clark, W. B. 1970. <u>Gold districts of California</u>. Bulletin 193. San Francisco: California Division of Mines and Geology.

Clifton, C. 1992. Stream classification and channel condition survey, with an inventory of sediment sources from roads and stream crossings conducted in the Last Chance and Spanish Creek watersheds. Quincy, CA: U.S. Forest Service, Plumas National Forest.

———. 1994. East Branch North Fork Feather River erosion control strategy. Quincy, CA: U.S. Forest Service, Plumas National Forest, East Branch North Fork Feather River Coordinated Resource Management Group.

Coleman, C. M. 1952. Pacific Gas and Electric of California: The centennial story of Pacific Gas and Electric Company 1852-1952. New York: McGraw-Hill Book Company.

Collins, B., and T. Dunne. 1990. Fluvial geomorphology and river-gravel mining: A guide for planners. Special Publication 98. Sacramento: California Division of Mines and Geology.

Costick, L. A. 1993. Lower south fork timber harvest plan: A decomposed granite restoration case study. In Proceedings of the conference on decomposed granite soils: Problems and solutions, edited by S. Sommarstrom, 171-73. Davis: University of California Extension.

———. 1996. Indexing current watershed conditions using remote sensing and GIS. In Sierra Nevada Ecosystem Project: Final report to Congress, vol. II, chapter 57. Davis: University of California, Centers for Water and Wildland Resources.

Cross, S. D. 1988. Riparian systems and small mammals and bats. In Streamside management: Riparian wildlife and forestry interactions, edited by K. Raedeke, 93-112. Contribution 59. Seattle: University of Washington, Institute of Forest Resources.

Cummins, K. W. 1992. Catchment characteristics and river ecosystems. In River conservation and management, edited by P. J. Boon, P. Calow and G. E. Petts, 125-35. Chichester: John Wiley and Sons.

Cummins, K. W., M. A. Wilzbach, D. M. Gates, J. B. Perry, and W. B. Taliaferro. 1989. Shredders and riparian vegetation. BioScience 39(1): 24-30.

Cuplin, P. 1985. Riparian area inventory and monitoring using large scale color infrared photography. In Riparian ecosystems and their management symposium, 69-71. Tucson: University of Arizona.

Cuplin, P., W. S. Platts, O. Casey, and R. Masinton. 1985. A comparison of riparian area ground data with large scale airphoto interpretation. In Riparian ecosystems and their management symposium, 67-68. Tucson: University of Arizona.

Curry, R. R. 1992. Eastern Sierra Nevada wetland assessment: Bridgeport basin study site - climatic change, irrigation, and wetland boundaries. In The history of water: Eastern Sierra Nevada, Owens Valley, White-Inyo Mountains, edited by C. A. Hall Jr., V. Doyle-Jones and B. Widawski, 396-414. Los Angeles: University of California, White Mountain Research Station.

Davenport, D. C. 1977. A nondestructive approach to reducing riparian transpiration. In Riparian forests in California: Their ecology and conservation, edited by A. Sands, 103-10. Publication 15. Davis: University of California, Institute of Ecology.

Davis, F. W., and D. M. Stoms. 1996. Sierran vegetation: A GAP analysis. In Sierra Nevada Ecosystem Project: Final report to Congress, vol. II, chapter 25. Davis: University of California, Centers for Water and Wildland Resources.

DeBano, L. F., and L. J. Schmidt. 1989. Improving southwestern riparian areas through watershed management. General Technical Report RM-182. Fort Collins, CO: U.S. Forest Service, Rocky Mountain Forest and Range Experiment Station.

DeBenedetti, S. H., and D. J. Parsons. 1979. Mountain meadow management and research in Sequoia and Kings Canyon National Parks: a review and update. In First conference on scientific research in the national parks, edited by R. M. Linn, 1305-11. Washington, DC: National Park Service.

Doppelt, B., M. Scurlock, C. Frissell, and J. Karr. 1993. Entering the watershed: A new approach to save America's river ecosystems. Washington DC: Pacific Rivers Council / Island Press.

Duane, T. P. 1996. Human settlement, 1850-2040. In Sierra Nevada Ecosystem Project: Final report to Congress, vol. II, chapter 11. Davis: University of California, Centers for Water and Wildland Resources.

Dudley, T., and B. Collins. 1995. Biological invasions in California wetlands: The impacts and control of nonindigenous species (NIS) in natural areas. Oakland: Pacific Institute for Studies in Development, Environment, and Security.

Dudley, T., and W. E. Dietrich. 1995. Effects of cattle grazing exclosures on the recovery of riparian ecosystems in the southern Sierra Nevada. Technical Completion Report UCAL-WRC-W-831. Davis: University of California, Water Resources Center.

Dudley, T., and M. Embury. 1995. Non-indigenous species in wilderness areas: The status and impacts of livestock and game species in designated wilderness in California. Oakland: Pacific Institute for Studies in Development, Environment, and Security.

Dunford, E. G., and P. W. Fletcher. 1947. Effect of removal of streambank vegetation upon water yield. Transactions American Geophysical Union 28: 105-10.

Dunne, T., and L. B. Leopold. 1978. Water in environmental planning. San Francisco: W. H. Freeman.

Dunne, T., T. R. Moore, and C. H. Taylor. 1975. Recognition and prediction of runoff-producing zones in humid regions. Hydrological Sciences Bulletin 20: 305-27.

Ehlers, R. 1956. An evaluation of stream improvement devices constructed eighteen years ago. California Fish and Game 42: 203-17.

Elmore, W. 1989. Rangeland riparian systems. In Proceedings of the California riparian systems conference: Protection, management, and restoration for the 1990's, edited by D. L. Abell, 93-95. General Technical Report PSW-110. Berkeley: U.S. Forest Service, Pacific Southwest Forest and Range Experiment Station.

Elmore, W., and R. L. Beschta. 1987. Riparian areas: Perceptions in management. Rangelands 9(6): 260-65.

_____. 1989. The fallacy of structures and the fortitude of vegetation. In Proceedings of the California riparian systems conference: Protection, management, and restoration for the 1990's, edited by D. L. Abell, 116-19. General Technical Report PSW-110. Berkeley: U.S. Forest Service, Pacific Southwest Forest and Range Experiment Station.

Erman, D. C. 1973. Invertebrate movements and some diel and seasonal changes in a Sierra Nevada peatland. Oikos 24: 85-93.

_____. 1976. Peat depth of Sierra Nevada fens, and profile changes from 1958 to 1972 in Mason Fen. Great Basin Naturalist 36(1): 101-107.

_____. 1992. Historical background of long-term diversion of the Little Truckee River. In The history of water in the Eastern Sierra Nevada, Owens Valley and White Mountains, edited by C. A. Hall, V. Doyle-Jones and B. Widawski, 415-27. Los Angeles: University of California Press.

Erman, D. C. and N. A. Erman. 1975. Macroinvertebrate composition and production in some Sierra Nevada minerotrophic peatlands. Ecology 56: 591-603.

Erman, D. C., and V. M. Hawthorne. 1976. The quantitative importance of an intermittent stream in the spawning of rainbow trout. Transactions of the American Fisheries Society 105: 675-81.

Erman, D. C., and D. Mahoney. 1983. Recovery after logging in streams with and without bufferstrips in northern California. Contribution 186. Davis: University of California, Water Resources Center.

Erman, D. C., J. D. Newbold, and K. B. Roby. 1977. Evaluation of streamside bufferstrips for protecting aquatic organisms. Contribution 165. Davis: University of California, Water Resources Center.

Erman, N. 1984. The use of riparian systems by aquatic insects. In California riparian systems: Ecology, conservation, and productive management, edited by R. E. Warner and K. Hendrix, 177-82. Berkeley: University of California Press.

_____. 1996. Status of aquatic invertebrates. In Sierra Nevada Ecosystem Project: Final report to Congress, vol. II, chapter 38. Davis: University of California, Centers for Water and Wildland Resources.

Faber, P. M., and R. F. Holland. 1988. Common riparian plants of California. Mill Valley: Pickleweed Press.

Federal Energy Regulatory Commission. 1986. Owens River basin: Seven hydroelectric projects, California. Final environmental impact statement. Washington DC: Federal Energy Regulatory Commission, Office of Hydropower Licensing.

_____. 1994. Draft environmental impact report / draft environmental impact statement: Clavey River project (FERC 10081-002). FERC/EIS-0074D. Washington DC: Federal Energy Regulatory Commission, Office of Hydropower Licensing.

Fleischner, T. L. 1994. Ecological costs of livestock grazing in western North America. Conservation Biology 8(3): 629-44.

Flett, M. A., and S. D. Sanders. 1987. Ecology of a Sierra Nevada population of Willow Flycatchers. Western Birds 18: 37-42.

Franklin, J. F., and J. Fites-Kaufmann. 1996. Analysis of late successional/old growth forests. In Sierra Nevada Ecosystem Project: Final report to Congress, vol. II, chapter 23. Davis: University of California, Centers for Water and Wildland Resources.

Furniss, M. J., T. D. Roelofs, and C. S. Yee. 1991. Road construction and maintenance. In Influences of forest and rangeland management on salmonid fishes and their habitats, edited by W. R. Meehan, 297-323. Bethesda, MD: American Fisheries Society.

Gaines, D. A. 1977. The valley riparian forests of California: Their importance to bird populations. In Riparian forests in California: Their ecology and conservation, edited by A. Sands, 57-85. Publication 15. Davis: University of California, Institute of Ecology.

Gard, R. 1972. Persistence of headwater check dams in a trout stream. Journal of Wildlife Management 36: 1363-67.

Goldman, S. 1993. Achieving effective erosion control at Lake Tahoe. In Proceedings of the conference on decomposed granite soils: Problems and solutions, edited by S. Sommarstrom, 152-60. Davis: University of California Extension.

Graber, D. 1996. Status of terrestrial vertebrates. In Sierra Nevada Ecosystem Project: Final report to Congress, vol. II, chapter 27. Davis: University of California, Centers for Water and Wildland Resources.

Gradek, P., L. Saslaw, and S. Nelson. 1989. An application of BLM's riparian inventory procedure to rangeland riparian resources in the Kern and Kaweah River watersheds. In Proceedings of the California riparian systems conference: Protection, management, and restoration for the 1990's, edited by D. L. Abell, 109-15. General Technical Report PSW-110. Berkeley: U.S. Forest Service, Pacific Southwest Forest and Range Experiment Station.

Grant, G. 1988. The RAPID technique: A new method for evaluating downstream effects of forest practices on riparian zones. General Technical Report PNW-220. Corvallis, OR: U.S. Forest Service, Pacific Northwest Forest and Range Experiment Station.

Grant, G., and F. J. Swanson. 1995. Morphology and processes of valley floors in mountain streams, western Cascades, Oregon. In Natural and anthropogenic influences in fluvial geomorphology: The Wolman volume, edited by J. E. Costa, A. J. Miller, K. W. Potter, P. R. Wilcock, 83-101. Geophysical Monograph 89. Washington, DC: American Geophysical Union.

Gregory, S. V., G. A. Lamberti, and K. M. S. Moore. 1989. Influence of valley floor landforms on stream ecosystems. In Proceedings of the California riparian systems conference: Protection, management, and restoration for the 1990's, edited by D. L. Abell, 3-8. General Technical Report PSW-110. Berkeley: U.S. Forest Service, Pacific Southwest Forest and Range Experiment Station.

Gregory, S. V., F. J. Swanson, W. A. McKee, and K. W. Cummins. 1991. An ecosystem perspective of riparian zones. BioScience 41(8): 540-51.

Greene, L. W., 1987. Yosemite: The park and its resources; A history of the discovery, management and physical development of Yosemite National Park, California. San Francisco: National Park Service.

Greenville Ranger District, 1985. Watershed condition survey and restoration plan for the Wolf Creek watershed. Greenville, CA: Plumas National Forest, Greenville Ranger District.

Groeneveld, D. P., and D. Or. 1994. Water table induced shrub-herbaceous ecotone: hydrologic management implications. Water Resources Bulletin 30(5): 911-20.

Hadley, R. F. 1961. Influence of riparian vegetation on channel shape in northeastern Arizona. Professional Paper 424-C. Reston, VA: U.S. Geological Survey.

Hagberg, T. 1995. Relationships between hydrology, vegetation and gullies in montane meadows of the Sierra Nevada. Master's thesis. Humboldt State University, Arcata.

Hakencamp, C. C., H. M. Valett, and A. J. Boulton. 1993. Perspectives on the hyporehic zone: Integrating hydrology and biology. Concluding remarks. Bulletin of the North American Benthological Society 12(1): 94-99.

Hall, J. G. 1960. Willow and aspen in the ecology of beaver on Sagehen Creek, California. Ecology 41:485-94.

Harmon, M. E., et al. 1986. Ecology of coarse woody debris in temperate ecosystems. Advances in Ecological Research 15: 133-302.

Harr, R. D., and R. A. Nichols. 1993. Stabilizing forest roads to help restore fish habitats: A northwest Washington example. Fisheries 18(4): 18-22.

Harris, J. H., S. D. Sanders, and M. A. Flett. 1987. Willow Flycatcher surveys in the Sierra Nevada. Western Birds 18: 37-42.

Harris, R. R., C. A. Fox, and R. Risser. 1987. Impacts of hydroelectric development on riparian vegetation in the Sierra Nevada Region, California, USA. Environmental Management 11(4): 519-27.

Harvey, B. C. 1986. Effects of suction dredging on fish and invertebrates in two California streams. American Journal of Fisheries Management 6: 401-409.

Harvey, B. C., T. E. Lisle, T. Vallier, and D. C. Fredley. 1995. Effects of suction dredging on streams: A review and evaluation strategy. Washington, DC: U.S. Forest Service.

Hawkins, C. P. et. al. 1994. Cumulative watershed effects: An extensive analysis of responses by stream biota to watershed management. Final report on cooperative agreement PSW-88-0011CA. Albany, CA: U.S. Forest Service, Pacific Southwest Forest and Range Experiment Station.

Heede, B. H. 1972. Flow and channel characteristics of two high mountain streams. Research Paper RM-96. Fort Collins, CO: U.S. Forest Service, Rocky Mountain Forest and Range Experiment Station.

Heede, B. H., 1990. Vegetation strips control erosion in watersheds. Research Note RM-499. Fort Collins, CO: U.S. Forest Service, Rocky Mountain Research Station.

Helvey, J. D. 1980. Effects of a north central Washington wildfire on runoff and sediment production. Water Resources Bulletin 16(4): 627-34.

Herbst, D. and R. Knapp. 1995a. Biomonitoring of rangeland streams under differing livestock grazing practices. Bulletin of the North American Benthological Society 14(1): 176.

_____. 1995b. Evaluation of rangeland stream condition and recovery using physical and biological assessments of nonpoint source pollution. Technical Completion Report UCAL-WRC-W-818. Davis: University of California, Water Resources Center.

254

Hewlett, J. D., and A. R. Hibbert. 1967. Factors affecting the response of small watersheds to precipitation in humid areas. In International symposium on forest hydrology, edited by W. E. Sopper and H. W. Lull, 275-90. New York: Pergamon.

Hibbert, A. R., 1983. Water yield improvement potential by vegetation management on western rangelands. Water Resources Bulletin 19: 375-81.

Hicks, T. 1995. Riparian monitoring plan for hydropower projects. Bishop, CA: U.S. Forest Service, Inyo National Forest.

Hill, K. J. 1994. Annual water quality report. Zephyr Cove, NV: Tahoe Regional Planning Agency.

Holmes, D. O. 1979. Cultural influences on subalpine and alpine meadow vegetation in Yosemite National Park. In First Conference on scientific research in the national parks, edited by R. M. Linn, 1267-72. Washington, DC: National Park Service.

Hot Springs Ranger District. 1994. South Creek ecosystem analysis. Porterville, CA: U.S. Forest Service, Sequoia National Forest.

Hughes, J. E. 1934. Erosion control progress report. Milford, CA: U.S. Forest Service, Plumas National Forest, Milford Ranger District.

Hunter, C. J. 1991. Better trout habitat: A guide to stream restoration and management. Washington, DC: Island Press / Montana Land Reliance.

Ice, G. G. 1995. Managing riparian zones and watersheds with state forest practice programs. In Watershed management: Planning for the 21st century, edited by T. J. Ward, 290-99. New York: American Society of Civil Engineers.

Inyo County Water Department. 1995. Owens Valley Water Reporter 8 (2).

Inyo National Forest. 1988. Land and resource management plan. Bishop, CA: U.S. Forest Service, Inyo National Forest.

_____. 1993. Interagency motor vehicle use plan revision- draft environmental impact statement. Bishop, CA: U.S. Forest Service and Bureau of Land Management.

James, L. A. 1994. Channel changes wrought by gold mining: Northern Sierra Nevada, California. In Effects of human-induced changes on hydrologic systems, edited by R. Marston and V. R. Hasfurther, 629-38. Bethesda, MD: American Water Resources Association.

Janda, R. J. 1966. Pleistocene history and hydrology of the upper San Joaquin River. Ph.D. dissertation, University of California, Berkeley.

Jennings, M. R. 1996. Status of amphibians. In Sierra Nevada Ecosystem Project: Final report to Congress, vol. II, chapter 34. Davis: University of California, Centers for Water and Wildland Resources.

Jensen, S. E., and W. S. Platts. 1989. Restoration of degraded riverine/riparian habitat in the Great Basin and Snake River regions. In Wetland creation and restoration: The status of the science, edited by H. A. Kusler and M. E. Kentula, 377-416. Corvallis: U.S. Environmental Protection Agency.

Johnson, R. R. 1971. Tree removal along southwestern rivers and effects on associated organisms. American Philosophical Society Yearbook 1970 : 321-322.

Johnston, C. A. 1991. Sediment and nutrient retention by freshwater wetlands. Critical Reviews of Environmental Control 21: 491-565.

_____. 1993. Material fluxes across wetland ecotones in northern landscapes. Ecological Applications 3: 424-40.

Jones and Stokes Associates. 1983. Characteristics of riparian vegetation at streamflow diversion sites on the eastern slope of the Sierra Nevada mountains. 84-RD-87. Rosemead, CA: Southern California Edison.

_____. 1989. Downstream effects of hydroelectric development on riparian vegetation: a joint PG&E /SCE research project. Sacramento: Jones and Stokes Associates.

Kaplan-Henry, T. A., H. A. Eddinger, and T. W. Henry. 1995. South Creek riparian ecosystem analysis, Hot Springs Ranger District, Sequoia National Forest. In Watersheds '94: Respect, rethink, restore; Proceedings of the fifth biennial watershed management conference, edited by R. R. Harris, R. Kattelmann, H. Kerner and J. Woled, 132-33. Davis: University of California, Water Resources Center.

Karr, J. R., and I. J. Schlosser. 1978. Water resources and the land-water interface. Science 201: 229-34.

Katibah, E. F., K. J. Dummer, and N. E. Nedeff. 1984. Current condition of riparian resources in the Central Valley of California. In California riparian systems: Ecology, conservation, and productive Management, edited by R. E. Warner and K. M. Hendrix, 314-21. Berkeley: University of California Press.

Kattelmann, R. 1989. Oversnow flow in the Sierra Nevada. In Proceedings international mountain watershed symposium: Subalpine processes and water quality, edited by I. G. Poppoff, C. R. Goldman, S. L. Loeb and L. B. Leopold, 220-25. South Lake Tahoe, CA: Tahoe Resource Conservation District.

_____. 1990. Floods in the high Sierra Nevada, California. In Hydrology in mountainous areas, vol. 2, edited by R. O. Sinniger and M. Monbaron, 311-17. Publication 194. Wallingford, England: International Association of Hydrological Sciences.

_____. 1992. Historical floods in the eastern Sierra Nevada. In The history of water in the Eastern Sierra Nevada, Owens Valley and White Mountains, edited by C. A. Hall, V. Doyle-Jones and B. Widawski, 74-86. Los Angeles: University of California Press.

_____. 1996a. Hydrology and water resources. In Sierra Nevada Ecosystem Project: Final report to Congress, vol. II, chapter 33. Davis: University of California, Centers for Water and Wildland Resources.

_____. 1996b. Impacts of floods and avalanches. In Sierra Nevada Ecosystem Project: Final report to Congress, vol. II, chapter 52. Davis: University of California, Centers for Water and Wildland Resources.

Kattelmann, R., and D. Dawson. 1994. Water diversions and withdrawal for municipal supply in the eastern Sierra Nevada. In Effects of human-induced changes on hydrologic systems, edited by R. A. Marston and V. R. Hasfurther, 475-83. Bethesda: American Water Resources Association.

Kauffman, J. B. 1988. The status of riparian habitats in Pacific Northwest forests. In Streamside management: riparian wildlife and forestry interactions, edited by K. J. Raedeke, 45-55. Seattle: University of Washington, Institute of Forest Resources.

Kauffman, J. B., R. L. Case, D. Lytjen, and D. L. Cummings. 1995. Ecological approaches to riparian restoration in northeast Oregon. Restoration and Management Notes 13(1): 12-15.

Kauffman, J. B., W. C. Krueger, and M. Vavra. 1983. Impacts of cattle on streambanks in northeastern Oregon. Journal of Range Management 36(6): 683-91.

Kauffman, J. B., and W. C. Krueger. 1984. Livestock impacts on riparian ecosystems and streamside management implications...a review. Journal of Range Management 37(5): 430-37.

Kaufmann, M., et al. 1994. An ecological basis for ecosystem management. General Technical Report RM-256. Fort Collins, CO: U.S. Forest Service, Rocky Mountain Forest and Range Experiment Station.

Keller, E A., and F. J. Swanson. 1979. Effects of large organic material on channel form and fluvial processes. Earth Surface Processes 4: 361-80.

Keller, E. A., and A. MacDonald 1995. River channel change: The role of large woody debris. In Changing river channels, edited by A. Gurnell and G. Petts, 217-235. Chichester: John Wiley and Sons.

Kinney, B. 1996. Conditions of rangelands before 1905. In Sierra Nevada Ecosystem Project: Final report to Congress, vol. II, chapter 3. Davis: University of California, Centers for Water and Wildland Resources.

Klebenow, D. A., and R. J. Oakleaf. 1984. Historical avifauna changes in the riparian zone of the Truckee River, Nevada. In California riparian systems: Ecology, conservation, and productive management, edited by R. E. Warner and K. M. Hendrix, 203-209. Berkeley: University of California Press.

Knapp, R. A. 1996. Non-native trout in natural lakes of the Sierra Nevada: An analysis of their distribution and impacts on native aquatic biota. In Sierra Nevada Ecosystem Project: Final report to Congress, vol. III. Davis: University of California, Centers for Water and Wildland Resources.

Knight, A. W., and R. L. Bottorff. 1984. The importance of riparian vegetation to stream ecosystems. In California riparian systems: Ecology, conservation, and productive management, edited by R. E. Warner and K. M. Hendrix, 160-67. Berkeley: University of California Press.

Kohen, D. S. et. al. 1994. Shaping the Future of Owens Lake. Pomona: California State University, Landscape Architecture, 606 Studio.

Kondolf, G. M. 1989. Stream-groundwater interactions along streams of the eastern Sierra Nevada, California: Implications for assessing potential impacts of flow diversions. In Proceedings of the California riparian systems conference: Protection, management, and restoration for the 1990's, edited by D. L. Abell, 352-59. General Technical Report PSW-110. Berkeley: U.S. Forest Service, Pacific Southwest Forest and Range Experiment Station.

_____. 1993. Lag in stream channel adjustment to livestock exclosure, White Mountains, California. Restoration Ecology 1: 226-30.

_____. 1995a. Five elements of effective stream restoration. Restoration Ecology 3(2):133-36.

_____. 1995b. Learning from stream restoration projects. In Proceedings of the fifth biennial watershed management conference, edited by R. Harris, R. Kattelmann, H. Kerner, and J. Woled, 107-10, Report 86. Davis: University of California, Centers for Water and Wildland Resources.

Kondolf, G. M., G. F. Cada and M. J. Sale. 1987. Assessing flushing-flow requirement for brown trout spawning gravels in steep streams. Water Resources Bulletin 23(5): 927-35.

Kondolf, G. M., G. F. Cada, M. J. Sale and T. Felando. 1991. Distribution and stability of potential salmonid spawning gravels in steep boulder-bed streams of the eastern Sierra Nevada. Transactions of the American Fisheries Society 120: 177-86.

Kondolf, G. M., R. Kattelmann, M. Embury, and D. C. Erman. 1996. Status of riparian habitat. In Sierra Nevada Ecosystem Project: Final report to Congress, vol. II, chapter 39. Davis: University of California, Centers for Water and Wildland Resources.

Kondolf, G. M., and W. V. G. Matthews. 1993. Management of coarse sediment on regulated rivers. Report 80. Davis: University of California, Water Resources Center.

Kondolf, G. M., and E. R. Micheli. 1995. Evaluating stream restoration projects. Environmental Management 19(1):1-15.

Kraebel, C. J., and A. F. Pillsbury. 1934. Handbook of erosion control in mountain meadows in the California region. Berkeley: U.S. Forest Service, California Forest and Range Experiment Station.

Krzysik, A. J. 1990. Biodiversity in riparian communities and watershed management. In Watershed planning and analysis in action, edited by R. E. Riggins, E. B. Jones, R. Singh and P. A. Rechard, 533-48. New York: American Society of Civil Engineers.

Kuehn, M. H. 1987. The effects of exceeding "probable maximum precipitation" on a severely burned watershed in the Sierra Nevada of California. In Landslide activity in the Sierra Nevada during 1982 and 1983, edited by J. V. De Graff, 27-40. San Francisco: U.S. Forest Service, Pacific Southwest Region.

LaBoa, J. et. al. 1994. Eastside pine. In Ecological support team workshop proceedings for the California spotted owl environmental impact statement, edited by E. Toth, J. LaBoa, D. Nelson and R. Hermit. San Francisco: U.S. Forest Service, Pacific Southwest Region.

LaFayette, R. A., and L. F. DeBano. 1990. Watershed condition and riparian health: Linkages. In <u>Watershed planning and analysis in action</u>, edited by F. E. Riggins, E. B. Jones, R. Singh and P. A. Rechard, 473-84. New York: American Society of Engineers.

Langley, R. D. 1984. SOFAR: A small-town water diversion project on the South Fork American River. In <u>California riparian systems: Ecology, conservation, and productive management</u>, edited by R. E. Warner and K. M. Hendrix, 505-14. Berkeley: University of California Press.

Larson, D. J. 1996. Historical water use priorities and public policies. In <u>Sierra Nevada Ecosystem Project: Final report to Congress</u>, vol. II, chapter 8. Davis: University of California, Centers for Water and Wildland Resources.

Lawton, H. W., P. J. Wilke, and W. M. Mason. 1976. Agriculture among the Paiute of Owens Valley. <u>Journal of California Anthropology</u> 3:13-50.

Laymon, S. A. 1987. Brown-headed cowbirds in California: Historical perspectives and management opportunities. <u>Western Birds</u> 18: 63-70.

Leiberg, J. B. 1902. <u>Forest conditions in the northern Sierra Nevada, California</u>. Professional Paper No. 8, Series H, Forestry 5. Washington DC: U.S. Geological Survey.

Lemons, J. 1979. Visitor use impact in a subalpine meadow, Yosemite National Park, California. In <u>First conference on scientific research in the national parks</u>, edited by R. M. Linn, 1287-92. Washington, DC: National Park Service.

Leopold, L. B. 1968. <u>Hydrology for urban land planning: a guide book</u>. Circular 554. Washington DC: U.S. Geological Survey.

Leopold, L. B. 1994. <u>A view of the river</u>. Cambridge: Harvard University Press.

Liddle, M. J. 1975. A selective review of the ecological effects of human trampling on natural ecosystems. <u>Biological Conservation</u> 7: 17-36.

Lindquist, D. S., and Y. Bowie. 1989. Watershed restoration in the northern Sierra Nevada: A biotechnical approach. In <u>Proceedings of the California riparian systems conference: Protection, management, and restoration for the 1990's</u>, edited by D. L. Abell, 436-40. General Technical Report PSW-110. Berkeley: U.S. Forest Service, Pacific Southwest Forest and Range Experiment Station.

Logan, C. A. 1948. History of mining and milling methods in California. In <u>Geologic guidebook along highway 49-Sierran gold belt the mother lode country</u>, edited by O. P. Jenkins, 31-34. San Francisco: California Division of Mines.

Los Angeles Department of Water and Power. 1995. Draft Mono Basin stream and stream channel restoration plan. Los Angeles: Department of Water and Power.

Loredo, I., D. Van Vuren, and M. L, Morrison. In press. Habitat use and migration behavior of the California tiger salamander. <u>Journal of Herpetology</u>.

Madej, M. A., W. E. Weaver, and D. K. Hagans. 1994. Analysis of bank erosion on the Merced River Yosemite Valley, Yosemite National Park, California, USA. <u>Environmental Management</u> 18(2): 235-50.

Mahoney, D. L., and D. C. Erman. 1984. The role of streamside bufferstrips in the ecology of aquatic biota. In <u>California riparian systems: Ecology, conservation, and productive management</u>, edited by R. E. Warner and K. M. Hendrix, 168-74. Berkeley: University of California Press.

Mahoney, D. L., and D. C. Erman. 1984. An index of stored fine sediment in gravel bedded streams. <u>Water Resources Bulletin</u> 20(3): 343-48.

Manley, P. N. 1995. Biological diversity and its measure: An assessment in lotic riparian ecosystems of the Lake Tahoe basin. San Francisco: U.S. Forest Service, Pacific Southwest Region.

Manley, P. N. and C. Davidson. 1995. Assessing risks and setting priorities for neotropical migratory birds in California. Draft manuscript on file, San Francisco: U.S. Forest Service, Pacific Southwest Region.

Marchetti, M. P.1994. Suspended sediment effects on the stream fauna of Humbug Creek. Master's thesis, University of California, Davis.

Marston, R. A. 1982. The geomorphic significance of log steps in forest streams. <u>Annals of the Association of American Geographers</u> 72: 99-108.

Martin, K. E. 1984. Recreation planning as a tool to restore and protect riparian systems. In <u>California riparian systems: Ecology, conservation, and productive management</u>, edited by R. E. Warner and K. M. Hendrix, 748-57. Berkeley: University of California Press.

Maser, C., and J. Sedell. 1994. <u>From the forest to the sea: The ecology of wood in streams</u>. Delray Beach, FL: St. Lucie Press.

McCleneghan, K., and R. E. Johnson. 1983. <u>Suction dredge gold mining in the mother lode region of California</u>. Administrative Report 83-1. Sacramento: Department of Fish and Game, Environmental Services Branch.

McDonald, P. M., and J. C. Tappeiner. Hardwood silviculture and ecology. In <u>Sierra Nevada Ecosystem Project: Final report to Congress</u>, vol. III. Davis: University of California, Centers for Water and Wildland Resources.

McGurk, B. J., 1989. Predicting stream temperature after riparian vegetation removal. In <u>Proceedings of the California riparian systems conference: Protection, management, and restoration for the 1990's</u>, edited by D. L. Abell, 157-64. General Technical Report PSW-110. Berkeley: U.S. Forest Service, Pacific Southwest Forest and Range Experiment Station.

McGurk, B. J., and D. R. Fong. 1995. Equivalent roaded area as a measure of cumulative effect of logging. <u>Environmental Management</u> 19(4): 606-21.

McKelvey, K. S., and J. D. Johnston. 1992. Historical perspectives on forests of the Sierra Nevada and the Transverse Ranges of southern California: Forest conditions at the turn of the century. In <u>The California Spotted Owl: A technical assessment of its current status</u>, edited by J. Verner et al., 225-46. Albany, CA: U.S. Forest Service, Pacific Southwest Research Station.

McWilliams, B., and G. Goldman. 1994. <u>The mineral industries in California: Their impact on the state economy</u>. Publication CNR 003. Berkeley: University of California, Division of Agriculture and Natural Resources.

McPhee, J. 1993. <u>Assembling California</u>. New York: Farrar, Straus, and Giroux.

Medina, A. L., 1990. Possible effects of residential development on streamflow, riparian plant communities, and fisheries in small mountain streams in central Arizona. <u>Forest Ecology and Management</u> 33/34: 351-61.

Meehan, W. R., F. J. Swanson, and J. R. Sedell. 1977. Influence of riparian vegetation on aquatic ecosystems with particular reference to salmonids and their food supply. In <u>Importance, preservation, and management of riparian habitat: A symposium</u>, edited by R. R. Johnson and D. A. Jones, 137-45. General Technical Report RM-43. Fort Collins, CO: U.S. Forest Service, Rocky Mountain Forest and Range Experiment Station.

Megahan, W. F., and P. N. King. 1985. Identification of critical areas on forest lands for control of nonpoint sources of pollution. <u>Environmental Management</u> 9(1): 7-18.

Menke, J. W. ed. 1977. <u>Proceedings of the workshop on livestock and wildlife-fisheries relationships in the Great Basin</u>. Davis: University of California.

Menke, J. W., C. Davis, and P. Beesley. 1996. Public rangeland / livestock grazing assessment. In <u>Sierra Nevada Ecosystem Project: Final report to Congress</u>, vol. II, chapter 30. Davis: University of California, Centers for Water and Wildland Resources.

Miller, A. H. 1951. An analysis of the distribution of birds in California. <u>University of California Publications in Zoology</u> 50: 531-643.

Minshall, G. W. 1994. Stream-riparian ecosystems: Rationale and methods for basin-level assessments of management effects. In <u>Ecosystem management: Principles and applications; eastside forest ecosystem health assessment</u>, edited by M. E. Jensen and P. S. Bourgeron, 149-73. General Technical Report PNW-318. Portland, OR: U.S. Forest Service, Pacific Northwest Research Station.

Minshall, G. W., J. T. Brock, and J. D. Varley. 1989. Wildfires and Yellowstone's stream ecosystems. BioScience 39(10): 707-15.

Mitsch, W. J., and J. G. Gosselink. 1986. Wetlands. New York: Van Nostrand Reinhold.

Morrison, M. L., et al. 1985. Natural history of vertebrates of Sagehen Creek basin, Nevada County, CA. Berkeley: University of California, Department of Forestry and Resource Management.

Mount, J. F. 1995. California rivers and streams: The conflict between fluvial processes and land use. Berkeley: University of California Press.

Moyle, P. B. 1996a. Biotic integrity of watersheds. In Sierra Nevada Ecosystem Project: Final report to Congress, vol. II, chapter 37. Davis: University of California, Centers for Water and Wildland Resources.

_____. 1996b. Status of aquatic habitat types. In Sierra Nevada Ecosystem Project: Final report to Congress, vol. II, chapter 35. Davis: University of California, Centers for Water and Wildland Resources.

Moyle, P. B., R. M. Yoshiyama, and R. A. Knapp 1996. Fish and fisheries of the Sierra Nevada. In Sierra Nevada Ecosystem Project: Final report to Congress, vol. II, chapter 36. Davis: University of California, Centers for Water and Wildland Resources.

Moyle, P., R. Zomer, R. Kattelmann, and P. Randall. 1996. Management of riparian areas in the Sierra Nevada. In Sierra Nevada Ecosystem Project: Final report to Congress, vol. III. Davis: University of California, Centers for Water and Wildland Resources.

Mullally, D. P., and J. D. Cunningham. 1956. Ecological relations of Rana mucosa at high elevations in the Sierra Nevada. Herpetologica 12(3): 189-98.

Murphy, M. L., and W. R. Meehan. 1991. Stream ecosystem. In Influences of forest and rangeland management on salmonid fishes and their habitats, edited by W. R. Meehan, 17-46, Special Publication 19. Bethesda, MD: American Fisheries Society.

Myers, L. H. 1987. Riparian area management: Inventory and monitoring riparian areas. Technical Reference 1737-3. Denver, CO: U.S. Bureau of Land Management.

Myers, M. 1992. Watershed improvement implementation schedule, Miami Basin. Mariposa, CA: U.S. Forest Service, Sierra National Forest, Mariposa Ranger District.

_____. 1993. Nichols Meadow restoration project, Mariposa Ranger District, Sierra National Forest. In Riparian management: Common threads and shared interests, edited by B. Tellman, H. J. Cortner, M. G. Wallace, L. F. DeBano and R. H. Hamre, 191. Fort Collins, CO: U.S. Forest Service, Rocky Mountain Forest and Range Experiment Station.

Naiman, R. J., et. al. 1992a. Fundamental elements of ecologically healthy watersheds in the Pacific Northwest coastal ecosystem. In Watershed management: Balancing sustainability and environmental change, edited by R. J. Naiman, 127-88. New York: Springer-Verlag.

Naiman, R. J., D. G. Lonzarich, T. J. Beechie, and S. C. Ralph. 1992b. General principles of classification and the assessment of conservation potential in rivers. In River conservation and management, edited by P. J. Boon, P. Calow and G. E. Petts, 93-123. Chichester: John Wiley and Sons.

Naiman, R. J., H. DeCamps, and M. Pollock. 1993. The role of riparian corridors in maintaining regional biodiversity. Ecological Applications 3: 209-12.

Naiman, R. J., J. J. Magnuson, D. M. McKnight, and J. A. Stanford. 1995. The freshwater imperative: A research agenda. Washington, DC: Island Press.

Nakamura, F., and F. J. Swanson. 1993. Effects of coarse woody debris on morphology and sediment storage of a mountain stream system in western Oregon. Earth Surface Processes and Landforms 18: 43-61.

National Research Council. 1992. Restoration of aquatic ecosystems: Science, technology, and public policy. Washington DC: National Academy Press.

_____. 1994. <u>Rangeland health: New methods to classify, inventory and monitor rangelands</u>. Washington DC: National Academy Press.

_____. 1995. <u>Wetlands: Characteristics and boundaries</u>. Washington DC: National Academy Press.

Nelson, C. W., and J. R. Nelson. 1984. The Central Valley riparian mapping project. In <u>California riparian systems: Ecology, conservation, and productive management</u>, edited by R. E. Warner and K. M. Hendrix, 307-13. Berkeley: University of California Press.

Nelson, D. et. al. 1994. Foothill riparian. In <u>Ecological support team workshop proceedings for the California spotted owl environmental impact statement</u>, edited by E. Toth, J. LaBoa, D. Nelson and R. Hermit. San Francisco: U.S. Forest Service, Pacific Southwest Region.

Newbold, J. D., D. C. Erman, and K. B. Roby. 1980. Effects of logging on macroinvertebrates in streams with and without buffer strips. <u>Canadian Journal of Fisheries and Aquatic Sciences</u> 37: 1076-85.

Newbury, R., and M. Gaboury. 1993. Exploration and rehabilitation of hydraulic habitats in streams using principles of fluvial behavior. <u>Freshwater Biology</u> 29: 195-210.

O'Connor, M. D. 1986. Effects of logging on organic debris dams in first order streams in northern California. Master's thesis, University of California, Berkeley.

Odion, D. C., T. L. Dudley, and C. M. D'Antonio. 1990. Cattle grazing in southeastern Sierran meadows: Ecosystem change and prospects for recovery. In <u>Plant Biology of Eastern California</u>, edited by C. A. Hall and V. Doyle-Jones, 277-92. Los Angeles: White Mountain Research Station, University of California.

Odion, D. C., R. M. Calloway, W. R. Ferren, and F. W. Davis. 1992. Vegetation of Fish Slough, an Owens Valley wetland ecosystem. In <u>The history of water in the Eastern Sierra Nevada, Owens Valley and White Mountains</u>, edited by C. A. Hall, V. Doyle-Jones and B. Widawski, 171-79. Los Angeles: University of California Press.

Odum, E. P. 1978. Ecological importance of the riparian zone. In <u>National symposium on strategies for protection and management of floodplain wetlands and other riparian ecosystems</u>, 2-4. Washington, DC: U.S. Forest Service.

Ohmart, R. D. 1994. The effects of human-induced changes on the avifauna of western riparian habitats. In <u>A century of avifaunal change in western North America</u>, edited by J. R. Jehl, Jr. and N. K. Johnson, 273-85. <u>Studies in Avian Biology</u> No. 15.

Overton, K. C., G. L. Chandler, and J. A. Pisano. 1994. <u>Northern/Intermountain regions' fish habitat inventory: Grazed, rested, and ungrazed reference stream reaches, Silver King Creek, California</u>. General Technical Report INT-311. Ogden, UT: U.S. Forest Service, Intermountain Research Station.

Pacific Rivers Council. 1995. <u>The urgent need for watershed protection and restoration in the Sierra Nevada: Native fish and streams at risk in California</u>. Sacramento: Pacific Rivers Council.

Palmer, T. 1994. <u>Lifelines: The case for river conservation</u>. Washington, DC: Island Press.

Parrish, J. L., and D. C. Erman. 1994. Critical questions for the Sierra Nevada: Recommended research priorities and administration. Report 34. Davis: University of California, Centers for Water and Wildland Resources.

Patten, D. T. 1986. <u>Riparian workshop, November 13-14, 1985</u>. San Ramon, CA: Pacific Gas and Electric and Southern California Edison.

Pawley, A., and J. F. Quinn. 1996. California watershed projects inventory database online. Davis: University of California, Division of Environmental Studies. Available from http://ice.davis.edu.

Pelzman, R. J. 1973. Causes and possible prevention of riparian plant encroachment on anadromous fish habitat. Administrative Report 73-1. Sacramento: California Department of Fish and Game, Environmental Services Branch.

Perkins, D. J., B. N. Carlsen, M. Fredstrom, R. H. Miller, C. M. Rofer, G. T. Ruggerone, and C. S. Zimmerman. 1984. The effects of groundwater pumping on natural spring communities in Owens Valley. In <u>California</u>

riparian systems: Ecology, conservation, and productive management, edited by R. E. Warner and K. M. Hendrix, 515-26. Berkeley: University of California Press.

Peterjohn, W. T., and D. L. Correll. 1984. Nutrient dynamics in an agricultural watershed: Observation on the role of a riparian forest. Ecology 65: 1466-75.

Petranka, J. W., M. P. Brannon, M. E. Hopey, and C. K. Smith. 1994. Effects of timber harvesting on low elevation populations of southern Appalachian salamanders. Forest Ecology and Management 67:135-47.

Pinay, G., and Decamps H. 1988. The role of riparian woods in regulating nitrogen fluxes between the alluvial aquifer and surface water: A conceptual model. Regulated Rivers: Research and Management 2: 507-16.

Pister, E. P., and J. H. Kerbavaz. 1984. Fish Slough: A case study in management of a desert wetland system. In California riparian systems: Ecology, conservation, and productive management, edited by R. E. Warner and K. M. Hendrix, 929-33. Berkeley: University of California Press.

Platts, W. S. 1979. Livestock grazing and riparian-stream ecosystems--an overview. In Proceedings, grazing and riparian-stream ecosystems forum, edited by O. B. Cope, 39-45. Vienna, VA: Trout Unlimited.

_____. 1984. Riparian system/livestock grazing interaction research in the intermountain west. In California riparian systems: Ecology, conservation, and productive management, edited by R. E. Warner and K. M. Hendrix, 424-29. Berkeley: University of California Press.

_____. 1991. Livestock grazing. In Influences of forest and rangeland management on salmonid fishes and their habitats, edited by W. R. Meehan, 389-423. Bethesda, MD: American Fisheries Society.

Platts, W. S., and R. L. Nelson. 1985. Streamside and upland vegetation use by cattle. Rangelands 7: 5-7.

Plumas National Forest. 1988. Land and resources management plan. Quincy, CA: U.S. Forest Service, Plumas National Forest.

Pomby, J. 1987. Mined land reclamation program. California Geology 40(1): 3-6.

Ponce, V. M., and D. S. Lindquist. 1990. Management strategies for baseflow augmentation. In Watershed Planning and Analysis, edited by R. E. Riggins, E. B. Jones, R. Singh and P. A. Rechard, 313-22. New York: American Society of Civil Engineers.

Raedeke, K. J., R. D. Taber, and D. K. Paige. 1988. Ecology of large mammals in riparian systems of Pacific Northwest forests. In Streamside management: Riparian wildlife and forestry interactions, edited by K. Raedeke, 113-32. Contribution 59. Seattle: University of Washington, Institute of Forest Resources.

Ralph, S. C., G. C. Poole, L. L. Conquest, and R. J. Naiman. 1994. Stream channel morphology and woody debris in logged and unlogged basins of western Washington. Canadian Journal of Fisheries and Aquatic Sciences 51: 37-51.

Range Watch. 1995. Sierra Nevada grazing impacts. Video tape. Posey, CA: Range Watch.

Ratliff, R. D. 1985. Meadows in the Sierra Nevada of California: state of knowledge. General Technical Report PSW-84. Berkeley: U.S. Forest Service, Pacific Southwest Forest and Range Experiment Station.

Reid, L. M. 1993. Research and cumulative watershed effects. General Technical Report PSW-141. Albany, CA: U.S. Forest Service, Pacific Southwest Research Station.

Reid, L. M., and T. Dunne. 1984. Sediment production from forest road surfaces. Water Resources Research 20: 1753-61.

Reynolds, F. L., T. J. Mills, R. Benthin, and A. Low. 1993. Restoring Central Valley streams: A plan for action. Sacramento: California Department of Fish and Game.

Rhodes, J., C. M. Skau, D. Greenlee, and D. L. Brown. 1985. Quantification of nitrate uptake by riparian forests and wetlands in an undisturbed headwaters watershed. In Proceedings of the North American Riparian Conference, 175-79. Fort Collins, CO: U.S. Forest Service, Rocky Mountain Forest and Range Experiment Station.

Ridenhour, R. L., C. Hunter, and W. J. Trush. 1995. Workplan: Mono Basin stream restoration (Rush Creek, Lee Vining Creek, and Parker Creek). Los Angeles: Department of Water and Power.

Rinne, J. N. 1990. The utility of stream habitat and biota for identifying potential conflicting forest land uses: Montane riparian areas. Forest Ecology and Management 33/34: 363-83.

Risser, P. G. 1995. The status of the science of examining ecotones. Bioscience 45(5): 318-25.

Risser, R. J., and R. R. Harris. 1987. Mitigation for impacts to riparian vegetation on regulated headwater streams. In Sierran Riparian Conference, edited by D. T. Patten, 42-47. San Ramon: Pacific Gas and Electric Company and Southern California Edison Company.

Robinson, G. E., and R. L. Beschta. 1990. Identifying trees in riparian areas that can provide coarse woody debris to streams. Forest Science 36: 790-801.

Robinson, T. W. 1965. Introduction, spread and aerial extent of saltcedar (Tamarix) in the western States. Professional Paper 491-A. Washington, DC: U.S. Geological Survey.

Roby, K. B. 1989. Watershed response and recovery from the Will Fire: Ten years of observation. In Proceedings of the symposium on fire and watershed management, edited by N. H. Berg, 131-36. Berkeley: U.S. Forest Service, Pacific Southwest Forest and Range Experiment Station.

Roby, K. B., and D. L. Azuma. 1995. Changes in a reach of a northern California stream following wildfire. Environmental Management 19(4): 591-600.

Roby, K. B., D. C. Erman, and J. D. Newbold. 1977. Biological assessment of timber management activity impacts and buffer strip effectiveness on national forest streams of northern California. San Francisco: U.S. Forest Service, Pacific Southwest Region.

Ruediger, R. 1991. Distribution and abundance of large wood in central Sierra streams. Sonora, CA: U.S. Forest Service, Stanislaus National Forest.

Sandecki, M. 1989. Aggregate mining in river systems. California Geology 42(4): 88-94.

Sanders, S. D., and M. A. Flett. 1989. Montane riparian habitat and Willow Flycatcher: Threats to a sensitive environment and species. In Proceedings of the California riparian systems conference: Protection, management, and restoration for the 1990's, edited by D. L. Abell, 262-66. General Technical Report PSW-110. Berkeley: U.S. Forest Service, Pacific Southwest Forest and Range Experiment Station.

Sands, A. ed. 1977. Riparian forests in California: Their ecology and management. Publication 15. Davis: University of California, Institute of Ecology.

Sands, A., and G. Howe. 1977. An overview of riparian forests in California: Their ecology and conservation. In Importance, preservation, and management of riparian habitat: A symposium, edited by R. R. Johnson and D. A. Jones, 98-115. General Technical Report RM-43. Fort Collins, CO: U.S. Forest Service, Rocky Mountain Forest and Range Experiment Station.

Schlosser, I. J., and J. R. Karr. 1981. Water quality in agricultural watersheds: Impact of riparian vegetation during base flow. Water Resources Bulletin 17(2): 233-40.

Schulenburg, R. 1994. Program status report, 1984 fish and wildlife habitat enhancement act (prop. 19). Sacramento: Wildlife Conservation Board.

Schwartz, M. W., D. J. Porter, J. M. Randall, K. E. Lyons. 1996. Impact of non-indigenous plants. In Sierra Nevada Ecosystem Project: Final report to Congress, vol. II, chapter 50. Davis: University of California, Centers for Water and Wildland Resources.

Sedell, J. R. 1984. Evaluating fish response to woody debris. In Pacific Northwest Stream Management Workshop, 222-45. Arcata: Humboldt State University.

Sedell, J. R., and G. H. Reeves. 1992. An ecosystem approach to the conservation and management of freshwater habitat for anadromous salmonids in the Pacific Northwest. Transactions of the North American Wildlife and Natural Resources Conference 57: 408-15.

Sedell, J. R., G. H. Reeves, and K. M. Burnett. 1994. Development and evaluation of aquatic conservation strategies. Journal of Forestry 92(4): 28-31.

Senter, E. 1987. Erosion control at Malakoff Diggings State Historical Park. Sacramento: Department of Water Resources, Central District.

Shevock, J. R. 1996. Status of rare and endemic plants. In Sierra Nevada Ecosystem Project: Final report to Congress, vol. II, chapter 26. Davis: University of California, Centers for Water and Wildland Resources.

Sigafoos, R. S., 1964. Botanical evidence of floods and floodplain deposition. Professional Paper 485A. Washington, DC: U.S. Geological Survey.

Skinner, C. N., and C. Chang. 1996. Fire regimes, past and present. In Sierra Nevada Ecosystem Project: Final report to Congress, vol. II, chapter 41. Davis: University of California, Centers for Water and Wildland Resources.

Skovlin, J. M. 1984. Impacts of grazing on wetlands and riparian habitat: A review of our knowledge. In Developing Strategies for Rangeland Management, 1001-1113. National Research Council. Boulder, CO: Westview Press.

Small, A. 1974. The Birds of California. New York: MacMillan Publishing Company.

Smith, F. E. 1977. A short review of the status of riparian forests in California. In Riparian forests in California: Their ecology and management, edited by A. Sands, 1-2. Davis: University of California, Institute of Ecology.

Smith, S. D., A. B. Wellington, J. L. Nachlinger, and C. A. Fox. 1991. Functional response of riparian vegetation to streamflow diversion in the eastern Sierra Nevada. Ecological Applications 1: 89-97.

Stanford, J. A., and J. V. Ward. 1988. The hyporehic habitat of river ecosystems. Nature 335: 64-66.

Stanford, J. A., and J. V. Ward. 1993. An ecosystem perspective of alluvial rivers: Connectivity and the hyporehic corridor. Journal of the North American Benthological Society 12: 48-60.

Stanislaus National Forest. 1988. Land and resources management plan. Sonora, CA: U.S. Forest Service.

Steinblums, I. J., H. A. Froehlich, and J. K. Lyons. 1984. Designing stable buffer strips for stream protection. Journal of Forestry 82(1): 49-52.

Stevens, L. E., B. T. Brown, J. M. Simpson, and R. R. Johnson. 1977. The importance of riparian habitat to migrating birds. In Importance, preservation, and management of riparian habitat: A symposium, edited by R. R. Johnson and D. A. Jones, 156-64. General Technical Report RM-43. Fort Collins, CO: U.S. Forest Service, Rocky Mountain Forest and Range Experiment Station.

Steward, J. 1934. Ethnography of the Owens Valley Paiute. American Archaeology and Ethnology 33:233-324.

Stine, S. 1991. Extent of riparian vegetation on stream tributary to Mono Lake, 1930-1940: an assessment of the streamside woodlands and wetlands, and the environmental conditions that supported them. Sacramento: California State Water Resources Control Board and Jones and Stokes Associates.

_____. 1994. Restoration conceptual plan: The concepts and principles guiding the restoration of Rush and Lee Vining Creeks, Mono County, California. Los Angeles: Department of Water and Power, Restoration Technical Committee.

Stine, S., D. Gaines, and P. Vorster. 1984. Destruction of riparian systems due to water development in the Mono Lake watershed. In California Riparian Systems: Ecology, Conservation, and Productive Management, edited by R. E. Warner and K. M. Hendrix, 528-33. Berkeley: University of California.

Stromberg, J., and D. Patten. 1989. Early recovery of an eastern Sierra riparian system after forty years of stream diversion. In Proceedings of the California riparian systems conference: Protection, management, and restoration of the 1990's, edited by D. L. Abell, 399-404. General Technical Report PSW-110. Berkeley: U.S. Forest Service, Pacific Southwest Forest and Range Experiment Station.

_____. 1991. Response of *Salix lasiolepis* to augmented streamflows in the upper Owens River. Sacramento: Jones and Stokes Associates.

_____. 1992. Mortality and age of Black Cottonwood stands along diverted and undiverted streams in the eastern Sierra Nevada, California. Madrono 39(3): 205-23.

Sudworth, G. B. 1900. Stanislaus and Lake Tahoe Forest Reserves, California, and adjacent territory. In Annual Reports of the Department of the Interior, 21st Annual Report of the U.S. Geological Survey, 505-61. Washington, DC: Government Printing Office.

Sullivan, K. 1994. An alternative view of riparian area management. Journal of Forestry 92(4): 29.

Swanson, F. J., J. F. Franklin, and J. R. Sedell. 1990. Landscape patterns, disturbance and management in the Pacific Northwest, U.S.A. In Changing landscapes: An ecological perspective, edited by I. S. Zonneveld and R. T. T. Forman, 191-213. New York: Springer-Verlag.

Swanson, F. J., S. V. Gregory, J. R. Sedell, and A. G. Campbell. 1982. Land-water interactions: The riparian zone. In Analysis of Coniferous Forest Ecosystems in the Western United States, edited by R. L. Edmonds, 267-291. Stroudsburg, PA: Hutchinson Ross Publishing Company.

Swanson, F. J., and R. E. Sparks. 1990. Long-term ecological research and the invisible place. Bioscience 40(7): 502-508.

Swanson, S. 1989. Using stream classification to prioritize riparian rehabilitation after extreme events. In Proceedings of the California riparian systems conference: Protection, management, and restoration of the 1990's, edited by D. L. Abell, 96-101. General Technical Report PSW-110. Berkeley: U.S. Forest Service, Pacific Southwest Forest and Range Experiment Station.

Tahoe Regional Planning Agency. 1988. Water quality management plan for the Lake Tahoe region. Zephyr Cove, NV: Tahoe Regional Planning Agency.

Taylor, D. W. 1982. Riparian vegetation of the Eastern Sierra: Ecological effects of stream diversions. Bishop, CA: U.S. Forest Service, Inyo National Forest.

_____. 1983. Assessing potential environmental impacts of small-hydro on riparian vegetation. Paper presented at workshop on small-hydro projects. Bishop, CA: Inyo County.

Taylor, D. W., and W. B. Davilla. 1985. Riparian vegetation in the Crane Valley project. San Ramon: Pacific Gas and Electric Company.

_____. 1986. Evaluation of riparian vegetation along the Lower North Fork Kings River and tributaries, Fresno County, California. San Ramon, CA: Pacific Gas and Electric Company.

Terrene Institute. 1994. Urbanization and water quality. Washington DC: Terrene Institute.

Thomas, J. W., C. Maser, and J. E. Rodiek. 1979. Riparian zones. In Wildlife habitat in managed forests: The Blue Mountains of Oregon and Washington, edited by J. W. Thomas. Agriculture Handbook 553. Washington, DC: U.S. Forest Service.

Tiller, R. L., and R. Tollefson. 1992. Restoration of riparian habitat on the Kern River Preserve. Watershed Management Council Newsletter 4(3): 10.

Todd, A. H. 1989. Watershed restoration and erosion control: Making it work in subalpine areas. In Proceedings international mountain watershed symposium: Subalpine processes and water quality, edited by I. G. Poppoff, C. R. Goldman, S. L. Loeb and L. B. Leopold, 290-99. South Lake Tahoe, CA: Tahoe Resource Conservation District.

Toth, E. et. al. 1994. Mixed conifer. In Ecological support team workshop proceedings for the California spotted owl environmental impact statement, edited by E. Toth, J. LaBoa, D. Nelson and R. Hermit. San Francisco: U.S. Forest Service, Pacific Southwest Region.

Trihey, E. W., and S. English. 1991. A conceptual plan for the restoration of aquatic and riparian habitats in Rush and Lee Vining Creeks, Mono County, California. Concord, CA: Trihey and Associates.

Troendle, C. A. 1993. Sediment transport for instream flow / channel maintenance. In Proceedings technical workshop on sediments, 31-34. Washington, DC: Terrene Institute.

U.S. Bureau of Land Management. 1994. Rangeland reform '94; draft environmental impact statement. Washington, DC: U.S. Department of the Interior.

U.S. Environmental Protection Agency. 1993. Monitoring protocols to evaluate water quality effects of grazing management on western rangeland streams. EPA 910/R-93-017. Washington, DC: Environmental Protection Agency, Water Division, Surface Water Branch.

U.S. Forest Service. 1995a. Pacific Southwest Region stream condition inventory handbook. Version 3.0. San Francisco: U.S. Forest Service, Pacific Southwest Region.

————. 1995b. Results of stream condition inventory of grazed and ungrazed meadow streams. Unpublished report. San Francisco: U.S. Forest Service, Pacific Southwest Region.

U.S. General Accounting Office. 1988. Public rangelands: Some riparian areas restored but widespread improvement will be slow. Washington, DC: U.S. General Accounting Office.

U.S. Soil Conservation Service. 1984. Foothills watershed area study, El Dorado unit. Placerville, CA: U.S. Soil Conservation Service.

————. 1989. East Branch North Fork Feather River erosion inventory report, Plumas County, California. Davis, CA: U.S. Soil Conservation Service, River Basin Planning Staff.

Van Haveren, B. P. and W. L. Jackson. 1989. Concepts in stream riparian rehabilitation. Transactions of the North American Wildlife and Natural Resources Conference 51: 280-89.

Vankat, J. L., and J. Major. 1978. Vegetation changes in Sequoia National Park, California. Journal of Biogeography 5: 377-402.

Vannote, R. L, G. W. Minshall, K. W. Cummins, J. R. Sedell, and C. E. Cushing. 1980. The river continuum concept. Canadian Journal of Fisheries and Aquatic Sciences 37: 130-37.

Vorster, P., and G. M. Kondolf. 1989. The effect of water management and land use practices on the restoration of Lee Vining and Rush Creeks. In Proceedings of the California riparian systems conference: Protection, management, and restoration of the 1990's, edited by D. L. Abell, 405-10. General Technical Report PSW-110. Berkeley: U.S. Forest Service, Pacific Southwest Forest and Range Experiment Station.

Wagoner, L. 1886. Report on forests of the counties of Amador, Calaveras, Tuolumne, and Mariposa. In First biennial report of the California State Board of Forestry for the years 1885-1886, 39-44. Sacramento: State Board of Forestry.

Walsh, K., R. Bowen, and H. Skibitzke. 1987. Aerial photograph interpretation of riparian vegetation/geomorphology relations on Bishop Creek. In Sierran Riparian Conference, edited by D. T. Patten, 2-4. San Ramon: Pacific Gas and Electric Company and Southern California Edison Company.

Walters, M. A., R. O. Teskey, and T. M. Hinckley. 1980. Impact of water level changes on woody riparian and wetland communities, volume VII, Mediterranean region, western arid and semi-arid region. Washington, DC: U.S. Fish and Wildlife Service.

Warner, R. E., and K. M. Hendrix eds. 1984. California riparian systems: Ecology, conservation, and productive management. Berkeley: University of California Press.

Weatherspoon, C. P., and C. N. Skinner. 1996. Landscape-level strategies for forest fuel management. In Sierra Nevada Ecosystem Project: Final report to Congress, vol. II, chapter 60. Davis: University of California, Centers for Water and Wildland Resources.

Welsh, H. H. 1993. A hierarchical analysis of the niche relationships of four amphibians from forested habitats in northwestern California. Ph.D. Dissertation, University of California, Berkeley.

Whitall, D. R., and S. S. Champion. 1989. Wetland enhancement in Blackwood Canyon. In Proceedings international mountain watershed symposium: Subalpine processes and water quality, edited by I. G.

Poppoff, C. R. Goldman, S. L. Loeb and L. B. Leopold, 83-90. South Lake Tahoe, CA: Tahoe Resource Conservation District.

Whitney, S. 1979. A Sierra Club naturalist's guide to the Sierra Nevada. San Francisco: Sierra Club Books.

Williams, G. P., and M. G. Wolman. 1984. Downstream effects of dams and alluvial rivers. Professional Paper 1286. Reston, VA: U.S. Geological Survey.

Wills, L. and J. Schramel. 1994. A grass roots perspective: Feather River coordinated resource management. In Overcoming obstacles: Proceedings of the fourth biennial watershed management conference, edited by J. Woled, 53-61. Davis: University of California, Centers for Water and Wildland Resources.

Wills, L. and J. C. Sheehan. 1994. East Branch North Fork Feather River, Spanish Creek and Lost Chance Creek non-point source water pollution study. Quincy, CA: Plumas Corporation.

Wolman, M. G. 1959. Factors influencing erosion of a cohesive river bank. American Journal of Science 257: 204-16.

Wood, S. H. 1975. Holocene stratigraphy and chronology of mountain meadows, Sierra Nevada, California. Ph.D. Dissertation, California Institute of Technology, Pasadena, California.

Woyshner, M. and B. Hecht. 1990. Sediment, solute and nutrient transport from Squaw Creek, Truckee River Basin, California. In Proceedings international mountain watershed symposium: Subalpine processes and water quality, edited by I. G. Poppoff, C. R. Goldman, S. L. Loeb and L. B. Leopold, 190-219. South Lake Tahoe, CA: Tahoe Resource Conservation District.

Zeiner, D. C., W. F. Laudenslayer, K. E. Mayer, and M. White eds. 1988. California's wildlife, volume II, birds; California Statewide Wildlife Habitat Relationships System. Sacramento: Department of Fish and Game.

_____. 1990a. California's wildlife, volume I, amphibians and reptiles; California Statewide Wildlife Habitat Relationships System. Sacramento: Department of Fish and Game.

_____. 1990b. California's wildlife, volume III, mammals; California Statewide Wildlife Habitat Relationships System. Sacramento: Department of Fish and Game.

Zimmerman, R. C., J. C. Goodlett, and G. H. Comer. 1967. Influence of vegetation on channel form of small streams. 255-75. Publication 75. Wallingford, England: International Association of Scientific Hydrology.

Appendix 1. Larger plants typical of riparian areas in the Sierra Nevada.
Trees

Alnus rhombifolia	white alder
Celtis reticulata	hackberry
Fraxinus latifolia	Oregon ash
Pinus ponderosa	ponderosa pine
Populus fremontii	Fremont cottonwood
Populus trichocarpa	black cottonwood
Salix laevigata	red willow

Shrubs

Baccharis glutinosa	water wally
Betula occidentalis	western birch
Cornus stolonifera	red osier dogwood
Forestiera neomexicana	desert olive
Phragmites communis var. *berlandieri*	reed
Rosa californica	wild rose
Rosa woodsii	wild rose
Salix exigua	coyote willow
Salix lasiolepis var. *bracelinae*	willow
Salix ligulifolia	willow
Salix lutea var. *watsonii*	willow

(from Walters et al. 1980; Faber and Holland 1988)

Appendix 2. Threatened and endangered species dependent on riparian habitat
(from Graber 1996)

Ambystoma californiense	California Tiger Salamander
Ambystoma macrodactylum	Long Toed Salamander
Hydromentes sp.	Owens Valley Web-Toed Salamander
Bufo canorus	Yosemite Toad
Rana aurora draytonii	Red-legged Frog
Rana boylei	Foothill Yellow-legged Frog
Rana muscosa	Mountain Yellow-legged Frog
Rana pipiens	Northern Leopard Frog
Scaphiopus hammondi	Western Spadefoot
Clemmys marmorata	Western Pond Turtle
Plegadis chihi	White-faced Ibis
Histrionicus histrionicus	Harlequin Duck
Bucephalia islandica	Barrow's Goldeneye
Pandion haliaetus	Osprey
Haliaetus leucocephalus	Bald Eagle
Empidonax trailii	Willow Flycatcher
Geothlypis trichas	Common Yellowthroat
Icteria virens	Yellow-breasted Chat
Agelaius tricolor	Tricolored Blackbird
Sorex lyelli	Mt. Lyell Shrew

Appendix 3.

MANAGEMENT AND LAND USE BUFFERS
by D. C. Erman, N. A. Erman, L. Costick, and S. Beckwitt

The region near streams and other aquatic ecosystems is defined in three ways: a transition or ecotone, a discrete habitat or community, and an area of special management or buffer between upslope land uses and the aquatic environment. No wonder that the terms and definitions vary with the context. Scientists and managers agree on the special nature of riparian areas. Both federal and California forest practice standards or rules specify restrictions and practices intended to protect streams and moderate disturbance from land use. The main issues are not about the special nature of riparian areas but rather how much area belongs in this category and what activities are acceptable. The ecological functions and process should be guides to use and protection.

The functions and processes take place in three areas at varying distances from the aquatic system: a community area, an energy area, and a land-use influence area The size of these areas will change depending on the characteristics that define them. Any one of the areas may be larger than the others; in other words the three areas are nested within each other but the order is determined by the characteristics which define them rather than an arbitrary hierarchy. One other fact is important in understanding the dimensions of the riparian area: it is not proportional to the size of the aquatic system. Ephemeral ponds, intermittent streams, and small springs are as important to the suite of species that depend upon them as large rivers are to another suite of species. Smaller aquatic systems in forested environments are dominated by the land system. Consequently, the impacts from changes in riparian forest structure and composition and from land disturbance result in major changes in the aquatic system (Erman et al. 1977, Minshall 1994).

The direction of state and federal protection of riparian areas has been based on broad classification of the aquatic system--presence of a life-form (fish-bearing vs. non-fish bearing, for example), size (rivers vs.spring runs), or permanence (year-round streamflow in most years vs. temporary flow in most years). Classification of aquatic habitats for management in this way does not recognize the connected nature of aquatic systems (upstream-downstream), does not recognize the needs of riparian dependent species, cannot work for the protection of aquatic biodiversity (which is particular to the type of system), or properly assist in the management of interconnected land-water systems. Shifting to a recognition of the community, energy, and buffering requirements of riparian areas will aid in protection and management of these areas.

The community area

For any aquatic habitat there is a suite of species that depend on the combination of land and water. Some spend most of their life in the water, some on the land. Most aquatic insects, for example, develop in water but spend a portion of the life cycle on land--feeding, mating, and resting (Erman 1996). Alder and cottonwood trees are always associated with nearby water-- spring, lake, stream, or groundwater near the surface. Of the total 401 Sierran species of mammals, birds, reptiles, and amphibians combined, 21% (84 species) depend on this community area near water, and of course many more use it occasionally or regularly to find food, water, shelter (Graber 1996). Nearly one-quarter (24%) of those dependent on the riparian area are at

270

risk of extinction. From a knowledge of the habitat requirements and life connections of the dependent species we should be able to define the general dimensions of this community area in the various regions and elevation zones of the Sierra. However, the exact requirements and hence the dimensions for many species are unknown. The water shrew (Sorex palustris) is likely confined to the virtual stream bank. Beaver (Castor canadensis) may move tens of meters from water to cut aspen or other trees, and cottonwood on relatively flat floodplains extend over 100 m from low-water channels. The California tiger salamander (Ambystoma californiense) which occurs in the foothills zone (Jennings 1996) lives in terrestrial habitats near temporary and permanent water used for breeding. Adults migrate up to 129 m (average 36 m) and juveniles up to 57 m (average 26 m) between their breeding site and terrestrial burrows (Loredo, et al. in press). Studies elsewhere on amphibians have found some species that live only in the cool, damp conditions near streams and up to several hundred meters from surface flow (Welsh 1994). Dramatic changes in riparian conditions by logging forests near headwater streams have greatly reduced populations of riparian-dependent and terrestrial salamanders in the Appalachians (Petranka, et al. 1994).

Thus, to provide for the living requirements of those organisms dependent for their survival on the special conditions of the riparian area, the primary management should be maintenance of these conditions. Even the natural role of disturbance, documented in this chapter and others, does not require in most situations, active restoration of the landscape in order to secure the habitat conditions necessary for the area.

The Energy Area

Major scientific understanding of the energy linkages between upstream and downstream (e.g., the "river continuum concept" [Vannote et al. 1981]) and exchanges between the land area and aquatic systems has emerged in the last two decades (see review by Murphy and Meehan 1991). Riparian areas contribute a year-round supply of organic material that ranges from nearly the total supply of food at the base of the food chain (small forested streams and springs) to critical quality food (transported organic matter into larger streams from smaller upstream sources). Wind-blown seeds and leaves are a significant source of material entering meadow reaches with little forest canopy. The type of organic material is also important. Easily decomposed plant material (e.g., parts with a relatively low carbon to nitrogen ratio such as alder leaves), those slow to decompose (such as Douglas-fir), as well as terrestrial insects carried in are needed to support a food web throughout the year. The surrounding riparian area also blocks energy from the sun and reradiation from the water (thus reducing temperature changes). And the role of large organic matter (trees, root-wads, debris dams) is of major importance to the structure of stream channels and complexity, to the routing of sediment, to the retention of nutrient supplies, and to the diversity of aquatic habitats. The dimensions of this region vary by the season (leaf fall of deciduous plants), by the hydrologic conditions (out of channel floods, size of stream), by the contributing area (large wood that can fall into the channel, plant parts and insects that blow in), and by the species mix (organic material breaks down and is useful as aquatic food at different times). A useful summary index of this area is the slope distance around the aquatic system equivalent to the height of the site potential tree. For the Sierra Nevada that height in many forest types is approximately 150 ft (46 m). However, the incorporation of wood and other organic material into streams will occur also during inundation of the flood plain. For larger streams in regions of gentle gradient, the width of a stream during major floods may extend much beyond 150 ft.

Riparian Buffer Area

Effects of land use disturbance are reduced by keeping such activities at a distance from the aquatic system and by maintaining a buffer area capable of absorbing disturbance. The likelihood of disturbance to a stream from most land uses increases as a function of proximity to a stream, the steepness of surrounding hillsides and the erodability of soils. These relationships, as in many risk factors, are probably multiplicative and therefore a doubling of slope has more than twice the risk of disturbance to the stream (i.e., an exponential change). Current practice for designing buffer systems based on risk rely on classification of the aquatic system (as mentioned above) and creating three or four categories of slope. As a consequence, a fixed width is chosen even though conditions on the land and requirements of the community would suggest a variable width. We propose a more direct system for estimating a variable width buffer system based on the community and energy area in combination with slope and other measurable risk factors.

For example, let us assume that a stream is in the mixed conifer zone. The determination of hillside slope can be made from topographic maps or from GIS. The SNEP GIS team has prepared a program that will calculate slope at 30 m increments along a stream channel. At each point, slope from five successive 30 m segments out from a channel are computed from the 30 m Digital Elevation Model. Slopes are then weighted 5, 4, 3, 2, 1 from closest to farthest away and divided by five to produce a weighted average slope over the 150 m (slopes closest to the stream have the greatest effect on the average). Let's also assume the stream has a community area defined by species as 110 ft (33.5 m) and an energy area that is 150 ft (46 m). Thus, a minimum region with maintenance of forest structure and minimal land disturbance is 150 ft for these two areas. This distance is then multiplied by the base of natural logs (e) raised to a power equal to 1+slope (in decimal form). If, for example, the slope were 25%, the equation is

$$\text{Buffer width (ft)} = 150 * e(1+0.25)$$

giving a value of 524 ft (160m). If the average slope were 50%, the buffer would be 672 ft (205 m). In the first case, an additional 374 ft (114 m) of buffer would be needed. Soil erodability, also available from soil maps and GIS, can be incorporated as the detachability value (Costick 1996) and the exponent would be expanded to 1+slope+detachability -slope x detachability. For example, if detachability were 0.30, the equation is

$$\text{Buffer width (ft)} = 150 * e(1+0.25+0.30-0.075)$$

giving a value of 656 ft (200 m). Extreme cases, when slope and detachability are both high, would result is even larger buffer zones and as slope and detachability approach zero buffer zones would become smaller--exactly the outcome common sense would indicate is appropriate. This additional area beyond 150 ft would not have the same land use restrictions as the community and energy areas. Its purpose is to highlight a region in which probability of disturbance may affect these areas and the aquatic system. Silvicultural procedures should minimize soil disturbance and in general retain sufficient forest structure to ameliorate microclimate change within the community area and minimize abrupt transition from upslope to the community area. Described as a "probability of disturbance" region places the responsibility on managers for designing practices that have higher standards and are more carefully matched to conditions where mistakes will matter more.

Current information and computer aided analytic methods are sufficient for layout of such a buffer system for many regions of the Sierra. Refinements in scale of Digital Elevation Models from 30 m to 10 m are underway and soil mapping continues to expand and be incorporated into GIS layers. Most forest and land managers today could determine first approximations based on habitat requirements, energy inputs, and hillside slope calculations to produce a logical, ecologically-based riparian management-protection system along the lines we have described. It would lead to better protection of riparian dependent organisms, of energy linkages between the land-water systems, and assist managers in tailoring land use activities to regions of greater need than is presently the case.

Vadose Zone Depth

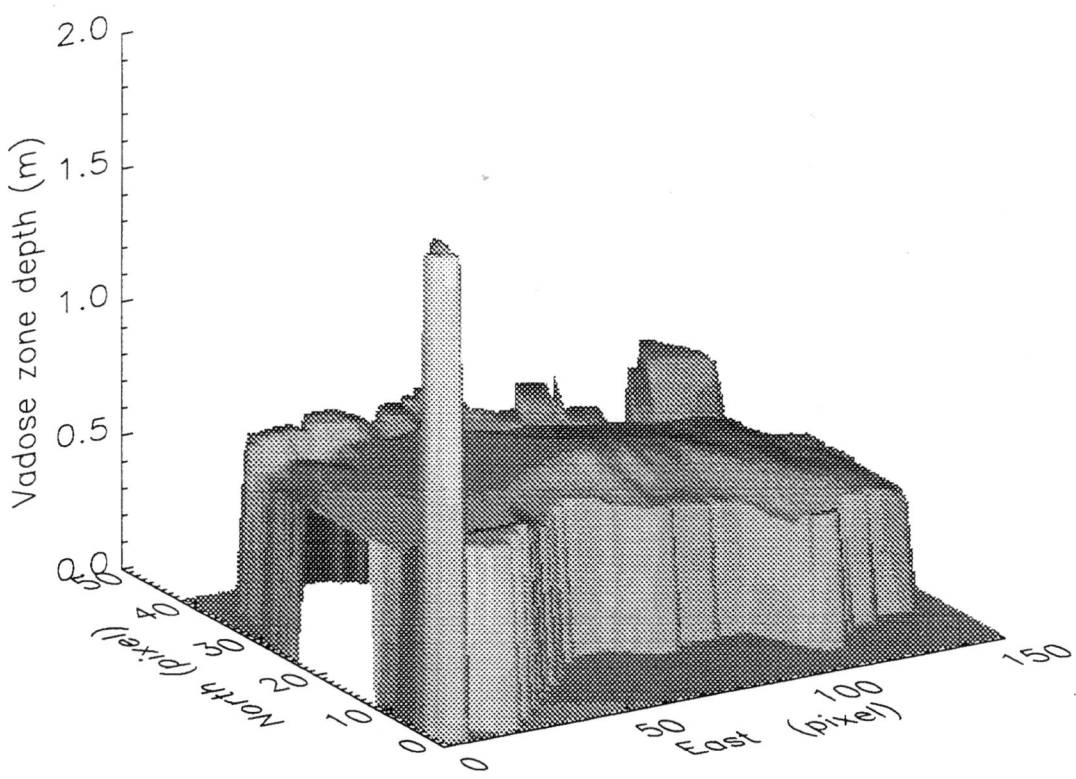

Figure 22.   Vadose Zone Depth

6

SUSAN L. USTIN
Department of Land, Air, and
    Water Resources
University of California
Davis, California

WESLEY W. WALLENDER
Department of Land, Air, and
    Water Resources
University of California
Davis, California

LARRY COSTICK
Department of Land, Air, and
    Water Resources
University of California
Davis, California

RENE LOBATO
Department of Land, Air, and
    Water Resources
University of California
Davis, California

SCOTT N. MARTENS
Department of Land, Air, and
    Water Resources
University of California
Davis, California

JORGE PINZON
Department of Land, Air, and
    Water Resources
University of California
Davis, California

QINGFU XIAO
Department of Land, Air, and
    Water Resources
University of California
Davis, California

Modeling Terrestrial and Aquatic Ecosystem Responses to Hydrologic Regime in a California Watershed

Sierra Nevada Ecosystem Project: Final report to Congress, vol. III, *Assessments, Commissioned Reports, and Background Information.* Davis: University of California, Centers for Water and Wildland Resources, 1996.

INTRODUCTION

This study is a part of the Sierra Nevada Ecological Project (SNEP), the goal of which was to provide an accurate hydrologic assessment and resources analysis study tool for use at watershed scales. During this project a model was developed, integrating various sources of information and allowing a synthesis of the hydrological processes for a watershed in the central Sierra Nevada Range. The SNEP case study of Camp Creek can provide a better understanding of ecosystem behavior and a set of management options for evaluating its' sustainability. One must keep in mind that model representations of physical hydrological laws are bound by the assumptions made for their elaboration; they only represent reality at particular space and time scales. In this report we will attempt to place the model in context of the assumptions and limitations and describe other methods for treating these processes.

Hydrological processes are influenced by factors like climate, topography, soil type and structure, and vegetation. Because these factors vary continuously in the landscape and interact together, it is difficult to predict the impacts of changes in any of their properties within the watershed without a simulating tool. The Surface-Subsurface Model is coupled with a Geographic Information System (GIS) that provides an easy way to manipulate large arrays of distributed data. Thus by changing the inputs and running the program, we can visualize and analyze their effects on the outputs, spatially and temporally. Finally, this model can be considered a management tool to predict the impact of landscape transformations like forest fires, logging, grazing or other activities on the hydrologic budget. The model can simulate the effects of complex interactive phenomena. It may improve our understanding of the hydrologic processes in a mountainous area.

What effect will changes in the water regime have on terrestrial ecosystems? This is a central question affecting predictions of ecosystem response to global climate change. Understanding what components of the hydrologic cycle and related ecosystem processes are sensitive to land use and climate change is critically important for the entire Sierra Nevada ecosystem. A far better understanding of regional hydrologic processes is needed if we are to understand how land management interacts with climate so that realistic strategies can be developed for balancing the demand for urban and agricultural water use. The interaction between climate and hydrologic systems is through plant water use. The biology of terrestrial and aquatic ecosystems depends on an integration of the quantity, quality, and temporal delivery of water resources, the complexity of which requires an integrated analysis of surface and subsurface processes and conditions. The distribution of terrestrial ecosystems is primarily determined by the interaction of climate and topography and the type and frequency of the disturbance regime on the landscape. The extreme Mediterranean climate in California and the frequency of fire create a highly dynamic landscape, where relatively small climate shifts can have significant impact on the local distributions of biome types. Water uptake and transpiration rates determine the amount of CO_2 available for photosynthesis, the mineral nutrition status of the plant, and limits the potential growth rate. Soil moisture, nutritional status, and disturbance regime (type and frequency) largely determine the impact of environmental "stresses." Population dynamics interfaces with the response to environmental stresses and determines whether directional succession will lead to changes in the distribution and abundance of plant communities on the watershed.

To a first approximation, canopy water use is driven by the surface energy budget, available soil moisture and the foliar biomass or surface area. The seasonality and distribution of soil moisture determine both the type of vegetation and the biomass accumulation. Several years of below normal precipitation can cause increased mortality to the forest directly, or indirectly, by increasing susceptibility to insects, pathogens, and wildfire as occurred during the drought of 1987-1993. If demand for latent heat exchange changes (due to a change in net radiation, either total or seasonal), or the supply of water (soil moisture either total or seasonal), then species distributions and/or densities and biomass will change. It is possible to predict the direction of changes in vegetation type or density under different climate change scenarios provided sufficient knowledge of seasonal soil moisture demand and energy budgets by different community types are understood. The ecosystem implications of climate change can be predicted through changes in evaporative demand, phenology, life history, and ultimately shifts in species distributions and biome boundaries. Such changes could be predicted by the ecohydrologic model.

CAMP CREEK CASE STUDY

The study site for this SNEP case study is the Camp Creek sub-basin of the Cosumnes River in the El Dorado National Forest, on the west side of the Sierra Nevada (Figure 1). The centered coordinate of the study area is: 38°42' north latitude and 120°23' west longitude. The reasons for selecting this watershed are: The Cosumnes basin is unique in the Sierra Nevada because it is a relatively low elevation undammed watershed (from 51 m to 2356 m). The watershed has typical west side forests including oak woodlands (lowest elevation), yellow pine, and red fir (highest elevations). Forests include early to late seral stages, and areas of recent wildfires, selected-cut, clear-cut, and re-planted forests. The complex mosaic of surface covers makes the study more realistic and useful to other watershed applications. The figure (from McGurk, this volume) also shows the locations of climate and hydrologic discharge stations within the Cosumnes River basin.

A smaller sub-watershed of a tributary into Camp Creek was used for hydrologic simulations and scenarios. The Snow Creek and Pebble Creek watersheds were selected by the SNEP team for several case study scenarios. Snow Creek is centered at 38°42' latitude and 120°25' longitude and is 3.55 km^2. Pebble Creek is centered at 38°42' latitude and 120°26' longitude and is 2.81 km^2.

Another advantage in studying Camp Creek is the availability of satellite data to drive the hydrology model. Satellite data provides a basis for enriching the spatial information in the model by making it possible to develop a truly spatially distributed hydrology model. The hydrology model is now running at the 30 meters spatial scale of TM images on the Camp Creek drainage. There is an excellent GIS database for this watershed that includes Landsat Thematic Mapper satellite images, DEMs, digital soil and geology maps, roads, forest vegetation and inventory maps, county build-out maps, and many other data layers in the SNEP database. Data from U.S. NOAA Climatological Weather Station data, California Climate Data Center (CDEC), California Irrigation Management and Information System (CIMIS) data, and data are from the forest service are also available. Quarter hour water level recording data was available for intermittent periods between January 1987 and June 1990 at three stations (Darlington Canyon, Pebble Canyon, and Little Light Canyon) within the watershed. Because there is no recorded stream cross section the data can't be converted to a hydrograph. We searched for existing hydrologic and weather data which could be used for model validation. Well data from four stations in Darlington Creek (Section 26, T10R14) were available from the Eldorado National Forest which were installed by the forest hydrologist and geologist to monitor herbicide transport with sub-surface flow. The wells are 38, 22, 65 and 16 ft deep, respectively. Well logs were available with water depth recorded manually beginning in Sept., 1991 and continued weekly through Sept. 29, 1992. Continuous recording rain and stream gauges were installed to complete the hardware for monitoring the hydrologic cycle and battery operated data loggers were installed. However, because of intermittent power failures, only incomplete data were provided. The forest also recorded tipping bucket rain gauge data at about 2780 m elevation but which was unreliable because of uncertainties during snow fall periods. Due to the limited nature of the hydrologic data for Darlington Canyon we excluded it from use in the current validation of the Ecohydrologic model. However, continued investment in the site would be useful for future validation work and the data stations should be maintained. Using recording devices designed for a wider range of weather contions may be an important upgrade for future studies.

The Eldorado National Forest also has adequate field-measured ecologic unit site data within and around the watershed to evaluate data quality for soils, geology, potential natural vegetation, and special features. The Forest Inventory Analysis (FIA) for Eldorado National Forest was used to evaluate vegetation characteristics and was a database on 26,000 trees from 241 plots.

The general structure of the model is shown in Figure 2. This schematic figure of a watershed illustrates the spatial relationships among the cells in the model and shows the connection between the

277

inputs and outputs for a cell. The model was run with cells having a size of 30m by 30m for the Camp Creek watershed. Another way to visualize these relationships is shown in Figure 3 which illustrates the inputs and outputs for a cell in the watershed. This figure describes some scenarios that might be considered using the model, such as climate processes, wildfires, and forest management and illustrates some environmental effects that might be evaluated.

OBJECTIVES

1. Complete the development of a linked Eco-hydrology Model.
2. Simulate hydrologic patterns over the Camp Creek watershed.

TERRESTRIAL ECOSYSTEMS AND HYDROLOGIC MODELS

Typically, ecosystem patterns (e.g., the yellow pine forest or the red fir forest) are recognized based on repeated community or structure units or their transitional forms within a larger mosaic. This complexity makes simple assumptions about vegetation patterns and water use prone to significant error. The explicit spatial distribution of ecosystems affects the transfer of energy and matter between systems. The amount and seasonal phenologic timing of canopy water use is dependent on the ecophysiological processes of the dominant species.   Similar seasonal and spatial (vertical and horizontal) patterns in root activity and soil water uptake make it essential to have detailed information about the distribution of type, density, and structure of vegetation within the watershed. Because there is an intimate interaction between the biologic system and the physical environment at small patch sizes, it presents difficult aggregation problems at watershed and regional scales without knowledge of the dynamics and the linearity of ecosystem processes.

It is necessary to predict spatially distributed patterns to predict the impact of possible climate variation, particularly if the impact associated with global warming is to be understood.   It is difficult to predict climate changes such as those that might result from atmospheric trace gas forcing. Long-term GCM estimates suggest that one effect of doubling the present atmospheric CO_2 concentration could be warmer winter minimum air temperatures, which would lift the snow line several hundred meters. Predicting the possible distribution of snowpack under these scenarios is difficult but important if hydrologic response is to be evaluated. These warmer winter storms would lead to more precipitation falling as rain and less as snow even if the total amount of precipitation did not change. Changing the distribution of precipitation would increase the probability of winter floods and decrease montane snow storage, the hydrologic component that is critical for the late summer water supply.   Either climate outcome would bring adverse effects to terrestrial and aquatic systems in the Sierra Nevada. Understanding hydrologic process and the hydrologic response to landuse and climate change requires an integration of all hydrologic components. It is not enough to develop the most inclusive and theoretically complex hydrologic model, because the input parameters need to be easy to derive from existing data sources and realistic. So some balance is needed between rigorous physically driven processes, scale of the processes, and data availability.

Most "physically based" hydrology models fall short in combining surface and subsurface flow much less including vegetation effects on the water budget. The technical meaning of physically based models have various interpretations. Generally what is meant is a "quasi-physical" model that uses simple physical equations for hydrologic phenomena. It must be kept in mind that the physical laws behind such models have been validated under specific and narrowly defined criteria and the linearity of the processes and appropriateness of multiple time/space scales may not be valid when applied over entire watersheds. Nonetheless, these models have largely been focused on regional scales while resources managers typically plan at a watershed scale. Furthermore, models do not fully exploit remote sensing data--the only near-contemporaneous spatially detailed data that exists.

Surface water simulators such as US Army Corps of Engineers TABS-MD calculate surface flow to streams but ignore the groundwater system. Similarly, groundwater analysis models (e.g. the USGS

MODFLOW) assume given or static inputs from the surface as boundary conditions which disconnected them from the vadose zone and vegetation effects. Jordan (1992) applied two of the best developed models, the SHE (Systeme Hydrologique Europeen; Abbott et al., 1986) and TOPMODEL (Topographic Models; Beven and Kirby, 1979), but could not model fast subsurface flows despite including all physical processes in the model. The SHE model used cells of 250m by 500m (1% of watershed). Gao et al. (1993), developed a fine scale (15 m by 15 m) spatially explicit physically-based surface-subsurface model to overcome the limitations of surface only or subsurface only approaches. They used a 1D Richard's equation to simulate unsaturated flow, a 2D groundwater flow equation assuming horizontal flow, a 2D kinematics wave equation to simulate overland flow, and stream flow was routed using the St. Venant equation. It was possible to model the basin solving the partial differential equations (PDEs) implicitly because (1) the watershed was only 4.4 ha. and well-instrumented, (2) the groundwater flow system was deep and isolated from the surface and as such was ignored, and (3) stream flow was not modeled. Even with these simplifying assumptions, the complexity of their approach is impractical at the scale of typical watersheds nor is the essential data to derive the model available. The model is computationally intensive due to the small time steps and very large matrix inversions that are necessary to solve implicit solutions of PDEs over large areas using grid cells of realistic size. Furthermore, the physically based models (described above and others) input parameters are largely depend on field observational data sources and existing maps. Finally, the interactions between hydrologic properties and ecological conditions (e.g., evapotranspiration rates and patterns) are not examined.

Even fewer models consider interactions of the physical hydrologic system with ecological conditions, despite obvious connections between plants and the interception of precipitation, soil water retention, and evapotranspiration. Hydrological models such as Regional Hydroecological Simulation system (RHESSys) are somewhat more biologically based but lack physical rigor. In recent years several models that address spatial and temporal information have been developed, such as the SiB2 model (Sellers et al., 1986), MTCLIM model (Running et al., 1987; Hungerford et al., 1989), and Forest-BGC model (Running and Coughlan, 1988), that can simulate climate and some hydrologic components for large scale studies. The minimum spatial scale in these models is on the order of kilometers and the temporal scale on the order of days. A distributed hydrology-vegetation model was developed for complex terrain (Wigmosta et al., 1994) that used 180 m spatial and one-day temporal scales to study surface and subsurface water movement. However, these models were developed for ecological studies so the main focus has been to predict evaporation and plant transpiration while ignoring both infiltration and surface flow. A simplifying assumption has been that the study area had a homogeneous soil and the surface cover parameterization used a preexisting vegetation map that may not correctly represent current vegetation distributions. The objectives, input parameters, and spatial and temporal resolution of these models have limited their application when applied to watershed scale hydrologic studies.

ECOHYDROLOGIC MODEL

The ecohydrologic model we developed for SNEP was derived from the rainfall event model of Xiao et al. (1996), and was modified to include surface energy balance and atmospheric exchange in order to compute an annual mass and energy balance hydrologic model. Explicit parameterization for energy budget and evapotranspiration was added by modifying the existing models to use the ET, carbon, and climate parameterizations described in MTCLIM and Forest BGC (Running et al., 1987; Running & Coughlan, 1988; Hungerford et al., 1989). Running & Coughlan (1988) used a simple physiological parameterization of canopy conductance and gas exchange developed for western conifer forests. Forest BGC uses simple physically-based formulations to calculate the characteristics of the vegetation surface as function of LAI, morphology, vegetation type, and soil reflectance properties. This combined model generates a dynamic representation of the spatial and temporal distributions of surface flow, infiltration, soil moisture, water table, subsurface flow, rainfall, evaporation, transpiration, snow pack, snow melt, and canopy interception (Figure 4). The vegetation type, leaf area index, canopy height, root zone depth, and soil moisture are used to calculate evapotranpiration, surface heat flux, canopy temperature, and soil temperature. The soil moisture, surface flow field, subsurface flow field, and infiltration are calculated from the hydrologic sub-model. The domain of the hydrology model is from the canopy/land surface to the bedrock and the time step varies from seconds during a precipitation event to days when changes in surface and subsurface flows are small.

MODEL DESCRIPTION

The spatially and temporally continuous surface-subsurface hydrologic flow model is integrated from five submodels which simulate the component hydrologic processes for each cell in the study area (Figures 3, 4). The precipitation submodel simulates spatial and temporal distribution of rainfall and snow over time. The physiological submodel predicts spatial and temporal distribution of evapotranspiration. The surface flow submodel simulates overland flow. The infiltration submodel simulates vertical water movement from the ground surface to the subsurface water table or to maximum infiltration depth. The subsurface sub-model calculates lateral ground-water flow. A vertical and horizontal mass balance is calculated for each cell at the end of each time step. Time steps are determined by the process requiring the shortest time step as determined by the CDF condition (Courant, et al., 1928). Our approach to modeling assumes simple physical relationships instead of applying the more rigorous higher-order transient differential equations used to estimate detailed local-scale hydrologic processes or the empirically based regional scale methods utilizing rainfall and stream gauge data. This simplifying decision makes the model more applicable to a minimum number of input parameters that are potentially available in sufficient spatial detail at regional scales. The linkages among the submodels are based on the mass balance.

Within each cell, all surface and subsurface flows are linked and water flows laterally between cells. Surface flow is stimulated as steady during a time step using Manning's equation. The equation is applied in the x and y directions of the horizontal plane and is a simplification of the two dimensional solution of the St. Venant equations. Forms of this equation have been widely applied in surface flow models (Abbott et al., 1986; Jordan, 1992; Gao et al., 1993). Surface roughness is derived from remote sensing data and available vegetation maps. Surface slope is derived from DEM data, and the water ponding depth is estimated from continuity of water movement. Infiltration is calculated using the method developed by Green and Ampt (1911). The parameters are all derived from available soil survey databases (e.g., USDA SCS or USDA Forest Service) and derived relations using standard equations (Maidment, 1993). A one-layered soil profile (surface undecomposed organic matter, root zone/unsaturated zone, and saturated zone) is used for calculating soil moisture distribution, unsaturated flow, and saturated subsurface flow. The horizontal water movement in the subsurface and ground water recharge are calculated from Darcy's Law. In the calculation for subsurface flow and determination of water table, the Dupuit assumption is assumed to be satisfied.

The study area is gridded at the same scale in X and Y directions (Figure 2). We assume the land surface and subsurface physical properties are homogenous within each grid cell even though the properties are heterogeneous over the whole study area. Figures 2 and 3 illustrated how the grid and the model are abstracted from the natural landscape. A mass balance is computed for each cell in the grid. Figure 5 shows a three dimensional representation of the hydrologic processes in the model and an X-Y plane view of the surface and subsurface flow paths. This figure describes the inputs and outputs in terms of the hydrologic fluxes.

The spatial scale of the model can be varied from meters to kilometers (depending on input data resolution) and temporal scales from seconds for storm studies to daily for ET and subsurface flow. This model is suitable for application to any study area because the model is not trained on empirical data. Because this model is physics-based, and uses remotely sensed data in a GIS database, it can be applied to any study area and produces surface and subsurface hydrographs as well as soil moisture history for all cells in the problem domain. All of the parameters and variables needed by this model are directly or indirectly found from satellite remote sensing data, USGS topographic data, available soil survey data, and meteorological data. Land use and construction layers (forest, roads, stream locations, buildings, and free surface water) are classified from Landsat TM data while others are from SNEP databases.

Climate Variables.

280

Several data sets are needed to drive the model including hourly precipitation and daily air temperature, relative humidity for the water year (September 1994-September 1995). To the extent that climate data were unavailable, the missing variables were derived from other information. Data sets were obtained from the National Climate Atmosphere Research Center in Boulder, CO, the US Weather Service Regional Archives, Reno, Nevada, the California Data Exchange Center (CDEC), and the California Irrigation Management Information System (CIMIS). In addition, some data was available for stations within the watershed from the USFS Eldorado National Forest and the Eldorado Irrigation District but these records were not continuous up to the current weather year. There are three USGS gauging stations within the watershed. Jenkinson Reservoir has inflow and outflow data records.

Precipitation

In the typical orographic precipitation regime, the local rainfall rate and cumulative rainfall are largely affected by the regional weather patterns as modified by local terrain features. Precipitation is a primary input to the hydrology model (Figure 5) which uses weather station estimates of precipitation, wind direction, air temperature, net solar radiation, and relative humidity that are spatially distributed over the watershed using the topography. We adapted much of the structure of the model MTCLIM (Mountain Microclimate Simulation Model) by Running et al., 1987 and Hungerford et al. 1988, to extrapolate routine NWS (National Weather Service) data to adjacent mountain terrain and make corrections for elevation differences between the station data and the cell. The main objective is to provide spatially distributed climate data on which to drive ecosystem models. There are 21 NOAA weather stations located in or near the Cosumnes River basin used for validation. Accuracy depends on how realistically weather station data can be extrapolated over a complex terrain. We used mean monthly regression equations developed from the 30-year long-term mean monthly rainfall record from seven weather stations located at mid-elevations in the central Sierra Nevada.

NOAA Climatological Data from sites identified in Table 1, were used to compute linear and third order monthly regressions for precipitation rates. We avoided stations with shorter data records and those located in sites where rainfall rates were possibly biased by their location. Since rainfall is strongly dependent on topographic elevation, we correlated rainfall and elevation by developing an empirical "environmental precipitation lapse rate" for the Camp Creek region. Because the weather stations are located approximately along the same latitudinal gradient, we assume that latitude is implicit in the function. In an initial examination of these data, we observed that rainfall generally increased with elevation up to about 2000 m and declined at higher elevations. Because of this nonlinearity, we computed two different monthly correlations, linear and third order (Table 2). The minimum monthly correlation coefficient for predicting rainfall as a function of elevation, for a third order regression was 0.86 (October). The best-fit 30 year mean monthly precipitation predictions for February (Figure 6a) and May (Figure 6b) are shown as a function of elevation.

Table 1. Weather stations with 30 year climate record.

WEATHER STATION	ELEVATION (M)
SACRAMENTO WSO CITY	7.62
PLACERVILLE	563.9
COLFAX	737.6
SALT SPRINGS	1128
LAKE SPAULDING	1571
BOWMAN DAM	1641
TWIN LAKES	2438

TABLE 2. Regression coefficients and coefficients of determination for the polynomial and first order equations relating mean monthly rainfall to elevation.

SNEP Camp Creek Case Study: EcoHydrological Model

	first order regression			third order regression				
	a	b	r^2	a	b	c	d	r^2
Jan	4.018	0.0014	0.90	3.9969	0.0009	4.0e-07	-5.0e-11	0.87
Feb	3.2104	0.0012	0.93	3.0319	0.001	2.0e-07	-4.0e-11	0.92
Mar	3.1003	0.0013	0.92	2.8997	0.0011	2.0e-07	-4.0e-11	0.90
Apr	1.5468	0.0007	0.91	1.2465	0.0009	1.0e-07	-1.0e-11	0.94
May	0.2086	0.0005	0.98	0.2764	0.0002	1.0e-07	-2.0e-11	0.99
Jun	0.0515	0.0002	0.98	0.1194	3.0e-05	5.0e-08	-5.0e-12	0.99
Jul	0.0579	6.0e-05	0.97	0.0511	8.0e-05	-9.0e-09	1.0e-12	0.98
Aug	-0.0181	0.0001	0.94	0.0759	-3.0e-05	6.0e-08	-5.0e-12	0.99
Sep	0.3403	0.0003	0.82	0.376	0.0001	9.0e-08	-1.0e-11	0.83
Oct	1.1248	0.0006	0.90	1.2075	0.0002	2.0e-07	-3.0e-11	0.86
Nov	3.1361	0.0013	0.93	3.1038	0.0009	3.0e-07	-5.0e-11	0.89
Dec	2.2861	0.0015	0.90	2.9583	0.0007	4.0e-07	-6.0e-11	0.87

TABLE 3. Weather stations with eight year climate record.

STATION'S ID	STATION'S NAME	ELEVATION (M)
3113	FOLSOM DAM	106.7
1428	CAMP PARDEE	200.6
2728	ELECTRA P.H.	217.9
6964	PLACERVILLE	563.8
3028	FIDDLETOWN D.R.	568.4
9582	WESTPOINT	859.5
6597	PACIFIC HOUSE	1049
7689	SALTSPRINGS P.H.	1128
0883	BLODGETT EXP. FOREST	1344
3891	HELL HOLE	1478
7489	ROBBS PEAK P.H.	1562
4713	LAKE SPAULDING	1571
0897	BLUE CANYON	1609
8332	SODA SPRINGS 1 E	2100
2671	ECHO SUMMIT SIERRA SKI	2240
9105	TWIN LAKES	2438

The fit of the data set were tested using a separate data set, a recent eight-year record (1987-1994) with both hourly and daily data obtained from 16 NOAA Climatological Data stations and the NCAR climate database. These sites crossed the same elevation gradient (Table 3) and latitude as the long-term dataset used to create the relationships. These data also show the that peak rainfall occurs in the mid-elevation range around the 2000 m contour. This result is consistent with recent model predictions for orographic precipitation (1994). Thus the short-term record from 16 stations located near the watershed displayed monthly precipitation and elevation patterns that were similar to the long-term mean precipitation patterns. We did not use these data directly because the short-term record was more noisy than the 30 year pattern. Because the short-term record spanned the drought years they were anomalous in their more sporadic rainfall distributions. A second reason for the greater noise in the eight year data set is because data records from several stations were incomplete and the missing data could also have biased the results. Again, first and third order regressions for monthly means showed good correlations, with regression coefficients greater than 0.87

The final data set used to evaluate weather generation is the California Irrigation Management Information System (CIMIS) weather station at Camino, CA and located within the Camp Creek study area. The regression between predicted and measured cumulative annual rainfall for the 1995 water year are shown in Figure 7. This figure provides an independent assessment of the accuracy of the weather predictions for a random location in the watershed and illustrates the reliability of the climate sub-model. The first order regression prediction closely approximated the measured precipitation at the Camino station. The third order regression prediction was slightly less good in this test of the prediction.

282

Net Radiation

The energy budget is driven by the net downward flux of radiation. Net radiation is the net sum of the downwelling short wave solar radiation and longwave sky radiation the upwelling shortwave and longwave radiation from the Earth's surface. Daily and hourly net radiation can be calculated by integrating hourly net radiation or total daily net radiation, extrapolated over the hours of daylight by assuming a sine function. Net shortwave radiation was used for all functions except snowmelt which requires total net radiation (including longwave radiation).

Net shortwave radiation for each cell was simulated in the model (following the methodology in MT-CLIM, Running and Coughlan, 1988) and was used to derive daily radiation budgets. These measures were adjusted for cloudiness using the Campbell and Bristow method and extrapolated spatially based on the solar zenith track for each time of day and date and the topographic conditions in each cell. Daily net shortwave radiation was modified by calculating an east and west horizon mask.

Energy Budget Equation

All organisms interact with the physical environment through energy exchange processes. In equilibrium, the rate of energy absorbed is equal to the rate of energy loss, through convective and radiative heat loss, and evapotranspiration. The simplest form of the energy budget equation is:

$$R_{net} = H + G + \lambda E \tag{1}$$

This form of the equation ignores minor sources of variance but includes the three major environmental components of the partitioning of solar energy. Rnet is the net radiation flux density. The soil heat storage (G) is generally small and <10% of the Rnet when soil moisture is not limiting. Most energy is dissipated as sensible heat flux (H) or latent heat flux density (λE). The balance of these components depends on several factors, including the availability of soil moisture for evapotranspiration, temperature, preceeding plant conditions, and relative humidity.

Vapor Pressure Deficit

The vapor pressure deficit is needed to calculate canopy conductance to water vapor. This is calculated from the dew point and the site average temperature.

Vapor Pressure (kPa) under ambient conditions is

$$e_a = 0.61078 \cdot e\left[\frac{17.269 \cdot T_{site}}{237.3 + T_{site}}\right] \tag{2}$$

where

T_{site} = mean daylight site Temperature $^\circ C$

The saturated vapor pressure in the atmosphere is determined by

$$e_s = 0.61078e\left[-\frac{17.269 \cdot T_{dew}}{237.3 + T_{dew}}\right] \tag{3}$$

where

283

e_a is the vapor pressure in the atmosphere

e_s is the saturated vapor pressure in the atmosphere at that temperature

T_{dew} = dew point, $°C$

The vapor pressure deficit VPD (kPa) is calculated as

$$VPD = e_a - e_s \qquad (4)$$

Albedo

The albedo of a cell depends on the fraction of canopy cover, F, and the presence of snow. Albedo of the canopy and albedo of the ground surface (non-canopy fraction of cell) are fixed inputs to the model. The fraction of canopy cover is estimated from lai as

$$F = lai / lai_{cc} \qquad (5)$$

where F is the fraction of cell area covered by canopy, lai is all-sided leaf area index, and lai_{cc} is leaf area index at canopy closure. The albedo of the cell, A_{cell}, is a weighted average of canopy albedo, A_{canopy}, and ground albedo, A_{ground}:

$$A_{cell} = (F * A_{canopy}) + ((1 - F) * A_{ground}) \qquad (6)$$

When the ground is snow-covered, A_{ground} is a function of the snow surface age and melt season of the form

$$A_{ground} = ab^{N^c} \quad \{NOTE: c \text{ is a superscript of } N \} \qquad (7)$$

where N is the age of the snow surface in days since last snowfall, and a, b, and c are coefficients that depend on season. During the accumulation season, the coefficients are 0.85, 0.94, and 0.58 respectively, and during the melt season they are 0.85, 0.82, and 0.46, respectively (Laramie and Schaake, 1972). The date of transition from accumulation season to melt season was estimated as March 15 from data in Smith (1982), but is a user-defined parameter.

Snow fall

There is decreasing catch efficiency in precipitation gages at higher altitudes with a higher proportion of snow making direct extrapolation somewhat inaccurate. Precipitation occurs as snowfall in our model if daily minimum temperature <= 0 C. According to Smith (1982, in Kattelmann et al., 1985), using daily minimum temperature and 0 C as the rain/snow threshold yields very accurate results for the Sierra Nevada. Smith accurately predicted observed precipitation type 88 percent of the time at the Central Sierra Snow Laboratory in Norden over a 10-yr period, and 96 percent of the time at Blue Canyon over a 12-yr period.

Snowmelt

Generally, energy fluxes affecting a snowpack are categorized as 1) radiative heat transfer, 2) sensible heat transfer by turbulent convection, 3) latent heat transfer (losses by evaporation and sublimation; gain by condensation of water), 4) heat advected to the pack by rainfall, 5) heat conduction through the snow-ground interface, and 6) internal latent heat exchange (loss by melting; gain by refreezing of liquid water).

We have incorporated an energy-balance method that estimates radiative transfer and heat advection to the snow, and assumes that the other fluxes are relatively small and can be neglected. Radiative transfer is the most important flux driving snowmelt in the Sierra Nevada (Kattelmann, 1990). Estimation of heat advected to the snowpack is important for prediction of rapid snowmelt due to rain-on-snow storm events.

Radiative transfer calculations include daily short- and long-wave radiation exchange with the snowpack. The snowpack is always assumed to be below the canopy. Net shortwave radiation at the top of the canopy is predicted as described above (Net Radiation). Incoming long-wave radiation flux is a function of atmospheric emissivity, air temperature, and estimated cloudiness.

Net shortwave radiation below the canopy (transmitted) is calculated by attenuating above-canopy shortwave radiation (incident) as a negative exponential function of leaf area index. If leaf area index is less than 1.0 then all incident radiation is assumed to be transmitted. Below canopy radiation is calculated as

$$I_t = I_o \, e^{-k * LAI} \tag{8}$$

where I_t is transmitted shortwave radiation, I_o is incident (above-canopy) shortwave radiation, LAI is one-sided leaf area index and k is an extinction coefficient (0.5).

Incoming longwave radiation to the snowpack under clear skies, L_{dc}, is calculated as

$$L_{dc} = e \, s \, T_a^4 \tag{9}$$

where e is effective emissivity, T is average daily air temperature (K), and s is the Stefan-Boltzmann constant. The effective emissivity of atmosphere and canopy overhead, e, is a function of atmospheric water vapor pressure, e_a, atmospheric transmissivity, t, and canopy cover, F. We used Sellers' (1965) coefficients for Brunt's (1932) equation expressing atmospheric emissivity, e_a, as a function of water vapor pressure at dew point temperature. This estimate was adjusted for cloudiness using the equation of Sugita and Brutsaert (1993),

$$C = 1.02 \, t^{-0.0227} \tag{10}$$

where C is a cloudiness scaler and t is atmospheric transmissivity. We used Bristow and Campbell's (1984) procedure to estimate atmospheric transmissivity, as described previously.

The effective emissivity, e, of the atmosphere and canopy overhead is then calculated as

$$e = (1 - F) \, (0.605 + 0.048 \, [e_a^{0.5}]) \, C + F \tag{11}$$

If the air temperature is below 0 C, then net longwave radiation to the snowpack can be estimated as

$$L_d = (e - 1) \, s \, T_a^4 \tag{12}$$

assuming the emissivity of snow as 1.0. When air temperature is above 0 C, the temperature of the snowpack is assumed to be 0 C and net longwave radiation is estimated as

$$L_d = e \, s \, T_a^4 - s(273)^4 \tag{13}$$

Heat advected to the snowpack by rainfall, R, is calculated based on the assumption that the snowpack is isothermal at the melting point

$$R = r_w \, c_w \, r \, (T_r - T_m) \tag{14}$$

where r_w is the density of water, c_w is the heat capacity of water, r is the amount of rainfall, T_r is the temperature of the rainfall (assumed equal to air temperature), and T_m is the melting point temperature.

All of the energy transferred to the snowpack is assumed to go towards converting snow to liquid (implying an isothermal snowpack) so that 334 kJ are required to melt 1 kg snow.

Penman-Monteith equation

The Penman equation (1948) estimates the evaporation loss for a day from an open water surface. Monteith (1963) proposed that evaporation could be predicted if the canopy and air resistance to water vapor flux were known. The Penman-Monteith Equation is used to calculate the evaporation of water from the canopy where the flux of water vapor is restricted below the potential rate of evaporation from an open surface of water. Evaporation from a free water surface provides an upper boundary for maximum evapotranspiration and the modified form of the equation provides an estimate of actual transpiration for a vegetated or soil surface in terms of environmental parameters of net radiation, vapor pressure deficit, and temperature, and the diffusive resistance to water vapor of the canopy. A combined form of these equations is commonly used:

$$\lambda E = \frac{s(R_n - G) + [\rho c_p (\rho'_{va} - (\rho'_{va} - \rho_{va}))/ r_H]}{\lambda_v [s + \gamma^*]} \qquad (15)$$

where

$$\gamma^* = 1 + \gamma r_{v/} r_H$$

here, λ_v is the latent heat of vaporization of water, E is the evapotranspiration, s is the slope of the saturation vapor density-temperature curve at the average temperature of the canopy, ρ is the density of moist air, c_p is the specific heat capacity of the air at constant pressure, ρ_{va} is the ambient vapor density, ρ'_{va} is the saturation vapor density of the air, and r_v is the canopy resistance to water vapor flux, and r_H is the aerodynamic resistance to water vapor transport, γ is the psychrometric constant $\rho c_{p/\lambda}$, , and γ^* defines the resistance function for a canopy. For a free water surface $r_v = r_H$.

Evapotranspiration

We modified the FOREST-BGC model (Running & Coughlan, 1988) which is an ecosystem process model that calculates carbon, water and nitrogen cycles in a forest ecosystem. The model treats canopy interception, evapotranspiration, transpiration, photosynthesis, growth, and maintenance respiration, carbon allocation above and below-ground, litterfall, decomposition and nitrogen mineralization on daily time steps.

Transpiration is calculated using the Penman-Monteith method following a methodology described by Running and Coughlan (1988). The transpiration rate derived from the Penman-Monteith equation m^3 H$_2$O s day^{-1} LAI^{-1} is multiplied by daylength (s day^{-1}) and LAI to obtain canopy transpiration m^3 H$_2$O s day^{-1} for a grid cell.

In BGC the aerodynamic resistance is a constant and assumes a well-ventilated conifer type canopy, an assumption that seems valid for pine and fir forests. However, the model does not distinguish between vegetation types (e.g., grasslands or chaparral) and so modification of the subroutines is necessary to improve characterization of other types of ecosystems. The aerodynamic resistance, r_a = s m^{-1}, is a reciprocal function of leaf area index (Running and Coughlan, 1988) as implemented in FOREST-BGC

$$r_a = 5.0 / (lai / 2) \qquad (16)$$

286

which assumes that the canopy is well ventilated with a conifer needle morphology. This assumption avoids the need for windspeed data.

Table 4 provides a description of the data inputs to the aboveground energy balance subunit of the model and the units.

Plant Water Uptake

Implicit to the logic used to estimate water uptake by vegetation is that rooting depth is equal to soil depth. Water is removed from the soil proportional to its availability; no preference is made between saturated or unsaturated zones. Therefore, given T (transpiration) in time Δt, the amount of water removed from the vadose zone is

$$T_g = T(W_v/W_v + W_g)) \qquad (17)$$

and from the groundwater zone is

$$T_g = T (W_g/(W_v + W_g)), \qquad (18)$$

where

W_v and W_g are the quantities of water in the vadose and groundwater zones, respectively,
T_v and T_g are subject to the constraint that they do no exceed W_v and W_g, respectively.

Canopy Conductance

The canopy conductance, G_c is modified by (1) solar radiation input, (2) temperature, (3) leaf water potential, and (4) absolute humidity deficit. It is a measure of the capacity for conductance of water vapor from the leaf to the air. In this formulation, no distinction between stomatal conductance and boundary layer conductance is made, therefore the canopy conductance is the sum of both of these terms.

(1) All leaf area receiving a defined minimum threshold radiation, as determined from the canopy light attenuation following a Beer's law extinction equation, will have conductance to water vapor. The Beer's Law canopy light extinction relationship for light environments at depth within the canopy is

$$\text{daily average short-wave radiation, } Q_i = (Q_o(1-e^{kLAI}))/(e^{kLAI}) \qquad (19)$$

where
Q_i = light transmittance, MJ m^{-2} day^{-1}
Q_0 = light intensity above canopy
k = Beer's Law extinction coefficient, assumed to be 0.5
LAI = Leaf area index

In canopies that have light transmission exceeding the radiation threshold, G_c is equal to that defined in relations (3) and (4) below. If the minimum daily radiation is less than the threshold, then canopy conductance is restricted to cuticular conductance which is defined as 0.00005 m s^{-1}.

(2) Minimum mean night air temperatures below freezing restrict canopy conductances to the cuticular conductance. Therefore, minimum night temperatures are used to reduce G_c. When below 0°C, conductance is reduced by 0.0002 m s^{-1} °C^{-1}.

Table 4. Soil, climate and plant parameters used for aboveground canopy evapotranspiration simulations.

Description	Units

Model Inputs:

      Site characteristics:

1. Geographic coordinate, latitude & longitude	$^\circ$
2. DEM	m
3. slope	$^\circ$
4. aspect	$^\circ$
5. vegetation type map	--
6. soil type map	--
7. geologic unit map	--
8. road map	--
9. Day of Year	day number

Input variables:

      Climate Data (hourly, daily):

10. Precipitation	m3 m^{-2}
11. Canopy interception, rain	m day^{-1}
12. Snow fall (equivalent water thickness)	m day^{-1}
13. Snowpack	m^3 m^{-2}
14. Snowmelt	m H$_2$O day^{-1}
15. Daily maximum air temperature	$^\circ$C
16. Daily minimum air temperature	$^\circ$C
17. Dew point temperature	$^\circ$C
18. Vapor Pressure Deficit	KPa
19. Daylight average air temperature	$^\circ$C
20. Average night minimum temperature	$^\circ$C
21. Canopy precipitation storage	m^3 m^{-2}

Soil Properties:

22. Soil water content	m^3 m-2
23. Soil water capacity	m^3
24. Soil-predawn Ψ	-Mpa
25. % organic matter	%
26. % clay	%
27. % sand	%

Table 4. Soil, climate and plant parameters used for aboveground canopy evapotranspiration simulations. (cont.)

Description	Units

Seasonal Characteristics:

28. Daylength	s day^{-1}

Canopy structure Characteristics:

29. Leaf area index	m^2 m^{-2}
30. Specific leaf area	m^3 kg^{-1}
31. Canopy light extinction coefficient	dimensionless
32. % Cover	%

Canopy Physiological Properties:
33. Spring minimum Ψ_l -MPa
34. Ψ_l at stomatal closure   -MPa
35. Maximum canopy conductance, H_2O m s^{-1}
36. Slope G_c humidity reduction   m s^{-2} μm^{-1}day^{-1}
37. Radiation G_c threshold   kJ m^{-2} day^{-1}
38. G_c H_2O, soil water control   multiplier
39. G_c H_2O, night minimum temp. reduction multiplier
40. G_c H_2O, humidity deficit reduction   multiplier
41. G_c H_2O, conductance radiation reduction multiplier
42. Final G_c H_2O m s^{-1}

Model Intermediates:
43. Penman-Monteith transpiration   m H_2O LAI^{-1} s^{-1}
44. Precipitation interception coefficient   m LAI^{-1} day^{-1}

Model Outputs:
45. Transpiration   m^3 m^{-2}
46. Evaporation   m^3 m^{-2}
47. Evaporation of canopy intercepted
       precipitation   m day^{-1}
48. Surface Water outflow   m^3 m^{-2}
49. Subsurface water outflow   m^3 m^{-2}
50. Surface water velocity $°$m sec^{-1}
51. Vadose zone water storage   m^3 m^{-1}
52. Surface ponding depth   m

(3) Decreasing soil water supply decreases transpiration through the influence of leaf water potential on canopy conductance. Daily maximum leaf water potential, $\Psi(MPa)$, is a reciprocal function of soil water supply, where

$$\Psi = \frac{0.2}{((Wv + Wg) / (d\phi))}$$ (20)

where
   d is soil depth and
   ϕ is soil porosity.

Canopy conductance, $G_c = $ m s^{-1}, is then calculated as

$$G_c = G_{c,max} - \Delta_{cc}(\Psi - \Psi_{min}),$$ (21)

where
   $G_{c,max}$ is maximum canopy conductance, m s^{-1}
   Δ_{cc} is the slope of the canopy conductance versus leaf water potential curve, m s^{-1} MPa^{-1} (see below), and
   Ψ_{min} is the minimum leaf water potential that induces stomatal closure (MPa)

Δ_{cc} is calculated from

$$\Delta_{cc} = G_{c,max} / (\Psi_{min} - \Psi_{min,spring}),$$ (22)

where
   $\Psi_{min,spring}$ is the spring minimum leaf water potential (MPa).

(4) Canopy conductance to water vapor is then computed as a function of first leaf water potential and modified by the absolute humidity deficit. Conductance declines under conditions of high vapor pressure deficit, where

$$G_c = G_{c\ max} - \text{slope} (G_{c\ max}/\Psi_{1\ stomatal\ closure} - \Psi_{1\ spring\ minimum})$$ (23)

and

$$G_{c\ VPD\ restriction,\ m\ s}{}^{-1} = G_{c\ max}\ \text{slope} (G_{cmax,\ m\ s}{}^{-1}/\Psi_{1\ stomatal\ closure,\ MPa} - \Psi_{1\ spring\ minimum,\ MPa})\ \text{absolute humidity deficit (m s}^{-1})$$

Canopy Interception

The canopy term for rainfall interception is proportional to LAI using an empirical factor derived from fraction of ground cover (Dickinson et al. 1991; Wigmosta et al. 1994), where interception = 10^{-4} * LAI*F (F= fraction of ground cover). Intercepted water may be evaporated (depending on Rnet), and the rest is assumed as storage. All precipitation is transferred to the ground the same day as the precipitation event occurs.

Evaporation from Soil

A Penman-Monteith approach was followed and an empirical relation was used to determine soil surface resistance. In this case, the canopy resistance term is replaced by a soil surface resistance, r_s. It is also possible to develop a less empirical relationship using soil properties. Wigmosta et al. (1994) determined soil evaporation using the minimum potential ET or soil desorptivity (a function of soil moisture content and soil properties; following the quasi-physical approach of Eagleson (1978a,b).

Vegetation Data Sets

The study used the USFS Calveg forest map to determine vegetation types and stocking class. There were two additional datasets used for validating the vegetation characteristics. These were the Forest Inventory Analysis (FIA) datasets and the Ecounit Inventory dataset. These latter datasets had information about forest structure, cover, and size classes from geographically located plots. Field observations were also conducted to evaluate the accuracy of predicting site conditions and sites having no canopy/bare soil. These sites were identified in the field using Trimble Navigation Pathfinder + Global Positioning System (GPS) recorder and differentially correcting for +/- 1 m recording accuracy in horizontal location and 2-3 m accuracy in the vertical location. In our current study we compared our SMA interpretation results with Forest Service Inventory Analysis data and about 241 plots where stand and soil data was obtained. We digitized that data and used it to validate our LAI and forest stand model. The extent of validation data for our current study is relatively unique. These results suggest that the model and data are parameterized at a scale useful for watershed level studies.

Leaf Area Index

Virtually all physiological models use a formulation of the Penman-Monteith equation multiplied by a function based on LAI, soil moisture, temperature, relative humidity, and daylength. LAI is the most important driver of ET and one place where data quality is poor and errors are large and significant. Typically, satellite data is used to derive a one time per year maximum "greenness" estimate which is distributed annually by assuming a probability distribution over time. Usually the assumption is that LAI is linear with NDVI or an empirical curve is used. Allometric equations may improve this relationship; especially where stand density or size information is available.

Estimation of Leaf Area Index

A Landsat Thematic Mapper satellite image from 1994 was used to estimate peak summer LAI using two methods. The first method was an estimate of canopy greenness based on a normalized ratio of the red and near-infrared bands. This index is called the Normalized Difference Vegetation Index and is computed as

$$NDVI = \frac{(TM\text{-}band\ 4 - TM\text{-}band\ 3)}{(TM\text{-}band\ 4 + TM\text{-}band3)} \qquad (24)$$

This index is sensitive to the amount of green foliage cover within a pixel. It has been widely used to estimate LAI using empirically derived scaling factors.

We also used another method to estimate LAI and % bare soil using a spectral mixing analysis. This technique assumes that the pixel spectrum is composed of the aerial proportional contribution of each of the objects in the pixel. Materials can be distinguished only if they are spectrally distinct. If they have distinctly different spectra then their individual contributions to the mixed pixel can be estimated. This was done for the TM scene and three classes were distinguished: bare soil/litter, green foliage, and "shade/shadow, " which captures the surface albedo variation. The contribution of topography to this spectral component was removed by calculating the variation in solar intensity as a function of topography. The residual shade represented a measure of the surface roughness and is related to the spacing and density of the canopy.

Sites lacking vegetation cover (bare soil) were compared to mapped estimates and % cover on the plot datasets.

The spectral mixing equation is

$$R_{ij} = \sum(F_{ij} R_{soil, j} + F_{ij} R_{veg, j} + F_{ij} R_{shade, j}) + error \qquad (25)$$

where
R_{ij} is the pixel radiance (or calibrated surface reflectance) for each band
F_{ij} is the fraction of each surface component in the pixel in each band
$R_{soil, j}$ is the radiance (or reflectance) of soil in each band j
$R_{veg, j}$ is the radiance (or reflectance) of green foliage in each band j
$R_{shade, j}$ is the radiance (or reflectance) of shade/shadows in each band j
error is the difference between the R_{ij} and the sum of the estimated spectral fractions in each pixel

We had no direct measure of LAI or an allometric relationship e.g., using DBH that had been developed for the site and species within our watershed. Comparisons between estimated LAI and canopy greenness were made to % cover from the Forest Service Ecounit site data. A constant scaling factor was applied to convert greenness to LAI using a linear interpolation and scaling between a maximum LAI of 1-12, and is equivalent to maximum NDVI. This comparison provides a estimate of all-sided LAI. Table 5-4 shows that the coefficients of determination (r^2) is significant at a probability p>0.0001. The FOREST BGC model uses an empirical relation of 2.2 to divide the all-sided LAI to get projected LAI. For reference, planar leaves in a canopy of spherically distributed leaf angles would have a theoretical value of 2.0.

Table 5-1 shows the results of a comparison between % total cover, % conifer cover, % shrub cover and total % vegetation cover from the Ecounit data set and NDVI and LAI (Table 5-2). None of these relationships had high coefficients of determination (r^2) even though some had significant probabilities (P) due to the large sample size (n). This relationship was also tested for topographic slope since some differences in illumination may not have been normalized by the NDVI. This relationship also had a low r^2. We also compared total herbaceous cover, topographic aspect, and hardwood cover against the % shade derived from the spectral mixture analysis after subtracting topographic shade from the analysis (Table 5-3). This relationship also showed a poor fit against the field data sets. The same comparison was performed for the FAI data set with similar results. There is a relatively poor fit between % cover (by forest type) or DBH (trunk diameter at breast height) and greenness as seen by the satellite. This poor fit is probably because of a combination of errors and the fact that as tree cover decreases within a plot, cover by the shrub and herbaceous layer increases. Thus, a better comparison to the satellite data would be total green foliage cover of all vegetation types. Since the model is only parameterized for a single vegetation layer, the greenness probably offers a closer estimate to total plot LAI.

Land Cover Type

In this study, vegetation type definitions followed the CALVEG inventory types as defined by the Forest Service. Thematic Mapper satellite data were used to directly determine vegetation patterns (type, density, LAI, % cover), spatial statistics and classifications. Several TM scenes, including summers of 1989, 1991, and 1994 are in our database and could be used to evaluate hydrologic processes during different water and climate years. We used the July 1994 TM scene to define vegetation type for all simulations reported here because it was the most nearly concurrent data for the 1995 water year which began in September 1994. Vegetation type was used to define rooting depth and LAI to define root mass. Results are combined to identify the percentage cover by canopy type, needle leaf forest, broad-leaf (or mixed) forest chaparral, grasslands, duff, bare soil, and rock (vegetation type and % cover). Either the Green Vegetation Fraction or NDVI (Normalized Difference Vegetation Index) may be used to identify the vegetation growth status and empirical relationships to estimate LAI (Leaf Area Index). These results are combined with the vegetation type map to derive interception and canopy aerodynamic resistance.

Soil Properties

Soil profiles, parent rock, soil structure, organic matter content, permeability, and water holding capacity within mapped units are derived from order three and/or order two soil survey data. These data, combined with the soil and litter fractions derived from the remote sensing analysis and DEM data, are used to identify the potential rooting depth, soil porosity, saturated hydraulic conductivity, and soil bulk density. The 20-30 m resolution our model is operating at is not realistic for mapping maximum soil heterogeneity but approximates real world situations and is as good as our database (or any database) allows at the present time.

Adding more soil layers would be physically more realistic as different species mine different depths of the soil profile or change depth as phenology progresses. The problem is in assigning a root depth (or active root depth) as a function of time, soil type, and vegetation type. There is very little data in the published literature to support a rigorous structuring of rooting depths and root biomass (or other parameters related to water uptake rates, e.g., root length density).

In this study, all of the soil physical and chemical data are from "Soil Survey Eldorado National Forest California", "Soil Survey of Eldorado Area, California", and "Laboratory Data and Descriptions for Some Typical Pedons of CA soil." The soil survey of the western Camp Creek region was done by USDA SCS and the eastern region of Camp Creek region was done by USDA forest service. Both soil surveys are in Order 3 scale. The data used for generating the data file, soilinfo.dat, are taken from Table 5, Table 6, and Table 10 of Soil Survey of Eldorado Area, California (USDA, 1974), and Laboratory Data and Descriptions for Some Typical Pedons of CA soil (SCS, 1973).

The soil attribute data are linked by the soil map units between the soil database and the digital soil survey map. The attribute data for the east side of the study area were directly digitized and input from the hardcopy of the USFS Eldorado National Forest soil survey report. The attribute data for the west side of the study area was abstracted from the STATSCO database.

The attribute data listed in the reports have a range of values (min. and max.) for each soil depth layer. The mean value for each layer was calculated based on the arithmetic average except for permeability which was calculated using the log mean. The model currently treats the soil profile as one layer but could be modified to run at more layers if data is available. The parameters for the soil layer were calculated using a weighted depth. The soil data in the data base includes:

> 1). Soil type (description)
> 2). Depth to bedrock (cm)
> 3). Hydraulic conductivity (cm s^{-1})
> 4). Porosity (dimensionless)
> 5). Field capacity (dimensionless, cm cm^{-1})
> 6). Effective suction at wetting front (kPa)
> 7). Available water capacity (dimensionless)

The soil data from the east side of the study was from hard copy of the Soil Survey Eldorado National Forest California and Laboratory Data and Descriptions for Some Typical Pedons of CA soil. For the west side of the study area, the data was from USDA National Resources conservation Service State Soil Geographic (STATSCO) data base.

Soil type is a value in the data base linked to the soil map unit symbols (presented by both soil survey agencies). The original soil map units used in the soil survey map and the soil type used in data file can be seen in the data file and are shown in Tables 4 and 5 of both soil survey reports. Depth to bedrock is the sum of the each depth in soil profile and is found in Tables 5 or 6 of the soil survey report.

The effective hydraulic conductivity can be directly estimated from the soil database. However, the saturated hydraulic conductivity which is given in this data base has a wide range; it varies from 0.2 to 6.0 in./hr. for the same soil. Without additional information, we may simply use the average value (or some other algorithm, e.g., log mean, geometric mean, or harmonic mean, etc.). Saturated hydraulic conductivity was estimated from the original multiple soil layer data set based on the harmonic mean which is generally used in hydrologic studies for integrating soil moisture. The original data for the west study area can be found in Table 6 of USDA Forest soil survey Soil Survey Eldorado National Forest California.

The porosity of the soil medium can be calculated from the measured bulk density. If the cation-exchange capacity of the clay (which is an indicator of the shrink-swell capacity of the clay), and the sand, clay, and organic matter percentage are available, then the bulk density at the water content for 33 kPa tension can be estimated from the following:

$$BD = 1.51 + 0.0025 \cdot S - 0.0013 \cdot S \cdot OM - 0.0006 \cdot C \cdot OM - 0.0048 \cdot C \cdot CEC \quad (26)$$

in which BD is the bulk density of < 2 mm material (gm/cm^3), S is percent sand, C is percent clay, OM is percent organic matter, and CEC is the ratio of cation-exchange capacity (CEC) of clay to the percent clay (CEC ranges from 0.1 to 0.9).

In this study, due to lack of the CEC data, we used sand, clay, and OM to estimation the mineral bulk density following the procedure and data chart developed by Rawls (1985).

$$Soil\ bulk\ density = \frac{100}{\dfrac{\%\ Organic\ matter}{Organic\ Matter\ Bulk\ Density} - \dfrac{100 - \%\ Organic\ Matter}{Mineral\ Bulk\ Density}} \quad (27)$$

Average organic matter bulk density equals 0.224 gm/cm^3. Bulk density is converted to porosity accordingly:

$$\phi = 1 - \frac{BD}{PD} \quad (28)$$

where PD is the particle density (2.65 gm/cm^3). Specific yield, used in the groundwater model, as assumed to be equal to porosity. The soil particle size distribution data and the chemical data for the east study area are listed in Table 6 and Table 5 of Soil Survey Eldorado National Forest California. Field capacity data are from Table 10 of "Soil Survey Eldorado National Forest California" and "Laboratory Data and Descriptions for Some Typical Pedons of CA soil".

The validity of the soil polygons for use in a hydrologic model of this scale was tested using data from the soil maps which were compared to FS plot data from the Ecounit Inventory. Because soil depth and % clay were the primary infiltration and water holding drivers they were compared by regression analysis. Figure 8a. shows the relationship between the estimated soil polygon % clay content of the soil (weighted average with depth) and the measured % clay content from the Ecounit study. The soil data base did not have a continuous range of % clay contents as seen in the figure. Several Ecounit soil samples were collected for each polygon type and these measured % clay values usually ranged over 20-30%. Thus, even though a significant regression with a positive slope was obtained, considerable scatter is found around the regression line. Not all soils had depth values associated with them but for those that did, we found a significant positive regression between measured depth and polygon value (Figure 8b). Again, substantial scatter is apparent. Nonetheless, these data show that polygon soil properties are within the range of measured values obtained at random point locations.   It would be possible to improve the input polygon data by determining a probability density distribution for these soil properties using the field data if this was determined to produce significant error in the infiltration patterns across the landscape.

Effective suction at the wetting front was estimated using the equation given by Rawls and Brakensiek (1982, 1983) by relating the Green-Ampt wetting front suction parameter to soil physical properties in the following equation:

$$H_f = \exp[6.53-7.326\phi+0.00158C2+3.809\phi2+0.000344SC$$
$$-0.04989S\phi+0.0016S2\phi2+0.0016C2\phi2-0.0000136S2C \qquad (29)$$
$$-0.00348C2\phi+0.000799S2\phi]$$

Available water capacity was estimated based on a weighted mean (by the thickness of each layer). The original data for the east side of the study area are listed in Table 6 of Soil Survey Eldorado National Forest California.

Digital Terrain Map.

Digital elevation maps were available for the study area at 1:24000 which yields an interpolated 30 m resolution in the horizontal and 12 m resolution in the vertical directions. ARC/Info was used to calculate slope and aspect at 1 pixel resolution and at a moving 9 pixel average resolution. The maps were compared to slopes created in GRASS for validation and were found to have a 1:1 relationship (R^2=0.999).

Because topographic gradients drive both the flow of water and the direction, the model is particularly sensitive to the accuracy of the topographic maps. The resolution of the digital USGS maps are about 30 m in the horizontal plane and 7 m in the vertical plane. We compared the elevation estimated from the USGS topographic data and the derived slope and aspect data to data from the Forest Service Ecounit and FIA datasets. Results from both comparisons yielded similar results with the same conclusions. Data from the Ecounit study are shown in Figure 9. It shows that the elevation predicted from the DEM is very close to the measured elevation. Aspect is also relatively well predicted from field measurements, while the worst case is found for estimating slope. The greater scatter in the predicted slope apparently results from both greater problems in mapping it accurately at the field scale and the differences in scales measured. When DEM data are aggregated to 5 x 5, 9 x 9, and 15 x 15 pixels, the relationship between measured and predicted values decreases. Thus, slopes are under-estimated which affects the accuracy in predicting runoff for all hydrologic models.

The DEM for the Camp Creek watershed is shown in Figure 10. The smaller Snow Creek watershed is shown in Figure 11 and the Pebble Creek watershed in Figure 12. Snow Creek and Pebble Creek are located within the watershed shown in Figure 10. The location of Snow Creek within the Camp Creek watershed can be seen in Figure 1.

Synthetic Terrain Map.

Several synthetic terrain maps were created for testing the surface flow module and anisotropy in modeled runoff. These included the gradient in x direction given by:

$$\delta z / \delta x = \frac{1}{8} \times \begin{bmatrix} -1 & 0 & 1 \\ -2 & 0 & 2 \\ -1 & 0 & 1 \end{bmatrix} \otimes DEM \tag{30}$$

and the gradient in y direction by

$$\delta z / \delta y = \frac{1}{8} \times \begin{bmatrix} -1 & -2 & -1 \\ 0 & 0 & 0 \\ 1 & 2 & 1 \end{bmatrix} \otimes DEM \tag{31}$$

then the slope and the aspect are defined by:

$$\text{slope} = [\ (\delta z/\delta x)^2 + (\delta z/\delta y)^2\ ]^{1/2} \tag{32}$$

for $\delta z/\delta x \neq 0$,   aspect = arctan[$(\delta z/\delta y)/(\delta z/\delta x)$] / [4×arctan(1)] × 180 + 270   if $\delta z/\delta x>0$

                         aspect = arctan[$(\delta z/\delta y)/(\delta z/\delta x)$] / [4×arctan(1)] × 180 + 90   if $\delta z/\delta x\leq0$

For $\delta z/\delta x = 0$,   aspect = 180   if $\delta z/\delta y>0$

                         aspect = 0   if $\delta z/\delta y\leq0$

Examples of the synthetic DEMs are shown in Figures 13 and 14 used for two of these tests.

The model was tested by several sets of generated surface flow parameters:
- Three rainfall types : point, polygon or constant over the area
- Three constant slopes : 10, 30, or 60 %
- Rotated in two kinds of grid orientations : normal to the N or to the NE direction
- Different shapes of landscape : steep plane, divergent, and convergent steep surfaces

To do this several DEM's were generated:
- Constant slope
- Composed of four valleys having four different slopes
- Octagonal DEM; created to test anisotropy
- A cone
- A valley with converging and/or diverging surfaces

Surface Flow

The mass balance principle is invoked to estimate the change in volume of water stored on the surface. Precipitation adds to the surface storage, infiltration may remove or add water to storage, and flow from adjacent cells adds or subtracts from storage. Consider precipitation and infiltration first. Our model assumes that precipitation, less a fraction intercepted by the canopy, arrives on the landscape and either infiltrates directly into the soil or contributes to water ponded on the soil surface. In the latter case, precipitation rate exceeds the potential infiltration rate. At the beginning of the rainfall event, due to the low initial water content of the soil, the infiltration rate is higher than the rainfall rate. With time, cumulative rainfall increases, and infiltration increases with rainfall, while infiltration rate decreases. Finally, at some time step, the rainfall rate exceeds the infiltration rate, and the excess rainfall causes ponding. At that time, surface flow begins. Water from groundwater seeps (exfiltration) may also contribute to surface flow. Thus, three causes of surface runoff are observed: saturation excess runoff, infiltration excess runoff, and subsurface flow that are described in detail by Famiglietti and Wood (1991).

In the first case the soil is saturated, in the second case the precipitation rate exceeds the infiltration rate, and in the third case exfiltration from groundwater contributes to the surface flow.

Knowing precipitation, infiltration, and discharges from the adjacent cells, a change in surface water storage in the cell of interest is:

$$\Delta S_s = \left[(P - I)\Delta x \Delta y + \sum_{i=1}^{4} Q_{s_i} \right] \Delta t \tag{33}$$

in which P is precipitation rate, I is infiltration rate, Δx and Δy are the cell dimensions in the x and y directions, respectively, and Q_s is the flow from the four adjacent cells during the time step Δt. Discharge is the product of velocity and area. Flow area is Δx or Δy multiplied by flow depth h_s. If inflow exceeds outflow, the h_s increases or if more water leaves than enters, it falls.

Water moves across adjacent cell boundaries based on physical processes and the topographic conditions. Figure 5 shows how the surface flow is calculated based on a two dimensional representation of water flux. The slope of the water surface is assumed to equal the slope of the ground surface, which is usually acceptable for gradually varied steady flow. Overland flows accumulate in depressions and in small streams which eventually merge into rivers, lakes, or ponds. In this phase, the transport of the water can be considered as free surface, gradually varied, sheet flow. The energy source for surface flow is gravity, which is consumed by friction, so the overland flow is considered as gradually varied sheet flow. Manning's equation states that the overland flow velocity is a function of surface geomorphologic and surface water ponding conditions. For the x direction,

$$u = \frac{1}{n} R^{2/3} S_x^{1/2} \tag{34}$$

in which u is velocity m/s, n is Manning's friction coefficient $L^{-1/3} T^{-1}$, R is hydraulic radius m (flow section area A m^2 over the wetted perimeter WP m), and S is bed slope m/m. For sheet flow, area is just flow depth h_s multiplied by unit width and, thus, hydraulic radius simplifies to flow depth.

$$u = \frac{1}{n} h_s^{2/3} S_x^{1/2} \tag{35}$$

$$Q_x = uA_x \tag{36}$$

and similarly for the y direction,

$$v = \frac{1}{n} h_s^{2/3} S_y^{1/2} \tag{37}$$

$$Q_y = vA_y. \tag{38}$$

There are two faces for the x direction and two for the y direction for a total four, as given in the mass balance equation Q_s.

Appropriate use of Manning's equation assumes particular conditions. Velocity is constant with depth; flow is uniform, that is depth, wetted section, velocity and discharge are constant along the channel; and the slope of the water surface is equal to the linear loss of head along the channel. For gradually varied flow, the equation applies at a location but the velocity changes as slope, roughness and depth varying spatially over the landscape. A constant Manning's n (0.1) was used because litter depth did not vary with vegetation types in this data base.

Field measurements (Starosolszky, 1987) showed that the Manning's equation yields estimates which agree with measured values for water at typical environmental temperatures (about $20^{\circ}C$) and flows at moderate depth (< 10 meters). Using this method for estimating the surface flow simplifies the model and minimizes parameter input into variables more readily derivable in GIS applications.

Subsurface Flow

The mass balance principle is also applied to the groundwater flow (Figure 5). Similar to surface flow, change in groundwater storage is:

$$\Delta S_g = \left[\left(R - ET_g \right) x \Delta y + \sum_{i=1}^{4} Q_{g_i} \right] \Delta t \qquad (39)$$

in which R is recharge, ET_g is water extraction by plants, Q_g is the lateral flow from the four adjacent cells during time step Δt. Again, if inflow exceeds outflow, water table depth h_g increases. The upper boundary is the water table and lower boundary is the bedrock which also defines the lower boundary of the soil layer. Drainage from the unsaturated vadose zone crosses the watertable and increases storage while plant water extraction decreases storage.

Lateral subsurface flow through the vertical edges or faces of each element is controlled by the thickness of the saturated layer and the slope or gradient of table elevation. There is no leakage through the bedrock. Since the slope or change in the depth of the water table is small between adjacent cells and the unconfined flow field is shallow in our system in the absence of sources and sink, the Dupuit assumption is satisfied. The Dupuits' assumption means that the flow moves in an horizontal plane (the isopotential lines are vertical). Darcy's law is limited to:

steady flow, $\dfrac{\partial h}{\partial t} = 0$ and laminar flow. $\qquad (40)$

Otherwise energy is wasted by viscous friction. But usually the following limits are acceptable: R_e represents the Reynolds' number, or the ratio of inertial forces over viscosity forces.

if $R_e < 1$, flow is laminar and Darcy's law applicable.
if $1 < R_e < 60$, Darcy's law is applicable with the correction proposed by Dupuits:
$q^n = -K \Delta H / L$
if $60 < R_e$, Darcy's law is not applicable.

In subsurface flows the velocity is usually very slow and Darcy's law can be used without considering the Reynolds' number. There is a problem with Darcy's law application for very low and very high values of the hydraulic conductivity K. Conductivity has no meaning in the case of a cracked rock, for example. In this case study, the conductivity at saturation ranges between 7.10^{-8} and $2.8 \ 10^{-4}$ ms^{-1}.

To simplify the problem, instead of solving Poisson's equation for steady state flow, Darcy's equation was solved directly for subsurface flow. The discharge Q per unit width for an aquifer thickness b in the x and y directions, respectively, is:

$$Q_x = q_{x^b} = -k\frac{\partial h_g}{\partial x}b \qquad\qquad Q_y = q_{y^b} = -k\frac{\partial h_g}{\partial y}b \qquad\qquad (41)$$

in which k is saturated hydraulic conductivity; hydraulic gradient is the change in total head with distance in the x and y direction $\dfrac{\partial h_g}{\partial x}$ and $\dfrac{\partial h_g}{\partial y}$, respectively. Total head in each cell is the elevation head defined by the base of the active soil layer plus the water table thickness b and the surface ponding depth h_s, if the water table is at or above the ground surface. The datum for the elevation head is the same as that used for the interpolated DEM data. Spatial distance along the head drop between two cells is the grid spacing.

Vadose zone

The surface and subsurface mass balance equations do not share a common variable and appear to be independent but are not. The vadose zone mass balance equation couples the surface and subsurface mass balance equations through I and R. Each element is bounded by the soil surface and the water table or bedrock in the absence of groundwater. Change in vadose water storage is:

$$\Delta S_v = \Big[(I - ET_v - R)\Delta x \Delta y \Big]\Delta t \qquad\qquad (42)$$

in which ET_v is water extracted by plants. Storage is the product of water content θ and thickness of the vadose zone h_v, and varies with time. Infiltration increases water stored in the vadose zone while water extraction by plants decreases storage. Recharge to the groundwater decreases θ and possibly h_v, as the water table rises. From field observations during rainfall events, the soil is not saturated below the surface and thus lateral flow in the vadose zone is negligible.

The vadose zone mass balance equation is coupled to the groundwater equation because h_v depends on h_s (groundwater elevation). To decouple the mass balance equations, the thickness of the vadose zone h_v is assumed constant during a time step and unadjusted water content θ^* is calculated. At the end of the time step, depth of the vadose zone and water content are adjusted to reflect the change in groundwater elevation ($\Delta h_s = h_{s,t+\Delta t} - h_{s,t}$).

$$h_{v,t+\Delta t} = h_{v,t} + \Delta h_s \qquad\qquad (43)$$

$$\theta_{t+\Delta t} = \frac{\theta^*_{t+\Delta t}h_{v,t} + \Delta h_s \theta_{fc}}{h_{v,t+\Delta t}} \qquad\qquad (44)$$

The water content of the incremental layer is field capacity.

Infiltration

Infiltration is the entry of water from the surface and its transport into the soil profile. Spatial and temporal dynamics of surface runoff and storage as well as subsurface flow and storage depend on estimates of infiltration. Water moving across the soil surface is a loss in the surface flow mass balance equation and a gain in the vadose zone and or groundwater mass balance equations.

In the case of no surface water ponding, infiltration rate is limited by the precipitation rate (model input). With ponding, infiltration rate is controlled by surface or subsurface conditions. Surface conditions constrain infiltration according to the potential infiltration rate I_{ga} estimated using the Green and Ampt equation (1911) or according to the depth of water ponding on surface which could infiltrate during the time step. Subsurface conditions might constrain infiltration according to the amount of unfilled storage in the vadose zone. If the vadose zone is filled, the groundwater table is the free water surface and the groundwater system can contribute to (exfiltration) or gain water from the surface flow.

Almost all subsurface flow models are based on Darcy's Law, and most approximate models give similar results. Vertessy et al. (1993) used a 1D Richard's equation to solve for unsaturated flow and a 2D Richard's equation was used for saturated flow over a 0.32 km^2 forest watershed. However, this detailed physical approach has not been applied to a large watershed.

The Green and Ampt (1911) model is most frequently used for larger watersheds because model assumptions simplify parameter estimation. In the Green-Ampt equation, the initial infiltration rate, the saturated infiltration rate, and soil physical properties are considered. The original Green-Ampt infiltration model was developed for ponded infiltration into a deep homogeneous soil with a uniform initial water content. In applying the Green-Ampt approach, two assumptions are made. First, there is a distinct and precisely definable wetting front. The matric potential at this wetting front remains effectively constant, regardless of time and position (i.e., dependent only on soil physical properties). The second, is that behind the wetting front the soil is uniformly wet and of constant conductivity. By neglecting the surface ponding depth the Green-Ampt rate equation has the form:

$$I_{ga} = k\left(1 + \frac{H_f M_d}{F}\right) \tag{45}$$

in which I_{ga} is potential infiltration rate m/s, k is effective hydraulic conductivity, m/s, H_f is effective matric potential at the wetting front m, M_d is the difference between saturation and initial water content $(\phi - \theta_i)$ m/m, θ_i is water content at the beginning of the precipitation event m/m, ϕ is soil porosity m/m, F is cumulative infiltration m, Notice that the infiltration rate is dependent on the water content at the beginning of the precipitation event which is determined by the vadose zone mass balance equation. In forward finite difference form,

$$I = \frac{F_{t+\Delta t} - F_t}{\Delta t} = k\left(\frac{F_{t+\Delta t} + H_f M_d}{F_{t+\Delta t}}\right) \tag{46}$$

$$F_{t+\Delta t}^2 - F_{t+\Delta t}\left(F_t + k\Delta t\right) - k\Delta t H_f M_d = 0 \tag{47}$$

$$F_{t+\Delta t} = \frac{-b + \sqrt{b^2 - 4ac}}{2a} \tag{48}$$

in which
$$a = 1$$
$$b = -\left(F_t + k\Delta t\right)$$
$$c = -k\Delta t H_f M_d.$$

$F_{t+\Delta t}$ is substituted into the finite differenced equation to give I_{ga}.

301

Mein and Larson (1973) adopted the Green-Ampt model for infiltration during rainfall. Just prior to surface ponding the infiltration rate I equals the rainfall rate R and the cumulative infiltration at the time to surface ponding is the same as the cumulative rainfall. Over a short time period (e.g., 1 second), we assume the rainfall is homogeneous and steady in each cell. The available water for infiltration is determined for each cell by the contributions of both rainfall and lateral surface flow. Ponding occurs when available water exceeds the sum of the rainfall and lateral surface flow. The surface water not only comes from rainfall, but also from adjacent cells via surface flow, so the cumulative infiltration is determined by both infiltration rate and the water supply from the surface.

The soil column becomes saturated when cumulative infiltration is greater than or equal to ϕ-θ_i times the soil depth. Next, the infiltration rate is limited by saturated hydraulic conductivity. When the subsurface is saturated, exfiltration may occur due to the subsurface flow. The surface-subsurface flow system is dominated by changes in the hydraulic head and changes in subsurface storage.

Recharge

Recharge R is either zero or saturated hydraulic conductivity:

$R = 0$ if $I \neq 0$
$R = k$ if $I = 0$ and $\theta_{fc} \leq \theta \leq \phi$

During infiltration, there is no recharge. If the Green and Ampt wetting front reaches the groundwater level during infiltration, the vadose zone vanishes and the water table immediately rises to the level of water on the land surface. After infiltration stops, the surface water recedes and groundwater moves down gradient. As water drains, a new vadose is created at the land surface.

Conversely, if infiltration stops before the advancing front meets the water table there is recharge. Water in the vadose zone, retained between field capacity and saturation and behind the wetting front, drains or recharges the groundwater at the rate of the effective hydraulic conductivity. Evapotranspiration is removed from the vadose zone if the water table is below the soil surface and it is removed from the groundwater flow compartment when the watertable rises above the soil surface.

Evapotranspiration

Evapotranspiration ET is derived from the above ground algorithm (Equation 5) and varies as a function of water stored in the groundwater and W_g vadose zone W_v. If the vadose zone is overtaken by the groundwater table, $ET_v = 0$ and all the water is extracted from the groundwater. Otherwise water is removed from the vadose zone ET_v storage and groundwater proportionately:

$$ET = \dot{\alpha}ET + \beta ET$$
$$= ET_v + ET_g$$

$$\alpha = \frac{W_v}{\left(W_v + W_g \right)}$$
$$\beta = \frac{W_g}{\left(W_v + W_g \right)}$$

(49)

$$W_v = h_v \theta$$
$$W_g = b\phi$$

in which W_v and W_g are depth of water stored in the vadose zone and the groundwater respectively. The groundwater is assumed fully saturated such that water content is equal to porosity ϕ. These equations are equivalent to Equation 5 for the estimate of evapotranspiration but show the ET in terms of soil water availability.

Boundary and Initial Conditions

To limit the region of the study domain, approximate boundary conditions must be determined before the model can be applied. Boundary conditions of the problem domain for the six different boundaries (in X, Y, and Z directions) follow. First, we define the flux across the bottom of the cell to be zero due to the presence of an impermeable bedrock layer. The flux at the top of the boundary is the rainfall rate which is determined from local precipitation data. Along the boundary in the X-Y plane, the assumption of prescribed head boundaries was made based on the DEM defining the natural watershed boundary. Since the soil depth is determined the head change over time can be calculated.

We used the assumption of Famiglietti and Wood (1994b) for initializing the hydrologic model by assuming that the local soil profile state is at gravitational equilibrium. Our model only used a one layer soil and we assumed that at the beginning of the simulation that there was no surface water ponding and that the total head was equivalent to the elevation head (i.e., there was no water table) except where free surface water existed. For the lakes, river channel, and streams, the total head is the sum of elevation head and the hydraulic head. This definition explicitly defines the surface and subsurface flows which are zero initially.

SNEP Scenario Testing and Simulation Results

One SNEP scenario was tested using five decadal forest conditions as estimated from John Session's model PROGNOSIS (see paper this volume for details). The scenario assumes that forest management follows the "Cal Owl Option A" plan which calls for a "modest" harvest. The PROGNOSIS model provides the predicted Vegetation Cover for the current year (decade 0) and for the next 50 years at decadal intervals. For the Snow Creek watershed (354.5 ha) we were provided with cover estimates for 74 vegetation units (Figure 15). This scenario amounted to a 11.55% average increase in LAI during this period. These vegetation values were substituted for the satellite derived imagery and annual ET (sum of daily ET) was estimated using the 1995 water year (Sept. 1994-Sept. 1995) as the base weather year. The model was re-run for each decadal cover estimate using the 1995 water year data set. We found a slight increase in ET for the 50 year period of 10.98% and equivalent to a mean increase of 2.5 cm. This increase in ET is consistent with results of the Leavesley Hydrologic Response Unit Model which predicted about half this increase (see McGurk this volume), and for which the change in ET is within the noise of the estimate. The advantage of our model is its time and space resolution that allow site specific management plans to be evaluated through simulations.

Table 6. Annual evapotranspiration predicted from the model for the Snow Creek watershed. Decade 0 begins initial forest condition. Model used rain year 1995 for each annual weather simulation and simulated ET at the end of each decade of forest growth.

Decade	Annual Transpiration	Weighted % Vegetation Cover
	cm yr^{-1} watershed^{-1}	
0	92693	45.5
1	95355	46.9
2	101158	50.3
3	103097	50.4
4	98762	48.6
5	102868	50.8

The most interesting observation is the large spatial pattern in ET within this watershed (as observed by the gray scale where black = lowest values and white equals highest. The maximum annual ET and weighted % vegetation cover is shown in Table 6. Transpiration was found to increase by 10.98% over the five decades while cover increased by 11.55%. To perform this analysis we disaggregated the 74 polygon cover values to 3939 pixels while the HRU model aggregated these patterns into three HRU polygons. The level of resolution is apparent in Figure 16 which shows the LAI derived from the NDVI analysis for this area. Several observations can be made, illustrating the value of this model. First, there is more continuous variation in LAI in the satellite data. Second, although the satellite patterns are generally observed in the polygon data, there is a difference in both location and size of the polygons relative to the satellite imagery. While the exact LAI values of the NDVI may be questioned, the spatial pattern represents more correctly the actual vegetation patterns than the polygon representation. Lastly, the initial LAI values derived from the satellite and shown in Figure 16 are higher than those in Figure 15, which were based on an allometric relationship. The difference in starting LAI at decade 0 is substantially greater (24% higher, assuming a maximum all-sided LAI of 12) than that for the 50 year change used in this scenario (11.55% difference over the 50 years). This result indicates the sensitivity of these models to input variables and their accuracy.

Results from the surface-subsurface model include: spatial patterns of cumulative precipitation, infiltration rate, surface flow velocity, subsurface flow velocity, water table elevation, surface water ponding depth, vadose zone depth. The rainfall event started at time zero and continued for seven hours. Precipitation increases with elevation, following the DEM (Figure 11).

The effect of spatially and temporally varying rainfall rates as well as spatially varying soil types and initial soil moisture contents, produce the temporal and spatial patterns observed in the instantaneous infiltration rate (not shown). The infiltration rate and cumulative infiltration are important factors in understanding pollution management. For example, essential soil nutrients are largely lost through vertical leaching. Thus, spatial maps of infiltration are of significant importance in understanding biogeochemical cycling in boreal ecosystems beyond the immediate role in the partitioning of the hydrologic budget.

The presence of surface water ponding and its spatial and temporal pattern during and after rainfall events is an important parameter for land use, flood control planning, and for hydraulic engineering. Figure 17 shows spatial patterns in surface ponding at 5 hours. From this image, one observes the strong dependence of surface ponding on terrain features. Surface ponding depth is 6 mm at the top of the hills and is 4 mm in the trough after 5 hours. Although not shown surface ponding depth in sites having steep slopes and high elevation has decreased, but the depth in the trough continues to increase. Later, most surface ponding is restricted to stream channels. The spatial and temporal patterns in surface ponding depth demonstrate the effect of both terrain features and precipitation patterns on surface water storage.

The surface flow velocity is important in the study of soil erosion, sediment yield, sediment transport, hydraulic engineering designs, soil nutrition, and redistribution of water resources. Figure 18 shows the spatial patterns in surface flow velocities at 7.4 hours. In the mountain regions, where the terrain is steep and the rainfall rate is high, the surface flow velocities are higher than in the trough. The surface flow velocity is equal to or greater than 1 m/s on steep slopes and is only a fraction of this in the low gradient trough areas.

Subsurface flow velocity is important for contamination studies as well as characterizing water resources distribution. The water table surface above DEM datum (Figure 19) demonstrates the variations in subsurface water resources. The water table reaches the soil surface at the time when the soil column becomes completely saturated. Drainage of water from the surface to the depth of the active layer is controlled by subsurface flow and infiltration. When the water table rises, the water table comes closer to the ground surface. At 7.4 hours the water surface is higher than in the trough and this gradient drives the groundwater to the trough. Because the gradient is steeper at higher elevation, the subsurface velocity is higher (Figure 20). Although the soil type varies (Figure 21), the conductivity is the same except for the south west corner. Soil in this corner is deeper and has a greater hydraulic conductivity than in remainder of the watershed. The water table drops sharply as shown by the spike in the thickness of the vadose zone (Figure 22, but not obvious from Figure 19 due to scale of the z axis).

REFERENCES

Abbott, M. B., J. C. Bathers, J. A. Cunge, P. E. O'Connell, and J. Rasmussen. 1986. An introduction to the European hydrological system--Systeme Hydrologique European, "SHE", 1: Structure of a physically-based, distributed modelling system. *Journal of Hydrology.* 87:61-77.

Beven, K. J. and M. J. Kirkby. 1979. A physically based, variable contributing area model of basin hydrology. *Hydrologic Science Bulletin.* 24:43-69.

Bristow, K. L. and G. S. Campbell. 1984. On the relationship between incoming solar radiation and daily maximum and minimum temperature. *Agricultural and Forest Meteorology.* 31:159-166.

Brunt, D. 1932. Notes on radiation in the atmosphere. I. *Quarterly Journal of the Royal Meteorological Society.* 58:389-420.

Courant, R., K. O. Friedrichs, and H. Lewy. 1928. Uber die partiellen differenzengleichngen der mathematishen physik. *Mathematishe Annalen.* 100:32-74.

Dickinson, R. E., A. Henderson-Sellers, C. Rosenzweig, and P. J. Sellers. 1991. Evapotranspiration models with canopy resistance for use in climate models. *Annual Review: Agricultural Forestry Meteorology.* 54:373-388.

Eagleson, P. S. 1978a. Climate, soil, and vegetation, 3. A simplified model of soil moisture movement in the liquid phase. *Water Resources Research.* 14:722-730.

Eagleson, P. S. 1978b. Climate, soil, and vegetation, 4. The expected value of annual evapotranspiration. *Water Resources Research.* 14:731-739.

Famiglietti, J. S. and E. F. Wood. 1991. Evapotranspiration and runoff from large land areas: land surface hydrology for atmospheric general circulation models. *Survey in Geophysics.* 12:179-204

Famiglietti, J. S. and E. F. Wood. 1994b. Application of multiscale water and energy balance models on a tallgrass prairie *Water Resources Research.* 30:3079-3093.

Gao, X., S. Sorooshian, and D. C. Goodrich. 1993. Linkage of a GIS to a distributed rainfall-runoff model. In *Environmental Modeling with GIS.* Edited by M.F. Goodchild, B. O. Parks, L. T. Steyaert. 182-187. New York: Oxford Press.

Glassy, J. M. and S. W. Running. 1994. Validating diurnal climatology logic of the MT-CLIM model across a climatic gradient in Oregon. *Ecological Applications.* 4:248-257.

Green, W. H. and G. A. Ampt. 1911. Studies on Soil Physics: 1. Flow of air and water through soil. *Journal of Agricultural Science.* 4:1-24.

Hungerford, R. D., R. R. Nemani, S. W. Running, and J. C. Coughlan. 1989. MTCLIM: A mountain microclimate simulation model. In *Research Paper INT-414.* Ogden, Utah: USDA For. Ser. Intermountain Research Station.

Jordan, J.P. 1992. Identification des processus de gration des crues -Application au bassin de la Haute Mentue" - Ph.D dissertation. Ecole Polytechnique rale de Lausanne, Switzerland.

Kattelmann, R. 1990. Effects of forest cover on a snowpack in the Sierra Nevada. In *Watershed Planning and Analysis in Action.* edited by R. E. Riggins, E. B. Jones, R. Singh and P. A. Rechard. 276-284. American Society of Civil Engineers. New York: New York.

Kattelmann, R.C., N. H. Berg, and M. K. Pack. 1985. Estimating regional snow water equivalent with a simple simulation model. *Water Resources Bulletin* 21(2):273-280.

Laramie, R.L. and J. C. Schaake, Jr. 1972. Simulation of the continuous snowmelt process. In *Report 143.* Cambridge, Massachusetts: Ralph M. Parsons Laboratory, Massachusetts Institute of Technology.

Leavesley, G. H., R. W. Litchy, B. M. Troutman, and L. G. Sandon. 1983. Precipitation-runoff modeling system: User's manual. In *U.S.G.S. Water Resources Investigations Report 83-4328.* p. 209.

Maidment D.R. 1993. *Handbook of Hydrology.* New York: McGraw-Hill.

Mein, R. G., and C. L. Larson. 1973. Modeling infiltration during a steady rain, *Water Resources Research.* 9:384-394.

Monteith, J. L. 1963. Gas exchange in plant communities. *Environmental control of plant growth.* edited by L. T. Evans. 95-112. New York: Academic Press.

Penman, H. L. 1948. Natural evaporation from open water, bare soil, and grass. In *Proceedings of the Royal Society of Agriculture.* 193: 120-145.

Rawls, W. J. and D. L. Brakensiek. 1983. A procedure to predict Green and Ampt infiltration parameters, *Advances in Infiltration.* 102-112. American Society of Agricultural Engineers.

Rawls, W. J., D. L. Brakensiek, and K. E. Saxton. 1982. Estimation of soil water properties, *Transactions of the American Society of Agricultural Engineering.* 25:1316-1320, 1328.

Rawls, W. J. and D. L. Brakensiek. 1985. Prediction of soil water properties for hydrologic modeling. In: *Watershed Management in the Eighties* American Society of Chemical Engineers. 293-299.

Running, S. W. and J. C. Coughlan. 1988. A general model of forest ecosystem processes for regional applications. 1. Hydrologic balance, canopy gas exchange and primary production processes. *Ecological Modeling.* 42:125-154.

Running, S. W., R. R. Nemani, and R. D. Hungerford. 1987. Extrapolation of synoptic meteorological data in mountainous terrain, and its use for simulating forest evapotranspiration and photosynthesis. *Canandian Journal of Forestry Research.* 17:472-483.

Soil Conservation Service. 1985. *Soil Survey of the Eldorado National Forest California.* Pacific Southwest Region: U.S.D.A. Forest Service.

Soil Conservation Service. 1973. *Soil Survey laboratory data and descriptions for some soils of California.* Soil Survey Investigations Report No. 24. Washington, D.C.: U.S.D.A. Soil Conservation Service.

Sellers, P. J., Y. Mintz, Y. C. Sud, and A. Dalcher. 1986. A simple biosphere model (SiB) for use within general circulation models. *Journal of Atmospheric Science.* 43:505-531.

Sellers, W.D. 1965. *Physical Climatology.* Chicago, Illinois: University of Chicago Press.

Sinclair, M.R. 1994. A diagnostic model for estimating orographic precipitation. *Journal of Applied Meteorology.* 33:1163-1175

Smith, J.L. 1982. The historical climatic regime and the projected impact of weather.

Starosolszky, O. eds. 1987. *Applied Surface Hydrology.* Littleton, Colorado: Water Resources Publications. 40-120.

Sugita, M. and W. Brutsaert. 1993. Cloud effect in the estimation of instantaneous downward longwave radiation. *Water Resources Research.* 29(3):599-605.

USDA Soil Conservation Service. 1974. *Soil Survey of Eldorado area, California.* Washington, D. C.: U.S.D.A. Soil Conservation Service and Forest Service.

Vertessy R. A., T. J. Hatton, P. J. O'Shaughnessy, and M. D. A. Jayasuriya. 1993. Predicting water yield from a mountain ash forest catchment using a terrain analysis based catchment model. *Journal of Hydrology.* 150:665-700.

Wigmosta M. S., L. W. Vail, and D. P. Lettenmaier. 1994. A distributed hydrology-vegetation model for complex terrain. *Water Resources Research.* 30:1665-1679.

Xiao, Q. F., S. L. Ustin, and W. W. Wallender. 1996. A spatial and temporal continuous surface-subsurface hydrologic model. *Journal Geophysical Research-Atmospheres.* In press.

Xiao, Q. F. 1994. A spatially and temporally continuous surface-subsurface hydrologic model. Master's thesis, Department of Land, Air, and Water Resources, University of California, Davis.

S#96-073R   PI: Susan L. Ustin and Dar Roberts, Scaling up from leaf to stands: Coupling ecophysiology with remote sensing.

A. Merit: How relevant to issues of global environmental change?

Several ecosystem models exist for scaling canopy gas exchange and decompositional processes from point models to regional models, including BGC, CASA and SiB. These models differ in their paramterizations of canopy and soil processes. Most are climate driven models that rely on GIS based vegetation, soil, and topographic maps and have look up tables for canopy functions. Remote sensing provides the only possibility for spatially explicit data to drive the models. What this study proposes to do is to improve the remote sensing inputs, using a modified Forest BGC model coupled with a climate simulator and a coupled surface-subsurface hydrologic model.

7

RONALD M. YOSHIYAMA
Department of Wildlife, Fish and
 Conservation Biology
University of California
Davis, California

ERIC R. GERSTUNG
California Department of Fish and Game
Inland Fisheries
Sacramento, California

FRANK W. FISHER
California Department of Fish and Game
Red Bluff, California

PETER B. MOYLE
Department of Wildlife, Fish and
 Conservation Biology
University of California
Davis, California

Historical and Present Distribution of Chinook Salmon in the Central Valley Drainage of California

Sierra Nevada Ecosystem Project: Final report to Congress, vol. III, *Assessments, Commissioned Reports, and Background Information*. Davis: University of California, Centers for Water and Wildland Resources, 1996.

309

INTRODUCTION

The vast expanse of the Central Valley region of California once encompassed numerous salmon-producing streams that drained the Sierra Nevada and Cascades mountains on the east and north and, to a lesser degree, the lower-elevation Coast Range on the west. The large areas that form the watersheds in the Sierra and Cascades, and the regular, heavy snowfalls in those regions, provided year-round streamflows for a number of large rivers which supported substantial-- in some cases prodigious-- runs of chinook salmon (*Oncorhynchus tshawytscha*). No less than 25 Central Valley streams supported at least one annual chinook salmon run, with at least 18 of those streams supporting two or more runs each year. In the Sacramento drainage, constituting the northern half of the Central Valley system and covering 24,000 sq mi (Jacobs et al. 1993), most Coast Range streams historically supported regular salmon runs; however, those "westside" streams generally had streamflows limited in volume and seasonal availability due to the lesser amount of snowfall west of the Valley, and their salmon runs were correspondingly limited by the duration of the rainy season. Some tributary streams, such as Cache and Putah creeks, did not connect with the Sacramento River at all during dry years, and salmon runs only entered them opportunistically as annual rainfall conditions allowed. In the San Joaquin drainage, composing much of the southern half of the Central Valley system and covering 13,540 sq mi (Jacobs et al. 1993), none of the westside streams draining the Coast Range had adequate streamflows to support salmon or any other anadromous fishes.

The great abundance of chinook salmon of the Central Valley was noted early in the history of colonization of the region by Euro-American people. However, following the California Gold Rush of 1849, the massive influx of fortune seekers and settlers altered the salmon spawning rivers with such rapidity and so drastically that the historic distributions and abundances of anadromous fish can be determined only by inference from scattered records, ethnographic information, and analysis of the natural features of the streams. Probably the only species for which adequate information exists to develop a reasonably complete picture is the chinook salmon-- the most abundant and most heavily utilized of the Central Valley anadromous fishes.

In this report, we consolidate historical and current information on the distribution and abundance of chinook salmon in the major tributary streams of the Central Valley in order to provide a comprehensive asssessment of the extent to which chinook salmon figured in the historical landscape of the Central Valley region.

THE FOUR RUNS OF CENTRAL VALLEY CHINOOK SALMON

Four runs of chinook salmon occur in the Central Valley system-- more precisely, in the Sacramento River drainage-- with each run defined by a combination of adult migration timing, spawning period, and juvenile residency and smolt migration periods (Fisher 1994). The runs are named on the basis of the upstream migration season. The presence of four seasonal runs in the Sacramento River lends it the uncommon distinction of having some numbers of adult salmon in its waters throughout the year (Stone 1883, Rutter 1904, Healey 1991, Vogel and Marine 1991). The fall and late-fall runs spawn soon after entering the natal streams, while the spring and winter runs typically "hold" in their streams for up to several months before spawning (Rutter 1904, CDFG 1993). Formerly, the runs also could be differentiated on the basis of their typical spawning habitats-- spring-fed headwaters for the winter run, the higher streams for the spring run, upper mainstem rivers for the late-fall run, and the lower rivers and tributaries for the fall run (Rutter 1904, Fisher 1994). Different runs often occurred in the same stream-- temporarily staggered but broadly overlapping (Vogel and Marine 1991, Fisher 1994), and with each run utilizing the appropriate seasonal streamflow regime to which it had evolved. On the average, the spring-run and winter-run fish generally were smaller-bodied than the other Central Valley chinook salmon, and late-fall run fish were the largest (Stone 1874, F. Fisher, unpubl. data).

Prior to the American settlement of California, most major tributaries of the Sacramento and San Joaquin rivers probably had both fall and spring runs of chinook salmon. The large streams that lacked either adequate summer flows or holding habitat to support spring-run salmon, which migrate upstream during the spring and hold over the summer in pools, had at least a fall run and in some cases perhaps a late-fall run. The fall run undoubtedly existed in all streams that had adequate flows during the fall months, even if the streams were intermittent during other parts of the year. Generally, it appears that fall-run fish historically spawned in the Valley floor and foothill reaches (Rutter 1904)-- below 500 ft elevation-- and most likely were limited in their upstream migration by their egg-laden and somewhat deteriorated physical condition. The spring run, in contrast, ascended to higher elevation reaches, judging from spawning distributions observed in recent years and the reports of early fishery workers (Stone 1874, Rutter 1904). A California Fish Commission report (CFC 1890) noted, "It is a fact well known to the fish culturists that the winter and spring run of salmon, during the high, cold waters, go to the extreme headwaters of the rivers if no obstructions prevent, into the highest mountains." Spring-run salmon, entering the streams while in pre-reproductive and peak physical condition well before the spawning season, were understandably better able to penetrate the far upper reaches of the spawning streams than were fall-run fish. The spring run, in fact, was generally required to utilize higher-elevation habitats-- the only biologically suitable places-- given its life-history timing. Spring-run fish needed to ascend to high enough elevations for over-summering in order to avoid the excessive summer and early-fall temperatures of the Valley floor and foothills-- at least to ~1,500 ft in the Sacramento drainage and most likely correspondingly higher in the more southerly San Joaquin drainage.[1] If they spawned in early fall, they needed to ascend even higher-- at least to ~2,500-3,000 ft in the Sacramento drainage-- to be within the temperature range (35-58°F) required for successful egg incubation. Spring-run fish which spawned later in the season did not have to ascend quite so high because ambient temperatures would have started to drop as autumn progressed, but presumably there were constraints on how long the fish could delay spawning-- set by decreasing streamflows (before the fall rains began), ripening of the eggs, and the fish's deteriorating physical condition.

The spring run was originally most abundant in the San Joaquin system, ascending and occupying the high-elevation streams fed by snow-melt where they over-summered until the fall spawning season (Fry 1961). The heavy snow-pack of the southern Sierra Nevada was a crucial feature in providing sufficient spring and early-summer streamflows, which were the highest flows of the year (F. Fisher, unpubl. data). Their characteristic life-history timing and other adaptive features enabled spring-run salmon to utilize high spring-time flows to gain access to the upper stream reaches-- the demanding ascent facilitated by high fat reserves, undeveloped (and less weighty) gonads, and a generally smaller body size. The more rain-driven Sacramento system was generally less suitable for the spring run due to lesser

---

[1] We use English units of measurements for distances and elevations in this paper for ease of comparison with information quoted from earlier published work. Some locations are given "river miles" (rm)-- the distance from the mouth of the stream under discussion to the point of interest.

amounts of snow melt and proportionately lower flows during the spring and early summer, but the spring run nonetheless was widely distributed and abundant in that system (Campbell and Moyle 1991). Some notable populations in the Sacramento drainage occurred in Cascades streams where coldwater springs provided adequate summer flows (e.g., Upper Sacramento and McCloud rivers, Mill Creek). These coldwater springs emanated from the porous lava formations around Mount Shasta and Mount Lassen and were ultimately derived from snow melt from around those peaks, and also from glacial melt on Mount Shasta.

The winter run-- unique to the Central Valley (Healey 1991)-- originally existed in the upper Sacramento River system (Little Sacramento, Pit, McCloud and Fall rivers) and in nearby Battle Creek (Fisher, unpubl. data); there is no evidence that winter runs naturally occurred in any of the other major drainages prior to the era of watershed development for hydroelectric and irrigation projects. Like the spring run, the winter run typically ascended far up the drainages to the headwaters (CFC 1890). All streams in which populations of winter-run chinook salmon were known to exist were fed by cool, constant springs that provided the flows and low temperatures required for spawning, incubation and rearing during the summer season (Slater 1963)-- when most streams typically had low flows and elevated temperatures. The unusual life-history timing of the winter run, requiring cold summer flows, would argue against such a run occurring in other than the upper Sacramento system and Battle Creek, seemingly the only areas where summer flow requirements were met. A similar constraint may apply to some extent to the late-fall run, of which the juveniles remain in freshwater at least over the summer and therefore require cold-water flows (Vogel and Marine 1991, Fisher 1994)-- whether from springs or from late snow-melt. The late-fall run probably spawned originally in the mainstem Sacramento River and major tributary reaches now blocked by Shasta Dam and perhaps in the upper mainstem reaches of other Sacramento Valley streams (Fisher 1994) such as the American River (Clark 1929). There are indications that a late-fall run possibly occurred also in the San Joaquin River, upstream of its major tributaries at the southern end of that drainage (Hatton and Clark 1942, Fisher 1994).

DISTRIBUTIONAL SURVEY: GENERAL BACKGROUND AND METHODS

As summarized by Clark (1929), makeshift barriers were built across Sierra Nevada streams as early as the Gold Rush period when mining activities significantly impacted salmon populations in a number of ways-- e.g., by stream diversions, blockages, and filling of streambeds with debris. Hydropower projects appeared in the 1890s and early 1900s, although most of the large irrigation and power dams were constructed after 1910 (Fisher, unpubl. data). The early hydropower dams of the early 1900s were numerous, however, and collectively they eliminated the major portion of spawning and holding habitat for spring-run salmon well before the completion of the major dams in later decades.

The early distributional limits of salmon populations within the Sierra Nevada and some Cascades drainages are poorly known, if at all, because of the paucity of accurate scientific or historical records pre-dating the heavy exploitation of populations and the destruction or degradation of stream habitats. It was not until the late 1920s and later that reliable scientific surveys of salmon distributions in Central Valley drainages were conducted. Reports by Clark (1929) and Hatton (1940) give information on the accessibility of various streams to salmon, and they identify the human-made barriers present at those times. They also give limited qualitative information on salmon abundance. These reports provide a valuable "mid-term" view of what salmon distributions were like in the first half of the century, after major environmental alterations had occurred and populations were significantly depleted compared to earlier times, but the survival of the populations was not yet imperiled to the extent it presently is. Fry (1961) provided the earliest comprehensive synopsis of chinook stock abundances in Central Valley streams, covering the period 1940-1959. Quantitative data were given by Fry (1961) for both spring and fall runs, but the fall-run estimates also included the winter and late-fall runs for the streams where those other runs occurred. Since then, fairly regular surveys of spawning runs in the various streams have been carried out by the California Department of Fish and Game and periodically summarized in the Department's "Administrative Reports".

In the following section we attempt to synthesize this earlier information with that available from more recent sources, with the aim of providing comprehensive descriptions for the major salmon-supporting streams of the Central Valley. For each of the major streams (excepting some tributaries in the upper Sacramento River system, for which little data exist) that are known to have had self-sustaining chinook salmon populations, we provide a narrative including their probable "original" distributions and later "mid-term" 1928-1940 distributions as indicated by published literature and unpublished documents.[2] The probable original distributions were determined by considering the presence of obvious natural barriers to upstream salmon migration together with historical information (e.g., accounts of gold miners and early settlers), and they apply to the salmon populations up to the period of intensive gold mining, ca. 1850-1890, when massive environmental degradation by hydraulic mining activities occurred. We also drew from ethnographic studies of Native American people. Much information on the material culture of the native peoples of California had been obtained by ethnographers during the early part of this century, who interviewed elder Native Americans from various groups. That information pertains to the life-experiences and traditions of the native informants during the period of their youth and early adulthood, and also to the mid-life periods of their parents and grandparents from whom they received information and instruction-- spanning essentially much of the middle and latter parts of the 19th century (e.g., Beals 1933, Aginsky 1943, Gayton 1948a). For the mid-term distributions, we relied heavily on the papers of Clark (1929) and Hatton (1940) and retained much of their original wording to faithfully represent the situation they reported at those times. We also give more recent and current (1990s) salmon spawning distributions based on government agency reports, published papers, and interviews with agency biologists.[3] The stream accounts are presented starting with the southernmost Sierra streams and proceeding northward. We also include accounts for several streams on the west side of the Sacramento Valley which are known to have had chinook salmon runs. They are representative of other small westside or upper Sacramento Valley streams that formerly sustained salmon stocks, if only periodically, but lost them because of extensive stream diversions and placement of man-made barriers.

We mention steelhead trout in several stream accounts, particularly where information on salmon is lacking. The intent is to show that certain stream reaches were accessible to at least steelhead and, hence, may have been reached also by chinook salmon-- particularly spring-run fish which typically migrated far upstream. However, the correspondence between the occurrence of steelhead and spring-run salmon in stream reaches was by no means complete. Steelhead aggressively ascend even fairly small tributary streams, in contrast to chinook salmon which generally utilize the mainstems and major forks of streams (Gerstung, pers. obs.). The migration timing of steelhead-- during the peak of the rainy season (January-March)-- aided their ascent into the small tributaries. Steelhead also are able to surmount somewhat higher waterfalls-- perhaps up to ~15 ft high-- while chinook salmon in California appear to be stopped by falls greater than 10-12 ft high (Gerstung, pers. obs.), depending on the abruptness of the drop. Furthermore, steelhead do not require as much gravel for spawning; e.g., steelhead formerly used westside streams in the upper Sacramento drainage (near Shasta Lake) that had small patches of gravel

---

[2] Unpublished documents are listed separately, following the References section, as are persons cited for personal communication ("pers. comm.").

[3] Agency abbreviations are: California Department of Fish and Game (CDFG); California State Board of Fish Commissioners (CFC); United States Commission for Fish and Fisheries, or U.S. Fish Commission (USFC).

interspersed among boulder substrate, which salmon generally shunned (Gerstung, pers. obs.). Yet, in terms of ascending the main stream reaches, it may be reasonably assumed that where steelhead were, spring-run salmon often were not far behind. Using the advantage of high spring flows, the salmon could have surmounted obstacles and reached upstream areas not much lower than the upper limits attained by steelhead in some streams.

Non-game fishes such as hardhead (*Mylopharodon conocephalus*), Sacramento squawfish (*Ptychochelis grandis*) and Sacramento sucker (*Catostomus occidentalis*) also provide hints about salmon distribution. Those species are typical of Valley floor and low- to mid-elevation foothill streams (Moyle 1976), and their recorded presence in stream reaches which are not blocked by obvious natural barriers is a good indication that anadromous salmonids likewise were able to ascend at least as far, and possibly even further upstream. The presence of non-game native fish populations above obvious barriers in some streams indicates that at least some of the natural barriers were formed subsequent to the initial dispersal of those species into the upper drainages.

DISTRIBUTIONAL SYNOPSES OF SALMON STREAMS

Kings River (Fresno Co.) Chinook salmon are known to have occurred at least periodically in the Kings River, the southernmost Central Valley stream that supported salmon. The Kings River, in the past, flowed into the northeast part of Tulare Lake, and its waters occasionally ran into the San Joaquin River during wet periods when water levels became high enough in Tulare Lake to overflow and connect the two drainages (Carson 1852, Ferguson 1914). Streamflows would have been greatest during the spring snow-melt period, so it is most likely that the spring run was the predominant or, perhaps, the only run to occur there. The spring-run fish would have had to ascend to high enough elevations (probably > 1,500 ft) to avoid excessive summer water temperatures, going past the area presently covered by Pine Flat Reservoir. The mainstem above Pine Flat Reservoir is of low gradient (Gerstung, pers. obs.) and free of obstructions for some distance (P. Bartholomew, pers. comm.), so the salmon probably were able to ascend ~ 10-12 mi beyond the present upper extent of the reservoir. The upper range of the bulk of salmon migration in the Kings River probably was near the confluence of the North Fork (Woodhull and Dill 1942). There is an undocumented note of "a few salmon" having occurred much further upstream at Cedar Grove (28 mi above present-day Pine Flat Reservoir) "in the past-- before Pine Flat Dam was constructed" (CDFG unpubl. notes). However, it is not clear if salmon could have reached that far, due to the presence of extensive rapids below around the area of Boyden Cave (3,300 ft elev.) and below Cedar Grove. The North Fork Kings River is very steep shortly above its mouth, and salmon most likely did not enter it to any significant distance (P. Bartholomew, pers. comm.).

Native American groups had several fishing camps on the mainstem Kings River downstream of Mill Flat Creek, including one used by the Choinimni people (a subgroup of the Northern Foothills Yokuts) at the junction of Mill Creek (~ 2 mi below the present site of Pine Flat Dam). There, the "spring salmon run" was harvested and dried for later use (Gayton 1948b). Gayton (1946) wrote: "On the lower Kings River, the Choinimni (Y) [denoting Yokuts] and probably other tribes within the area of the spring salmon run (about May) held a simple riverside ritual at their principal fishing sites. The local chief ate the first salmon speared, after cooking it and praying to Salmon for a plentiful supply. Then others partook of a salmon feast, and the season, so to say, was officially open." The existence of a well-established salmon ritual among the native people would seem to indicate that salmon runs in the Kings River were not uncommon, even if they did not occur every year (e.g., in years of low precipitation). Drawing on testimony from one native informant, Gayton (1948a) also reported that salmon "were well known and greatly depended upon" by the Chunut people (a subgroup of Southern Valley Yokuts) who dwelt on the eastern shore of Tulare Lake-- essentially the downstream terminus of

315

the Kings River. A second Chunut informant interviewed by Latta (1977) similarly attested to the presence of salmon, and evidently steelhead, in the Lake: "There were lots of fish in Tulare Lake. The one we liked best was *a-pis*, a bit [sic] lake trout. They were real big fish, as big as any salmon, and good meat. ... Sometimes the steelheads came in the lake too; so did the salmon. We called the steelheads *tah-wah-aht* and the salmon *ki-uh-khot*. We dried lots of fish. When it was dried and smoked, the salmon was the best." It is evident, therefore, that salmon entered Tulare Lake at least on occasion, where they were taken by Chunut fishers. The different tribes of Yokuts people around Tulare Lake and the lower Kings River each had territorial limits (Gayton 1948a, Latta 1977), and transgressions apparently were vigorously repulsed (e.g., Gayton 1948a, Cook 1960). Furthermore, there would have been little reason for the Chunut to have made special fishing excursions to areas away from Tulare Lake, given that the Lake contained an abundance and variety of high-quality fish resources (Gayton 1948a, Latta 1970). It, therefore, does not seem likely that the Chunut traveled out of their territory to the Kings River to obtain salmon, nor have we found any indication in the ethnographic literature that they did so.

Diversions from the Kings River and other streams for agricultural irrigation occurred from the early years of American settlement and farming in the San Joaquin Valley. The reduced streamflows undoubtedly diminished the frequency of salmon runs-- and perhaps extinguished them altogether-- for a period spanning the late-19th to early-20th centuries. The California Fish and Game Commission reported that after a channel was dredged out between the Kings and San Joaquin rivers ca. 1911, salmon began reappearing in the Kings River-- "a few" in the spring of 1911, a "very considerable run" in 1912 which ascended to Trimmer Springs (rm 125) near the upper end of present-day Pine Flat Reservoir, and another "very considerable run" in June 1914 (Ferguson 1914). Several small chinook salmon were caught by a CDFG biologist in the fall of 1942 near the town of Piedra on the mainstem Kings River (~2 mi downstream of the mouth of Mill Creek; W. Dill, pers. comm.); those fish were notable in that they were precociously mature males-- i.e., running milt (W. Dill, pers. comm.). A single ~5-inch chinook salmon (with "very enlarged testes") was later captured in September 1946 in the mainstem "about 8 miles above the junction of the North Fork Kings River (W. Dill- CDFG letter). Moyle (1970) later collected juvenile chinook salmon (~4 in total length) in April 1970 from Mill Creek, shortly above its mouth. Salmon that spawned in Mill Creek likely ascended the stream at least several miles to the vicinity of Wonder Valley (P. Bartholomew, pers. comm.). Salmon runs in the Kings River were observed to occur more frequently after the construction of the Kings River Bypass in 1927, with "especially noticeable runs" in 1927, 1938 and 1940 (Woodhull and Dill 1942).

The Kings River salmon run was probably bolstered by, or perhaps even periodically reestablished from, the San Joaquin River population, particularly after series of dry years during which the run would have progressively diminished. The termination of natural streamflows down the channel of the San Joaquin River since 1946, except during exceptionally wet years, resulted in the extirpation of salmon runs in both the Kings and upper San Joaquin rivers.

San Joaquin River (Fresno Co.) Spring and fall runs of salmon formerly existed in the upper San Joaquin River, and there may also have been a late-fall run present, but all salmon runs in the San Joaquin River above the confluence of the Merced River were extirpated by the late-1940s. The spring run historically ascended the river past the present site of Kerckhoff Power House in the Sierra foothills to spawning grounds in the higher reaches (CDFG 1921). A natural barrier shortly upstream of the mouth of Willow Creek, near present-day Redinger Lake, may have posed an obstruction to salmon (E. Vestal, pers. comm.). However, there is some evidence that salmon traveled further upstream to a point just below Mammoth Pool Reservoir (~3,300 ft elevation), where habitat suitable for spring-run salmon exists. The oral history of present-day Native American residents in the region includes references to salmon occurring there (P. Bartholomew, pers. comm. based on interviews with Native American informants). Suckers presently occur in the stream up to the location of a velocity barrier ~0.25-0.5 mi below

Mammoth Pool Dam, suggesting that salmon likewise could have made the ascent to that point (P. Bartholomew, pers. comm.). Based on the absence of natural barriers, it is likely that salmon entered two tributaries of the upper San Joaquin River near Millerton Reservoir-- Fine Gold Creek, possibly "as far upstream [~6 mi] as opposite Hildreth Mtn", and Cottonwood Creek, which they probably ascended as least 2 mi (E. Vestal, CDFG unpubl. notes and pers. comm.).

Native Americans belonging to Northern Foothill Yokuts groups, including the Chukchansi people from Coarse Gold Creek and the Fresno River, fished for salmon in the San Joaquin River near the area of Friant (Gayton 1948b). According to Gayton's (1948b) ethnographic account, the salmon were watched for "When the Pleiades were on the western horizon at dusk", and a first salmon ritual was held by several different Yokuts tribes when the first salmon of the season was caught. Large quantities of salmon were dried for storage: "They were put in a sack [skin?] and packed home with a tumpline. A man carried about two hundred pounds of fish" (Gayton 1948b). The areas further up the San Joaquin drainage, above the Yokuts, were occupied by Monache (Western Mono) groups. Gifford (1932) stated that the "Northfork Mono", who lived on the "North Fork" San Joaquin River (also called Northfork Creek or Willow Creek), Whiskey Creek and nearby areas, fished for and ate salmon as well as trout. The Northfork Mono also were said to have held first salmon rites (Aginsky 1943). However, it is not clear how far up Willow Creek salmon ascended.

The construction and operation of Kerckhoff Dam (ca. 1920) for power generation blocked the spring-run salmon from their spawning areas upstream and seasonally dried up ~14 mi of stream, below the dam, where there were pools in which the fish would have held over the summer (CDFG 1921). Later in the decade, Clark (1929) reported that the salmon spawning beds were located in the stretch between the mouth of Fine Gold Creek and Kerckhoff Dam and in the small tributary streams within that area, covering a stream length of ~36 mi; a few scattered beds also occurred below the town of Friant. At the time of Clark's (1929) writing, there were four dams on this river that impeded the upstream migration of salmon: the "Delta weir" (in a slough on the west side of the river, 14 mi southeast of Los Banos); Stevenson's weir (on the main river east of Delta weir); Mendota weir (1.5 mi from the town of Mendota); and the impassable Kerckhoff Dam, 35 mi above Friant. The first three were irrigation diversion projects. Friant Dam had not yet been constructed. In addition to the barriers themselves, reduced streamflows due to irrigation diversions impeded and disoriented uncounted numbers of migrating salmon which went astray in the dead-end drainage canals on the Valley floor, where they abortively spawned in the mud (Clark 1930).

Hatton (1940) considered the upper San Joaquin River in 1939 to possess the "most suitable spawning beds of any stream in the San Joaquin system", and "even in the dry year of 1939, most of the suitable areas were adequately covered with water and the water level was satisfactorily constant." Hatton reported that the spawning beds in the San Joaquin River were located along the 26 mi from Lane's Bridge up to the Kerckhoff Power House, all of which were accessible, and the "best and most frequently used areas" were between Lane's Bridge and Friant. The stream above Friant, where it entered a canyon was generally unsuitable, comprising mainly bedrock, "long, deep pools" and "short stretches of turbulent water". He also estimated that the planned Friant Dam would cut off 16 mi of stream where spawning occurred, which represented ~36 percent of the spawning beds with a spawner capacity of 7,416 salmon. At that time (1939), Hatton considered the spawning beds below Friant Dam to be "so underpopulated that even after the completion of the dam more than adequate areas will still be available, if water flows are adequate". The expected negative impact of Friant Dam was not so much the elmination of spawning areas above the dam as the diversion of water from the stream channel downstream. Quoting Hatton (1940), it was "hoped that seepage from the dam and returned irrigation water will provide sufficient flow to make spawning possible". It would seem that the deleterious consequences of vestigial streamflows and polluted irrigation drainage on salmon were not yet fully appreciated at that time.

Hatton (1940) stated that the San Joaquin River where spawning occurred was "singularly free

317

of obstructions and diversions", but there were obstructions further downstream. The lowermost barrier below the spawning beds was the Sack Dam of the Poso Irrigation District, "several miles below Firebaugh" (near Mendota), which in an average water year "destroys any possibility of a fall run up the San Joaquin" because its "compete diverson of water leaves the stream bed practically dry between that point and the mouth of the Merced River" (Hatton 1940). The sand bags constituting this dam were left in place until they were washed out by the winter floods. The only other obstruction below the spawning beds was the Mendota Weir, which was equipped with a "satisfactory fishway"; however, there were eight unscreened diversions above the dam which Hatton viewed as "a serious menace to the downstream migrants".

The numbers of salmon that at one time existed in the San Joaquin River were, by some accounts, tremendous. Clark (1929) stated that "Fifty or sixty years ago, the salmon in the San Joaquin were very numerous and came in great hordes." Indeed, it is recorded that ca. 1870 the residents of Millerton on the banks of the San Joaquin, were kept awake "by the 'myriads of salmon to be heard nightly splashing over the sand bars in the river'" (California State Historical Association 1929), the noise being "comparable to a large waterfall" (Northern California Historical Records Survey Project 1940). The site of Millerton presently lies covered by Millerton Reservoir. In reference to the fall run (and evidently steelhead), one early observer in correspondence with State Fish Commissioner B.B. Redding wrote: "...in the fall the salmon and salmon-trout find their way up here in large quantities. Last fall I helped to spear quite a number, as that is about the only way of fishing in this part of the county; but below the San Joaquin bridge I understand they were trapped in a wire corral by ranchers and fed to hogs; they were so plentiful" (USFC 1876b). The former spring run of the San Joaquin River has been described as "one of the largest chinook salmon runs anywhere on the Pacific Coast" and numbering "possibly in the range of 200,000-500,000 spawners annually" (CDFG 1990). Blake (1857) noted in reference to salmon in the vicinity of Fort Miller (just upstream of Millerton) in 1853: "It is probable, however, that they are not abundant, as the mining operations along the upper part of the stream and its tributaries sometimes load the water with impurities." While Blake's conjecture regarding the salmon evidently was not accurate at the time, it foreshadowed events to come. Although Clark (1929) reported that a "very good run" of salmon was seen at Mendota in 1916-1917 and a "fairly good" one for 1920, "very few" fish were seen in 1928 and Clark considered the salmon in the San Joaquin River to be "fast decreasing". By then there was essentially only a spring run, the water being too low later in the year to support a fall run (Clark 1929). The decline of the salmon resource was, of course, noted by the river inhabitants. Particularly affected were Native Americans who depended upon the runs for sustenance. In the words of a Yokuts man named Pahmit (William Wilson) in 1933: "Long time 'go lots salmon in San Joaquin River. My people-- maybe 2-3 thousand come *Coo-you-illik* catch salmon-- catch more salmon can haul in hundred freight wagons. Dry 'em-- carry 'em home." [Since 1909] "no salmon in river. White man make dam at old Indian rancheria *Kăh-wăh-chu*-- stop fish-- now Indian got no fish. Go river-- water there, but no fish. White man got no fish. White man got no money. Injun got no fish-- Injun got no money--*everybody* broke. That's bad businesss." (Frank Latta unpubl. papers, field notes). Coo-you-illik ("Sulphur Water") was a Dumna Yokuts village at the later site of Fort Miller (Latta 1977). The salmon were well-remembered by non-Native Americans also: "The salmon fishing in the San Joaquin River was out of this world. It was one of the finest spawning rivers for salmon. ...There were hundreds and hundreds. ...The salmon looked like silver torpedoes coming up the river " (Anthony Imperatice interview, 11 February 1988; in Rose 1992).

In spite of the general decline of salmon in the upper San Joaquin River due to increasingly inhospitable environmental conditions, particularly for the fall run, both the spring run and the fall run managed to persist. Hatton (1940) reported that the fall run occurred in "some years", "making a hazardous and circuitous journey" through natural sloughs and irrigation canals, from near the mouth of the Merced River and "miraculously" entering the San Joaquin River again above Mendota weir. By

1942, the upper San Joaquin River was stated by Clark (1943) to have had "a fair-sized spring run of king [chinook] salmon for many years" and a fall run that had "been greatly reduced". In addition to those two runs, there were indications that a late-fall run formerly may have existed in the San Joaquin River (Van Cleve 1945). In 1941, a run apparently of appreciable size entered the river, starting about December 1 and continuing through at least December 10 (Hatton and Clark 1942). The authors concluded that "a run of several thousand fish may enter the upper San Joaquin River during the winter months, in addition to the spring run during March, April and May" (Hatton and Clark 1942). This December run has been viewed as a possible late-fall run (Fisher 1994) because peak migration of late-fall-run fish characteristically occurs in December, at least in the Sacramento River system. A more likely alternative, however, is that the migration observed by Hatton and Clark was simply the fall run, having been delayed by unfavorable conditions that evidently typified the river in the early fall months. Clark (1943) in fact stated that a "late-fall run of salmon occurs after this sand dam [the Sack Dam near Firebaugh] is washed or taken out in late November", clearly indicating that the fall run was usually blocked from ascending past that point any earlier. Furthermore, spawning of Central Valley fall-run stocks tend to occur progressively later in the season in the more southerly located streams (Fisher, unpubl. data), and the spawning migration period is known to include December in the San Joaquin basin tributaries (Hatton and Clark 1942, T. Ford, pers. comm.). Yet, an actual late-fall run may have existed in earlier times in the San Joaquin River. Historical environmental conditions in the mainstem reach of the San Joaquin River just above the Valley floor may have been suitable for supporting late-fall-run fish, which require cool-water flows during the summer juvenile-rearing period. Writing of the San Joaquin River near Fort Miller in late July, 1853, Blake (1857) noted: "The river was not at its highest stage at the time of our visit; but a large body of water was flowing in the channel, and it was evident that a considerable quantity of snow remained in the mountains at the sources of the river. A diurnal rise and fall of the water was constantly observed, and is, without doubt, produced by the melting of the snow during the day. The water was remarkably pure and clear, and very cold; its temperature seldom rising above 64°Fahrenheit while that of the air varied from 99° to 104° in the shade."

Fry (1961) reported that during the 1940s prior to the construction of Friant Dam, the San Joaquin River had "an excellent spring run and a small fall run". At that time the San Joaquin River spring run was considered probably "the most important" one in the Central Valley (Fry 1961), amounting to 30,000 or more fish in three years of that decade, with a high of 56,000 in 1945 (Fry 1961) and an annual value of "almost one million dollars" (Hallock and Van Woert 1959). In 1946, the sport catch in the San Joaquin Valley included an estimated 25,000 salmon produced by the upper San Joaquin River, with perhaps another 1,000 taken by the ocean sport fishery (CDFG 1955 unpubl. document). In addition, the commercial harvest, averaged for the period 1946-1952, accounted for another 714,000 pounds of salmon that originated from the San Joaquin River (CDFG 1955 unpubl. document). The last substantial run (> 1,900 fish) occurred in 1948 (Warner 1991). The salmon runs were extirpated from the upper San Joaquin drainage, above the confluence with the Merced River, as a direct result of the completion of Friant Dam (320 ft high) in 1942 and associated water distribution canals (viz., Madera and Friant-Kern canals) by 1949 (Skinner 1958). The dam itself cut off at least a third of the former spawning areas, but more importantly, the Friant Project essentially eliminated river flows below the dam, causing the ~60-mi stretch of river below Sack Dam to completely dry up (Skinner 1958, Hallock and Van Woert 1959, Fry 1961). While not attributing the collapse of the Sacramento-San Joaquin spring salmon fishery soley to Friant Dam, Skinner (1958) noted the "striking coincidence" that in the 1916-1949 (pre-Friant) period, the spring-run catch averaged 664,979 lbs (31% of the total Sacramento-San Joaquin commercial catch) and in 1950-1957 (post-Friant) it averaged 67,677 lbs (6% of the total catch)-- a 90% reduction in absolute poundage. Skinner (1958) further chronicled the telling correlation between events in the development of the Friant Project, their effects on year-classes of fish, and the rapid deflation of the spring in-river fishery-- the latter falling from a high catch of 2,290,000 lbs in 1946 to a low of 14,900 lbs in 1953. Efforts by CDFG biologists to preserve the last cohorts of the upper San Joaquin spring-run salmon in 1948, 1949 and 1950-- thwarted by insufficient streamflows and excessive poaching-- ended in failure (Warner 1991). Since the closure of Friant Dam, highly polluted irrigation drainage during much of the year has comprised essentially all of the water flowing down the course of the San Joaquin River along the Valley floor until it is joined by the first major tributary, the Merced River (San Joaquin Valley Drainage Program 1990). In only very wet years in recent times have salmon occasionally been able to ascend to the upper San Joaquin River, the latest record being that of a single 30-in male (possibly spring-run) caught by an angler on July 1, 1969 below Friant Dam (Moyle 1970).

The San Joaquin River salmon runs were the most southerly, regularly occurring large populations of chinook salmon in North America, and they possibly were distinctly adapted to the demanding environmental regime of the southern Central Valley. The California Fish Commission (CFC 1875, USFC 1876b) regarded the summertime migration of the fall run during the seasonally hot portion of the year as extraordinary: "Large numbers pass up the San Joaquin River for the purpose of spawning in July and August, swimming for one hundred and fifty miles through the hottest valley in the State, where the temperature of the air at noon is rarely less than eighty degrees, and often as high as one hundred and five degrees Fahrenheit, and where the average temperature of the river at the bottom is seventy-nine degrees and at the surface eighty degrees." The Commissioners noted that during August-September of 1875-1877, the average monthly water temperatures for the San Joaquin River where two bridges of the Central Pacific Railroad crossed (at 37°50'N, 121°22'W and 36°52'N, 119°54'W) were within 72.1-80.7°F (considering both surface and bottom water) and maximal temperatures were 82-84°F (CFC 1877). The high temperature tolerance of the San Joaquin River fall-run salmon inspired interest in introducing those salmon into the warm rivers of the eastern and southern United States (CFC 1875, 1877, USFC 1876a,b). Quoting the California Fish Commission (CFC 1875): "Their passage to their spawning grounds at this season of the year, at so high a temperature of both air and water, would indicate that they will thrive in all the rivers of the Southern States, whose waters take their rise in mountainous or hilly regions, and in a few years, without doubt, the San Joaquin Salmon will be transplanted to all of those States."

Perhaps it was this hardiness of the fall-run fish that enabled them to persist through years of depleted streamflows to make their occasional, "miraculous" sojourns up the San Joaquin drainage mentioned by Hatton (1940). Nothing is known of the physiological and genetic basis of the seemingly remarkable temperature tolerances of upper San Joaquin River fall-run salmon, because that population has been long extinct. It is not known to what degree the remaining fall-run populations in the other tributaries of the San Joaquin basin possess the temperature tolerances and genetic characteristics of the original upper San Joaquin River fall-run. Because of extreme fluctuations in year-to-year run sizes in recent times and the probable loss of genetic variation during population bottlenecks, it is likely that present-day fall-run salmon of the San Joaquin tributaries are genetically different from their forebears, or at least from the former upper San Joaquin River fall run. Similarly, the spring-run fish of the upper San Joaquin River perhaps also were physiologically and genetically distinctive due to their extreme southerly habitation. After completion of Friant Dam, spring-run fish began to utilize areas below the dam (Clark 1943). Approximately 5,000 spring-run fish were observed by Clark (1943) over-summering in pools below the dam during May-October 1942, where water temperatures had reached 72°F by July. The fish remained in "good condition" through the summer, and large numbers were observed spawning in riffles below the dam during October and November (Clark 1943). A temperature of 80°F has been regarded as the upper thermal limit for San Joaquin River spring-run fish, above which most of them would have died (CDFG 1955 unpubl. document), although much lower temperatures (40-60°F) are necessary for successful incubation of the relatively temperature-sensitive eggs (Seymour 1956, Beacham and Murray 1990).

Merced River (Merced Co.) Both spring- and fall-run salmon historically occurred in the Merced River, although now only the fall run exists and is the most southerly occurring native chinook salmon run (CDFG 1993). According to one gold miner's account, Native Americans were observed harvesting salmon in the spring of 1852 at Merced Falls, where their "rancheria" (village) was located (Collins 1949). Oral history obtained from local residents (Snyder unpubl. memorandum, 9 May 1993) indicates that salmon occurred in the area between Bagby and Briceburg near the branching of the North Fork. There is a 20-ft waterfall below Briceburg (Stanley and Holbek 1984), but it probably was not steep enough to have posed a substantial obstacle to salmon (see below). Another gold miner's journal (Perlot 1985) indicates that salmon were caught in abundance on the mainstem Merced River some unspecified distance above the confluence of the South Fork-- probably approaching the vicinity of El Portal (~2,000 ft elevation). The section of river above El Portal is of high gradient and would have presented a rigorous challenge to migrating fish; thus, it is not clear if substantial numbers of salmon, if any, were able to ascend beyond that point.

There has been disagreement on whether any salmon reached Yosemite Valley. Shebley (1927) stated that in 1892 "steelhead and salmon ascended the Merced River to Wawona [South Fork] and into Yosemite Valley [on the mainstem] as far as the rapids below the Vernal-Nevada Falls", taking advantage of the high spring floods to surmount the low dams that were present in the river at that time. However, Shebley provided no evidence to support his statement, which was later discounted (Snyder 1993 unpubl. memo.). The absence of any clear reference to salmon in the early historical accounts of the Yosemite Valley (e.g., Muir 1902, 1938, 1961, Hutchings 1990), and the present lack of archeological and ethnographic evidence to show that native peoples subsisted on salmon in the higher elevation parts of the drainage (Snyder 1993 unpubl. memo.), seem to argue against the past occurrence of salmon there, at least in significant numbers. Snyder (unpubl. 1993 memo.), noted that there are no references to salmon in the native folklore of the Yosemite region, nor to terms related to the procedures of salmon fishing as there are in the cultural milieu of native inhabitants of the lower elevations. The paucity of suitable spawning gravels in Yosemite Valley (Gerstung, pers. obs.) also would indicate that few, if any, salmon ascended that far, although the presence of "speckled trout" (=rainbow trout, *Oncorhynchus mykiss*) in Yosemite Valley was noted in some early accounts (Caton 1869, Lawrence 1884, Hutchings 1990). Yet, B.B. Redding of the California Fish Commission noted in 1875 that "A few years since, they [salmon] spawned near the Yosemite Valley. A dam built for mining purposes, some four or five years since, prevented them from reaching this spawning-ground" (USFC 1876b). It appears, therefore, that salmon at one time and in unknown numbers had approached the vicinity of Yosemite Valley, even if they did not enter the Valley proper. For the present, the area around El Portal may be the best estimate of the historical upstream limit of salmon distribution in the mainstem Merced River, unless supporting evidence for Shebley's (1927) statement can be found.

Salmon most likely entered the South Fork Merced River at least as far as Peach Tree Bar, ~7 mi above the confluence with the mainstem, where a waterfall presents the first significant obstruction (P. Bartholomew, pers. comm.). Hardheads are limited in their upstream distribution by the waterfall, and Sacramento suckers occur even further upstream to the vicinity of Wawona (Toffoli 1965, P. Bartholomew, pers. comm.). Salmon, which often spawn in the same reaches frequented by those species (Moyle 1976, Gerstung, pers. obs.), undoubtedly reached as least as far as Peach Tree Bar. It is possible that salmon surmounted the waterfall and ranged above Peach Tree Bar, but there is no confirmatory historical information available. If they did so, their upstream limit would have been a 20-ft waterfall located near the entry of Iron Creek, ~4 mi below Wawona (Gerstung, pers. obs.). The North Fork Merced River is a relatively low watershed (~1,300 ft elevation at the lower end), but there are substantial falls located ~1 mi above the mouth (T. Ford, pers. comm.; E. Vestal, CDFG unpubl. notes) which would have prevented further penetration into the drainage by salmon. This evidently was the cascade mentioned by the gold miner J.-N. Perlot which "had at all times been an insurmountable obstacle for the fish", thus accounting for his observations that the North Fork "contained no kind of fish whatsoever, not the least white-bait, not the smallest gudgeon" (Perlot 1985).

As early as 1853, a temporary dam was erected by fishermen ~10 mi below Merced Falls, thereby blocking the salmon from their upstream spawning areas (Collins 1949). In the following decades, a succession of dams was built at Merced Falls and at locations upstream up to the Yosemite National Park boundary-- including the 120-ft high Benton Mills Dam at Bagby (built in 1859) and a later (1900) dam at Kittredge, 4 mi below Bagby (Snyder 1993 unpubl. memo). Those dams had already impeded the upstream migration of salmon by the 1920s, but it was the construction of Exchequer Dam that permanently barred the salmon from their former spawning grounds (CDFG 1921). Clark (1929) stated that the existant spawning beds were on "occasional gravel bars" located between the river mouth and Exchequer Dam, with "about 12 miles" of streambed available. These are in the lower river and therefore pertain to fall-run fish. As of 1928, there were three obstructions to migrating salmon: Crocker Huffman irrigation diversion dam near Snelling; Merced Falls ~3 mi upriver, where there was a natural fall and the 20-ft Merced Falls Dam with a defunct fishway; and Exchequer Dam, 20 mi above Merced Falls. A decade later, Hatton (1940) considered the spawning areas to occur between "a point half a mile downstream from a line due south of Balico" and Exchequer Dam. Of this 42.2-mi stretch, only 24.1 mi was accessible to salmon due to obstructions; there were four beaver dams, passable under "usual water conditions", and four impassable rock dams lacking fishways and allowing only "seepage" to pass downstream. Above these rock dams was the Merced Falls Dam, equipped with a fishway but inaccessible to the salmon because of the downstream obstructions and low water flows. Presently (1995), natural spawning by fall-run fish principally occurs in the stretch above Highway 59 to the Crocker-Huffman diversion dam, the upstream limit of salmon migration (CDFG 1993). The Merced River Hatchery (operated by CDFG) is located by this dam. Fall-run spawners ascending to this point are captured at the dam's fish ladder, for use as hatchery brood stock, or are diverted into the adjacent artificial spawning channel where spawning can also occur.

Clark (1929) had reported both spring and fall runs of salmon present in the Merced River. He mentioned reports by early residents of the river who recalled great runs of migrating upriver to spawn in summer and fall, "so numerous that it looked as if one could walk across the stream on their backs". An early newspaper account (Mariposa Gazette, 26 August 1882) reported "... the water in the Merced river has become so hot that it has caused all the salmon to die. Tons upon tons of dead fish are daily drifting down the river, which is creating a terrible stench, and the like was never known before." Judging from the date, the reference was to spring-run salmon; the fall-run fish would not have entered the tributaries so early, assuming they behaved similarly to the Sacramento River fall run. By 1928, the runs were greatly depleted; several hundred fish were reported in the Merced River in November 1928. According to Clark (1929), very low flow conditions due to irrigation diversions during the spring, summer and early fall had "just about killed off the spring and summer runs" (the "summer" run now considered to be the early portion of the fall run), and only fish arriving in late fall after the rains were able to enter the river. These fish were probably a late-running component of the fall run, rather than a true late-fall run (sensu Fisher 1994) because there was no mention by Clark (1929) of early residents referring to salmon runs in December or later that would have been more characteristic of the late-fall run. Clark also refered to late fall as including November in his account for the Mokelumne River, which is a somewhat earlier run time than is characteristic of most late-fall-run fish. Even in recent years when drought conditions and extensive irrigation diversions had reduced streamflows to very low levels, the salmon did not spawn in the Merced River "until after the first week of November when water temperatures [had] become tolerable" (CDFG 1993).

Fry (1961) considered the Merced River to be "a marginal salmon stream" due to the removal of water by irrigation diversions, and he stated that there was "a poor fall run and poor spring run". Run-size estimates for the fall run were 4,000 fish for 1954 and <500 fish for every other year during the period 1953-1959 (Fry 1961). No numerical estimates were available for the spring run at that time. After 1970, fall-run sizes increased to an annual average of 5,800 fish, reaching 23,000 spawners in 1985, due to increased streamflows released by the Merced Irrigation District and operation of the Merced River Hatchery (CDFG 1993). As in other San Joaquin basin tributaries, spawning escapements in the Merced River have dropped to "seriously low levels" in recent years, numbering less than 200 fish in 1990 and 1991, including returns to the Merced River Hatchery (CDFG 1993, Fisher, unpubl. data). However, the fall run numbered over 1,000 spawners in both 1992 and 1993, and reached almost 5,000 fish in 1994 (Fisher, unpubl. data), perhaps auguring a partial recovery of the stock. The Merced River Hatchery, operated since 1971 by CDFG, has received a major fraction of the spawning run in the Merced River, accounting for 5-39% of the annual runs during the 1980s and 19-67% of the runs in 1990-1994 (Fisher, unpubl. data). Late-fall-run salmon are said to occur occasionally in the Merced River (CDFG 1993). The spring run of this river no longer exists.

Tuolumne River (Stanislaus, Tuolumne counties) At least spring and fall runs originally utilized the Tuolumne River. Clavey Falls (10-15 ft high), at the confluence of the Clavey River, may have obstructed the salmon at certain flows, but spring-run salmon in some numbers undoubtedly ascended the mainstem a considerable distance. The spring-run salmon were most likely stopped by the formidable Preston Falls at the boundary of Yosemite National Park (~50 mi upstream of present New Don Pedro Dam), which is the upstream limit of native fish distribution (CDFG unpubl. data). Sacramento suckers (*Catostomus occidentalis*), riffle sculpins (*Cottus gulosus*) and California roach (*Lavinia symmetricus*) were observed during stream surveys between Early Intake and Preston Falls (CDFG unpubl. data; Moyle, unpubl. data), and spring-run salmon probably occurred throughout that reach as well. If they were present in the Tuolumne drainage, steelhead trout probably ascended several miles into Cherry Creek, a tributary to the mainstem ~1 mi below Early Intake, and perhaps spring-run salmon also entered that stream. Steep sections of stream in the Clavey River and the South and Middle forks of the Tuolumne shortly above their mouths most likely obstructed the salmon (T. Ford, pers. comm.), although squawfish are found within the first mile of the Clavey River and suckers and roach occur up to 10-15 mi upstream (EA Engineering, Science and Technology 1990 unpubl. report). A large (25-30 ft) waterfall in the lower South Fork (Stanley and Holbek 1984) probably prevented further access up that fork. The North Fork, with a 12-ft waterfall ~1 mi above the mouth, likewise offered limited access. Overall, probably few, if any, salmon entered those upper reaches of the Tuolumne drainage (T. Ford, pers. comm.). The waterfalls just below present Hetch Hetchy Dam on the mainstem, ~10 mi above Preston Falls, evidently stopped all fish that might have ascended that far, for John Muir wrote that the river was barren of fish above the falls (Muir 1902). There are no indications that salmon ever reached Hetch Hetchy Valley or Poopenaut Valley further downstream (Snyder 1993 unpubl. memo.). Just as with the Merced River, there is no archeological or ethnographic evidence indicating that salmon were part of the subsistence economics of the native inhabitants of the higher elevations along the upper Tuolumne River (Snyder 1993 unpubl. memo.).

The first written record of salmon in the Tuolumne River is that of the Fremont Expedition of 1845-1846. Fremont's (1848) journal entry for 4 February 1846 reads: "...Salmon was first obtained on the 4th February in the To-wal-um-né river, which, according to the Indians, is the most southerly stream in the valley in which this fish is found." It is not clear whether Fremont's party caught the salmon or obtained them from the local native inhabitants. In any case, it would seem from the wording of the account that the fish were the beginning of a run (i.e., spring run) rather than the continuation of one which for some reason could not be procured earlier by the party. Although the bulk of the spring-run salmon migration occurs during April-June, at least in the Sacramento drainage (Fisher 1994), spring-run fish have occasionally appeared in their spawning streams in early February (e.g., in Butte Creek during 1995, F. Fisher, unpubl. data; they also were observed sometime in February 1946 in the

American River, Gerstung 1971 unpubl. report). The occurrence of salmon in the Tuolumne River in those early years was also noted by John Marsh, who had arrived in California in the mid-1830s. Quoting Marsh, the pioneer Edwin Bryant wrote in his journal, "... the river of the Towalomes; it is about the size of the Stanislaus, which it greatly resembles, ... and it particularly abounds with salmon" (Bryant 1849).

Significant blockage of salmon runs in the Tuolumne River began in the 1870s when various dams and irrigation diversion projects were constructed, although dams and water diversions associated with mining had been present as early as 1852 (Snyder 1993 unpubl. memo.) and undoubtedly had some impact. Wheaton Dam, built in 1871 at the site of present-day La Grange Dam, may have blocked the salmon to some degree (T. Ford, pers. comm.). La Grange Dam, 120 ft high and considered an engineering marvel when completed in 1894, cut off the former spring-run spawning areas. Mining and other activities that degraded the river habitat probably affected the salmon runs, but to an unknown degree. John Muir (1938) recorded in his journal in November, 1877: "Passed the mouth of the Tuolumne... It is not wide but has a rapid current. The waters are brown with mining mud. Above the confluence the San Joaquin is clear..."

Clark (1929) stated that the spawning grounds in 1928 extended from the town of Waterford to La Grange, over 20 mi of "good gravel river". At the time, there were two dams of major significance: La Grange Dam and Don Pedro Dam (built in 1923) 13 mi upriver, which was 300 ft high and formed a large irrigation reservoir (Clark 1929). Hatton (1940) later stated that the spawning beds in the Tuolumne River lay between a point 2.2 mi below the Waterford railroad bridge and the La Grange Power House. As of 1939, the Modesto Weir (a low structure) had no water diversion and was passable to salmon because the flash boards were removed "several weeks in advance of the fall run" (Hatton 1940). The rest of the Tuolumne River was clear of obstructions up to the impassable La Grange Dam. Spawning now (1995) occurs in the ~20-mi stretch from the town of Waterford (rm 31) upstream to La Grange Dam (EA Engineering, Science and Technology 1992). La Grange Dam remains a complete barrier to salmon and thus defines the present upstream limit of their spawning distribution (CDFG 1993). The total area of spawning gravel presently considered available to salmon in the lower Tuolumne River (below La Grange Dam) is 2.9 million sq ft (EA Engineering, Science and Technology 1992).

The California Fish Commission (CFC 1886) noted that the Tuolumne River "at one time was one of the best salmon streams in the State", but that salmon had not ascended that stream "for some years." At the time of Clark's (1929) writing, salmon generally still were "scarce" in the Tuolumne River. As of 1928, both spring and fall runs still occurred, but the spring run was inconsequential, "amounting almost to nothing" (Clark 1929). Clark reported, however, "a good run" (evidently the fall run) for 1925 that surpassed any of the runs seen in the several years prior to that. Presently, only the fall run exists in appreciable numbers in the Tuolumne River. In the past, fall-run sizes in the Tuolumne River during some years were larger than in any other Central Valley streams except for the mainstem Sacramento River, reaching as high as 122,000 spawners in 1940 and 130,000 in 1944 (Fry 1961). Tuolumne River fall-run fish historically have comprised up to 12% of the total fall-run spawning escapement for the Central Valley (CDFG 1993). The average population estimate for the period 1971-1988 was 8,700 spawners (EA Engineering, Science and Technology 1991), but run sizes in most recent years have been extremely low-- fewer than 130 spawners in each of the years 1990-1992 and <500 fish in both 1993 and 1994 (Fisher, unpubl. data).

It has been stated that "a small population" of late-fall-run fish exists in the Tuolumne River (CDFG 1993), but the existence of such a run appears to be based mainly on the occurrence of juveniles in the river during the summer and on observations of occasional spawning in later months (January-March) than is typical for fall-run fish (T. Ford, pers. comm.). However, hydrological conditions in the Tuolumne River during the past few decades have not been conducive to the maintenance of a late-fall run-- notably the lack of consistent, cool flows during the summer to support the juveniles (CDFG 1993).

It is possible that the infrequent observations of fish with late-fall-run timing characteristics have been strays from the Sacramento River system and their progeny. Late-emerging or slow-growing fry belonging to fall-run fish, perhaps of hatchery origin, could also account for some of the juveniles that have been observed over-summering in the river.

Stanislaus River (Stanislaus, Calaveras counties). Both spring and fall runs originally occurred in the Stanislaus River. Salmon are known to have occurred in the vicinity of Duck Bar, 4.5 mi below the town of Stanislaus, which is now covered by the upper end of New Melones Reservoir. A long-time Native American resident named Indian Walker caught them there in fish traps to sell to the white community (Cassidy et al. 1981). Beals' (1933) ethnographic account states that salmon went up the Stanislaus River as far as Baker's Bridge-- the location of which is unknown to us but very likely it was innundated by New Melones Reservoir. A more recent account (Maniery 1983) reports that Miwok residents of "Murphy's Rancheria", a village near the town of Murphy that was occupied ca. 1870-1920, caught salmon at Burns Ferry Bridge ("below the old road to Copperopolis") and at Camp Nine (~ 13 mi upstream of the town of Melones). Spring-run and perhaps some fall-run salmon probably went up the forks considerable distances because there are few natural obstacles (B. Loudermilk, pers. comm.). In the North Fork, suckers and hardhead occurred up to the confluence of Griswold Creek (Northern California Power Authority 1993 unpubl. report), so salmon may have ascended at least to that point. The North Fork Stanislaus River is accessible to salmon up to McKay's Point (~ 8 mi above the confluence with the Middle Fork), where the gradient steepens. Any salmon passing that point most likely were blocked 5 mi further upstream by a 15-ft waterfall, above Board's Crossing. Similarly, there are no substantial obstacles on the Middle Fork up to the reach above the present site of Beardsley Reservoir (3,400 ft elev.) (E. Vestal, pers. comm.), although the steep gradient may have deterred most salmon. The South Fork is a small drainage and is unlikely to have supported more than a few, if any, salmon because of the paucity of habitat. We have seen no suggestions of salmon having occurred in the South Fork Stanislaus River, and for the present we do not include it as a former salmon stream.

Damming and diversion of water on the Stanislaus River, for both mining and irrigation, began soon after the Gold Rush. The earliest "permanent" dam on the river was the original Tulloch Dam, constructed in 1858 just downstream of the present Tulloch Dam (Tudor-Goodenough Engineers 1959). The original Tulloch Dam was a relatively low structure and evidently had an opening at one end (Tudor-Goodenough Engineers 1959), and its impact on the salmon runs, therefore, may not necessarily have been significant. Clark (1929) stated that the salmon spawning beds were located in over 10 mi of stream, from the marshlands above Oakdale to Knight's Ferry. Dams on the river by that time included 20-ft Goodwin Dam (completed in 1913) 18 mi above Oakdale, which had a fishway and was at times negotiable to salmon, and the 210-ft, impassable Melones Dam (completed in 1926), above the town of Melones. The spawning beds in 1939 were reported by Hatton (1940) to extend from Riverbank Bridge to the Malone Power House, although of this 32.7-mi distance, the 9.3 mi between Goodwin Dam and the Power House was "only rarely accessible to salmon". Hatton stated that the fishway over Goodwin Dam was "seldom passable" and that the fluctuating water level caused by hydroelectric operations above Goodwin Dam and the "almost complete diversion of water at the dam" made it "very nearly an impassable barrier". Fry (1961) also mentioned the blockage of migration by Goodwin Dam, the operation of which also caused low and warm flows downstream during the summer and "violent" water fluctuations (due to power-generation releases) during the fall and winter. Presently, the salmon do not ascend the Stanislaus River further than Goodwin Dam, which regulates streamflows from Tulloch Reservoir and diverts water for irrigation and power generation (CDFG 1993). Much of the spawning occurs on the extensive gravel beds in the 23-mi stretch from Riverbank upstream to Knights Ferry, which are essentially on the Valley floor (T. Ford, pers. comm.). Upstream of Knights Ferry, where the river flows throgh a canyon, spawning is concentrated at Two-mile Bar (~ 1 mi above Knights Ferry) but also occurs in scattered pockets of gravel (T. Ford, pers. comm.).

The California Fish Commission (1886) state that while the Stanislaus River in the past had been among the best salmon streams in the state, only occasionally was a salmon seen "trying to get over one of its numerous dams." Much later, Clark (1929) reported that the Stanislaus River "has a good spring and fall run of salmon", but he also stated that their abundance was "about the same as in the Tuolumne" where he had described them to be "scarce". Given these contradictory statements, it is not clear how abundant, even qualitatively, the salmon were in the Stanislaus at the time of Clark's survey (late-1920s). Historically, the spring run was the primary salmon run in the Stanislaus River, but after the construction of dams which regulated the streamflows (i.e., Goodwin Dam and, later, Melones and Tulloch dams), the fall run became predominant (CDFG 1972 unpubl. report). Fry (1961) described the Stanislaus River as "a good fall run stream for its size" but it had "almost no remaining spring run". Run-size estimates were 4,000-35,000 and averaged ~11,100 fall-run fish for the 1946-1959 period preceeding the construction of Tulloch Dam (in 1959); in the following 12-year period (1960-1971), the average run size was ~6,000 fish (Fry 1961, CDFG 1972 unpubl. report). Fall-run sizes since 1970 have ranged up to 13,621 (average ~3,600) spawners annually (Fisher, unpubl. data). The Stanislaus River fall run historically has contributed up to 7% of the total salmon spawning escapement in the Central Valley (CDFG 1993). Numbers of fall-run spawners returning to the Stanislaus River in recent years have been very low-- <500 fish annually during the period 1990-1993 and 800 fish in 1994 (Fisher, unpubl. data).

Presently (1995) there is essentially only the fall run, although small numbers of late-fall-run fish are said to occur (CDFG 1993). A lesser run in the winter (most likely late-fall run fish) reportedly occurred in the Stanislaus River in earlier times (CDFG 1972 unpubl. report). One gold miner's account mentions a salmon, "which must have weighed twenty-five pounds", caught in the Stanislaus River during December 1849 (the exact date unknown, but suggested to have been just after December 19) (Morgan 1970)-- a run time consistent with the peak migration period of the late-fall run, but also with the end of the fall run (Fisher 1994). As in the Tuolumne River, the occurrence of late-fall-run salmon in recent years could be due to strays moving in from the Sacramento River system.

Calaveras River (Calaveras Co.) The Calaveras River is a relatively small, low elevation drainage that receives runoff mainly from rainfall during November-April (CDFG 1993). This river was probably always marginal for salmon, and it lacks suitable habitat for spring-run fish (E. Gerstung, pers. obs.). Chinook salmon runs were known to have occurred on an "irregular basis" (CDFG 1993), although Clark (1929) reported that the Calaveras River was "dry most of the summer and fall" and so had no salmon. There was until recently an unusual salmon run in winter which spawned in late-winter and spring, but it is unknown if that run existed before the dams were built on the river. The presence of this "winter run" was documented for 6 years in the period 1972-1984 and it numbered 100-1,000 fish annually (CDFG 1993). The fish ascended to New Hogan Dam, and they held and spawned in the reach just below the dam (T. Ford, pers. comm.). Management of streamflows by the U.S. Army Corps of Engineers entailed high-flow releases from New Hogan Dam interspersed with periods of very low flow, which undoubtedly contributed to the apparent demise of this run (T. Ford, pers. comm.). Bellota Dam, 15 mi below New Hogan Dam, and at least two other diversion dams are known to have blocked upstream salmon migration during periods of low streamflow (CDFG 1993). The run's extirpation may also have been hastened, if not guaranteed, by persistently low streamflows due to the 1987-1992 drought and to irrigation diversions. It may be that the existence of salmon in this river during recent decades has been mainly the result of suitable conditions created by the dams, and perhaps their natural historical occurrence there was limited to exceptionally wet years. Fall-run salmon-- perhaps those destined for other San Joaquin River tributaries-- occasionally enter the Calaveras River when suitable fall streamflows occur. For example, several hundred fall-run fish were observed during the fall of 1995 at Bellota Dam, where they were temporarily blocked (CDFG unpubl. data).

Mokelumne River (San Joaquin, Amador counties) The Mokelumne River, in its original state, apparently supported at least fall and spring salmon runs. Some evidence suggests that a late-fall run also occurred at one time. In what is probably the earliest record of salmon in the Mokelumne River, the fur trapper Jedediah Smith, having encamped on "Rock River" (Mokelumne River), wrote in his journal for 22 January 1828: "Several indians came to camp and I gave them some tobacco. They brought with them some fine salmon some of which would weigh 15 or 20 lbs. I bought three of them and one of the men killed a deer..." (Sullivan 1934). The salmon that would have been present during that part of January in "fine" condition most likely were late-fall run or perhaps spring-run, although the timing seems extraordinarily early for the latter. Smith's party evidently was on the lower Mokelumne River on the marshy Valley floor, for "...although the ground was rolling the horses sank at every step nearly to the nees [sic]" (Sullivan 1934). Two decades later, the 49ner Alfred Doten similarly recorded (for 22 December 1851): "Saw three fine salmon, which were brought from the Moqueleme-- they averaged about 20 lbs a piece" (Clark 1973). That date is consistent with the peak migration time of the late-fall run, and although late stragglers of the fall run cannot be completely discounted, it is somewhat more likely that late-fall run fish would have been present in a physical condition that could be described as "fine".

Salmon ascended the river at least as far as the vicinity of present-day Pardee Dam (completed in 1928). Reportedly, a large waterfall (30+ ft high) was present at Arkansas Ferry Crossing, 1 mi downstream of the Pardee Dam site in a narrow rocky gorge (R. Nuzum, pers. comm.), and it may have posed a serious, if not complete, barrier to the fall run. The site of the waterfall was inundated by Camanche Reservoir, and no natural obstructions presently exist between Camanche Reservoir and Pardee Dam (S. Boyd, pers. comm.). Spring-run salmon undoubtedly would have ascended past that point in order to reach higher elevations where water temperatures were suitable for over summering. Steelhead were believed to have spawned mostly in the reaches above Pardee Dam (Dunham 1961 unpubl.). Because there are no impassable falls between Pardee and the Electra powerhouse 12 mi upstream, spring-run salmon undoubtedly also reached the latter point. Bald Rock Falls (30 ft high), 7 mi beyond Electra, is a complete fish barrier (Woodhull 1946); native fish such as hardhead and squawfish are known to have reached it (Woodhull 1946), so the falls can be reasonably taken as a likely upstream limit for salmon and steelhead as well.

However much the salmon runs had recovered from the habitat degradation of the gold mining era, the runs were believed to have started another decline after Woodbridge Dam (15 ft high) was constructed in 1910 at the town of Woodbridge (Dunham 1961 unpubl. report). Fry (1961) cited Woodbridge Dam as having been "a serious fish block" for many years, as well as providing "often too little water for the passage of salmon", and he mentioned industrial and mining pollution as having been "very serious" at times. As of 1928 the salmon spawning grounds extended from the river mouth above tidewater for ~15 mi to above Woodbridge Dam (Clark 1929). There was a small fishway at this dam which had very little water flowing down it during summer and fall (Clark 1929). Clark reported that only a fall run occurred, "usually quite late". He stated that a "considerable run" migrated upriver each year, although not as large as in former years, and that the flashboards in Woodbridge Dam were taken out in late fall (November) to allow passage of the salmon. Although this is possibly an indication of a late-fall run, it seems more likely that the fish for the most part were a late-running fall run, delayed by the lack of water. The true late-fall run, as currently recognized (Fisher 1994), probably would not have been present in the Mokelumne River or other tributaries in significant numbers until December at the earliest. However, the earliest historical references to salmon (noted above) seem to indicate that late-fall run salmon actually occurred in the Mokelumne River at least until the mid-19th century.

The construction of Pardee Dam in 1928 presented an insurmountable obstacle, cutting off the upper spawning areas (Dunham 1961 unpubl. report). Hatton (1940) stated that spawning beds on the

Mokelumne River occurred in the 22.5 mi between Lockeford Bridge and Pardee Dam. At that time (1939), the irrigation dam at Woodbridge had a fishway but was impassable at times due to "fluctuating water levels", and Hatton was of the opinion that probably most of the migrating spawners did not ascend to the spawning beds until the dam's weir boards were removed, usually "around the first week in November".

Fall-run salmon are now stopped at the lower end of Camanche Reservoir, ~ 10 mi below Pardee Dam. They spawn in the reach from Camanche Dam downstream to Elliott Road (J. Nelson, pers. comm.), and 95% of the suitable spawning habitat is within 3.5 mi of Camanche Dam (CDFG 1993). Prior to the completion of Camanche Reservoir (1964), the fall run also spawned upstream from Camanche Dam up to the canyon ~3 mi below Pardee Dam (CDFG 1993). The Mokelumne River Hatchery, operated by CDFG, was built in 1965 as mitigation specifically for that spawning stock component (CDFG 1993; J. Nelson, pers. comm.).

Fry (1961) reported that counts of fall-run spawners passing Woodbridge Dam ranged from < 500 (in two separate years) to 7,000 fish during the period 1945-1958, and there were partial counts of 12,000 fish each in 1941 and 1942. Fry also stated that the spring run appeared to be "practically extinct". Over the period 1940-1990, total annual run sizes ranged between 100-15,900 fish (CDFG 1993); the runs averaged 3,300 spawners during 1940-1963 (prior to impoundment of Camanche Reservoir) and 3,200 spawners during 1964-1990 (post-impoundment) (CDFG 1993). The most recent annual run-size estimates for the fall run have been 367-3,223 (average ~ 1,760) total spawners during 1990-1994, with hatchery returns composing 16-69% of the run; the number of natural spawners during this period ranged from 182 fish (in 1991) to 1,305 (in 1994) and averaged 756 fish (Fisher, unpubl. data).

Cosumnes River (El Dorado Co.) The Cosumnes River, a branch of the Mokelumne River, historically has been an intermittent stream and from earliest times offered limited access to salmon. Yet, the river derives its name from the Cosumne tribe of the Valley Yokuts-- the "People of the Salmon Place" in the language of the neighboring Miwok people (Latta 1977). Only a fall run is definitely known to have occurred in this river. There is no indication that a spring run ever existed here (J. Nelson, pers. comm.) and the atypical streamflow regime and low elevation of the drainage make it unlikely that there was one. There is a 30-ft falls a half mile below Latrobe Highway Bridge which has been viewed as a barrier, although the salmon probably did not usually reach that far upriver. If any fish were able to surmount that obstacle, they would have been stopped by a second waterfall (50 ft high) at the Highway 49 crossing 8.5 mi further upstream. Because of the limited time available for migration into this stream, it is likely that few fish ascended past Michigan bar (rm 31).

Clark (1929) reported the presence of "a considerable run" (fall run) which he stated to be equal in abundance to that in the Mokelumne River. At that time the spawning grounds extended from the river mouth above tidewater to the irrigation diversion dam near the town of Sloughhouse, which was a barrier to the salmon. In 1939, the spawning grounds on the Cosumnes River extended along the 15.2 mi stretch from Sloughhouse Bridge up to the falls below Latrobe Highway Bridge (Hatton 1940). Hatton (1940) reported that the best spawning areas were between the Sloughhouse and Bridgehouse bridges; just above Bridgehouse the river passed through a canyon where bedrock largely replaced the gravel beds. At that time (1939), the 18-ft high Bridgehouse Dam was the only permanent dam on the river, having two "apparently satisfactory fishways" but an unscreened diversion. The lower end of the stream was dry during the months when irrigation diversions were taken, but in late fall "a run of undetermined size" took place (Hatton 1940). The fall run presently spawns in the reach from downstream of the Highway 16 crossing (Bridgehouse Bridge) up to the falls below Latrobe Road (J. Nelson, pers. comm.). Additional spawning habitat occurs downstream of the Highway 16 crossing to Sloughhouse Bridge, but below that point the substrate is largely sand and unsuitable for spawning (Gerstung, per. obs.). The sole dam in the river-- Granlees Diversion Dam (located 1 mi upstream of the Highway 16 crossing)--

presently may pose an obstacle to salmon migration because its fish ladders are sometimes inoperative. The salmon generally cannot ascend the river until late-October to November, when adequate flows from rainfall occur (CDFG 1993).

Fry (1961) reported run-size estimates for the fall run of <500 to 5,000 fish for the period 1953-1959. Historically, the run size has averaged ~1,000 fish, but recent runs have numbered no more than 100 individuals (CDFG 1993), when there was water in the streambed. In many years there has been insufficient streamflow to maintain connection with the San Joaquin River. No salmon have been observed in the Cosumnes River for at least the last four spawning seasons (1991-1994) (Fisher, unpubl. data).

American River (Sacramento, Placer counties) Spring, fall and posssibly late-fall runs of salmon ascended the American River and its branches and were blocked to varying degrees by a number of natural obstacles, at least one which no longer exists. In the North Fork, steelhead trout were observed during CDFG surveys in the 1930s at Humbug Bar, above where the North Fork of the North Fork enters (CDFG unpubl. data); because there are no substantial falls below that point, spring-run salmon no doubt also easily ascended that far. Mumford Bar, ~7 mi above Humbug Bar, was one of several salmon fishing spots for the native Nisenan people, at which "salmon [were] taken with bare hands during heavy runs" (Beals 1933). If the salmon, like steelhead trout, were able to surmount the waterfall at Mumford Bar, they would have had clear passage ~4 mi further upstream to a 10-ft waterfall at Tadpole Creek (2,800 ft elevation), which is too steep for kayakers to boat over (Stanley and Holbek 1984). If salmon were able to jump that waterfall, their upper limit would have been another 7 mi upstream at the 60-ft falls at Royal Gorge (4,000 ft elev.), which likely was the uppermost barrier to steelhead (CDFG unpubl. data). That uppermost limit would accord with Beals' (1933) statement that salmon reportedly ranged above the elevational limit of permanent habitation (~4,000 ft) of the Nisenan people of the area. On the Middle Fork American River, falls that had existed before the gold-mining era at Murderer's Bar, ~3 mi above the confluence with the North Fork, obstructed the salmon at least to some degree (Angel 1882). During spawning time, the salmon "would accumulate so thickly in a large pool just below, that they were taken in great numbers by merely attaching large iron hooks to a pole, running it down in the water, and suddenly jerking it up through the mass". That scene was not exceptional, for the "Salmon at that time ran up all the streams as far as they could get until some perpendicular barrier which they could not leap prevented further progress", and "During these times, the Indians supplied themselves with fish, which they dried in the sun" (Angel 1882). It is likely that the dense aggregations of salmon harvested by the native people below the natural obstacles were fall-run fish, impeded by the low fall-season streamflows. The spring run, ascending during the spring flood flows, presumably would have been able to transcend some of those same obstacles. Spring-run salmon probably were able to ascend the Middle Fork a fair distance due to the absence of natural barriers above Murderer's Bar. In 1938, the spawning area for salmon was reported to extend up the Middle Fork to below the mouth of Volcano Creek (1,300 ft elev.) (Sumner and Smith 1940); salmon likely reached the confluence with the Rubicon River (1,640 ft elev.), which we presently take as the historical upstream limit. Steelhead were observed in the Rubicon River during the early CDFG surveys, but a 15-ft waterfall ~4-5 mi upstream from the mouth was a likely barrier to them and to any salmon that ascended that far.

In the South Fork American River, a major part of the salmon runs went at least as far as Salmon Falls, below which they concentrated; large numbers were harvested there by gold miners and Native Americans in 1850 and 1851 (CFC 1875). As recounted by Special Indian Agent E.A. Stevenson (31 December 1853 letter to Superintendant of Indian Affairs T.J. Henley; in Heizer 1993), "I saw them at Salmon Falls on the American river in the year 1851, and also the Indians taking barrels of these beautiful fish and drying them for winter." The site of Salmon Falls is now covered by Folsom Reservoir, and there has been disagreement on whether the 20-ft falls originally were a complete barrier to migrating salmon. It seems likely that it was the fall run-- egg-laden and migrating during low streamflows-- that would have been largely blocked, especially before the major fall rains had swelled the streams. But even the fall run may not have been completely barred by the falls-- their dense concentration there and at other places perhaps being bottlenecks where some fraction of the run rested or was stalled until streamflows increased before ascending further. Salmon Falls was blasted sometime near the turn of the century, by one account to create passage for log drives down the river (CDFG unpubl. notes) and by another to allow the salmon to go further upstream, but the latter attempt was said to have ended in failure (Cassidy et al. 1981). The California Fish Commission report for 1888-1890 (CFC 1890) mentions "the removal of obstructions at Salmon Falls, in the American River". The falls were also later blasted in 1935 by the California Division of Fish and Game "to make them more passable for steelhead trout and salmon" (CDFG unpubl. notes). However, there is evidence that salmon did in fact ascend the South Fork past Salmon Falls in earlier times, prior to the attempts to modify the falls. Henry W. Bigler, one of the Mormon workmen at Sutter's Sawmill at Coloma during the fateful winter of 1847-1848, wrote in his diary, "Our grub was mainly unbolted flour, pork, mutton, salmon, peas, tea, coffee and sugar" (Gudde 1962). Based on a review of that and other documents, Gay (1967) added: "Beef and beans also formed part of the diet. ...the pork, mutton and beef was freshly killed on the spot; while the river rewarded anyone who had piscatorial inclinations with a nice catch of salmon." A gold miner's account (Steele 1901) states: "In the latter part of August [1852] a band of forty or fifty Indians camped on the opposite bank of the river, spending about two weeks mining and fishing... Here, with long spears, they caught many fine salmon". The location was "Texas Bar on the south fork of the American River", one-half mile upstream of Chili Bar and "about two miles from Placerville" (Steele 1901). Also, Voegelin (1942) reported the following ethnographic information given in 1936 by a 65-year old Nisenan informant who had lived all her life in the vicinity of Camino (~ 5 mi east of Placerville and due south of present Slab Creek Reservoir on the South Fork): "Salmon obtainable within area, in American River. No salmon caught until certain time in summer; first fish cooked, divided and eaten by all members of community, for 'good luck'." The implication is that the fish were spring-run, becoming obtainable as streamflows dropped during the summer, and also that there was an annual first salmon ceremony-- indicating that a regular run of salmon went up the South Fork American River. Furthermore, Beals (1933), based upon his ethnographic survey of elder Nisenan informants in 1929 reported that salmon "Ascended S. fork American r. to Strawberry near summit." However, we view Beals' statement broadly-- i.e., that salmon went up to the general area approaching the present town of Strawberry-- because it is less specific than other ethnographic references to salmon that we have included. There is a 30-ft waterfall, with an incline of 45° (Gerstung, pers. obs.) at Eagle Rock, ~ 12 mi downstream of Strawberry, which kayakers portage around (Stanley and Holbek 1984). There are also several steep stretches above Eagle Rock up to Strawberry, and very little suitable habitat (pools and gravel beds), so salmon probably did not ascend past Eagle Rock in significant numbers, if at all. The vicinity of Eagle Rock (4,600 ft elev.), therefore, most likely was the approximate upper limit for salmon in the South Fork.

Hydraulic mining during the 1850-1885 period caused the deposition of large quantities of sediments into the American River, as was true for many other Sierra streams. By one estimate, ~ 257 million cubic yards of gravel, silt and debris from mining operations were washed into the American River (Sumner and Smith 1940, citing Gilbert 1917). Again quoting Indian Agent Stevenson (31 December 1853 letter, in Heizer 1993): "The rivers or tributaries of the Sacramento formerly were clear as crystal and abounded with the finest salmon and other fish. ... But the miners have turned the streams from their beds and conveyed the water to the dry diggings and after being used until it is so thick with mud that it will scarcely run it returns to its natural channel and with it the soil from a thousand hills, which has driven almost every kind of fish to seek new places of resort where they can enjoy a purer and more natural element." According to one gold miner's account, in the summer of 1851 "Salmon were then caught in the river" at Horseshoe Bar on the North Fork American River, ~7 mi above the confluence with the South Fork, "and fried salmon was no uncommon dish" (Morgan 1970). By 1860 a sand bar had formed across the mouth of the American River on the Sacramento River (CDFG 1993). The silting over of the spawning beds in the mainstem and forks due to mining activities nearly exterminated the salmon runs in the American River (Gerstung 1989). Stone (1874) wrote, "The American Fork was formerly a prolific salmon river, but the mining operations on its banks have rendered it so muddy that the salmon have abandoned it altogether, and none ascend it now." Similarly, the California Fish Commission (1886) wrote: "The American is a shallow, muddy stream... But few fish are found in the lower part of the stream. ... This river, prior to placer mining, was one of the best salmon streams in the State. Of late years no salmon have ascended it."

Somewhat later, the construction of dams that lacked adequate fish passage facilities caused the further diminishment of the runs (Gerstung 1989). The 68-ft high Old Folsom Dam (completed in 1895), 27 mi upstream from the mouth, initially was an impassable barrier to salmon and blocked them from reaching the forks of the American River for about 36 years (Sumner and Smith 1940). A fish ladder was built for Old Folsom Dam in 1919, but Clark (1929) stated that salmon were never known to have passed above it, although steelhead probably did; an effective fish ladder for salmon was later constructed in 1931 (Sumner and Smith 1940). Another potential barrier to salmon was a 16-ft high dam built in 1899 by the North Fork Ditch Company on the North Fork American River near Auburn, a few miles downstream of the confluence with the Middle Fork; a rock chute fishway was provided in 1912, but it allowed difficult passage and few salmon used it (Sumner and Smith 1940). The 140-ft high North Fork Debris Dam (completed in 1939), 2 mi above the confluence with the Middle Fork, posed yet another impassable barrier and assured the extirpation of the salmon run in the North Fork (Sumner and Smith 1940).

Clark (1929) stated that the run of salmon in the American River had "always been a late-fall migration", although he provided no further details, and he also noted that this river "[had] known great runs". An early gold miner noted salmon migrating up the American River ~7 mi east of Sutter's Fort on 1 December 1848, of which "thirty-five splendid salmon" were procured by "well-directed rifle-ball" (Buffum 1959). Early December coincides with the upriver migration periods of both fall and late-fall runs; however, it is appreciably later than the peak migration presently observed for the Sacramento Valley fall run (September-October) but within the peak migration period for the late-fall run (December) (Fisher 1994). The implication seems to be that a late-fall run occurred in the American River, posssibly in substantial numbers. However, it is more likely that the run was a fall run that had a relatively late or extended migration season, combined perhaps with some unknown numbers of true late-fall-run fish. The spring run is known to have entered the American River as early as February, as occurred in 1946 (Gerstung 1971 unpubl. report).

Clark (1929) described the 1927-1928 salmon run as "very good" and noted that residents on the river had seen no noticeable decrease in the run size over the previous 20 years, although the run reportedly had been devastated by early mining operations. Spawning occurred from the river mouth to Old Folsom Dam ~1 mi above the town of Folsom, "a distance of 30 mi of good gravel river." In the 1940s, both the spring and fall runs began to re-establish themselves in the American River above Old Folsom Dam. Counts at the fishway at Old Folsom Dam showed that the spring run reached a maximum of 1,138 fish in 1944 and the fall run reached 2,246 fish in 1945 (Gerstung 1971 unpubl. report). The spring-run count dropped to 42 fish in 1945, 16 in 1946, and 3 fish in 1947; both the spring and fall runs reportedly were decimated after the fish ladder on Old Folsom Dam was destroyed by flood waters in 1950 (Gerstung 1971 unpubl. report). The spring run was finally extirpated during the period of construction of present-day Folsom Dam and Nimbus Dam (the latter completed in 1955) (Gerstung 1971 unpubl. report).

Fry (1961) noted the presence, at least through 1951, of "a small spring run" which became mixed with the "much larger fall run" during spawning. Total run sizes were 6,000-39,000 spawners annually during the period 1944-1959; these comprised mainly the fall run but included "a small but unknown proportion of spring run fish" in the years when the total counts exceeded 30,000 (Fry 1961). During 1944-1955, an estimated average of 26,500 salmon (range 12,000-38,652) spawned annually in the mainstem American River below the town of Folsom; ~73% of the spawners utilized the 5-mi stretch between Old Folsom Dam and the present site of Nimbus Dam, and the remainder spawned further downstream (Gerstung 1971 unpubl. report). In recent decades, spawning escapements of the fall run have ranged from 30,000 to 90,000 annually (Gerstung 1989); spawning escapements averaged 43,200 fish during 1980-1989 and 23,350 fish during 1990-1994 (range ~10,600-36,200 fish in the latter period) (Fisher, unpubl. data). The fall run formerly spawned not only above the site of Nimbus Dam but above Folsom Dam as well (J. Nelson, pers. comm.). Fall-run salmon presently are limited in their upstream migration by Nimbus Dam and spawn mainly downstream from the dam to just above the Watt Avenue crossing (J. Nelson, pers. comm.); the habitat downstream of Watt Avenue presently consists mainly of pools unsuitable for spawning (Gerstung, pers. obs.).

Bear River (Placer Co.) The Bear River, the second largest tributary to the Feather River, formerly contained salmon, but evidently only a fall run. The run reportedly was "substantial" (CDFG 1993) but has not occurred in its former numbers for decades (J. Nelson, pers. comm.) They ascended as far as present day Camp Far West Reservoir, where a waterfall in that vicinity probably barred their further passage. No waterfall exists there now, so it evidently was submerged or built upon during the construction of Camp Far West Reservoir and Dam (J. Hiskox, pers. comm.). There are no natural barriers above Camp Far West Reservoir at least to Rollins Reservoir 24 mi upstream, next to present-day Chicago Park (J. Hiskox, pers. comm.). According to one native Nisenan informant who had resided most of her life around Chicago Park, there were no salmon in that area (Voegelin 1942), so the salmon evidently were completely blocked by the waterfall near Camp Far West.

Clark (1929) stated that the Bear River "has never been known to be a salmon stream", with only an occasional salmon observed there. Clark reported the presence of an impassable dam near the town of Lincoln (which is not on the river but lies ~9 mi south of Camp Far West Reservoir). As with other Sierra streams, hydraulic mining activities caused substantial sedimentation problems in the Bear River such that by 1876 its channel had become completely filled (CDFG 1993). According to early historians, "Near Wheatland the river has altered its course for several miles, making a new channel half a mile south of the old bed. The banks of this stream were once twenty-five to thirty feet high. Its channel has been filled up, and the water is so thick and heavy with sediment that in summer there is scarcely any stream at all. From 1866 to 1869, the stream almost ceased to run except on Sundays, the water on other days being used by the miners" (Chamberlain and Wells 1879). The impact on the salmon runs extant at that time would have been catastrophic, and undoubtedly accounts for the apparent historical scarcity of salmon prior to Clark's (1929) assessment. Indeed, it was written: "Bear, Yuba and Feather rivers were full of salmon, and the Indians speared them by the hundred in the clear water. When the river began to be muddy, the fish became scarce. The Indians even then speared them, and although unable to see the fish, they could tell their position with unerring precision by the ripples made in their passage through the water" (Chamberlain and Wells 1879). The change in the Bear River was so profound that the California Fish Commission would later write, "Bear has lost all claim to the name of river. ... It never was noted as a fish stream, although a few salmon and perch were taken from its waters in early days" (CFC 1886).

Presently, the fall run occurs only occasionally, when heavy rains and dam spillage provide adquate flows (CDFG 1993). At those times, the run may number in the "hundreds" (CDFG 1993). The spawning distribution has its upper limit at the South Sutter Irrigation District (SSID) diversion dam, 15 mi above the confluence with the Feather River and 0.5 mi below Camp Far West Reservoir. The spawning areas extend from the SSID dam downstream ~6 mi to a point near Highway 65, although there are additional spawning gravels extending 4-5 mi further downstream to Pleasant Grove Road (J. Nelson, pers. comm.). There is no suitable upstream holding habitat for spring-run salmon in the Bear River (J. Nelson, pers. comm.).

Yuba River (Yuba Co.) Both spring and fall runs originally occurred in the Yuba River. In the North Fork Yuba River, salmon were caught by PG&E workers in the Bullards Bar area during the 1898-1911 period of operation of the Yuba Powerhouse Project; the ditch tenders at the diversion dam "would nail two or three salmon on boards, place them body down in the ice-cold ditch stream, and ten hours later the night's dinner would come floating down" to the powerhouse on the Valley floor (Coleman 1952). In later years, the salmon ascended in "considerable numbers" up to Bullards Bar Dam during its period of construction (1921-1924)-- "so many salmon congregated and died below it that they had to be burned" (Sumner and Smith 1940). There are no natural barriers above the Bullards Bar Dam site, so salmon presumably had been able to ascend a considerable distance up the North Fork. There is photographic evidence of steelhead (also called "salmon-trout" in early writings) occurring further upstream at Downieville at the mouth of the Downie River (CDFG file records). In their historical account of Sierra County, Fariss and Smith (1882) related the following episode: "While encamped on Jersey flat Jim Crow one day killed with a small crow bar a salmon-trout which weighed fourteen pounds. It was boiled in the camp kettle... afterwards gold was found in the bottom of the kettle." Jersey Flat (formerly Murraysville) was located across the river from Downieville (Fariss and Smith 1882). The California Fish Commission (CFC 1875) stated that in 1850 and 1851, "large quantities [of salmon] were taken by the miners and by Indians ... as far up as Downieville on the Yuba", as well as at other points on the American and Feather rivers. There are no natural obstructions from Downieville upstream to Sierra City, where Salmon Creek enters, so steelhead and spring-run salmon most likely were able to traverse that stretch as well. The steelhead probably ascended the higher gradient reaches further up and their absolute upstream limit would have been Love Falls, but salmon most likely did not reach as far. Except for a 10-ft falls in the lower reach of the Middle Fork Yuba River, there are no significant natural obstructions and salmon therefore may have had access to a considerable portion of the Middle Fork. Both salmon and steelhead were observed in the lower part of the Middle Fork, near where the North Fork joins, during a CDFG survey in 1938 (CDFG unpubl. data). Steelhead were found as far upstream as the mouth of Bloody Run Creek near Moores Flat (CDFG unpubl. data). Whether salmon also were able to ascend that far remains conjectural because direct information on their distribution is lacking and it is uncertain if many of them were able to surmount the 10-ft falls on the lower river. Similarly, little is known of the original distribution of salmon in the South Fork Yuba River-- the salmon population was severely depressed and access up the stream long since obstructed by dams by the time the CDFG surveys were conducted in the 1930s. There are records of salmon occurring within 1-2 mi upstream of the mouth of the South Fork Yuba River (CDFG unpubl. data). A substantial cascade with at least a 12-ft drop, located 0.5 mi below the juncture of Humbug Creek (California Resources Agency 1972, Stanley and Holbek 1984), may have posed a significant obstruction to salmon migration, but it was not necessarily a complete barrier. This cascade, or "step-falls", is similar in dimensions and comformation to cascades on other streams which salmon are known to have surmounted (P. Lickwar, pers. comm.). Steelhead are known to have ascended further up the South Fork as far as the juncture of Poorman Creek near the present town of Washington (CDFG unpubl. data), and perhaps spring-run salmon historically also reached that point. Among the tributary streams of the lower Yuba River, salmon and steelhead were observed to ascend Dry Creek at least 5-6 mi in past decades (e.g., in the 1960s; Gerstung, pers. obs.), and they occasionally still do when streamflows are high. Steelhead also went up Deer Creek a quarter of a mile where they were stopped by impassable falls (Gerstung, pers. obs.), but we have no records of salmon in that stream.

The Yuba River, along with the Feather and Bear rivers, sustained some of the most intensive hydraulic mining carried out during the gold-mining years (1850-1885) (CDFG 1993), and the effects on the salmon runs were undoubtedly severe. Indeed, by 1876 the channel of the Yuba River reportedly had become completely filled and the adjoining agricultural lands covered with sand and gravel (CDFG 1993)-- a marked deterioration of the river as salmon habitat. Chamberlain and Wells (1879) wrote: "At Timbuctoo ravine it is claimed that the Yuba river has been filled with a deposit, eighty feet in depth. ... At Marysville, the depth of the deposit is about twenty-two feet. At a point, in front of the city, the river was considerably deeper than at any point above or below; this has been filled up to the regular line of the bottom, the deposit being over thirty feet in thickness. The bottom-lands along the Yuba and Bear rivers have been covered to a depth of five to ten feet, extending, in some places, one and one-half miles back from the streams." It was estimated that during the period 1849-1909, 684 million cubic yards of gravel and debris due to hydraulic mining were washed into the Yuba River basin (Sumner and Smith 1940, citing Gilbert 1917).

Clark (1929) reported that the salmon spawning grounds extended from the river mouth up to the town of Smartsville, but that very few salmon (evidently spring run) went past that point further upstream. As of 1928, there was the "Government barrier" dam (Daguerre Point Dam) near the town of Hammond below Smartsville which served to catch sediments washed down the river from mining and dredging operations further upriver. Although fishways had been provided at this dam, they were destroyed by floods in winter 1927-1928, but in any event few salmon reportedly went further upriver to spawn (Clark 1929). Daguerre Point Dam (15 ft high), located ~11 mi east of Marysville on the Valley floor (at 120 ft elev.), was said to have "almost completely blocked king salmon runs since its construction in 1910"; salmon did surmount that dam in occasional years because they were observed in large numbers in the North Fork Yuba River during the early 1920s at Bullards Bar (Sumner and Smith 1940). Prior to the construction of Daguerre Point Dam, "heavy runs of salmon" reportedly occurred in Dry Creek and Deer Creek upstream of the dam site, but "few, if any," were present in 1938 (Sumner and Smith 1940). An even earlier structure, Barrier No. 1, (built in 1904-1905), was 4.5 mi above the later site of Daguerre Point Dam and probably hindered salmon until floods destroyed it in 1907 (Sumner and Smith 1940). Clark (1929) also reported that located on the South Fork Yuba north of Nevada City was Edison Dam, a power project dam that had a "good fish ladder and screens." There evidently were other dams on the Yuba River which were washed out or damaged during the winter of 1927-1928. Fry (1961) later stated that the Yuba River "was seriously handicapped" for many years by a diversion dam (evidently Daguerre Point Dam) which lacked a functional fish ladder and below which there "was often very little water". Although adequate fish ladders were later provided, the low-water conditions remained as of 1959 (Fry 1961). Construction of Englebright Dam 12.5 mi further upstream (282 ft elev.) in the late-1930s eliminated much spring-run salmon habitat and "severely reduced the spring run" (CDFG 1990). Englebright Dam presently is the upstream limit of salmon distribution. Although most of the salmon spawning habitat occurs in the 7.8 mi of river on the open Valley floodplain downstream of Daguerre Point Dam (CDFG 1993), the greater part of the run now generally spawns above Daguerre Point (J. Nelson, pers. comm.). The fall run previously spawned in the entire stretch from Englebright Dam downstream to Simpson Lane (Marysville), below which the substrate is too sandy (J. Nelson, pers. comm.). The spring run, when the fish were common in the recent past, spawned in the area between Engelbright Dam and Highway 20 (J. Nelson, pers. comm.).

Salmon originally migrated into the Yuba River in large numbers to spawn. The California Fish Commission reported that in 1850 "the salmon resorted in vast numbers to the Feather, Yuba, American, Mokolumne [sic], and Tuolumne Rivers", and on the Yuba River as late as 1853, "the miners obtained a large supply of food from this source"; however, by 1876 the salmon no longer entered those streams (CFC 1877). At the time of Clark's (1929) report, a fall run occurred in late fall and there was an occasional, "slight" spring run. He stated that "Very little could be learned" about past salmon abundances in this river, but at that time (1928) the salmon (essentially the fall run) were "holding their own and not decreasing." Fry (1961) reported fall-run sizes of 1,000-10,000 fish for the period 1953-1959. The assessment by the California Department of Fish and Game (CDFG 1993) was that the Yuba River "historically supported up to 15% of the annual run of fall-run chinook salmon in the Sacramento River system." Fall-run sizes during the period 1953-1989 ranged within 1,000-39,000 fish and averaged 13,050 annually (CDFG 1993). More recently (1990-1994), annual run-size estimates for the fall run have varied from 4,000 to ~36,200 spawners (Fisher, unpubl. data). Fry (1961) noted that the spring run had "virtually disappeared". A remnant spring run has managed to persist up to now (1995) in "minimal numbers" (J. Nelson, pers. comm.), but the run has been genetically mixed with the fall run due to spatial overlap of their spawning grounds, as has been the case also in the Feather and American rivers (J. Nelson, pers. comm.). These mixed spring-run fish are now present in "minimal numbers" (J. Nelson, pers. comm.).

Feather River (Yuba, Butte, Plumas counties) The Feather River, noted by one early traveler in 1843 as "tributary to the Sacramento and still richer in salmon" (Van Sicklen 1945), was renowned as one of the major salmon-producing streams of the Sacramento Valley. R.H. Buckingham, of the California Fish Commission, wrote in the Sacramento Bee (31 December 1885), "In years gone by, some of the fishermen of Sacramento would ascend the Feather river as far as Yuba City, to fish for salmon, which were very plentiful at times, Indians catching as many as two hundred in a single night with spears." Salmon originally ascended a considerable distance into the Feather River system, particularly the spring run which spawned in the higher streams and headwaters. They went up the West Branch at least to the site of Stirling City (F. Meyer, pers. comm.), and also up along the entire length of the North Fork Feather River through the area now covered by Lake Almanor and into the surrounding tributary streams (>4,200 ft elev.). Copies of early correspondence sent to the CDFG state that large numbers of spring-run fish ("thousands") entered the North Fork, most of which were stopped by Salmon Falls ~2-2.5 mi above the town of Seneca (CDFG letters no.1, no.2), although a few fish were able to surmount the falls and proceed further upstream (CDFG letter no.1). Flows from the many springs that fed the Lake Almanor area (formerly Big Meadows), together with streamflows from further up the North Fork, undoubtedly were sufficient for salmon to have ascended through the lakebed area and up the North Fork another 6 mi or more (J. Nelson, pers. comm.). Judging from streamflows that occur in the Hamilton Branch of the North Fork above Lake Almanor, salmon most likely ascended that branch for several miles, possibly to within a very short distance of present-day Mountain Meadows Reservoir (J. Nelson, pers. comm.). Spring-run salmon are also known to have ascended Indian Creek, a tributary of the East Branch of the North Fork, at least as far as Indian Falls (near the junction of Highways 89 and 70); they concentrated there and were harvested by Native Americans, although the falls were not necessarily the upper limit of their distribution in that stream (J. Nelson, pers. comm.). In reference to two other North Fork tributaries, Hanson et al. (1940) stated that the quality of spawning habitat was good in Yellow Creek and excellent in Spanish Creek, although by that time salmon were blocked from reaching the streams by a diversion dam downstream. The previous distribution of salmon in those two streams is unknown, but Yellow Creek probably was used at least to some extent; a substantial waterfall above the mouth of Spanish Creek (R. Flint, pers. comm.) possibly barred salmon from ascending that stream. In the Middle Fork Feather River, the salmon were stopped shortly above Lake Oroville by Bald Rock Falls (18 ft high) and Curtain Falls (30 ft) immediately above. Spring-run salmon were observed spawning below Bald Rock Falls in the 1960s before Oroville Dam was built, and fishermen often caught large numbers of salmon from the pool below the falls (Gerstung, pers obs.). In Fall River, a tributary of the Middle Fork, the 640-ft Feather Falls ~1 mi above the mouth certainly was a barrier. The South Fork Feather River, according to Hanson et al. (1940), had "much more spawning gravel per mile of stream than either the Middle or North Fork", but at that time nearly all of the streamflow was diverted for irrigation into the Forbestown and Palermo canals. Prior to the diversion of the stream, spring-run salmon may have ascended to the vicinity of Forbestown, near the present upper limit of the South Fork arm of Lake Oroville.

Clark (1929) reported both spring and fall runs present in the Feather River. The main spawning beds extended for 30 mi from the river mouth up to Oroville. At that time (1928), the spring-run fish evidently still went up all four branches above Oroville, which were all suitable as spawning habitat, up to points where they were blocked by dams. Several dams in the Feather River drainage presented obstacles to salmon in 1928. The Sutter-Butte Dam 6 mi below Oroville was a 5-ft high irrigation diversion dam with a reportedly ineffective fishway and lacking fish screens on the intake ditches, although the salmon nonetheless surmounted it (Clark 1929). Miocene Dam near the town of Magalia on the West Fork was 12.5 ft high power project with no fishway or fish screens. Stirling City Dam, also on the West Fork, was 8 ft high and supplied a powerhouse; it had a fish ladder but Clark stated that salmon never reached this far upriver. On the North Fork was the Great Western Power Company dam equipped with a fish ladder, although water diversions to the powerhouse dried up the river for "a number of miles" when streamflow was low (Clark 1929). Clark was not aware of any barriers to salmon on the Middle Fork Feather River, but he noted that the South Fork had two irrigation diversion dams: Dam No. 1 on Lost Creek, which took "nearly all the water from the South Fork during the summer months", and Dam No. 2 located on the main fork and lacking a fishway.

Clark (1929) stated that both spring and fall runs were "very heavy in the Feather River previous to the building of obstructions". Clark asserted that early mining operations may have reduced the runs "somewhat", but that it was the building of dams that had "about destroyed the spring run". However, the impact of early mining operations on salmon habitat, while not quantifiable, nonetheless was undeniably substantial during their heyday. John Muir (1938), referring to water turbidity as he traveled along the Sacramento River wrote in November 1877: "...the Sacramento is clear above the confluence of the Feather." Somewhat earlier, Stone (1874) noted that poor water quality resulting from intense mining activity was the reason for the absence of salmon from the Feather, Yuba and American rivers. A decade later, Stone (1883) again observed: "...the Feather River, the Yuba, the American Fork, have long ago been completely ruined as spawning grounds, in consequence of the immense deposit of mud in them, caused by the hydraulic mining operations on these rivers. Not a salmon ever enters these streams now. Except possibly at a time of very high water, these streams are so thick with mud that it would kill any fish attempting to ascend them." A graphic account was given by Chamberlain and Wells (1879): "A detailed statement of the loss by mining debris it is impossible to make, but its ravages can be seen on every hand. The surface of the country has undergone a change; the streams diverted from their obstructed channels, have been compelled to seek new courses and outlets for their mud-burdened waters. The banks of Feather, Yuba, and Bear rivers, were, formerly, several feet above the ordinary level of the water, and the steamers and sailing vessels were enabled to make easy and convenient landings. The streams were as clear as crystal, at all seasons of the year, and thousands of salmon and other fishes sported in the rippling waters, their capture being a favorite amusement of both the white man and the native. But now the channels have become choked with sediment, the waters heavy and black with its burden of mud, and the fish been compelled to seek other localities. ... The bed of the Feather river, from Oroville to the mouth of Yuba river has been raised six or eight feet." Even in 1904 Rutter would write: "The water of the upper part of the Sacramento River and the upper tributaries is quite clear, and continues so until the mouth of the Feather River is reached, from which point to the mouth it is very muddy. It is in the muddy water between the mouth of Feather River and Vallejo that the salmon for the markets are taken" (Rutter 1904).

Clark described the fall run as "large, although not extremely abundant" and having "fallen off in the last few years". He suggested that the salmon populations showed a 3- or 4-year cycle, based on statements by river residents. Fry (1961) reported run-size estimates for the fall run of 10,000-86,000 fish for the period 1940-1959, and of 1,000 to ~4,000 fish for the spring run. The fall run spawned mainly in the mainstem, while most of the spring run spawned in the Middle Fork, with a few spring run entering the North Fork, South Fork and West Branch (Fry 1961). Just prior to the completion of Oroville Dam (in 1967), a small naturally-spawning spring run still existed in the Feather River, but the Oroville project cut off all the orginal spring-run habitat (CDFG 1993). Currently, the fall run has its upstream limit at Oroville Dam fish barrier, spawning from there downstream to a point ~2 mi above the Gridley Road crossing (J. Nelson, pers. comm.). There is also a hatchery-sustained population of "spring-run" fish that has been genetically mixed with the fall run (Fisher 1994) and which spawns in the 0.5-mi stretch between the fish barrier immediately below Oroville Dam and downstream to Highway 7 (J. Nelson, pers. comm.). The hybrid spring-run fish hold over the summer in deep pools within the so-called "low-flow" section of the river between Thermolito Diversion Dam (5 mi below Oroville Dam) and the downstream Thermolito Afterbay Outlet (CDFG 1993). They are spawned artificially in the Feather River Hatchery and also spawn naturally in the river during late-September to late-October (CDFG 1993). The "spring run" thus overlaps temporally as well as spatially with the fall run-- which is the cause of the hybridization between the runs. The hybrids consistently enter the hatchery as the early component of the spawning run, but infusion of fall-run genetic material into the hybrid population by artificial hatchery selection continues to dilute the genetic integrity of the putative (hybrid) spring-run fish (Fisher, unpubl. data).

The Feather River Hatchery, located at the town of Oroville, was built by the California Department of Water Resources to mitigate for loss of upstream spawning habitat of salmon and steelhead due to the building of Oroville Dam (CDFG 1993). The California Department of Fish and Game began operation of the hatchery in 1967 (CDFG 1993). The Feather River Hatchery presently is the only source of eggs from "spring-run" chinook salmon in the Central Valley and is viewed as a key component in plans for restoration of spring-run populations (CDFG 1993). Population estimates for the period 1982-1991 indicated an average of 2,800 "spring-run" fish, compared to the average of 1,700 fish prior to the construction of Oroville Dam (CDFG 1993). The hybrid spring-run stock has increased since the early 1980s and numbered >5,000 fish in 1989 (Campbell and Moyle 1991). The higher numbers for the more recent period are attributed to the consistent supply of cold water to the hatchery and to the "low-flow" section of the river (CDFG 1993). Fall-run fish also have increased since completion of Oroville Dam, averaging 39,100 spawners prior to the project and 51,400 fish afterwards (CDFG 1993). In addition, anglers are estimated to have harvested 10,000 fish (spring and fall runs combined) each year in the past decade (pre-1993) (CDFG 1993). Fall-run sizes in the most recent period 1990-1994 have averaged 40,390 fish annually (range ~31,100-51,400), including both hatchery and natural spawners, compared to an annual average of 50,390 fish (~30,500-69,000) during the 1980s (Fisher, unpubl. data).

The CDFG attempted to introduce a late-fall run into the Feather River in the fall of 1970 by planting over one million eyed eggs from Coleman National Fish Hatchery (CDFG 1974). The Feather River Hatchery received returning age-3 and age-4 adults for two generations (during 1973-1978) following the plant, but the run subsequently failed to persist.

Butte Creek (Butte Co.) Spring and fall runs of salmon, and evidently a late-fall run, historically utilized Butte Creek. The spring run ascended at least as far as approximately the present site of Centerville Head Dam near DeSabla. PG&E company employees at one time had reported salmonids migrating past the site to areas upstream (J. Nelson, pers. comm.), but it is not known how much further upstream they went, or whether they were salmon or steelhead. A waterfall (25+ ft high) ~0.5-1 mi below Centerville Head Dam previously had been viewed as a barrier to salmon migration, but the presence of one salmon carcass above the waterfall during a CDFG spawning survey in early 1995 (J. Nelson, pers. comm.) indicates that some portion of the spring run historically may have spawned in reaches further upstream. Steelhead are believed to have ascended as far upstream as Butte Meadows (Flint and Meyer 1977 unpubl.

report), but it is likely that the salmon did not reach that far (J. Nelson, pers. comm.). Clark (1929) described Butte Creek has having been known as "a very fine salmon stream" and "a good spawning ground". He stated that there was only a fall run present, "as the water is very low and warm in the summer". At that time (1928) so much water was being diverted from the stream during most of the summer and fall that the fall run was stated by Clark to have been "almost destroyed". However, it appears that Clark did not fully recognize that the flow conditions he observed in the summer and fall, while detrimental to the fall run or to any salmon that might be present in the lower creek, did not preclude the existence of the spring run. Spring-run fish, migrating during the time of high flows, would have been well upstream during the summer-fall period when Clark evidently made his observations. Flint and Meyer (1977 unpubl. report) stated that the spring run "historically provided a good fishery in Butte Creek"; they also mentioned the presence of a late-fall run which "migrates up Butte Creek in January-February and spawns immediately after arriving at the spawning beds."

Clark (1929) reported the presence of two duck club weirs and three irrigation dams on the creek, but all were low enough to be surmounted by salmon if there was enough water. He specifically mentioned a drainage canal ("833") which carried "considerable water" and in which adult salmon became stranded, to "die in the mud". There were a few spawning beds in the lower creek, but he noted that the few fish that entered the creek spawned in the upper reaches, if they were able to surmount the irrigation dams and ditches. Presently, there are 10 diversion dams in Butte Creek above Butte Slough that divert water for various uses (e.g., power generation, irrigation, domestic supply), and all impair salmon migration-- in some cases by dewatering sections of the stream (CDFG 1993). These barriers affect the upstream migration of the different runs to different degrees, because of seasonal variation in streamflows; e.g., fall-run fish are most affected, having to migrate when flows are inadequate to allow passage over the barriers.

According to Hanson et al. (1940), Butte Creek reportedly was "a very fine salmon stream in the past" but was no longer suitable for salmon due to extensive mining and hydroelectric development that had occurred in the watershed. Fry (1961) noted that Butte Creek had a spring run but "almost no fall run", setting it apart from most small streams in the northern Sacramento Valley which had mainly, or only, a fall run. The many removable dams on the creek blocked or reduced flows late into the fall, and the fall run could not surmount them. Fry (1961) reported that the spring run ranged from <500 to 3,000 fish during the period 1953-1959. As late as the 1960s, the spring run numbered >4,000 in Butte Creek, with smaller numbers of fall and late-fall fish (CDFG 1993). More recent annual estimates of spring-run numbers range from <200 to >1,000 adults (CDFG 1993). The fall run remains small, numbering "a few fish to as many as 1,000" (CDFG 1993) because of the very low late-summer and fall flows (Fisher, pers. obs.). There are also late-fall-run salmon in Butte Creek, but their numbers are unknown (CDFG 1993).

The fall-run salmon generally spawn below the Parrott-Phelan Dam (J. Nelson, pers. comm.). Unlike spring runs in other streams, spring-run fish in Butte Creek presently spawn in the lower part of the creek at relatively low elevation (~1,000 ft), where they are blocked by the Centerville head dam. However, the water there is unusually cold, comparable in temperature to that typically found at ~2000-ft elevation (Fisher, unpubl. data). Although the spring run in Butte Creek migrates and spawns at the same times as spring-run fish in other streams, it appears to be a somewhat different "breed" in that the fry emerge in December; some of these fry migrate out immediately while others migrate out in the spring (CDFG 1993), and the remaining fraction remains in the stream until the following fall (1 yr after they had been spawned) (Fisher, pers. obs.). This is in contrast to the pattern seen in streams where spring-run fish spawn in the colder, high-elevation reaches (i.e., Mill and Deer creeks). There the fry do not emerge from the gravel until March, and they remain in the streams over the summer to migrate out in September-October (Fisher, unpubl. data). Spring-run adults are present in Butte Creek in early February, March and April, in contrast to Feather River "spring-run" (hybrid) fish which do not enter that river until May or June.

Big Chico Creek (Butte Co.) Big Chico Creek contains marginally suitable habitat for salmon and probably was opportunistically used in the past. Spring, fall and late-fall runs have occurred in this creek (CDFG 1993). Fry (1961) gave estimates of 50 fall-run (including late-fall run) fish in 1957, 1,000 spring-run fish in 1958, and 200 spring run in 1959. Fry (1961) also reported that a barrier had been removed from the creek in summer 1958, thus providing an additional 9 mi of habitat for salmon up to Higgins Hole (a deep pool), above which is another natural barrier (Outdoor California 1958, Travanti 1990). The lower barrier-- a 14-ft falls in the Iron Canyon area created by rocky debris from a rock slide that occurred around the time of the San Francisco earthquake of 1906-- blocked upstream access for what had previously been a "sizable" salmon run (Outdoor California 1958). The present distribution of salmon in Big Chico Creek thus is probably not much different from what it had been originally. The spring run has been able to ascend further upstream during spring flows than is reached by the fall run, and thus is both spatially and temporally isolated from the fall run, as is true in some other streams. The current upper limit of the spring run and steelhead is essentially Higgins Hole, ~0.5-1 mi above the crossing of Ponderosa Way, although with high enough streamflows the fish can ascend a half mile further upstream (J. Nelson, pers. comm.). The fall run typically spawns below the Iron Canyon Fish Ladder in Bidwell Park, in the lower one-third or one-fourth of the creek (J. Nelson, pers. comm.).

The average annual run-size of the spring run is believed to have been <500 fish during the 1950s-1960s, but is now considered to be only a remnant (CDFG 1993). The fall and late-fall runs recently have been highly variable, and presently the fall run occurs in very low numbers due to the lack of water in late summer and fall (CDFG 1993). The Iron Canyon fish ladder was damaged by high flows during the winter of 1994-95, thereby blocking the spring salmon run in 1995; in that year, ~100 salmon were captured below the obstruction and transported further upstream (J. Nelson, pers. comm.) Big Chico Creek has been heavily planted with Feather River "spring-run" fish, which evidently had been genetically mixed with fall-run fish. In the last decade or so, very few, if any, of these hybrid spring-run spawners have returned to the creek (Fisher, unpubl. data). Intensive pumping of water from lower Big Chico Creek for irrigation takes a heavy toll of young salmon migrants during all but very high streamflow conditions and is likely responsible for the recent population declines in this stream.

Deer Creek (Tehama Co.) Both spring- and fall-run salmon occurred in Deer Creek, which is a cold, spring-fed stream. The Yahi branch of the Yana people occupied both the Deer and Mill creek drainages, and for whom salmon and other fishes were an important secondary food source (Johnson 1978). The celebrated Ishi, last of the Yahi, demonstrated to anthropologists the Yahi methods of procuring fish, and Ishi himself was said to have "used a salmon spear most expertly" (Pope 1918).

Prior to the 1940s, the spring-run salmon salmon ascended Deer Creek for ~40 mi from its mouth up to the 16-ft high Lower Deer Creek Falls (Hanson et al. 1940), located ~1 mi below the mouth of Panther Creek. According to Hanson et al. (1940), salmon were never known to have passed Lower Deer Creek Falls. Clark (1929) stated that spawning beds extended from the creek mouth (near the town of Vina) to about 10 mi into the foothills, which he described as "a good spawning ground when there is water"; he was, however, evidently referring only to the fall run.

Clark (1929) reported the presence of two irrigation diversion dams on the creek: Stanford Vina Dam, ~3 mi east of Vina, 5 ft high but with a fish ladder and screens installed on the irrigation ditches, and Deer Creek Irrigation District Dam, 8 mi east of Vina. The latter dam had no fish ladder, because it was not considered to be an obstruction to salmon, but it also lacked fish screens at that time (Clark 1929). According to Clark (1929), there was a "small spring run" but "quite a large fall run" and salmon had been "very numerous" in Deer Creek "until the diversion dams removed most of the water from the creek." Clark furthermore stated that "the spring run has never been successful as the fish come up in the spring and summer and lay in the holes until fall before spawning', and "The water becomes too warm for them and they die before they can spawn." Clark may have made this latter statement based on limited observations on fish relatively low in the drainage or during years of low streamflows; spring-run fish are presently known to be capable of over-summering in the pools in Deer Creek (e.g., Needham et al. 1943; Fisher, pers. obs.). Clark stated that the fall run was more successful, when there was "sometimes enough water in late fall", but even the fall run was "very small" at that time (1928) due to irrigation diversions from the creek. Decreased streamflows and consequently high water temperatures in the early summer caused mortalities of up to several hundred late-migrating adult salmon in the years 1945-1947 (Moffett 1949).

As part of the Shasta Fish Salvage Plan (to mitigate for construction of Shasta Dam), a fish ladder was constructed around Lower Deer Creek Falls in 1942-1943 (Needham et al. 1943, Moffett 1949). By the end of 1943, salmon were able to ascend ~5 mi further upstream to Upper Deer Creek Falls, a "sheer drop" of ~20 ft (Hanson et al. 1940), which is the present major upstream barrier. There is, however, a fish ladder at the Upper Falls that is occasionally used by a few salmon (Moyle, pers. obs.). Hence, the amount of stream available for over-summer holding and for spawning (particularly for the spring run) has been increased. To compensate for the loss of spawning habitat in the upper Sacramento drainage caused by construction of Shasta and Keswick dams, Sacramento River spring-run salmon were caught at Keswick and transported to Deer Creek during the 1940s to mid-1950s (Needham et al. 1943, Moffett 1949, Fry 1961), but those transfers had no noticeable effect on the spring run in Deer Creek (Fry 1961). Deer Creek is currently believed to have sufficient habitat to support "sustainable populations" of 4,000 spring-run and 6,500 fall-run salmon (CDFG 1993). In recent years, most of the flow in the lower 10 mi of the creek on the Valley floor has been diverted, and in "many years" all of the natural flow from mid-spring to fall is depleted by the three diversion dams and four diversion ditches (CDFG 1993). Although all of the diversion structures have fish screens and fish ladders, inadequate flows sometimes impede or prevent the upstream passage of salmon (CDFG 1993).

The fall run presently still exists, spawning at lower elevations than the spring run and later in the fall, after ambient temperatures have become cooler. The two runs thus are both spatially and temporally isolated for spawning. The center of the present summer-holding and spawning areas for the spring run is the A-line Bridge (at ~2,900 ft elevation), which lies between Lower Deer Creek Falls and the U.S. Forest Service (Potato Patch) Campground further upstream. The spring run spawns from late August to early October (having held over the summer in the upstream reaches), while the fall run cannot enter the lower creek to spawn until stream flows increase in late October (Fisher, pers. obs.).

Fry (1961) reported spring-run population estimates of <500 to 4,000 fish for the period 1940-1956, and fall run estimates ranging from <500 to 12,000 fish for the period 1947-1959. From 1950 onward, the number of fall-run spawners has ranged over 10-12,348 fish annually, averaging ~600, but since 1985 has numbered 16-900 fish, averaging ~300 (Fisher, unpubl. data). The spring run has varied within 77-3,500 fish (average ~1,360) annually since 1950, and within 77-1,500 fish (average ~550) since 1980 (Fisher, unpubl. data). The spring-run population in Deer Creek is one of only four remaining naturally spawning spring-run chinook populations in California considered to be genetically pure and demographically viable (CDFG 1990)-- the only other Central Valley population being the one in nearby Mill Creek.

Mill Creek (Tehama Co.) Both spring and fall are present in Mill Creek, and occasionally late-fall run fish also occur (CDFG 1993). Clark (1929) described Mill Creek as "a celebrated salmon stream" that had "some very large runs". Clark (1929) stated that the spawning beds extended from the U.S. Bureau of Fisheries egg station and hatchery (located ~1 mi above the creek mouth) for a distance of 2 mi to Clough Dam. Most habitat for salmon, either for holding or spawning, is currently viewed as extending from the mouth of Little Mill Creek (~1,500 ft elevation) up to the area around Morgan Hot Spring

(~5,000 ft) (Fisher, pers. obs.). Some spring-run salmon in Mill Creek reportedly spawn in stream reaches well in excess of 5,000 ft elevation (CDFG 1993) near the boundary of Lassen National Park-- among the highest altitudes known for salmon spawning in North America. All the original upstream habitat suitable for spring-run salmon is still intact, and no major changes have been made on this stream (Fisher, pers. obs.).

Mill Creek is spring-fed and generally cold enough to sustain a spring run. However, it is unusual in that there is an elevational temperature inversion. The upper creek is fed by water from Lassen National Park, where there are many hot springs, but further downstream the lateral influx from coldwater springs results in cooler temperatures (Fisher, pers. obs.). Mill Creek also differs from other streams of the eastside Central Valley drainage in having high silt load and turbidity during the spring snow-melt, the silt originating naturally from volcanic and glacial materials in Lassen Volcanic National Park (CDFG 1993).

Clark (1929) reported three dams on Mill Creek: the Molinas Water Company dam, with fish screens on its diversion ditches and "not considered an obstruction"; 16-ft high Clough Dam, an irrigation diversion project equipped with fish screens but with a poor fishway, which was seldom passable due to low water; and a third, unnamed 7-ft high dam further upstream, with screened diversion ditches. However, these dams were in the lower reaches of the creek, essentially on the Valley floor, and they probably posed no real obstruction to spring-run fish during the spring flows. Presently, there are three dams in the lower eight miles of the creek which divert most of the natural flow (CDFG 1993). All three dams have fish screens, and the lowermost and uppermost dams have operative fish ladders (CDFG 1993). However, the fish ladder on Clough Dam (the middle and tallest dam) functions poorly during certain flow conditions (CDFG 1993) and may therefore impede upstream migration.

Clark (1929) noted that salmon abundance in this creek was reflected by the egg takes at the U.S. Bureau of Fisheries egg station, which collected eggs from fall-run fish but not from the spring run. The station operated during 1902-1945, closing down after completion in 1945 of the Coleman National Fish Hatchery on Battle Creek (CDFG 1993). The egg takes peaked during 1904-1906 but were generally high from 1903 to 1918, dropping substantially during the later years 1919-1924. Clark stated that female salmon in this system produced about 5,000 eggs each, thus allowing estimates to be made of female spawner abundance from the total egg takes by the station; he also stated that there were "at least half again the number of males" (i.e., males were 50% or more as abundant as females). Thus, at the peak productivity in 1905 (30 million eggs taken), there were an estimated 9,000 spawners present (including 6,000 females). In 1924, one of the years of lowest egg production, 2.3 million eggs were taken, which translated to 450 female and 675 total spawners in the creek.

Clark (1929) mentioned the presence of both fall and spring runs, but he described the spring run as "very small and decreasing each year." It is possible, however, that Clark did not realize that spring run fish ascended far upstream and held there over the summer, and he therefore may have underestimated their presence. Fry (1961) reported spring-run numbers of <500 to about 3,000 fish in the 1947-1959 period, while the fall run ranged between 1,000-16,000 spawners. Fry stated that most of the fall run spawned below Clough Dam, while "for all practical purposes the entire spring run" went upstream past the dam.

In recent decades, the spring-run population size has varied from zero fish, during the severe drought in 1977, to 3,500 fish in 1975 (CDFG 1993, Fisher, unpubl. data), but the trend has been downward from an annual average of 2,000 fish in the 1940s to ~300 in the 1980s (CDFG 1990). Since 1983, the spring run has ranged between 73 and 844 spawners annually, averaging ~300 (Fisher, unpubl. data). Fall-run sizes have ranged between 0 and 16,000 spawners since 1952, usually hovering near 1,500 fish (Fisher, unpubl. data). The CDFG (1993) reported an average annual fall-run size of 2,200 fish for the 38 years of record. In the last decade (1985-1994), the fall run has numbered from the hundreds up to ~4,200 fish, but the run has been absent during some years due to low seasonal streamflows (Fisher, unpubl. data). As in Deer Creek, the spring and fall runs are separated temporally, the fall run ascending the creek during fall flows well after the spring-run fish have finished spawning (Fisher, pers. obs.). There is also spatial separation of the spring and fall runs in both Mill and Deer creeks, with spring-run fish spawning well upstream from the fall-run fish and thus further minimizing the posssibility of hybridization (CDFG 1990). Late-fall run salmon have been occasionally observed spawning in the lower reaches of the creek (CDFG 1993).

Antelope Creek (Tehama Co.) Both spring and fall runs, and probably a late-fall run, originally occurred in Antelope Creek. Spring-run salmon ascended the creek at least to where the North and South forks join (where several salmon were observed a few years ago (by Lassen National Forest biologists), and they probably held there over the summer. The few spring-run fish that now enter the creek ascend the North and South forks ~5-6 mi to the vicinity of the Ponderosa Way crossings-- their probable historical upper limit-- beyond which there is little suitable habitat (Fisher, pers. obs.).

As in Mill and Deer creeks, the low late-summer and fall streamflows limit the accessibility of the creek to fall-run fish. There are currently two water diversions on Antelope Creek operated by the Edwards Ranch (50 cfs) and by the Los Molinos Mutual Water Company (70 cfs) (CDFG 1993). During the typical flow-diversion season (April 1-October 31), operation of both diversions usually dries out the lower reach of the stream (CDFG 1993), thus impeding or preventing the upstream migration of both spring and fall runs.

The spring run formerly numbered 200-300 fish annually, with lows down to 50 fish (Fisher, unpubl. data). The CDFG (1993) gave an estimated historical run size of 500 fish No regular estimates of run size have been made recently, but occasional checks indicate that Antelope Creek currently has no more than a remnant spring run which probably is not self-sustaining; 2-3 individuals at most have been seen in the last few years. The fall run in Antelope Creek generally has been small. During the period 1953-1984, the fall run ranged in size between 50-4,000 fish, with an annual average of ~467 fish (CDFG 1993). Population estimates have not been made in recent years due to the scarcity of the salmon, and the run may be extirpated (CDFG 1993).

Battle Creek (Tehama Co.) Both spring and fall runs of salmon originally occurred in Battle Creek, and there is evidence that a winter-run was also present. Rutter (1904) reported the capture in September and early October of newly emerged fry of a size that could only have been the winter run, and in 1939 Needham et al. (1941) observed salmon spawning in Battle Creek during May and June-- the typical winter-run spawning time (Slater 1963, Fisher 1994). The North Fork of Battle Creek contains a series of springs near the town of Manton which would have provided cold-water flows required for the summertime spawning and rearing of the winter run, despite Slater's (1963) assertion that the winter run would not normally spawn successfully in Battle Creek, or in Deer and Mill creeks, because of high (>70°F) water temperatures during the summer. However, the winter run was largely eliminated after hydroelectric development of the creek in 1910-1911, which cut off the spawning habitat. A formerly large spring run also was significantly reduced by the loss of habitat at that time and it may have been completely eliminated for a period thereafter, as indicated in CDFG (1990). However, spring-run fish have been observed in more recent times (including 1995) passing the Coleman National Fish Hatchery at the fish barrier dam (T. Healey, pers. comm.). Spring-run and a few winter-run salmon were observed in the Eagle Canyon area of the North Fork Battle Creek during summer 1995 (T. Healey, pers. comm.).

Surveys conducted prior to the construction of Shasta Dam indicated that the reaches above Coleman National Fish Hatchery could support >1,800 spawning pairs of salmon (CDFG 1993). The North Fork of Battle Creek, especially Eagle Canyon, contains deep, cold pools-- ideal summer holding habitat for spring-run salmon (CDFG 1993), and significant areas of spawning gravel have been determined to exist from Coleman Powerhouse on the mainstem up to Macumber Dam on the North Fork and on the South Fork between South Powerhouse and South Diversion Dam (CDFG 1993). It is likely that much of those areas had been previously used by salmon before blockage of migration and the alteration of the streamflow regime. In the North Fork, salmon have been observed as far upstream as Volta Powerhouse above Manton (T. Healey, pers. comm.). Hanson et al. (1940) reported the presence of a waterfall on the South Fork near the Highway 36 crossing, which evidently was a natural barrier to salmon.

Clark (1929) reported that Battle Creek had a fall run and a "small" spring run. As of 1928, there was a U.S. Bureau of Fisheries egg-collecting station and hatchery (Battle Creek Hatchery) located about 1.5 mi above the creek mouth. The station collected eggs from the fall run but allowed the spring run to pass upstream (Hanson et al. 1940). Spawning by spring run occurred in the 5-mi stretch between the egg station and the upstream dams (Clark 1929). Clark (1929) reported the presence of three power dams and plants: the Coleman plant 6 mi above the mouth, with an operative fish ladder and screens on the diversion canals; a second dam, 30 ft high and equipped with "a good fish ladder and ditch screens", on the South Fork ~20 mi above the Coleman plant; and the Volta plant on the North Fork. Clark stated that despite the presence of fish ladders, the water was often so low that the dams were impassable to fish.

Natural spawning of salmon in Battle Creek presently occurs in the stretch between the creek mouth and the Coleman National Fish Hatchery weir 6 mi above the mouth, and is "still significant" (CDFG 1993). The salmon for the most part are blocked at the hatchery, and natural spawning that formerly occured upstream has been largely eliminated by this blockage and by low flows due to hydropower operations of Pacific Gas and Electric (CDFG 1993). There are presently four unscreened hydropower diversions on the North Fork, three unscreened hydropower diversions on the South Fork, two storage reservoirs and a system of canals and forebays in the drainage, as well as two "significant" agricultural diversions (one unscreened) on the main stem (CDFG 1993).

The records for egg takes (for the fall run) at the U.S. Bureau of Fisheries egg station indicated peak spawner abundances generally occurring in the period 1896-1907; the egg takes remained fairly high until 1916, after which there seemed to be an overall decline until 1924 (Clark 1929). Translating the egg takes to numbers of females (assuming 5,000 eggs per female, after Clark (1929)) gives a peak of 10,000 females for 1904 and a low of 200 females for 1924. According to Clark (1929), the spring run, which was allowed to spawn naturally in the creek, amounted to "almost nothing"; only six or seven spring-run salmon were seen in 1928. The old Battle Creek Hatchery, which took fall-run spawners from the creek, operated through 1945 (Fry 1961). The larger Colemen Hatchery began operations in 1943 and took small numbers (<1,200) of spring-run fish from Battle Creek in 1943-1946, but during that period Coleman Hatchery received most of its fish (both spring- and fall-run) from fish-salvage efforts at Keswick Dam and from the Balls Ferry Racks on the mainstem Sacramento River (Moffett 1949, Fry 1961). Coleman Hatchery started taking fall-run fish locally from Battle Creek in 1946 (Moffett 1949, Fry 1961).

During the period 1946-1956, the spring run numbered ~2,000 fish in most years (Fry 1961, Campbell and Moyle 1990). The spring run has since been either extirpated or is nearly so (Campbell and Moyle 1990). Abundance data for the winter run in Battle Creek are almost nonexistent, although Slater (1963) reported that on 22 May 1962, 457 winter-run fish were counted and a population size of 2,687 fish was estimated for the 2-mi stretch below Coleman Hatchery. Numbers of fall spawners ranged over 3,000-30,000 fish and averaged 15,000 during 1946-1959 (Fry 1961). In 1995, approximately 1,000-4,000 fall-run salmon ascended past the Coleman Fish Hatchery Dam (CDFG unpubl. data).

The Coleman Hatchery also has maintained a late-fall run, but returns of adults have not been consistently strong enough to sustain the run and the hatchery relies on obtaining late-fall spawners from the Keswick fish trap below Keswick Dam on the Sacramento River.

Mainstem Sacramento River and Upper (Little) Sacramento River (Solano, Yolo, Sacramento, Sutter, Colusa, Glenn, Butte, Tehama, Shasta counties) The Sacramento River, regarded by Clark (1929) as "the most important salmon stream in the state" and by Fry (1961) as "the largest and best salmon stream of the Central Valley", has the sole distinction among the salmon-producing rivers of western North America of supporting four runs of chinook salmon-- spring, fall, late-fall and winter.

Salmon originally ascended the Sacramento drainage into the Upper, or Little, Sacramento River (called the Destruction River in some early accounts) in large numbers at least to the falls near the town of Sims, ~31 mi upstream of the site of Shasta Dam. Large numbers of juvenile salmon were observed in the vicinity of Sims during the summer of 1898 by Rutter (1904), who estimated a probable density of "as many as 10,000 young salmon to the mile in the Upper Sacramento... or between a half and three quarters of a million in all the headwaters of that stream." Juveniles were also captured in Hazel Creek, "a favorite spawning stream both for salmon and trout", which joins the Sacramento River near Sims (Rutter 1904). Clark (1929) stated that the falls at Sims stopped most of the salmon, although "a few fish" were able to surmount them. However, Stone (1874) reported that in July 1871 "hundreds of salmon, averaging 15 pounds apiece", were caught by anglers at Upper Soda Springs, upriver of Sims and just below the town of Dunsmuir. Furthermore, the native Wintu people were said to have fished for salmon (during July) upriver of Sims, between Castle Crag depot 5 mi south of Dunsmuir and Shasta Retreat ~1 mi above Dunsmuir (Voegelin 1942). According to one Wintu informant, the salmon fishing activities involved "200-300 people" and lasted 2-3 weeks (Voegelin 1942), indicating that substantial numbers of salmon were able to ascend the falls past Sims. Once over the falls, salmon would have had clear access up to the present site of Mt Shasta City, and it appears that they were able to ascend almost the entire length of the river to the site of present-day Box Canyon Dam and Lake Siskiyou, where several spring-fed streams enter the Upper Sacramento River from the east (Mt. Shasta). Rutter (1904) reported netting "Nearly 500" juvenile salmon in a single seine haul from a pool at the head of Box Canyon, near Sisson in August 1897, and he stated that it was not uncommon "to catch over a hundred at a time in many of the pools of the headwaters." It is possible that the large numbers of young salmon observed by Rutter were to some extent due to plantings of salmon fry into the Upper Sacramento from Sisson (Mount Shasta) Hatchery, a practice started in 1888 (CFC 1890, Shebley 1922). However, salmon were abundant enough in the remote reaches of the Upper Sacramento River prior to any hatchery plantings to gain notice in the first report of the California Fish Commission (CFC 1871): "Salmon are caught by the Indians in the small streams that empty into the Sacramento from the sides of Mount Shasta, at an elevation of more than four thousand feet above the level of the sea; to reach which they must have passed through at least fifty miles of almost continuous rapids." A similar quote was attributed to Dr. David Starr Jordan: "They are known to ascend the Sacramento as far as the base of Mount Shasta, or to its extreme headwaters-- about four hundred miles" (CFC 1890); this statement likewise antedates any possible results from plantings of young salmon in the Upper Sacramento River in 1888 and later, due to the minimum generation time of three years for chinook salmon.

Both fall and spring runs occurred in the Upper Sacramento River, and the winter run was reported to have spawned in the headwaters near Mt Shasta (Stone 1874). The late-fall run, with its requirement of cool summer flows for fry and juvenile rearing, also can be inferred to have ascended at least the lower reaches of the Upper Sacramento where such flows existed. Stone (1874) stated that the salmon ascended the Upper Sacramento River "in great numbers, and make the clear waters of this stream the principal spawning-ground of the salmon of the Great Sacramento River, with one exception" (the exception being the McCloud River). Clark (1929) described the Upper Sacramento River as an "ideal spawning stream" with "wonderful spawning beds" along its entire length. He stated that "the salmon were extremely abundant" prior to construction of the Southern Pacific Railroad through the Sacramento Canyon, and that "the run was almost destroyed" by the construction work ca. 1884-1887. Erosion of rocks and sediments into the river blocked and muddied the water, and the railroad workers reportedly blasted areas holding the salmon to catch the fish (Clark 1929). As noted by Shebley (1922), many fish were used to feed the 9,000 laborers camped along the Sacramento River, but "there was wanton destruction in the way they were killed". Furthermore, a mining tunnel, located just above the confluence with the Pit River, essentially prevented the migration of the fall run when flows were low in August-September during the 1880s. The tunnel's diversion of water from a short stretch of the Upper Sacramento River evidently accounted for the greatly depressed fall run "for a long while past", until the tunnel was closed in 1890 (CFC 1890). In the only quantitative assessment of salmon abundance for this stream, Hanson et al. (1940) estimated that the Upper Sacramento River in 1938 had a "potential spawning capacity" of 14,303 redds. This should be viewed as a minimal estimate because the spawning capacity estimates given by Hanson et al. (1940) for other streams generally are lower than the run sizes that subsequently have been observed for those streams (Fisher, unpubl. data).

On the mainstem Sacramento River on the Valley floor, the Anderson-Cottonwood Irrigation District (ACID) diversion dam (built 1917) at Redding was an almost complete barrier to salmon during the irrigation season (April-October) for about 10 yrs (1917-1927) (Hanson et al. 1940). Despite the contention by the ACID authorities that an open section of the dam was adequate to allow the passage of salmon (CFGC 1921), it was determined that salmon did not use that spillway and that very few fish surmounted the dam at any point along it (McGregor 1922). Further testimony regarding the ineffectiveness of the original "fishway" was given by upstream residents who reported that salmon had become "extremely scarce since the erection of the dam"; as one pioneer fisherman of the area noted, "Why would we journey miles down the river from our homes to fish at the dam if we could get fish up where we belong?" (McGregor 1922). Clark (1929) stated that the dam "nearly exterminated the salmon run at that point of the river". Clark presumably was referring to the winter and spring runs because the dam routinely was dismantled during October; the fall run for the most part had clear access up the river and, therefore, probably was not significantly affected. After installation of a new fish ladder on the dam, reportedly "quite a number of salmon" passed over, "but nothing to compare with conditions before the dam was constructed" (Clark 1929). The ACID dam continues to pose some fish-passage problems (CDFG 1993). The Glenn-Colusa Irrigation District (GCID) diversion facility has been another significant obstacle to salmon, but mainly for downstream-migrating juveniles which are destroyed in large numbers by the pumping operations (Phillips 1931, CDFG 1993). However, by far the greatest factor to affect the salmon runs of the Sacramento River in recent times has been Shasta Dam, completed in 1943. Shasta Dam barred the salmon entirely from their former spawning grounds in the Upper Sacramento, McCloud and Pit River drainages, thus removing those areas from salmon production. In addition, ~13 mi of salmon habitat in the mainstem Sacramento River above Shasta and Keswick dams, up to the confluence of the Upper Sacramento and Pit rivers, were no longer accessible. Operation of the Coleman National Fish Hatchery in Battle Creek was intended to compensate for the habitat loss. Presently, the upstream distribution of salmon in the Sacramento River is delimited by Keswick Dam, a flow-regulating dam 9 mi below Shasta Dam. Fall-run salmon spawn in the mainstem Sacramento River where spawning gravels occur from Keswick Dam dowstream to below the town of Tehama (Clark 1929, Gerstung, pers. obs.)-- a distance of ~67 mi. Fall-run spawning escapements in the mainstem Sacramento River averaged 252,000 fish annually during the period 1952-1959, 159,200 fish in the 1960s, 88,400 in the 1970s, 108,300 in the 1980s, and 65,700 fish in the period 1990-1994 (Fisher, unpubl. data).

McCloud River (Shasta Co.). The McCloud River, once denoted by the California Fish Commission as "the best salmon-breeding river in the world" (CFC 1890), originally supported both spring and fall runs of salmon, as well as a winter run (Stone 1874, Hanson et al. 1940, Needham et al. 1941). According to native Wintu informants, the spring run was "heavier" than the fall run in both the McCloud and Sacramento rivers, and the average size was "approximately twenty pounds", with occasional fish

345

weighing as much as 65 and 70 pounds (DuBois 1935). The winter run appears to have been the least abundant of the three runs, with small numbers of of spawners reported by various workers (Stone 1874, Schofield 1900, Rutter 1904, Hanson et al. 1940). Salmon ascended the McCloud River up to the impassable Lower Falls (20 ft high), ~6 mi above present Lake McCloud (Rutter 1904, Wales 1939, Hanson et al. 1940). Hanson et al. (1940) reported observations of salmon (evidently winter-run) spawning during May and June, 1939, in the McCloud River between Big Springs and Lower Falls (~1.5-mi distance). However, the reach from Big Springs to Lower Falls was ecologically less suitable than areas downstream for salmon because of relatively low streamflows. Big Springs (rm 49) is where two large springs feed the McCloud River and which, in the past, contributed well over half the minimum streamflow measured near the mouth of the river; Big Springs, therefore, was somewhat of an "ecological barrier" to salmon (Wales 1939). Ethnographic information similarly indicates that salmon did not ascend in significant numbers past a bend in the river at rm 32, 1 mi below Lake McCloud: the "salmon got no further, just got there" (Guilford-Kardell and Dotta 1980). That point was the location of a Wintu village named Nurumwitipom ("salmon come back") or Nurunwititeke ("falls back where the salmon turn back") (Guilford-Kardell 1980). The native people, primarily interested in harvesting the salmon in quantity, evidently paid little heed to the presumably small numbers of salmon that ascended past the main fishing sites into the less suitable upper reaches. It would seem that if salmon had ascended in large numbers to the uppermost limit, Lower Falls, that point most likely would have been a major fishing site, just as other barrier falls on other streams had been (e.g., Burney Falls in the Pit drainage and Salmon Falls on the South Fork American River). A few salmon reportedly were observed in Squaw Valley Creek, the largest tributary to the McCloud, in September 1938, and they probably also entered the lower reaches of several other tributary streams (e.g., Star City, Claiborne and Caluchi creeks) (Wales 1939).

Clark (1929) described the McCloud as "a good spawning stream" throughout its length. As of 1928 there were no dams or other artificial obstructions on the river except for the racks of the U.S. Fish Commission egg station (Clark 1929). Hanson et al. (1940) estimated that the McCloud River potentially could support 25,097 redds, and they reported salmon spawning in 1939 near the mouth, at Big Springs, and at "several other places below the Lower Falls." They also estimated that the lower 5 mi of Squaw Valley Creek, a tributary entering the McCloud River ~29 mi upstream of the mouth, could support ~830 redds (Hanson et al. 1940).

After its establishment on the McCloud River in 1872 by the noted fish culturist Livingston Stone, the U.S. Fish Commission egg-collecting station (Baird Station) soon was taking the spawn from almost all of the returning salmon (Clark 1929). During the early years of its operation (1872-1883), most of the eggs collected were shipped out of California for the main purpose of establishing runs in East Coast rivers, which in almost all attempts were failures (USFC 1892, Clark 1929, Towle 1987). Production of salmon in the McCloud itself could not be sustained. A precipitous drop in salmon numbers entering the McCloud River occurred in 1883, caused by railroad construction along the Sacramento River (Stone 1885a,b). In 1884 the scarcity of salmon led to the temporary closure of the egg station (Stone 1885a, Clark 1929).

Clark (1929) presented a tabulation of egg takes by the Baird Station in the years 1872-1924, which illustrated the decline in salmon abundance during the later years compared with earlier years. Aside from the first year operation (1872) in which 50,000 eggs were collected, the egg takes ranged from ~1 million to over 12 million eggs during the period 1873-1883, the first phase of operation prior to its temporary closure (Clark 1929). Eggs were taken from spring-run fish in that period, but the demise of that run led to cessation of operations in 1884-1887. The egg station resumed activities in 1888 and continued to 1924, but taking eggs primarily from the fall run; the spring run was still decimated (CFC 1890, Stone 1893), nor would it ever fully recover. In recognition of the depleted condition of the Sacramento River salmon stocks, Baird Station was reactivated for the expressed purpose of "aiding in the maintenance of the salmon fisheries of the Sacramento River" (USFC 1892). During that latter period of operation (1888-1924), between 1 million and 29.9 million eggs were taken annually, and the peak production (in 1903) was from about 5,600 females (Clark 1929). From about 1907 onward, the egg takes showed a fairly steady decline down to about 1-1.5 million eggs per year. By 1924, there were only "about 260 fish at the racks", which produced 1.2 million eggs (Clark 1929).

Stone (1876b) had estimated that in 1874, the first year in which a weir was set across the McCloud River for capturing the salmon, "Tens of thousands, not to say hundreds of thousands, which would perhaps be the nearer the truth" passed upstream before the weir was finished, and "thousands more" were blocked after its completion. After the hiatus in the mid-1880s, the salmon (fall run) returned in large numbers to the McCloud River in the 1890s and early-1900s-- according to elder Wintu informants, "So thick on the McCloud it looked like you could walk across them" (Guilford-Kardell and Dotta 1980). Clark (1929) reported both spring and fall runs still present in the McCloud River as of 1928, with the fall run "not as heavy as the spring", but by that time both runs were greatly depleted.

Excessive fishing pressure by commercial gillnetters in the Sacramento River undoubtedly depressed the spawning runs into the McCloud River. In the early 1880s, the fishermen reportedly had the Sacramento River completely blocked with their gill nets (CFC 1884, McEvoy 1986). The McCloud River runs were also significantly affected by downstream obstructions in the Sacramento River-- first by the Anderson-Cottonwood Dam in the period 1917-1927 (Clark 1929) and ultimately by Shasta Dam (starting in 1943; Slater 1963). The latter completely blocked access upriver and thereby extirpated all runs of salmon and other anadromous fishes into the McCloud River and other upper Sacramento tributaries.

Pit River (Shasta Co.). The Pit River system covers an extensive area, according to Clark (1929) comprising "at least half of the main Sacramento River". The Achumawi people (referred to in the past as the "Pit River Indians") are reported to have controlled ~50 mi of salmon streams in their territory (Olmsted and Steward 1978). The salmon ascended in large numbers at least to Pit River Falls (rm 75). Voegelin's (1942) ethnographic account states that "Salmon ascend Pit River as far as falls at site of Pit 1 power house, in Achomawi area". The presence of spring-run salmon in Hat Creek, a tributary of the Pit River below Pit River Falls, was reported by Rutter (1904), and the occurrence of a winter run (spawning in "the headwaters") was indicated by Stone (1874). Despite their occurrences in Hat Creek observed by early fishery workers, salmon evidently were not present there in significant numbers during the latter part of the 19th century, but they supposedly had been abundant in earlier times. One ethnographic account states that among the Atsuwegi people, who controlled most of the Hat Creek drainage, "salmon were obtained only by invitation of the western Achumawi on Pit River" (Garth 1978) to where the Atsuwegi made salmon-fishing expeditions in the fall, and giving the Achumawi part of the catch as payment to trespass (Garth 1953). Garth's (1953) survey of Atsuwegi informants indicated that salmon were "rarely seen in Hat Creek", and Voegelin (1942), drawing from an interview in 1936 with a 79-year-old Atsuwegi informant, recorded: "Not many salmon in Hat Creek; occasionally a good run". However, Kniffen's (1928) earlier ethnographic summary, in describing the Hat Creek Valley, states that "Formerly the streams contained an abundance of salmon, pike, trout, and suckers". Garth (1953) reported that a waterfall located "about a mile below Caasel [Cassel] on Rising River", was a favorite fishing place of the Atsuwegi people, who called it "ani" [salmon] "wecéici" [jumping]. This reference is evidently to a stretch of Hat Creek which contains cascades and was sometimes called "Rising River"; it is located just downstream of the mouth of the true Rising River. The latter is a wide, slow-flowing tributary to Hat Creek which lacks salmon habitat (Gerstung, pers. obs.). Shebley (1922) stated that although salmon abundance in Hat Creek was so low in 1886 and 1887 as to cause abandonment of the newly constructed (1885) Hat Creek Hatchery, a "large run" of salmon formerly entered Hat Creek and the spawning beds only "a few years before had been covered with thousands of spawning fish." Rutter (1908) also reported that Hat Creek was "a salmon stream of some importance", but with "a number of rapids that make its ascent difficult." Available spawning habitat and suitable conditions also occur in Kosk and Burney creeks, two other tributaries, where it is likely that winter-run salmon spawned. The Achumawi people owned fish weirs situated at Burney Falls, where they evidently caught salmon (Garth 1953). Burney Falls, a 129-ft double waterfall located ~1 mi above the mouth of Burney Creek, was an obvious historical barrier to salmon.

Rutter (1904), referring to the spring run, stated that "some of the earlier ones even pass Pit River Falls and ascend Fall River to its source"; those "earlier ones" most likely comprised some number of winter-run fish. He also stated that "they are not found in Pit River above the mouth of Fall River"-- indicating that the salmon runs entered the cool and partially spring-fed Fall River for spawning, rather than continue up the relatively warm Pit River. Garth's (1953) ethnographic account similarly reported that salmon seldom ascended the Pit River above Fall River Mills, located at the mouth of Fall river. Prior to the time of Rutter's (1904) report, a fishway had been excavated out of the rock formation on the southern side of Pit River Falls, in 1881 (Throckmorton 1882). Pit River Falls (65 ft high) was "thought by many to rival in beauty any to be seen in the Yosemite Valley" (Rutter 1908), and which Rutter, in his 1904 paper, stated had been impassable for salmon prior to the modification. Yet Rutter (1908) later noted that "each side is broken by ledges, so that it is possible in high water for fish to pass"-- perhaps suggesting that salmon also could have surmounted the falls on the side opposite where the fishway was situated. In any event, Powers (1877), in discussing the first-salmon ritual (probably for the spring run) of the Achumawi on the Pit River, wrote: "After the vast crystal volume of Fall River enters and overcomes the swampiness of the snaky Pit, then salmon are caught, the Indians say, though the whites assert that they do not ascend above a certain tremendous cataract which is said to exist on the lower river." The "tremendous cataract" undoubtedly was Pit River Falls-- which, it seems, did not actually pose a complete barrier to the salmon, as the Achumawi evidently knew. Powers had made his observations on the Achumawi and other native groups during the early 1870s (primarily in the summers of 1870 and 1871; Heizer 1976), well before any attempt to modify the falls. Thus, it is probable that spring-run salmon, and perhaps winter-run, originally surmounted the Pit River Falls and entered the Fall River some distance up its 15-mi length. Kniffen (1928) similarly noted that the Fall River delimited the easternmost area where salmon were an important component of the native people's food economy in that region, and it "also marked the upper limit of the salmon run". Salmon historical abundance in the Fall River cannot be clearly determined, but after construction of the fishway, they reportedly passed over Pit River Falls "in considerable numbers" (Rutter 1908).

Clark (1929) stated that the spawning beds extended from the river mouth (where the river joins the McCloud and Little Sacramento rivers) to the Pit 4 dam, and there were suitable beds also in Squaw Creek and two or three smaller creeks. Access up the river was completely cut off by several power projects dams constructed during the period 1922-1927. Proceeding from the lowest to highest upriver, they were: Pit 4, 7 mi below Burney and Burney Falls, 60 ft high and without fish passage facilities; Pit 3, 9 mi above Pit 4, impassable to salmon; and Pit 1 near the town of Fall River Mills on the Fall River, and also impassable. (Clark 1929).

Stone (1874) stated that the salmon "come up Pit River in great numbers in the spring", but as the weather became warmer in late June or early July the salmon reportedly all "left Pit River for the colder waters of the McCloud". Stone thought it "probable that they ascend[ed] the upper waters of the Pit River also to a limited extent". Clark (1929) later noted both a spring run and a fall run occurring in the Pit River. Comparing with the earlier years of Stone's time, Clark described the salmon population in the Pit River in 1928 as "very small." He mentioned statements from long-time residents of the river indicating that the Pit River formerly "was one of the best for salmon" but that the salmon had "decreased considerably". Based on his observations made in July 1923, Clark estimated that "at the most" 150-200 salmon were stopped at the base of Pit 4 dam, and that they probably comprised the entire spring run (Clark 1929). Hanson et al. (1940) estimated that the lower 28 mi of the Pit River, "from the mouth to

348

Fender's Ferry", potentially could support 14,402 salmon nests. As with the Little Sacramento and McCloud rivers, construction of Shasta Dam eliminated salmon runs into the Pit River drainage.

Cottonwood Creek (Tehama Co.) Cottonwood Creek, a tributary on the westside upper Sacramento Valley, historically supported both spring and fall runs and, presumably, also a late-fall run. The spring-run fish formerly migrated to the headwaters of the South and Middle forks of Cottonwood Creek-- above Maple Gulch on the South Fork (CDFG 1993) and ~8 mi into Beegum Creek on the Middle Fork (CDFG unpubl. data and notes). According to Hanson et al. (1940), the North Fork has a two-part falls (15 ft and 10 ft high) that forms a natural barrier ~5 mi upstream of Ono; below the falls, the stream has only a limited amount of suitable pools and spawning gravel to support salmon.

The past abundance of salmon in Cottonwood Creek reportedly had been "considerable", but by 1928 it had only "a very slight fall run" (Clark 1929). Clark stated that the salmon spawned near the mouth of the creek because low water flows did not allow them to ascend further. He reported the presence of an irrigation diversion (lacking a fishway) 25 mi above the mouth on the South Fork, although salmon rarely reached that point, and several other smaller ditches for irrigation diversions.

In recent years prior to 1993, fall, late-fall and hybrid fall-spring runs occurred in Cottonwood Creek (CDFG 1993). The fall-run size ranged between "a few hundred" to >8,000 fish, with an annual average of 1,000-1,500 (CDFG 1993). The late-fall run numbered <500 fish, spawning in the mainstem and the lower reaches of the North, Middle and South forks (CDFG 1993). The spring run is believed to have averaged ~500 fish historically (CDFG 1993), but there are no recent run-size estimates. Low spring flows and high water temperatures may prevent the upstream migration of the spring run during some years (CDFG 1993). Presently, there are only the bare remnants of a salmon run in Cottonwood Creek. Individuals appear only occasionally and do not constitute a self-sustaining population. Eight adult spring-run salmon were observed by CDFG personnel during the summer of 1995 in the vicinity of the North and South forks (T. Healey, pers. comm.).

Stony Creek (Tehama Co.) Stony Creek is a west-side tributary in the Sacramento drainage and formerly supported spring run and fall runs. Stony Creek reportedly was "a very good salmon stream" prior to the placement of the irrigations dams (Clark 1929). Kroeber (1932), drawing from ethnographic data, stated that "Salmon, for instance, ran up Stony creek through Wintun as far as Salt Pomo territory." The downstream (eastern) border of the latter has been placed at the confluence of Stony Creek and Little Stony Creek, ~5 mi below Stonyford (McLendon and Oswalt 1978), so that point would have been the upstream range of the salmon. By 1928, both spring and fall runs were nonexistant due to irrigation diversions that kept the stream dry except during the rainy season (Clark 1929). At that time, there were two permanent dams on the creek: the Orland Project Dam (20 ft high, built ca. 1914) 4 mi west of Stonyford, and a dam on Big Stony Creek (90 ft high, "too high for a fish ladder") (Clark 1929). There was also a dam across Stony Creek where an irrigation canal built by the Glenn Colusa Irrigation District (GCID) crossed the creek ~3-4 mi upstream of its mouth. This dam was usually washed out in high water, but most of the time it would have been a barrier to salmon, had there been any water in the creek (Clark 1929). Presently there are three storage reservoirs on the creek (CDFG 1993). There is "excellent" spawning gravel within the ~20 mi of stream between the creek mouth and the lowermost dam, Black Butte Dam, which would be a barrier to salmon (CDFG 1993). However, the GCID canal, downstream of Black Butte Dam, continues to completely bar salmon migration any further upstream (CDFG 1993); this canal-crossing barrier is now seldom washed out except when flood control releases are made from Black Butte Reservoir.

Miscellaneous small Sacramento Valley tributaries In addition to Antelope, Cottonwood and Stony creeks, more than a dozen other small tributaries in the upper Sacramento Valley occasionally supported fall-run salmon during the period 1940-1959 in years of early and heavy rains, and a few of those streams also had spring runs (Fry 1961). In Clear Creek, spring-run salmon were observed in 1949 and 1956 (Azevedo and Parkhurst 1958 unpubl. report); they most likely ascended past the present site of Whiskeytown Reservoir to somewhere above the French Gulch area (~1,400 ft elevation). Clear Creek in some years still supports a substantial fall run; in 1995, the fall run was estimated to have numbered up to 10,000 spawners (CDFG unpubl. data). Thomes Creek supported a small spring run. Murphy (1946) observed 3 adult salmon in early August 1946 in a pool situated within The Gorge area below Lake Hollow, 8 mi upstream from the town of Paskenta; however, no salmon were observed in that stream during a later survey in the 1960s (T. Healey, pers. comm.). In contrast, spring-run salmon probably did not utilize the Cow Creek drainage to any significant extent either because there is no suitable over-summering habitat (i.e., deep bedrock pools), as in the South Fork, or because natural barriers prevented access to the headwaters, as in the other forks. Fall-run salmon presently occur in the mainstem Cow Creek up to where the South Fork joins, and they ascend the South Fork up to Wagoner Canyon. In the North Fork Cow Creek, fall-run fish are stopped by falls near the Ditty Wells fire station of the California Department of Forestry. Occasionally, late-fall run salmon also occur in Cow Creek. Fall-run salmon reportedly migrated 20 mi up Stillwater Creek to spawn in 1938, when the fall rains began early (Hanson et al. 1940). Cache and Putah creeks, two intermittent streams on the west side of the lower Sacramento drainage, have supported fall salmon runs only during wet years within historical times (Shapovalov 1947). Salmon have been observed as far upstream as Capay Dam in Cache Creek (Hanson et al. 1940, Shapovalov 1947) and near the town of Monticello in Putah Creek (Shapovalov 1947). In even earlier times (ca. A.D. 1450-1650), Putah Creek provided salmon to the local Native Americans in at least some minor quantity (Schulz 1994, unpubl. manuscript). Fry (1961) reported that the combined fall runs (including late-fall) for the miscellaneous Sacramento tributary streams totaled 1,000-13,000 fish annually during 1940-1959. The spring-run totals, available for only three years in that period, were <500 fish in two years and 1,000 fish in the third (1956). During the period 1953-1969, the Cow Creek drainage alone supported a fall run that averaged 2,800 fish (CDFG 1993). Currently (1994), the combined fall runs in these miscellaneous streams, if existant, are inconsequential and the spring runs essentially no longer occur (CDFG 1993).

DISTRIBUTION: PRÉCIS

It has been estimated that prior to the placement of man-made obstructions in the salmon streams of the Sacramento and San Joaquin drainages, there were "at least 6000 linear miles of streambed suitable and available to spawning salmon" (Clark 1929), although the process by which that figure was determined was not explained. However, given the sheer magnitude of that estimate, it is evident that not only spawning habitat but all lengths of stream traversed or occupied by salmon (i.e., migration corridors and holding areas) were included. The actual amount of spawning habitat originally used by, or available to, Central Valley salmon, therefore, is not clearly known. By 1928, the amount of spawning stream habitat had been reduced to an estimated 510 linear mi and reportedly at least 80 percent of the spawning grounds were cut off by obstructions-- which include 11 dams in the San Joaquin system and 35 dams in the Sacramento system that posed partial or complete barriers to salmon (Clark 1929). Van Cleve (1945) later estimated a somewhat lesser loss of 75% of the original spawning habitat due to all causes. In 1993, the amount of existant spawning habitat for salmon and steelhead in the Central Valley system was estimated by the California Department of Fish and Game to total less than 300 mi (CDFG 1993).

We estimated from map distances the lengths of stream that have been lost as salmon habitat in each of the major Central Valley drainages due to installation of barriers or reduction of streamflows that made passage of salmon impossible under usual conditions (Table 1, Map). We included lengths of stream that salmon are known or can be inferred to have had access to, whether for holding or spawning purposes. These estimated stream lengths are minimum estimates because we have considered only the mainstems and the major forks and tributaries as salmon habitat. Numerous small 3rd- and 4th-order streams undoubtedly were utilized to some degree by salmon, for which records do not exist, although the numbers of salmon using those smaller streams would have been small. Furthermore, the full extent of the historical distribution of salmon even in the major stream reaches is not clearly known for some drainages (e.g., Middle Fork American River, mainstem and South Fork Merced River). Based on the available information, our estimates indicate that the amount of habitat that was lost differs greatly from drainage to drainage. In the Bear River, for example, the length of stream accessible to salmon has changed very little, while in Deer Creek it has actually increased by several miles due to artificially improved fish passage over natural barriers. In most drainages, considerable portions of the former salmon-supporting reaches are no longer accessible to salmon, and some drainages have been entirely removed from salmon production (i.e., McCloud, Pit, Upper (Little) Sacramento, upper San Joaquin rivers). The general pattern has been the elimination of the higher foothill and mountain reaches in the Sierra Nevada and Cascades from the distributional range of chinook salmon.

Summing the stream-by-stream estimates of accessible salmon habitat (for streams tabulated in Table 1), we obtain a total of 1,014 mi of main stream lengths remaining of the 2,113 mi of Central Valley streams originally available to chinook salmon-- indicating an overall loss of 52%. We did not include Sacramento-San Joaquin Delta in our calculations, where ~700 mi of river channels and sloughs were available to salmon, to various degrees, as migration corridors or rearing areas. In contrast to previously cited estimates which specified only spawning habitat, our figures include the lengths of stream available to salmon as migration corridors (e.g., the lower Sacramento and San Joaquin rivers) as well as holding and spawning habitat. We note that our figures include ~220 mi in the lower Sacramento River (below Tehama), ~50 mi in the lower San Joaquin River (below the confluence of the Merced River), and the lower reaches of several tributaries which contain no spawning habitat. It is likely that those lower Sacramento and San Joaquin reaches historically were used as rearing areas (at least during certain flow regimes) as the juveniles moved downstream, but in recent times they have become less suitable for rearing due to alterations in channel morphology and other environmental conditions. In terms of spawning habitat only, the proportionate loss from the amount originally available far exceeds the value of 52% because the upper stream reaches that have been cut off contained a relatively large proportion of the available spawning habitat. In contrast, much of the remaining lengths of stream in the lower drainages now traversed or occupied by salmon cannot be used for spawning. Of the total length of stream courses presently accessible, less than one-third in the San Joaquin drainage and probably less than a half in the Sacramento drainage are suitable as spawning habitat. Excluding stream courses that were used only as migration corridors (and only minimally for juvenile rearing), we roughly estimate that ~82% of the original spawning and holding habitat for salmon in the Central Valley drainage is no longer available. Thus, the CDFG's (CDFG 1993) earlier assessment that ~95% of the chinook salmon spawning habitat that was originally available has been lost seems reasonably accurate; however, the frequently cited estimate that over 6,000 mi of habitat were once available for spawning (Clark 1929) is probably overly high by a factor of three.

The extent of habitat loss for steelhead most likely was much higher than that for salmon because steelhead were undoubtedly more extensively distributed. Due to their superior jumping ability, the timing of their upstream migration which coincided with the winter rainy season, and their less restrictive preferences for spawning gravels, steelhead could have utilized at least hundreds of miles of smaller tributaries not accessible to the earlier-spawning salmon.

REFERENCES

Aginsky, B.W. 1943. Culture element distributions: XXIV Central Sierra. *University of California Publications in Anthropological Records* 8: 390-468.

Angel, M. 1882. *History of Placer County.* Thompson and West, Oakland, California. 416 pp.

Beacham, T.D. and C.D. Murray. 1990. Temperature, egg sizes, and development of embryos and alevins of five species of Pacific salmon: a comparative analysis. *Transactions of the American Fisheries Society* 119: 927-945.

Beals, R.L. 1933. Ethnology of the Nisenan. *University of California Publications in American Archaeology and Ethnology* 31: 335-410.

Blake, W.P. 1857. Geological Report. No. 1. Itinerary, or notes and general observations upon the geology of the route. *Explorations and surveys for a railroad route from the Mississippi River to the Pacific Ocean.* War Department. Vol. 5. Part II. Washington, D.C.

Bryant, E. 1849. *What I saw in California: being the journal of a tour, in the years 1846, 1847.* D. Appleton and Company, New York. 480 pp.

Buffum, E.G. 1959. *Six months in the gold mines: from a journal of three years' residence in upper and lower California 1847-8-9.* J.W. Caughey (ed.). The Ward Ritchie Press, Los Angeles. 145 pp.

California Fish and Game Commission (CFGC). 1921. An important decision on the fishway law. *California Fish and Game* 7: 154-156.

California Department of Fish and Game (CDFG). 1921. San Joaquin River salmon. Hatchery Notes, W.H. Shebley (ed.). *California Fish and Game* 7: 51-52.

Calfornia Department of Fish and Game (CDFG). 1974. *Feather River Hatchery Administrative Report 74-5.*

California Department of Fish and Game (CDFG). 1990. *Status and management of spring-run chinook salmon.* Report by the Inland Fisheries Division to the California Fish and Game Commission, Sacramento. May 1990. 33 pp.

California Department of Fish and Game (CDFG). 1993. *Restoring Central Valley streams; a plan for action.* Compiled by F.L. Reynolds, T.J. Mills, R. Benthin and A. Low. Report for public distribution, November 10, 1993. Inland Fisheries Division, Sacramento. 129 pp.

California State Board of Fish Commissioners (CFC). 1871. *(1st Biennial) Report of the Commissioners of Fisheries of the State of California for the years 1870 and 1871.* (Reprinted in *California Fish and Game* 19: 41-56, January 1933).

California State Board of Fish Commissioners (CFC). 1875. *(3rd Biennial) Report of the Commissioners of Fisheries of the State of California for the years 1874 and 1875.* Sacramento, California.

California State Board of Fish Commissioners (CFC). 1877. *(4th Biennial) Report of the Commissioners of Fisheries of the State of California for the years 1876 and 1877.* Sacramento, California.

California State Board of Fish Commissioners (CFC). 1884. *(8th) Biennial Report of the Commissioners of Fisheries of the State of California, for the years 1883-4.* Sacramento, California.

California State Board of Fish Commissioners (CFC). 1886. *(9th) Biennial report of the Commissioners of Fisheries of the State of California for the years 1885-1886.* Sacramento, California.

California State Board of Fish Commissioners (CFC). 1890. *(11th) Biennial report of the State Board of Fish Commissioners of the State of California for the years 1888-1890.* Sacramento, California.

California State Historical Association. 1929. Millerton, landmark of a vanished frontier. *California History Nugget* 2: 114-117.

Campbell, E.A. and P.B. Moyle. 1991. Historical and recent population sizes of spring-run chinook salmon in California. In: *Proceedings, 1990 Northwest Pacific chinook and coho salmon workshop,* pp. 155-216. American Fisheries Society, Humboldt State University, Arcata, California.

Carson, J.H. 1852. *Recollections of the California mines. An account of the early discoveries of gold, with anecdotes and sketches of California and miners' life, and a description of the Great Tulare Valley.* Reprinted by Biobooks, Oakland, California (1950). 113 pp.

Cassidy, J., M. Daley-Hutter, C. Nelson and L. Shepherd. 1981. *Guide to three rivers. The Stanislaus, Tuolumne and South Fork of the the American.* Friends of the River Books, San Francisco. 295 pp.

Caton, J. D. 1869. Trout fishing in the Yosemite Valley. *American Naturalist* 3: 519-522.

Chamberlain, W.H. and H.L. Wells. 1879. *History of Sutter County, California.* Thompson and West, Oakland, California. 127 pp. Reprinted by Howell-North Books, Berkeley, California. 1974.

Clark, G. H. 1929. Sacramento-San Joaquin salmon (*Oncorhynchus tshawytscha*) fishery of California. Division of Fish and Game of California, *Fish Bulletin* No. 17: 1-73.

Clark, G.H. 1930. Salmon spawning in drainage canals in the San Joaquin Valley. Calif. Fish and Game 16: 270.

Clark, G.H. 1943. Salmon at Friant Dam-- 1942. *California Fish and Game* 29: 89-91.

Clark, W.V.T. 1973. *The journals of Alfred Doten 1849-1903.* Vol. 1. University of Nevada Press, Ren. 808 pp.

Coleman, C.M. 1952. *PG and E of California. The centennial story of Pacific Gas and Electric Company 1852-1952.* McGraw Hill, New York. 385 pp.

Collins, C. 1949. *Sam Ward in the gold rush. Stanford University Press, Stanford, California.* 189 pp.

Cook, S.F. 1960. Colonial expeditions to the interior of California. Central Valley, 1800-1820. *University of California Publications in Anthropological Records* 16: 239-292.

DuBois, C. 1935. Wintu ethnography. *University of California Publications in American Archaeology and Ethnology* 36: 1-148.

Fisher, F.W. 1994. Past and present status of Central Valley chinook salmon. *Conservation Biology* 8: 870-873.

Fariss [no initials] and C.L. Smith. 1882. *Fariss and Smith's History of Plumas, Lassen and Sierra counties, California, and biographical sketches of their prominent men and pioneers.* Reprinted 1971, Howell-North Books, Berkeley, California. 507 pp.

Ferguson, A.D. 1914. General conditions and some important problems. *State of California Fish and Game Commission Twenty-third Biennial Report for the years 1912-1914*, pp. 27-29. Sacramento, California.

Fremont, J.C. 1848. *Geographical memoir upon Upper California, in illustration of his map of Oregon and California.* Report to the United States Senate, 30th Congress, 1st Session, Miscellaneous No. 148. Washington, D.C. 64 pp.

Fry, D.H., Jr. 1961. King salmon spawning stocks of the California Central Valley, 1940-1959. *California Fish and Game* 47: 55-71.

Garth, T.R. 1953. Atsuwegi ethnography. *University of California Publications in Anthropological Records* 14: 129-212.

Garth, T.R. 1978. Atsuwegi. In: *Handbook of North American Indians.* Vol. 8. California, pp. 236-248. R.F. Heizer (ed.), Smithsonian Institution, Washington, D.C.

Gay, T. 1967. James W. Marshall. *The discoverer of California gold. A biography.* The Talisman Press, Georgetown, California. 558 pp.

Gayton, A.H. 1946. Culture-environment integration: external references in Yokuts life. *Southwest Journal of Anthropology* 2: 252-268.

Gayton, A.H. 1948a. Yokuts and Western Mono ethnography I: Tulare Lake, Southern Valley, and Central Foothill Yokuts. *University of California Publications in Anthropological Records* 10: 1-142.

Gayton, A.H. 1948b. Yokuts and Western Mono ethnography II: Northern Foothill Yokuts and Western Mono. *University of California Publications in Anthropological Records* 10: 143-302.

Gerstung, E.R. 1989. Fishes and fishing in the forks of the American River: then and now. In: *The American River. North, Middle and South forks.* The Wilderness Conservancy. Protect American River Canyons, Auburn, California. 320 pp.

Gifford, E.W. 1932. The Northfork Mono. *University of California Publications in American Archaeology and Ethnology* 31: 15-65.

Gilbert, G.K. 1917. Hydraulic-mining débris in the Sierra Nevada. *United States Geological Survey Professional Paper No. 105.* Washington, D.C.

Gudde, E.G. 1962. *Bigler's chronicle of the West. The conquest of California, discovery of gold, and Mormon settlement as reflected in Henry William Bigler's diaries.* University of California Press, Berkeley. 145 pp.

Guilford-Kardell, M. and J. Dotta. 1980. Papers on Wintu ethnography: 239 Wintu villages in Shasta County circa 1850. *Occasional papers of the Redding Museum No. 1*, Redding Museum and Art Center, Redding,

California. 131 pp.

Hallock, R.J. and W.F. Van Woert. 1959. A survey of anadromous fish losses in irrigation diversions from the Sacramento and San Joaquin Rivers. *California Fish and Game* 45: 227-296.

Hanson, H.A., O.R. Smith and P.R. Needham. 1940. An investigation of fish-salvage problems in relation to Shasta Dam. *United States Bureau of Fisheries Special Scientific Report No. 10.* Washington, D.C. 202 pp.

Hatton, S.R. 1940. Progress report on the Central Valley fisheries investigations. *California Fish and Game* 26: 334-373.

Hatton, S.R. and G.H. Clark. 1942. A second progress report on the Central Valley fisheries investigations. *California and Game* 28: 116-123.

Healey, M.C. 1991. Life history of chinook salmon (*Oncorhynchus tshawytscha*). <u>In</u>: *Pacifc salmon life histories*, pp. 313-393. C. Groot and L. Margolis (eds.), UBC Press, Vancouver.

Heizer, R.F. 1976. Editor's Introduction. *Tribes of Calfornia*, by Stephen Powers. University of Callifornia Press, Berkeley. 480 pp.

Heizer, R.F. 1993. *The destruction of California Indians.* University of Nebraska Press, Lincoln. 321 pp.

Hutchings, J.M. 1990. *In the heart of the Sierras. Yo Semite Valley and the Big Tree Groves.* P. Browning (ed.), Great West Books, Lafayette, California. 505 pp.

Jacobs, D., E. Chatfield, L. Kiley, G.M. Kondolf, L. Loyd, F. Smith, D. Walker, and K. Walker. 1993. *California's Rivers. A Public Trust report.* California State Lands Commission, Sacramento. 334 pp.

Johnson, J.J. 1978. The Yana. <u>In</u>: *Handbook of North American Indians.* Vol. 8. California, pp. 361-369. R.F. Heizer (ed.), Smithsonian Institution, Washington, D.C.

Kniffen, F. 1928. Achomawi geography. *University of California Publications in American Archaeology and Ethnology* 23: 297-332.

Kroeber, A.L. 1932. The Patwin and their neighbors. *University of California Publications in American Archaeology and Ethnology* 29: 253-423.

Latta, F.F. 1977. *Handbook of Yokuts Indians.* Bear State Books, Santa Cruz, California. 765 pp.

Lawrence, J.H. 1884. Discovery of the Nevada Fall. *Overland Monthly (second series).* Vol. 4, No. 22 (October 1884): 360-371.

Maniery, J.G. 1983. A chronicle of Murphys Rancheria (Mol-Pee-So): an historic Central Sierra Miwok village. *Journal of California and Great Basin Anthropology* 5: 176-198.

McGregor, E.A. 1922. Migrating salmon at Redding Dam. *California Fish and Game* 8: 141-154.

McLendon, S. and R.L. Oswalt. 1978. Pomo: Introduction. <u>In</u>: *Handbook of North American Indians.* Vol. 3. California, pp. 274-288. R.F. Heizer (ed.), Smithsonian Institution, Washington, D.C.

Moffett, J.W. 1949. The first four years of king salmon maintenance below Shasta Dam, Sacramento River, California. *California Fish and Game* 35: 77-102.

Morgan, D.L. 1970. *In pursuit of the golden dream. Reminiscences of San Francisco and the northern and southern mines, 1849-1857,* by Howard C. Gardiner. Western Hemisphere, Inc., Stoughton, Massachusetts. 390 pp.

Moyle, P.B. 1970. Occurrence of king (chinook) salmon in the Kings River, Fresno County. *California Fish and Game* 56: 314-315.

Moyle, P.B. 1976. *Inland fishes of California.* University of California Press, Berkeley. 405 pp.

Muir, J. 1902. *Our National Parks.* Houghton, Mifflin and Company, Boston, Massachussetts. 370 pp.

Muir, J. 1938. *John of the Mountains. The unpublished journals of John Muir (ed. by L. M. Wolfe).* Houghton Mifflin Co., Boston. 459 pp.

Muir, J. 1961. *The mountains of California.* Doubleday and Co., Inc., Garden City, New York. 300 pp.

Murphy, G.I. 1946. A survey of Stony Creek, Grindstone Creek and Thomes Creek drainages in Glenn, Colusa and Tehama counties, California. *California Department of Fish and Game, Inland Fisheries Branch Administrative Report No. 46-14.* Sacramento.

Needham, P.R., H.A. Hanson and L.P. Parker. 1943. Supplementary report on investigations of fish-salvage problems in relation to Shasta Dam. *United States Fish and Wildlife Service, Special Scientific Report No. 26.* 30 June 1943. 52 pp.

Needham, P.R., O.R. Smith and H.A. Hanson. 1941. Salmon salvage problems in relation to Shasta Dam, California, and notes on the biology of Sacramento River salmon. *Transactions of the American Fisheries Society* 70: 55-69.

Northern California Historical Records Survey Project. 1940. Inventory of the county archives of California. No. 10. Fresno County (Fresno). Division of Professional and Science Projects, Work Projects Administration. July 1940.

Outdoor California. 1958. Salmon get a freeway up a rugged canyon. August 1958, pp. 4-5.

Perlot, J.-N. 1985. *Gold seeker. Adventures of a Belgian argonaut during the Gold Rush years.* Translated by H.H. Bretnor, H.R. Lamar (ed.), Yale University Press, New Haven, Connecticut. 451 pp.

Phillips, J.B. 1931. Netting operations on an irrigation canal. California Fish and Game 17: 45-52.

Pope, S.T. 1918 Yahi archery. University Publications in American Archaeology and Ethnology 13: 104-152. Reprinted in: *Ishi, the last Yahi. A documentary history.* R.F. Heizer and T. Kroeber (eds.), University of California Press, Berkeley. 1979. 242 pp.

Powers, S. 1877. *Tribes of California. Contributions to North American Ethnology*, Vol. III. Department of the Interior, U.S. Geographical and Geological Survey of the Rocky Mountain Region. Washington, D.C. Reprinted by University of California Press, Berkeley. R.F. Heizer, ed. 1976. 480 pp.

Rose, G. 1992. *San Joaquin. A river betrayed.* Linrose Publ. Co., Fresno, California. 151 pp.

Rostlund, E. 1952. Freshwater fish and fishing in native North America. *University of California Publications in Geography* 9: 1-314.

Rutter, C. 1904. Natural history of the quinnat salmon. A report of investigations in the Sacramento River, 1896-1901. *Bulletin of the United States Fish Commission* 22: 65-141.

Rutter, C. 1908. The fishes of the Sacramento-San Joaquin Basin, with a study of their distribution and variation. *Bulletin of the Bureau of Fisheries.* Vol. 27 (1907): 103-152.

San Joaquin Valley Drainage Program. 1990. *Fish and wildlife resources and agricultural drainage in the San Joaquin Valley, California.* Vol. 1. October 1990. Sacramento, California. 166 pp.

Schofield, N.B. 1900. Notes on an investigation of the movement and rate of growth of the quinnat salmon fry in the Sacramento River. *Fifteenth Biennial Report of the State Board of Fish Commissioners of the State of California, for the years 1897-1898*: 66-71.

Seymour, A.H. 1956. Effects of temperature upon young chinook salmon. Ph.D. dissertation. University of Washington, Seattle.

Shapovalov, L. 1947. Report on fisheries resources in connection with the proposed Yolo-Solano development of the United States Bureau of Reclamation. *California Fish and Game* 33: 61-88.

Shebley, W.H. 1922. A history of fishcultural operations in California. *California Fish and Game* 8: 62-99.

Shebley, W.H. 1927. History of fish planting in California. *California Fish and Game* 13: 163-173.

Skinner, B. 1958. Some observations regarding the king salmon runs of the Central Valley. *Water Projects Miscellaneous Report No. 1.* California Department of Fish and Game. 14 October 1958. 14 pp.

Slater, D.W. 1963. Winter-run chinook salmon in the Sacramento River, California with notes on water temperature requirements at spawning. *United States Fish and Wildlife Service Special Scientific Report-- Fisheries No. 461.* November 1963. 9 pp.

Stanley, C. and L. Holbek. 1984. *A guide to the best whitewater in the state of California.* Friends of the River Books, Palo Alto, California. 281 pp.

Steele, J. 1901. *Camp and cabin. Mining life and adventure, in California during 1850 and later.* Reprinted by The Lakeside Press, R.R. Donnelley and Sons Co., Chicago. 1928. 377 pp.

Stone, L. 1874. Report of operations during 1872 at the United States salmon hatching establishment on the McCloud River. *United States Commission of Fish and Fisheries, Report for 1872 and 1873*: 168-215. Washington, D.C.

Stone, L. 1876a. Report of operations in California in 1873. *United States Commission for Fish and Fisheries, Report of the Commissioner for 1873-4 and 1874-5*, Appendix B, pp. 377-429.

Stone, L. 1876b. Report of operations during 1874 at the United States salmon-hatching establishment on the M'Cloud River, California. *United States Commission of Fish and Fisheries, Report of the Commissioner for 1873-4 and 1874-5*: 437-478.

Stone, L. 1883. Account of operations at the McCloud River fish-breeding stations of the United States Fish Commission, from 1872 to 1882 inclusive. *Bulletin of the United States Fish Commission*, Vol. 2 for 1882: 217-236.

Stone, L. 1885a. History of operations at the fish hatching stations on the McCloud River, California, from the beginning, August, 1872, to October, 1884. *Bulletin of the United States Fish Commission*, Vol. 5 for 1885: 28-31.

Stone, L. 1885b. Report of operations at the United States salmon-breeding station on the McCloud River, California, during the year 1883. *United States Commission of Fish and Fisheries, Report of the Commissioner for 1883*, Part XI, pp. 989-1000.

Sullivan, M.S. 1934. *The travels of Jedediah Smith. A documentary outline including the journal of the great American pathfinder.* The Fine Arts Press, Santa Ana, California. 195 pp.

Sumner, F.H. and O.R. Smith. 1940. Hydraulic mining and debris dams in relation to fish life in the American and Yuba Rivers of California. *California Fish and Game* 26: 2-22.

Throckmorton, S.R. 1882. Description of the fish-way in Pitt River, California. *Bulletin of the United States Fish Commission* 1: 202-203.

Toffoli, E.V. 1965. Chemical treatment of the Merced River, Mariposa County. California Department of Fish and Game, *Inland Fisheries Branch Administrative Report No. 65-14.* Sacramento.

Towle, J.C. 1987. The great failure: nineteenth-century dispersals of the Pacific Salmon. *California Geographical Society* 27: 75-96.

Tudor-Goondenough Engineers. 1959. *Summary report on the Tri-Dam Project. Stanislaus River, California.* San Francisco, California. January 1959. 99 pp.

Travanti, L. 1990. The effects of piscicidal treatment on the fish community of a northern California stream. M.S. thesis, California State University, Chico. 67 pp.

United States Commission of Fish and Fisheries (USFC). 1876a. The propagation of food-fishes in the waters of the United States. *Report of the Commissioner for 1873-4 and 1874-5.* Washington, D.C.

United States Commission of Fish and Fisheries (USFC). 1876b. Correspondence relating to the San Joaquin River and its fishes. *Report of the Commissioner for 1873-4 and 1874-5.* Part XXIII, pp. 481-483. Washington, D.C.

United States Commission of Fish and Fisheries (USFC). 1892. *Report of the Commissioner for 1883*: pp. xxxv-xxxvi.

Van Cleve, R. 1945. Program of the Bureau of Marine Fisheries. *California Fish and Game* 31: 80-138.

Van Sicklen, H.P. 1945. *A sojourn in California by the King's orphan. The travels and sketches of G.M. Waseurtz af Sandels, a Swedish gentlemen who visited California in 1842-1843.* The Book Club of California, San Francisco.

Voegelin, E. 1942. Culture element distributions: XX. Northeast California. *University of California Publications in Anthropological Records* 7: 47-252.

Vogel, D. A. and K. R. Marine. 1991. *Guide to upper Sacramento chinook salmon life history.* Report to U.S. Bureau of Reclamation, Central Valley Project. CH2M Hill, Inc., Redding, California. 55 pp.

Wales, J.H. 1939. General report of investigations on the McCloud River drainage in 1938. *California Fish and Game* 25: 272-309.

Warner, G. 1991. Remember the San Joaquin. In: *California's salmon and steelhead. The struggle to restore an imperiled resource*, pp. 61-69. A. Lufkin (ed.), University of California Press, Berkeley.

Woodhull. C. 1946. A preliminary investigation of the Mokelumne River from Tiger Creek to Pardee Reservoir. *California Division of Fish and Game, Bureau of Fish Conservation, Administrative Report 46-16.* 28 pp.

Woodhull, C. and W. Dill. 1942. The possibilities of increasing and maintaining a run of salmon (*Oncorhynchus tshawytscha*) in the Kings River, California. *California Division of Fish and Game, Bureau of Fisheries Conservation (Inland Fisheries Division) Administrative Report 42-26.* 32 pp + figures.

Unpublished Documents

Azevedo, R.L. and Z.E. Parkhurst. 1958. The upper Sacramento River salmon and steelhead maintenance program, 1949-1956. United States Fish and Wildlife Service, unpubl. report.

California Department of Fish and Game (CDFG). 1955. Fish and game water problems of the Upper San Joaquin River. Potential values and needs. Statement submitted to the Division of Water Resources at hearings on the San Joaquin River water applications, Fresno, California. 5 April 1955. 51 pp.

Calfornia Department of Fish and Game (CDFG). 1972. Report to the California State Water Resources Control Board on effects of the New Melones Project on fish and wildlife resources of the Stanislaus River and Sacramento-San Joaquin Delta. Region 4, Anadromous Fisheries Branch, Bay-Delta Research Study, and Environmental Services Branch, Sacramento. October 1972.

CDFG letter no.1. Letter from H.A. Kloppenburg, U.S. Forest Service District Ranger, 23 April 1941, to R. VanCleve, CDFG.

CDFG letter no.2. Letter from R. Belden, 29 April 1941, to Calif. Fish and Game Commission.

CDFG unpubl. field data and notes. Stream survey data, fish counts at dam fishways, notes and photographs on file at CDFG offices, Red Bluff, Sacramento and Rancho Cordova.

California Resources Agency. 1972. California Protective Waterway Plan, 1972. Appendix (by C. Trost). Sacramento, California.

Dill, W. Letter, 24 September 1946, to Donald H. Fry, Jr. CDFG, Fresno.

Dunham, R. 1961. Report on the pollution of the Mokelumne River. Unpubl. CDFG report, 27 June 1961. Sacramento, California.

EA Engineering, Science and Technology. 1990. Report to the Federal Regulatory Commission. Application for license-- major unconstructed project. Clavey River Project No. 100181. Exhibit E, Report 3: Fish, wildlife, and botanical resources. Submitted by Tuolumne County and Turlock Irrigation District.

EA Engineering, Science and Technology. 1991. Tuolumne River salmon spawning surveys, 1971-1988. EA Engineering Fishery Report, October 1991, Appendix 3.

EA Engineering, Science and Technology. 1992. Lower Tuolumne River spawning gravel availability and superimposition report. EA Engineering Fishery Report, February 1992, Appendix 6.

Flint, R.A. and F.A. Meyer. 1977. The De Sabla-Centerville Project (FERC No. 803) and its impact on fish and wildlife. CDFG report, October 1977.

Gerstung, E.R. 1971. A report to the California State Water Resources Control Board on the fish and wildlife resources of the American River to be affected by the Auburn Dam and Reservoir and the Folsom South Canal and measures proposed to maintain these resources. California Department of Fish and Game unpubl. report, Sacramento. June 1971.

Latta, F. Unpubl. Papers, Field Notes: Frank Latta interview with Pahmit (William Wilson), 1 July 1933. Yosemite Research Library, Yosemite National Park.

Northern California Power Authority. 1993. Griswold Creek Diversion Project application for license for major unconstructed project. Submitted to U.S. Federal Energy Regulatory Commission. December 1993.

Schulz, P. D. 1994. Fish remains from YOL-182: a prehistoric village in the lower Sacramento Valley, October 10, 1994. Brienes, West and Schulz, P.O. Box 184, Davis CA 95617. 18 pp.

Snyder, J. B. (Historian, Yosemite National Park, National Park Service). 1993 Memorandum to Park Superintendent Mike Finley: "Did salmon reach Yosemite Valley or Hetch Hetchy?" 9 May 1993 manuscript. P.O. Box 577, Yosemite National Park. 8 pp.

Sources for Personal Communications

Phil Bartholomew. CDFG, Region 4, Oakhurst.
Steve Boyd. East Bay Municipal Utilities District (EBMUD), Oakland, California.
Leon Davies. Department of Wildlife, Fish and Conservation Biology, University of California, Davis.
William A. Dill. CDFG (retired), Region 4, Fresno.
Richard Flint. CDFG, Region 2, Oroville.
Tim Ford. Turlock and Modesto Irrigation Districts, Turlock, California.
Terry Healey. CDFG, Region 1, Redding.
John Hiskox. CDFG, Region 2, Nevada City.
Pete Lickwar. U.S. Fish and Wildlife Service, Energy and Power Branch. Sacramento.
Bill Loudermilk. CDFG, Region 4, Fresno.
Fred Meyer. CDFG, Region 2, Rancho Cordova.
John Nelson. CDFG, Region 2, Ranco Cordova.
Robert C. Nuzum. East Bay Municipal Utilities District (EBMUD), Oakland, California.
Eldon Vestal. CDFG (retired), Region 4, Fresno.

Table 1. Estimated changes in lengths of stream available to chinook salmon in the major salmon-supporting drainages of the Central Valley. The values for stream lengths originally available and subsequently lost are in most cases minimum estimates because the full extent of the former salmon distributions is incompletely known.[1]

Drainage	Length (mi) of stream historically available[2]	Length (mi) of stream presently accessible[3]	Length (mi) of stream lost (or gained)[4]	Percent lost (or gained)
Sacramento Valley				
Mainstem Sacramento River[5]	299	286	13	4
Pit River	99	0	99	100
McCloud River	43	0	43	100
Upper (Little) Sacramento River	52	0	52	100
Battle Creek	53	6	47	89
Antelope Creek	32	32	0	0
Mill Creek	44	44	0	0
Deer Creek	34	38	(4)	(12)
Big Chico Creek	24	24	0	0
Butte Creek	53+	53	>0	>0
Feather River	211	64	147	70
Yuba River	77	21	56	73
Bear River	16	16	0	0
American River	161	28	133	83
Clear Creek	25	16	4	16
Cottonwood Creek	79	79	0	0
Stony Creek	54	~3	51	94
San Joaquin Valley				
Mainstem San Joaquin River[6]	50	50	0	0
Cosumnes River	34	34	0	0
Mokelumne River	69	46	23	33
Calaveras River	~38	38	0?	0?
Stanislaus River	113	46	67	59
Tuolumne River	99	47	52	53
Merced River	99	43	56	57
Upper San Joaquin River[7]	171	0	171	100
Kings River	84	0	84	100

[1] Additional, minor streams such as Thomes, Paynes, Cache and Putah creeks and perhaps a dozen others in the Sacramento Valley historically supported salmon runs (Fry 1961)-- probably only the fall run and only during wet years when streamflows were adequate. The historical upstream distribution of salmon in those streams is too poorly known to allow inclusion in this table. Futhermore, current salmon production in those streams is limited because of a number of factors, including low streamflows, habitat degradation and obstruction by irrigation canal crossings (CDFG 1993).

[2] Lengths of all stream reaches known or presumed to have been traversed or utilized by salmon in the drainage are included.

[3] Length between the mouth of the stream and the current upstream limit.

[4] Length of stream gained is given in parentheses; this situation applies only to Deer Creek.

[5] From Rio Vista in the northern Sacramento-San Joaquin Delta, upstream to the confluence of the Upper (Little) Sacramento and Pit rivers.

[6] From Mossdale in the southern Sacramento-San Joaquin Delta, upstream to the confluence of the Merced River. This stretch lacks spawning gravels and serves primarily as a migration corridor.

[7] Includes the mainstem San Joaquin River above the confluence of the Merced River.

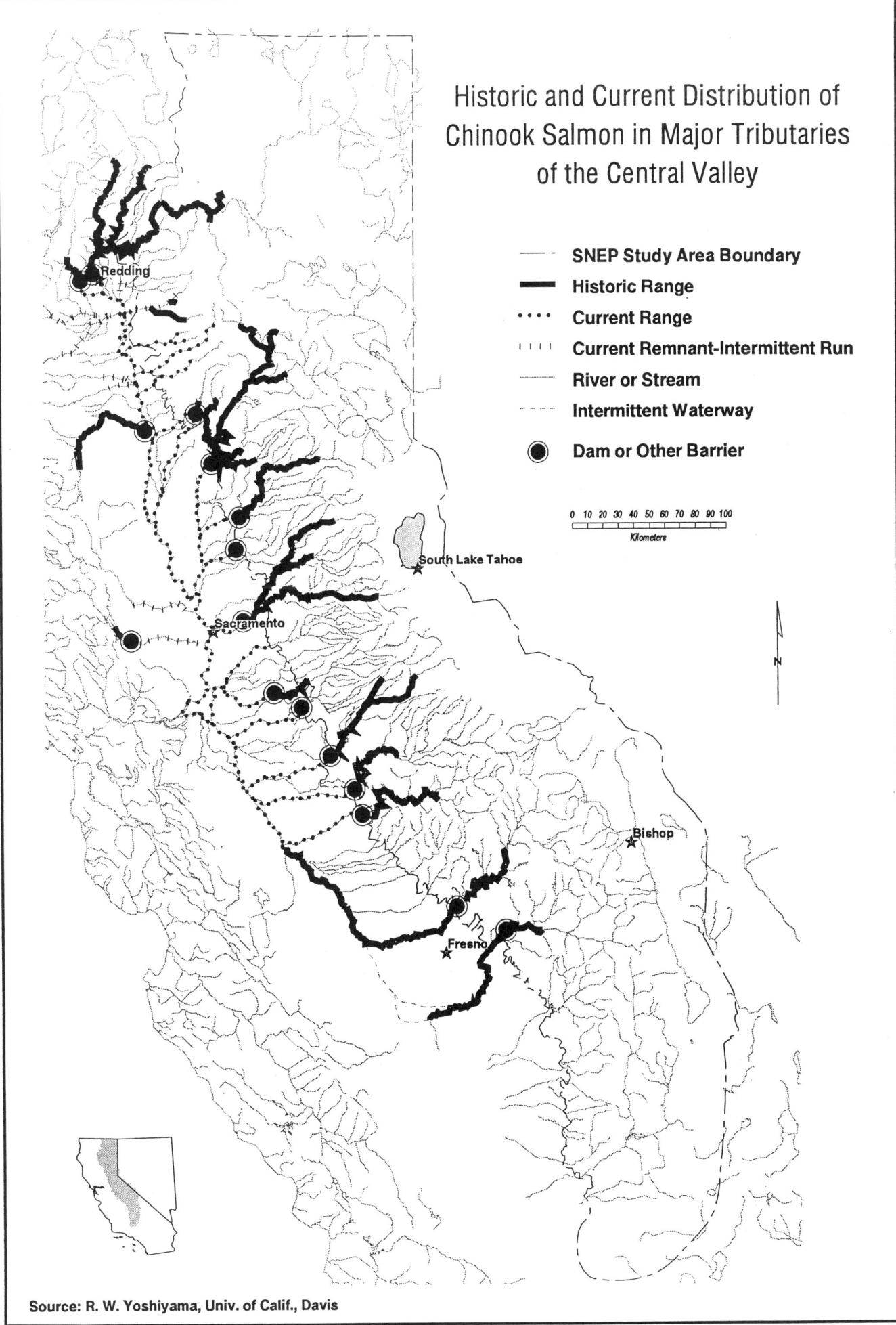

Historic and Current Distribution of Chinook Salmon in Major Tributaries of the Central Valley

SNEP Study Area Boundary
Historic Range
Current Range
Current Remnant-Intermittent Run
River or Stream
Intermittent Waterway
Dam or Other Barrier

0 10 20 30 40 50 60 70 80 90 100
Kilometers

Redding

South Lake Tahoe

Sacramento

Bishop

Fresno

N

Source: R. W. Yoshiyama, Univ. of Calif., Davis

361

SNEP GIS December 01, 1995

ROLAND A. KNAPP
Sierra Nevada Aquatic Research
    Laboratory
University of California
Mammoth Lakes, California
and
Marine Science Institute
University of California
Santa Barbara, California

8

Non-Native Trout in Natural Lakes of the Sierra Nevada: An Analysis of Their Distribution and Impacts on Native Aquatic Biota

Sierra Nevada Ecosystem Project: Final report to Congress, vol. III, *Assessments, Commissioned Reports, and Background Information.* Davis: University of California, Centers for Water and Wildland Resources, 1996.

This report was funded in part by the Sierra Nevada Ecosystem Project (SNEP). Under the agreement with SNEP, I agreed to conduct a literature review of the distribution of non-native trout in the Sierra Nevada, and their impacts on native aquatic biota. Because existing literature did not allow an adequate analysis of the current trout distribution, I have included results based on a compilation of data from the California Department of Fish and Game and the National Park Service. The geographic information system (GIS) data compilation effort was funded by the U.S.D.A. Pacific Southwest Research Station.

ABSTRACT

The objective of this study was to describe the current distribution of introduced trout in the Sierra Nevada relative to the historic fish distribution, and to review the impacts of introduced trout on native aquatic biota. Historically, trout were absent above approximately 1800 m in the Sierra Nevada. In the mid-1800's, however, widespread trout introductions were begun to move fish into formerly fishless lakes and streams to enhance recreational fishing. Trout stocking is now conducted by the California Department of Fish and Game, and the current program is intended to supplement and maintain existing populations of non-native trout. As a result of past and current trout stocking, the proportion of trout-containing lakes in the Sierra Nevada has increased from less than 1% of all lakes larger than 1 ha (N=4000+) to approximately 63% of all such lakes. National forests have a much higher proportion of lakes containing non-native trout than national parks, with trout in at least 85% of the lakes larger than 1 ha. Only 7% are known to be fishless. In Sequoia, Kings Canyon, and Yosemite National Parks, the proportion of lakes with fish has increased from less than 1% to approximately 35-50% of such lakes. The greater number of fishless lakes in the national parks than national forests is due in part to the termination of fish stocking in park lakes in the 1970's. Recent surveys in Sequoia, Kings Canyon, and Yosemite National Parks show that trout have disappeared from 29-44% of previously stocked lakes. Although data on the distribution of non-native trout in Sierran streams is generally lacking, data from Yosemite National Park suggests that trout are likely to occur in at least 60% of all streams. Given the current ubiquity of trout in the formerly fishless portion of the Sierra Nevada, their impacts on native aquatic biota are likely widespread.

Introduced trout are affecting the distribution of a wide range of native aquatic species in the Sierra Nevada, including native fishes, amphibians, zooplankton, and benthic macroinvertebrates. The introduction of non-native trout has caused widespread declines of native trout species such as golden trout as a result of hybridization, competition, and predation. The decline of at least one amphibian species, the mountain yellow-legged frog, has been attributed largely to predation by introduced trout. Predation by introduced trout has also caused dramatic changes in zooplankton and benthic invertebrate species composition in lakes, shifting the dominant species in these communities from large-bodied to small-bodied forms.

The majority of lakes stocked by the California Department of Fish and Game lie within designated wilderness areas, areas managed for their natural values. Given that trout stocking serves to maintain an artificial fishery that has substantial impacts on native aquatic biota, and that continuation of this fishery is strongly supported by portions of the public, the ongoing stocking of trout poses inherent management conflicts. Resolution of these conflicts will require additional research on the ecological and sociological consequences of alternatives to the current trout stocking program that provide a better balance between the needs of aquatic ecosytems and those of recreational interests.

Key Words: alpine habitats, biodiversity, cold water fisheries, lakes, recreation, streams, watersheds, wilderness, food chains, amphibians, aquatic invertebrates, introduced species, plankton, Sierra bioregion, conservation biology, endangered species, federal lands, geographic information systems, land management, park management, restoration.

INTRODUCTION

The Sierra Nevada is largely federally-owned, with the majority of its 5 million hectares lying within national parks, national monuments, and national forests (Palmer 1988). Eighty-four percent of the national park acreage and 24% of the national forest acreage is designated wilderness (Palmer 1988). Because national parks and wilderness areas are supposedly managed primarily for natural ecosystems, a widely-held public perception is that the Sierra Nevada, particularly the higher elevation areas, are largely protected from anthropogenic impacts. Although recent research on forest ecosystems, fire ecology, and air quality illustrate that anthropogenic influences are impacting even the most remote portions of the Sierra Nevada (see SNEP chapters), until recently there has been little evidence to suggest that high elevation aquatic ecosystems are at risk. Recent research, however, suggests that these ecosystems are among the most disturbed in the range.

Prior to the mid-nineteenth century, nearly all lakes and streams in the Sierra Nevada above 1800 m (6000') were fishless. As a result of 150 years of fish stocking throughout the Sierra Nevada, however, all watersheds now contain as many as five non-native trout species (Jenkins et al. 1994). Although fish stocking was curtailed in Sequoia, Kings Canyon, and Yosemite National Parks in the 1970's and completely halted in 1991, stocking of non-native trout species continues in the national forests, including designated wilderness.

Although the stocking of trout into lakes and streams has long been viewed as an activity that benefits recreationists and has few negative consequences, results of recent research into the effects of non-native trout on naturally-fishless ecosystems is challenging this view. Studies of aquatic ecosystems in the Sierra Nevada show that introduced trout can have severe impacts on native trout (e.g., Gerstung 1988), amphibians (Bradford 1989; Bradford et al. 1993), zooplankton (Stoddard 1987), and benthic macroinvertebrates (Melack et al. 1989; Bradford et al. 1994a), and suggest that some aquatic species might be driven to extinction by the current nearly ubiquitous distribution of non-native trout (Bradford et al. 1993). Similar effects of non-native trout appear to be common in mountain ranges throughout western North America (e.g., Anderson 1971; Bahls 1992). Interest in the effects of non-native fishes on aquatic ecosystems is likely to increase rapidly during the next decade, as several amphibian species are listed under the federal Endangered Species Act.

The purpose of this report was to provide an overview of the historic (i.e., pre-1850) and current fish distribution in the Sierra Nevada, and to review the impacts of non-native trout on Sierran aquatic ecosystems. Specifically, the report is divided into four major sections to address the following topics:

(1) The historic distribution of native fishes in the Sierra Nevada. An understanding of the historic distribution provides the basis for comparisons with the current trout distribution, and is critical in order to assess the magnitude of changes that have occurred as a result of trout stocking.

(2) The history of trout stocking in the Sierra Nevada. This brief review will summarize the agencies and groups responsible for fish stocking from the mid-nineteenth century to the present, and will highlight recent changes in fish stocking practices in the Sierra Nevada.

(3) The current state of knowledge pertaining to present-day trout distributions in the Sierra Nevada. This review utilizes information obtained from published papers, agency documents, and a geographic information system (GIS), to provide an overview of the current distribution of non-native trout in portions of three national forests and three national parks in the Sierra Nevada. This review also serves to highlight gaps in the available information pertaining to the distribution of non-native trout in the Sierra Nevada.

(4) The impacts of non-native trout on aquatic ecosystems in the Sierra Nevada. An improved understanding of these impacts will assist in designing aquatic ecosystem management strategies for which the consequences (both beneficial and harmful) are as well understood as possible.

Based on the review of the distribution of non-native trout in the Sierra Nevada and their impacts on native aquatic species, I then (1) discuss the risks associated with current management of aquatic ecosystems in the Sierra Nevada, (2) outline several alternatives to the current management of aquatic ecosystems and briefly discuss the ecological and sociological consequences of each alternative, (3) recommend several immediate changes to the current trout stocking program, and (4) suggest directions for future research aimed at providing a better understanding of the ecological consequences of alternatives to the current trout stocking program in the Sierra Nevada.

METHODS

The general geographic boundaries of this study coincide with those adopted by the Sierra Nevada Ecosystem Project (figure 1). Information on the historic fish distribution, the history of trout stocking, and the impacts of non-native trout on aquatic ecosystems within the study area was acquired through literature surveys of published papers and unpublished reports. Literature searches were conducted using CD-ROM facilities at the University of California, Santa Barbara. These searches were supplemented with information obtained during visits to offices of the California Department of Fish and Game (DFG) and the National Park Service. Information on the current fish distribution in the Sierra Nevada was obtained through literature reviews and compilation of data from the DFG and the National Park Service. Stocking records for lakes within the study area and any available site-specific information was obtained from the DFG Regions 2, 4, and 5 (northern Sierra, western Sierra, and eastern Sierra, respectively). These records were compiled into a geographic information system (GIS) utilizing 1:100,000 and 1:24,000 USGS digital line graphs (DLG's) of hydrologic features, with additional coverages including elevation, watershed boundaries, and land ownership.

RESULTS: FISH DISTRIBUTIONS

The GIS revealed major information gaps pertaining to the current distribution of trout in the Sierra Nevada. First, current lake-specific information is lacking for large portions of the Sierra Nevada. For example, DFG Regions 2 and 4 had information primarily on lakes that are currently stocked with trout. Within these regions, there was little information on lakes that are not currently stocked but are still likely to contain non-native trout (e.g., as a result of past stocking). In contrast, DFG Region 5 had information on approximately 95% of the lakes larger than 1 ha within their jurisdiction. Yosemite and Sequoia-Kings Canyon National Parks both had data on a large proportion of lakes within their jurisdiction, although records from Yosemite National Park were more extensive and more detailed.

The second data gap pertains to the current distribution of trout in streams within the study area. This distribution is very poorly described by existing data, and records are available only for Yosemite National Park. As a result, I was unable to provide a detailed analysis of fluvial trout distributions within the study area, and was forced to restrict the scope of this report primarily to trout distributions in lakes.

As a result of these data gaps, I obtained summary information for the entire study area, but all detailed analyses of the current distribution of trout in the Sierra Nevada are based on Sequioa, Kings Canyon, and Yosemite National Parks and that portion of the Sierra Nevada within DFG Region 5 (figure 1). The presented data serve to describe the current trout distribution in a portion of the Sierra Nevada, cover a large fraction of the historically fishless areas in the Sierra Nevada (figure 1 and 2) where the most dramatic changes in fish distribution have occurred, and illustrate the large differences in trout distributions between national forests and national parks.

Historic fish distribution

Nearly all lakes and streams in the Sierra Nevada above 1800 m (6000') were historically fishless, but several native fish species were found historically in streams, rivers, and a few lakes at lower elevations around the perimeter of the Sierra Nevada (figure 2). A description of these native fish distributions is given in Moyle et al. (1995).

Brief history of trout stocking

Although many fish species have been introduced to the Sierra Nevada (Moyle 1976), trout were by far the most commonly introduced group at elevations above the valley floors. Starting in the mid-1800's and continuing until the 1960's, trout have been introduced into formerly fishless streams and lakes to provide recreational fishing (Christenson 1977). Although some of these introductions were interbasin transfers of trout native to the Sierra Nevada (e.g., golden trout, rainbow trout, Lahontan cutthroat trout), many were introductions of trout species not native to California. These included brook trout (Salvelinus fontinalis), lake trout (Salvelinus namaycush), and Atlantic salmon (Salmo salar) from eastern North America, kokanee salmon (Oncorhynchus nerka) from northwestern North America, and brown trout (Salmo trutta) from Europe (Christenson 1977). Early trout planting efforts were aimed primarily at establishing trout in formerly fishless waters, and were carried out largely by sporting groups (e.g., Bishop Fish Planting Club, Sierra Club, Visalia Sportsmens Club). In addition, the U.S. military conducted extensive trout planting in Sequoia, Kings Canyon, and Yosemite National Parks (Christenson 1977). In the early 1900's, the California Fish and Game Commission (the precursor to the current California Department of Fish and Game) began coordinating the fish planting effort, and by the 1940's fish stocking was conducted almost entirely by the California Department of Fish and Game (DFG). Today, the DFG is responsible for nearly all authorized trout stocking throughout the Sierra Nevada, although the emphasis has changed from introducing trout into fishless lakes and streams to stocking waters to augment or maintain existing non-native trout populations.

Sequoia, Kings Canyon, and Yosemite National Parks began phasing out trout stocking in 1969 as a result of recommendations in the Leopold Report (Leopold 1963). In 1972, the National Park Service (NPS) released its policy that stated, "No artificial stocking of fish species exotic to a park will occur; artificial stocking of fish or eggs may only be employed to reestablish a native species. Naturally barren waters will not be stocked with either native or exotic fish species" (NPS 1975). Limited stocking was continued until 1991, when an agreement was negotiated with the DFG to terminate all fish stocking in these parks. Trout stocking is permitted on all other federal lands in the Sierra Nevada (67% of the Sierra Nevada; Palmer 1988), including national forest wilderness areas, except those waters within wilderness areas that were not stocked prior to federal wilderness designation (Bahls 1992).

Although concern over the impacts of non-native trout on aquatic biota in the Sierra Nevada is increasing (Bradford et al. 1994a; Knapp 1995a, Bahls (1992) concluded that trout stocking is generally conducted with only minimal concern for native fish species (including trout), amphibians, and other native aquatic biota. Paradoxically, this is true even in federally designated wilderness areas, where lands are supposed to be managed in such a way as to maintain their natural conditions (Kloepfer et al. 1994). Although some states in the western U.S. attempt to minimize impacts to aquatic ecosystems by stocking trout only into lakes that have been surveyed, this is not the case in California (Bahls 1992). In addition, there appears to be little emphasis on determining whether currently-stocked lakes are actually self-sustaining. In a recently surveyed portion of the Sierra Nevada, the majority of stocked lakes do not need to be stocked to maintain their fish populations (Matthews and Knapp 1995).

Current fish distribution

Despite over a century of effort being expended to stock trout in the Sierra Nevada, information on the current distribution of trout is rudimentary at best. While DFG and NPS records indicate that all major watersheds in the Sierra Nevada contain at least one species of introduced trout, lake-specific and stream-specific information on the presence or absence of fish is generally incomplete and outdated. Much of the DFG data is not computerized, and has never been summarized to provide an overview of the current distribution of trout in the Sierra Nevada. Although estimates of the number of trout-containing versus troutless waters have been published for portions of the Sierra Nevada, these estimates were based on interviews with fishery managers (Bahls 1992) or on the results of surveys from a very small number of waters scattered throughout the Sierra Nevada (Jenkins et al. 1994), and may not provide an accurate picture of the Sierra-wide distribution of trout.

Sierra-wide trout distribution. Bahls (1992) reported that of 4,131 mountain lakes in California (lakes higher than 800 m; these are primarily in the Sierra Nevada), 63% contained introduced fish and 52% were currently stocked. Of the estimated 37% of lakes that remain fishless, most are small (<2 ha), shallow (<3 m), and generally incapable of supporting trout populations (Bahls 1992). Only 3% of larger lakes (>2 ha, >3 m deep) remain fishless. Based on a survey of 30 randomly selected high elevation lakes (>2400 m and >1 ha) throughout the Sierra Nevada, Jenkins et al. (1994) used the Environmental Monitoring and Assessment Program (EMAP) procedure (Paulsen et al. 1991) to extrapolate their results to all lakes above 2400 m in the study region. Jenkins et al. (1994) estimated that 1404 lakes in the Sierra Nevada met their selection criteria, and projected that one or more species of non-native trout would occur in 63%. Based on the relative frequency of occurrence, golden trout were projected to occur in 36% of lakes, rainbow trout in 33%, brook trout in 16%, brown trout in 8%, and cutthroat trout in 0.5% of lakes.

  <u>Trout distribution on three national forests</u>. Christenson (1977) suggested that as many as 95% of California's naturally fishless mountain lakes outside of national parks currently contain fish. Although there are no published descriptions of the distribution of non-native trout on national forests, analysis of the data from DFG Region 5 suggests that this estimate may be quite accurate. The Sierra Nevada portion of the DFG Region 5 includes approximately 700 mountain lakes larger than 1 ha and 16 reservoirs. The DFG Region 5 database includes information on 649 lakes and all 16 reservoirs. The 649 lakes include 452 lakes on the Inyo National Forest, 116 lakes on the Sierra National Forest, and 81 lakes on theToiyabe National Forest. Eighty-four percent of the lakes lie within four federally-designated wilderness areas (Ansel Adams, Golden Trout, Hoover, and John Muir), 2% lie within a Forest Service Research Natural Area (Harvey Monroe Hall), and the remaining 14% lie outside of wilderness areas. The majority of the lakes lie between 3000-3500 m (mean=3179 m, S.D.=285), and nearly all have surface areas of less than 10 ha (mean=6.0 ha, S.D.=13.4). Although all 649 were originally without trout, 85% now contain non-native trout, 7% are fishless, and the status of the remaining 8% is unknown. Fish-containing and fishless lakes do not differ in their elevations (Mann-Whitney U-test: U=1.0, P>0.3; figure 3), but fish-containing lakes are significantly larger than fishless lakes (Mann-Whitney U-test: U=6.6, P<0.001; figure 4). Brook trout are the most common species (51% of lakes), followed by rainbow trout, golden trout, brown trout, cutthroat trout, and kokanee salmon and hybrid trout populations. The frequency of occurrence of these fish species changes with elevation (figure 5), with the most common species being rainbow trout at the lowest elevations, brook trout at intermediate elevations, and golden trout at the highest elevations. Although fishless lakes are found at nearly all elevations (figure 3 and 5), they are relatively uncommon (figure 5) and nearly all are very small (<2 ha)(figure 4). Fishless lakes are most common at low and high elevations, and least common at intermediate elevations (figure 5). Many of these lakes may be fishless because they are too small and shallow to support fish populations.

  The DFG regularly stocks trout into 46% of the 649 lakes. The remaining 54% either contain self-sustaining trout populations or are fishless. Thirty-five percent of the stocked lakes are stocked annually and 65% are stocked every two years. Stocked lakes are significantly lower in elevation than unstocked lakes (Mann-Whitney U-test: U=2.6, P<0.01; figure 6) and significantly larger than unstocked lakes (Mann-Whitney U-test: U=8.8, P<0.0001; figure 7). Of the 302 stocked lakes, nearly all are stocked with rainbow or golden trout fingerlings.

  Although the mountain lakes within DFG Region 5 are subject to regular fish stocking, they are surveyed infrequently. During the past ten years (1985-94), only 32%

were surveyed for fish and 14% have never been surveyed. In addition, surveys have typically been restricted to fish populations, with no effort being made to determine the status of native aquatic species. The hundreds of small lakes and ponds not represented in the DFG Region 5 database also have not been surveyed.

Figures 8 and 9 illustrate the dramatic changes in fish distributions that have occurred within DFG Region 5 since approximately 1850. Prior to fish stocking, the upper portion of the French Creek and Piute Creek watersheds was entirely fishless (figure 8). Today, nearly all of the larger lakes (≥ 1 ha) and a substantial proportion of the smaller ponds (<1 ha) contain fish (figure 9). Only two lakes are known to remain in a fishless condition. Within these watersheds, the DFG Region 5 has information on 56 of the lakes, and 70% of these are regularly stocked with trout. No information is available on the streams, but because trout readily move out of lakes to colonize inlet and outlet streams, nearly all stream sections shown in figure 9 are likely to contain non-native trout.

Trout distribution in national parks - Numerous gillnet and snorkeling surveys of non-native trout have been conducted in Sequoia, Kings Canyon, and Yosemite National Parks, but these surveys have generally been limited to a small subset of the total number of lakes in each park. Assuming that the sampled lakes are representative of park lakes, all three national parks contain a substantially greater proportion of fishless lakes than do national forests.

Extensive study of non-native trout distributions in Yosemite National Park lakes and streams was conducted during 1951-52 (Wallis 1952). This study involved the compilation of all available historical lake information (e.g., stocking records, angler surveys), and surveys of 78% of 343 park lakes larger than 1 ha and the majority of park streams. Based on his surveys, Wallis (1952) concluded that approximately 62% of the lakes and 78% of streams contained non-native trout populations.

Since the study by Wallis (1952), the number of lakes containing non-native trout has declined as a result of the termination of fish stocking. Botti (1977) surveyed 102 lakes in Yosemite National Park that had been stocked between 1963 and 1977, and found that non-native trout had disappeared from 22%. An additional 22% were likely to become fishless because of a lack of suitable spawning habitat. Therefore, 66% of the lakes surveyed by Botti (1977) should still contain non-native trout populations. Lakes that lost their trout populations after stocking was halted were at significantly lower elevations (Mann-Whitney U-test: U=5.2, P<0.0001; figure 10) and were smaller (P<0.003; figure 12) than lakes that retained trout. Of the lakes that lost their trout populations, nearly all were those formerly stocked with rainbow trout (figure 11). In contrast, brook trout were only lost from three lakes after the termination of trout stocking. As a result, the relative abundance of the four non-native trout found by Botti (1977) changed markedly after trout stocking was halted (figure 12). The combination of data from Wallis (1952) and Botti (1977) suggests that approximately 34% of Yosemite National Park lakes still contain fish (Elliot and Loughlin 1992). The stocking history and current trout status in Yosemite National Park lakes and streams is shown in figure 13.

Similar trout distributions are found in Sequoia and Kings Canyon National Parks. A recent survey of 312 of 2801 naturally fishless lake-sites (lakes and adjacent ponds, if present) scattered throughout Sequoia and Kings Canyon National Parks found introduced trout in 46% (Bradford et al. 1993). However, a considerable amount of inter-drainage variation in the relative proportions of fish-containing versus fishless lakes is apparent from a second survey by Bradford et al. (1994a). This survey included 104 lakes in a particularly remote portion of Kings Canyon National Park, and trout were only found in 17%.

As in Yosemite National Park, the greater proportion of fishless lakes in Sequoia and Kings Canyon National Parks than on national forest lands is due at least in part to the termination of fish stocking. Zardus et al. (1977) sampled 137 lakes that had been stocked with trout between 1963 and 1977, and found that 13% of the lakes had returned to a fishless condition by 1977. An additional 16% were expected to eventually revert to a fishless condition because of poor spawning habitat.

RESULTS: IMPACTS OF TROUT ON NATIVE AQUATIC SPECIES

Trout are highly-effective predators and their impacts on prey species are well-documented (e.g., Northcote 1988). This impact may be particularly severe in oligotrophic lakes such as those found in the Sierra Nevada, since the relatively simple food webs of such lakes are believed to make them especially sensitive to impacts from introduced species (Li and Moyle 1981; McQueen, et al. 1986). In fact, based on an extensive survey of lakes in the Sierra Nevada, Bradford et al. (1994a) concluded that "the most profound human impacts on aquatic communities in the High Sierra appear to be related to historical and on-going stocking of exotic fish species into High Sierra waters". The following review documents the effect of introduced trout on native fishes, amphibians, zooplankton, lake benthic invertebrates, stream benthic invertebrates, and community structure in the Sierra Nevada.

Native fishes

The native fish fauna of the Sierra Nevada has been altered substantially by the introduction of non-native trout, with impacts of introductions being particularly severe for native trout. The range of the two golden trout subspecies was greatly reduced by the 1970's as a result of non-native trout introductions (USFS 1982). Extensive hybridization with introduced rainbow trout and displacement by introduced brook trout precipitated the listing of the Little Kern golden trout under the Endangered Species Act. Since its listing, non-native trout have been eradicated from the entire Little Kern River and pure populations of Little Kern golden trout are being re-established. During the 1950's and 1960's, introduced brown trout displaced the California golden trout from much of the South Fork Kern River. Recovery of this subspecies required the removal of brown trout from over 100 km of river and the construction of two fish barriers. The recent discovery of brown trout above the lower barrier, however, has increased the likelihood of brown trout reinvading the upper South Fork Kern River. Because of this threat, the U.S. Fish and Wildlife Service is currently considering listing the California golden trout under the Endangered Species Act.

The status of native rainbow trout on the west side of the Sierra Nevada is unclear. Although rainbow trout populations probably still occur in most streams and rivers where they occurred historically, extensive introgression with introduced hatchery rainbow trout is likely. Although no data are currently available to support this possibility in the Sierra

373

Nevada, introgression has been documented between hatchery rainbow trout and the native rainbow trout of the upper Sacramento Basin (Oncorhynchus mykiss stonei; (Behnke 1992).

The habitat of the Lahontan cutthroat trout has been reduced by over 90% throughout its native range by massive habitat alteration, water diversions, and overfishing. In the remaining highly isolated populations, however, cutthroat trout are subject to hybridization and competition with and predation by introduced trout (Gerstung 1988). Because of the severity of its decline, the Lahontan cutthroat trout was listed under the Endangered Species Act in 1970. The recently released Lahontan cutthroat trout recovery plan (Coffin and Cowan 1995) calls for the removal of non-native trout from portions of the native range of Lahontan cutthroat trout as a critical recovery strategy. Declines of non-trout fishes in the Sierra Nevada are widespread (Moyle and Nichols 1973; Moyle and Nichols 1974; La Rivers 1994), but the few studies detailing the causes of these declines suggest that they have been caused primarily by habitat alteration and not trout introductions (e.g., Moyle and Nichols 1974).

Amphibians

Numerous native species of amphibians are found in the Sierra Nevada (see Jennings 1995 for a detailed review). Several anuran species are reported to be declining in abundance (Yosemite toad: Bufo canorus; California red-legged frog: Rana aurora draytonii; foothill yellow-legged frog: R. boylii; and mountain yellow-legged frog: R. muscosa: Moyle 1973; Hayes and Jennings 1986; Bradford 1991; Sherman and Morton 1993; Bradford et al. 1994b; Drost and Fellers 1994). Declines of the three Rana species have been attributed in part to predation by introduced fishes, including trout (e.g., Hayes and Jennings 1986; Bradford 1989; Bradford et al. 1993). The California red-legged frog and the foothill yellow-legged frog are found in the western foothills of the Sierra Nevada below 1500 m, and inhabit ponds and streams, respectively (Zweifel 1955). The proposed negative effect of introduced fishes on the California red-legged frog and the foothill yellow-legged frog is based largely on observations of a lack of overlap between either of the species and introduced fishes (Hayes and Jennings 1986). These data, however, are confounded by the fact that habitats containing introduced fishes are also frequently inhabited by the bullfrog (Rana catesbeiana) (Hayes and Jennings 1986), another introduced species proposed as a cause for the decline (Moyle 1973; Hayes and Jennings 1986). In addition, former habitats of these species that now contain introduced fishes have often also been altered by land management practices. As a result, the importance of introduced fish relative to bullfrogs and habitat alterations as a factor leading to the declines of the California red-legged frog and the foothill yellow-legged frog remains unclear (Hayes and Jennings 1986).

The mountain yellow-legged frog is endemic to the Sierra Nevada and a few sites in southern California. Historically, the mountain yellow-legged frog was widespread throughout the Sierra Nevada at elevations above 1500 m (Zweifel 1955), having been present in all major watersheds on the west and east sides of the Sierra Nevada. However, based on a recent resurvey of historic localities in the central Sierra Nevada, Drost and Fellers (1994) reported that the mountain yellow-legged frog was present in fewer than 15% of the sites where it was found in 1915.

Several attributes of this species make it particularly vulnerable to predation and subsequent extirpation by non-native trout. First, adult mountain yellow-legged frogs are highly aquatic and are found primarily in lakes (most of which now contain trout). Second, in contrast to tadpoles of other Sierran anurans that complete metamorphosis to the terrestrial stage in a single summer, mountain yellow-legged frog tadpoles generally require at least two years before metamorphosis to the terrestrial stage. This overwintering requirement restricts breeding to bodies of water that are deep enough to avoid oxygen depletion when ice-covered (>1.5 m; Mullally and Cunningham 1956; Bradford 1983). The majority of these deeper lakes, however, now contain introduced trout.

There is substantial evidence that introduced trout have severely reduced the abundance of mountain yellow-legged frogs in the Sierra Nevada. As early as 1924, Grinnell and Storer (1924) reported that mountain yellow-legged frog tadpoles and introduced trout rarely co-occur in lakes and ponds in the Sierra Nevada. This observation has been quantified repeatedly in different parts of the Sierra Nevada (Bradford 1989; Bradford and Gordon 1992; Bradford et al. 1993; Drost and Fellers 1994). This lack of overlap is assumed to be the result of predation by trout on the mountain yellow-legged frog, an assertion supported by Needham and Vestal (1938), who observed trout preying on mountain yellow-legged frogs in a lake into which trout had recently been introduced. Given that the presence of fish generally makes a pond or lake unsuitable for mountain yellow-legged frogs, that lakes smaller than 1 ha are generally too shallow to support mountain yellow-legged frogs (Matthews and Knapp 1995), and that 34-85% of formerly fishless lakes larger than 1 ha now contain introduced trout (see Results: Current fish distribution), the amount of suitable habitat for mountain yellow-legged frogs has likely been reduced by a similar amount.

In addition to the direct impact that non-native trout have on mountain yellow-legged frogs via predation, Bradford et al. (1993) proposed that fish could also impact mountain yellow-legged frogs indirectly by isolating remaining populations. They reported that fish introductions into lakes in Sequoia and Kings Canyon National Parks have resulted in a four-fold reduction in effective mountain yellow-legged frog population sizes and a 10-fold reduction in connectivity between populations. Because amphibian populations often fluctuate widely under natural conditions (Pechmann et al. 1991; Gulve 1994), and small populations are more likely to go extinct under stochastic population fluctuations than are large populations (Wilcox 1980; Hanski 1989; Hanksi and Gilpin 1991), Bradford et al. (1993) proposed that the reduction in mountain yellow-legged frog population size caused by trout introductions is likely to have increased the rate at which individual populations are extirpated. In addition, they suggested that the increased isolation of mountain yellow-legged frog populations would reduce the probability of recolonization of formerly occupied sites. This reduction could result from the smaller size of potential source populations, increased distance from source populations, and predation by introduced trout on dispersing frogs (Bradford et al. 1993). Increased isolation of remaining populations could also result in increased inbreeding with a resulting decrease in genetic diversity within populations (Reh and Seitz 1990).

In a recent study, Blaustein et al. (1994) proposed that the transmission of pathogens by introduced fishes may be another means by which trout introductions indirectly impact amphibian species such as the mountain yellow-legged frog. Blaustein et al. (1994) reported that the extremely high mortality of western toad (<u>Bufo</u> <u>boreas</u>) egg masses in a lake in the Cascade Mountains in Oregon was caused by a <u>Saprolegnia</u> fungal infection. This fungus is frequently found on trout raised in hatcheries, including on those species commonly introduced into lakes in the Sierra Nevada (Seymour 1970; Richards and Pickering 1978; Pohl-Branschield and Holtz 1985; Willoughby 1986). The recent discovery of <u>Saprolegnia</u> fungus infecting eggs of the mountain yellow-legged frog in the Sierra Nevada (Knapp 1993a) suggests that this proposed impact should be investigated more fully in Sierran amphibians.

Several additional anuran and salamander species are found in the Sierra Nevada, but direct impacts to these species from introduced trout are either unlikely because of a lack of overlap in habitat use between the amphibian species and introduced trout, or are likely but undocumented. All of the non-<u>Rana</u> anuran species in the Sierra Nevada (western toad, Yosemite toad, Pacific chorus frog) are largely terrestrial and generally breed in shallow ponds. Because these ponds are subject to desiccation in summer and freezing in winter and are therefore unlikely to contain fish, direct effects of introduced trout on these amphibian species are probably minimal. Most salamanders found in the Sierra Nevada (<u>Ensatina</u> sp., <u>Hydromantes</u> sp., <u>Batrachoseps</u> sp.) live and breed in semi-aquatic sites such as springs and seeps, and are therefore also unlikely to be impacted by introduced trout. However, the long-toed salamander (<u>Ambystoma</u> <u>macrodactylum</u>), found in the central and northern Sierra Nevada, appears to be restricted largely to fishless lakes (Bradford and Gordon 1992). Similar distributions have been described for the long-toed salamander in other mountain ranges, and for other species of lake-dwelling salamanders whose habitat contains introduced trout. For example, in lakes in North Cascades National Park, densities of the long-toed salamander were reduced in the presence of introduced trout (Liss and Larson 1991). The closely-related <u>Ambystoma</u> <u>gracile</u> was also much less common in lakes containing introduced trout than in fishless lakes. Burger (1950) reported the extinction of neotenic <u>Ambystoma</u> <u>tigrinum</u> <u>nebulosum</u> in a mountain lake in Colorado after the introduction of trout. Therefore, ample evidence exists that trout can impact lake-dwelling ambystomatid salamanders, and suggests that the effect of introduced trout on long-toed salamander populations in the Sierra Nevada should be investigated more thoroughly.

Although existing data suggests that the introduction of trout into Sierran lakes has caused local extirpations of at least one amphibian species (mountain yellow-legged frog), there are no published studies that have investigated the likelihood of amphibians recolonizing habitats if fish are removed or disappear as a result of a termination in stocking. Some recent survey data, however, suggests that mountain yellow-legged frogs can readily recolonize lakes from nearby refugia. Zardus et al. (1977) presented biological data on 137 lakes in Sequoia and Kings Canyon National Parks, including the presence or absence of mountain yellow-legged frogs and introduced trout. They reported finding trout but no frogs in three lakes in the Palisade Basin ("Barrett Lakes 1, 2, and 3"). Stocking was apparently discontinued in these lakes in the late 1970's or early 1980's. When these lakes were revisited in 1993, Barrett Lake 3 still contained fish and no mountain yellow-legged frogs, but Barrett Lakes 1 and 2 had reverted to a fishless condition and contained large mountain yellow-legged frog populations (>100 adults;

Knapp 1993b). Several nearby ponds and lakes were probably never stocked with trout (Jenkins et al. 1994), and mountain yellow-legged frogs in Barrett Lakes 1 and 2 probably recolonized from these refugia. Second, in a study of the aquatic biota of several lakes in Kings Canyon National Park, Taylor and Erman (1980) reported that all lakes in their study contained trout, including "Lower Sixty" Lake. When this lake was revisited in 1990, it was fishless and contained a very large mountain yellow-legged frog population (>500 adults; Knapp 1990). Although it is possible that mountain yellow-legged frogs were present in "Lower Sixty" Lake during the Taylor and Erman (1980) study (since they apparently did not survey the lake for mountain yellow-legged frogs during their research), the scarcity of lakes in which trout and frogs coexist (Bradford 1989) makes it more likely that mountain yellow-legged frogs recolonized this lake after the disappearance of introduced trout. Several nearby lakes have never been stocked with trout, contain large mountain yellow-legged frog populations (Zardus, et al. 1977; Knapp 1993a), and could have served as sources for recolonization of "Lower Sixty" Lake. A third potential example of recolonization by mountain yellow-legged frogs is apparently occurring in Wolf Creek Lake, located north of Yosemite National Park. The California Department of Fish and Game poisoned this lake in 1991-92 to remove the resident brook trout population. No mountain yellow-legged frogs were seen in the vicinity of the lake before or during the treatment. In 1994, however, DFG biologists reported seeing mountain yellow-legged frog adults and tadpoles in a small pond immediately adjacent to the lake (Knapp 1995b).

Zooplankton

The ability by fishes to dramatically alter lake zooplankton assemblages is widely recognized (e.g., Carpenter et al. 1985, 1987). The introduction of fish to a lake generally shifts the zooplankton community from one dominated by large-bodied species to one dominated by smaller-bodied species as a result of size-selective fish predation (Northcote 1988). Several studies have documented this effect of introduced trout on zooplankton communities in lakes in the Sierra Nevada. Stoddard (1987) found that the presence or absence of fish (primarily salmonids) was by far the most important predictor of the distribution of zooplankton species among 75 alpine and subalpine lakes in the central Sierra Nevada, with large-bodied species found in fishless lakes and small-bodied species found in lakes with trout. Other studies on Sierran lakes have produced very similar results (Richards et al. 1975; Morgan et al. 1978; Goldman et al. 1979; Melack et al. 1989; Bradford et al. 1994a). Effects of trout on zooplankton communities have also been reported for lakes in the Rocky Mountains and Europe (Anderson 1971, 1972; Northcote et al. 1978; Dawidowicz and Gliwicz 1983; Bahls 1990).

Fish introductions may result in the extirpation of vulnerable zooplankton species. In Sierran lakes, large bodied Daphnia and Diaptomus species are commonly found in fishless lakes but are rarely found in lakes with trout (Reimers 1958; Melack et al. 1989; Bradford et al. 1994a). These results are in agreement with the results of a model by Walters and Vincent (1973) that predicted that large-bodied zooplankton species would be eliminated by trout predation even at low trout densities. Although these Daphnia and Diaptomus species have apparently been extirpated from many lakes in the Sierra Nevada, they are still relatively common in the range (e.g., Melack et al. 1989; Bradford et al.

1994a). In constrast, the phantom midge, <u>Chaoborus</u> <u>americanus</u>, may have been extirpated from the Sierra Nevada by introduced trout (Stoddard 1987). <u>C</u>. <u>americanus</u>, is common in high elevation lakes throughout western North America, but Stoddard (1987) did not find <u>C</u>. <u>americanus</u> in any of his samples from Sierran lakes. <u>C</u>. <u>americanus</u> was also absent from Sierran lakes sampled by Silverman and Erman (1979), Melack et al. (1989) and Bradford et al. (1994a). The possibility that trout introductions are responsible for the absence of <u>Chaoborus</u> in the Sierra Nevada is supported by studies showing the complete elimination of <u>Chaoborus</u> from lakes by introduced trout (Northcote et al. 1978).

Although trout introductions in the Sierra Nevada can apparently cause the extirpation of vulnerable zooplankton species from lakes, it is not clear whether these species reappear in lakes that revert to their original fishless condition. Some studies show that vulnerable zooplankton species do not reappear (Reimers 1958; Anderson 1972, 1974; Leavitt, et al. 1994), while others show that they do (Walters and Vincent 1973; Bahls 1990). Many zooplankton taxa have resting stages (e.g., Thorp and Covich 1991), including those of one species recently shown to remain viable for over 300 years (Hairston et al. 1995). If Sierran zooplankton also have long-lived resting stages, this "egg bank" could allow recovery of the original zooplankton community after fish disappearance. On the contrary, the introduction of fish may cause changes in lake food webs that reduce the ability of some zooplankton species to recolonize (Leavitt et al. 1994). Therefore, further research is necessary to determine the effects of trout introductions on Sierran lake food webs and zooplankton colonization dynamics.

Lake benthic macroinvertebrates

In addition to their effects on zooplankton communities, fish are also capable of altering the structure of lake benthic macroinvertebrate communities. In the Sierra Nevada, high elevation fishless lakes contain mayfly larvae (Ephemeroptera), caddisfly larvae (Trichoptera), aquatic beetles (Coleoptera), and true bugs (Corixidae) that are absent in lakes that contain introduced trout (Reimers 1958; Melack et al. 1989; Bradford et al. 1994a). Similar results have also been documented in other mountain ranges in the western United States (Walters and Vincent 1973; Bahls 1990). No data is currently available to determine the rate at which benthic macroinvertebrates recolonize lakes after trout disappearance.

Stream benthic macroinvertebrates

In contrast to the research effort that has been devoted to quantifying the impact of introduced trout on native lake biota, few studies have examined their effect on native stream biota. In the only study of trout impacts on Sierra Nevada stream benthic taxa that I am aware of, Melack et al. (1989) found significant differences in the macroinvertebrate assemblages of fish and fishless streams; these effects, however, were confined to a minority of the taxa present. Studies outside the Sierra Nevada are equivocal on the impacts of trout, with some studies showing no effect of trout on stream macroinvertebrates (e.g., Allan 1982; Culp 1986), and others showing strong effects (e.g., Hemphill and Cooper 1984; Cooper 1988; Flecker and Townsend 1994). Cooper et al.

(1990) suggest that vulnerability of particular taxa to trout predation is likely a function of a species exchange rate (i.e., immigration/emigration), with taxa with low exchange rates being more vulnerable than those with high exchange rates. If true, then stream communities may be more resistant than lake communities to changes caused by trout predation because of the much greater magnitude of prey exchange in streams.

In addition to direct predation effects on stream macroinvertebrates, trout can also have non-lethal effects. These effects include changes in diel behavior patterns (Douglas et al. 1994), diets, and growth rates (Wiseman et al. 1993).

Community-wide effects

Although the effect of introduced trout on native aquatic biota is often presented as an interaction between two trophic levels (e.g., trout preying on amphibians, trout preying on zooplankton), large changes in one trophic level (e.g., as a result of trout introductions) can have important cascading effects on all parts of the food web (Carpenter and Kitchell 1993). Although multiple trophic level consequences of fish introductions have not received much attention until recently, several potential community-wide effects of trout introductions have been suggested for aquatic ecosystems in the Sierra Nevada. Jennings et al. (1992) demonstrated that the garter snake, Thamnophis elegans, depends heavily on frog tadpoles as prey items, and they suggested that the decline of amphibians in the Sierra Nevada may also result in the decline of T. elegans. Because introduced trout are likely to be one of the causal factors leading to the decline of at least one Sierran amphibian (Bradford 1989; Bradford et al. 1993), trout may also indirectly cause the decline of T. elegans. The loss of tadpoles from aquatic communities may also have impacts on lower trophic levels, since tadpoles can significantly reduce algal biomass (Dickman 1968) and alter lake nutrient cycling (Seale 1980).

Changes in the zooplankton community in lakes as a result of fish predation may also have community-wide consequences. In subalpine Castle Lake (northern Sierra Nevada), a decrease in the density of rainbow trout following the cessation of trout stocking caused an increase in introduced zooplanktivorous fishes, a decrease in zooplankton, a decrease in water transparency, and an increase in primary productivity (Brett et al. 1994; Elser et al. 1995). In a study of alpine lakes in Canada, the loss of all non-native trout following the termination of trout stocking resulted in the an increase in grazing zooplankton and a decrease in phytoplankton abundance (Leavitt et al. 1994). Similar results were found by Stenson et al. (1978) and Carpenter et al. (1985). Similar trophic cascades have also been documented in streams (Power 1990; Flecker and Townsend 1994).

INTERPRETATIONS AND MANAGEMENT IMPLICATIONS

My review shows that although trout were historically absent from large portions of the Sierra Nevada, they are now nearly ubiquitous throughout the range as a result of introductions. National parks have proportionally more fishless waters, due in part to the termination of trout stocking in the national parks and the continued stocking of trout in national forests. This change in national park stocking policies has allowed numerous lakes to revert to their original fishless condition. Introduced trout are having considerable deleterious effects on native fishes (including trout), amphibians, zooplankton, lake macroinvertebrates, and probably stream macroinvertebrates. Introduced trout are also likely causing community-wide effects as a result of direct impacts cascading to other trophic levels. These effects may reduce the chances of lakes reverting to their former community composition even after trout disappear or are removed.

The majority of natural lakes in the Sierra Nevada lie within designated national forest and national park wilderness areas. These areas are supposed to be managed to preserve their original condition (Kloepfer et al. 1994), in part to serve as refugia for species unable to tolerate the more anthropogenically-altered habitats, and to provide control areas against which the effects of anthropogenic influences can be measured. My report suggests that lakes and probably other aquatic habitats in the Sierra Nevada, including those in wilderness areas, may be so extensively modified by the introduction of non-native trout that they are unable to serve as refugia or as control areas. One species may already have disappeared (the phantom midge) and several others endemic to the Sierra Nevada have suffered dramatic population declines (e.g., golden trout, mountain yellow-legged frog). Continued decline of these species will likely result in listing under the Endangered Species Act, a step that could have far-reaching consequences for the management of aquatic ecosystems throughout the Sierra Nevada. The simplest and perhaps most effective way to reduce impacts of introduced trout is to modify current trout stocking programs to cause the die-out of some introduced trout populations. Such modification is perhaps most critical in wilderness areas to recreate their natural conditions. Below, I present three trout stocking alternatives for Sierra Nevada wilderness areas that differ in their consequences for the distribution of non-native trout and native aquatic species.

Alternative 1

Strategy: Continue the current policies of intensive trout stocking into national forest waters, and no stocking of trout into national park waters.

Consequences: The distribution of trout in the Sierra Nevada would remain much as it is today. In national parks, populations of some native aquatic species would expand as they recolonize habitats that have recently reverted to their naturally fishless condition. Populations of other less mobile species or species whose movement is restricted by the continued presence of trout in streams (e.g., the mountain yellow-legged frog) would persist in highly fragmented configurations, although fragmentation would decrease slowly as additional habitats were recolonized. These consequences to national park waters are common to all alternatives. On national forests, populations of most native aquatic species would exist in highly fragmented configurations. Particularly sensitive taxa (e.g., mountain yellow-legged frogs) would continue to decline. On a Sierra-wide scale, national parks would become increasingly isolated refugia within a landscape of unsuitable national forest habitat. The increased isolation of populations of native aquatic species within national parks would likely result in the eventual extirpation of some species from the Sierra Nevada.

As a result of increasing evidence that introduced trout are having considerable impacts on native aquatic species, continued intensive fish stocking on national forests may meet with considerable resistance from members of the public. In addition, if native aquatic species decline to the point where they are listed under the Endangered Species Act, trout stocking would likely come under increased scrutiny from the U.S. Fish and Wildlife Service.

Alternative 2

Strategy: In national forest wilderness areas, continue trout stocking only in waters along heavily-traveled areas such as trail corridors. Within these areas, stock only waters that contain non self-sustaining trout populations. Continue the current policy of no trout stocking in national park waters.
Consequences: The distribution of trout would change in national forest drainages as some lakes in low-visitation areas reverted to a fishless condition. Populations of some native aquatic species would expand as they recolonized these recently fishless habitats. Populations of other less mobile species or species whose movement was restricted by the continued presence of trout in streams would persist in fragmented configurations. However, because fishless lakes would be recreated in all drainages, fragmentation of habitats for native aquatic species would be reduced compared with that resulting from Alternative 1. Across the Sierra Nevada, the trend toward increasing habitat fragmentation and population isolation would likely be halted, and may be reversed, as habitats in all drainages were slowly recolonized by native aquatic species. Populations of native aquatic species in national parks would be connected to populations on national forests by numerous drainages containing viable populations.

Resistance from angling groups and local communities to a termination of stocking in lakes within lightly-visited areas would be substantial given the public perception that fishing opportunities would disappear without stocking. Resistance would be less than under a "no stocking" alternative. Phasing out stocking over a several year period would further reduce resistance.

Alternative 3

Strategy: Terminate all trout stocking in national forest wilderness and continue the policy of no trout stocking in national park waters.
Consequences: The distribution of trout on national forests would change as 10-20% of the lakes reverted to their formerly fishless condition. After trout populations stabilized, populations of some native aquatic species would expand as they recolonized habitats that had recently reverted to their naturally fishless condition. Populations of other less mobile species or species whose movement is restricted by the continued presence of trout in

streams would persist in highly fragmented configurations, although fragmentation would decrease slowly as additional habitats were recolonized. In addition, because fishless lakes would be recreated in all drainages, fragmentation of habitats for native aquatic species would be reduced compared with that resulting from implementation of Alternative 2. Across the Sierra Nevada, the trend toward increasing habitat fragmentation would be reversed as habitats in all drainages were slowly recolonized by native aquatic species. Populations of native aquatic species in national parks would be connected by numerous drainages to populations on national forests.

Resistance from angling groups and local communities to halting trout stocking in all national forest wilderness areas would be considerable, and could lead to a backlash against protection of native aquatic species. As an example of the probable reaction to the complete cessation of trout stocking, when the Forest Service recently decided to terminate all trout stocking in the Desolation Wilderness and Mokelumne Wilderness, an outpouring of public reaction against the proposal forced the Forest Service to adopt a policy of evaluating stocking practices on a lake by lake basis. Resistance could be reduced by phasing out stocking over a several year period.

RECOMMENDATIONS FOR IMMEDIATE CHANGES IN STOCKING PROGRAMS

Although changes in fish stocking programs appear to be needed in order to maintain and restore populations of several native aquatic species, these changes will likely take years or decades to implement. Several immediate changes could reduce the impacts of trout stocking while changes to current policies are being decided upon and implemented.

(1) Trout stocking should occur only in lakes that have been surveyed for sensitive native aquatic species and for non-native trout. This would eliminate the stocking of lakes that contain sensitive species (e.g., mountain yellow-legged frogs) or that contain self-sustaining non-native trout populations.

(2) The aircraft used by the DFG to stock backcountry lakes should be outfitted with navigational systems to allow target lakes to be unmistakably identified before the trout are dropped. As of 1994, stocking planes did not have any navigational equipment, and target lakes were identified only by aerial photographs. Although the error rate associated with the current methodology is unknown, several incidences have occurred in recent years in which trout of the wrong species where stocked into a lake, and in one case, a fishless lake was stocked. The navigational system should also be configured to record the locations of all lakes into which trout were dropped. This would allow the determination of error rates associated with trout stocking, and would aid in determining what the sources of error are.

(3) The California Department of Fish and Game should be required to prepare environmental documentation under the California Environmental Quality Act (CEQA) to disclose the impacts of stocking trout into waters within wilderness areas. Currently, all fish stocking is classified as a "categorical exemption" under the California Code of Regulations (Title 14, Section 15301.j) because it is believed not to have a significant effect on the environment. Given the numerous published accounts of negative impacts of introduced trout on native aquatic biota in the Sierra Nevada, this exemption does not appear justified, particularly in wilderness areas.

RECOMMENDATIONS FOR FUTURE RESEARCH

A substantial research effort will be necessary in order to determine the full impacts of trout on aquatic ecosystems in the Sierra Nevada, and to better understand how these impacts can be reduced or eliminated. Several of the most critical research needs are discussed below.

(1) In order to determine the extent to which creation of additional fishless habitats will benefit native aquatic species, a better understanding of the rates at which extirpated species recolonize lakes is critical.

(2) Of the aquatic species native to the Sierra Nevada, the mountain yellow-legged frog appears to be the most strongly affected by the presence of non-native trout. It is therefore critical to conduct a metapopulation analysis for this species to determine the extinction probabilities for this species under different trout stocking management strategies. Critical information for such an analysis is still unavailable, including survivorship of all life stages, degree of natural population fluctuations, and dispersal capabilities of all life stages.

(3) Because mountain yellow-legged frogs utilize streams as movement corridors between lakes, and apparently do not utilize streams that contain fish (Bradford et al. 1993), it may be necessary to reintroduce this species to formerly occupied habitat after the habitat reverts to its naturally fishless condition. Although two reintroductions have recently been conducted in the Sierra Nevada, additional reintroductions are needed to evaluate the feasibility of this approach.

ACKNOWLEDGMENTS

This study was supported in part by the Sierra Nevada Ecosystem Project as authorized by Congress (HR 5503) through a cost-reimbursable agreement No. PSW-93-001-CRA between the USDA Forest Service, Pacific Southwest Research Station, and the Regents of the University of California, Wildland Resources Center. Funding to Roland Knapp and Robert Jellison for the GIS and DFG data compilation was provided by a cooperative agreement between the USDA Forest Service, Pacific Southwest Research Station and the University of California, Marine Science Insitute. Biologists with the DFG and NPS provided access to stocking records and databases. Kathleen Matthews (USDA-Pacific Southwest Research Station) provided financial and logistical support, Jim Muck (USDA-Pacific Southwest Research Station) assisted with data compilation, and Robert Jellison (Marine Science Institute, University of California) provided GIS expertise and logistical support. Comments by Peter Moyle, Don Erman, and Nancy Erman on an earlier draft greatly improved the paper.

REFERENCES

Allan, J.D. 1982. The effects of reduction in trout density on the invertebrate community of a mountain stream. *Ecology* 63:1444-1455.

Anderson, R.S. 1971. Crustacean plankton of 146 alpine and subalpine lakes in Western Canada. *Journal of the Fisheries Research Board of Canada* 28:311-321.

_____. 1972. Zooplankton composition and change in an alpine lake. *Verhandlung Internationale Vereinigung fur Theoretische und Angewandte Limnologie* 18:264-268.

_____. 1974. Crustacean plankton communities of 340 lakes and ponds in and near the national parks of the Canadian Rocky Mountains. *Journal of the Fisheries Research Board of Canada* 31:855-869.

Bahls, P. 1990. *Ecological implications of trout introductions to lakes of the Selway Bitterroot Wilderness, Idaho.* Master's Thesis, Oregon State University.

_____. 1992. The status of fish populations and management of high mountain lakes in the western United States. *Northwest Science* 66:183-193.

Behnke, R.J. 1992. *Native trout of western North America.* American Fisheries Society Monograph 6.

Blaustein, A.R., D.G. Hokit, R.K. Ohara, and R.A. Holt. 1994. Pathogenic fungus contributes to amphibian losses in the Pacific Northwest. *Biological Conservation* 67:251-254.

Botti, S. 1977. Status of fish populations in 102 planted lakes. Unpublished file report, U.S. Department of the Interior, National Park Service, Yosemite National Park, California.

Bradford, D.F. 1983. Winterkill, oxygen relations, and energy metabolism of a submerged dormant amphibian, Rana muscosa. *Ecology* 64:1171-1183.

_____. 1989. Allotopic distribution of native frogs and introduced fishes in high Sierra Nevada lakes of California: implication of the negative effect of fish introductions. *Copeia* 1989:775-778.

_____. 1991. Mass mortality and extinction in a high-elevation population of Rana muscosa. *Journal of Herpetology* 25:174-177.

_____, and M.S. Gordon. 1992. Aquatic amphibians in the Sierra Nevada: current status and potential effects of acidic deposition on populations. Final Report, Contract No. A932-139. California Air Resouces Board. Sacramento.

_____, F. Tabatabai, and D.M. Graber. 1993. Isolation of remaining populations of the native frog, Rana muscosa, by introduced fishes in Sequoia and Kings Canyon National Parks, California. *Conservation Biology* 7:882-888.

_____, S.D. Cooper, and A.D. Brown. 1994a. Distribution of aquatic animals relative to naturally acidic waters in the Sierra Nevada. Final Report, Contract No. A1323-192. California Air Resources Board. Sacramento.

_____, D.M. Graber, and F. Tabatabai. 1994b. Population declines of the native frog, Rana muscosa, in Sequoia and Kings Canyon National Parks, California. *Southwestern Naturalist* 39:323-327.

Brett, M.T., et al. 1994. Species-dependent effects of zooplankton on planktonic ecosystem processes in Castle Lake, California. *Ecology* 75:2243-2254.

Burger, W.L. 1950. Novel aspects of the life history of two amphibians. *Journal of the Tennessee Acadamy of Science* 25: 252-257.

Carpenter, S.R., J.F. Kitchell, and J.R. Hodgson. 1985. Cascading trophic interactions and lake productivity. *Bioscience* 35:634-639.

_____, et al. 1987. Regulation of lake primary productivity by food web structure. *Ecology* 68:1863-1876.

_____, and J.F. Kitchell. 1993. *The trophic cascade in lakes.* Cambridge University Press. New York, New York.

Christenson, D.P. 1977. History of trout introductions in California high mountain lakes. Pages 9-15. In: *Symposium on the management of high mountain lakes in California's National Parks.* California Trout, Inc. and the American Fisheries Society.

Coffin, P.D., and W.F. Cowan. 1995. Lahontan cutthroat trout (<u>Oncorhynchus clarki henshawi</u>) recovery plan. U.S. Fish and Wildlife Service, Portand, Oregon.

Cooper, S.D. 1988. The responses of aquatic insects and tadpoles to trout. *Verhandlung Internationale Vereinigung fur Theoretische und Angewandte Limnologie* 23:1698-1703.

_____, S.J. Walde, and B.L. Peckarsky. 1990. Prey exchange rates and the impact of predators on prey populations in streams. *Ecology* 71:1503-1514.

Culp, J.M. 1986. Experimental evidence that stream macroinvertebrate community structure is unaffected by different densities of coho salmon fry. *Journal of the North American Benthological Society* 5: 140-149.

Dawidowicz, P., and Z.M. Gliwicz. 1983. Food of brook charr in extreme oligotrophic conditions of an alpine lake. *Environmental Biology of Fishes* 8:55-60.

Dickman, M. 1968. The effect of grazing by tadpoles on the structure of a periphyton community. *Ecology* 49:1188-1190.

Douglas, P.L., G.E. Forrester, and S.D. Cooper. 1994. Effects of trout on the diel periodicity of drifting in baetid mayflies. *Oecologia* 98:48-56.

Drost, C.A., and G.M. Fellers. 1994. Decline of frog species in the Yosemite section of the Sierra Nevada. Cooperative National Park Resources Studies Unit NPS/WRUC/NRTR-94-02.

Elser, J.J., C. Luecke, M.T. Brett, and C.R. Goldman. 1995. Effects of food web compensation after manipulation of rainbow trout in an oligotrophic lake. *Ecology* 76:52-69.

Elliot, M.J., and M.H. Loughlin. 1992. Historical overview of fishery management in Yosemite National Park 1877-1992. Natural Resources Report, draft. Yosemite National Park, California.

Flecker, A.S., and C.R. Townsend. 1994. Community-wide consequences of trout introduction in New Zealand streams. *Ecological Applications* 4:798-807.

Gerstung, E.R. 1988. Status, life history, and management of the Lahontan cutthroat trout. *American Fisheries Society Symposium* 4:93-106.

Goldman, C.R., M.D. Morgan, S.T. Threlkeld, and N. Angeli. 1979. A population dynamics analysis of cladoceran disappearance from Lake Tahoe, California-Nevada. *Limnology and Oceanography* 24:289-297.

Grinnell, J., and T.I. Storer. 1924. *Animal life in the Yosemite*. University of California Press. Berkeley, California.

Gulve, P.S. 1994. Distribution and extinction patterns within a northern metapopulation of the pool frog, <u>Rana</u> <u>lessonae</u>. *Ecology* 75:1357-1367.

Hanski, I. 1989. Metapopulation dynamics: does it help to have more of the same? *Trends in Ecology and Evolution* 4:113-114.

_____, and M. Gilpin. 1991. Metapopulation dynamics: brief history and conceptual domain. *Biological Journal of the Linnean Society* 42:3-16.

Hairston, N.G. Jr., R.A. Van Brunt, C.M. Kearns, and D.R. Engstrom. 1995. Age and survivorship of diapausing eggs in a sediment egg bank. *Ecology* 76:1706-1711.

Hayes, M.P., and M.R. Jennings. 1986. Decline of ranid frog species in western North America: are bullfrogs (<u>Rana</u> <u>catesbeiana</u>) responsible? *Journal of Herpetology* 20:490-509.

Hemphill, N., and S.D. Cooper. 1984. Differences in the community structure of stream pools containing or lacking trout. *Verhandlung Internationale Vereinigung fur Theoretische und Angewandte Limnologie* 22:1858-1861.

Jenkins, T.M. Jr., et al. 1994. Aquatic biota in the Sierra Nevada: current status and potential effects of acid deposition on populations. Final Report, Contract A932-138. California Air Resources Board, Sacramento.

Jennings, M.R. 1995. Status of amphibians in the Sierra Nevada of California. Final Report, Contract 94-05496N, Sierra Nevada Ecosystem Project, Davis, California.

Jennings, W.B., D.F. Bradford, and D.F. Johnson. 1992. Dependence of the garter snake <u>Thamnophis</u> <u>elegans</u> on amphibians in the Sierra Nevada of California. *Journal of Herpetology* 26:503-505.

Knapp, R.A. 1990. Unpublished field notes describing the distribution of trout and mountain yellow-legged frogs in selected lakes in Sixty Lakes Basin, Kings Canyon National Park. Sierra Nevada Aquatic Research Laboratory, University of California.

_____. 1993a. Conversation with G. Fellers, Herpetologist, National Biological Service, Pt. Reyes National Seashore, California, March 8.

_____. 1993b. Unpublished field notes describing the distribution of trout and mountain yellow-legged frogs in selected lakes in Palisade Basin, Kings Canyon National Park. Sierra Nevada Aquatic Research Laboratory, University of California.

_____. 1995a. Conversation with C. Knutson, Inland Fisheries, California Dept. of Fish and Game, Davis, California, April 18.

_____. 1995b. Conversation with C. Milliron and D. Wong, Department of Fish and Game, Region 5, Bishop, CA, February 19.

Kloepfer, D., J. Watson, and P. Byrnes. 1994. *The Wilderness Act handbook*. The Wilderness Society, Washington, D.C.

LaRivers, I. 1994. *Fish and fisheries of Nevada*. University of Nevada Press. Reno, Nevada.

Leopold, A.S. 1963. Wildlife management in the National Parks. Report to the Secretary of the Interior.

Leavitt, P.R., et al. 1994. Fossil pigment records of phytoplankton in trout-stocked alpine lakes. *Canadian Journal of Fisheries and Aquatic Sciences* 51:2411-2423.

Li, H.W., and P.B. Moyle. 1981. Ecological analysis of species introductions into aquatic systems. *Transactions of the American Fisheries Society* 110:772-782.

Liss, W.J., and G.L. Larson. 1991. Ecological effects of stocked trout on North Cascades naturally fishless lakes. *Park Science* 11:22-23.

Matthews, K.R., and R.A. Knapp. 1995. Distribution of trout in the John Muir Wilderness, Inyo and Sierra National Forests. Unpublished data. U.S.D.A. Pacific Southwest Research Station, Albany, California.

McQueen, D.J., J.R. Post, and E.L. Mills. 1986. Trophic relationships in freshwater pelagic ecosystems. *Canadian Journal of Fisheries and Aquatic Sciences* 43:1571-1581.

Melack, J.M., et al. 1989. Chemical and biological characteristics of Emerald Lake and the streams in its watershed, and the responses of the lake and streams to acidic deposition. Final Report, Contract No. A6-184-32. California Air Resources Board, Sacramento

Morgan, M.D., S.T. Threlkeld, and C.R. Goldman. 1978. Impact of the introduction of kokanee (Oncorhynchus nerka) and opposum shrimp (Mysis relicta) on a subalpine lake. *Journal of the Fisheries Research Board of Canada* 35:1572-1579.

Moyle, P.B. 1973. Effects of introduced bullfrogs, Rana catesbeiana, on the native frogs of the San Joaquin Valley, California. *Copeia* 1973:18-22.

_____. 1976. *Inland fishes of California*. University of California Press, Berkeley.

_____, and R.D. Nichols. 1973. Ecology of some native and introduced fishes of the Sierra Nevada foothills in central California. *Copeia* 1973:478-490.

_____, and R.D. Nichols. 1974. Decline of the native fish fauna of the Sierra Nevada foothills, central California. *American Midland Naturalist* 92:72-83.

Moyle, P.B, R.M. Yoshiyama, R.A. Knapp. 1995. Fish and fisheries of the Sierra Nevada. Final Draft Report, Sierra Nevada Ecosystem Project, Davis, California.

Mullally, D.P., and J.D. Cunningham. 1956. Ecological relations of Rana muscosa at high elevations in the Sierra Nevada. *Herpetologica* 12:189-198.

Needham, P.R., and E.H. Vestal. 1938. Notes on growth of golden trout (Salmo aguabonita) in two High Sierra lakes. *California Fish and Game* 24:273-279.

Northcote, T.G. 1988. Fish in the structure and function of freshwater ecosystems: a "top-down" view. *Canadian Journal of Fisheries and Aquatic Sciences* 45:361-379.

_____, C.J. Walters, and J.M.B. Hume. 1978. Initial impacts of experimental fish introductions on the macrozooplankton of small oligotrophic lakes. *Verhandlung Internationale Vereinigung fur Theoretische und Angewandte Limnologie* 20:2003-2012.

NPS (National Park Service). 1975. Management policies. U.S. Department of the Interior, National Park Service. Section IV: 7-8.

Palmer, T. 1988. *The Sierra Nevada: a mountain journey*. Island Press, Washington D.C.

Paulsen, S.G., et al. 1991. EMAP-Surface waters monitoring and research strategy, fiscal year 1991. U.S. Environmental Protection Agency, Washington, D.C.

Pechmann, J.H.K., et al. 1991. Declining amphibian populations: the problem of separating human impacts from natural fluctuations. *Science* 253:892-895.

Pohl-Branscheid, M. and W. Holtz. 1990. Control of spawning activity in male and female rainbow trout (Oncorhynchus mykiss) by repeated foreshortened seasonal light cycles. *Aquaculture* 86:93-104.

Power, M.E. 1990. Effects of fish in river food webs. *Science* 250:811-814.

Reh, W., and A. Seitz. 1990. The influence of land use on the genetic structure of populations of the common frog Rana temporaria. *Biological Conservation* 54:239-249.

Reimers, N. 1958. Conditions of existence, growth, and longevity of brook trout in a small, high altitude lake of the eastern Sierra Nevada. *California Fish and Game* 44:319-333.

Richards, R.C., C.R. Goldman, T.C. Frantz, and R. Wickwire. 1975. Where have all the Daphnia gone? The decline of a major cladoceran in Lake Tahoe, California-Nevada. *Verhandlung Internationale Vereinigung fur Theoretische und Angewandte Limnologie* 19:835-842.

Richards, R.H., and A.D. Pickering. 1978. Frequency and distribution patterns of Saprolegnia infection in wild and hatchery-reared brown trout Salmo trutta L. and char Salvelinus alpinus L. *Journal of Fish Diseases* 1:69-82.

Seale, D.B. 1980. Influence of amphibian larvae on primary production, nutrient flux, and competition in a pond ecosystem. *Ecology* 61:1531-1550.

Seymour, R.L. 1970. The genus Saprolegnia. *Nova Hedwigia* 30:1-124.

Sherman, C.K., and M.L. Morton. 1993. Population declines of Yosemite toads in the eastern Sierra Nevada of California. *Journal of Herpetology* 27:186-198.

Silverman, G., and D.C. Erman. 1979. Alpine lakes in Kings Canyon National Park, California: baseline conditions and possible effects of visitor use. *Journal of Environmental Management* 8:73-87.

Stenson, J.A.E., et al. 1978. Effects of fish removal from a small lake. *Verhandlung Internationale Vereinigung fur Theoretische und Angewandte Limnologie* 20:794-801.

Stoddard, J.L. 1987. Microcrustacean communities of high-elevation lakes in the Sierra Nevada, California. *Journal of Plankton Research* 9:631-650.

Taylor, T.P., and D.C. Erman. 1980. The littoral bottom fauna of high elevation lakes in Kings Canyon National Park. *California Fish and Game* 66:112-119.

Thorp, J.H., and A.P. Covich. 1991. *Ecology and classification of North American freshwater invertebrates*. Academic Press. San Diego, California.

USFS (U.S. Forest Service). 1982. Golden Trout Wilderness management plan. Inyo and Sierra National Forests.

Wallis, E.O. 1952. Comprehensive review of trout fishery problems of Yosemite National Park: A report of the Yosemite Trout Investigations, 1951-1953. U.S. Department of the Interior, National Park Service, Yosemite National Park.

Walters, C.J., and R.E. Vincent. 1973. Potential productivity of an alpine lake as indicated by removal and reintroduction of fish. *Transactions of the American Fisheries Society* 102:675-697.

Wilcox, B.A. 1980. *Insular ecology and conservation*. Pages 97-117. In: M.E. Soule and B.A. Wilcox (eds.). Conservation biology. Sinauer Associates, Massachusetts.

Willoughby, L.G. 1986. An ecological study of water as the medium for growth and reproduction of the <u>Saprolegnia</u> from salmonid fish. *Transactions of the British Mycological Society* 87:493-502.

Wiseman, S.W., S.D. Cooper, and T.L. Dudley. 1993. The effects of trout on epibenthic odonate naiads in stream pools. *Freshwater Biology* 30:133-145.

Zardus, M., T. Blank, and D. Schultz. 1977. Status of fishes in 137 lakes in Sequioa and Kings Canyon National Parks, California. Unpublished file report, U.S. Department of the Interior, National Park Service, Sequioa-King Canyon National Parks.

Zweifel, R.G. 1955. Ecology, distribution, and systematics of frogs of the <u>Rana boylei</u> group. *University of California Publications in Zoology* 54:207-292.

FIGURES

391

Report Study Areas

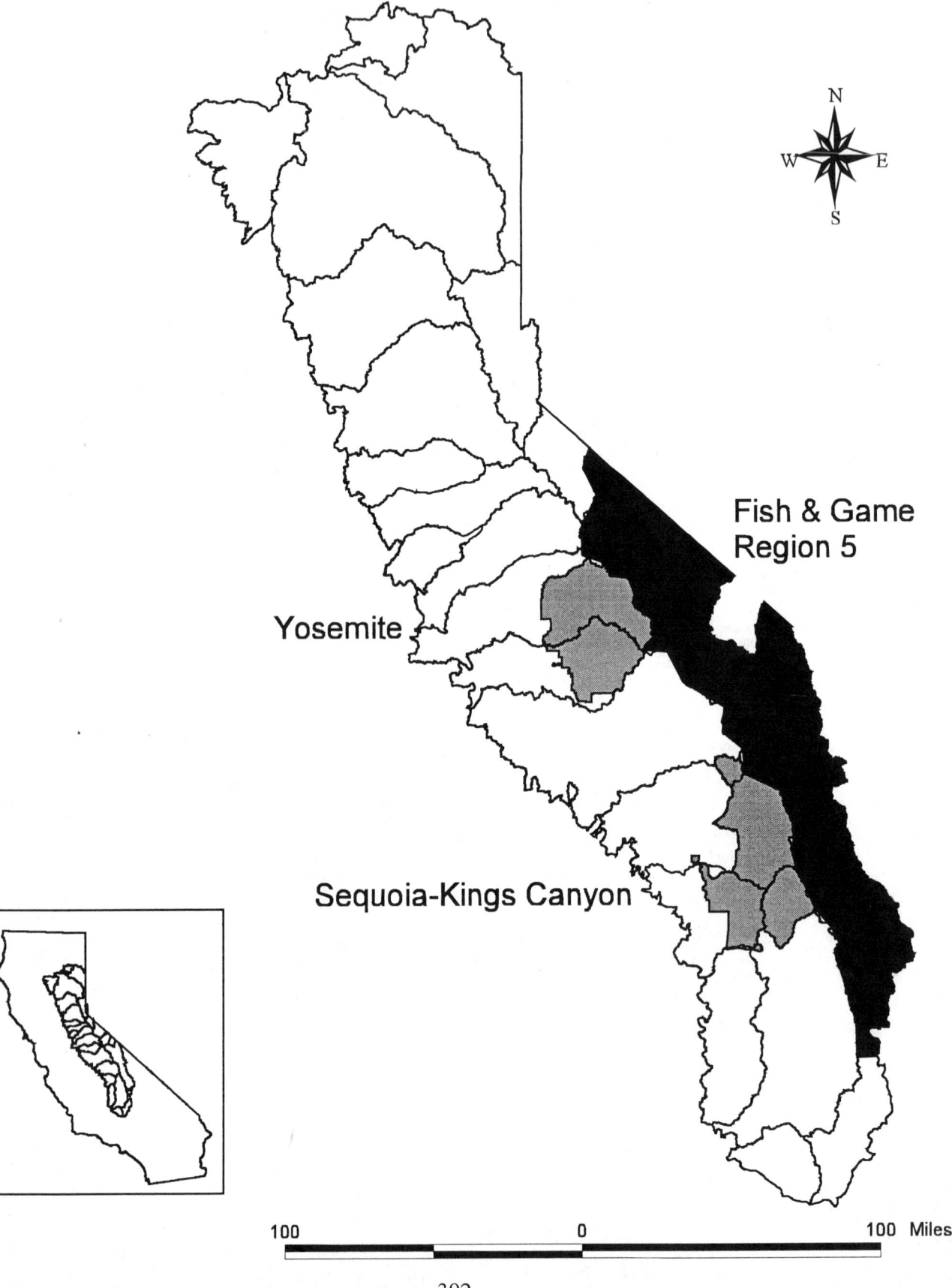

Fish & Game
Region 5

Yosemite

Sequoia-Kings Canyon

N
W E
S

100   0   100   Miles

392

Figure 1. A map of the SNEP study area boundary, showing the portions of the Sierra Nevada covered in detail in this report.

Figure 2. A map showing the historical fishless area in the Sierra Nevada. The map was drawn by Paul Randall (UC Davis); the boundaries of the fishless area are based on the available literature on historical distributions of native fishes and on discussions with Eric Gerstung, California Department of Fish and Game.

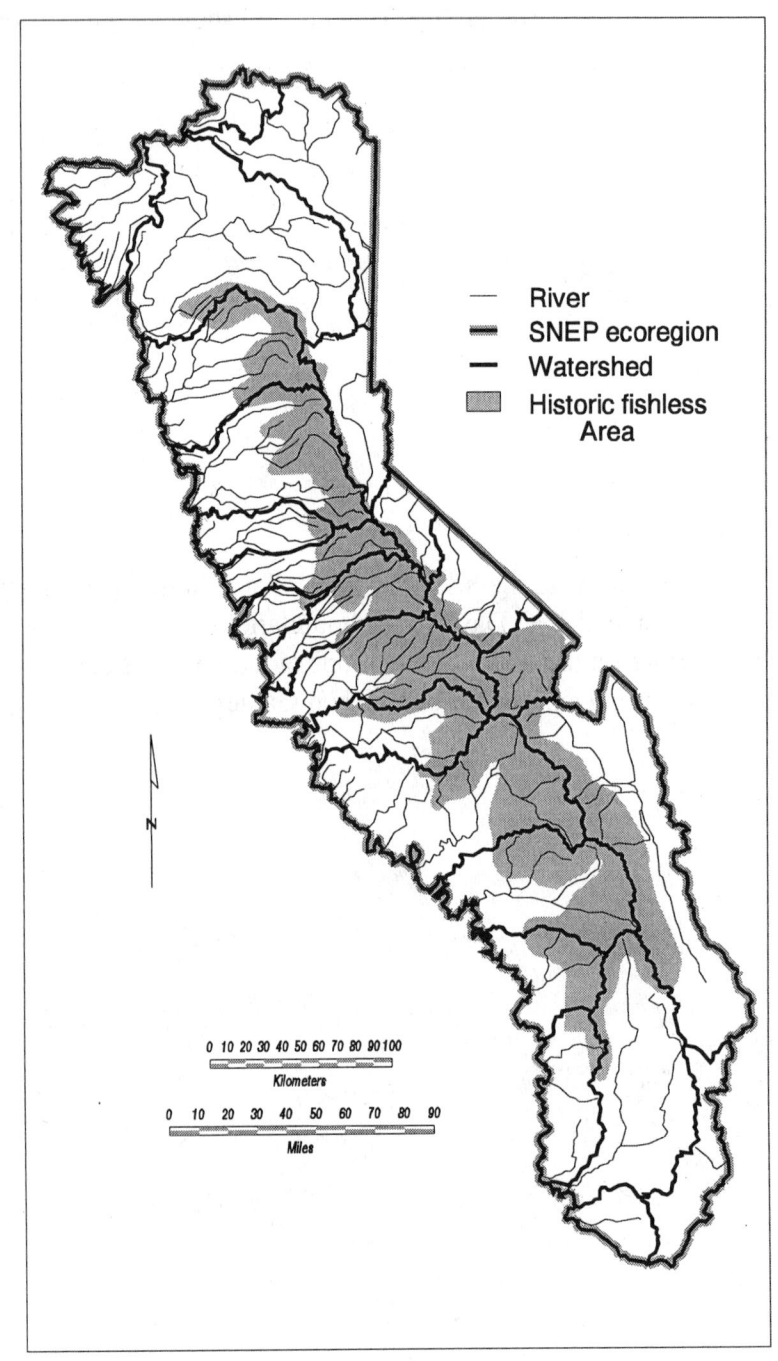

River

SNEP ecoregion

Watershed

Historic fishless
Area

0 10 20 30 40 50 60 70 80 90 100
Kilometers

0 10 20 30 40 50 60 70 80 90
Miles

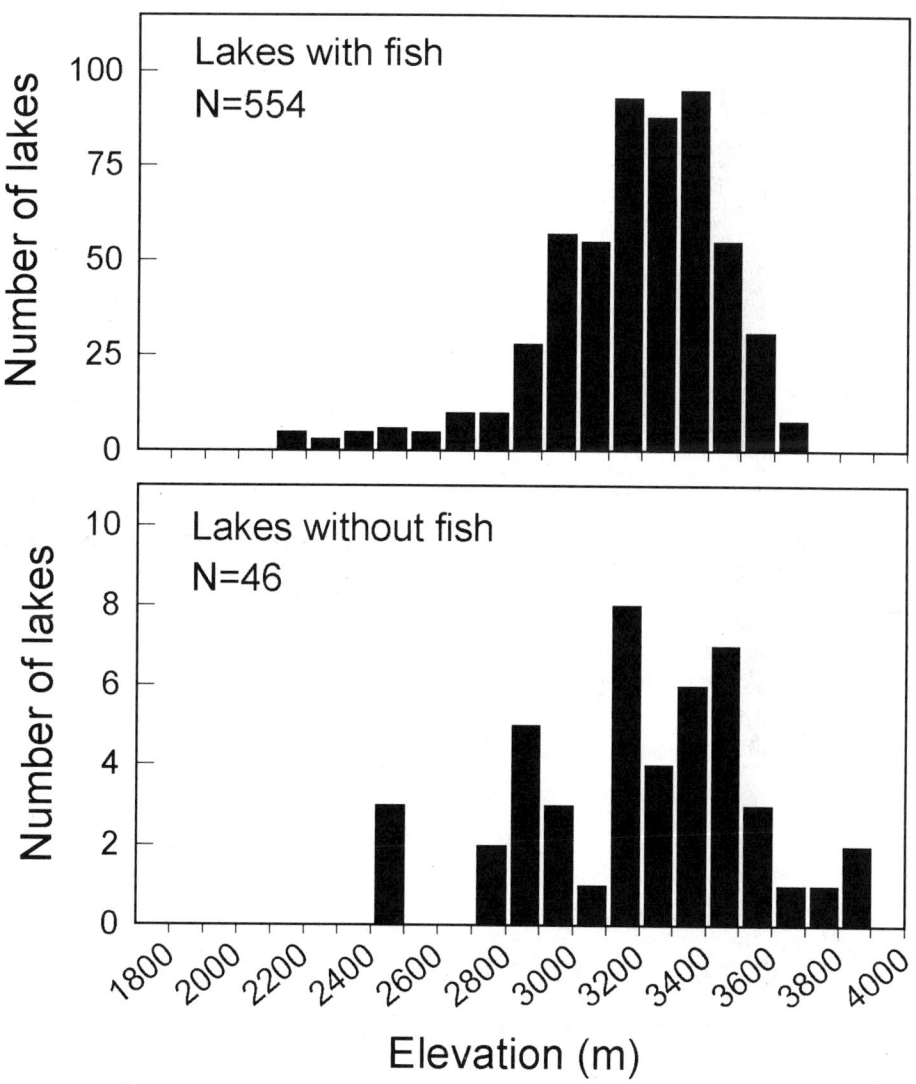

Figure 3. Frequency histograms showing the elevational distribution of lakes with and without fish within the jurisdiction of Region 5 of the California Department of Fish and Game. Lakes with fish are not different in their elevations than lakes without fish.

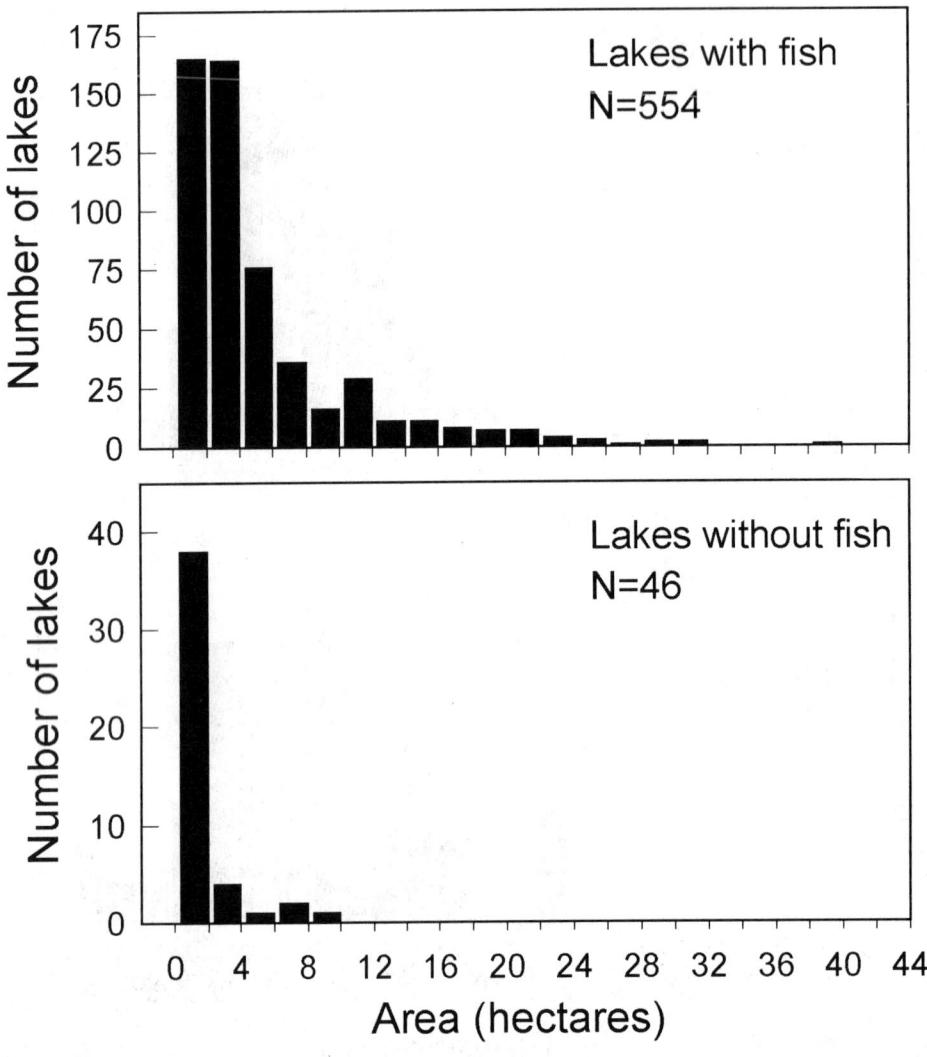

Figure 4. Frequency histograms showing the size distribution of lakes with and without fish within the jurisdiction of Region 5 of the California Department of Fish and Game. Lakes with fish are significantly larger than lakes without fish.

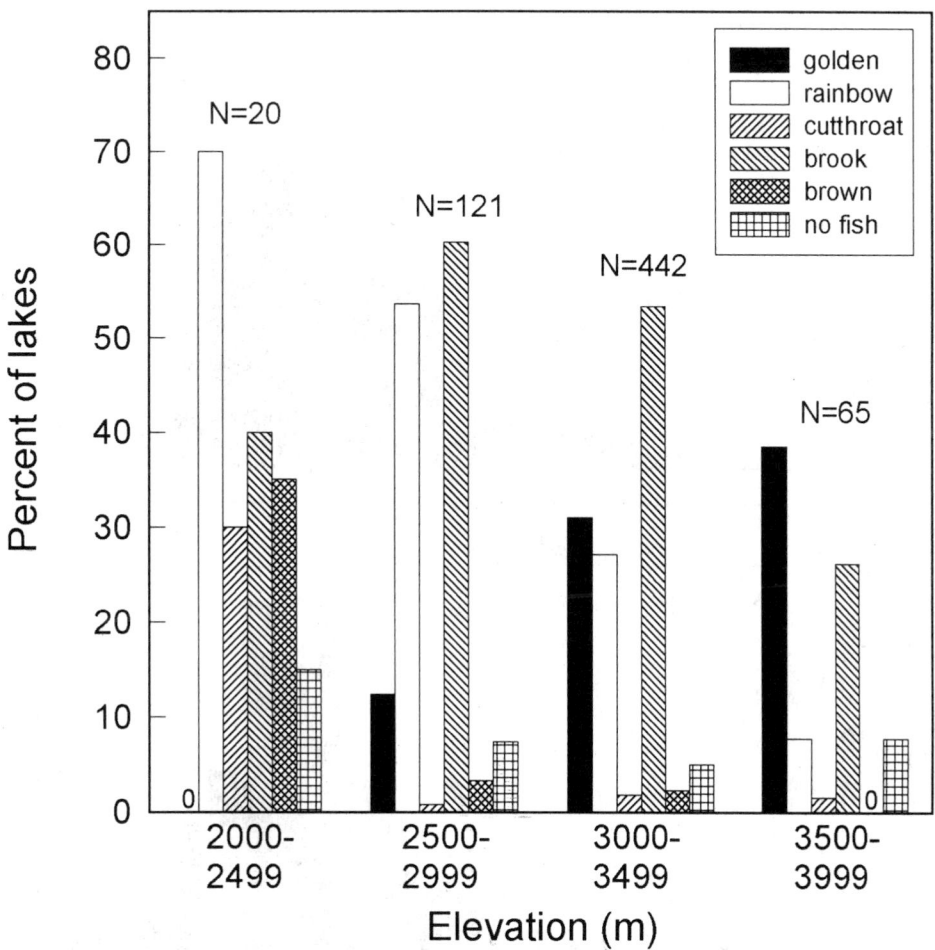

Figure 5. The relative frequency of five introduced trout species and fishless lakes at different elevations. The lakes are within the jurisdiction of Region 5 of the California Department of Fish and Game.

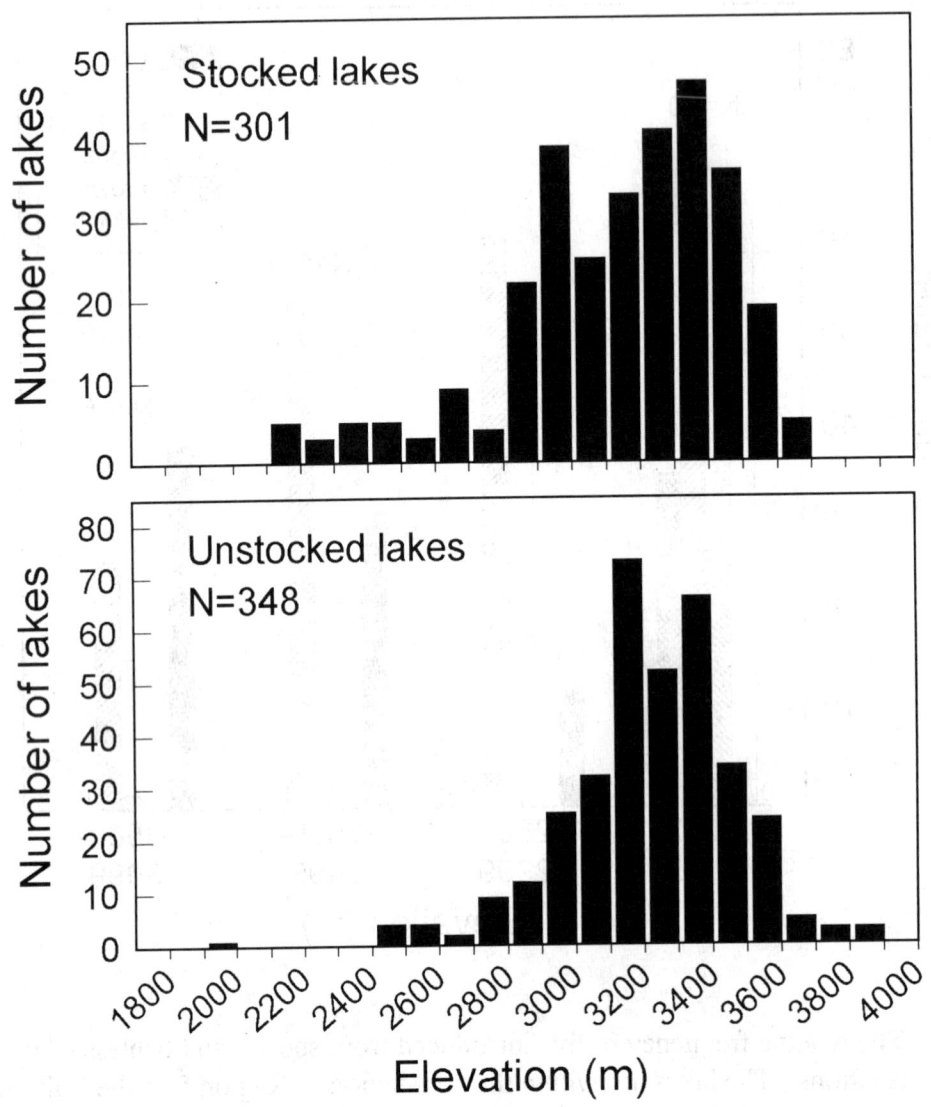

Figure 6. Frequency histogram showing the elevational distribution of stocked and unstocked lakes within the jurisdiction of Region 5 of the California Department of Fish and Game. Stocked lakes occur at significantly lower elevations than unstocked lakes.

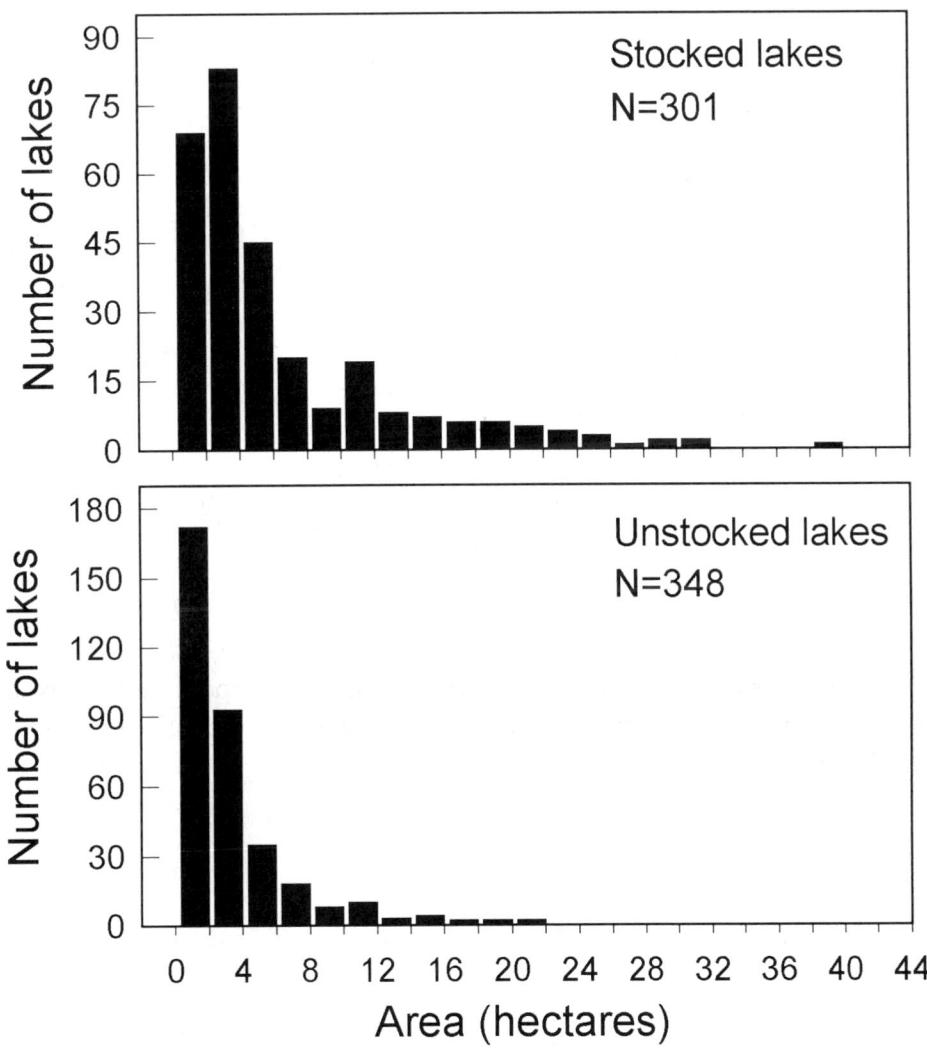

Figure 7. Frequency histograms showing the size distribution of stocked and unstocked lakes within the jurisdiction of Region 5 of the California Department of Fish and Game. Stocked lakes are significantly larger than unstocked lakes.

Figure 8. A map showing the historic fish distribution in the upper Piute Creek and French Creek watersheds, Sierra National Forest. The distribution is based on historical evidence (see text).

Upper Piute Cr. / French Cr. Watersheds
Historic Fish Distribution

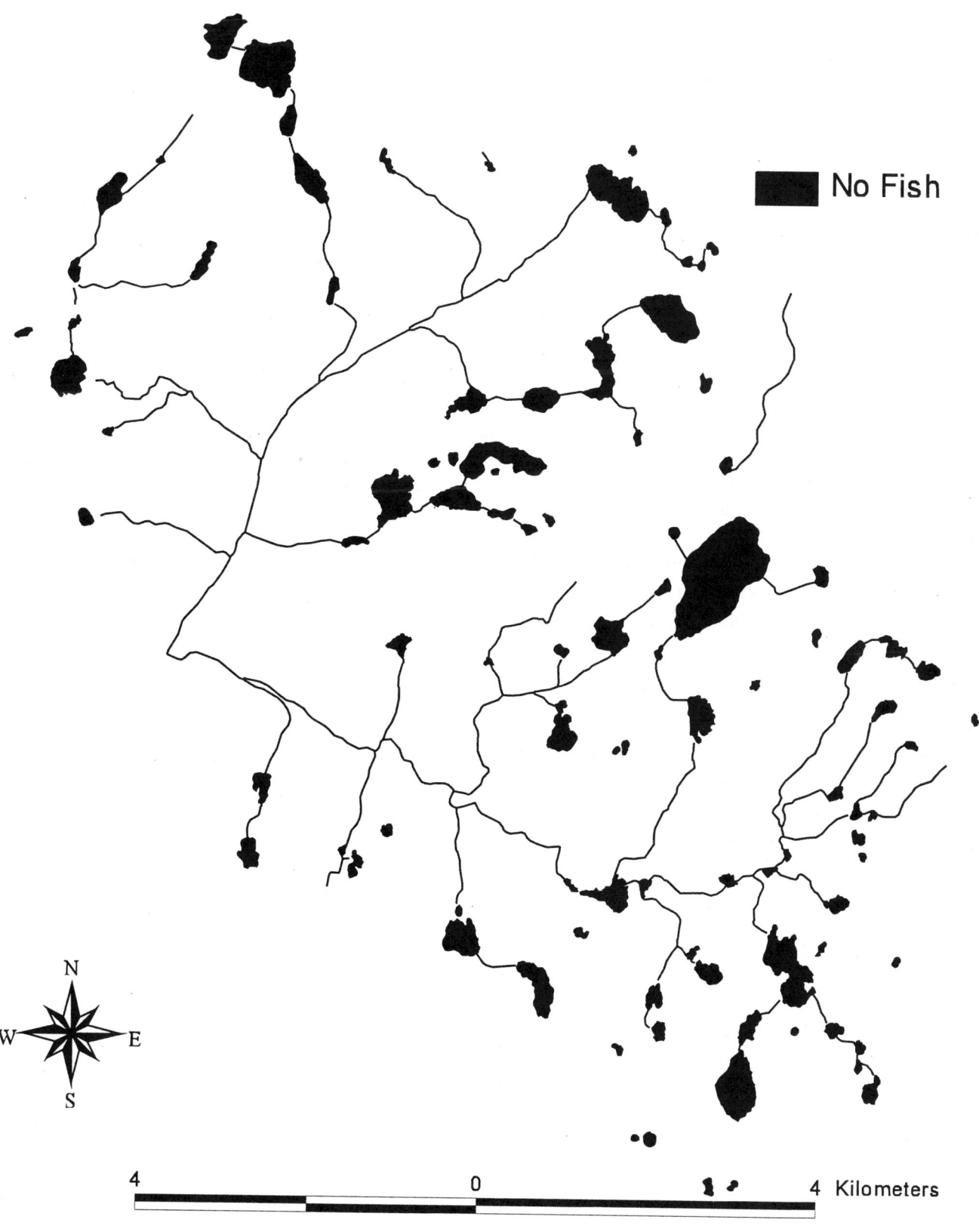

■ No Fish

N
W E
S

4   0   1   4 Kilometers

401

Figure 9. A map showing the current fish distribution in the upper Piute Creek and French Creek watersheds, Sierra National Forest. The distribution is based on records provided by Region 5 of the California Department of Fish and Game.

Upper Piute Cr. / French Cr. Watersheds
Current Fish Distribution

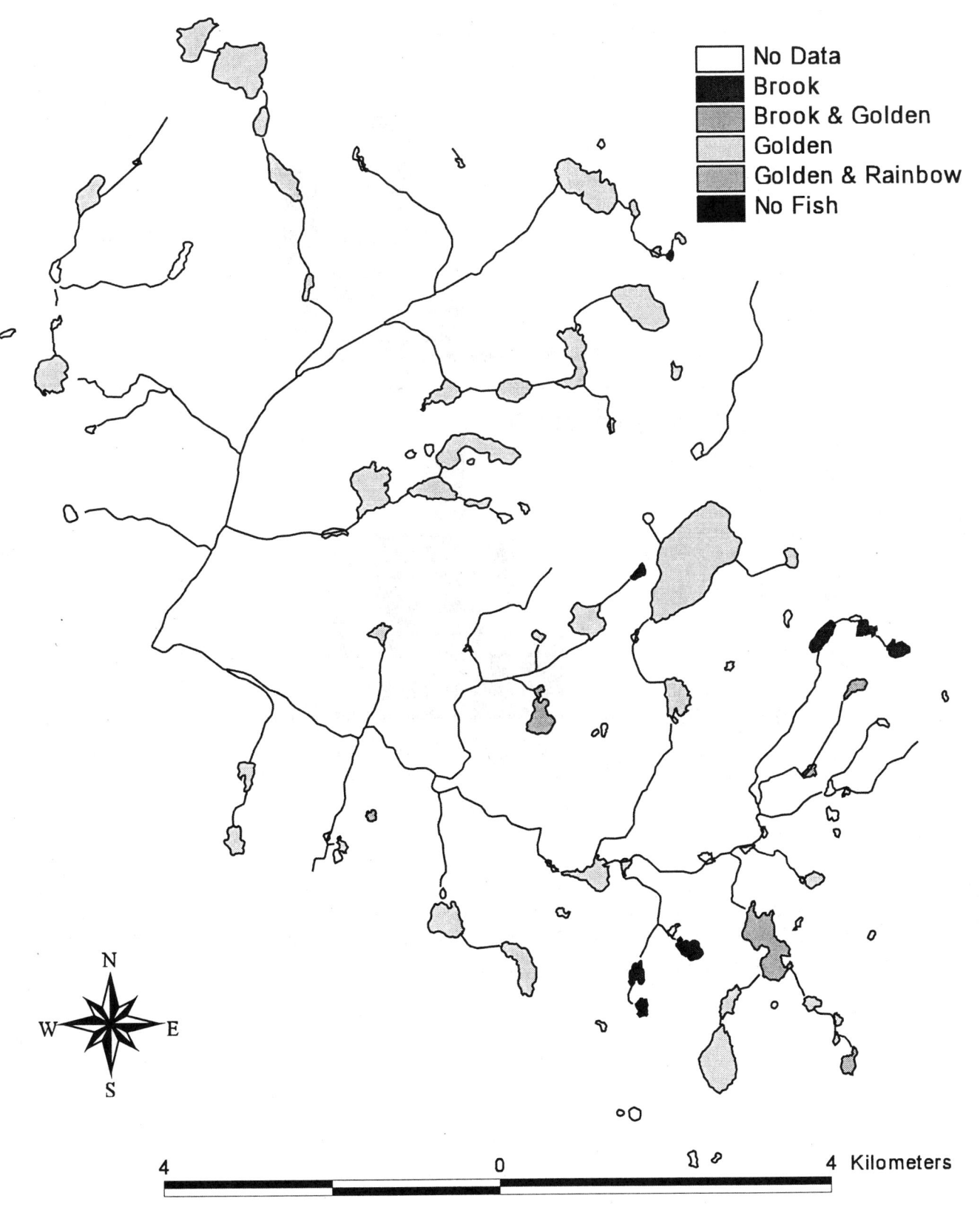

No Data
Brook
Brook & Golden
Golden
Golden & Rainbow
No Fish

N
W   E
S

4   0   4 Kilometers

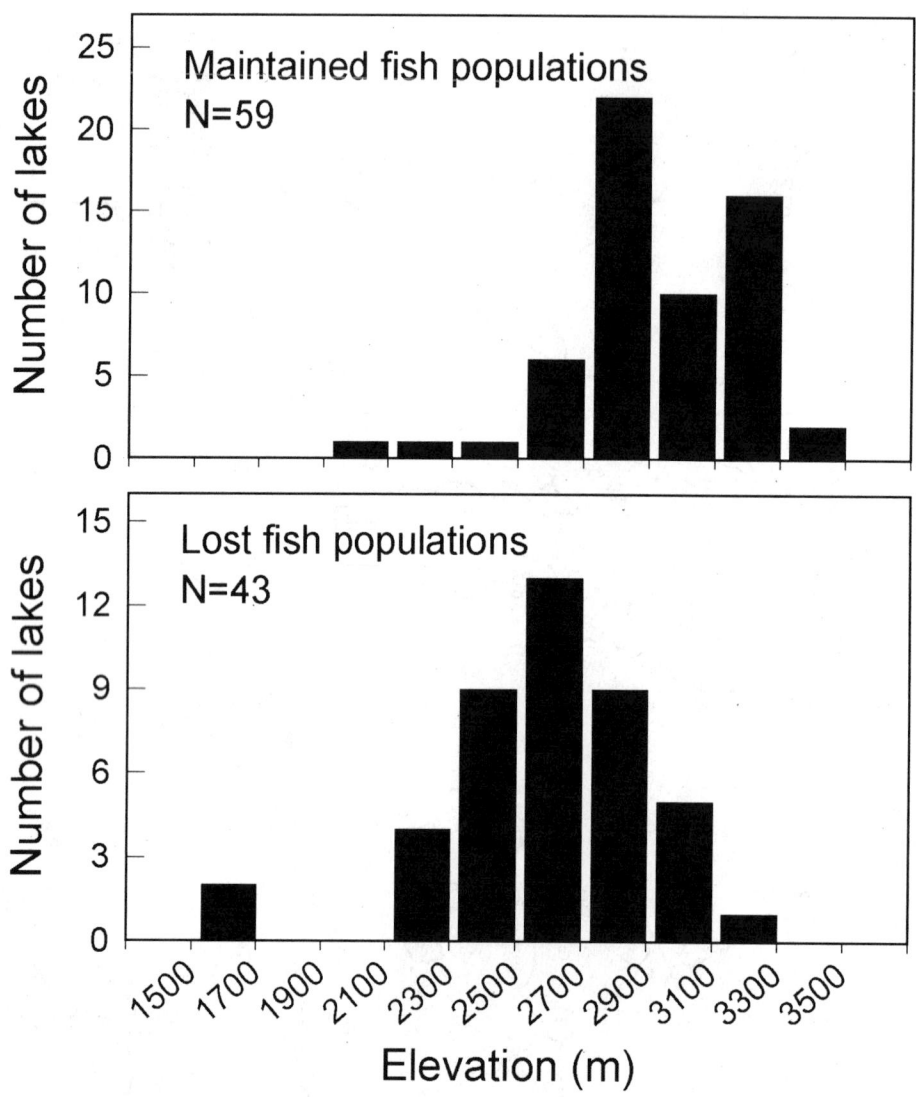

Figure 10. Frequency histograms showing the elevational distribution of lakes that maintained and lost fish populations in Yosemite National Park. Lake that maintained fish populations are found at higher elevations than lakes without fish. Data are from Botti (1977).

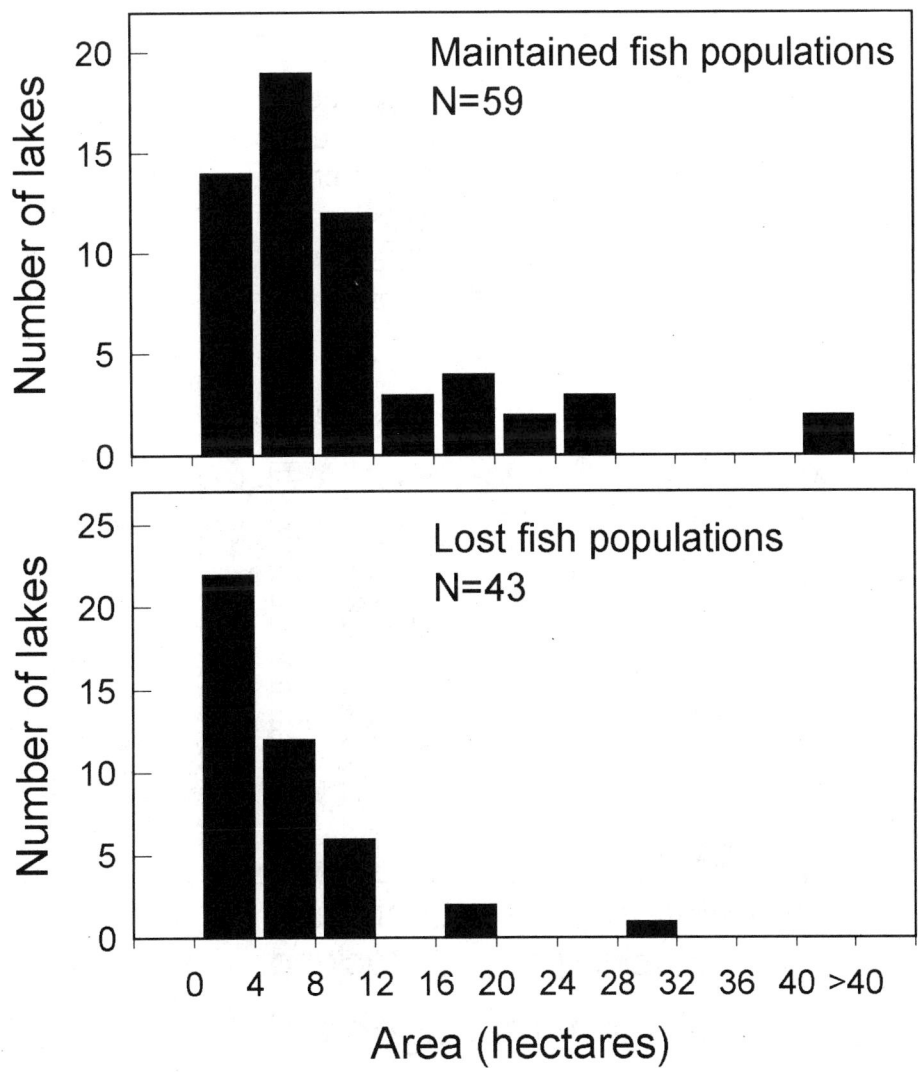

Figure 11. Frequency histograms showing the size distribution of lakes that maintained and lost fish populations in Yosemite National Park. Lakes that maintained fish populations are significantly larger than lakes without fish. Data are from Botti (1977).

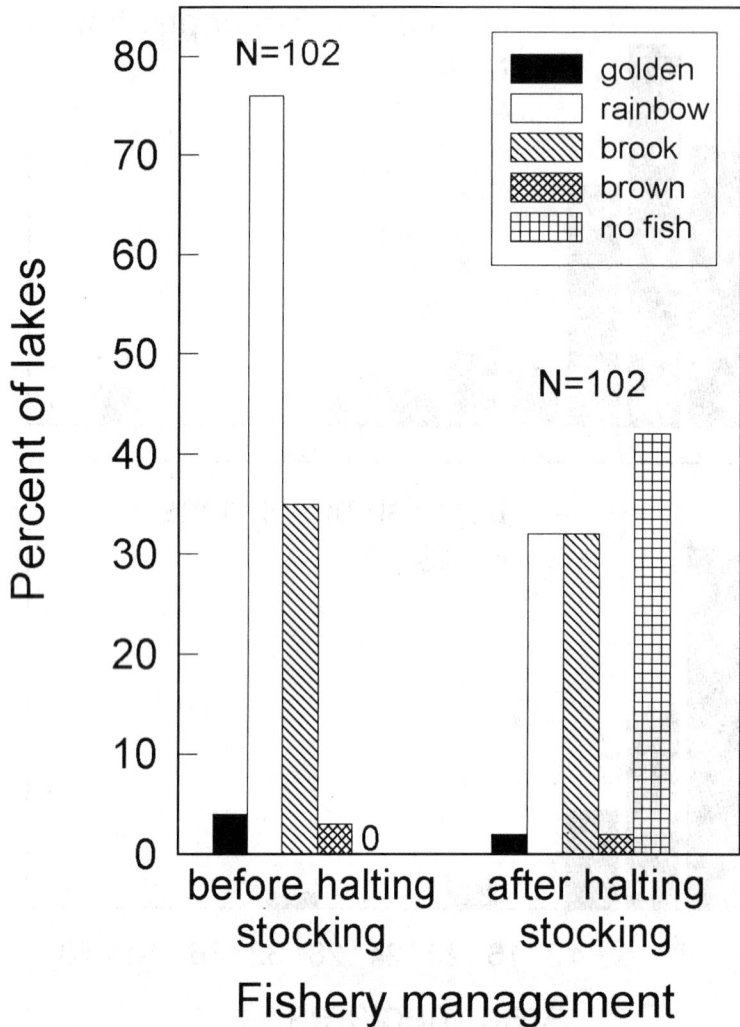

Figure 12. The relative frequency of four introduced trout species and fishless lakes in Yosemite National Park before and after trout stocking was halted. Data are from Botti (1977).

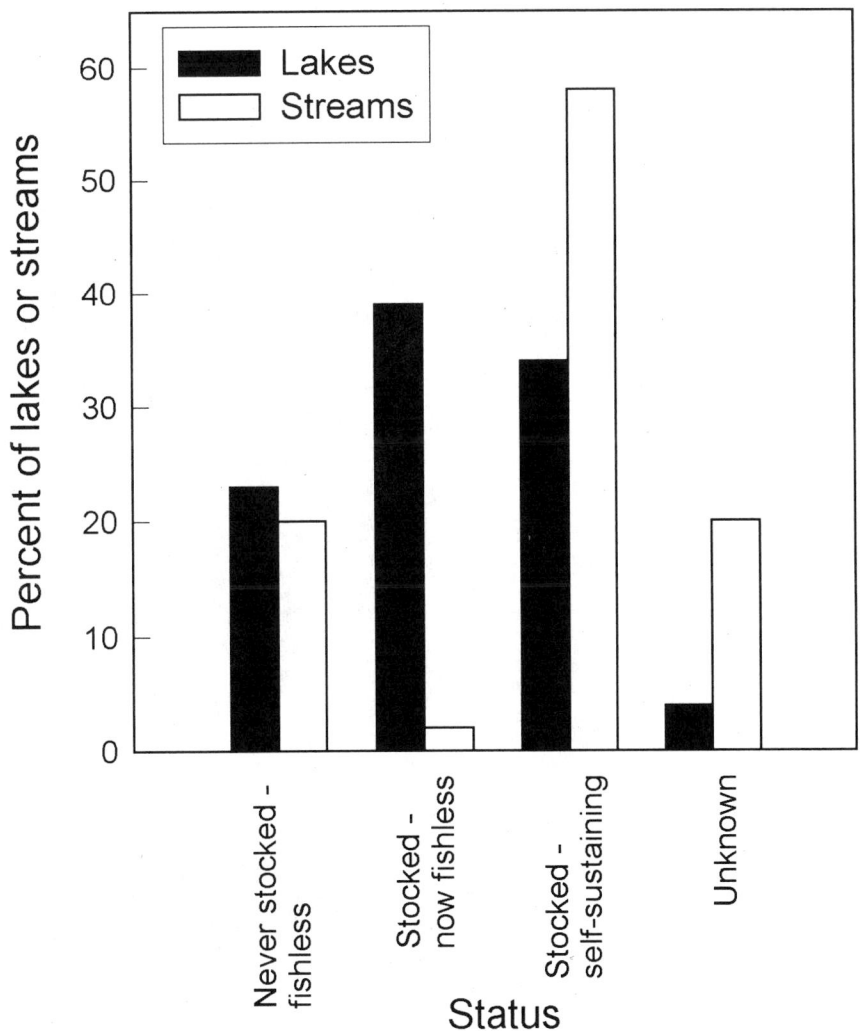

Figure 13. Frequency histograms showing the status of Yosemite National Park lakes and streams with respect to stocking history and the presence or absence of trout. Data are from Elliot and Loughlin (1992) and Wallis (1952).

PETER B. MOYLE
Department of Wildlife, Fish, and
    Conservation Biology
University of California
Davis, California

PAUL J. RANDALL
Department of Wildlife, Fish, and
    Conservation Biology
University of California
Davis, California

RONALD M. YOSHIYAMA
Department of Wildlife, Fish, and
    Conservation Biology
University of California
Davis, California

Potential Aquatic Diversity Management Areas in the Sierra Nevada

Sierra Nevada Ecosystem Project: Final report to Congress, vol. III, *Assessments, Commissioned Reports, and Background Information.* Davis: University of California, Centers for Water and Wildland Resources, 1996.

INTRODUCTION

This chapter is a supplement to the chapter by Moyle in SNEP Volume 2, called "Options for the conservation of aquatic biodiversity in the Sierra Nevada." One of the main options discussed is the establishment of a system of Aquatic Biodiversity Management Areas (ADMAs), consisting of two main types of ADMAs: watersheds and Significant Natural Areas (SNAs). The "Options" chapter should be consulted for definitions and descriptions of the the two types of ADMAs and how the examples presented here were chosen. In this chapter, we present descriptions of 42 ADMA watersheds (Table 1) that were selected for their representativeness of habitat conditions throughout the range and for their ability to support native aquatic organisms. We also present three descriptions of potential SNAs, as examples of a much more extensive system that needs developing..

The 42 ADMA watershed accounts constitute a catalog of potential ADMA watersheds for the Sierra Nevada. Each entry in the catalog presents a short description of the watershed to indicate why it has been chosen for inclusion in the ADMA watershed system. This catalogue should be considered to be a starting place for the development of a representative system of watersheds given special management to maintain aquatic biodiversity in the Sierra Nevada. Suggestions for additions and deletions are welcome, as is additional information on the watersheds proposed here.

We emphasize that all watersheds in the Sierra Nevada should be managed as if biodiversity matters. This catalog is designed, however, to help set priorities for biodiversity management, given limited resources.

Table 1. Potential ADMA watersheds of the Sierra Nevada region.

WEST SIDE DRAINAGES

Sacramento River Tributaries
1. Antelope Creek
2. Dye Creek
3. Mill Creek
4. Pine Creek
5. Deer Creek
6. Big Chico Creek

Feather River Drainage
7. Yellow Creek
8. Middle Fork Feather River

Yuba River Drainage
9. Lavezolla Creek/Downey River

American River Drainage
10. North Fork, American River
11. Rubicon River above Hell Hole Res.
12. Jones Fork of Silver Fork (above Union Valley Reservoir)
13. Rock Creek

Cosumnes River Drainage
14. Entire drainage

Calaveras River Drainage
15. North Fork Caleveras River

Mokelumne River Drainage
16. North Fork, Mokelumne River

Stanislaus River Drainage
17. North Fork, Stanislaus River
18. South Fork, Stanislaus River above Pinecrest Reservoir
19. Rose Creek

Tuolumne River Drainage
20. Clavey River
21. South Fork, Tuolumne River

Merced River Drainage
22. Entire drainage above McClure Reservoir

Upper San Joaquin Drainage
23. Mariposa Creek above Mariposa Reservoir
24. East Fork, Chowchilla River
25. Finegold Creek

Kings River Drainage
26. Rancheria Creek
27. South and Middle Forks, Kings River

Tule River Drainage
28. North and Middle Forks, Tule River

Kaweah River Drainage
29. South Fork, Kaweah River

Tulare Lake Foothill Drainages
30. Deer Creek

Kern River Drainage
31. Kern River above Isabella Reservoir

32. North Fork, Kern River
33. South Fork, Kern River

EAST SIDE DRAINAGES

Eagle Lake Drainage
     34. Entire drainage, including Pine Creek
Susan River/Honey Lake Drainage
     35. Willow Creek
Truckee River Drainage
     36. Upper Little Truckee River
     37. Sagehen Creek
Carson River Drainage
     38. East Fork, Carson River
Walker River Drainage
     39. West Walker River drainage
     40. Buckeye Creek
Mono Lake Basin
     41. Mono Lake
Owens River Drainage
     42. Convict Creek

Name: Antelope Creek

Drainage: Sacramento

Cal Watershed No.: 509.63000

County: Tehama

Location: Entire drainage from headwaters on Turner Mountain to its mouth on the Sacramento River, just south of Red Bluff.

Elevation: 70 to 2079 m; mean 1074 m

Drainage Area: 374 km^2

Description: Antelope Creek is a three-forked stream draining the slopes of Turner Mountain; its north fork begins at Pear Lake, the middle fork at Diamond Lake and the south fork originates on the southeast slope of Turner Mountain. It flows through dense conifer forest in its upper reaches, drops rapidly through a deep shady canyon lined with conifers, and continues through oak woodland and grassland where it leaves the Lassen National Forest. Deep pools in the reach between Paynes Place and the NF and SF confluence provide limited holding habitat for spring run chinook salmon. The stream then flows through the Tehama Wildlife Refuge Management Area and eventually into the Sacramento Valley, through land which is occupied by privately owned ranchland and orchards. Multiple diversions are present in the lowermost reach, resulting in reduced water flows in the spring and summer. The channel is highly braided in the lower reaches and finally reaches the Sacramento River in several locations.

Aquatic Province: Sacramento-San Joaquin

Habitat Types: A2120 Conifer forest snowmelt stream; A2140 Foothill canyon ephemeral stream; A2412 Forest stream; A2413 Spring stream; A2421 Resident rainbow trout stream; A2422 Rainbow trout/cyprinid stream; A2431 Spring run chinook stream; A2442 Fall run chinook spawning stream; A2443 Hardhead/squawfish stream.

Native Fishes: Spring run chinook salmon (R), fall run chinook salmon (R), rainbow trout (A), Pacific lamprey (R), squawfish (C), hardhead (R), Sacramento sucker (C), riffle sculpin (C), speckled dace (C) and California roach (C).

Amphibians: Foothill yellow-legged and California newts present in Indian Creek, tributary to Antelope Creek. Overall status of amphibians in Antelope Creek is uncertain, but populations are likely where habitat is suitable.

Other Vertebrates: Beaver present. Western pond turtle, aquatic garter snake also reported on Indian Creek. Important corridor for Tehama deer herd and golden eagle nesting habitat.

Invertebrates: Summer sampling in the upper reaches found macroinvertebrates neither diverse nor abundant. A cursory survey of Indian Creek indicated many species of aquatic insects present.

Riparian: Upper reaches of Antelope Creek banded by thin strip of alders, dogwoods, cedars, willows, firs, leafy emergents and grasses. Riparian woodland for lower half of Indian Creek described in ecological survey by Keeler-Wolf.

Human Impacts: Logging (clearcuts are present), cattle grazing, and recreation (fishing, camping) impact upper drainage. There are 4WD roads throughout most of the watershed, but stream access is mostly limited to foot trails. In the lower reaches, water diversions reduce flow during spring and summer, reducing access for anadromous fishes and providing habitat for introduced fishes. Grazing, agriculture, roads, and other land uses have greatly altered lowermost reaches of creek.

Ownership: Upper drainage mostly in Lassen National Forest, some private lands; lower drainage is mostly privately owned with a small area managed by the state (Tehama Wildlife Refuge).

Existing Protection: Fishing is limited to catch and release only in Tehama Wildlife Refuge. Indian Creek is managed by USFS as a Research Natural Area.

IBI Score: 80

Significant Natural Area (Aquatic): Indian Creek

Overall Quality Rating: 2.4 above diversions; 2.8 for valley floor reach; 2.0 for Indian Creek.

Reasons for Rating: A relatively modest sized drainage with no dams but considerable impacts from logging, grazing and roads. A small population of spring run chinook still spawns in this creek. It is the northernmost tributary to Sacramento River that supports a spring chinook spawning run before Red Bluff Diversion Dam. Indian Creek drainage is a nearly pristine habitat containing threatened foothill yellow-legged frogs and other native aquatic organisms.

Notes: Antelope forms a cluster of spring run chinook streams with Deer, Antelope, and Butte Creeks and is part of a group of Sacramento River tributaries dominated by native fishes.

UCD Surveys?: Yes, most recently in 1993.

Sources:
1. Lassen National Forest Management Plan, Appendix E: Wild and Scenic Rivers Evaluation.
2. Keeler-Wolfe, T. 1990. Ecological Surveys of Forest Service Research Natural Areas in California, Technical Report PSW-125.

Date of Compilation: 19 December 1994 **Compiler:** PR & PBM

ADMA WATERSHED

Name: Mill Creek   **Drainage:** Mill Creek

Cal Watershed No.: 509.42000   **County:** Tehama

Location: Entire drainage from headwaters in Lassen National Park to Sacramento River.

Elevation: 65 to 3130 m; mean 1597 m

Drainage Area: 402 km^2

Description: Mill Creek headwaters include hot mineral-laden water from springs in Lassen Volcanic National Park and small, high gradient streams in heavily forested areas. These tributaries coalesce in Mill Creek Meadows, where the creek is a meandering meadow stream. The creek then flows along Highway 172 through a heavily used mixed conifer forest before plunging into a deep canyon, which flows in part through the Ishi Wilderness Area. The upper canyon contains deep pools that harbor spring run chinook salmon, while the lower canyon is remarkably deep, narrow, and swift. The valley reaches flow through private ranchland and orchards and the creek is diverted at several places so little flow reaches the Sacramento River. The lower reaches are also altered by channelization and contain smallmouth bass and other exotic fishes. They are also important spawning areas for fall run chinook and other migratory fishes.

Aquatic Province: Sacramento-San Joaquin

Habitat Types: A2120 Conifer snowmelt stream; A2140 Foothill/canyon ephemeral stream; A2412 Forest stream; A2413 Spring; A2416 Hot springs outflow; A2421 Resident rainbow trout; A2431 Spring run chinook stream; A2442 Fall chinook spawning stream; A2443 Hardhead/squawfish stream.

Native Fishes: Fall run chinook salmon (R), spring run chinook salmon (R), Pacific lamprey (R), rainbow trout (A), Sacramento squawfish (C), hardhead (R), Sacramento sucker (C), California roach (C), riffle sculpin (C).

Amphibians: Cascade frogs, foothill yellow-legged frogs, Pacific tree frogs, California newts.

Other Vertebrates: Pacific pond turtles, aquatic garter snakes.

Invertebrates: Abundant and diverse.

Riparian zone: Mostly in good condition, except in lowermost reaches. Oaks, cottonwood, willow, and sycamores grow along the lower reaches of the creek. Foothill pine and chaparral vegetation is common in the middle reaches. Mixed conifer is found in the upper reaches.

Human Impacts: Logging, cattle grazing, camping and fishing all occur in USFS lands. Access to middle reaches of Mill Creek is limited to foot trails, providing some natural protection. Mill Creek meadows has been heavily grazed. Water diversions in lower reaches significantly reduces flow so little water reaches the Sacramento River in the summer. Clough Dam represents a partial barrier to movements of migratory fish. Town of Los Molinos is along the last km or of stream. Introduced fishes are present in lower reaches.

Ownership: Headwaters are in Lassen National Park. About half the upper drainage is in Lassen National Forest, including the Ishi Wilderness Area in the lower elevations. Below the USFS boundary the land is all privately owned.

Existing Protection: National Park manages headwaters; Ishi Wilderness Area in middle reaches. The Nature Conservancy has a conservation easement on Mill Creek meadows.

Significant Natural Areas (Aquatic): None described.

Overall Quality Rating: 2.1 above valley floor; 2.8 on valley floor.

Reasons for Rating: Mill Creek has no dams or diversions except in its lowest reach. Native fish communities are still present including spring run chinook salmon.

IBI Score: 93

Notes: Spring run chinook salmon probably qualify as a threatened species under both state and federal law, but efforts are now underway to protect its populations without listing. A Mill Creek Conservancy has been formed by private landowners to develop conservation plans for the watershed.

UCD Surveys?: Yes. Survey of entire drainage done in 1987.

Sources:

Wild and Scenic River Evaluation; EIS for Forest Plan, Lassen National Forest.

Sato, G. S. and P. B. Moyle. 1988. Survey for fish populations on Deer and Mill Creeks, unpublished report.

Date of Compilation: 23 December 1994   **Compiler:** PR and PBM

ADMA WATERSHED

Name: Dye Creek   **Drainage:** Upper Sacramento River

Cal Watershed No.: 509.62000   **County:** Tehama

Location: Entire drainage from headwaters to Sacramento River.

Elevation Range: 67 to 700 m; mean 383 m

Drainage Area: 105 km^2

Description: Dye Creek is a small foothill drainage sandwiched between the Mill Creek and Antelope Creek watersheds. It has two main forks, both in deep lava-walled canyons that are cool enough to support trout populations. There is a well-developed, if narrow, corridor of riparian trees and vines along the creek. During summer, the creek in the lower canyon is a trickle between pools and supports large populations of California roach and speckled dace. As the creek emerges from the canyon, there is a steep cascade that flows into a long deep pool that seems to mark the upstream limit of squawfish and hardhead. A pond on a dammed section of creek at the headquarters of the Dye Creek Preserve (TNC) serves as source of exotic fish and frogs in the drainage. The lower reaches of the creek flow through seasonal pasturelands and sections of it are rip-rapped. The reach just above the Sacramento River is used seasonally as a rearing area for juvenile chinook salmon and other riverine fishes.

Aquatic Province: Sacramento-San Joaquin

Habitat Types: A2140 Foothill/canyon ephemeral stream; A2412 Forest stream; A2413 Spring; A2421 Resident rainbow trout; A2442 Fall chinook spawning stream (?); A2443 Hardhead/squawfish stream.

Native Fishes: Fall run chinook salmon (R), Pacific lamprey (?), rainbow trout (C), Sacramento squawfish (C), hardhead (?), Sacramento sucker (C), California roach (A), speckled dace (A).

Amphibians: Bullfrogs abundant in lower canyon, but native frogs may be present higher. California newts.

Other Vertebrates: Pacific pond turtles, aquatic garter snakes.

Invertebrates: In a cursory survey (June 1995), they did not appear to be particularly abundant or diverse.

Riparian zone: Mostly in good condition, except in lowermost reaches. Oaks, cottonwood, willow, fig (non-native) and sycamores grow along the lower reaches of the creek. Foothill pine and chaparral vegetation is common in the middle reaches. Condition of riparian zone is improving because of TNC management practices.

Human Impacts: Cattle grazing and hunting (mainly pigs) have been the principal activities in the past, which have been continued by TNC, although at a reduced level. Water diversions in lower reaches probably reduce flow so little water reaches the Sacramento River in the summer. Introduced fishes and frogs are present in lower reaches and a pond at the TNC headquarters is probably a major source.

Ownership: Almost the entire drainage is owned by The Nature Conservancy, with exception of some land along the lower most reaches.

Existing Protection: The Nature Conservancy manages the watershed as both as reserve and as a working cattle ranch.

Significant Natural Areas (Aquatic): None described

Overall Quality Rating: 2.1 above ranch headquarters; 2.8 below.

Reasons for Rating: Dye Creek has no dams or diversions except in its lowest reach. Native fish communities are still present, although bullfrogs seem to dominate the amphibian community.

IBI Score: 80

Notes: TNC welcomes research on their land.

UCD Surveys?: Yes. Quick survey of lower drainage done in June, 1995 by R. L. Leidy and P. B. Moyle.

Sources: Paul Maslin, CSU Chico, personal communication; George Stroud, TNC.

Date of Compilation: 16 July 1995   **Compiler:** PBM

ADMA WATERSHED

Name: Pine Creek   **Drainage:** Upper Sacramento R.

Cal Watershed No.: 509.16000   **County:** Tehama

Location: Entire drainage from headwaters (Bennett Spring) on Cohasset Ridge to Sacramento River.

Elevation: 55 to 1220 m; mean 637 m

Drainage Area: 281 km^2

Description: Pine Creek is a small foothill drainage just south of the Deer Creek drainage and north of the Big Chico Creek drainage. Typical summer flows are 0.23 m3/sec but the creek dries up in its lowermost reaches. The upper creek and its tributaries flow through a deep lava-walled canyons and is cool enough to support trout. There is a well-developed, if narrow, corridor of riparian trees and vines along the creek. During summer, the creek in the lower canyon is a trickle between pools and presumably supports large populations of California roach and speckled dace. As the creek emerges from the canyon, there is a large diversion dam over which the water plunges into a deep (4+m) pool that seems to be the upper limit to squawfish and hardhead. The lower reaches of the creek flow through seasonal pasturelands (some irrigated). The reach just above the Sacramento River is used seasonally as a rearing area for juvenile chinook salmon and other riverine fishes.

Aquatic Province: Sacramento-San Joaquin

Habitat Types: A2140 Foothill/canyon ephemeral stream; A2412 Forest stream; A2413 Spring; A2421 Resident rainbow trout; A2442 Fall chinook spawning stream (?); A2443 Hardhead/squawfish stream.

Native Fishes: Fall run chinook salmon (R), Pacific lamprey (C), rainbow trout (C), Sacramento squawfish (C), hardhead (C), Sacramento sucker (C), California roach (A), speckled dace (A), riffle sculpin (C), hitch (R), tule perch (R).

Amphibians: Not known

Other Vertebrates: Not known

Invertebrates: Not known

Riparian zone: Mostly in good condition, except in lowermost reaches. Oaks, cottonwood, willow, fig (non-native) and sycamores grow along the lower reaches of the creek. Foothill pine and chaparral vegetation are common in the middle reaches.

Human Impacts: Cattle grazing and water diversions are main factors affecting watershed. Water diversions in lower reaches probably reduce flow so little water reaches the Sacramento River in the summer. Introduced fishes and probably frogs are present in lowermost reaches but not particularly abundant.

Ownership: Private, although uppermost headwater are in Lassen NF.

Existing Protection: None

Significant Natural Areas (Aquatic): None described

Overall Quality Rating: 2.1 above diversion dam (131 m elevation); 2.4 below.

Reasons for Rating: Pine Creek is dominated by native fishes, even in its lowermost reaches. Presumably the rugged country through which it flows limits access of both people and cattle to much of the stream.

IBI Score: 80

Notes: Similar to nearby Dye Creek

UCD Surveys?: No

Sources:

Paul Maslin, CSU Chico, personal communication.

Grant, G. C. 1992. Selected life history aspects of Sacramento squawfish and hardhead minnows in Pine Creek, Tehama County, California. Unpublished M.S. thesis, CSU Chico. 86 pp.

Date of Compilation: 16 July 1995   **Compiler:** PBM

Name: Deer Creek

Drainage: Sacramento River

Calwater No.: 509.20000

County: Tehama

Location: Entire drainage from headwaters to mouth on Sacramento River north of Woodson Bridge State Recreation Area.

Elevation Range: 60 to 2389 m; mean 1224 m

Drainage Area: 540 km^2

Description: Deer Creek is the largest tributary to the lower Sacramento River without a major dam\reservoir. The headwaters are small, high gradient tributaries in mixed conifer forest, which coalesce in Deer Creek meadows. In the meadows, the creek is a meandering meadow stream that has been altered by grazing and recreational use. It then flows along Highway 32 in a heavily used (recreation, logging) ponderosa pine forest before plunging into a deep, inaccessible canyon. The lower part of the canyon reach, which flows through foothill pine-oak savannah, is in the Ishi Wilderness Area. The canyon contains deep pools that harbor spring run chinook salmon in summer and provide habitat for most of the native fishes, in a classic pattern of zonation. The lowermost reaches flow through private ranchlands and orchards, which are irrigated with creek water. Diversions in several places can dry up the creek in late summer. The lower reaches are also altered by channelization, levees, and roads but still provide spawning habitat for fall run chinook salmon and other native fishes ascending from the Sacramento River.

Aquatic Province: Sacramento-San Joaquin

Habitat Types: A2120 Conifer snowmelt stream; A2412 Forest stream; A2421 Resident trout stream; A2431 Spring chinook stream; A2443 Hardhead-squawfish stream; A2442 Seasonal spawning stream.

Native Fishes: Pacific lamprey (C), fall (C) and spring run (C) chinook salmon, rainbow trout (A), hardhead (A), Sacramento squawfish (A), California roach (A), speckled dace (A), Sacramento sucker (A), riffle sculpin (A), tule perch (C).

Amphibians: Foothill yellow-legged frogs (R), cascade frogs (R), Pacific tree frogs (C), Sierra newts.

Other Vertebrates: Pacific pond turtle (P), otters (C), dippers (C).

Invertebrates: Abundant and diverse.

Riparian zone: Riparian vegetation not well-developed in most places because of steep canyons, but is typically mixed conifer. Deer Creek meadows is the largest meadow system in the drainage and has been altered by extensive grazing (few willows, etc., left). Lowermost reaches have floodplain with cottonwoods and oaks, whose condition varies with location.

Human Impacts: Roads (esp. Highways 32 and 36) affect parts of the upper drainage, providing access to anglers and campers. Upper drainage is heavily grazed, especially Deer Creek meadows, creating a degraded meadow stream and favoring exotic brown trout. Selective logging occurs throughout the drainage but impact on stream has been minimal, although roads on steep slopes are a potential problem. Diversions on lowermost reaches may create passage problems at times for salmon and other fishes, and make lower reaches uninhabitable for most native fishes. Extensive channel alteration has taken place between Sacramento River and Leninger Road. Poaching may affect salmon populations.

Ownership: About half the upper drainage is in Lassen National Forest, with a checkerboard of land ownership with private timber companies. The lowermost reaches are all on privately owned ranch and farmland.

Existing Protection: Part of the middle-lower reaches flow through the Ishi Wilderness Area. Catch and release fishing permitted only in canyon sections. Cub Creek is a USFS RNA.

Significant Natural Areas (Aquatic): Cub Creek

Overall Quality Rating: 2.2 overall. 2.1 for reaches above Leninger Road (2.3 for Deer Creek meadows) and 2.9 for valley floor reach.

Reasons for Rating: Deer Creek is still dominated by its native fish communities and is one of the last refuges for spring run chinook salmon. While the uppermost reaches are roaded and accessible, the middle reaches flow through some of the wildest country in California, especially considering the low elevations. This is the best example of a natural Sacramento River tributary stream remaining, through a combination of size and habitat variety. The lowermost reaches are highly altered but not irreversibly so, especially if summer diversions are reduced.

IBI Score: 93

Notes: Spring run chinook salmon probably qualify as a threatened species under both state and federal law, but efforts are now underway to protect its populations without listing. The Deer Creek Conservancy, an organization of landowners within the drainage, is actively seeking ways to reduce human impact on the watershed.

UCD Surveys?: Numerous because this has been a major study site for native fishes. Major survey in 1986-87.

Sources:

Baltz, D. M. and P. B. Moyle. 1993. Invasion resistance to introduced species by a native assemblage of California stream fishes. Ecol. Applications 3:246-255.

Moyle, P. B. and D. M. Baltz. 1985. Microhabitat use by an assemblage of California stream fishes: developing criteria for instream flow determinations. Trans. Amer. Fish. Soc. 114:695-704.

See also Mill Creek sources.

Date: 20 October 1994   **Compiler:** PBM

ADMA WATERSHED

Name: Big Chico Creek   **Drainage:** Sacramento River

Calwater No.: 509.14000   **County:** Butte and Tehama

Location: Entire drainage from Lassen National Forest near Chico Meadows to its confluence on Sacramento River.

Elevation: 50 to 1831 m; mean 940 m.

Drainage Area: 187 km^2

Description: Big Chico Creek begins in Lassen National Forest as the confluence of two small unnamed tributaries near Chico Meadows. For the first 55 km the stream flows through a deep, volcanic canyon surrounded by oak woodland in a north-south direction, adjacent to Highway 32. Deep, bedrock pools in this reach support a small number of spring run chinook salmon as well as native cyprinids. A barrier near Ponderosa Way crossing is the upstream end for salmon migration. About 8 km downstream is the Iron Canyon fish ladder which provides upstream passage for anadromous fishes. The creek then turns to the west and flows about 16 km through the Central Valley including Bidwell Park area in the City of Chico. The last few miles of stream run through ranches and farmlands where much of it gets diverted before it meets the Sacramento River. In many years there is insufficient flow for a fall run chinook spawning migration in Big Chico Creek.

Aquatic Province: Sacramento-San Joaquin

Habitat Types: A2120 Conifer forest snowmelt stream; A2130 Foothill/valley ephemeral stream; A2140 Foothill canyon ephemeral stream; A2412 Forest stream; A2421 Resident rainbow trout stream; A2431 Spring chinook stream; A2442 Fall chinook spawning stream; A2443 Hardhead/squawfish stream.

Native Fishes: Fall chinook salmon (R), spring chinook salmon (R), Pacific lamprey (C), hardhead (C), Sacramento squawfish (C), Sacramento sucker (C), California roach (A), speckled dace (R), riffle sculpin (C), rainbow trout (A).

Amphibians: No records

Other Vertebrates: Yellow-billed cuckoos recorded near mouth.

Invertebrates: Benthic invertebrates were studied in detail from Ponderosa Way road crossing down to Bidwell park to see the effects of a rotenone treatment on the aquatic insects, by Paul Maslin of CSU Chico. Baseline data existed prior to treatment.

Riparian zone: Thin belt of riparian vegetation along much of stream, although some is urbanized. Bidwell Park in Chico contains excellent examples of Great Valley Mixed Riparian Forest and Valley Oak Riparian Forest. At the mouth are remnants of Great Valley Cottonwood Riparian Forest.

Human Impacts: Diversions (M & T pumps) are significant in the lower reaches causing reverse flow at the mouth of the Sacramento River during critical outmigration for salmonids, possibly directing the fish into unscreened pumps. The Iron Canyon fish ladder has been recognized as a partial barrier due to poor construction, but has been recently repaired. Rotenone treatment of lower reaches in 1986 killed most of the native fishes and recovery was slow due to drought. Smallmouth bass recolonized rapidly after treatment and have dominated in sections below Iron Canyon barrier. Recreational uses are high within Bidwell Park, including fishing, swimming and OHV use.

Ownership: Only 1 mile of the headwaters is within Lassen NF. Some land in middle reaches is managed by BLM. Downstream from USFS boundary is almost entirely private, except for Bidwell Park, managed by City of Chico.

Existing Protection: None

Significant Natural Areas (Aquatic): None identified

Overall Quality Rating: 2.3 above Iron Gate Dam; 2.5 through Bidwell Park/City of Chico; 2.9 downstream of city.

Reasons for Rating: One of the few remaining tributaries that can still support spring run chinook salmon. Lower reaches still have a native fish assemblage in foothill regions.

IBI Score: 60

Notes: Lower reaches were poisoned (rotenone) by CDFG in 1986 to benefit anadromous salmonid populations. Operation was of dubious success and mainly seemed to favor exotic smallmouth bass. This drainage is included as an ADMA despite its relatively low IBI score because of its high recovery potential.

UCD Surveys?: Yes, 1980s.

Sources:

CH2M Hill, Inc. 1993. Assessment of Big Chico Creek Salmon and Steelhead Production. Unpublished Report.

Lassen National Forest. Environmental Impact Statement of Forest Management Plan, Appendix E: Wild and Scenic Rivers Evaluation.

Maslin, P. 1987. Follow-up studies on the Rotenone Treatment of Chico Creek, Unpublished report, CSU Chico.

Maslin, P., et al. 1994. A Critical Evaluation of the Rotenone Treatment of Big Chico Creek. Unpublished report, CSU Chico.

Travanti, L. 1990. The effects of piscidal treatment on the fish community of a northern California stream. Unpublished M.S. thesis, CSU Chico. 67 pp.

Compiled: 16 July 1995   **Compiler:** PR and PBM

ADMA WATERSHED

Name: Yellow Creek   **Drainage:** North Fork Feather River

Calwater No.: 518.43010-43020   **County:** Plumas

Location: Yellow Creek is a tributary to the North Fork Feather River. The confluence is along Highway 70 at the PG&E power plant. The upper and middle portions drain the mountains southwest of Lake Almanor in Lassen NF. Includes tributary Soda Creek.

Elevation: 735 to 2141 m; mean 1604 m

Drainage Area: 197 km^2

Description: Yellow Creek is a spring-fed meadow stream. The middle reaches are 3rd-4th order, with moderate gradients. The upper-middle sections (near the PG&E campground) are typical of a meadow/valley stream, consisting of a meandering channel lined with grasses and willows, having a low gradient, slow velocity, and muddy substrate. The lower-middle sections are higher velocity, medium gradient, run- and riffle-dominated sections.

Aquatic Province: Sacramento-San Joaquin

Habitat Types: A1210 Alpine lake; A1240 Dystrophic pond; A2120 Conifer forest snowmelt stream; A2412 Forest stream; A2413 Spring stream; A2421 Resident rainbow trout stream.

Native Fishes: Rainbow trout (C). Non-native brown trout (A) and brook trout (C) also present.

Amphibians: None seen in Yellow Creek by UCD survey crew in 1993, despite extensive searching, but native frogs probably present.

Other Vertebrates: Wolverine and goshawk reported around Green Island Lakes.

Invertebrates: Aquatic macroinvertebrates are abundant, diverse, and dominated by snails, perlid stonefly larvae, and corydalid larvae.

Riparian zone: Lake and bog type wetlands are present in headwaters of Soda Creek drainage. Wet meadows are present in much of the drainage but especially around Green Island Lakes and Soda Creek. Riparian zone often well developed, with alders, aspen, willows, and leafy emergent plants.

Human Impacts: Grazing is heavy in the upper and middle sections of Yellow Creek near the PG&E campground. Logging has occurred in the past although it is less evident in the downstream areas. Mining has been done extensively in the past and the portion of the stream nearest the campground receives heavy fishing and other recreational use.

Ownership: Lassen National Forest

Existing Protection: Green Island Lakes and Soda Ridge are USFS Research Natural Areas. Yellow Creek is managed as a wild trout stream by the California Department of Fish and Game.

Significant Natural Areas (Aquatic): Green Island Lakes, Soda Creek

Overall Quality Rating: 2.5 Yellow Creek; 2.1 Soda Creek and Green Island Lakes

Reasons for Rating: Yellow Creek is a fairly typical Sierra drainage in that it has been heavily used by for grazing, logging, mining, recreation, etc. However, its unique attributes (e.g. springs, Soda Creek, meadows) are gradually being recognized and improvements are happening.

IBI Score: 68

Notes: Soda Creek is relatively inaccessible and needs to be surveyed for amphibians and other organisms. Yellow Creek has an excellent reputation for its wild trout fishery.

UCD Surveys?: Yes, 1993.

Sources:

Keeler-Wolf, T. 1990. Ecological surveys of Forest Service Natural Areas in California. PSW Tech. Rpt. 125.

Date: 27 December 1994　　　　　　　　　　**Compiler:** PR, PBM

ADMA WATERSHED

Name: Middle Fork Feather River　　　　　**Drainage:** Feather River

Calwater No.: 518.3000　　　　　　　　　　**County:** Butte, Plumas

Location: From Oroville Reservoir upstream 175 km. to headwaters in Sierra Valley.

Elevation: 305 to 2631 m; mean 1653 m

Drainage Area: 2919 km^2

Description: The Middle Fork begins in the flat, agricultural Sierra Valley, into which flow numerous small tributaries. The river in this area consists of a series of parallel but meandering channels (many of them channelized) on the valley floor, many of which are dry in summer. Collectively, the Sierra Valley above Portola contains 200 km of trout stream, 50 km of warmwater stream and at least 160 km of canals and sloughs. Also present are one natural lake, and two major reservoirs (Frenchman Reservoir, Davis Reservoir). Some water from the Truckee River is diverted into the Valley via a canal.

Between the mouths of Big Grizzly Creek and Sulphur Creek (at Clio), the Middle Fork is generally a low gradient, slow moving river with mostly warm water fishes, including several exotic species. Sulphur Creek is a cold spring-fed tributary containing a large wild trout population in addition to native cyprinids. The river below Clio runs through flat pastures in Mohawk Valley and is typically warm water containing few trout. Between Graeagle and Nelson Point the stream gradient increases, channel becomes more narrow, and cooler waters support more trout and fewer cyprinids. River is very developed along this reach and road access creates heavy fishing pressure.

Nelson Creek is a major tributary that enters near the top of the Middle Fork canyon and contains a large population of wild rainbow trout. The lower reaches contain numerous pools and spawning gravel, making it one of the most important spawning tributaries of the Middle Fork. Below Nelson Creek, the Middle Fork drops into a canyon with some reaches containing steep granitic walls over 600 m high and numerous cascades. Wild rainbow trout are the dominant species with native nongame fish present in small numbers. This section of river has good water quality, high aquatic insect production and an abundant rainbow trout population. The Middle Fork then empties into Oroville Reservoir. The Fall River enters the Middle Fork near its mouth on Oroville, cascading over Feather Falls (206 m high); it may deserve status as a separate ADMA.

Aquatic Province: Sacramento-San Joaquin

Habitat Types: A1210 Alpine lakes; A2120 Conifer forest snowmelt stream; A2130 Foothill/valley ephemeral stream; A2412 Conifer forest stream; A2413 Spring; A2414 Meadow stream; A2421 Resident rainbow trout stream; A2422 Rainbow trout/cyprinid stream; A2443 Hardhead/squawfish stream; A2446 Squawfish/sucker spawning stream.

Native Fishes: Sacramento squawfish (C), Sacramento sucker (C), hardhead (P?), California roach (?), speckled dace (C), riffle sculpin (C), rainbow trout (A).

Amphibians: No amphibians were seen by UCD survey crew sampling Nelson Creek in 1993 but native frogs should be present.

Other Vertebrates: Waterfowl habitat in Sierra Valley.

Invertebrates: Moderately diverse and abundant in Nelson Creek.

Riparian Zone: Sierra Valley was presumably once a continuous marsh/meadow. Today, freshwater marshes are located in scattered areas on the west side of Sierra Valley and in the Marble Hot Springs area. Riparian vegetation of the Sierra Valley is typically willow, alders, cottonwoods and grasses. Canyon is steep sided with little room for riparian vegetation.

Human Impacts: Oroville Dam cuts off access of chinook salmon and steelhead to drainage. Grazing and water diversion is extensive in Sierra Valley; riparian zone and freshwater marsh habitats have been reduced. Introduced fish species are common in the Valley and Upper Middle Fork. Northern pike were introduced illegally into Frenchman Reservoir and it is not certain whether or not eradication efforts by CDFG were successful. Lahontan redside, mountain sucker, and other fishes from the Great Basin have been introduced via an irrigation canal from the Little Truckee River. Two upper drainages have dams on them. Recreational use, including fishing, is high for middle and upper reaches and in the tributary streams. Logging has been a major activity in the drainage and suction dredging and other mining operations have been active for decades in the upper drainage.

Ownership: Much of the drainage is in Plumas National Forest with some in Tahoe National Forest. The Sierra Valley and most of the land along the main river down to mouth of the canyon is privately owned. In addition, the upper watershed contains Plumas-Eureka State Park and two large state game refuges.

Existing Protection: Entire river between Beckwourth (Sierra Valley) and Oroville Reservoir is designated a Wild and Scenic River. The lowermost reaches are included in Feather Falls National Scenic Area. Nelson Creek is managed as a wild trout stream by CDFG.

Significant Natural Areas (Aquatic): None noted.

Overall Quality Rating: 2.9 for main river in Sierra Valley; 2.4 for un-dammed tributaries in upper drainage on National Forest land; 2.5 for river from Portola to Nelson Creek; 2.4 for Middle Fork canyon reach and tributaries.

Reasons for Rating: The Middle Fork of the Feather is a large drainage with aquatic habitats ranging from irreversibly degraded to near-pristine. It therefore provides a good representation of the aquatic habitat types in this portion of the Sierra Nevada. Although there are two large reservoirs on the upper end, there is sufficient flow down most of the river to still maintain a natural hydrologic regime. Many of the tributaries are also in good condition and maintain a diversity of aquatic organisms. The Sierra Valley has been highly altered by human activity yet is unusual for its extensive marshlands and spring systems; special consideration should be given to expanding natural/protected areas in the valley.

IBI Score: 63. The Middle Fork is included as an ADMA despite this score because of the diversity of habitats and the high potential of many areas to respond to biodiversity-oriented management.

Notes: A thorough review of existing information on the watershed is needed, along with additional surveys of aquatic and riparian habitats. Invertebrate and amphibians surveys are needed for spring areas in Sierra Nevada to identify the biologically richest remaining areas.

UCD Surveys?: Nelson Creek, 1993.

Sources:

Palmer, T. 1993. The Wild and Scenic Rivers of America.

California Department of Fish and Game. July, 1961. Fish and Wildlife Resources of Proposed Water Development on the Middle Fork Feather River.

California Department of Water Resources. October, 1973. Natural Resources of the Sierra Valley Study Area.

Date: 28 December 1994   **Compiler**: RY, PBM

ADMA WATERSHED

Name: Lavezolla Creek / Upper Downie River   **Drainage:** Yuba River

Cal Watershed No.: 517.52000   **County:** Sierra

Location: From headwaters to union just above Downieville.

Elevation: 935 to 2253 m; mean 1680 m

Drainage Area: 74 km^2

Description: The Lavezzola Creek and the Upper Downie River unite above Downieville to form a major tributary to the North Fork Yuba River. Both streams cascade through deep, steep-walled canyons lined with a mixture of second-growth conifers and oaks. The upper reaches of the two streams appear to accessible only by trail and the watersheds appear to be in good condition. However, in the 1850s much of the watershed was denuded to supply timber for the building of Downieville and its mines. Placer mining also took place in the creeks and they are still the locus of mining claims. The headwaters include some small lakes (e.g., Spencer Lakes, Hawley Lake). Wild rainbow trout are common to abundant in most areas but their native distribution is not known. Lavezzola Creek is managed as a wild trout stream by CDFG.

Aquatic Province: Sacramento-San Joaquin

Habitat Types: A1151 Outcrop pools (?); A1152 Mountain ponds; A1210 Mountain lakes; A2120 Conifer forest snowmelt stream; A2412 Forest stream; A2413 Spring; A2414 Meadow stream; A2421 Resident rainbow trout stream.

Native Fishes: Rainbow trout (A), other fishes may be present in lowermost reaches, just above their confluence.

Amphibians: Unknown, but mountain yellow-legged frogs may present.

Other Vertebrates: Deer migration corridor through North Fork Yuba River drainage.

Invertebrates: Not known but a caddisfly proposed for federal listing as an endangered species (category 1), *Goeracea oregona*, is endemic to New York Ravine, a downstream tributary to NF Yuba. Two other caddisfly species that are federally listed (category 2) also occur in NY Ravine.

Riparian, Wetland Habitats: Narrow riparian zone along creek reasonably well developed.

Human Impacts: Some mining, logging, grazing, and recreational use take place in drainage.

Ownership: Entirely within Tahoe NF, with small private inholdings and mining claims scattered throughout drainage.

Existing Protection: Lavezzola Creek managed as a wild trout stream by CDFG.

Significant Natural Areas (Aquatic): None identified.

Overall Quality Rating: 2.3

Reasons for Rating: Two streams are in reasonably good condition because of their steep terrain which discourages use. Although they were devastated during the Gold Rush, they have shown remarkable recovery, which should be allowed to continue.

IBI Score: 67

Notes: More information is needed on this drainage, especially about invertebrates.

UCD Surveys?: No

Sources:

US Forest Service. 1994. Wild and Scenic River Assessment in Environmental Impact Statement for the Tahoe National Forest.

Gerstung, E., et al. 1977. Sierra County Wildlife Conservation Element. Unpublished Report, Dept. of Fish and Game, June 1977.

Date: 28 December 1994   **Compiler:** RY, PBM

ADMA WATERSHED

Name: North Fork American River   **Drainage:** American River

Calwater No.: 514.50000   **County:** Placer

Location: From the headwaters in the Cedars area down to Iowa Hill Bridge, SE of Colfax.

Elevation: 183 to 2709 m; mean 1302

Drainage Area: 900 km^2

Description: The North Fork American headwater area is characterized as a broad glaciated valley composed of several steep gradient tributaries surrounded by patches of forest interspersed with exposed granite bedrock. Much of this area is on private land and contains two separate research reserves. The river below Serena Creek changes to a high gradient stream with numerous rapids and several falls 20-50 feet high in a V-shaped canyon. The canyon at Royal Gorge has depths up to 1050 meters. Below the Gorge the gradient decreases and the river becomes more braided and meandering within a narrow alluvial valley. Red fir and mixed conifer forest is the dominate vegetation type in the upland area. The streambed widens to 100 feet in some places and contains extensive gravel beds. The canyon narrows then widens at Green Valley then closes again at Giant Gap, where the river becomes constricted by a narrow bedrock canyon. Oak woodland and chaparral are the dominant vegetation in the lower reaches. The reach ends at Iowa Hill Bridge, site of the upper end of the proposed Auburn Dam.

Aquatic Province: Sacramento-San Joaquin

Habitat Types: A1151 Outcrop pools (?), A1152 Mountain ponds; A1210 Alpine lakes; A2120 Conifer forest snowmelt stream; A2130 Foothill/valley ephemeral stream; A2412 Forest stream; A2413 Spring; A2421 Resident rainbow trout stream; A2422 rainbow trout/cyprinid stream.

Native Fishes: Rainbow trout (A); Sacramento sucker (A); Sacramento squawfish (C); hardhead (C); California roach (C); riffle sculpin (C). Chinook salmon and steelhead once present but excluded by downstream dams.

Amphibians: Mountain yellow-legged frogs reported in some areas.

Other Vertebrates: Golden Eagle and Peregrine Falcon nesting areas in upper canyon.

Invertebrates: No records.

Riparian zone: Very diverse group of plant communities along the river canyon. Dense overstory on the north facing slopes dominated by conifers and more sparse vegetation on the south facing slopes with canyon live oak as a common species. Unaltered red fir and yellow pine stands along the river canyon have been identified as California Natural Areas. CNPS lists *Veronica cusickii* as the only rare plant in the North Fork (1977) and it is found in high alpine meadows on north facing slopes. Remoteness of the canyon, unaltered flows and the limited timber harvesting has resulted in little impacts to streamside vegetation.

Human Impacts: Timber harvest and mining activity has been very limited although some private timber lands could have some adverse impacts to river in the future. Privately landowners in the Cedar area have taken an active role in protecting the area and public access is very limited. There are only two road crossings in the entire reach, the Iowa-Hill Bridge at the lowest end and the Soda Springs crossing in the Cedar area. Most river access is by foot trails. Hiking, fishing and boating are the major recreational uses on the river.

Ownership: 42 km of the main river is in Tahoe National Forest, 19.2 km on BLM land. Private lands in the Cedars and scattered sections throughout the drainage.

Existing Protection: From the Cedars to Iowa Hill Bridge over 61 km is designated as National Wild and Scenic River. Most of this same section, over 59 km, is managed as a Wild Trout Stream. There are two research areas, the University of California Natural Reserve System (6.9 km2) and the USFS Onion Creek Experimental Forest (11.7 km2). The private landowners association is also very active in preserving the upper reaches of the river. There are 10 km2 acres of Natural Areas in the watershed representing unaltered stands of red fir, yellow pine, meadow and riparian areas.

Significant Natural Areas (Aquatic): The Cedars (UCNRS Reserve); Sugar Pine Point RNA; Onion Creek RNA

Overall Quality Rating: 2.3

Reasons for Rating: Much of the drainage is unaltered because of its rugged features and roadless areas. There are over 60 km of free-flowing river with most of its original native fishes still present except for anadramous fish. Large areas of protected or recognized natural areas.

IBI Score: 70

Notes: This river has potential for restoration of salmon and steelhead, if the fish can be moved over Folsom and Natomas dams.

UCD Surveys?: Yes, 1993

Sources:

US Forest Service. 1978. North Fork American Wild and Scenic River Study Report, Tahoe National Forest, 1978.

California Department of Fish and Game. 1977. North Fork American River Waterway Management Plan, California Department of Fish and Game, 1977.

Palmer, T. 1993. The Wild and Scenic Rivers of America.

Date Compiled: December 19, 1994   **Compiler:** PR

ADMA WATERSHED

Name: Rubicon River   **Drainage:** American River

Cal Water Basin No.: 514.45000   **County:** El Dorado

Location: From headwaters in Desolation Wilderness to inlet to Hell Hole Reservoir.

Elevation Range: 1447 to 2990 m; mean 2215 m

Drainage Area: 172 km^2

Description: The headwaters of the Rubicon begin in the Rockbound Valley of Desolation Wilderness Area, which was originally without fish. Steep gradient snowmelt tributaries flow into alpine lakes, which discharge their water into the river. The river is characterized by long runs and riffles with frequent pools. At the lower end of Rockbound Valley the flow is captured in part by Rubicon Reservoir and Rockbound Lake, which are connected by a tunnel. The river then drops into a steep, glaciated canyon with patches of late successional forests adjacent to stream. Stream access is limited to foot trails for the entire drainage. The river eventually flows into Hell Hole Reservoir.

Aquatic Province: Sacramento-San Joaquin

Habitat Types: A1151 Outcrop pools; A1152 Mountain ponds; A1210 Alpine lakes; A2110 Alpine snowmelt stream; A2120 Conifer forest snowmelt stream; A2412 Forest stream; A2413 Spring; A2421 Resident rainbow trout stream.

Native Fishes: Rainbow trout. Non-native brown trout and brook trout also present.

Amphibians: Mountain yellow-legged frogs

Other Vertebrates: No records.

Invertebrates: No records.

Riparian Zone: Narrow and coniferous along most of river because of steep canyon walls.

Human Impacts: Stream partially regulated for power production. Hiking, camping, fishing are main activities in the watershed. Some logging also present. Grazing a major problem in meadows.

Ownership: El Dorado NF with some private inholdings

Existing Protection: Desolation Wilderness and Granite Chief wilderness areas for headwaters.

Significant Natural Areas (Aquatic): None designated.

Overall Quality Rating: 2.5.

Reasons for Rating: This alpine watershed is in a glaciated landscape that is largely in wilderness areas, containing native frogs etc. Presumably rainbow trout were native to the canyon below 2000 m. While the lower half of this river reach is partially regulated, the flow regime is close to the one that originally existed. This watershed is a good example of a high alpine systems fed by many small lakes.

IBI Score: 64

Notes: The upper Rubicon may not be the best choice for a high alpine ADMA in the middle Sierra Nevada but most other regions have similar drawbacks (introduced trout, small dams).

UCD Surveys?: Yes, 1993

Sources:

Wild and Scenic Affected Environment, Tahoe NF EIS, 1994.

Personal communication with Tahoe NF hydrologist, James Bergman.

Date: 28 December 1994   **Compiler:** PR, PBM

ADMA WATERSHED

Name: Jones Fork, Silver Fork   **Drainage:** South Fork American

Calwater No.: 514.34010 and 34011   **County:** El Dorado

Location: From headwaters in Desolation Wilderness to Union Valley Reservoir.

Elevation: 1522 to 2818 m; mean 1926 m

Drainage Area: 66 km^2

Description: Jones Fork originates in the Desolation Wilderness around Maud and Gertrude Lakes, which are located in subalpine meadows. The stream flows over exposed granitic rock and drops into a high gradient, boulder dominated channel surrounded by coniferous forest. In the lower reaches the creek becomes a low gradient channel composed of many large, sandy bottomed shallow pools with undercut banks and abundant root wads. Sacramento suckers inhabit this low gradient reach along with rainbow trout. There are large patches of gravel in the riffle areas that have been reported to support a kokanee spawning run from Union Valley Reservoir. There is a steep bedrock drop just upstream of the reservoir that is a fish barrier during low flows.

Aquatic Province: Sacramento-San Joaquin

Habitat Types: A1151 Outcrop pool (?); A1151 Mountain pond; A1210 Alpine lake; A2120 Conifer forest snowmelt stream; A2412 Forest stream; A2421 Resident rainbow trout stream; A2422 Rainbow trout/cyprinid stream.

Native Fishes: Rainbow trout, Sacramento sucker; non-native brown trout, brook trout, and kokanee also present.

Amphibians: Pacific treefrogs and western toads reported in the meadow areas around Maud Lake. Mountain yellow-legged frogs present in scattered areas.

Other Vertebrates: Mountain garter snakes observed in meadow areas.

Invertebrates: No records

Riparian zone: Because of steep rocky terrain, the riparian zone is narrow and sparse, consisting of alders, willows, grasses, shrubs and cedars. Indian rhubarb is abundant within stream channel in the lower reaches.

Human Impacts: Large clearcuts on private land are present in drainage above Union Valley Reservoir. Grazing has degraded stream banks and created significant erosion in the middle reaches. Camping and fishing pressure is high along middle reaches as well as the headwater areas. Some stream restoration work was attempted in the middle reaches to help gravel recruitment, but substrate is mostly fines and small gravels.

Ownership: Mostly El Dorado NF, with private timber lands in lower drainage.

Existing Protection: None

Significant Natural Areas (Aquatic): None noted

Overall Quality Rating: 2.4

Reasons for Rating: Although the watershed has been disturbed by grazing, logging, roadbuilding and recreational activities, it is basically in good condition and contains native fish and amphibians. However, high elevation areas were originally fishless.

IBI Score: 68

Notes: Jones Fork is one of a few places where Sacramento suckers are found above 1400 m elevation.

UCD Surveys?: Yes, 1993

Sources: Personal communication, George Elliot, El Dorado NF, 1994.

Date: 29 December 1994   **Compiler:** PR, PBM

ADMA WATERSHED

Name: Rock Creek   **Drainage:** South Fork American

Calwater No.: 514.32020-32031   **County:** El Dorado

Location: From headwaters along Georgetown Divide, south of Wentworth Springs Road, to the confluence to South Fork American River, about 4 km north of Placerville.

Elevation: 305 to 1427 m; mean 844 m

Drainage Area: 216 km^2

Description: The headwaters of Rock Creek are on the southern slopes of Georgetown Divide. The watershed includes other large drainages such as Whaler Creek, Bear Creek and Traverse Creek. The main creek is a third order, low elevation canyon stream flowing in a north-south orientation over steep granitic substrate. The watershed is extensively roaded as the result of a long history of mining and logging but access to much of the creek is limited by steep terrain.

Aquatic Province: Sacramento-San Joaquin

Habitat Types: A2130 Foothill/valley ephemeral stream; A2412 Forest stream; A2413 Spring; A2421 Resident rainbow trout stream; A2422 Rainbow trout/cyprinid stream; A2445 California roach stream.

Native Fishes: Rainbow trout, Sacramento sucker, riffle sculpin, Sacramento squawfish, California roach.

Amphibians: Pacific treefrogs common. Bullfrogs present in some areas. Historical report of red-legged frog where bullfrogs now exist. Foothill yellow-legged frogs may be present but not verified.

Other Vertebrates: Western pond turtles and aquatic garter snakes reported in Whaler Creek.

Invertebrates: El Dorado NF has conducted a study for EIS on effects of OHV stream crossings on aquatic insects. Preliminary results indicate over 130 taxa (down to genera) occur in Rock Creek. Presence of endemic or rare species is not known.

Riparian zone: Condition of zone variable, depending on amount of mining and recreational activity.

Human Impacts: Logging, gravel mining and OHV use are present in the drainage (there are several OHV stream crossings in the upper drainage). Although housing development is in close proximity to the upper drainage, access to the stream is limited to 4WD in most places. There is a small diversion dam just below Rock Creek road crossing, but it has minimal impact on downstream flows.

Ownership: Much of drainage is in El Dorado NF while the remainder is private, mainly private timber lands.

Existing Protection: None

Significant Natural Areas (Aquatic): None designated. Traverse Creek may deserve this designation because of its native fish populations.

Overall Quality Rating: 2.6

Reasons for Rating: Rock Creek is a fairly large drainage in foothill region that has no major dams and minimal diversions and is largely on USFS lands. The watershed has been fairly heavily used for mining, logging, and recreation over the past 140 years but has not been irreversibly damaged. One of the best examples of a diverse foothill drainage remaining.

IBI Score: 78

Notes: The IBI score may be a high because it assumes native frogs are present.

UCD Surveys?: Yes, 1993.

Sources:

Personal communication, George Elliot, El Dorado NF, 1994.

Stream surveys by BLM, 1979-80.

Date: 28 December 1994   **Compiler:** RY, PBM

ADMA WATERSHED

Name: Cosumnes River   **Drainage:** San Joaquin

Calwater No.: 532.2000   **County:** El Dorado (upper), Amador, Sacramento

Location: Entire drainage from headwaters on Iron Mountain Ridge to its mouth on the Mokelumne River, just above the Delta.

Elevation: 59 to 2342 m; mean 824 m

Drainage Area: 1638 km²

Description: The Cosumnes River drains much of southern El Dorado County, with the North, Middle, and South Forks uniting in the vicinity of Highway 49 to form the main river. The main river joins the Mokelumne River just before it enters the Delta. The upper reaches of the three forks (and their tributaries) are perennial, high gradient streams traversing through forests of mixed conifer and deep granitic canyons. Channels are complex, with substrates dominated by boulders and cobble. The upper drainage is heavily roaded from logging and mining. In the middle reaches, there are many small diversions on tributary streams, but flow regimes and native fish communities are largely intact. Below Highway 49, the main river flows through the oak savannahs of large ranches. There are frequent large pools. The lowermost reaches meander through orchards, farmland, and the expanding suburbs of Sacramento. At the mouth, the river is lined with remnant riparian forest.

Aquatic Province: Sacramento-San Joaquin

Habitat Types: A1110 Floodplain pool (?), A1260 Valley marsh; A1330 Valley sloughs and backwaters; A2120 Conifer snowmelt stream; A2130 Foothill ephemeral stream; A2412 Forest stream; A2413 Spring; A2414 Meadow stream; A2421 Resident trout stream; A2422 rainbow trout/cyprinid stream; A2442 Fall chinook spawning stream; A2443 Hardhead/squawfish stream; A2445 California roach stream; A2446 Sucker-squawfish spawning stream.

Native Fishes: Rainbow trout (A), Sacramento squawfish (C), Sacramento sucker (A), California roach (C), speckled dace (R), hardhead (C), chinook salmon (R), Pacific lamprey (C). Other lowland fishes, such as hitch, Sacramento blackfish, and splittail present in lower river.

Amphibians: Poorly known but native ranid frogs are scarce.

Other Vertebrates: Poorly known but presumably a fairly complete representation of the native fauna, from otters to dippers to pond turtles.

Invertebrates: Aquatic insects diverse and abundant in many areas. A number of unusual or endemic stoneflies (Plecoptera) in drainage. More than 300 taxa of aquatic insects are known from the drainage, including 70 species of stoneflies.

Riparian Zone: Highly variable in condition but most riparian types for the western Sierra are in the watershed.

Human Impacts: This drainage has been heavily altered by logging, grazing, placer mining, and recreation, as well as agriculture along its lowermost reaches. There are many small diversions but no large dams. The human population of the region is growing rapidly and so increasing demands on the river and its watershed are likely.

Ownership: Upper drainage is largely in El Dorado National Forest; lower drainage (below highway 49) is largely privately owned. The Nature Conservancy has a preserve near the mouth.

Existing Protection: TNC Cosumnes River Preserve at mouth

Significant Natural Areas (Aquatic): Jackass Canyon; Bendorf stream and spring; Stump Spring; Camp Creek

Overall Quality Rating: 2.8.

Reasons for Rating: This drainage has received heavy human use since the Gold Rush but the lack of a major dam on the system means that the hydrograph is fairly natural. Non-native fishes have invaded or been planted in much of the drainage but there are significant areas with native fishes still present. The drainage contains the southernmost populations of speckled dace in the Sacramento-San Joaquin drainage. Camp Creek above its diversion is a fairly large tributary drainage (to the North Fork) that rates higher (2.4) than most of the rest of the drainage because its nearly inaccessible canyon has reduced human impacts.

IBI Score: 60

Notes: This drainage is the focus of a major watershed management effort led by The Nature Conservancy. The remaining native biota of the drainage should respond well to biodiversity-oriented management.

UCD Surveys?: Yes, 1993.

Sources:

Bottorff, R. L. 1990. Ph.D. dissertation, UC Davis; R. L. Bottorff, personal communication.

Date: 28 December 1994   **Compiler:** PBM, PR

ADMA WATERSHED

Name: North Fork Calaveras River   **Drainage:** Calaveras River

Cal Watershed No.: 533.20000   **County:** Calaveras

Location: From headwaters just above Calaveras Reservoir, located about 24 km east town of Jackson, to New Hogan Reservoir.

Elevation: 244 to 1403 m, mean 637 m

Drainage Area: 317 km^2

Description: This is a fourth order foothill stream flowing almost entirely on private land. The flow is intermittent in the summer but the channel contains deep pools that support mostly native species. The river flows through oak woodland and chaparral plant communities with a diverse riparian community along the channel.

Aquatic Province: Sacramento-San Joaquin

Habitat Types: A2130 Foothill/valley ephemeral stream; A2443 Hardhead/squawfish stream; A2445 California roach stream; A2446 Squawfish/sucker spawning stream.

Native Fishes: Rainbow trout (C), California roach (A), Sacramento squawfish (P?), Sacramento sucker (C), Hardhead (P?).

Amphibians: Foothill yellow-legged frogs present

Other Vertebrates: Western pond turtles

Invertebrates: Unknown

Riparian, Wetland Habitats: Unknown

Human Impacts: Cattle grazing is present throughout the drainage.
Mining and private timber harvest are also widespread. There is a small reservoir in the headwaters, but holds little water, and flow is mostly unimpeded.

Ownership: Mostly private with some BLM parcels.

Existing Protection: None

Significant Natural Areas (Aquatic): None identified.

Overall Quality Rating: 2.6

Reasons for Rating: Past stream surveys on BLM land have observed a large percentage of native fishes as well as rare amphibians and turtles. Flows have been reported to be largely unaltered. Due to private land ownership, condition of the land is mostly unknown. Presence of native species indicates drainage is still in relatively good shape.

IBI Score: 80

Notes: Gary Fregane of State Parks and Recreation owns over 80 acres along the NF Calaveras River and supplied the information on native aquatic fauna.

UCD Surveys?: None

Sources:

Bureau of Land Management. 1980. Fisheries Inventory of Sierra Foothill Streams on Public Land in 1979, unpublished, 1980.

Fregane, Gary, private land owner and State Parks and Recreation biologist, personal communication, November, 1994.

Date: 30 December, 1994   **Compiler:** PR

ADMA WATERSHED

Name: North Fork Mokelumne River   **Drainage:** San Joaquin

Calwater No.: 532.60010-60023   **County:** Calaveras, Amador, Alpine

Location: From Highland Lakes to Salt Springs Reservoir.

Elevation Range: 1214 to 3100 m; mean 2354 m

Drainage Area: 402 km^2

Description: The upper 14 km of river are a meadow stream flowing through a broad glaciated valley containing well defined red fir, sub-alpine and riparian vegetation. This section is closely paralleled by highway 4 and receives high recreational use. Hatchery trout are stocked in this reach. The remaining 29 km of river flow within the Mokelumne Wilderness Area. The river makes a rapid descent at the upper wilderness boundary into a deeply incised canyon which is over 1200 m deep in places. There are several waterfalls and the canyon walls are very steep, making river access difficult. Wild trout fishing is excellent and angling pressure is low. The river eventually flows into Salt Springs Reservoir which is operated by PG&E for hydroelectric power.

Aquatic Province: Sacramento-San Joaquin

Habitat Types: A1151 Outcrop pools (?), A1152 Mountain ponds; A1210 Alpine lake; A2120 Conifer snowmelt stream; A2412 Forest stream; A2413 spring; A2414 Meadow stream; A2421 Resident rainbow trout stream.

Native Fishes: Rainbow trout. Non-native brown trout also present.

Amphibians: No recent records available but mountain yellow-legged frogs probably present.

Other Vertebrates: Possible pine marten and fisher migration corridor. Dippers and beaver also present.

Invertebrates: No records available

Riparian, Wetland Habitats: Variable from meadow type in headwater area to narrow band in river canyon. Condition and vegetation types unknown.

Human Impacts: Recreational use in headwater area includes hiking, camping and fishing with motorized access. Access to wilderness areas is limited to foot trails. Salt Springs Reservoir limits upstream and downstream movement for trout.

Ownership: Entire stretch of river (approx. 43 km) is within Stanislaus NF.

Existing Protection: Over 29 km is within Mokelumne Wilderness Area which receives limited public use due to rugged terrain and roadlessness.

Significant natural areas (aquatic): None designated

Overall Quality Rating: 2.3

Reasons for Rating: Much of the drainage is lightly disturbed, especially portion in the wilderness area, although non-native trout present in lakes and streams.

IBI Score: 64

Notes: Relative low IBI score due to high percentage of watershed that was originally fishless but now contains trout.

UCD Surveys?: No

Sources:

Wildlife and Scenic River Study Appendix E of the Environmental Impact Statement for the Stanislaus National Forest.

Date: 30 December 1994   **Compilers:** PR, PBM

ADMA WATERSHED

Name: South Fork Stanislaus River   **Drainage:** San Joaquin

Calwater No.: 534.30010 and 30011   **County:** Tuolumne

Location: From headwaters in Emigrant Wilderness to Pinecrest Reservoir.

Elevation Range: 1645 to 3001 m; mean 2450 m

Drainage Area: 71 km²

Description: Roughly 22 km of the upper South Fork has no road access. The headwaters are in Emigrant Wilderness Area where the stream flows through broad glacial valleys with some meadows and patches of fir and mixed conifer forests. The river then descends into a U-shaped, glacially carved granitic canyon. Recreational use is moderate in the Wilderness Area with fishing and hiking present.

Aquatic Province: Sacramento-San Joaquin

Habitat Types: A1151 Outcrop pools (?); A1152 Mountain ponds; A1210 Alpine Lakes; A2120 Conifer forest snowmelt stream; A2412 Forest stream; A2413 Spring; A2414 Meadow stream; A2421 Resident rainbow trout stream.

Native Fishes: Rainbow trout (A)

Amphibians: Tree frogs and western or Yosemite toad tadpoles observed in Three Meadows, 1993.

Other Vertebrates: Migration corridor for martens, fishers and wolverines.

Invertebrates: Unknown

Riparian, Wetland Habitats: Variety of wetland habitat types from wet meadows in headwater region to narrow bands of riparian in river canyon.

Human Impacts: Recreational use in headwaters include fishing and camping with access provided only by foot trails. Pinecrest Reservoir region is heavily used for recreation. Livestock grazing and some OHV use present in meadow areas.

Ownership: Entire reach is within Stanislaus NF.

Existing Protection: Upper half of drainage flows within Emigrant Wilderness Area. Proposed Wild and Scenic River from headwaters to New Melones Dam.

Significant Natural Areas (Aquatic): Three Meadows

Overall Quality Rating: 2.1

Reasons for Rating: Watershed is in excellent condition because of limited human use in most of it. Large native amphibian population is present.

IBI Score: 53

Notes: Low IBI score the result of extensive invasion of high elevation areas by non-native trout.

UCD Surveys?: Yes, 1993.

Sources:

Wild and Scenic River Study in Appendix E of Environmental Impact Statement for Stanislaus NF.

Date: 30 December 1994   **Compilers:** PR, PBM

ADMA WATERSHED

Name: Rose Creek   **Drainage:** Stanislaus River

Calwater No.: 534.22010-22013   **County:** Tuolumne

Location: Rose Creek drains Star Ridge north of Sonora, and empties into New Melones Reservoir.

Elevation Range: 307 to 1600 m; mean 1020 m

Drainage Area: 113 km^2

Description: Rose Creek is located in a deep, steep-sided, low elevation canyon. Summer flows are low and much of the bottom substrate is dominated by granite bedrock. Habitat in late summer is generally shallow riffles connecting deep pools.

Aquatic Province: Sacramento-San Joaquin

Habitat Types: A2130 Foothill/valley ephemeral stream; A2422 Rainbow trout/cyprinid stream; A2445 California roach stream.

Native Fishes: Rainbow trout (C), California roach (C).

Amphibians: None observed in 1993.

Other Vertebrates: Unknown

Invertebrates: Aquatic insects were moderately diverse and abundant.

Riparian Zone: Often dense thickets of willow and blackberry.

Human Impacts: Mining is extremely heavy in the area and occurs in many forms including suction dredging. Several claims and many people are involved. Recreational use is heavy, especially ORV use. Some parts of the stream contain human refuse.

Ownership: Mostly within Stanislaus NF with some fragments of private land.

Existing Protection: None

Significant Natural Areas (Aquatic): None

Overall Quality Rating: 2.9

Reasons for Rating: Watershed is heavily abused by mining activity but it merits inclusion as an ADMA watershed because much of the watershed is restorable and portions are in reasonably good condition as indicated by riparian vegetation. It could become an important refuge for California roach, an increasingly uncommon fish in the San Joaquin drainage.

IBI Score: 68

Notes: Taxonomic status of roach merits investigation.

UCD Surveys?: Yes, 1993.

Sources:

Date: 29 December 1994   **Compiler:** RY, PBM

ADMA WATERSHED

Name: Clavey River   **Drainage:** Tuolumne River

Calwater No: 536.40000   **County:** Tuolumne

Location: Entire drainage, from headwaters to mouth on Tuolumne River. Includes Cottonwood Creek, Thirteenmile Creek, Hull Creek, Two Mile Creek, Trout Creek, Reed Creek, and Bear Creek.

Elevation Range: 306 to 2808 m; mean 1409

Drainage Area: 930 km^2

Description: The main river (length ca. 51 km) is a 5th order tributary to the Tuolumne River. Lower reaches flow through steep, north-south oriented granitic canyon. Much of habitat consists of deep pools connected by short riffles and runs, with frequent waterfalls. Tributaries are steep, bouldery, and lined with granite outcrops and deep forest. The upper reaches are accessible by forest roads but easy access for the reach from 3NO1 bridge to mouth is only at a single crossing, 1NO4 bridge.

Aquatic Province: Sacramento-San Joaquin

Habitat Types: A1151 Outcrop pools (?); A1152 Mountain ponds; A1210 Alpine lakes; A2110 Alpine snowmelt stream; A2120 Conifer forests snowmelt stream; A2411 Alpine stream; A2142 Forest stream; A2413 Spring; A2421 Resident rainbow trout stream; A2422 Rainbow trout\cyprinid stream; A2443 Sacramento sucker\squawfish stream

Native Fishes: Rainbow trout (A), California roach (A), hardhead (C), Sacramento squawfish (C), Sacramento sucker (A). Squawfish and hardhead are confined to the lower 2-3 km. Rainbow trout are throughout the drainage.

Amphibians: Foothill yellow-legged frogs (R), mountain yellow-legged frog (R), Pacific tree frog (C), western toad (C); Sierra newt (C), ensatina (C), California slender salamander (R), arboreal salamander (R), limestone salamander (R).

Other Vertebrates: Pacific pond turtles may be present. Dippers and other aquatic birds common.

Riparian Zone: Riparian zone is narrow because of steep canyons but is mostly in good condition.

Invertebrates: Aquatic insects abundant and diverse.

Human Impacts: Proposed site of major dam(s) for Turlock Irrigation District. Logging and roads in upper watershed create some erosion, along with camping and ORV use. Some gold dredging in accessible areas.

Ownership: Entirely in Stanislaus National Forest

Existing Protection: Wild Trout Stream (CDFG); proposed for Wild and Scenic River Status.

Significant Natural Areas (Aquatic): Bell Meadow RNA; Bourland Meadow candidate RNA.

Overall Quality Rating: 2.0

Reasons for Rating: Because of its north-south orientation and steep canyon, there has been comparatively little human use of this drainage. It is one of the most pristine drainages in California. It is remarkable in that it is one of the few large drainages (perhaps the only such drainage) in the Sierra Nevada containing **only** native fishes. The lack of exotic trout is especially unusual. The Clavey River watershed also contains a good representation of the native amphibian fauna.

IBI Score: 92

UCD Surveys?: Yes, 1993.

Notes: The proposed dam project was shelved in 1995 for environmental and economic reasons. There is active interest in protecting the Clavey River by Friends of the River, Friends of the Clavey, Tuolumne River Preservation Trust, and other environmental groups.

Sources:

EA Engineering, Science and Technology. 1990. Clavey River Project Exhibit E: Environmental Report. Report 3: Fish, Wildlife and Botanical Resources. Turlock Irrigation District.

California Department of Fish and Game. 1985. Unpublished wild trout surveys.

Date: 20 October 1994   **Compiler:** PBM

ADMA WATERSHED

Name: South Fork Tuolumne River   **Drainage:** Tuolumne

Calwater No.: 536.8000   **County:** Tuolumne

Location: Entire drainage from headwaters (Yosemite National Park) to mouth on Tuolumne River.

Elevation Range: 486 to 2802 m; mean 1660 m

Drainage Area: 233 km²

Description: Headwaters in YNP are typical high gradient, boulder dominated streams in mixed conifer forests. Main river has moderate gradient and is crossed repeatedly by Highway 120 and other roads through Stanislaus

National Forest. Lowermost reaches (below Highway 120) are in steep canyon, where the habitat is dominated by bouldery riffles and runs which periodically open into large, deep pools.

Aquatic Province: Sacramento-San Joaquin

Habitat Types: A2412 Forest stream; A2421 Resident rainbow trout stream; A2422 Rainbow/trout cyprinid stream; A2443 Sacramento sucker/squawfish stream

Native Fishes: Rainbow trout (A), Sacramento sucker (C), Sacramento squawfish (C), California roach (C), hardhead (R?). Some brown trout present as well.

Amphibians: No recent records of ranid frogs.

Other Vertebrates:

Invertebrates: Aquatic insect fauna moderately diverse and abundant.

Riparian Zone: Mostly narrow in canyons but typically in good condition.

Human Impacts: Drainage has been logged and grazed in many areas. Moderate recreational use in middle reaches because of easy road access.

Ownership: Headwaters, Yosemite National Park. Most of rest of drainage is Stanislaus National Forest.

Existing Protection: YNP headwaters, lower portions included in Wild and Scenic River designation for Tuolumne River

Significant Natural Areas (Aquatic): None identified

Overall Quality Rating: 2.3

Reasons for Rating: Although watershed is fairly accessible and has been logged, roaded, and grazed, the headwaters (1.0?) and the mouth are in exceptionally good condition (2.1). It appears to have a largely native fish fauna.

IBI Score: 72

Notes:

UCD Surveys?: Yes, 1986, 1993.

Sources:

Date: 6 October 1994   **Compiler:** PBM

Name: Merced River   **Drainage:** Merced River

Calwater No.: 537.30000-60000   **County:** Mariposa and Madera

Location: Entire drainage from headwaters on Mt. Lyell to McClure Reservoir, including North Fork (origins on Pilot Ridge) and South Fork (origins in Yosemite).

Elevation Range: 303 to 3850 m; mean 1823 m

Drainage Area: 2361 km²

Description: The Merced is a free-flowing river that has its origins in rugged, glacially-carved mountains (most famously in the spectacular cliffs and domes of Yosemite National Park) and then plunges through a deep gorge and through the foothills before being stopped by McClure Reservoir (Exchequer Dam). The mainstem flows through a complete range of mountain-foothill vegetation types, although it has Highway 140 running along it for much of its length. The North Fork is primarily a foothill drainage (with origins on Pilot Ridge, elevation ca. 1500-1800 m), while the South Fork also has its origins in Yosemite N.P. (2000-2500 m). The South Fork descends through a rugged canyon after leaving YNP. The North Fork is perhaps the least disturbed of the three forks, including Bull Creek, a mid-elevation tributary.

Aquatic Province: Sacramento-San Joaquin

Habitat Types: A1152 Mountain ponds; A1210 Alpine lakes; A2110 Alpine snowmelt stream; A2120 Conifer forest snowmelt stream; A2130 Foothill ephemeral stream; A2411 Alpine stream; A2412 Forest stream; A2421 Resident rainbow trout stream; A2422 Rainbow trout/cyprinid stream; A2443 Hardhead/squawfish stream; A2445 California roach stream(?).

Native Fishes: Rainbow trout (A), riffle sculpin (A), Sacramento sucker (A), Sacramento squawfish (C), hardhead (R?), California roach (C). Introduced smallmouth bass and brown trout present in main river, which may limit native fishes, especially hardhead. Main river is planted with catchable rainbow trout by CDFG.

Amphibians: Mountain and foothill yellow-legged frogs historically present; both now very rare. Other native amphibians also increasingly rare in drainage, although bullfrogs are common in the North Fork drainage.

Other Vertebrates: Western pond turtles, river otters, dippers, many riparian species.

Invertebrates: Moderately abundant and diverse.

Riparian Habitats: There is a narrow strip of riparian vegetation along most of the main river that has been altered by human activity. As a result there are six threatened/rare plant species: *Allium yosemitense*; *Clarkia lingulata*; *Eriophyllum congdonii*; *E. nubigenum*; *Lewisis congdonii*; and *L. disepala*. However, the riparian corridor is more or less continuous on non-roaded banks and in reasonably good condition along North and South forks. Riparian vegetation in especially good condition in lower Bull Creek, tributary to North Fork, although upper part of drainage burned in 1987.

Human Impacts: Because Highway 140 runs along much of the main river, there are homes, power lines and other structures along the corridor. The river receives heavy recreational use in Yosemite National Park and along much of the corridor. In-river gold dredging is widespread outside the Park. Much of lower drainage, esp.

along North and South Forks was site of intensive mining activity in past. Considerable roading in lower drainage.

In many sections, access is limited by steep canyon walls. Grazing seems to be a problem in some areas (e.g., headwaters, Sweetwater Creek).

Ownership: Much of drainage is in Yosemite National Park, Sierra and Stanislaus National Forests, and land managed by BLM. Only about 4% of the river proper flows through private land.

Existing Protection: Headwaters in Yosemite National Park. The Merced River above Briceburg and the South Fork Merced were declared Wild and Scenic in 1987. The portions on public land were designated for "moderate use" by the USFS (Record of Decision, 1991).

Significant Natural Areas (Aquatic): Bishop Creek (Research Natural Area 55).

Overall Quality Rating: Overall rating is 2.6, with headwaters rating 2.1, mainstem from Yosemite to Briceburg, 2.8, foothill reaches of all three forks 2.5; upper South Fork, 2.2, upper north fork, 2.3.

Reasons for Rating: Ratings are tentative. Headwaters of mainstem in Yosemite often in near-pristine condition, although non-native trout widespread; other headwaters crossed by roads. Mainstem has highway on banks and non-native fish in stream along with natives. Foothill areas often heavily roaded and mined. These areas need to be more carefully surveyed for native fishes and amphibians, including main river below Briceburg.

IBI Score: 63 (North Fork, 67).

Notes: Spring-run chinook salmon may have once occurred as high as Yosemite Valley. Drainage was site of early investigations of animal distributions (J. Grinnell and T. I. Storer. 1924. Animal life in the Yosemite, Univ. California Press). Some spring systems present that need to be inventoried, especially in limestone areas of North Fork (Bower Cave area).

UCD Surveys?: Yes, 1993.

Sources:

Appendix E. Forest Plan, Sierra National Forest.

California Department of Fish and Game. 1984. Unpublished field notes, Wild Trout Program.

Date: 6 October 1994   **Compiler:** PBM

ADMA WATERSHED

Name: Mariposa Creek   **Drainage:** San Joaquin

Calwater No.: 538.00010-00060   **County:** Mariposa

Location: Entire drainage, from ca. 1 km above Mariposa Reservoir to headwaters near town of Mariposa

Elevation Range: 182 to 1278 m; mean 580

Drainage Area: 242 km^2

Description: A small (1-2 cfs in late summer, wetted channel 1-2 m wide), warm, frequently intermittent foothill stream that flows through oak woodland and small rocky canyons. Much of the summer water is in sandy-bottomed pools and gradients are generally low, especially in lower reaches.

Aquatic Province: Sacramento-San Joaquin

Habitat Types: A2130 Foothill ephemeral stream; A2444 Hitch stream; A2445 California roach stream

Native Fishes: Hitch (C), California roach (C), Sacramento sucker (C). Introduced green sunfish and mosquitofish abundant in lower reaches of stream.

Amphibians: No recent records

Other Vertebrates: No recent records

Invertebrates: No recent records

Riparian Zone: Upper reaches often with fairly good canopy over stream (50-60%) but lower reaches exposed, with few riparian trees.

Human Impacts: Heavy grazing in riparian zone and surrounding hills, roads along streams in places.

Ownership: Entire drainage is on private lands.

Existing Protection: None

Significant Natural Areas (Aquatic): None noted

Overall Quality Rating: 2.8

Reasons for Rating: Mariposa Creek is an example of a small foothill drainage that contains mainly hitch and California roach, two declining fish species in the San Joaquin drainage. The lower reaches are now dominated by non-native fishes, which may be expanding their range upstream in response to decline in habitat quality (e.g., reduced pool depth, increased temperatures, etc.) caused by grazing and other activities.

IBI Score: 64

Notes: This creek needs a thorough biological survey. Mariposa County has had a stream restoration program in place for the reaches near the town of Mariposa.

UCD Surveys?: Some sampling done in 1970 and 1986.

Sources: Brown and Moyle 1987, 1993.

Date: 23 October 1994   **Compiler:** PBM

ADMA WATERSHED

Name: East Fork, Chowchilla River   **Drainage:** San Joaquin

Calwater No.: 539.11020-11031   **County:** Madera and Mariposa

Location: From mouth (junction with Middle Fork) to headwaters in Sierra National Forest

Elevation Range: 303 to 1948 m; mean 978 m

Drainage Area: 151 km²

Description: The East Fork is largely a foothill stream, intermittent in places during summer, flowing through oak-digger pine woodland and grazing land. The middle to lower reaches contain large deep, boulder and bedrock pools, often with sandy bottoms. These reaches have exposed channels with little riparian cover and show the effects of heavy grazing. The upper reaches and headwaters are small trout streams dominated by boulders with some deep (2 m) pools.

Aquatic Province: Sacramento-San Joaquin

Habitat Types: A2130 Foothill ephemeral stream; A2412 Forest stream; A2413 Spring (?); A2421 Resident rainbow trout stream; A2443 Hardhead/squawfish stream.

Native Fishes: Hardhead (A), Sacramento squawfish (A), Sacramento sucker (C), California roach (C), rainbow trout (C, headwaters).
Exotic green sunfish present in small numbers.

Amphibians: No recent records

Other Vertebrates: No recent records

Invertebrates: No recent records

Riparian Zone: Very limited in foothill areas because of canyon walls and heavy grazing. Often well developed in forested upper reaches and headwaters.

Human Impacts: Heavy grazing throughout drainage. Upper part of drainage extensively roaded.

Ownership: Mostly on private land; headwaters in Sierra NF

Existing Protection: None

Significant Natural Areas (Aquatic): None noted so far but springs in drainage (e.g., Salt Spring) merit investigation.

Overall Quality Rating: 2.7

Reasons for Rating: Much of the drainage flows through foothill land that has been heavily grazed so the banks are collapsed and the channel is wide and sandy in places. However, it supports largely native fishes, including exceptionally large numbers of hardhead, a species disappearing rapidly from the San Joaquin drainage.

446

IBI Score: 58

Notes: Has considerable restoration potential.

UCD Surveys?: Yes. Sampled in both 1970 and 1985-86 surveys.

Sources: Brown and Moyle 1987, 1993.

Date: 22 October 1994   **Compiler:** PBM

ADMA WATERSHED

Name: Finegold Creek   **Drainage:** San Joaquin

Calwater No.: 540.11010 to 540.11022   **County:** Merced

Location: Entire drainage from headwaters to mouth on Millerton Reservoir

Elevation Range: 182 m to 1462 m; mean 638 m

Drainage Area: 243 km^2

Description: Finegold Creek is a largely intermittent foothill stream that flows through digger pine-oak woodland and pastureland. Many of the smaller tributaries dry up completely although some (e.g., Little Fine Gold Creek) have permanent flows. Most reaches consist of a few bouldery pools 1-2 m deep in summer, connected by long sandy-bottomed sections of stream. The pools are the principal fish habitat because flows often become subsurface in summer in the sandy sections. The creek and its larger tributaries are small in summer (1-2 m wide) but flows rise quickly during winter rains.

Aquatic Province: Sacramento-San Joaquin.

Habitat Types: A2130 Foothill/valley ephemeral stream; A2413 springs; A2444 Hitch stream; A2446 Squawfish-sucker stream.

Native Fishes: Sacramento sucker (R), hitch (C). Lower reaches are dominated by non-native fishes, especially green sunfish, which can invade from Millerton Reservoir.

Amphibians: None recorded in recent years

Other Vertebrates: No records

Invertebrates: No records

Riparian Zone: Many areas heavily grazed with collapsing banks, but oaks, digger pine, and willows still provide 30-60% shade of stream in most areas.

Human Impacts: Most of drainage is grazed by livestock. Numerous roads through drainage, and some houses. Stockponds store water of seasonal tributary drainages. Reservoir at lower end is constant source of non-native fishes.

Ownership: Mostly private land; some headwater areas in Sierra NF.

Existing Protection: None

Significant Natural Areas (Aquatic): Little Fine Gold Creek

Overall Quality Rating: 2.9

Reasons for Rating: This drainage is marginal as an ADMA watershed but most similar drainages in the foothills are in even worse condition. The aquatic fauna is dominated by non-native fishes in most of the drainage, except in Little Finegold Creek which is dominated by Sacramento hitch. Roads, grazing, and reservoir have reduced the overall quality of the watershed.

IBI Score: 50

Notes: If efforts were made to restore the riparian habitats and pools of the creek, much of the drainage could be recolonized by hitch.

UCD Surveys?: 1970 and 1983.

Sources: Brown and Moyle, 1993.

Date: 3 December 1994   **Compiler:** PBM

ADMA WATERSHED

Name: Rancheria Creek   **Drainage:** North Fork, Kings

Calwater No.: 552.33060-3306   **County:** Fresno

Location: Entire drainage from headwaters to mouth on North Fork of Kings River

Elevation: 1441 to 3043 m; mean 2489 m

Drainage Area: 67 km^2

Description: Rancheria Creek is a high gradient alpine stream that has its origins in the small streams and lakes of the John Muir Wilderness area. It then plunges downward through some of the least disturbed late successional mixed conifer forest in the southern Sierra Nevada.

Aquatic Province: Sacramento-San Joaquin

Habitat Types: A1152 Mountain pond; A1210 Alpine lake; A2110 Alpine snowmelt stream; A2120 Conifer snowmelt stream; A2411 Alpine stream; A2412 Forest stream; A2414 Meadow stream; A2421 Resident rainbow trout stream.

Native Fishes: Rainbow trout

Amphibians: No records

Other Vertebrates: No records

Invertebrates: No records

Riparian Zone: Narrow but near-pristine most areas.

Human Impacts: Only one small road enters the watershed so the main impacts have been light recreation and some grazing.

Ownership: Entirely in Sequoia National Forest

Existing Protection: Headwaters in John Muir Wilderness Area

Significant Natural Areas (Aquatic): None identified

Overall Quality Rating: 1

Reasons for Rating: This is one of the most pristine drainages anywhere in the Sierra Nevada, thanks to its relative inaccessibility and steep terrain which has prevented most logging.

IBI Score: 92. This score assumes rainbow trout were originally found in most of drainage and that ranid frogs are present.

Notes: A thorough survey of the watershed is needed.

UCD Surveys?: No

Sources: E. Beckwitt, personal communication.

Date: 29 December 1994   **Compiler:** PBM

ADMA WATERSHED

Name: Middle and South Forks, Kings River   **Drainage:** San Joaquin

Cal Watershed No.: 552.34000   **County:** Fresno

Location: From the confluence of North Fork Kings River upstream to the headwaters of both Middle Fork and South Fork. Also includes Mill Flat Creek as well as other tributaries.

Elevation Range: 304 to 4313 m; mean 2601

Drainage Area: 2471 km²

Description: The Kings River begins in Kings Canyon National Park, flowing entirely through public land and has the greatest vertical drop without a dam in the U.S. Most of this reach has been designated as a Wild and Scenic River. The river is one of the largest of California's designated wild trout streams and is noted for its extremely high water quality.

The Middle Fork begins near Muir Pass at Helen Lake, at 3541 m elevation. The upper reaches of the river plunges over dozens of waterfalls and through several meadow habitats in a classic V-shaped canyon. No roads access the river, only the Pacific Crest Trail provides public access. The canyon walls rise up to 2000 meters in some sections with spectacular granite peaks like Tehipite Dome adding to the high scenic quality of the river. The lower 11.2 km flows through Monarch Wilderness and has no trail access.

The South Fork begins below Mather Pass in a broad granitic basin with several glacial lakes and some of the southernmost glaciers in the U.S. Trails parallel sections of the river and penetrate most of the high country. The middle reaches of the South Fork flow within a heavily forested, U-shaped valley characterized by wooded flats and meadows. Highway 180 parallels the river from Cedar Grove recreation area to Boyden Cave. The lower section of the river plunges down through one of the deepest canyons in the nation and consists of a series of cascades and chutes with numerous deep pools. The lower 18 km is managed as a Wild Trout stream by CDFG.

The Middle and South Forks converge below Highway 180 bridge crossing, each of comparable size to form the beginning of the mainstem. The Kings River is free-flowing for roughly 32 km until it empties into Pine Flat Reservoir. In the upper reaches the river runs fairly straight, moderate gradient hemmed in by steep slopes. In the middle and lower reaches, the channel widens and the river often meanders around large cobble and boulder bars. Long pools connected by shorter, turbulent riffles are the predominant habitat type. This section is the largest in volume of California's wild trout rivers.

Mill Flat Creek is a large tributary that empties into the Kings River about 3 miles upstream of the North Fork. The creek is a low gradient, low elevation stream and is an important spawning stream for several native fishes in the Kings river. The lower most sections are in foothill oak woodland with deep (1-2 m) pools and extensive sand and gravel bottomed riffles and runs. Summer flows are typically 6-10 m3/min and summer temperatures are usually 22-28 C.

Aquatic Province: Sacramento-San Joaquin

Habitat Types: A1152 Mountain pond; A1210 Alpine lakes; A2110 Alpine snowmelt stream; A2120 Conifer forest snowmelt stream; A2130 foothill ephemeral stream; A2411 Alpine stream; A2412 Forest stream; A2413 Spring; A2414 Meadow stream; A2415 Glacial melt stream; A2421 Resident rainbow trout stream; A2422 Rainbow trout/cyprinid stream; A2443 Hardhead/squawfish stream.

Native Fishes: Rainbow trout (A), Sacramento sucker (A), California roach (C), hardhead (R), Sacramento squawfish (A), riffle sculpin (C), Kern brook lamprey (R).

Amphibians: Foothill and mountain yellow-legged frogs (R?), Pacific tree frogs (C), Mt Lyell salamander (R), Sierra newt (C). Non-native bullfrogs present in lower Mill Flat Creek.

Other Vertebrates: Abundant and diverse, e.g. western pond turtles, aquatic garter snakes, bald eagle, peregrine falcon, willow flycatcher, dippers, and other aquatic birds.

Invertebrates: Aquatic insects appear to be abundant and diverse.

Riparian Zone: Much of the upper drainage has a very narrow riparian community in the steep canyon areas. Meadows in the glacial basin and sections of the canyons add to the diversity of plant communities. State listed rare plants observed in the upper watershed are Tompkins sedge, Congdon's bitterroot, Muir's raillardella and Tehipite jewel flower (last 2 only found on the MF). Other unusual plants include Hall's daisy and Kings Canyon Jewel flower. The Cedar Grove valley reach of the South Fork is lined with a narrow band of alder, cottonwood, black oak, willow, and pine.

Human Impacts: Most of the drainage is protected by the National Park and by its relatively inaccessible terrain. The South Fork and mainstem Kings probably receive the most impact from recreation in the form of camping, fishing, hiking and boating. There has been a proposal to build the Rodgers Crossing dam about 3 km above Pine Flat Reservoir. Road access is limited to sections of the mainstem Kings above Pine Flat Reservoir and from Highway 180, which runs along 29 km of the South Fork. The amount of timber harvest occurring on USFS land is not known. Monarch Wilderness on the lower Middle Fork would prevent any harvest activity.

Ownership: The entire watershed is on public land, with a few private inholdings. 88.8 km are in the Kings Canyon National Park and 59.2 km flow within Sequoia and Sierra National Forest. The Middle Fork has 43.2 km in Kings Canyon NP, while the lower 12.8 km are in Sierra NF. The South Fork has 45.6 km in Kings Canyon NP and 19.2 km in Sierra NF. The 30 km of the mainstem Kings River from the confluence of the forks to Pine Flat Reservoir has Sierra NF on the north and Sequoia NF on the south.

Existing Protection: National Wild and Scenic River status was designated from the headwaters of the Kings River to about 9.6 km below the confluence of the Middle and South Forks. The lower 17.6 km of the Kings is classified as a special management area; only an act of Congress can approve the construction of a dam. The California Department of Fish and Game manages the lower section of the South Fork and the mainstem Kings above Pine Flat Reservoir as a Wild Trout Stream. The lower reaches of the Middle Fork is in the Monarch Wilderness. Most of the Mill Flat Creek drainage has no special protection.

Significant Natural Areas (Aquatic): None identified but Zumalt Meadows and other areas in Kings Canyon N.P. qualify. Fox Springs and other spring systems in the Mill Flat Creek drainage merit investigation.

Overall Quality Rating: 2.0 for the Middle Fork, 2.2 for the South Fork and mainstem.

Reasons for Rating: Extensive protection throughout the drainage exists in the form of Wild and Scenic River status, National Park management area, and Wild Trout management by Fish and Game. The wild trout population is considered one of the best in California. Several native nongame fish species are present, including a rare population of brook lamprey above a major dam. Several endemic plant species are present in the drainage as well as giant sequoia groves. The Middle Fork deserves a higher rating because the entire drainage is protected either by National Park or USFS Wilderness areas. It also has no road access and limited trail access.

IBI Score: 80

Notes:

UCD Surveys?: Yes, 1986, 1993 (Mill Flat Creek).

Sources:

Brown, L. R. and _____. 1993. Distribution, ecology, and status of the fishes of the San Joaquin River drainage, California. California Fish and Game 79:96-114.

California Department of Fish and Game. 1985. Wild trout surveys (unpublished data).

Committee to Save the Kings River. 1987. The Kings River, A Report on its Qualities and its Future.

Mulligan, M. J. 1975. The ecology of fish populations in Mill Flat Creek: tributary to the Kings River. Unpublished M.S. thesis, CSU Fresno, 135 pp.

Palmer, T. 1993. The Wild and Scenic Rivers of America.

US Forest Service. 1990. Kings River Special Management Area and Kings, South Fork Kings and Middle Fork Kings Wild and Scenic Rivers Draft Environmental Impact Statement, USFS Sierra NF and Sequoia NF.

Snider, W. M. 1981. Wild trout management of a west slope Sierra Nevada stream. California Department of Fish and Game Inland Fisheries Admin. Rpt. 81-3. 21 pp.

Date: December 16, 1994   **Compiler:** PR, PBM

ADMA WATERSHED

Name: North and Middle Forks, Tule River   **Drainage:** Tule River

Calwater No.: 555.12000   **County:** Tulare

Location: Approximately 24 km east of Porterville. From the headwaters of the North Fork and Middle Fork to the confluence of both forks, just east of Springville.

Elevation Range: 301 to 3088 m; mean 1477 m

Drainage Area: 540 km²

Description: Headwaters of the North Fork and North Fork of the Middle Fork (NFMF) begin in the southern boundary of Sequoia National Park. The NFMF Tule River flows mostly within Sequoia National Forest through a steep rugged canyon surrounded by mixed conifer forest in the upper reaches and oak woodland in the lower end. Steep gradients along with large granitic boulders create a series of cascading plunge pools interspersed with some riffle and runs. Doyle Springs contributes significant mineral laden water to the stream, resulting in heavy travertine deposits downstream. The travertine has been reported to reduce macroinvertebrate habitat as well as trout spawning habitat. There are two diversion dams on NFMF and a pump in Doyle Springs that reduce flows for hydroelectric power.

The South Fork of the Middle Fork Tule River originates near Camp Nelson in Sequoia National Forest flowing through a rocky canyon surrounded by mixed conifer in the upper reaches and vegetated by scrub oak, chamise and scattered yucca plants in the lower sections. Highway 170 runs adjacent to stream from Camp Nelson to town of Springville, but stream access is limited by steep canyon walls. A water diversion exists just below the confluence of the north and south forks of the Middle Fork Tule River. Below the diversion, the gradient begins to flatten, water temperatures increase, and trout are replaced by warm water fish species.

The North Fork begins as a steep gradient, forested stream dominated by trout. The creek decreases in gradient at Milo, and flows through private grazed pastureland. Flows are somewhat reduced by diversions for stock water ponds and very little flow makes it to the mainstem in the summer months.

Aquatic Province: Sacramento-San Joaquin

Habitat Types: A2120 Conifer forest snowmelt stream; A2130 Foothill/valley ephemeral stream; A2140 Foothill canyon ephemeral stream; A2412 Forest stream; A2413 Spring; A2414 Meadow stream; A2421 Rainbow trout stream; A2422 Rainbow trout/cyprinid stream; A2443 Hardhead/squawfish stream; A2445 Roach stream.

Native Fishes: Hardhead (R), Sacramento squawfish (C), Sacramento sucker (C), California roach (A), Rainbow trout (A).

Amphibians: Unknown

Other Vertebrates: Rattlesnakes, dippers, garter snakes.

Invertebrates: Some work done on the NFMF Tule River has shown relatively low abundance of aquatic invertebrates as a result of mineralized deposition from Doyle Springs. It is possible that endemic species are associated with mineral springs in the upper Middle Fork. No information is known for the North Fork.

Riparian, Wetlands: White alder is the dominant riparian species in the MF Tule River. One study found no significant difference in alder growth for diverted sections on the NFMF Tule with non-diverted sections on the SFMF Tule river. Diversions on the NFMF may promote the abundant population of floating aquatic plants and the heavy travertine deposition. Doyle Springs supplies a constant year round flow to the NFMF, although over 5 cfs gets diverted. Other springs on the un-diverted SFMF also create travertine deposition downstream. The mainstem middle Fork flows mostly through foothill pine oak woodland plant community, with large cottonwood and alders along the stream floodplain. The North Fork flows through mixed conifer forest and sequoia stands in the upper reaches. The lower section run through a broad grassland with several cattle ranches.

Human Impacts: There are two water diversions on the NFMF, one on Hossack Creek, and a pump in Doyle Springs. They collectively divert water to the Tule River Conduit which leads to a PG&E powerhouse at the confluence of the forks. Another diversion is just below the forks and runs to another powerhouse, operated by Southern Cal Edison near Springville. Blowout of this diversion ditch eroded hillside and deposited high levels of sediment into the Middle Fork. Highway 170 runs along the Middle Fork in the lower sections and there is heavy fishing pressure in the upper reaches of the Middle Fork at Doyle Springs residential area and Camp Nelson. Brown trout dominate the sections below the NFMF diversions and the upper reaches of the SFMF. Introduced species are found in the lower reaches of the MF and NF. Much of the water in the North Fork Tule is diverted for pastureland and little reaches the mainstem in the summer.

Ownership: A small section of the headwater area is in Sequoia National Park. Most of the Middle Fork drainage and a small section of the North Fork is in Sequoia National Forest. Most of the NF Tule is on private ranchlands, with a small section of private forested land in the headwaters. A section of the upper NFMF Tule flows through Mountain Home State Forest.

Existing Protection: Headwaters in Sequoia National Park. Small area in State Forest.

Significant Natural Areas (Aquatic): Doyle Springs and other mineral springs need to be investigated.

Overall Quality Rating: 2.7

Reasons for Rating: Several native fishes exist in the lower reaches of the North and Middle Forks although introduced fishes are also present and flows are partially regulated. Upper reaches of the forks are more remote, have unaltered flows and conditions favor native rainbow trout. The presence of so many diversions makes this drainage a tenuous choice as an ADMA watershed; however much of the river is very restorable and native fishes are still present. The watershed was chosen in part for its many unusual features that may include endemic invertebrates.

IBI Score: 56

Notes: The reaches of stream affected by diversions have been intensively studied by PG&E.

UCD Surveys?: Yes, 1970, 1986, 1993.

Sources:

Brown, L. and Moyle, P. 1987. Survey of the fishes of the mid-elevation streams of the San Joaquin Valley. Unpublished Report. 263 pp.

California Department of Fish and Game. 1985. Unpublished surveys, Wild Trout Program.

Woodward Clyde Consultants. 1985. Tule River Project (FERC 1333) Fisheries, Riparian and Water Quality Technical Reports.

Date Compiled: December 12, 1994   **Compiler:** PR, PBM

ADMA WATERSHED

Name: South Fork Kaweah River   **Drainage:** San Joaquin

Calwater No.: 553.42000   **County:** Tulare

Location: Entire drainage, from headwaters to mouth on mainstem Kaweah River, just above Kaweah Reservoir.

Elevation Range: 218 to 3430 m; mean 1520 m

Drainage Area: 224 km^2

Description: A classic small (summer flows ca. 8-10 cfs) San Joaquin tributary stream. It is a permanent stream, with boulder-bedrock substrate dominating. Lowermost reaches are warm in summer, supporting native cyprinids and suckers in deep pools among the boulders. Some houses and roads are present near the stream, but the riparian zone is largely continuous. Middle reaches are in a canyon with deep pools, in which the water is often cool enough to support trout. Upper reaches flow through Sequoia National Park and originate in part from a number of alpine lakes.

Aquatic Province: Sacramento-San Joaquin

Habitat Types: A1210 Alpine lakes; A2110 Alpine snowmelt stream; A2120 Conifer forest snowmelt stream; A2130 Foothill/valley ephemeral stream; A2411 Alpine stream; A2412 Forest stream; A2421 Resident rainbow trout stream; A2443 Hardhead/squawfish stream.

Native Fishes: Rainbow trout (A), Sacramento squawfish (C), California roach (A), Sacramento sucker (A), hardhead (R), riffle sculpin (C). Chisel-lipped variety of California roach predominant, indicating isolation of drainage (Brown et al. 1993).

Amphibians: Foothill yellow-legged frogs formerly in lower reaches of river but now probably absent. Mountain yellow-legged frogs may be present in high elevation areas.

Other Vertebrates: Dippers.

Invertebrates: No records available.

Riparian Zone: Thin because of steep topography but well-developed where possible, with cottonwoods and willows. Largely continuous.

Human Impacts: Housing development in lower reaches. Several road crossings provide access to river. Some water diversions occur on private lands in lower section of river. National Park waters in upper reaches have been stocked with trout, although lakes and streams historically were probably fishless.

Ownership: Upper reaches in Sequoia National Forest (Grouse Creek) and Sequoia National Park; middle and lower reaches on private lands.

Existing Protection: Headwaters in Sequoia NP. Lower reaches protected in part by steep terrain but have no formal protection.

Significant Natural Areas (Aquatic): None identified.

Overall Quality Rating: 2.1 for headwaters; most of rest of drainage averages 2.5.

Reasons for Rating: Headwaters contain introduced trout populations, otherwise would probably rate 1. Watershed outside SNP is grazed and logged and contains scattered housing but is a reasonably good condition.

IBI Score: 72

Notes: Middle Fork of Kaweah (including Marble Fork) probably also qualifies as ADMA watershed (confined to Sequoia National Park). Has been sampled by CDFG Wild Trout Program and contains rainbow trout, brown trout, and Sacramento suckers.

UCD Surveys?: Yes, 1973, 1986.

Sources:

Brown, L. R., _____, W. A. Bennett, B. D. Quelvog. 1992. Implications of morphological variation among populations of California roach *Lavinia symmetricus* (Cyprinidae) for conservation policy. Biological Conservation 62:1-10.

Brown, L. R. and _____. 1993. Distribution, ecology, and status of the fishes of the San Joaquin River drainage, California. California Fish and Game 79:96-114.

Date: 6 October 1994   **Compiler:** PBM

ADMA WATERSHED

Name: Deer Creek   **Drainage:** Buena Vista Lake

Calwater No.: 555.20000   **County:** Tulare

Location: This is a small independent drainage located about 25 km northwest of Isabella Reservoir. Its headwaters are in Sequoia National Forest (California Hot Springs area) and it disappears into the canals and fields of the San Joaquin Valley floor. Presumably it was once tributary to the now-drained Buena Vista Lake (Kern River sink).

Elevation Range: 182 to 2512 m; mean 994 m

Drainage Area: 297 km²

Description: The headwaters of Deer Creek (including Tyler Creek and Cold Springs Creek) are forest streams of moderate gradient flowing through steep rocky canyons. The southernmost grove of giant sequoia is present in the headwaters. Middle reaches fed by hot springs, mostly developed. In the foothills, Deer Creek is small (summer flows less than 5 cfs) and warm (22-30 C), flowing over gravel and bedrock with scattered shallow (< 1 m) pools. The channel is increasingly shallow and braided as the result of grazing.

Aquatic Province: Sacramento-San Joaquin

Habitat Types: A2130 Foothill ephemeral stream; A2412 Forest stream; A2413 Spring (?); A2421 Rainbow trout stream; A2422 Rainbow trout\cyprinid stream; A2446 Squawfish/sucker stream.

Native Fishes: Rainbow trout (A), California roach (C), Sacramento squawfish (C), Sacramento sucker (A).

Amphibians: No observations

Other Vertebrates: No observations

Invertebrates: Aquatic insects seem to be diverse and abundant in forested reaches.

Riparian Zone: In forested areas, there is a good riparian canopy although understory is sparse. In foothills, there are scattered cottonwoods, oaks, and willows but the riparian vegetation is largely depleted by grazing.

Human Impacts: Heavy grazing along lower creek. Heavy recreational use in California Hot Springs area. Road runs along much of middle reaches of creek.

Ownership: Headwaters in Sequoia National Forest. California Hot Springs area mostly private, as are the foothill portions of watershed.

Existing Protection: None, except that provided to giant Sequoia groves.

Significant Natural Areas (Aquatic): None known but spring systems (including hot springs) should be investigated.

Overall Quality Rating: 2.2 in headwaters, 2.7 in foothills

Reasons for Rating: Generally has high restoration potential. Headwaters in Sequoia NF in reasonably good condition, as indicated by populations of wild trout. Lower reaches contain only native fishes but there is some evidence the channel is gradually becoming wider and shallower, so less likely to sustain native fish populations.

IBI Score: 68

Notes: This watershed is one of three small "independent" watersheds in the region (others: White River and Posos Creek) that still contain predominately native fishes. Deer Creek seems to contain the most fishes and be in the best condition, although the other two watersheds also merit special management. All three need thorough surveys for native fishes, invertebrates, and amphibians.

UCD Surveys?: Yes, 1973, 1986, 1993.

Sources:

Brown, L. R. and ____. 1993. Distribution, ecology, and status of the fishes of the San Joaquin River
 drainage, California. California Fish and Game 79:96-114.

Date: 20 October 1994   **Compiler:** PBM

ADMA WATERSHED

Name: North Fork, Kern River   **Drainage:** Kern

Calwater No.: 554.24000   **County:** Tulare

Location: Headwaters to junction with South Creek, above crossing of Highway 41 (about 30 km above Isabella
Reservoir); includes entire Little Kern River drainage.

Elevation Range: 1181 to 4412 m; mean 2666 m

Drainage Area: 2034 km^2

Description: This watershed drains on the steep, granitic slopes of the high Sierra through dozens of small
streams. Much of the Little Kern River basin was glaciated, so the river flows through a U-shaped valley and
drains a number of small cirque lakes. Below this area, most of the basin was not glaciated so the river meanders
through broad alluvial flats that are separated by low pine-covered ridges. The meadows are composed of
unconsolidated sands and sediments, so are highly subject to erosion as the result of grazing. The valley streams
are typically low gradient, shallow, meandering streams, with sand and gravel substrates. There is little riparian
vegetation, so the streams are fairly exposed.

Aquatic Province: Sacramento-San Joaquin.

Habitat Types: A1152 Mountain pond; A1210 Alpine lakes; A2110 Alpine snowmelt stream; A2120 Conifer
forest snowmelt stream; A2411 Alpine stream; A2412 Forest stream; A2414 Meadow stream; A2423 Kern golden
trout stream.

Native Fishes: Little Kern golden trout (C), Sacramento sucker (C). Non-native fishes include rainbow trout(C)
and brown trout (C)

Amphibians: Mountain yellow-legged frog; endemic slender salamanders.

Other Vertebrates: No information available.

Invertebrates: No information available.

Riparian Zone: Little true riparian vegetation in meadows. In canyons there are typically sparse growths of pine
where soil conditions permit.

Human Impacts: The introduction of non-native rainbow and brown trout greatly reduced the populations of
native golden trout and efforts are now underway to restore many of the streams to golden trout only streams.

Grazing is a major factor increasing erosion of the streams in the unstable soils of the meadows. Recreational use is relatively light.

Ownership: Almost entirely in Sequoia National Forest, with some private inholdings.

Existing Protection: Some headwaters in Golden Trout Wilderness Area. The Little Kern golden trout is a federally listed threatened species, which confers considerable protection on its habitats.

Significant Natural Areas (Aquatic): Kern Hot Spring, Soda Springs Creek

Overall Quality Rating: 2.3

Reasons for Rating: Although this is a high mountain region that minimally disturbed by logging and mining, grazing has had a major impact on the meadows and secondarily the streams. The Kern Plateau region contains many endemic or unusual animals and plants.

IBI Score: 76

UCD Surveys?: No

Sources:

Knapp, R. A. and T. L. Dudley. 1990. Growth and longevity of golden trout, *Oncorhynchus aquabonita*, in their native streams. California Fish and Game 76:161-173.

Date: 30 December 1994   **Compiler:** PBM

ADMA WATERSHED

Name: South Fork, Kern River   **Drainage:** Kern

CalWater Basin No.: 554.23000   **County:** Kern

Location: Entire drainage, from mouth on Isabella Reservoir to headwaters in Golden Trout Wilderness Area, Inyo National Forest.

Elevation: 874 to 3688 m; mean 2347 m

Drainage Area: 1374 km^2

Description: The South Fork Kern River drains some of the highest peaks in the Sierra Nevada, dropping through steep granitic gorges and long, wide meadows and fed by numerous tributaries. The drainage is in the Kern Plateau, a region which was not glaciated during the Pleistocene and contains many unusual biotic and geologic features as a result. The meadows are typically dominated by pinon pine, juniper, and sagebrush. Monache Meadows is the largest meadow system in the Sierra Nevada. The drainage is mostly in wilderness areas so has few roads although Highway 178 parallels the last 15 km of river. The high elevation parts of the drainage are covered with subalpine forests dominated by foxtail and lodgepole pine. A large cottonwood-alder riparian forest exists along part of the lowermost reaches.

Aquatic Province: Sacramento-San Joaquin

Habitat Types: A1152 Mountain pond; A1210 Alpine lakes; A2110 Alpine snowmelt stream; A2120 Conifer forest snowmelt stream; A2411 Alpine stream; A2412 Forest stream; A2414 Meadow stream; A2423 Kern golden trout stream.

Native Fishes: South Fork Kern golden trout (C), Sacramento sucker (C). Non-native fishes include rainbow trout(C) and brown trout (C).

Amphibians: Mountain yellow-legged frog; endemic slender salamanders.

Other Vertebrates: Yellow-billed cuckoo (lower reaches).

Invertebrates: No information available.

Riparian Zone: The lowermost reaches supports the largest contiguous cottonwood/willow riparian forests in the state. In gorges, the riparian zone is narrow and rocky. The meadow systems are large and expansive and of a unique physiographic variety found only in the southern Sierra.

Human Impacts: The river ends in a reservoir. Farms and ranches occur along the lowermost reach, which is also paralleled by a highway. Extensive grazing by livestock occurs in meadows throughout the drainage. The drainage is a popular back country recreation region including off-road vehicle use in some areas. A small airport exists in Monache Meadows. Introduced fishes, especially brown trout, displace native golden trout.

Ownership: 88% of the drainage is in Sequoia and Inyo National forests, while 12% is private (mostly the lowermost reach in South Fork Valley).

Existing Protection: 76% of the drainage is in three wilderness areas (Dome Land, Golden Trout, South Sierra) and another 12% is managed by the USFS as well. The Nature Conservancy has created the Kern River Preserve to protect riparian forest in South Kern Valley. The USFS sections have been given Wild and Scenic River designation.

Significant Natural Areas (Aquatic): None identified.

Overall Quality Rating: 2.2 for reaches in wilderness areas, 2.5 for reach in South Fork Valley.

Reasons for Rating: Except for the effects of grazing, motorized recreation, and introduced trout, the USFS portions of the drainage are fairly pristine. The South Fork Valley contains a remarkable riparian forest but the river is dominated by non-native fishes.

IBI Score: 72

Notes: A considerable amount of research on the flora and fauna of this watershed has been conducted.

UCD Surveys?: No.

Sources:

Sequoia National Forest Long Range Management Plan.

Odion, D. C., T. L. Dudley, and C. M. D'Antonio. 1988. Cattle grazing in southeastern Sierran meadows: ecosystem change and prospects for recovery. Pages 277-292 in C. A. Hall and V. Doyle-Jones, eds. Natural history of the White-Inyo Range. Vol. 2. White Mountain Research Station, UC Los Angeles.

Date: 10 November 1994   **Compiler:** PBM

ADMA WATERSHED

Name: Eagle Lake   **Drainage:** Eagle Lake

CalWater No.: 637.31000 and 32000   **County:** Lassen

Location: Entire drainage, including Pine Creek watershed.

Elevation Range: 1585 to 2444 m; mean 1789 m

Drainage Area: 1113 km^2

Description: The Eagle Lake watershed is closed basin with Eagle Lake as its terminus. It is located in a semi-arid plateau landscaped by ancient volcanoes and lava flows. The southern half of the basin is characterized by steep, pine-covered slopes, while the northern half is more arid, with rounded mountains (including the highest peak, Fredonyer) dominated by juniper and sagebrush. The principal drainage that feeds the lake is Pine Creek, which has its headwaters in alpine lakes in the Caribou Wilderness near Lassen National Park and flows 70 km to reach Eagle Lake. Other much smaller drainages include Papoose Creek and Merrill Creek. The alpine tributaries of Pine Creek are intermittent most of the time and the creek does not become permanent until Stephen's Meadow, the first of a series of wide meadows (Pine Creek Valley, McCoy Flat) through which the creek flows and gathers water before reaching the lake. The lowermost reaches flow through mixed conifer forest and are intermittent or dry in summer. Eagle Lake is a large (area ca. 90 km^2), alkaline (pH 8.4-9.6), lake with three basins, two shallow (max depth ca. 5 m) and one deep (max. depth ca. 23 m). There are numerous springs in the basin, which may or may not drain into lake tributaries. The only outlet to the lake is Bly Tunnel, built in 1922, and now blocked, but still siphoning some water from the lake.

Aquatic Province: Great Basin

Habitat Types: C1120 Mountain pond; C1210 Alpine lake; C1221 Great Basin scrub perennial pool; C1222 Spring pool; C1313 Caldera lake; C1320 Eagle Lake; C2110 Alpine snowmelt stream; C2120 Conifer snowmelt stream; C2130 Great Basin scrub snowmelt stream; C2212 Exposed alpine stream; C2213 Spring stream; C2215 Meadow stream; C2333 Pine Creek; C2340 Speckled dace stream.

Native Fishes: Eagle Lake trout (C), Eagle Lake tui chub (A), speckled dace (A), Tahoe sucker (A), Lahontan redside (A). Non-native brook trout present in Pine Creek.

Amphibians: Pacific tree frogs (C), western toad (C), Cascade frog (R), spadefoot toad (U)

Other Vertebrates: Osprey, bald eagle, white pelican, western grebe, Clark's grebe, eared grebe, double crested cormorant, various herons and egrets are abundant on Eagle Lake, as are a variety of migratory shorebirds and waterfowl. Three species of garter snakes are common along the streams.

Invertebrates: Fauna of lake is low in diversity but abundant; several presumably endemic molluscs. Wide variety of forms in ponds and streams in drainage.

Riparian Zone: Meadow and sagebrush flats (presumably once meadow) predominant riparian habitat along permanent streams. Lake shore ranges from Jeffrey-yellow pine forest to juniper-sagebrush desert.

Human Impacts: Grazing and logging in the past have caused major changes to the Pine Creek drainage, making it largely inaccessible to Eagle Lake trout. Both activities still taking place but at reduced levels. Recreational use of the lake and lake shore is fairly heavy in places and a small community (Spaulding) exists that is expanding. Drainage is extensively roaded.

Ownership: Pine Creek drainage is mostly in Lassen National Forest, although Stephens Meadow (a crucial spawning and rearing area for Eagle Lake trout) is privately owned. The land around the lake is a mixture of public (USFS, BLM) and private ownership.

Existing Protection: Some headwaters in Caribou Wilderness Area but most has no special protection. Eagle Lake is managed by the California Department of Fish and Game as a trophy trout fishery.

Significant Natural Areas (Aquatic): Stephens Meadow, Papoose Meadow, Mahogany Lake.

Overall Quality Rating: 2.3

Reasons for Rating: Eagle Lake is largest lake in California still without significant exotic species, an intact native lake ecosystem. However, Eagle Lake trout are maintained entirely by hatcheries. The drainages feeding the lake are in the process of being restored, although they have suffered heavy logging, grazing, and roading in the past.

IBI Score: 72

Notes: CSU Chico and UC Davis maintain a field station on Eagle Lake for teaching and research in the area. Lassen National Forest is developing a Coordinated Resource Management Plan for the Pine Creek watershed.

UCD Survey Numbers: Several years of quantitative sampling of Pine Creek and Eagle Lake.

Sources:
Unpublished reports, P. B. Moyle, University of California, Davis
Eagle Lake Ranger District, Lassen NF, 1994. Draft Environmental Assessment, Pine Creek Coordinated Resource Management Plan. 33 pp. + appendices.

Date: 30 November 1994   **Compiler:** PBM

ADMA WATERSHED

Name: Willow Creek   **Drainage:** Susan River

Calwater No.: 637.40010-40030   **County:** Lassen

Location: Entire drainage, from headwaters (Murrer's Meadows, near Eagle Lake) to bridge on Belfast Road, which marks the approximate spot where the creek emerges from the canyon to flow through agricultural land.

Elevation Range: 1275 to 2401 m; mean 1659

Drainage Area: 653 km^2

Description: Headwaters are springs along meadow and Bly Tunnel, from Eagle Lake. Upper ca. 12 km heavily grazed meadow/forest stream, <1% gradient. Diverted for irrigation and channelized etc. through Willow Creek valley (ca. 15-20 km), including state wildlife refuge. Lower 20-25 km of mainstem flows through deep lava canyon, often steep and rocky (1-4% gradient), water tea-colored. Minimum summer flows 5-15 m3 per min., highest in lower reaches. Summer temperatures approach or exceed 25 C in most areas, so marginal for trout. Large brown trout present in lower canyon in low numbers and are sought by anglers, although access is difficult. Tributaries (e.g., Pete's Creek) to the lower creek drain large areas of dry scrub and canyon and have been unexplored from a biological perspective. One of the sources of Pete's Creek is Horse Lake, a large playa which is usually dry in summer.

Aquatic Province: Great Basin

Habitat Types: C1110 Alkali playa lake; C2120 Conifer forest snowmelt stream; C2213 Spring stream (seeps); C2332 Sucker/dace/redside stream.

Native Fishes: Tui chub (C), Lahontan redside (A), speckled dace (A), Tahoe sucker (A), mountain sucker (C, only occurrence in Susan River Drainage.), Paiute sculpin (C). Abundance very high in canyon. Mountain sucker present in small numbers in canyon only. Very small numbers of rainbow trout in upper reaches; brown trout in canyon.

Amphibians: Non-native bullfrogs abundant throughout drainage.

Other Vertebrates: Upper reaches important feeding areas for aquatic birds (egrets, herons, terns, etc.). Three species of garter snakes in riparian areas (western, aquatic, common).

Invertebrates: Diverse aquatic insect and mollusc fauna, very dense in places, especially where aquatic plants abundant. Signal crayfish present in lowermost reaches (mouth of canyon).

Riparian Zone: Heavily impacted by grazing throughout, especially meadow systems. Riparian zone narrow in canyons.

Human Impacts: Heavily grazed in upper reaches, so little development of riparian vegetation, stream wide and shallow. Valley is irrigated pasture/hay lands/wildlife refuge, so water returned to stream is warm and turbid. BLM lands in canyon have also been heavily grazed but impact reduced in recent years. Logging and wildfires in surrounding hills.

Ownership: Most of upper reaches through Willow Creek Valley in private ranch land, although forested land in drainage a mixture of public (USFS) and private ownership. Some CDFG land in valley (refuge). Canyon is mainly BLM land.

Existing Protection: Canyon is in proposed wilderness area. BLM recognizes unique nature of canyon and is managing it to reduce human impacts.

Significant Natural Areas (Aquatic): None identified, although Murrer's Meadow (headwaters) may qualify.

Overall Quality Rating: Upper reaches, 2.6, valley reaches, 2.9, canyon reaches 2.2.

Reasons for Rating: With the exception of cutthroat trout, the drainage contains all the native fishes of the region, including mountain sucker (a CDFG Species of Special Concern). The invertebrate fauna is rich and probably contains a number of endemic species, especially molluscs. While the entire drainage has been heavily grazed and logged, none of the damage to the stream system is irreversible, except the replacement of native leopard (?) frogs by bullfrogs.

Notes: Headwaters are close to the Eagle Lake Field Station (CSU Chico) so creek has been used for student studies. Bly Tunnel delivers some Eagle Lake water to the creek.

IBI Score: 68

UCD Surveys?: Yes, by students from Eagle Lake Field Station

Sources:
Houk, A., R. Kaufman, and P. B. Moyle. 1994. Distribution and status of fishes of Willow Creek, Lassen County. Unpublished Report, UC Davis.
Aceituno, M. 1980. 1980 Willow Creek survey. File Report BLM, Susanville.
Moyle, P. B., et al. 1991. Fishes of Bly Tunnel, Lassen County, California. Great Basin Naturalist 51:267-270.

Date: 20 October 1994   **Compiler:** PBM

ADMA WATERSHED

Name: Upper Little Truckee River   **Drainage:** Truckee River

Calwater No.: 636.00010-00022   **County:** Sierra (mostly); Nevada (some headwaters)

Location: Entire upper drainage, from headwaters to Stampede Reservoir. Includes Independence and Webber Lakes, Independence Creek and Cold Stream. Some of lower reaches run along Highway 89.

Elevation Range: 1704 to 2767 m; mean 2114 m

Drainage Area: 232 km^2

Description: Headwaters are a small, high gradient forested streams. Independence and Webber lakes are large natural alpine lakes containing native fishes. The streams reaches below the lakes are largely a braided meadow streams with a fine-substrate bottoms and dense riparian vegetation (in places). Perazzo Meadows along the main lower Truckee River are broad, heavily grazed, and surrounded by mixed conifer forest on the uplands.

Aquatic Province: Great Basin

Habitat Types: C1240 Fen; C1311 Alpine lake (with native fish); C2120 Conifer forest snowmelt stream; C2214 Conifer forest stream; C2310 Trout headwater; C2331 Sucker/dace/redside stream with cutthroat trout; C2350 Whitefish/cutthroat trout/sucker stream.

Native Fishes: Lahontan cutthroat trout (upper Independence Creek and Independence Lake) (R), mountain whitefish (C), Tahoe sucker (A), Lahontan redside (A), Lahontan speckled dace (A), mountain sucker (C), Paiute sculpin (A). Non-native brown trout and rainbow trout in most streams sections. Other non-native fishes in lakes.

Amphibians: Not known

Other Vertebrates: Various aquatic birds (dippers, egrets, etc.). Introduced beaver may play a major role in stream ecology.

Invertebrates: Moderately diverse and abundant.

Riparian Zone: Willow often abundant in meadows but riparian areas often altered by livestock.

Human Impacts: Much of the drainage has been logged in recent years. Independence Lake is "notched" and levels are lowered annually for water deliveries, increasing late-season flows down Independence Creek. Much of the flow of the Little Truckee above its confluence with Independence Creek is diverted (in part illegally) into a ditch for use by ranchers in the Sierra Valley (Erman 1992). Heavy grazing in meadows and on streambanks. Considerable recreational use of drainage. Highway 89 runs along part of the main Little Truckee River and other roads parallel the river and tributaries.

Ownership: Mixed private and public ownership, although headwaters are mostly in Tahoe NF.

Existing Protection: None

Significant Natural Areas (Aquatic): Independence Lake

Overall Quality Rating: 2.6

Reasons for Rating: Drainage has been logged and grazed for 100+ years and has been extensively roaded but it is still in good enough condition so that it supports a full spectrum of native fishes. Independence Lake and upper Independence Creek are among the few places where Lahontan cutthroat (federally listed threatened species) still persist in their natural range (rating 2.2). The Little Truckee River from the diversion to Stampede Reservoir is rated 2.9 because of the combined effects of Highway 89, Stampede Reservoir, the upstream diversion, high late summer flows down Independence Creek, and heavy grazing on the surrounding meadows. Lakes in drainage are among few in Sierra Nevada to which fish are native.

IBI Score:

Notes: This is one of two several watersheds (including Sagehen Creek, also listed as an ADMA watershed) that are part of the Little Truckee River drainage but that are now isolated from each other by Stampede and Prosser Reservoirs. The upper Little Truckee Watershed is the only watershed of the three containing cutthroat trout and large lakes.

UCD Surveys?: Yes, 1993 and previously.

Sources:

E. Gerstung, CDFG, personal communication; D. Erman, UCD, personal communication.

Erman, D. C. 1992. Historical background of long-term diversion of the Little Truckee River. Pages 415-427 in C. A. Hall, V. Doyle-Jones, and B. Widawski (eds.). The history of water: Eastern Sierra Nevada, Owens Valley, White-Inyo Mountains. White Mountain Research Station Symposium 4.

Date: October 20, 1994   **Compiler:** PBM

ADMA WATERSHED

Name: Sagehen Creek

Drainage: Truckee

Calwater No.: 636.00030-00031

County: Nevada and Sierra

Location: Headwaters on Carpenter Ridge and Sagehen Hills to mouth on Stampede Reservoir

Elevation Range: 1827 to 2623 m; mean 2091

Drainage Area: 44 km^2

Description: Sagehen Creek is a small alpine stream that drains numerous boggy meadows and logged-over forest lands. Its uppermost headwaters are high gradient, rocky streams while the lower tributaries are short, often seasonal, forest and meadow streams. The middle reaches are lined with meadows and mixed conifer forest and there are numerous beaver dams that create a succession of small ponds. Below the crossing of highway 89, the creek meanders through meadows between forested hills before ending in Stampede Reservoir. The reservoir is created by a dam on the Little Truckee River. Besides the creek, the watershed contains numerous springs of various sizes and chemistry, most with constant temperatures (3.5-9 C). There are also a number of fens in the drainage.

Aquatic Province: Great Basin

Habitat Types: C1120 Mountain pool; C1240 Fen; C2110 Alpine snowmelt stream; C2120 Conifer forest snowmelt stream; C2213 Springs; C2214 Conifer forest stream; C2215 Meadow stream; C2310 Trout headwater; C2320 Trout/sculpin stream; C2331 Sucker/dace/redside stream.

Native Fishes: Piaute sculpin (A), Tahoe sucker (A), mountain sucker (R), Lahontan redside (C), speckled dace (?), mountain whitefish (R). Nonnative trout (brown, rainbow, brook) abundant.

Amphibians: Few records

Other Vertebrates: Garter snakes common, dippers, etc.

Invertebrates: Abundant and diverse N. Erman (1989) identified 77 species of caddisflies (Tricoptera) from the drainage and noted the diversity of other aquatic invertebrates as well, although the exceptional diversity is partly related to the many studies that have taken place in the watershed.

Riparian Zone: Much of the riparian zone is alpine meadow and fens.

Human Impacts: Drainage has been extensively logged and grazed, especially by sheep. Sagehen Creek is heavily fished, especially where Highway 89 crosses it. Stampede Reservoir has a major effect on the fish fauna of the lower reaches (D. Erman 1986).

Ownership: Entire drainage is in Tahoe National Forest.

Existing Protection: No fishing allowed in vicinity of Sagehen Creek Field Station.

Significant Natural Areas (Aquatic): See notes

465

Overall Quality Rating: 2.4

Reasons for Rating: Drainage is in reasonably good condition considering the history of use and the creek is dominated by native aquatic species (except for trout).

IBI Score:

Notes: Site of the Sagehen Creek Field Station of University of California, Berkeley. As a consequence, the creek and surrounding areas are among the most studied ecosystems in the Sierra Nevada. The size of the watershed is smaller than other ADMA watersheds in the Sierra Nevada but unified landownership, the spring-fed nature of the stream, its present isolation (by the reservoir) and the intensive studies in the drainage justify its treatment as an ADMA watershed rather than a significant natural area.

UCD Surveys?: Yes

Sources:

Erman, D. C. and N. A. Erman. 1975. Macroinvertebrate composition and production of some Sierra Nevada minerotrophic peatlands. Ecology 56:591-603.

Erman, D. C. 1986. Long-term structure of fish populations in Sagehen Creek, California. Trans. Amer. Fish. Soc. 115:682-692.

Erman, N. A. 1989. Species composition, emergence, and habitat preferences of Trichoptera of the Sagehen Creek basin, California, USA. Great Basin Naturalist 49:186-197.

Date: 26 November 1994   **Compiler:** PBM

ADMA WATERSHED

Name: East Fork Carson River   **Drainage:** Carson River

Cal Watershed No.: 632.10000   **County:** Mono

Location: From headwaters to the confluence with Bryant Creek (including Bryant Creek) in Nevada.

Elevation: 1522 to 3459 m; mean 2325 m

Drainage Area: 893 km^2

Description: The river originates at the eastern base of the Sierra Nevada crest in the Carson-Iceburg Wilderness Area which is managed by the Toiyabe National Forest. Steep gradient tributaries flow north through forested canyons and subalpine meadows which contain the last refuges for Paiute cutthroat trout. Most of these meadows are grazed by cattle, but some areas contain cattle exclosures to protect trout habitat. The upper reaches are only accessible by foot trails. The river through the East Carson River Canyon, in a wide flood plain vegetated with willow and aspen groves. Highways 89 and 4 follow the lower reaches of the river canyon altering the topography of the east bank. The river continues into Nevada and eventually meets the West Fork and empties in the Carson Sink.

Aquatic Province: Great Basin

Habitat Types: C1311 Alpine lakes; C2110 Alpine snowmelt stream; C2120 Conifer forest snowmelt stream; C2130 Great basin scrub snowmelt stream; ?C2212 Alpine stream; C2213 Spring stream; C2214 Conifer stream; C2215 Meadow stream; C2310 Trout headwater; C2320 Cutthroat trout/Paiute sculpin stream; C2350 Whitefish/cutthroat trout/sucker stream.

Native Fishes: Paiute cutthroat trout (R), Lahontan cutthroat trout (R), mountain whitefish (C), Paiute sculpin (A), Tahoe sucker (A), mountain sucker (C), speckled dace (C), Lahontan redside (C).

Amphibians: Mountain yellow-legged frogs observed in Whitecliff Lake.

Other Vertebrates: Dippers.

Invertebrates: Many streams have fairly fine substrates, so invertebrate diversity is low in these areas.

Riparian, Wetland Habitats: Riparian vegetation ranges from sedge/rush and grass/forbs/sagebrush to mixed conifer forest in the uplands. Meadow streams have been heavily grazed although some sections of streams are protected by cattle exclosures. Meadow vegetation is dominated by Nebraska sedge and silver sagebrush communities.

Human Impacts: Grazing occurs in most of the meadow areas, although riparian areas of the river with Paiute cutthroat trout have been fenced off. Camping and fishing are present throughout the drainage; fishing pressure is especially high along the highway sections. Mine tailings and effluent is a problem in the lower reaches. Introduced trout are displacing the native cutthroat, leaving small headwater tributaries with barriers as the last refuges.

Ownership: Predominantly in Toiyabe NF with some sections in BLM land and private lands. Lower section in State of Nevada.

Existing Protection: Wild Trout Management Area in the headwaters of the drainage allows no fishing in areas that still contain Paiute cutthroat trout. Headwaters are also in the Carson-Iceburg Wilderness Area which allows access only by foot.

Significant Natural Areas (Aquatic): Silver King Creek above Llwellyn Falls (Paiute cutthroat trout stream); Whitecliff Lake (fishless lake with frogs)

Overall Quality Rating: 2.3 in Wilderness , 2.5 below Silver King Creek confluence.

Reasons for Rating: Headwater tributaries are one of the last remaining refuges for Paiute cutthroat trout, a federally listed endangered species. Wilderness Area has only trail access. Outside the wilderness areas, the river and the watershed is accessible and roaded, but the fish fauna is largely native.

IBI Score: 64

Notes:

UCD Surveys?: Informal, 1994.

Sources:

California Department of Fish and Game. 1986. Survey of Fish Populations in Carson River Drainage, IFD Admin. Report 86.

California Department of Fish and Game. 1983. Fish survey of Carson River drainage, 1983. IFD admin. report no. 86-1.

Compiled: December 23, 1994   **Compiler:** PR, PBM

ADMA WATERSHED

Name: West Walker River   **Drainage:** Walker River

Cal Watershed No.: 631.40000   **County:** Mono

Location: From the headwaters adjacent to Hoover Wilderness Area to Sonora Junction at the confluence of Little Walker River, including the Little Walker River drainage.

Elevation Range: 1557 to 3566 m; mean 2505 m

Drainage Area: 846 km^2

Description: West Walker River originates on the eastern slope of the Sierras in Toiyabe National Forest just north of Yosemite National Park. Little Walker River has its headwaters in Hoover Wilderness Area. The headwater tributaries flow north through steep forested terrain eventually coming together in a broad valley near Sonora Junction. Most of the drainage is inaccessible by road with the exception of Highway 108 which runs parallel to the West Walker River in the lower section of the watershed.

Aquatic Province: Lahontan

Habitat Types: C1311 Alpine lakes; C2120 Alpine snowmelt stream; C2120 Conifer forest snowmelt stream; C2130 Great basin scrub snowmelt stream; C2212 Alpine stream; C2213 Spring stream; C2214 Conifer stream; C2215 Meadow stream; C2310 Cutthroat trout headwater; C2320 Cutthroat trout/Paiute sculpin stream; C2350 Whitefish/cutthroat trout/sucker stream

Native Fishes: Lahontan cutthroat trout (R), speckled dace (C), mountain whitefish (C), Paiute sculpin (C), Lahontan redside (C), mountain sucker (R), Tahoe sucker (A). Non-native rainbow trout, brook trout, and brown trout abundant.

Amphibians: Unknown

Other Vertebrates: Unknown

Invertebrates: Moderately diverse and abundant (description for Molybdenite Creek)

Riparian, Wetland Habitats: Dense willow and aspen thickets in riparian areas, but meadows affected by grazing.

Human Impacts: Hunting, horseback riding and fishing occurs in drainage. Few roads restrict public access. Area along Highway 395 is altered by road, USMC Mountain Warfare Training Center, and other roadside development.

Ownership: USFS Toiyabe NF for most of the drainage with a portion of privately owned land at Sonora Junction.

Existing Protection: Headwaters of Little Walker River is in Hoover Wilderness Area.

Significant Natural Areas (Aquatic): Little Walker River (headwater sections with Lahontan cutthroat trout)

Overall Quality Rating: 2.4

Reasons for Rating: Some sections of headwater streams still contain Lahontan cutthroat trout, although introduced trout are present in downstream areas. Most of the drainage is accessible by foot trails only, so disturbance to streams is relatively low.

IBI Score: 68

Notes:

UCD Surveys?: Yes, 1993

Sources:

Ellison, J. P. 1980. Diets of mountain whitefish, *Prosopium williamsoni*, and brook trout, *Salvelinus fontinalis*, in the Little Walker River, Mono County, California. California Fish and Game 66:96-104.

Compiled: 30 December, 1994   **Compiler:** PR

ADMA WATERSHED

Name: Buckeye Creek   **Drainage:** East Walker River

Calwater No.: 630.40020-40022   **County:** Mono

Location: From headwaters to Bridgeport Valley. By-Day Creek is a disjunct part of the watershed.

Elevation: 2071 to 3604 m; mean 2787 m

Drainage Area: 91 km²

Description: Third order, moderate gradient, boulder substrate dominated eastern Sierran trout stream.

Aquatic Province: Great Basin

Habitat Types: C2120 Conifer forest snowmelt stream; C2214 Conifer forest stream; C2310 Trout headwater.

Native Fishes: Lahontan cutthroat trout (R, in By-day Creek only); Mountain whitefish (C). Non-native rainbow, brown, and brook trout present.

Amphibians: No records

Other Vertebrates: No records

Invertebrates: No records

Riparian Zone: Riparian zone consisting of aspen, willow, cottonwood and Jeffery Pine in reasonably good condition in much of middle drainage. Heavily grazed meadows present in many areas.

Human Impacts: Grazing has degraded stream banks and reduced riparian vegetation in important meadow areas that support threatened cutthroat trout. Logging is also present in the drainage.

Ownership: Most of the drainage is within Toiyabe NF. Meadows in middle reaches of By-day Creek are privately owned.

Existing Protection: None, although Lahontan cutthroat trout are a federally listed threatened species.

Significant Natural Areas (Aquatic): By-Day Creek (not usually connected directly to creek since it flows into Bridgeport Valley).

Overall Quality Rating: 2.5

Reasons for Rating: Watershed has many natural attributes, including native fishes, but has been degraded by grazing, road, and introduced trout.

IBI Score:

Notes: By-Day Creek are one of the few remaining streams in California where native cutthroat trout still occur.

UCD Surveys?: Yes, 1993 and previously.

Sources:

Coffin, P. D. and W. F. Cowan. 1995. Lahontan cutthroat trout *(Oncorhynchus clarki henshawi)* recovery plan. USFWS, Portland. 108 pp.

Date: 29 December 1994   **Compiler:** PBM, PR

ADMA WATERSHED

Name: Mono Lake   **Drainage:** Mono Lake

Calwater No.: 601.00000   **County:** Mono

Location: Entire drainage from headwaters to Mono Lake, including "dry" drainages on Nevada side.

Elevation: 2179 to 3976 m; mean 2428

Drainage Area: 1747 km^2

Description: The Mono Basin has three broad aquatic habitat areas: (1) Mono Lake, a large, terminal, alkaline lake, (2) steep forested drainages on the eastern side of the Sierran Crest and (3) broad desert washes of the Great Basin. Mono Lake is a highly saline lake with an abundant population of endemic brine shrimp (*Artemia monica*) and other aquatic invertebrates which are an important food source for migrating waterfowl. The lake is renowned for its tufas, towers of calcium carbonate and argonite, that rise up above the water surface. The area around the lake is geologically diverse, comprised of lava buttes, sand dunes and desert washes. The major tributaries to Mono Lake originate from snowmelt of the eastern Sierras and springs. These streams and alpine lakes were historically fishless but now contain at least six species of fish. The streams are all regulated and the lower reaches of Rush, Lee Vining, and other creeks had been dry as the result of diversions until recently. They are now in a recovery phase.

Aquatic Province: Great Basin

Habitat Types: C1120 Mountain pool; C1130 Great Basin scrub pool; C1210 Alpine lake; C1222 Spring pool; C1232 Mono Lake; C2110 Alpine snowmelt stream; C2120 Conifer forest snowmelt stream; C2130 Great Basin scrub snowmelt stream; C2211 Glacial melt stream; C2213 Spring stream; C2214 Conifer forest stream; C2215 Meadow stream; C2221 Desert scrub stream.

Native Fishes: No fish were native to the basin; the streams flowing into Mono Lake now contain rainbow, brown and eastern brook trout, as well as threespine stickleback, Owens sucker, and tui chub.

Amphibians: Great Basin spadefoot toads breed in small permanent ponds in the dunes. Mountain yellow-legged frog in some high elevation areas.

Other Vertebrates: Over 100 species of waterbirds and shorebirds have been observed at Mono Lake. California Gull, Eared Grebe, Wilson's Phalarope, and Red-necked Phalarope are especially dependent on brine shrimp and flies during significant portions of their life cycle.

Invertebrates: The endemic Mono brine shrimp, alkali fly (and seven other species of flies) are a major food source for several species of birds. The brine shrimp have been proposed for inclusion on the federal endangered species list.

Riparian Zone: The once expansive riparian forests along the creeks died following the complete diversion of the streams. With the restoration of minimum stream flows, some recovery of riparian communities is expected. Willows and wild rose are common along streams. At higher elevations, aspen groves are found along streams as well as hillsides where spring and seeps are present. Wet meadows, dominated by sedges, grasses and forbs are found in the basin as well. Approximately 35 percent of the exposed lake shore is a marsh plant community, mostly with a mosaic of bullrush and saltgrass. There are numerous alpine lakes and alpine meadows in the upper drainages on the eastern Sierra crest (upper Lee Vining watershed well described in the USFS ecological survey for the Harvey Monroe Hall RNA; one of the best botanically known RNAs).

Human Impacts: Water diversions by City of Los Angeles from Rush, Parker, Walker and Lee Vining Creeks have significantly lowered Mono Lake water level and increased salinity levels as well as drying up streams. Recent historic legal settlements have resulted in increased flows in the creeks and to the lake. A subsequent reduction in invertebrate populations have decreased the available food supply for several species of migratory waterfowl. Sheep and cattle grazing have degraded riparian and meadow areas. Recreational uses range from OHV use to sightseeing to fishing in the streams.

471

Ownership: Most of the land area is managed by Inyo NF. Mono Lake is owned by the State of California.

Existing Protection: The Mono Basin National Forest Scenic Area is managed by Inyo National Forest. Harvey Monroe Hall Research Natural Area is the oldest RNA in California (1933). Recent (1994) decisions by the State Water Resources Control Board will raise lake levels and maintain permanent flows in the streams.

Significant Natural Areas (Aquatic): Harvey Monroe Hall Research Natural Area, located 1.6 km north of Tioga Pass, includes 15 alpine lakes, several meadows and 3 glaciers.

Overall Quality Rating: 2.1 Mono Lake, 2.5 headwater areas, 3+ for streams below diversions.

Reasons for Rating: Mono Lake's unique saline ecosystem is still intact and has been protected by recent actions and decisions. The upper watershed is in USFS Wilderness Areas with high diversity of plant communities and wetland habitats, although exotic fish are common. The streams below the diversion will take many years to recover from the devastation they experienced and even then the "recovered" ecosystems will be dominated by exotic trout.

IBI Score: 36 for stream systems overall (but should improve as riparian and instream habitats recover). The lake cannot be scored using the IBI system but has high biotic integrity.

Notes: Mono Lake and the surrounding basin have been intensively studied because of the long dispute over the water rights (resolved in 1994).

UCD Surveys?: Yes (Lee Vining Creek).

Sources:

Keeler-Wolf, T. 1990. Ecological Surveys of Forest Service Research Natural Areas, PSW Technical Report No. 125.

Patten D. T. and Mono Basin Ecosystem Study Committee. 1987. The Mono Basin Ecosystem: effects of changing lake level. National Academy Press, Washington, D.C. 272 pp.

State Water Resources Control Board. 1994. Mono Lake basin water right decision 1631. 212 pp.

USFS. 1989. Inyo National Forest, Mono Basin National Forest Scenic Area, Comprehensive Management Plan.

Compiled: 28 December, 1994   **Compiler:** PR, PBM

ADMA WATERSHED

Name: Convict Creek and Lake   **Drainage:** Owens River

Calwater No.: 603.10060-10061   **County:** Mono

Location: From headwaters lakes on the northeast slope of the Mammoth Crest to Crowley Reservoir.

Elevation Range: 2058 to 3909 m; mean 2854 m

Drainage Area: 72 km²

Description: Convict Creek arises from several small lakes on the northeast slopes of Mammoth Crest and flows north dropping rapidly into Convict Lake. Below Convict Lake the stream is a series of boulder-strewn pools and cascades until it drops into Long Valley where the creek turns east toward Crowley Reservoir. The creek meanders through sagebrush flats, meadows, and pasturelands that are heavily grazed by cattle (land managed by Los Angeles Water and Power).

Aquatic Province: Great Basin

Habitat Types: C1210 Alpine Lakes; C2110 Alpine snowmelt stream; C2120 Conifer forest snowmelt stream; C2130 Great Basin scrub snowmelt stream; C2212 Exposed alpine stream; C2214 Conifer forest stream; C2215 Meadow stream.

Native Fishes: Owens sucker were originally found in the lower creek up to and including Convict Lake (the only lake in the Owens drainage with native fish). Dominant non-native fishes are rainbow trout, brown trout, and brook trout.

Amphibians: Mountain yellow-legged frogs present.

Other Vertebrates: Nothing unusual

Invertebrates: Abundant and diverse, but altered by predation from exotic fish.

Riparian Zone: Riparian vegetation is largely absent from the lowermost reaches due to grazing. In the reaches above Convict Lake, riparian vegetation (willows, alder) is often well-developed.

Human Impacts: Introduced trout dominate the fish biota for most of the drainage. Cattle have degraded the lower reaches of the creek, causing bank instability and removal of riparian vegetation. The meadows along the creek in this area may be flood irrigated.

Ownership: Most of watershed down to Highway 395 is in Inyo National Forest; the lowermost reaches are LADWP land.

Existing Protection: Watershed above Convict Lake is in John Muir Wilderness Area

Significant Natural Areas (Aquatic): None identified.

Overall Quality Rating: 2.4 above Convict Lake, 2.6 in the lake and below.

Reasons for Rating: Drainage in wilderness area mainly affected by exotic trout, grazing and recreational use. Lowermost reaches heavily grazed.

IBI Score: 68

Notes: Site of Sierra Nevada Research Laboratory of the University of California.

UCD Surveys?: No

Sources:

Deinstadt, J. M., G. F. Sibbald, J. D. Knarr, and D. M. Wonmg. 1985. Surveys of Fish Populations in streams of the Owens River drainage: 1983-84. California Department of Fish and Game IFD Admin. Report 85-?. 102 pp.

Reimers, N., J. A. Maciolek, and E. P. Pister. 1955. Limnological study of the lakes in Convict Creek Basin, Mono County, California. USFS Fishery Bulletin 56:437-503.

Date: August 1 1995   **Compiler**: PBM

AQUATIC SIGNIFICANT NATURAL AREAS OF THE SIERRA NEVADA: EXAMPLES

Aquatic Significant Natural Areas (SNAs) are watersheds or portions of watersheds that are notable for their concentration of native organisms, as habitat for rare or endangered species, or for their relatively pristine nature. They also are small in area so are less suitable for "multiple use" management than watershed ADMAs . Most require fairly intense management and protection to maintain their value for the protection of aquatic biodiversity and are therefore more likely to be thought of as traditional preserves. The areas listed here are only examples because we lacked the time during the SNEP process to do an intensive identification investigation of potential SNAs.

AQUATIC SIGNIFICANT NATURAL AREA

Name: Independence Lake and Creek   **Drainage:** Little Truckee River

Calwater No.: 105.31026   **County:** Nevada

Location: Upper Independence Creek from headwaters to (and including) Independence Lake.

Elevation: 2118 (lake)-2500 m

Drainage Area:

Description: Drainage above Independence Lake is a small, high gradient forested stream. Independence Lake is a large natural alpine lake. The exit from the lake has been "notched" so that the lake level can be lowered for water supply.

Aquatic Province: Great Basin

Habitat Types: C1310 Alpine lake (with native fish); C2120 Conifer forest snowmelt stream; C2214 Conifer forest stream; C2310 Cutthroat trout headwater; C2331 Sucker/dace/redside stream with cutthroat trout.

Native Fishes: Lahontan cutthroat trout (C), Tahoe sucker (A), Lahontan redside (A), Lahontan speckled dace (C), mountain sucker(?), Paiute sculpin (C).

Amphibians: Not known

Other Vertebrates: Not known

Invertebrates: Moderately diverse and abundant.

Riparian Zone: Narrow but present

Human Impacts: Much of the drainage has been logged in recent years. Lake has been "notched" at mouth so levels can be lowered annually for water deliveries. Heavy grazing occurs in meadows and on streambanks in places. Considerable recreational use of drainage, but access mainly by foot trail.

Ownership: Headwaters and part of lake is in Tahoe NF but half of lake near outlet is privately owned, as is first 2 km of stream below lake.

Existing Protection: Lahontan cutthroat trout is a federally listed threatened species.

ADMA Watershed: Part of Upper Little Truckee River ADMA watershed.

Overall Quality Rating: 2.3

Reasons for Rating: Drainage has been logged and grazed for 100+ years but is still in reasonably good condition. Lake and upper creek are among the few places where Lahontan cutthroat trout still persist in their natural range.

IBI Score: 84

Notes: Independence Lake is unusual for an alpine lake in the Sierra Nevada in that it naturally contained fishes.

UCD Surveys?: Yes, 1993.

Sources:

E. Gerstung, CDFG, personal communication; D. Erman, UCD, personal communication.

Date: 20 October 1994   **Compiler:** PBM

SIGNIFICANT NATURAL AREA

Name: Three Meadows   **Drainage:** South Fork Stanislaus

Calwater No.:   **County:** Tuolumne

Location: Upper headwaters of northern tributary to South Fork Stanislaus River. About 1.5 km north of Waterhouse Lake on the Emigrant Wilderness boundary.

Elevation: ca. 2400 m

Drainage Area:

Description: Small subalpine meadow with perennial, fishless stream. Meadow has mostly grasses and low herbaceous groundcover surrounded by red fir forest. Stream biota included large number of tree frogs and toad tadpoles.

Aquatic Province: Sacramento-San Joaquin

Habitat Types: A2120 conifer forest snowmelt stream; A2412 Forest stream; A2414 Meadow stream

Native Fishes: None

Amphibians: Pacific tree frogs abundant in lower meadow; *Bufo* sp. in middle meadow. Mountain yellow-legged frog probably present.

Other Vertebrates: Unknown.

Invertebrates: A cursory survey indicated aquatic insects were not particularly diverse or abundant, but unusual or endemic forms are probably present.

Riparian, Wetland Habitats: Wet meadow habitat with riparian vegetation along water's edge.

Human Impacts: Cattle grazing and ORV use in meadows.

Ownership: Entirely within Stanislaus NF.

Existing Protection: None

ADMA Watershed?: Part of South Fork Stanislaus ADMA watershed.

Overall Quality Rating: 2.4

Reasons for Rating: A natural meadow system that shows signs of continuous abuse by humans and livestock, yet seems to be an important breeding area for amphibians.

IBI Score: Not applicable

Notes: A thorough biological inventory of this meadow system is needed.

UCD Surveys?: Yes, 1993.

Sources:

Date: 29 December 1994   **Compiler:** PR, PBM

SIGNIFICANT NATURAL AREA

Name: Mill Creek   **Drainage:** Feather River

Calwater No.: 518.42000   **County:** Plumas

Location: From headwaters in Bucks Lake Wilderness to inlet at Bucks Lake.

Elevation Range: 1571-2111 m

Drainage Area:

Description: The watershed contains 1st to 4th order streams with an estimated mean annual precipitation of ca. 230 cm inches. The upper reaches are in a steep granitic canyon which has limited access. The lower section of the creek is more accessible and contains a 20 m waterfall, about 3 km above Bucks Lake, that historically was an upstream fish barrier. Mill Creek is surrounded by a mixed conifer forest dominated by red firs, interspersed with large patches of manzanita chaparral.

Aquatic Province: Sacramento-San Joaquin

Habitat Types: A1280 Sphagnum bog; A2120 Conifer snowmelt stream; A2412 Forest stream; A2421 Resident rainbow trout stream.

Native Fishes: Rainbow trout. Non-native brook trout present above barrier.

Amphibians: Unknown

Other Vertebrates: Unknown

Invertebrates: 1993 summer spot survey describes aquatic insects as being low in diversity and abundance dominated by small mayflies.

Riparian, Wetland Habitats: Short alder and willow thickets along stream margin. Submerged and raised bog habitat types as well as wet and moist meadow wetlands are present within the USFS Research Natural Area.

Human Impacts: Cattle grazing has been a consistent pressure in this watershed for many years. By end of summer, grazing exerts a strong visual impact on the vegetation of the bog, meadow and riparian areas. Camping and fishing pressure also have negative impacts to the area above Bucks Lake. However, a significant stretch of the stream is very difficult to access from the road and should be relatively undisturbed.

Ownership: Mostly Plumas NF land interspersed by private land.

Existing Protection: Bucks Lake Wilderness Area in the upper reaches and Mount Pleasant Research Natural Area, both managed by Plumas NF. Potential USFS RNA.

ADMA Watershed?: No

Overall Quality Rating: 2.2

Reasons for Rating: Unique assemblage of aquatic habitats with existing management to protect these areas.

IBI Score: Not rated because of uncertainty of original fish distribution

Notes: May contain one of the fastest maturing and reproducing red fir forests in the Sierras. Unusually high mean annual precipitation creates unusual ecological conditions.

UCD Surveys?: Yes, 1993.

Sources:

Keeler-Wolfe, T. 1990. Ecological Surveys of USFS Research Natural Areas in California, Gen. Tech. Report PSW-125.

Date: 24 December 1994   **Compiler:** PR, PBM

ROBERT J. LAACKE
USDA Forest Service
Pacific Southwest Research Station and
    Range Experiment Station
Redding, California

JOHN C. TAPPEINER
USDI Forest and Rangeland Ecosystem
    Science Center
and
College of Forestry
Oregon State University
Corvallis, Oregon

10

Red Fir Ecology and Management

Sierra Nevada Ecosystem Project: Final report to Congress, vol. III, *Assessments, Commissioned Reports, and Background Information.* Davis: University of California, Centers for Water and Wildland Resources, 1996.

ABSTRACT

Red fir forests have been less affected by humans than the mixed conifer forests, because they were not burned nor cleared for mining, and because they were too far from the early markets for timber. Therefore until recently there has been less research and experience in their ecology and management than in the mixed conifer forests.

Forest soils are likely to be more affected by management than those in the mixed conifer forests because a large share of their nutrient capital is in the forest floor. Thus logging and scarification for site preparation site must be done with considerable care.

Regeneration can be obtained by natural seeding, advanced regeneration and by planting. It appears that regeneration following timber harvest or fire can be achieved. The potential for regeneration varies throughout the Sierra. In the southern Sierra, shade along with ample seed supply appear to be important for regeneration on south, exposed sites. Planting is less likely to succeed on these sites than on north slope, unless shelter trees are left to provide shade. Advanced regeneration is frequently present in the understory of red fir stands. If logging is done carefully, it will respond and grow. Along with new natural seedlings and planting on some sites, advanced regeneration can provide adequate regeneration.

Red fir forests have the potential for high yields of wood. It can grow at high densities for long periods of time and then respond to thinning or density management. Thus, it can be managed under a variety of silvicultural systems, including evenage systems with long rotations and unevenaged systems.

INTRODUCTION

Red fir forests are a major component of the forest cover of the Sierra Nevada. Most of the early work on forest ecology and management was done in the mixed conifer forest where the early timber harvest was concentrated, and where fire was much more common. There is a growing body of knowledge about red fir forests and their management. Information ranges from research on basic ecology and on silviculture including: regeneration, thinning and regeneration methods. Much of the current work is being done mainly in the southern Sierras, earlier work was done further north. The purpose of this paper is to summarize information from the literature and experience that provides a back ground for silvicultural practices for managing red fir forests.

Ecological Understanding

Of the forest systems directly influenced by modern human activity, one of the least altered from its "natural state" is perhaps the Red Fir forest, an ecosystem dominated by its defining species, California Red Fir (*Abies magnifica*) and the varietal Shasta red fir (*A. magnifica* var. *shastensis*). Although most extensive in the higher elevations of California's Sierra Nevada, these forests also occupy equivalent elevational positions from the central and southern Cascades of Oregon into the northern coast ranges of California (Laacke 1990). Red fir is probably the least altered of the Sierra Nevada ecosystems for a combination of reasons: first, the short time during which these systems have been subject to significant harvest or road building activity; second, the relative lack of species capable of replacing those present; and third, the characteristics of natural fire in red fir.

A combination of heavy snows, long winters, short growing seasons, soils with nutrients accumulated in the forest floor, and a variety of other attributes associated with high-elevation, mountainous terrain made the red fir forests less suited to agriculture and other uses compared to lower elevation forests. As a result, large scale human access to the high country was postponed until very late in the process of European settlement. Barring local impacts, such as the narrow corridors harvested for fuel wood during building of the railroads and concentrations of livestock around new population centers (Leiberg 1902), incursion into the red fir forests was late in coming. The extensive pine and mixed-conifer forests at lower, more accessible elevations in the Sierra Nevada and elsewhere were available to produce the wood needed. Logging had begun by 1943 (Oostings and Billings 1943) but it wasn't until the two decades following 1953 that harvest of red fir forests began to be significant (Bolsinger 1980). Even so, as recently as 1962, the standard silviculture textbook (Baker 1962) stated that little silviculture information about red fir and that the type remained too small, variable and secondary in value to merit special consideration.

Many of the same physical and climatological characteristics that had limited human presence in the red fir forests also limit the number and kinds of plants and animals that can flourish there. Although far from depauperate, the red fir forest may generally contain fewer and a less diverse flora and fauna than do lower elevation forests (Barbour and Woodward 1985, Gordon and Bowen 1978). For example, the number of vertebrate wildlife species that are present in red fir forests as permanent residents or even as transients is significantly less than forests lower in elevation (Laudenslayer and Grenfeld 1983, Mayer and Laudenslayer 1988, Timossi et al. 1993, Zeiner et al. 1988). Red fir supports fewer species in nearly all categories and is most deficient in those that are present all year (between 46 and 54% of the other forest types.)

The red fir forests are generally included of several plant associations especially in the southern and central Sierra (USDA 1994). There are potentially competitive tree species all through the red fir forest (white fir, Jeffrey pine, incense-cedar, sugar pine at lower elevations; western white pine, lodgepole pine). Frequently these species are part of with different plant associations (for example red fir/lodgepole pine/hawksweed) and successional trends and respones to disturbance and management can vary considerable among associations. Red fir is well adapted to heavy snows and ice; saplings bent double by the snow can straighten during the next growing season (Gordon 1978). White fir has complementary ecological capabilities although it may be generally better suited to elevations below the red fir and, in the ebb and flow of climate change, forests dominated by either red fir or white fir probably "move up and down hill".

Because red fir forests are located in the high elevations with a short summer, it is perhaps surprising that wildfire frequencies in red fir are not particularly different, now or in the past, than forests of lower elevations. Fire affects in red fir forests are differently than in mixed conifer and eastside pine forests. Although moderate to high severity fires do occur in red fir and produce large patches of regeneration, fire regimes in red fir forests appear to be dominated by low- and moderate-intensity fires that result in small scattered groups of regeneration (Kilgore 1971, Kilgore 1973, Agee 1990, Taylor 1993, Taylor and Halpern 1991) rather than extensive areas of even age stands. Fires appear to be a major historic element in creating small openings in dense forests and preparing seedbeds for regeneration. However the history of fires in red fir forest has not been well documented throughout the range of this forest type.   The pattern of small groups of even-sized (and sometimes even-aged) trees is similar to that produced by windthrow, insect kill, lightning, or pathogens. All of these variables results in creation of sites for establishment of new seedlings, thinning of small trees, and release existing regeneration to grow faster. These disturbance factors result in the naturally patchy distribution of different size trees in the red fir forest.

It is often assumed that red fir stands are even-aged (Rundel et al. 1988) because the trees are even-sized. However, even aged stands, including even-aged by small group stands, are probably unusual in natural red fir. Regeneration can be a continuous process over reasonably large areas, occurring beneath existing trees and in openings created by fire, windthrow, insects, and disease (Barbour and Woodward 1985, Taylor and Halpern 1991). The shade tolerant nature of the species allows reasonable growth to occur under a variety of conditions and as a result, trees in even-sized stands, or clumps, can vary in age by more than 100+ years.

A major consideration in red fir forest management is the nature of its soils (see Poff and Powers). Soils are young, and much of the nutrient capital occurs in dead organic material or the forest floor. Thus, silvicultural systems and harvesting techniques that avoid widespread soil disturbance, are likely to be a good management practices for the future.

The reasonably extensive harvest and management efforts of the last 30 or so years concentrated on artificial regeneration even though successful artificial regeneration of red fir was rare until the latter years of this period when enough was learned about nursery culture and handling of red fir to make it possible. Because of this difficulty large amounts of Jeffrey pine (a natural component of the red fir forest) were planted as it was possible to achieve successful artificial regeneration with the pine in some cases. On the larger plantations and wildfire rehabilitation efforts, planting Jeffrey pine had the effect of temporarily changing the forest from red fir to pine. However, natural red fir seedlings became dominant even before the pines reach maturity.

Management of Red Fir Forests

Most of the information developed from experiments with regeneration and tests of different regeneration methods was done in the red fir/ white fir association and much of it at Swain Mountain. Therefore the following discussion is mainly relevant to management of red fir-white fir not mixture of red fir and lodgpole pine or hemlock.

Silvicilturally, red fir forests are quite different than pine and mixed conifer forests, because the management of these forests focuses primarily on a single tree species with little opportunity for managing mixtures of conifers and hardwoods. The primary reason for silvicultural practices in red fir forests is for wood production. There is less reason to treat stands to reduce fire hazard and insect impacts. Fire potential is inherently much lower in these forests than in the other Sierra Nevada forest types. Even though there may be considerable dead organic matter and fuel concentrations in red fir forests, intense, stand replacing fires covering large areas have been uncommon. Also, there has not been the general occurrence of insects that have been common in mixed conifer forests or white fir stands/red fir at the lower elevations, even during the droughts of the 1980's and 1990's. Dwarf mistletoe that is common in red fir forests and large trees that often have stem decay in them, may be an important part of wildlife habitat. These factors undoubtedly reduce the yield of merchantable timber, but they also have significant wildlife habitat value. Their net effect depends upon the relative importance of timber production and habitat.

Some management might improve wildlife habitat. Even though these forests are generally quite dense and their understories typically have sparse or non-existent layers of shrubs or herbs, some management could be done to enhance habitat for wildlife that use shrubs forbs and grasses for cover and forage. At lower elevations there is generally a seed bank of *Ceanothus* and *Manzanita sp.* and other species in the forest floor (Quick 1959 and Weatherspoon 1987), that produces a substantial cover if trees are removed by timber harvest or fire and many of these are preferred browse species. Red fir seedlings become established beneath these shrubs and eventually overtop and replace them. This is usually a fairly long process and the shrub communities are likely to persist for 30 to 50+ years before being replaced by the fir.

Another case where some management for other than timber production may be beneficial is the thinning of dense, young stands of red fir that have been established after timber harvest or other disturbance. Red fir natural regeneration often produces young stands with very high stocking (800+ seedlings/acre). These stands have the potential for becoming quite dense and for growing only very small trees in the near future. Thinning dense, young stands to produce larger trees in a shorter time may benefit both wildlife and timber production objectives.

Potential for Wood Production

Red fir stands have the potential for high yields of commercial wood. Even though initial stand growth is often slow, growth rates may accelerate after about 50 years of age. Growth remains high for a number of years. For example, Shumacher (1928) reports net volumes on average site quality at age 50 that range only from 2,450 to 5,000 ft^3/acre but increase considerably from 11,650 to 23,000 ft^3/acre at 120 years. Since mortality was not measured in this study, actual yields would probably be greater. Furthermore, red fir stands respond well to thinning even at relatively old ages. Oliver (1988) reports the results of thinning 100 year old stands of red fir and white fir whose basal areas ranged from 320 to 498 ft^2/acre before thinning and 142 to 363 ft^2/acre after thinning. Volume increments for 10 years after thinning ranged from 189 to 337 ft^3 or 1,404 to 1,776 bd. ft/acre/year. Compared to ponderosa pine, for example, red fir stands can grow at high densities for long periods of time and still maintain stand and individual tree vigor. This positive response to a partial cutting over a wide range of stand densities suggests that there is considerable silvicultural flexibility and a range of options for managing red fir. When thinning is undertaken, however, excessive damage to the boles of remaining trees must avoided to prevent infection by decay fungi .

Natural Regeneration

Natural regeneration is common in red fir forests (Barbour and Woodward 1985). Throughout unmanaged stands, there are often seedlings and saplings of a wide range of sizes and ages that occur in openings caused by death of individual or small groups of overstory trees (Taylor and Halpern 1991). Seedlings and saplings are common in stands in which sanitation and salvage, which harvested individual trees. Natural regeneration is favored by a good seed supply, some shade during the first 2 - 3 years following germination and a mineral soil seed bed (Gordon, 1970). High temperatures in undisturbed forest floor organic layers cause high rates of mortality of 1 to 2 year old red fir. Thus, shade aids seedling establishment on undisturbed sites (Ustin et al. 1984). Also exposure of mineral soil aids survival because temperatures at the seedlings stems are reduced and probably the effects of pathogens are decreased. Gordon (1970) reports lower maximum temperatures (150° F) on mineral soil than in one inch deep forest floor (163°F), but even with mineral soil seed beds, shade enhanced survival.

A study of different regeneration methods (Gordon, 1979) in red fir and red and white fir stands verified the importance of abundant seed, seed bed preparation, and shade for natural regeneration. Seedlings were most abundant on the narrowest clearcuts and under shelter woods with the largest number of trees. Ten years following harvesting seedlings were present from several seed crops, but they were most abundant from the crops that most closely followed disturbance from logging. In this experiment, even the minimum number of seedlings that occurred on the clearcuts exceeded the stocking (300/acre) required by state law (Gordon, 1979).

Seedlings that become established in small openings in the understory of red fir stands grow slowly. But they can respond to the removal of overstory trees by logging or natural disturbance. For example, Gordon (1973) reports the response of natural red fir regeneration to removal of the overstory. Trees ages were 39 to 45 years at time of release and height ranged from 2.2 to 5.0 feet. For about 5 years after overstory removal, there was no increase in growth. However, after 10 -12 years, average height growth increased four times and annual rings per inch decreased from 70 to 100 to 7 to 12 rings per inch (Gordon, 1978). He concluded that advanced regeneration would restock the site and produce a new stand. Similarly, Oliver (1985) found red fir seedlings and saplings that appeared to be badly damaged grow ing rapidly after thinning or complete overstory removal.

The work discussed above (Gordon1970, 1973, 1979) was begun in the late 1950's and early 1960's mainly at Swain Mountain on the Lassen National Forest. The stocking and growth of regeneration on these study sites remain high although the growth of the seedling growth was inversely related to the density of the overstroy trees (Laacke and Tomascheski In press). Recent observations indicate that on some sites, the effects of making openings in red fir forests may cause regeneration problems in the future. The initial openings had little regeneration of grasses or sedges immediately following cutting. However, the density of these species increased and apparently developed their potential for regeneration. In subsequent cutting in adjacent stands, these species were much more aggressive and formed dense covers sooner than in the initial cutting. Based on experience on other sites, it is likely that populations of gophers will also likely increase with the cover of grasses and sedges.

Artificial Regeneration

Planting is also a method of red fir regeneration that has been developed over the last two decades. Studies of seed production (Gordon 1978); collection (Oliver, 1974); nursery production and handling of seedlings have developed insight into the physiology of this species and its response to nursery, storage, and planting techniques. A key to the production of planting stock is obtaining dormancy in the nursery and lifting at the proper time so that seedlings have the potential for vigorous root growth after planting (Jenkinson et al. 1993). Cold storage for about 4 months between the time of lifting and out planting.

Planting at high elevations late spring and early summer is difficult. Deep snow may prevent access to planting sites until late spring or early summer when long days and elevated temperatures cause more demand for water than the small root systems of the seedlings can supply. Planting just after snow melt, in cold soils, delays initiation of seedling root growth and the seedling tops can desiccate before their roots can supply water. Research indicates that with proper handling of seedlings, site preparation, and attention to weather and soil conditions, sufficient rates of seedling survival can be obtained. Operationally success of planting red fir has not been as successful as planting ponderosa pine and Douglas-fir.

A further difficulty of red fir plantation establishment on some sites is the combination of herbaceous vegetation gopher browsing. Where dense herbaceous communities provide summer habitat for gophers, above- and below- ground brow grazing on planted and natural red fir seedlings in the summer and winter can be fatal. Although resistance to gopher damage increases with tree size, even large saplings (3 m+) are damaged and killed when gopher populations age high (Gross and Laacke 1984).

Silvicultural Systems

Information in the literature and experience suggest that red fir can be managed under a variety of stand structures and silvicultural systems (Gordon, 1970); however, long-term experience and records of red fir management are lacking. Natural evenage stands of white fir and red fir have developed after large fires; however, stand establishment may take considerable time. Burned sites were initially stocked with shrubs. Then after about 30 to 50 years, the fir seedlings that became established under the shrubs overtopped them and formed dense evenage or even size stands. These stands appear to become unevenaged disturbance occurs in them. After about 100 - 120+ years, perhaps longer, gaps are formed in these stands from root diseases, snow, wind and insects; regeneration occurs in the gaps and the development of an unevenage stand begins.

Evenage management, should be tried at least on a limited basis. One drawback to this system appears to be that shrubs, grasses, sedges invade after clearcutting and retard seedling establishment. Also, gophers often occupy clearcuts and delay regeneration establishment. Because of slow red fir establishment on some clearcuts throughout the Sierras, Jeffrey pine was planted. On most of these sites, red fir became established under the shrubs, along with the Jeffrey pine. In time, these stands will likely become red fir. How long it will take will vary from site to site depending upon the relative stocking and growth rates of the two species.

An important consideration in the management of red fir forests is nutrient conservation. Compared to other forest types, apparently in true fir forests a large proportion of the forest nutrient capital is in the litter on the forest floor (Powers and Edmund 1992). Therefore, practices such as broadcast burning of slash that oxidizes the organic matter could result in considerable loss of nitrogen. Some disturbance of the forest floor and exposure of mineral soil is needed for natural seedling establishment, however.

The choice of regeneration method and silviculture system will likely vary with management objectives but also with location within the Sierra. It appears that unevenage management or systems that make small openings in the forest canopy are suitable for managing red fir on a range of sites , although shelterwood and clearcutting methods will likely work on north slopes and more generally in the northern Sierras.

With careful logging and site preparation on many sites natural regeneration will become established Either group selection, single tree selection , or a combination of these methods could be used. When beginning to implement these systems, natural openings that contain natural regeneration could be expanded in order to release established seedlings and saplings, and to obtain additional regeneration at the edges of the openings (Gordon 1973). In dense stands, thinning and making openings in the overstory by removing one to three large trees would likely provide sites for natural regeneration. Soil disturbance associated with logging would probably expose sufficient mineral soil to provide a suitable seed bed. As with any ground based logging methods, a careful planning and use of designated skid trails is needed to minimize soil compaction. Trees to be left after logging would depend upon stand management objectives. Groups of large (40 in. + DBH) old trees , some with decay and mistletoe in them could be retained for cavity nesters, aesthetics, a more diverse structure, or old growth component. Among them could be grown smaller vigorous trees. This combination of groups of small and large trees would yield timber and provide a continuous forest cover, except where openings (1 to 2+ acres) were made to provide patches of shrubs or to regenerate fir.

Ferrell (1980, 1983) has provided guidelines for assessing tree fir vigor and mortality based on crown characteristics. The guidelines can be used to determine which trees are likely to die or produce snags and cavities and which are the trees that are rapidly growing into the larger size classes and producing merchantable wood. They are quantitative guides for determining trees to leave or remove to regulate stand density in thinning or unevenage silvicultural systems.

Initial guidelines for unevenage management can be approximated from information in the literature. Assuming average stand diameters of 30 - 36 inches, Gordon's (1979) regeneration cuttings at Swain Mountain left about 50 to 70 ft^2/acre basal area in the heaviest cut (10 trees/acre remaining) and from 150 - 210 ft^2/acre basal area in the lightest cut (30 trees/acre remaining). Most regeneration occurred at the higher densities. Furthermore, these densities were within the range (137 - 263) in which Oliver (1988) found substantial volume and diameter growth rates. Windthrow averaged less than one tree/acre over all of Oliver's thinning treatments. On windy, exposed ridges more blowdown could be expected. However, Gordon (1973) found less windthrow among shelterwoods and small openings than along clearcut edges. Thus, it appears that with careful selection of leave trees, logging systems planning and implementation, regeneration can be obtained and diverse stand structures can be maintained.

REFERENCES

Agee, James K. 1990. The historical role of fire in Pacific Northwestern forests. In Walstad, Radosevich, and Sandberg, eds. *Natural and prescribed fire in the Pacific Northwest.* Oregon State University Press. Corvallis, OR pp. 25-38.

Barbour, Michael G. and Roy A. Woodward. 1985. The shasta red fir forest of California. *Canadian Journal of Forest Research.* 15:570-576

Baker, Frederick S. 1962. The California region. pg 460-502 In: Barrett, John W., ed. *Regional Silviculture of the United States.* New York: Ronald Press Co.

Bolsinger, Charles C. 1980. California forests: trends, problems, and opportunities. *Resource Bull. PNW-89.* Portland, OR: US Department of Agriculture, Forest Service, Pacific Northwest Forest and Range Experiment Station; 137 p.

Ferrell, G. T. 1980. Risk-rating systems for mature red fir and white fir in nothern California. *USDA Forest Service Gen. Tech. Report PSW-39*, 29p., Pacific Soutwest Experiment Station, Albany, CA

Ferrell, G. T. 1983. FGrowth classification systems for fed fir and white fir in northern California. *USDA Forest Service, Gen. Tech. Report PSW 72,* 18p., Pacific Southwest Experiment Station, Albany, CA

Gordon, Donald T. 1973. Released advanced reproduction of white and red fir ... growth, damage, mortality. *Res. Paper PSW-95. Berkeley, CA: Pacific Southwest Forest and Range Experiment Station, Forest Service*, US Department of Agriculture 12 p.

Gordon, Donald T. and Eugene E. Bowen. 1978. Herbs and brush on California red fir regeneration sites: a species and frequency sampling. *Res. Note PSW-329. Berkeley, CA: US Department of Agriculture, Forest Service,* Pacific Southwest Forest and Range Experiment Station. 10 p.

Gordon, Donald T. 1978. California red fir literature: some corrections and comments. *Forest Science* 24(2):52-57.

_____. 1979. Successful natural regeneration of white and red fir--influence of several factors. *USDA Forest Service Research Paper* PSW 58, Berkeley, CA

Gross, Rob and Robert J. Laacke. 1984. Pocket gophers girdle large true firs in northeastern California. *Tree Planters' Notes.* Vol 35(2):28-30.

Jenkinson, J. L. , J. A. Nelson and M. E. Huddleson. 1993. Improving planting stock quality-the Humoldt experience. *US Forest Service Gen. Tech. Report PSW-GTR-143, Albany, CA, 219p.*

Kilgore, Bruce M. 1971. The role of fire in managing red fir forests. *Transactions of the North American Wildlife and Natural. Resources Conference* 36:405-416.

Kilgore, Bruce M. 1973. The ecological role of fire in Sierra conifer forests: its application to national park management. *Quaternary Research* 3: 496-513.

Kimmey, James W. 1950. Cull factors for forest-tree species in northwestern California. *Forest Survey Release No. 7. Berkeley, CA: California Forest and Range Experiment Station, Forest Service, US Department of Agriculture 30 p.*

Kimmey, James W. 1957. Application of indicator cull factors to white and red fir stands in the Sierra Nevada. *Forest Research Notes No. 127. Berkeley, CA: California Forest and Range Experiment Station, Forest Service, US Department of Agriculture 5 p.*

Laacke, Robert J. and Jeanne H. Tomascheski. In Press. Effects of residual trees on height growth of natural true fir seedlings. Res. Paper PSW-000. Berkeley, CA: California Forest and Range Experiment Station, Forest Service, US Department of Agriculture.

Laacke, Robert J. and Jeanne H. Tomascheski. 1986. Shelterwood regeneration of true fir: conclusions after 8 years. *Forest Service, US Department of Agriculture Res. Paper PSW-184.* Berkeley, CA: Pacific Southwest Forest and Range Experiment Station.

Laacke, Robert J. 1990 *Abies magnifica* A. Murr. California Red Fir. pg 71-79. In Burns and Honkala, eds. *Silvics of North America: volume 1. Conifers.* Agriculture Handbook 654 Forest Service, US Department of Agriculture.

Laudenslayer, W.F. Jr. and W.E. Grenfeld Jr. 1983. A list of amphibians, birds, and mammals of California. *Outdoor California* 44:5-14.

Leiberg, John B. 1902. Forest conditions in the northern Sierra Nevada, *California. Professional Paper No. 8, Series H, Forestry 5.* Washington, DC: Geological Survey, US Department of the Interior 194 p.

Mayer, K.E. and W.F. Laudenslayer Jr. 1988. *A guide to wildlife habitats of California.* California Dep. Forestry and Fire Protection. Sacramento CA. 166pp.

Oostings, H.J. and W.D. Billings. 1943. The red fir forest of the Sierra Nevada: *Abietium magnificae. Ecological Monographs* 13(3):260-274.

Powers, R. F. and R. L Edmonds. 1992. Chapter 4. Nutrient management of subalpine *Aibes* forests. In:H. N. Chappell, G. F. Weetman, and R. E. Miller (ed). *Forest fertilization: sustaining znd improving nutrition and growth of western forests.* Seattle WA, University of Washington Institute of Forest Resources.

Quick, C. R. 1959. Ceanothus seeds and seedlings on burns. *Madrono* 16: 23-30.

Rundel, Philip W., David J. Parsons, and Donald T. Gordon. 1988. Montane and subalpine vegetation of the Sierra Nevada and Cascade Ranges. pp 559-599 In Barbour, Michael, G. and Jack Major eds. *Terrestrial Vegetation of California.* California Native Plant Society Special Publication Number 9.

Show, S.B. and E.I. Kotok. 1924 The role of fire in the California pine forests. *Department Bull. No. 1294. Washington, DC: US Department of Agriculture* 80 p.

Schumacher, Francis X. 1926. Yield, stand and volume tables for white fir in the California pine region. Bulletin 407. Berkeley, CA: *University of California, Agricultural Experiment Station* 26 p.

Schumacher, Francis X. 1928. Yield, stand and volume tables for red fir in California. Bulletin 456. Berkeley, CA: *University of California, Agricultural Experiment Station* 29 p.

Taylor, Alan. 1993. Fire history and structure of red fir (*Abies magnifica*) forests, Swain Mountain Experimental Forest, Cascade Range, northeastern California. *Canadian Journal of Forest Research* 33:1672-1678.

Taylor, Alan and Charles B. Halpern. 1991. The structure and dynamics of *Abies magnifica* forests in the southern Cascade Range, USA. *Journal of Vegetation Science* 2:180-200

Timossi, I., et al. 1993. *California wildlife habitat relationships microcomputer database* Version 5.0. State of California, The Resources Agency, Dept. of Fish and Game. Sacramento.

USDA Forest Service. 1994. Guide to forested communities of the upper montanein the central and southern Sierra Nevada. Forest Service, Pacific Southwest Region. R5- ECOL-TP-3, 164p.

Ustin, S. L. , R. A. Woodward, M. G. Barbour, and J. L. Hatfield. 1984. Relationships between sunfleck dynamics and red fir seedling distribution. *Ecology* 65: 1420-1428.

Weatherspoon, C. Phillip. 1987. Preharvest prescribed burning for vegetation management: effects on Ceanothus velutinus seeds in litter and duff. In Proceedings of the Ninth Annual Forest Vegetation Management Conference. November 4-5 Redding, California.

Zeiner, D.C., et al. eds. 1988a. *California statewide wildlife habitat relationships system,* Volume I, amphibians and reptiles. State of California, The Resources Agency, Dept. of Fish and Game. Sacramento.

Zeiner, D.C., et al. eds. 1988b. *California statewide wildlife habitat relationships system,* Volume II, birds. State of California, The Resources Agency, Dept. of Fish and Game. Sacramento.

Zeiner, D.C., et al. eds. 1988c. *California statewide wildlife habitat relationships system,* Volume III, mammals. State of California, The Resources Agency, Dept. of Fish and Game. Sacramento.

WILLIAM W. OLIVER
USDA Forest Service
Pacific Southwest Forest and
    Range Experiment Station
Redding, California

GEORGE T. FERRELL
USDA Forest Service
Pacific Southwest Forest and
    Range Experiment Station
Redding, California

JOHN C. TAPPEINER
USDI Forest and Rangeland Ecosystem
    Science Center
and
College of Forestry
Oregon State University
Corvallis, Oregon

11

Density Management of Sierra Nevada Forests

Sierra Nevada Ecosystem Project: Final report to Congress, vol. III, *Assessments, Commissioned Reports, and Background Information.* Davis: University of California, Centers for Water and Wildland Resources, 1996.

LIST OF FIGURES

INTRODUCTION

Stand density and species composition have a major impact on stand growth and development as well as on many aspects of forest ecology and management. Its of major concern to the Sierra Nevada because there are many stands in the Sierras that began after fire, mining and logging, and often these stands are growing at high densities. Stand density affects, tree growth rates and vigor; cover for wildlife; fuels and fire potential and behavior; understory tree, shrub, and herb density; growth and yield of forest products. The literature on the relationships of stand density, growth, and yield in the 19th and 20th centuries in Europe is comprehensive (Assmann 1970). Those results have been corroborated by studies in North America (Smith 1986 and Daniel, Helms and Baker 1979). The purpose of this section is to discuss work relevant to the Sierra Nevada forests.

Measures of Stand Density

Several acceptable measures of stand density that have been used in Sierra Forests for many years: stocking (trees/ha), stand density index (number of trees in relation to average tree size) (Reineke 1933), and basal area. These are absolute measures. When they are compared to the maximum a site can support, such as "normal" basal area (Dunning and Reineke 1933, Schumacher 1928, 1930; Meyer 1938) a measure of the degree of full site occupancy is produced that is independent of site productivity, tree species and often age. These measures can be considered standards against which to compare individual stands. More recent studies by researchers at the U.S. Forest Service, Pacific Southwest Research Station, have examined the development of stands growing at a range of densities. They have begun to determine how factors such as tree mortality; growth rates of individual trees and stands; crown size and other stand and tree parameters are related to stand density.

Tree and Stand Growth

As trees grow, stand density increases, trees become more crowded and less resources (water, light, nutrients) are available for maintaining tree and stand vigor. For example, Oliver (In Press) studied the development of a ponderosa pine stand at five densities from stand ages 20 to 40 years on a productive site at 4,000 ft. near Foresthill in the Sierra Nevada. At 20 years of age the densest plots had 507 tree/acre, and 144 ft^2 of basal area; the least dense plots had 77 trees/acre and 64 ft^2/acre of basal area. At 40 years of age, the character of these plots was quite different. In the low density plots, tree diameters averaged 21.2 inches and live crown ratios averaged 70 percent. Values were 13.5 inches and 54 percent, respectively, in the high density plots. In addition, an understory of white fir, Douglas-fir, and sugar pine, and some ponderosa pine became established in the low density plots (Oliver and Dolph 1992).

The density of young stands on productive sites changes much more rapidly than the density of older stands or stands on less productive sites. For example, Oliver (In Press) reports that total basal area growth of the ponderosa pine plots at Foresthill ranged from 4.7 to 9.0 ft^2/acre/year at 21 to 25 years of age and 3.8 to 5.6 ft^2acre/year at 36 to 40 years of age. Thus, these young stands on productive sites increased density very rapidly. Even though they were thinned three times in a 20-year period, net basal areas that ranged from 38 to 144 ft^2/acre at age 20 years had increased to 93 and 190 ft^2 at 40 years. In contrast to Foresthill, a plantation of trees similar in size and thinned to similar densities on a less productive site was growing more slowly. Total basal area growth between the ages of 28 and 38 ranged from 2.2 to 6.6 ft^2/acre/year (Oliver 1979).

Stand densities in red and white fir stands generally are much higher than they are in ponderosa pine stands--320 to 498 ft^2/acre of basal area in one study (Oliver 1988). After reducing stand density to basal areas of 140 to 365 ft^2/acre, this 100-year-old true fir responded to thinning with increased diameter growth. Net basal area growth rates were 3.9 to 6.3 ft^2/acre/year, and it appeared that within about 10 to 15 years these stands would have regrown to their previous densities.

Forest stands maintain a relatively constant rate of biomass production or volume growth rate over a wide range of stand densities. The effects of stand density on stand and tree growth can be generalized from Figure 1. adopted from Smith (1986) and Daniel et al. (1979). At very low densities or numbers of trees per acre, an increase in density causes a proportional increase in volume growth (Zone A). As density increases, volume growth continues to increase but at a lower rate because trees begin to compete with each other for site resources (Zone B). Then growth is constant over a wide range of stand densities (Zone C). However, net growth in Zone C is likely to decrease because mortality is often higher at higher densities. This relationship has been demonstrated for red fir (Daniel, Helms, and Baker 1979; Oliver 1988). Oliver (1988) found that after thinning, net volume growth of true fir stands ranged from 196 to 213 ft^3/acre/year at basal areas of 140 to 170 ft^2/acre. At basal area of 200 to 260 ft^2/acre, growth was somewhat greater-217 to 317 ft^3/acre/year, but no significant relationship existed between stand growth and density over this range of basal areas. Diameter growth, as expected, was significantly greater at lower basal areas. Oliver (In Press) found a similar relationship in the young ponderosa pine plantation at Foresthill. Net or gross volume growth was not significantly related to stand densities that ranged from 51 to 168 ft^2/acre of basal area. Net stand growth across this range of stand densities was 174 to 165 ft^3/acre/year--less at the higher densities because of insect related mortality.

Understory Vegetation and Stand Development

In young stands, stand density and growth may be affected by understory vegetation, particularly shrubs. Also, the interaction of trees and shrubs varies by site productivity. For example, Oliver (1984) found that tree growth in a young ponderosa pine stand on a site of low productivity was related more to manzanita density than to tree density. Once the density of manzanita was reduced, tree and stand growth were regulated by tree density. On a more productive site after 20 years of growth with understories of primarily manzanita and deer brush, trees growing without shrubs were larger and had produced about 40 percent more cubic volume than trees with shrubs (Oliver 1990). Despite covering 77 percent of the area, shrubs appeared to have far less impact than on the less productive site--not preventing stand development but only delaying it. Oliver (1990) estimated that at a 15-foot spacing stands with a shrub understory would have an averaged stand diameter of 12 inches about 7 years later than stands without shrubs.

Stand Density and Insect Populations

There is considerable evidence that the susceptibility of a stand to forest insects is related to its density. However, factors such as drought, root disease, mistletoe, and possibly air pollution also are important. White fir trees under stress from Fomes annosus root decay (Ferrell and Smith 1976) and moisture stress from mechanical damage have been shown to be susceptible to the fir engraver beetle. Even sections of individual white fir trees infected by true mistletoe were shown to be under moisture stress and more susceptible to attack than uninfected parts of trees or entire trees (Ferrell 1974). Undoubtedly there is considerable interaction among these variables and stand density. During a severe drought the effects of stand density may become paramount. For example, Ferrell 1980 developed a method of predicting the likelihood of mortality of red and white fir based on crown and bark characteristics. However, when studying the outbreak of the fir engraver beetle that occurred at Lake Tahoe, during the drought of the late 1980's, he found tree characteristics inadequate for predicting mortality on either a tree or stand basis. About 98 percent of the variation in mortality could be explained by models using only white fir basal area and total stand basal area.

After reviewing the literature on the fir engraver beetle, Berryman and Ferrell (1988), concluded that stand density management to reduce the food supply provided by trees of poor vigor (to the extent that it is practical in western North American forests) may be the best long-term approach to controlling western fir engraver. Other researchers have reached this conclusion for the mountain pine beetle (Waring and Pitman 1985).

Storm damage and related insect mortality have been shown to be related to stand density. At the high stand densities in the Foresthill study at age 40 about 20 percent of the trees had been killed by insects and an additional 5 to 10 percent had been damaged by winter snow and wind breakage (Oliver In Press). Similar storm damage to dense stands was reported by Powers and Oliver (1970). In addition to breeding in trees of low vigor, bark beetles may breed in the broken tops of storm-damaged trees, and then spread to adjacent healthy trees. In a study in northeastern California on a site less productive than that at Foresthill, a range of stand densities was established in a 28 year old ponderosa pine stand. Trees/acre ranged from 43 to 456/acre; basal area from 13 to 86 ft^2/acre. At age 62, approximately 200 trees/acre and about half of the basal area or volume in the high density treatments have been killed by bark beetles.

Stand Density Management

Total biomass or volume production generally increases with stand density. However, tree mortality, caused by inter-tree competition, insect mortality and storm damage (as discussed above) also increases with density. Of course, tree size and vigor increase as competition (i.e. stand density) decreases. It is important to stress that net production or yield of wood is relatively constant beyond a certain density (Zone C)(Figure 1).

Other variables important to forest management are related to stand density. A productive understory-- conifers, hardwood and shrubs, herbs, grasses-- generally becomes established in stands of low density with few overstory trees. This affects forage for wildlife and livestock and also cover for wildlife. However, in more open stands understory vegetation and the large crowns of the trees may result in high fuel loads and fire potential unless the crowns are pruned and understory density is reduced (by grazing, cutting, burning, or herbicides). In dense stands, dead trees will increase fuel loading from snags and logs on the forest floor. Although snags and logs are important habitat for some wildlife species, dead trees in very dense stands will likely be too small to provide cavities or to persist as snags or logs on the forest floor.

Objectives for regulating stand density in Sierra Nevada forests are ecological, as well as managerial. These include reduction of fuels and fire potential, regulation of species composition, enhancing the development of large trees, wood production, and regulation of the understory of shrubs and conifer regeneration. Most of these objectives are "interactive". For example, thinning to develop fire resistance by reducing overstory density and fuel ladders of understory shrubs and

Figure 1. Theoretical biomass production of forest stands, and some tree and stand characteristics in relation to stand density. In zone A biomass production increases rapidly with increasing density. In zone B, biomass increases with density, but less rapidly than in A, because trees compete with each other. In C there is little increase in net or total biomass with density, but generally more mortality, as density increases, from inter-tree competition.

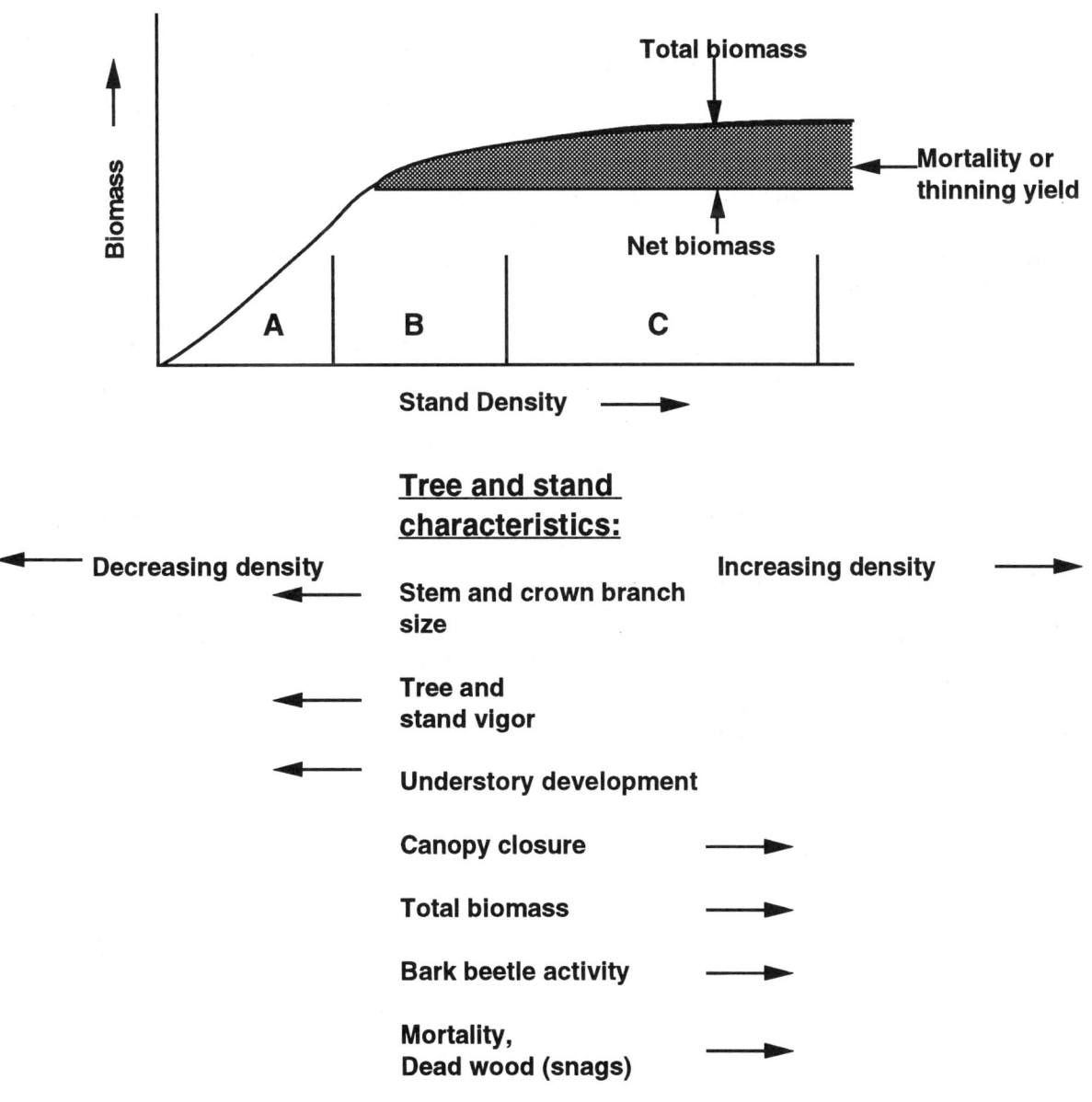

conifers also will tend to reduce susceptibility to insect-caused mortality, and to accelerate development of old-growth characteristics, i. e. large trees with full crowns. Thinning will yield merchantible wood, as well. Shade-tolerant conifers, however, will likely regenerate in the understory of these stands. Periodic underburning or mechanical tree removal would be needed to retain fire resistance.

Regulation of species composition is a compelling part of density management. White fir, incense cedar and to a lesser degree, Douglas-fir, are shade-tolerant species that are easily established beneath an overstory. In the absence of fire, during the 20th century, they have undoubtedly contributed to increased stand density. In addition to increasing fuels and fuel ladders, these species compete with large ponderosa and sugar pine. They also increase shade within stands and thereby reduce the likelihood of natural pine establishment.

The desired density of forest stands depends upon management objectives, site productivity, species composition and age of the stands, and frequency of treatments. Stands that are being managed for spotted owls would undoubtedly have relatively dense overstories, as well as multiple understory layers. Whereas, those for which the objectives were reduced fuels and fire potential would be open with few trees and shrubs in the understory. For a given site quality or potential productivity, mixed conifer stands would be denser than ponderosa pine stands.

Managing stand density by thinning needs considerable planning and care. Slash resulting from thinning can be a fire hazard. Also, if stands are thinned in the spring, fresh slash may be habitat for bark beetles (populations of which could build up in the slash and then move to green trees). Not all snags, slash, or trees of poor vigor need to be removed. Some should be left for species that use cavities or depend upon dead wood. However, the abundance of dead wood that is left should not be sufficient to encourage build-up of bark beetles nor become hazardous fuels.

Timing treatments to the rate of stand development is an important consideration in density management of forest stands. The rate of stand development and future stand density and vigor must be anticipated. For example, young stands of ponderosa pine grow rapidly. If they become very dense, crowding causes individual tree crowns' size and density to decrease. In this condition, in addition to stands becoming more susceptible to insects, diameter growth decreases and height to diameter ratios increase. Thus, crowded stands are susceptible to snow and wind damage especially after thinning. According to Oliver (In Press) thinning regimes kept live crown ratios (percent of tree boles with crowns) from about 55 to 75 percent. All trees responded well to thinning although the western pine beetles were active in plots at high densities.

References

Assmann, E. 1970. *The principles of forest yield study*. Pergamon Press.New York, NY 506p.

Berryman, A. A. and G. T. Ferrell. 1988. The fir engraver beetle in the western United States (ed) A. A. Berryman. *Dynamics of forest insect populations: patterns, causes, implications*. Plenum Press, New York. p.555-577.

Daniel, T. W., Helms, J. A., and Baker, F.S. 1979. *Principles of silviculture*. McGraw Hill, New York. 500p.

Dunning, D. and L. H. Reineke. 1933. Preliminary yield tables for second-growth stands in the California pine regions. *U.S. Department of Agriculture Tech. Bulletin 354.* 23p.Washington D.C.

Ferrell, G. T. 1974. Moisture stress and fir engraver attack in white fir infected by tree mistletoe. *Canadian Journal of Entomology*. 106: 315-318.

_____. 1978. Moisture stress threshold of susceptibility to fir engraver beetles in pole size white fir. *Forest Science* 24: 85-92.

_____ 1980. Risk-rating systems for mature red fir and white fir in northern California. *U.S.D.A. Forest Service General Technical Report*. PSW-39, Berkeley, CA

_____. 1983. Growth, classification systems for red fir and white fir in northern California. *U.S.D.A. Forest Service General. Technical. Report*. PSW-72 Berkeley, CA

_____. 1989. Ten year risk-rating system for California red and white fir. *U.S.D.A. Forest Service General. Technical. Report*. PSW-115, Berkeley CA

Ferrell, G. T., W. J. Otrosing, and C. J. Demars, Jr. 1994. Predicting susceptibility of white fir during a drought associated outbreak of the fir engraver in California. *Canadian Journal of Forest Research* 24:302-305.

Ferrell, G. T. and R. Smith, Jr. 1976. Indicators of Fomes annosus and bark beetle susceptibility in sapling white fir. *Forest Science* 22: 365-369.

Meyer, W. H. 1938. Yield of evenage stands of ponderosa pine. *U.S.D.A. Forest Service Technical*, Bulletin. 630.Washington D.C.

Oliver, W. W. 1979. Fifteen year growth patterns after thinning a ponderosa-Jeffrey pine plantation in northeastern California. *U.S.D.A. Forest Service Research Paper. PSW-141*. 10p. Berkeley, CA

_____. 1984. Brush reduces growth of thinned ponderosa pine in northern California.*U.S.D.A. Forest Service Research Paper PSW-172*. Berkeley, CA

_____. 1988. Ten-year growth respsonse of a California red and white fir saw timber stand to several thinning intensities. *Western Journal of Applied Forestry.* 3: 41-43.

_____. 1990. Spacing and shrub competition influence 20-year development of planted ponderosa pine. *Western Journal of Applied Forestry* 5: 79-82.

_____. In Press. Growth and yield of planted ponderosa pine repeatedly thinned to different stand densities. *Western of Journal of Applied Forestry*

Oliver, W. W. and K. L. Dolph. 1992. Mixed conifer-seedling growth varies in response to overstory release. *Forest Ecology and Management.* 48: 179-183.

Reineke, L. H. 1933. Perfecting a stand-density index for even-aged forests. *Journal of Agricultural Research* 46: 627-638.

Schumacker, F. X. 1928. Yield, stand and volume tables for red fir in California. *University of California Agriculture Experiment. Station. Bulletin. 456.* Berkeley, CA

Schumacher, F. X., 1930. Yield, stand, and volume tables for white fir in California. University of California. Agriculture Experiment Station. Bulletin. 491.

Smith, D. M. 1986. *The practice of silviculture.* Wiley and Sons. New York. 527p.

JOHN C. TAPPEINER
USDI Forest and Rangeland Ecosystem
    Science Center
and
College of Forestry
Oregon State University
Corvallis, Oregon

PHILIP M. McDONALD
USDA Forest Service
Pacific Southwest Research Station
Redding, California

12

Regeneration of Sierra Nevada Forests

Sierra Nevada Ecosystem Project: Final report to Congress, vol. III, Assessments, Commissioned Reports, and Background Information. Davis: University of California, Centers for Water and Wildland Resources, 1996.

501

ABSTRACT

The purpose of this document is to summarize the literature and experience with regard to regeneration of Sierra Nevada forests. We have drawn heavily on studies that focus on the regeneration of mixed conifer and true fir forests--that is mainly on studies conducted in the Sierra Nevada on ponderosa and sugar pine, white fir, red fir and Douglas-fir. Most of Natural regeneration from seed, planting, and advanced regeneration can all be used to regenerate Sierra Nevada forests.

Regeneration is a critical part of forest management, because it helps to insure that forests maintain the desired species composition and stocking after fire, logging, insect epidemics or other distubances to the forest. We stress that the knowledge of the principles of forest regeneration alone does not insure successful regenration. On-site assesment of such factors as seed prodcution, potential affects from competing species, as well as planting techniques, and seedling handling in the nursery are most important. See Hobbs et al. (1992) for a thorough treatment of many phases of forest regeneration.

INTRODUCTION

The ability to regenerate forests after disturbances such as fire, timber harvest, housing developments, etc., is an important part of forest management in the Sierra Nevada. Methods of regeneration include: a) natural seedling establishment after disturbance, b) planting, and c) advanced regeneration - seedling, saplings already on the site prior to disturbance. All methods can be successful, but their use must be determined site by site after evaluating variables such as species of seed sources; microclimate; soils; potential competition from shrubs; vigor, species, and distribution of advanced regeneration; and the desired species composition of the future stand. In practice, combinations of these methods can be used, and sometimes all three may be used simultaneously.

On sites managed for timber production, federal and state regulations have a major influence on the method of regeneration used. Generally the regulations require that sites be regenerated within 3 to 5 years of the removal of the large trees in the stands. Thus managers often choose to plant in order to insure compliance with regulations.

The need to develop reliable methods to regenerate Sierra forest was recognized well over a half century ago (Dunning 1923). Large fires from mining, logging, and railroads had resulted in hundreds of thousands of acres of shrub fields, and it was apparent that they would return to forests only very slowly, and that the future stands would often be true fir, not mixed conifer.

Baker's (1955) analysis of regeneration practices in California was an important step in a concerted effort to develop reforestation practices for Sierra forests. He pointed out that summer drought and competition for soil water from shrubs and other vegetation were major variables in reforestation and that a seedling's ability to become established in these conditions depended upon its physiological condition, genetics (seed source) and often upon a reduction in competition to make soil moisture available to regeneration. Using these principles, from about 1955 through 1980 forest research and management organizations focused on the development of regeneration methods. This work resulted in guidelines for seed collection and handling, nursery production and planting of seedlings, and site preparation and vegetation controls (Schubert and Adam 1971). Major improvements for production and establishment of planting stock were being developed, and work on natural seedling establishment and effectiveness of advance regeneration was also underway during this period. In the 1960's it was recognized that competition from shrubs and sprouting hardwoods was affecting the growth and survial of conifer plantation, and consequently work was done to understand the nature of competition and how to control it (Conard and Radosevich 198 , McDonald and Fiddler 1993a, 1993b).

Natural Conifer Regeneration

Sierra Nevada conifers have the potential for successful natural regeneration on many sites. Most of today's Sierra Nevada forests were established naturally from seed. The key questions concerning natural regeneration is not if it will succeed but how long will it take, and what will be the stocking rate, species composition, structure, and growth rate of the next forest? In the interest of forest management for multiple resources, what is the role of natural regeneration? How can natural regeneration and planting be combined to insure a forest that provides future societies a range of options?

Factors Affecting Natural Regeneration

For natural regeneration to be successful, there must be adequate seed supply, and seedlings must germinate on microsites where there is a reasonable probability of survival. Sierra Nevada conifers collectively produce seed on a fairly regular basis. However, for any one species, annual production and years between adequate seed crops vary enormously (Tappeiner 1966, McDonald 1992). For example, Fowells and Schubert (1956), who studied cone and seed production from 1926 to 1953 in the central Sierra Nevada, report only about six adequate seed crops for ponderosa pine and three or four for sugar pine during this period. Cone and seed predation by insects, rodents (Tevis 1953) and birds were often high; over 30% of the pine cones produced, but only 10% of the white fir cones. Cone and seed production of the true firs is more consistent than for pines (Gordon 1986).

Seedfall and dispersal generally occur in September and October. During the winter, seed overcomes dormancy, but it is also susceptible to further predation. Beetham (1962) working in the southern Sierra Nevada found that seed predation of sugar pine and ponderosa pine was high, but it was negligible for incense cedar, white fir, and giant sequoia. Similarly Tevis (1953) found that chipmunks preferred seed of the pines to those of white fir and incense cedar. Predator preference for Douglas-fir cones and seed appears to be similar to sugar and ponderosa pine (Tappeiner 1966). Seed dispersal does not appear to be limiting where there has not been extensive disturbance. However, after large fires that kill many trees in young forests, lack of seed could substantially reduce the stocking of the next stand, and the rate of forest development.

Survival of first year conifer seedlings is strongly dependent upon microsite and weather. A favorable microsite (Ustin et al.1984, Laacke and Tomocheski 1986, Tappeiner and Helms 1971, Gordon 1970 and 1978, Stark 1963, Schubert 1956, Baker 1952) generally consists of:

1. a light shade that reduces the evaporative capacity of the air and the high and low extreme temperatures at the soil surface sites;

2. bare mineral soil or a fire or mechanical disturbance to the forest that reduces the habitat of pathogen, invertebrates and rodents (Baker 1951, Gordon 1970 and 1979, McDonald 1976a&b, 1973);

3. lack of vegetation that severely competes for light and soil water, or that produces heavy litter-fall that covers seedlings.

These three conditions are optimal for early seedling establishment; the extent to which they must be met depends upon variables such as weather, miocroclimate (slope, aspect), and species. For example, condition two appears to be more important for sugar pine and ponderosa pine than it does for true fir and incense cedar (Seter et al 1986, Tappeiner and Helms 1971). Conditions one and three might become less important on north-northeast slope during a relatively cool summer.

Note that timing of the occurrence of these conditions is also important. A fire may result in a mineral soil seed bed (#2) suitable for Douglas-fir, ponderosa or sugar pine, but these species might not produce seed for several years following the fire, or the seed source may be destroyed. After a fire, on many Sierra sites, a dense shrub community becomes established which would slowly (50+ years) be overtaken by white fir that become established beneath the shrubs. So the potential for either rapid growth of a pine stand or the very slow, gradual development of a fir stand depends upon the timing and coincidence of soil disturbance and seed production. Generally the true firs, especially white fir, can become established in low light environments on undisturbed forest floor . . . environments in which Douglas-fir and ponderosa pine would not survive. However, true fir growth is often very slow in these environments (Tappeiner and Helms 1971) and older seedlings (20-30+ years) may die if there is no disturbance to the overstory that increases light.

Natural regeneration of conifers has been studied under operational implementation of silvicultural systems. The strip and uniform shelter wood methods have resulted in successful regeneration of white and red fir (Gordon 1970, 1979, Laacke and Tomacheski 1986) and mixed conifer forests (McDonald 1976b, 1983, and Dunlap and Helms 1983).

Advance Regeneration

Advance regeneration of all species, but particularly of white fir, red fir, and incense cedar and tanoak often occurs in the understory of natural and managed stands. It is often the result of an opening of the canopy by thinning or windthrow, for example, or natural variation of canopy density. Populations of natural seedlings may be considered "seedling banks" (Grime 1981). Natural seedlings become established in the understory and grow slowly or persist for many years. If there is a disturbance to the overstory some may respond and become the new overstory trees. Also, older seedlings may die, and be replaced in the understory by new germinants (Tappeiner and McDonald 1984).

Several studies indicate that after release from overstory trees, advance regeneration will grow quite well and provide the stocking for a new stand (Tesch and Korpella 1993, Helms and Standiford 1985, Oliver 1985, Gordon 1973, Dunning 1923, and Van Alten 1959). The rate of growth of advanced regeneration after release can be predicted from measurement of pre-release live crown percent and annual height growth (Helms and Standiford 1985). Douglas-fir seedlings that are bent and otherwise damaged during logging may recover in about five years (Tesch et al. 1993). However, damage to white fir may cause serious stem decay (Aho and Filip 1982).

Advance regeneration may regenerate a stand after logging, windthrow or insect and disease mortality, but it is not likely to survive intense fire. On sites where advanced regeneration is irregularly distributed and composed of only shade-tolerant species it may be desirable to interplant with pine and/or Douglas-fir to insure a well-stocked mixed conifer stand. On dry sites, especially on the eastside of the Sierra, advanced ponderosa pine regeneration is much more common, but on some sites, interplanting may be used to insure sufficient stocking.

Conclusions

A summary of the literature and experience with natural regeneration of Sierra Nevada conifer indicates that:

> * Shade tolerant species such as California white fir, incense cedar, and red fir reproduce well in microsites ranging from exposed to shaded understory. The true fir species will seed into shrub communities, overtop them, and eventually produce pure stands.

> * Ponderosa pine, Douglas-fir, sequoias, and sugar pine will not reproduce reliably in shaded understory sites, nor in brushfields. Timing of disturbance to the forest floor in an open environment and seed availability is necessary for their establishment. In addition, competition from shrubs and grasses must be minimal for the first several years.

* A light shade aids early establishment. Too much shade will reduce later seedling growth.

* Natural regeneration of Sierra Nevada conifers can be used to regenerate sites after logging providing that there is a sufficient seed source, the proper microenvironment, and that forest managers can use the necessary treatments: for example, timing scarification of the forest floor to coincide with a seed crop; controlling grass and shrub communities.

* Use of advance regeneration is a good method of regenerating a stand after disturbance. Careful logging and interplanting with shade intolerant species are often required to insure future well-stocked mixed conifer stands.

Planting

The ability to successfully plant the major tree species is an important part of forest management of Sierra forests. Planting can be used, if needed, to rapidly regenerate sites after disturbance. It is also a method of keeping shade-intolerant species like ponderosa pine, sugar pine, and giant sequoia in the mixed conifer forests. For example, on many sites after a large, intense fire, pine seed may not be available for natural regeneration. Consequently, the site may be covered with stands of shrubs, which after 50+ years may be overtopped or replaced by white fir, since pine would not become established under a cover of shrubs. However, planting pines immediately after fire will generally insure that those species will be a part of the future stand.

Today there are at least five nurseries (both agency and commerical) that can produce conifer seedlings for reforestation of Sierra Nevadas species. The major environmental variable that constrains tree seedling establishment in Sierra forests is the summer drought. Variables such as browsing by vertebrates and invertebrates, cold spring or fall temperatures, or other factors are locally important, but periods of high temperatures and low precipitation often extending from late spring through early fall are of overriding importance. Seedlings must be in a physiological condition and in a microenvironment that enables them to survive on the water that is stored in the soil after the rains stop. This means that they must be able to produce roots that can extract water from the soil, and that the planting site is free of intense competition for soil water from other plants.

The original research on the physiology of ponderosa pine seedlings showed that nursery practices greatly influenced the seedlings' capacity to produce roots (Stone, and Schubert 1959; Stone et. al. 1962; Stone and Jenkinson 1970 and 1971). For example, if seedlings are lifted from the nursery bed too early in the fall, before cold weather has induced dormancy, or too late in the winter, when top growth has begun, their capacity to produce new roots is greatly reduced.

Jenkinson has continued this research using root growth capacity (RGC or the potential to produce new roots after being outplanted)) as an index of seedling vigor. He has documented that root growth capacity is directly related to survival of field planted seedlings (Jenkinson 1976, 1978, 1979, and 1980). Furthermore, the development of RGC in the nursery is dependent upon the seed source, and that it has a strong genetic component. For example, for some Sierra Nevada ponderosa seed sources RGC peaks about mid-January; some maintain high RGC from November to February, while RGC for other seed sources peaks in January or February (Jenkinson 1980). Similar patterns occur for red and white fir.

Sowing schedules also and seed handling are also important. Sowing sugar pine and Douglas-fir in the winter increases the vigor of the resulting seedlings. For example, sugar pine seedlings from February sowings averaged 1.4 to 2.1 times taller than those from April or May sowings (Jenkinson 1993b). Also, they were much less susceptible to soil borne pathogens and seedling survival was 5 times greater with early sowings. Apparently early sowing enables beneficial mycorrhizal infection of seedlings in the colder soils, while pathogenic fungi are favored by warmer soils. Later sowing (April and May) works well for ponderosa and Jeffrey pine, however.

The results of the work on seedling physiology can be summarized as "windows" within which nursery and outplanting operations should occur in order to maintain seedling RGC, and thus insure a high probability of survival of planted seedlings. Nursery sowing should be done early enough to avoid pathogen activity and enhance mycorrhizal infection of seedlings. A lifting window "opens" about December after a sufficient fall and early winter cold period and is generally "closed" in February or early March by warming and potential for top and root growth. Seedlings must be lifted during this window and put in cold storage to maintain their RGC.

A planting window occurs between the period of soil warming to 40°F+ in the spring and soil surface drying in the early summer. Actual dates vary with elevation and aspect of the planting site. Thus forest managers must schedule planting operations to correspond to the availability of warm soils with plentiful soil moisture. This often means that they must have access to cold storage facilities so that they can maintain RGC while waiting for proper planting conditions.

Vegetation Management

On most sites throughout the Sierra Nevada there is the potential for rapid establishment of shrubs, herbs, and grasses after disturbance from fire or logging. Control of competing vegetation and its effects on conifer stand establishment has received lots of attention from both forest management organizations and researchers, after it was recognized that competition from shrubs and herbaceous plants (sometimes along with poor quality planting stock) was often the cause of plantation failure. On some sites sprouting hardwoods are also a major component of the reestablishing vegetation. Buried seed of shrubs such as deerbrush, ceanothus, cherry and manzanita are often present on many sites. Disturbance stimulates their germination and a dense shrub community results. Also shrubs and hardwoods sprout from buds on below-ground burls or at the base of their stems. Bearclover and bracken fern often have a dense network of rhizomes below-ground from which aerial stems are produced after disturbance. On the east side of the Sierra, grasses are often the major invaders after disturbance.

Shurbs and herbs are an important part of forest stands because, for example, they provide habitat for various wildlife species, fix nitrogen on some sites, help stabilize soil nutrients, and prevent erosion. However, depending upon their density, these plants may be severe competitors not only with conifers, but among themselves. For example, dense covers of hardwoods (Harrington et al. 1991 and Hughes et al. 1987) will overtop and kill shrubs and herbs that are preferred browse, as well as causing conifer mortality or severely limiting conifer growth. McDonald and Fiddler (1989) documented the effect of manzanita on a native grass (Stipa sp.) and found that Stipa density ranged from 50,000 plants/acre on sites where there was little manzanita to only 553 plants/acre on sites well stocked with manzanita.

In the Sierra Nevada, the major impact of shrubs and hardwoods is likely to be on the species composition of the next stand. Ponderosa and sugar pine and Douglas-fir are generally not likely to become established under a dense cover of shrubs. The true firs, especially white fir are best suited to these conditions. If pine and Douglas-fir seed is present and germinate within 1-2 years after disturbance then it is likely that these species will be present in the next stand. If not, the stand will probably remain a shrub community for many years (50+ yr) and then slowly be overtopped by white fir, providing a fir seed source is present.

The effects of competition on conifer growth is well understood (Walstad and Kuch 1987, Tappeiner et al.1991 ,McDonald and Fiddler 1989). Competition reduces conifer seedlings growth in both height and diameter, and it may make them susceptible to insects as well as grazing damage from rodents and ungulates (McDonald and Radosevich 1992, Tappeiner and Radosevich 1982). In many cases competition for soil moisture, combined with damage, results in seedling mortality. For example, McDonald and Radosevich (1992) reported that survival of 8-year-old ponderosa pine seedlings was reduced from 90% of maximum to less than 20% as shrub biomass increased form about 1000 kg/ha to 7000+ kg/ha. Most shrub communities in the Sierra are capable of producing well over 7000 kg/ha above ground biomass (Hughes et al. 1987).

The options for controlling competing vegetation during conifer regeneration include mulching to control grasses and herbs, manual control by cutting or grubbing, grazing and herbicides. McDonald and Fiddler (1993) have recently evaluated these alternatives for the Sierras. Based on their 40 studies in a range of vegetation types in California, and on other research, they concluded that all methods will release conifer seedlings from severe competition and enable the development of a new stand. Because herbicides were effective in controlling shrubs, the density or numbers of herbs and grasses was usually greater following their use of herbicides, than after manual treatments or grazing.

The land managers' objectives and costs also dictate the choice of methods. If regeneration and a new stand of conifers is important, then release is needed only to insure survival and eventual growth of enough trees of the proper species to produce the desired future stand. This may require only a spotwise manual cutting of shrubs or hand application of herbicide. No treatment at all may be needed if conifer are established soon after disturbance and/or only moderately dense shrub communities develop. If, on the other hand, rapid stand growth for cover, slope stabilization or wood production is desired, then more intensive treatments will be considered. As stated above, state and federal regulations regarding the time required to establish regeneration will also affect the decision on methods of vegetation control.

Literature Cited

Aho, P. E., and G. M. Filip. 1982. Incidence of wounding and Echinodontium tinclorium infestation in advanced white fir regeneration. *Canadian Journal of Forest Research* 12:705-708.

Baker, F. S. 1942. Reproduction of ponderosa pine at low elevations in the Sierra Nevada. *Journal of Forestry* 40:401-404.

Baker, F. S. 1951. Reproduction of pine on old railroad grades in California. *Journal of Forestry* 49:577.

Baker, F. S. 1955. *California forest regeneration problems.* State of California Division of Forestry, Sacramento, CA. 45p.

Beetham, N. M. 1962. *The ecological tolerance range of the seedling stage of Sequoia gigantea.* Dissertation Abstracts 24:479-480.

Conard, S. G., and S. R. Radosevich. 1982. Post-fire succession of white fir in the northern Sierra Nevada. *Madrono* 29: 42-56.

Dunning, D. 1923. Some results of cutting in the Sierra Nevada forests of California. *U.S. Department of Agriculture Technical Bulletin 1176.*

Dunlap, J. M., and J. A. Helms. 1983. First year growth of planted Douglas and white fir seedlings under different shelterwood regimes. *Forest Ecology and Management* 5:255-268.

Fowells, H. A., and G. H. Schubert. 1951. Natural reproduction in certain cutover pine-fir stands. *Journal of Forestry* 49:192-196.

_____ and _____. 1956. Seed crops of forest trees in the pine region of California. *U.S. Department of Agriculture Technical Bulletin 1150.*

Fowell, H. A., and N. Stark. 1965. Natural regeneration in relation to environment in the mixed conifer forest type of California. *U.S. Department of Agriculture, Forest Service Research Paper PSW 24,* Berkeley, CA

Gordon, D. T. 1970. Natural regeneration of white and red fir--influence of several factors. *U.S. Department of Agriculture, Forest Service Research Paper PSW 58*, Berkeley, CA.

_____ 1973. Released advanced reproduction of white and red fir...growth, damage, mortality. *U.S. Department of Agriculture, Forest Service Research Paper PSW 95*, Berkeley, CA.

_____1978. White and red fir cone production in northeastern California: Report of a 16 year study. *U.S. Department of Agriculture, Forest Service Research Paper PSW 99*, Berkeley, CA. 12p.

Gordon, D. T. 1979. Successful natural regeneration cuttings in California true fir. *U.S. Department of Agriculture, Forest Service , Research Paper PSW 140*, Berkeley, CA.

Grime, J. P. 1979. *Plant strategies and vegetation processes.* John Wiley and Sons, New York, 222p.

Harrington, T. B., J. C. Tappeiner and T. F. Hughes. 1991.Predicting average growth and size distributions of Douglas-fir saplings competing with sprout clumps of tanoak or Pacific madrone. *New Forests* 5:109-130.

Helms, J. A., and R. B. Standiford. 1985. Predicting release of advanced reproduction of mixed conifer species in California following overstory removal. *Forest Science* 31:3-15p.

Hobbs, S. D. S. D. Tesch, P. W. Oyston, R. E. Stewart, J. C. Tappeiner, G. E. Wells. 1992. Reforestation practices in southwestern Oregon and northern California. *Forest Research Lab, Oregon State University,* Corvallis, OR, 465p.

Hughes, T. F., C. R. Latt, J. C. Tappeiner, and M. Newton. 1987. Biomass and leaf area estimates for varnish-leaf ceanothus, deerbrush, and white leaf manzanita. *Western Journal of Applied* Forestry 2:124-128p.

Jameson, E. W. 1952. Food of deer mice Peromyscus maniculatus and P. boylei in the northern Sierra Nevada. California *Journal of Mammology* 33:50-60p.

Jenkinson, J. L. 1980. Improving plantation establishment by optimizing growth capacity and planting times of western yellow pine. *U.S. Department of Agriculture, Forest Service Research Paper PSW-154*, Berkeley, CA. 22p.

Jenkinson, J. L. and A. H. McCain. 1993. Winter sowings produce 1-0 sugar pine planting stock in the Sierra Nevada. *U.S. Department of Agriculture, Forest Service Research Paper PSW-RP-219.* Albany, CA. 10p.

Jenkinson, J. L., J. A. Nelson, and Mary Huddleson. 1993. Improving planting stock quality--the Humboldt Experience. *U.S. Department of Agriculture, Forest Service General Technical Report PSW-GTR-143*, Berekeley, CA 219p.

Laacke, R. J., and J. H. Tomascheski. 1986. Shelterwoodregeneration of true fir conclusions after eight years. *U.S. Department of Agriculture, Forest Service Research Paper PSW 184*, Berkeley, CA. 7p.

Laacke, R. J., and G. O. Fiddler. 1986. Overstory removal: stand factors related to success and failure. *U.S. Department of Agriculture, Forest Service Research Paper ,PSW 183,* 6p.

McDonald, P. M. 1970. Seed dispersal in small clearcuttings in north-central California. U.S. Department of Agriculture, Forest Service Research Paper PSW 150, Berkeley, CA. 5p.

McDonald, P. M. 1976a. Forest Regeneration and seedling growth from five major cutting methods in north-central California. *U.S. Department of Agriculture, Forest Service Research Paper, PSW 115*, Berkeley, CA.

_____.1976b. Shelterwood cutting in a young-growth mixed conifer stand in north- central California. *U.S. Department of Agriculture, Forest Service Research Paper 117,* Berkeley, CA.

_____.1978. *Silviculture - Ecology of three native California Hardwoods on high sites in north central California* PhD Thesis, Oregon State University, Corvallis, OR. 309p.

_____.1983. Clearcutting and natural regeneration management implications for the northern Sierra Nevada. *U.S. Department of Agriculture, Forest Service Technical Report 70,* Berkeley, CA.

_____. 1992. Estimating seed crops of conifer and hardwood species. *Canadian Journal of Forest Research* 22: 832-838.

McDonald, P. M., and G. O. Fiddler. 1993a. Feasibility of alternatives to herbicides in young conifer plantations in California. *Canadian Journal of Forest Research* 2015-2022.

_____and _____. 1993b.Vegetative trends in a youngconifer plantation after 10 yrs of grazing by sheep. *U.S. Department of Agriculture,Forest Service Research Paper PSW-RP-215,* Albany CA., 9p.

Oliver, W. W. 1985. Growth of California red fir advanced reproduction after overstory removal and thinning.*U.S. Department of Agriculture, Forest Service Research Paper PSW 180,* Berkeley, CA. 6p.

_____1986. Growth of California red fir advanced regeneration after overstory removal and thinning. *U.S. Department of Agriculture, Forest Service Research Paper PSW 180,* Berkeley, CA.

Schubert, G. H. 1956. Early survival and growth of sugar pine and white fir in clear cut openings. *U.S. Forest Service, California Forest and Range Experiment Station, Research note 117,* Berkeley, California

Schubert, G. H. , and R. S. Adams. 1971. *Reforestation practices for conifers in California,* State of California, Division of Forestry, Sacramento, CA. 359p.

Selter, C. M., W. D. Pitts, and M. G. Barbour. 1986. Site microenvironment and seedling survival of Shasta red fir. *American Midland Naturalist* 115:288-300p.

Stark, N. 1963. Natural regeneration of Sierra Nevada mixed conifers after logging. *Journal of Forestry* 63:456-60.of California.

Tappeiner, J. C. 1967. *Natural r egeneration of Douglas-fir and white fir in the SierraNevada of Califronia,* Phd Thesis , University of California, Berkekey, 237p.

Tappeiner, J. C., and J. A. Helms. 1971. Natural   regeneration of Douglas-fir and white fir in the Sierra Nevada of California. *American Midland Naturalist* 86:358-370p.

Tappeiner, J. C., and P. M. McDonald. 1984. Development of tanouk understories in conifer stands. *Canadian Journal of Forest Research* 14:271-277p.

511

Tesch, S. D., K. B. Katz, and E. J. Korpela. 1993. Recovery of Douglas-fir seedlings and saplings wounded during overstory removal. *Canadian Journal of Forest Research.* 23:1684-1694.

Tesch, S. D., and E. J. Korpella. 1993. Douglas-fir and white fir advanced regeneration for renewal of mixed conifer forests. *Canadian Journal of Forest Research.* 23:1427-1437.

Tevis, L. P. 1953. Effect of vertebrate animals on the seed crop of sugar pine. *Journal of Wildlife Management* 1 7:128-131p.

Ustin, S. L., R. A. Woodward, M. G. Barbour, and J. L. Hatfield. 1984. Relationships between sunfleck dynamics and red fir seedling distribution. *Ecology* 65:1420-1428.

Von Althen, F. W. 1959. *A contribution to the study of edge effects on the regeneration of small forest openings in the Sierra Nevada.* M. F. Professional paper. Forestry, University of California, Berkeley

Worthington, N. P. 1953. Reproduction following small group cuttings in Douglas-fir. *Research note 85. U.S. Department of Agriculture, Forest Service*, Pacific Northwest Forest and Range Experiment Station.

MIKE LANDRAM
USDA Forest Service
Pacific Southwest Region
San Francisco, California

13

Status of Reforestation on National Forest Lands Within the Sierra Nevada Ecosystem Project Study Area

Sierra Nevada Ecosystem Project: Final report to Congress, vol. III, *Assessments, Commissioned Reports, and Background Information.* Davis: University of California, Centers for Water and Wildland Resources, 1996.

ACKNOWLEDGEMENTS

Many people were involved in this effort. I would like to thank John Tappeneir and John Fiske for asking the questions and for guidance. The mapping and inventory products used in this report were produced by the Forest Service Remote Sensing Lab and Pacific Meridian Resources in Sacramento. Refining and interpreting that information would not have been possible without Ralph Warbington's program support, Deborah Nicoll's computer support, and many a helpful session with Kevin Casey, Kama Kennedy, Mark Rosenburg and Eric Spry. Analysis of the mapping and inventory products was made possible by the people at SNEP GIS; I want to thank Karen Gabriel and Russ Jones for periodic assistance and most especially John Gabriel, creator of GIS map products and queries that became the heart of this analysis. Additional thanks goes to Richard Teck of the Timber Management Support Center in Fort Collins for help with the visualization graphics and FVS support, Chris Riper of SNEP for the graphics work on current plantation condition, Larry Wilson (contractor) for programming and graphics display of the variation among sample points, Chuck Stadelman of the Regional Office for programming Stand Record System reports, the Silviculture Development Unit in Redding (Gary Fiddler, Walt Leonard, Eric Yerkes, and crew) for field inventories, and Bill Hay of the Regional Office for computer support with the document. Those that provided peer reviews added immeasurably to the final product. For those reviews, I would like to thank John Helms, John Fiske, Bob Rogers, Dave Bakke, Ralph Warbington, Doug Leisz, and 3 SNEP reviewers whose identity is unknown to me.

ABSTRACT

The reforestation program on national forest lands within the SNEP Study Area is successful; stocking objectives are achieved in the near term (within 5 years of harvest or planting) on 80% to 90% of the land where reforestation is needed depending on the method used to evaluate success. Older plantations are growing at rates sufficient to meet the modelled expectations in forest plans. Four-percent of the total forestland consisted of plantations in 1991 (estimated at 5% in 1995). Inventory statistics for 170,000 acres planted before 1981 are provided. Current declining survival rates, reductions in workforce size, potential reduction in workforce skill, decline in funds, decline in organizational consensus to reforest, and a plethora of often competing objectives converging on areas that need reforestation all increase risks of reforestation failures in the near term. The likelihood of inadequate plantation maintenance is increasing with reduced funding and workforce size.

Keywords: reforestation, wood, wildlife, wildfire, vegetation management, fuel management, thinning, shrubs, databases

TABLE OF CONTENTS

Appendix A - Reforestation Success Rate Calculations

Appendix B - Status of Reforestation after Final Harvest

Appendix C - Older Plantation Projected Average Volume at Age 55

Appendix D - Land Area Table

Appendix E - Status of Plantation Inventories

Appendix F - Wildlife Habitat Relationships Stages

Appendix G - Current Plantation Condition Graphics

Appendix H - Variation Among Inventory Sample Points

Appendix I - Traditional Program Indicators

PURPOSE

This report was commissioned by John Tappeiner for the Sierra Nevada Ecosystem Project. Its purpose is to develop information about reforestation on national forests within the study area. The National Forests included are the Modoc, Lassen, Plumas, Tahoe, Eldorado, Stanislaus, Inyo, Sierra, and Sequoia. The following set of questions were asked and have been answered in this report:

1. How successful is the Forest Service reforestation program?

2. Is plantation tree growth sufficient to meet Forest Service wood production objectives in forest plans?

3. What is the extent of plantations on the national forests?

4. Over what period of time has plantation acreage accumulated?

5. What are the number, size, and acreage characteristics of plantations planted after fire compared to after harvest?

6. How much older plantation acreage is in each of the various forest types?

7. What kind of wildlife habitats are provided by the older plantations?

8. What is the proportion of different tree species in the older plantations?

9. How does shrub cover compare to tree cover in the older plantations, and what are the most common shrub species?

10. What are the mortality trends in the older plantations?

11. What is the average plantation structure in older plantations?

12. How variable are the older plantations?

CONCLUSIONS AND OUTLOOK FOR THE FUTURE

The knowledge, skills, organization, and desire to reforest lands that have been burned, harvested, or otherwise denuded is evidenced by the substantial inventory of plantations established since about 1960 (over 300,000 acres). The Forest Service has successfully reforested most locations where it set out to do so (80%-90% near term depending on method used to evaluate). Current declining survival rates (variety of causes), reductions in workforce size, potential reduction in workforce skill, decline in funds, decline in organizational consensus to reforest, and a plethora of often competing objectives converging on areas that need reforestation all increase risks of reforestation failures in the near term. The likelihood of inadequate plantation maintenance is increasing with reduced funding and workforce size.

The proportion of forest land affected by the reforestation program to date is small and current rates of treatment are declining as regeneration harvesting declines. The annual acreage planted will soon return to the average level experienced in the 1970s. Regeneration harvests are changing both in type and in quantity. Most of the anticipated near term reforestation will occur on burned lands that have been harvested. The eastern portions of the Plumas and Tahoe National Forests and the south end of the Stanislaus National Forest have the largest burned areas in need of reforestation.

The fire hazard effected by the current condition of plantations established in the 1960s and 1970s is a concern. Shrub removal, dead and down fuel removal, and pruning of lower tree limbs would lower the hazard. Funding available for investments in hazard reduction is not likely on a large scale. As tree crowns close and intertree competition affects more acreage, combined thinnings and reduction of shrub densities would lower the hazard. This will likely happen as trees attain a merchantable size. It will happen sooner in locations that have a market for small sized material.

The knowledge, skills, organization, and desire to monitor and report on the status of reforestation is less evident than the reforestation itself. Available maps and records contain some inaccuracies, making assessment and disclosure problematic. The techniques developed and results described in this report represent state of the art, yet accuracy remains limited. The outlook for substantial improvements in this area is neutral because improvements in availability of Geographic Information Systems (GIS) and other technology will be offset with reductions in skilled and experienced employees, available field time, and opportunities to manage more complete and accurate databases.

INTRODUCTION

The reforestation program in the Pacific Southwest Region of the Forest Service, like most forest management programs, has experienced increasing scrutiny in the 1990s. Reforestation success is a primary current issue. Although substantial investments in monitoring for tree survival, stocking, and release needs have been made on each planted stand; the need to ascertain and communicate reforestation success in a comprehensive way, addressing the entire landbase, is relatively new. Consequently, efforts to do just that are also relatively new. This report is another step toward fullfilling that need.

Reforestation practices are generally well understood and documented (Schubert, 1971. USDA-FS, 1983. Hobbs, 1992). The last major Region 5 Forest Service assessment of the program dealt with its vegetation management aspects (USDA-FS, 1988). Additional information on reforestation, or regeneration, is contained in Helms and Tappenier, 1995.

Terms and Definitions

Afforestation - The establishment of trees on an area from which they have always been absent in modern history.

Artificial reforestation - The purposeful collection of tree seed that is subsequently distributed elsewhere in the forest or that is grown into seedlings in a nursery and subsequently planted.

Basal area - The cross sectional area (expressed in square feet per acre) of tree stem measured at a point 4 1/2 feet above the ground surface; a measure of density.

Forest land - Land that is now or is naturally capable of being occupied by more than a 10% cover of trees.

Natural reforestation - The reliance on seed falling from trees that reside on or near the location where reforestation is desired.

Quadratic mean diameter - The diameter of a tree of average basal area.

Reforestation - The establishment of trees on an area from which they were present but have been removed.

Reforestation success - There is no one generally accepted definition for this term. The term generally refers to the characteristics of new tree establishment that satisfy owner objectives. These characteristics typically include measures of tree condition at points in time at levels of cost. This report will look at "success" in a variety of ways.

Stocked - As used in this report, stocked means the area of interest contains a level of stocking that meets or exceeds objectives. In practice, objectives vary from stand to stand in response to the variety of multiple uses for which plantations are managed. This report, by necessity, simplifies criteria to facilitate analysis at the SNEP study area scale.

Stocking - As used in this report, stocking refers to the quantity of trees of desirable species and condition on an area of interest.

Reforestation History

Artificial Reforestation - Little was known about either artificial or natural reforestation in California when the Forest Service began experimenting around 1905 (Ayers, 1958). An unknown quantity of land, extensive enough to attract attention, had been burned or logged and was occupied by vegetation other than the desired trees. Experiments in artificial reforestation were conducted off and on from about 1905 to 1930, by which time enough had been learned about seeding, nursery practices, planting techniques, and subsequent care that investments in operational-scale reforestation (hundreds of acres per year) seemed justified. Seeding experiments had generally unreliable results, so further efforts focused primarily on planting. Planting on an operational scale occurred from 1930 to 1945. About 6,000 acres of plantations from this time period persist today. Overall success remained fairly low, however (Fowells, 1948). Operational problems with nursery management, control of competing vegetation, and animal damage were paramount. The seeding done during this period once again proved generally unsuccessful. Efforts continued from 1945 to 1960 in similar fashion, resulting in another 20,000 acres that persist today. Most of the earlier operational problems were overcome during this period (Buck, 1974). Large wildfires during the period also served to elevate the need to reforest. Regeneration harvesting (creates openings that need reforestation) designed for artificial reforestation began operationally in the 1960s , increased slowly in the 1970s, rapidly in the 1980s, and is now in decline. The combination of ability to reforest, the increasing acreage in openings created by harvest and wildfires, and a desire to grow more wood led to plans calling for an increase in the amount of reforestated land. The rate of reforestation increased during the 1960s, decreased in the 1970s, increased again in the 1980s, and is now decreasing as regeneration harvesting declines.

Natural Reforestation and Cutting Practices - The total acreage reforested through natural seeding following harvest, wildfire, or other disturbances is unknown. Emphasis and dependence on natural reforestation varied significantly on Forest Service lands. The following discussion describes policies, cutting practices, and what we know about the results for four periods: 1905-1945, 1945-1960, 1960-1990, and 1991-present.

Tree harvests under Forest Service administration were conducted from about 1905 to 1945 in such a way to encourage natural reforestation (Buck, 1974). About 40% to 80% of the merchantable volume was cut, the most healthy individuals being left to parent the next generation; species or individuals with low market value were often left (Buck, 1974. Dunning, 1923). These harvests occurred on an undetermined amount of land but probably covered less than 5% of the forest land in total (less than 400,000 acres). In modern silviculture terminology, these harvests were shelterwood seed cuts. Generally, slash was burned after harvests and no further action was taken. No attempt to monitor results in a systematic fashion was made. Subsequent natural establishment of tree seedlings was highly variable, extremely successful in places and extremely unsuccessful in others. No formal reforestation records were kept. These land areas are spatially-lost in history. Most likely, these areas appear in one of several current inventoried conditions. Some probably failed to reforest, have never been planted, and are now mapped as sparsely stocked forest land. Some were probably planted and are now mapped as plantations. Some were probably successful and are now mapped as well stocked natural stands. Some were probably partially successful and are now mapped as poor to medium- stocked natural stands.

From 1945 to 1960, the creation of openings with a natural reforestation objective was de-emphasized in favor of salvage of timber over large land areas that would otherwise become unmerchantable; construction of a road system was desired and financed by this type of cutting (Buck, 1974). About 15% to 30% of the merchantable volume was cut, concentrating on individuals with the poorest health or form. In modern silviculture terminology, these harvests were a combination of thinnings, sanitation, and salvage cuttings. Thousands of acres were cut during this period in this fashion; some of which had been aquired from private owners after removal of the best quality trees.

From 1960 through 1990, various combinations of thinning, salvage, and increasing amounts of even-aged regeneration harvests (clearcuts and seed cuts; mostly followed by artificial reforestation) were employed. Delineation of land areas (stands) that could be mapped, treated, and monitored became increasingly common place, especially where regeneration harvests occurred. Harvest levels reached a peak in the late 1980s. Reliance on natural reforestation declined steadily through the 1960s, reaching the stable and low level in the 1970s which persists today. Rarely relied on in planting operations today, natural seedlings commonly supplement stocking of planted seedlings.

From 1991 to date, even-aged regeneration harvests have been de-emphasized in favor of uneven-aged regeneration harvests (selection cuts or group selection cuts) and thinnings. Salvage after fire or drought induced insect mortality is increasing. Total harvest levels are declining. Natural reforestation remains a supplemental practice.

Assessing the Reforestation Program

Program Level Indicators - This report is limited by the data available at a regional office. Knowledge that would improve its accuracy exists in Ranger district offices but is impratical to access.

Traditional Regional indicators (Appendix I) used to manage the program are:

- A set of annual reports that disclose seedling survival, acreage accomplishments (planting, associated treatments), certification of success, and future reforestation needs (USDA-FS, 1956-1965. USDA-FS, 1966-1994). These reports have been analyzed in this effort. They are not spatial (they do not report on individual plantations; maps are kept in district offices) and do not link to events of prior years.

- Funding levels, both appropriated by Congress and retained from timber sale proceeds under authority of the Knudson-Vandenburg Act (KV).

- Funding requests by the Forests to the Region for the various reforestation treatments.

- Unit costs (the cost per acre to accomplish a given reforestation treatment).

Evolving present and future indicators are:

- Stand records, which have been automated and available to program managers since 1989 (USDA-FS, 6/95, SRS). Although they are not currently linked to computerized Geographic Information Systems (GIS) which are spatial, they do have spatial characteristics and events are partly linkable to events of prior years. These records are the current source for the annual reports mentioned above. The reforestation aspects of these records have been analyzed in this effort.

- Vegetation mapping and inventory for the entire SNEP Study Area, using consistent methodology and including plantations (USDA-FS, 6/95, FIA), became available in GIS for the first time in 1995; part of an increasingly sophisticated inventory program that was accelerated in response to emerging bioregional issues, primarily the California Spotted Owl. The new inventories have been analyzed in this effort.

Stand Level Indicators - Section 4 (d)(1) of the National Forest Management Act (NFMA) states "that all forested lands...shall be maintained in appropriate forest cover with species of trees, degree of stocking, rate of growth, and conditions of stand designed to secure the maximum benefits of multiple use sustained yield management in accordance with land management plans." It goes on to require that "All...lands treated...shall be examined after the first and third growing seasons and certified...as to stocking rate".

The Region 5 certification criteria (USDA-FS, July, 1991), applied at the stand level, are:

- A minimum number of established commercial trees per acre by forest type and site class.
- At least 50 percent stocked plots. "Stocked" means meets the minimum number criterium.
- Stocking well distributed over the area.

The minimum numbers and distribution criteria are assigned by silviculturists on a stand by stand basis, given overall forest plan and project level management direction.

FINDINGS

Question 1 - *How successful is the Forest Service reforestation program?*

Answer: The program is about 80% to 90% successful, depending on the method used to evaluate success.

Methods and Discussion:

There is no one generally accepted professional standard for defining, measuring, or describing success of an entire reforestation program. Three methods are offered here.

Method 1

This method considers *year of planting* as a beginning point. About 90% of the acres initially planted between 1988 and 1992 were stocked at time of last survey. The success rate after harvest is about the same as it is after fire (Appendix A).

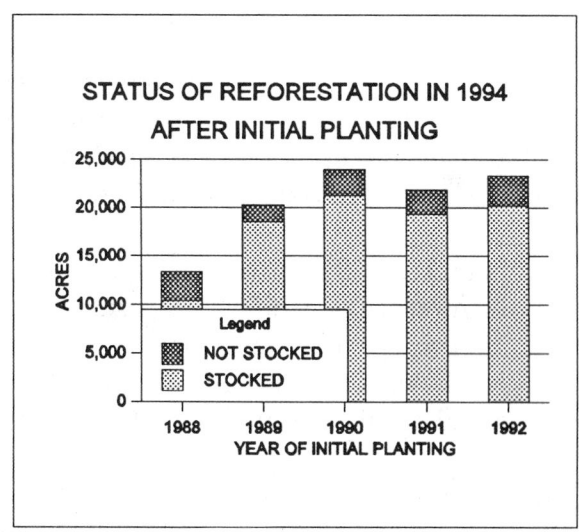

The automated Stand Record System (SRS) provided the basis for these statements (USDA-FS, 6/95, SRS). Each ranger district maintains a computer database of historical, current, and planned future events for each stand where such events are being tracked. There are 37 ranger districts, and therefore 37 databases, within the SNEP study area. The databases are physically located in Kansas City, Missouri; they are accessed remotely. The system was installed in 1989; since record keeping priorities emphasize the present over the past, it is more likely that the record of events is more complete and accurate from 1989 on than from prior years. The contents of the databases change daily at the discretion of district employees. Mylar maps indicating the location of stands are kept at the district offices; they are not available electronically.

Initial planting is defined as the first time an area is planted during reforestation. The initial planting records also contain, as an *option*, the ability to identify the disturbance that caused the need to reforest (usually fire or harvest). All plantings subsequent to the initial planting are referred to as replantings.

Stocking surveys are required by law at the end of the first and third growing seasons after planting. The stocking survey records in SRS contain, at local *option*, the ability to store an estimate of the number of *trees per acre* found. Another *option* on those records indicates that conditions are ***progressing*** toward meeting objectives for quantity, distribution, and quality of desired tree species.

When objectives are ensured without further treatments, a record that ***"certifies"*** reforestation is stored in SRS. Those that make the decisions to certify have a conservative bias. There is a tendency to withhold certification until the likelihood of tree persistence is virtually certain. Even low risks of fire, insect damage, animal damage, or dessication from moisture competition with competing vegetation are often viewed as cause to withhold certification. As a result, compliance with the policy of making certification determinations and documenting those determinations is sporadic.

Given the above, the 37 databases were queried for places initially planted between 1988 and 1992. Queries for early years were made; records in the database from earlier years are not sufficiently present for this analysis. The years 1993 and 1994 were excluded because insufficient time has passed to conduct a third-year survey.

For purposes of this analysis, the term "stocked" is defined as:
1. A record of certification exists, or
2. A record of survey indicating a progression toward certification exists, or
3. The total trees per acre on the last survey date exceed 149, which is the standard used for mixed conifer type in Regional scale planning .

The result was 89,789 stocked acres out of 102,771 planted acres, indicating a success rate of 87%. Separating the areas between those where fire created the reforestation need and those where harvest created the need, did not indicate any significant difference in success. Appendix A contains supporting data tables. No effort was made to quantify why 13% of the total do not meet the "stocked" criteria. In some cases, no record of survey exists on the databases. In other cases, additional treatments are planned but have not been carried out.

Method 2

This method considers *year of harvest* as a beginning point. Seventy-nine percent of the area that received regeneration harvests (including fire salvage) in 1988 and 1989 were stocked at the end of 1994. Thirteen percent of the area had not been planted pending availability of herbicides to control competing vegetation. Several reasons account for delay on 7% of the area, which is scheduled for planting or replanting. 1% of the area is not stocked and no further attempt to reforest is anticipated due to a change in land allocation (Appendix B). *Note:* It is typical for an area to be planted one or more years after the year in which it was harvested.

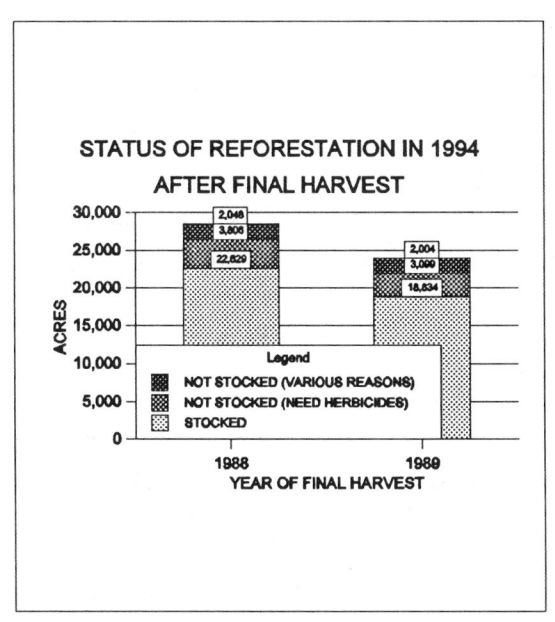

These results come from recent attempts (1993-1994) by the Forest Service to standardize reporting of reforestation status after harvest. The automated stand record system has been helpful, but not completely reliable, due to missing data or acreage imbalances on the records. The general results (see Appendix B) are reliable.

Method 3

Comparing historic reports of acres planted in a particular year to current inventory of acres that originated in that same year implies a lower than intuitive success rate and indicates difficulties with available information; this comparison is unreliable as an indicator of success.

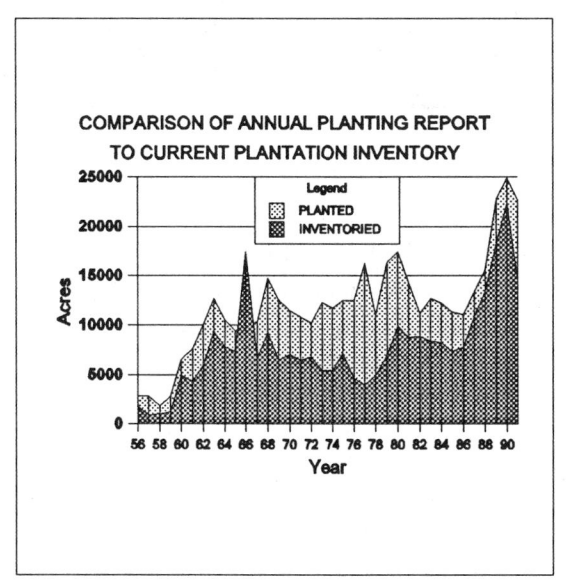

The current inventory of plantation acres is based on GIS plantation layers that have been incorporated into the Pacific Southwest Region's forest mapping program; they are available as part of comprehensive vegetation maps. These plantation layers were constructed by ranger district employees, using local records and 1991 imagery that shows openings in the forest. Most of them were constructed in late 1991, and include areas planted in that year. Each stand is labeled with a year of plantation origin corresponding to the year of planting. The accuracy of historic information with which to prepare and label these maps varies; they represent the best available information on location and age of plantations.

The annual planting reports, on file in the Regional Office, disclose acreage planted by year; however, these acres have no locations associated with them.

An adequate comparison of the mapped acres with the acres reported as reforested was impossible for the following reasons:

- Planting reports mix initial planting and replanting (sometimes done because of failure, to increase stocking; or to add new species) together and should, therefore, be reduced by the amount of replanting before making a comparison. There is no way to determine how much of the total planting is replanting for most of the period. *Note:* it is possible to make that split from 1988 forward. For the period 1988 through 1991, replanting accounted for 8% of the total.

- The year of origin on the plantation maps is not always the year of initial planting. Where site preparation had to be repeated, the year of replanting is recorded as the year of origin.

- The minimum mapping size for the plantation maps is 5 acres, but smaller reforested areas were included in the reports. There is no way to determine how much of the total planting was done on areas less than 5 acres in size for most of the period. *Note:* It is possible to make that split from automated stand records from about 1988 forward. For the period 1988 through 1991, areas less than 5 acres accounted for about 3% of the total.

- Some plantations have burned. The acreage is not known but is likely less than 3%.

- Some older plantations, having developed sufficient crown closure and crown diameter resembling natural stands, are no longer identified as plantations on the plantation maps. The extent of area in this condition is unknown, but is likely not significant.

Question 2 - *Is plantation tree growth sufficient to meet Forest Service wood production objectives in forest plans?*

Answer: Yes.

The 170,000 acres reforested before 1981, based on projection of current inventory, will exceed cubic foot per acre volumes used in forest plan modeling (Appendix C).

AGE (yrs)	PROJECTED VOLUME (merch. cu. ft./ac.)	FOREST PLAN VOLUME (merch. cu. ft./ac.)
55	3,600	3,400

* Forest Vegetation Simulator projection of current inventory

** RAMPREP bare-ground projection

Methods and Discussion:

Forest Plan Volume

The planned yield of 3,400 cubic feet per acre at age 55 is based on planning records on file in the Regional Office. The current forest plans in the SNEP study area were developed during the 1980s. A computer projection model named RAMPREP was used to forecast timber yields (Levitan, 1991). Estimates were made for regenerated stands on every national forest, by forest vegetation type and site class. These yield tables predict total volume per acre by decade (10 year increments). The time when trees attain an average diameter of 13 inches was estimated to be the first time that a commercial harvest could be made. That time varies with site quality, level of stocking, and species. In the SNEP study area, there is more plantation acreage in the Mixed Conifer Type than any other, and the average site quality is R-5 Site Class III. Forest plan modeling assumed Site Class III areas would attain an average diameter of 13 inches at age 55. In the planning process, yield tables functioned as input to an optimizing routine called FORPLAN, which schedules harvests of different types on different land areas subject to different constraints. The time scheduled by FORPLAN for harvest in regenerated stands varies from forest to forest. Not all forest plans schedule harvest (thinnings) in plantations at age 55. For purposes of this comparison, that complexity is ignored; if yields can meet RAMPREP, they will also meet any delayed entry scheduled by FORPLAN. Most of the RAMPREP regenerated yield tables are on file in the Regional Office; values from them are:

RAMPREP VOLUME AT AGE 55 FOR SITE CLASS III MIXED CONIFER	
FOREST	NET CUBIC FOOT YIELD PER ACRE
MODOC	2,880
LASSEN	3,310
PLUMAS	2,930
TAHOE	2,910
ELDORADO	3,340
STANISLAUS	3,490
SEQUOIA	4,250
SIMPLE AVERAGE	3,372

Note: The yields projected in forest planning serve as a checkpoint to test whether a given even-aged stand is meeting land management planning timber growth criteria. Whether there would be a commercial thinning in a particular stand at age 55, or any other age, is determined by a site-specific silvicultural prescription, not by the plan.

Projected Volume

The projected yield of 3,600 cubic feet per acre is based on the current inventory of actual performance to date (average age 23), projected to age 55. Region 5 Forest Inventory data were used (USDA-FS, June, 1995, FIA). Those are the most consistent, comprehensive inventory data available. A summary of the inventory is provided in Appendix E.

There are 85 mapped plantation strata within the SNEP study area. Strata delineations are based on national forest, forest type, and plantation year of origin year when the trees were planted).

With some exceptions, plantations whose year of origin is 1981 or later were considered one age class. The 25 strata in this age class have *not* been inventoried; investment in an inventory was not deemed prudent because conditions in young plantations can change more rapidly than in older ones and because reforestation work (stocking surveys, release treatments, animal damage control, precommercial thinnings) is ongoing.

With some exceptions, plantations whose year of origin is 1980 or sooner were mapped in one of three age classes (1971-1980, 1961-1970, before 1961). The 60 strata in these age classes, occupying about 170,000 acres, *have* been inventoried. Inventory data from each of these 60 strata were projected into the future using the Forest Vegetation Simulator (FVS, formerly PROGNOSIS). FVS is a commonly used individual tree, distance-independent growth model (Wykoff, 1982). The SORNEC variant of the model was used to project plantations on the Modoc and Lassen National Forests. The WESSIN variant was used for all others. Summary statistics for the 60 strata were averaged together weighted by the acreage in each stratum. Appendix C displays the average statistics table from the projections.

Question 3 - *What is the extent of plantations on the national forests?*

Answer: Through 1991, about 300,000 acres (4% of the forest land) were plantation. About 80,000 additional acres have been planted since then.

There are about 7.6 million acres of forest land (land that is now or is naturally capable of being occupied by trees) in the study area (Appendix D). Through 1991, about 4% of the forest land is occupied by trees that were planted. About 2% of the forest land is not stocked (either unplanted, or failed and need replanting), most of which burned in large fires on the Stanislaus and Plumas National Forests in 1987.

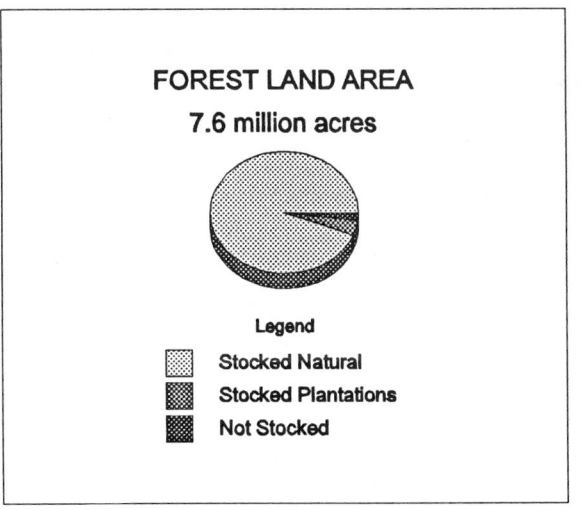

Methods and Discussion:

These land area statistics were calculated by the SNEP GIS lab using Region 5 Forest Service Forest Inventory GIS Vegetation Layers. A combination of remote sensing, photogrammetry, and field data collection techniques was employed to produce the maps (USDA-FS, June, 1995, FIA). Each national forest was mapped separately. The smallest unit of mapping is a polygon. Within a national forest, polygons of similar forest type, tree size, and tree density are grouped into a stratum, an area to be field sampled and described as a statistical population. Many strata are defined on each forest (USDA-FS, 1994).

The source for the plantation portion of the maps is ranger district records. The source imagery upon which plantation boundaries were drawn dates to 1991 (either ortho photos, color infrared photos, or spot 10 meter imagery). Instructions were to draw boundaries only for plantations where openings are visable on the 1991 imagery. Openings created after 1991 are not included. Plantation map coverage is complete through 1991 and incomplete from 1992 on. District employees transferred plantation boundaries onto mylar registered to 7 1/2 minute USGS quadrangles for geographic referencing in GIS (letter of instruction dated 9/9/91). These plantation updates were done in different years (see Appendix E) but 1991 imagery was used by all. Each plantation has been labeled with the major forest type within which it occurs, and with its year of origin (the year it was initially planted or the replant year if poor survival necessitated another site preparation). All acreage with origin prior to 1992 is accounted for because the imagery upon which plantation boundaries were drawn dates to 1991. The acreage accounting for origin after 1991 is a partial accounting. Only plantations where openings were created prior to 1992 with subsequent planting occuring before year of update are included. The plantation information supercedes the remotely sensed description that it overlaps.

Stocked plantations are assigned to strata based on the forest type in which they occur and the age of the plantation. Some areas that received shelterwood seed cuts (seed trees remain) and some areas that received overstory removals (removal of the largest size class in natural stands that are stocked with trees of a younger age class) were included as stocked plantations in these maps, but the acreage in these categories is insignificant and has not been included in acreage statistics. Future mapping will not label these areas as plantations unless they have been planted.

The not-stocked category applies to land areas that have been harvested but not yet planted (site preparation pending), areas where plantings to date have failed and additional work is needed, and areas that have burned but are not yet planted.

Identification of all remaining forestland (natural origin) is done by remote sensing.

Question 4 - *Over what period of time has plantation acreage accumulated?*

Answer: 1935 to present.

Through 1991, the most recent year for which regional level plantation maps are available, plantations cover about 300,000 acres; about 170,000 acres were planted prior to 1981 (forest inventory available, Appendix E); about 130,000 acres were planted from 1982 through 1991 (forest inventory not conducted, 1st and 3rd year survival exams provide stand level inventory). An estimated 80,000 additional acres have been planted since 1991.

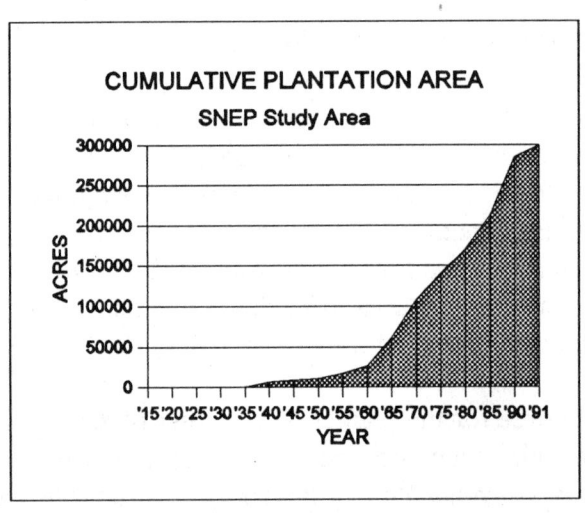

Methods and Discussion:

These figures were calculated in GIS from the vegetation layers. Appendix E discloses acreage by forest, forest type, and stratum designation. The reason for separating acreage planted prior to 1981 is that a forest inventory using consistent inventory design has been done on those areas; a comparative inventory has not been done on the younger plantations, those planted after 1980 (various local inventories and stocking surveys exist for the younger plantations, they are located in district offices, sample designs vary, and area coverage is incomplete; for these reasons, they have not been used in this assessment). The estimate of additional acreage planted since 1991 is not map based, it comes from annual reports for the period.

Question 5 - *What are the number, size, and acreage characteristics of plantations planted after fire compared to after harvest?*

Answer: The number of plantations following harvests greatly exceeds the number following fires. Half the acres in plantations were created following harvests, the other half following fire. Plantations following harvest average about 15 acres in size. Plantations following fire average about 340 acres in size.

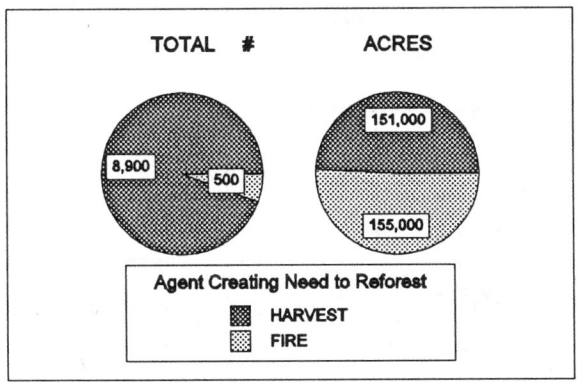

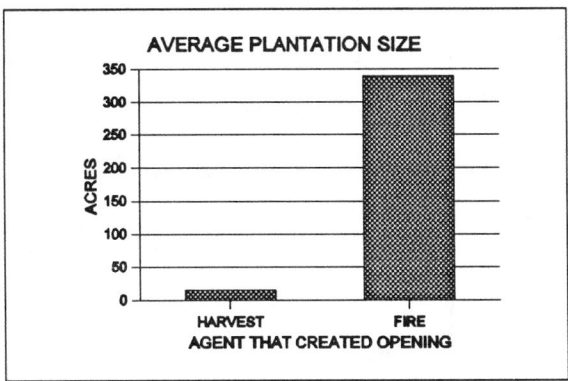

Methods and Discussion:

The method used to make these estimates utilized two GIS layers: the vegetation layer discussed earlier and a layer that contains the outer perimeter boundary of all wildfires (over 500 acres) that have occurred from about 1920 to present. The fire boundary layer was created recently from historic maps, primarily fire history atlases kept on ranger districts; boundaries are approximate. The accuracy of acreage estimates in this analysis is limited by that approximation.

First, using just the vegetation layer, the interior boundaries of all adjacent plantation polygons were eliminated, creating single plantation polygons surrounded by non-plantation polygons.

Second, using only the vegetation layer and a size criterion of 40 acres, a calculation was made of number of polygons, acreage, and average size for all plantations less than 41 acres and for all plantations over 40 acres.

Third, using only the vegetation layer and a size criterion of 80 acres, a calculation was made of number of polygons, acreage, and average size for all plantations less than 81 acres and for all plantations over 80 acres.

Fourth, the fire history and vegetation layers were compared and the total plantation acreage within the fire boundaries and outside the fire boundaries was calculated.

These calculations yielded the following:

METHOD	ASSUMED CAUSED BY HARVEST			ASSUMED CAUSED BY FIRE		
	TOTAL NUMBER	TOTAL ACRES	AVG. SIZE	TOTAL NUMBER	TOTAL ACRES	AVG. SIZE
Fire Layer Compared to Vegetation Layer		151,000 acres outside fire history boundaries			155,000 acres inside fire history boundaries	
40 Acre Criterion	8,245 polygons less than 41 ac.	105,000 acres less than 41 ac.	13 acres	1109 polygons more than 40 ac.	201,000 acres more than 40 ac.	181 acres
80 Acre Criterion	8,870 polygons less than 81 acres	139,000 acres less than 81 ac.	16 acres	484 polygons more than 80 acres	166,000 acres more than 81 ac.	344 acres

In terms of total area in plantation caused by fire, the values determined by comparing the fire and vegetation layers seem more reliable. This method assumes that all plantations inside a fire boundary are the result of a fire and that all plantations outside those boundaries are the result of a harvest. Neither assumption is completely accurate. The 40-acre criterion method assumes that all plantations less than 41 acres are the result of harvest. Knowing that clearcuts in the Sierras did not begin to any great extent until the late 1960s , and knowing that they were restricted to a 40-acre maximum by policy (later written into regulation), this assumption is attractive. However, the practice only applied to events within a single timber sale; subsequent cuts adjacent to previous ones have resulted in plantations over 40 acres.

Because the 80-acre criterion yielded a total area split more closely comparing to the vegetation/fire layer comparison method, it is used as an estimate of the split in number of plantations and average plantation size. Notice that average size caused by harvest is relatively insensitive to the method used while the average size caused by fire is relatively sensitive.

Question 6 - *How much older plantation acreage is in each of the various forest types?*

Note: Plantations planted before 1981 (hereafter called "older plantaions") have been inventoried using a consistent methodology (Appendix E; USDA-FS, 6/95, FIA). The remainder of these findings apply to these lands only (about 170,000 acres). Because these plantations were over 10 years old at time of inventory, the following information portrays the kind of conditions that exist after reforestation treatments are completed and stands begin to develop forest structure. Many of these areas have been precommercially thinned (no resulting wood product). Most of them have *not* been commercially thinned, but many may be in the next 10 to 20 years. The lack of consistent, comprehensive inventory for plantations planted after 1980 is a limitation of this report. It cannot be assumed that they will attain conditions similar to the following.

Answer:

Plantations occur in SAF forest cover types (Eyre, 1980) Sierra Nevada mixed conifer (85,000 acres), Interior ponderosa pine (38,000), white fir (14,000), Jeffrey pine (14,000), Pacific ponderosa pine (11,000), and red fir (7,000). See Appendix E.

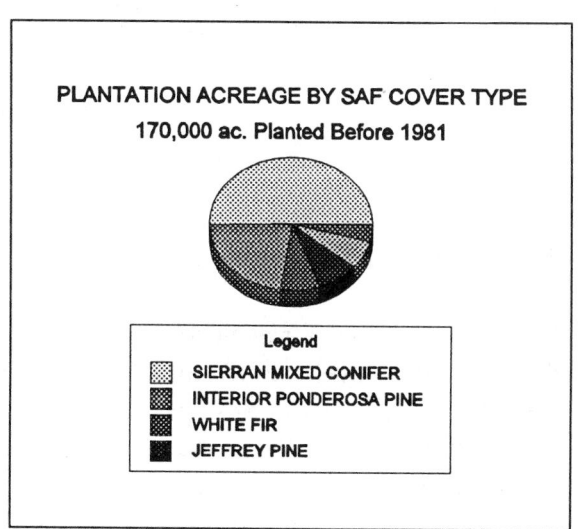

Methods and Discussion:

These calculations were made in GIS using the vegetation layer. Appendix E discloses the forests and strata that comprise them. Since roughly half the acreage is in the Mixed Conifer Type, average statistics for the entire study area are strongly influenced by conditions in the mixed conifer plantations.

Question 7 - *What kind of wildlife habitats are provided by the older plantations?*

Answer:

The habitats provided in 1991 by these plantations were primarily sparse closure sapling size and open closure pole size habitats (Mayer, 1988).

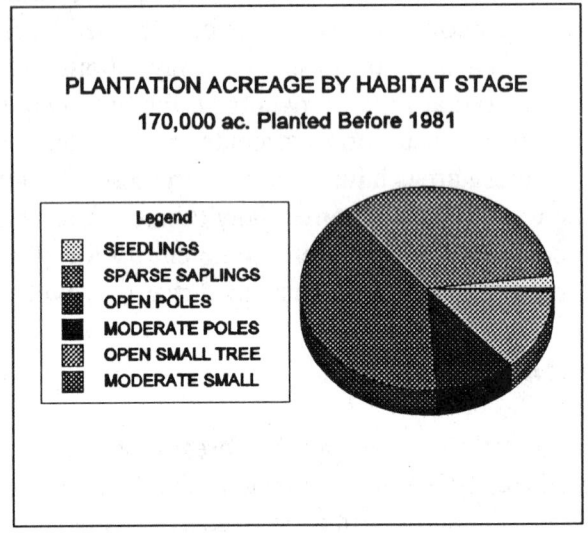

Methods and Discussion:

The inventory data for each stratum were analyzed with the Forest Vegetation Simulator using decision rules developed for the California Spotted Owl EIS (USDA-FS, January, 1995) to assign a Wildlife Habitat Relationships Stage (Mayer, 1988). For the most part, plantations are currently providing habitat for those species that prefer sparse closure sapling size and open closure pole size tree conditions. The range in habitats provided tends to increase as plantations age. Notice the variation in habitat ratings between the three ages in the mixed conifer type (Appendix F).

Question 8 - *What is the proportion of different tree species in the older plantations?*

Answer:

About 65% of all trees are either ponderosa pine or Jeffrey pine. White fir and incense-cedar are seeding in naturally underneath the planted pines in some cover types (Appendix G).

> *Note:* About 2% of all trees are sugar pine, a species of special interest because blister rust is a threat.
>
> *Note:* About 2% of all trees are hardwoods, all of natural origin, primarily California black oak.

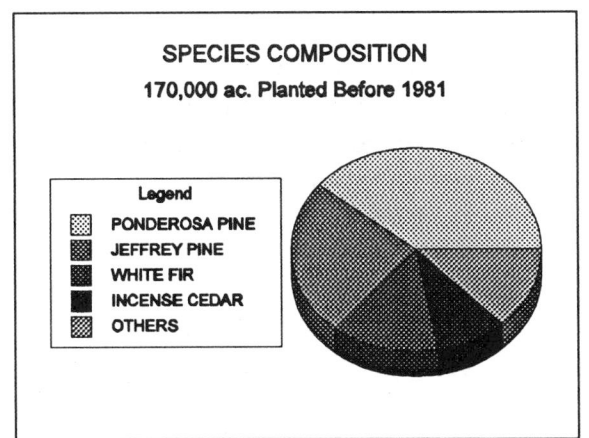

SPECIES COMPOSITION
170,000 ac. Planted Before 1981

Legend
- PONDEROSA PINE
- JEFFREY PINE
- WHITE FIR
- INCENSE CEDAR
- OTHERS

Methods and Discussion:

Tree per acre statistics were calculated for each stratum using either Region 5 Forest Inventory software (USDA-FS, June, 1995) or the Forest Vegetation Simulator (Wykoff, 1982). Strata statistics were averaged proportional to acreage, first by major forest type, then for the entire SNEP study area.

Pines (Ponderosa and Jeffrey) have been favored in the Mixed Conifir Type because it is more economical to use them (they are easier to grow in nurseries and survive better in the field), because they have historically had a higher timber value, and because there was a desire to offset the shift in species composition away from fir that is dominating in many natural stands.

The magnitude of incense-cedar and white fir natural regeneration that has occurred after planting is adequate enough to be evident in entire study area averages, showing up most notably in the seedling and sapling size classes (Appendix G).

Species of particular interest such as sugar pine and most hardwoods are present in small numbers; sugar pine probably at significantly lower than historic levels because of blister rust disease, early emphasis on cutting sugar pine for high market values, and difficulties with producing large quantities of reliable high quality nursery stock.

Question 9 - *How does shrub cover compare to tree cover in the older plantations, and what are the most common shrub species?*

Answer:

Average shrub cover is twice as great as tree cover (average tree age is 23 years). Greenleaf manzanita and mountain whitethorn are the most common shrub species (Appendix G).

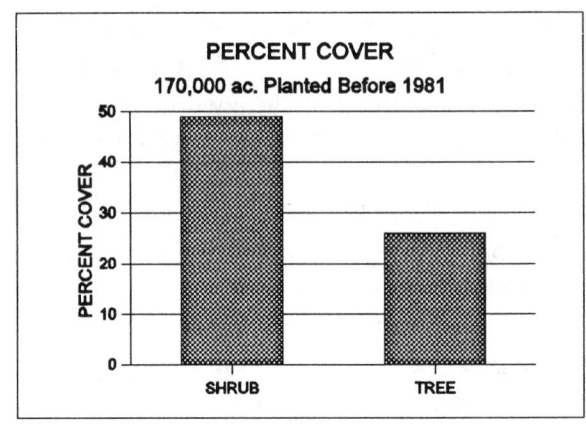

Methods and Discussion:

Individual sample points were installed in the field during forest inventory to sample conditions within a stratum. Cover estimates shown in Appendix G were obtained for each stratum from inventory software (FIA) outputs, then acre-weighted averages were developed by forest type, then overall.

Overall shrub cover of about 50% is about twice that of the trees. Most of these plantations began with very little shrub cover. Most of them received some type of release treatment intended to temporarily reduce competition between shrubs and trees, thus insuring establishment of trees. The resilient nature of many shrub species is evident. Their presence now, as these plantations grow through poletimber sizes, is of greatest concern from a fire hazard standpoint. The hazard will not decline until the stands get older.

Question 10 - *What are the mortality trends in the older plantations?*

Answer:

Tree mortality risk from inter-tree competition is low (about 85% of the 3,091 sample points had less than 120 square feet of basal area at time of inventory, see Appendix H). This risk will increase significantly as density increases over the next 10 to 20 years unless thinnings are done. The combined effect of shrub and tree competition increases overall tree mortality risk, especially on low quality sites.

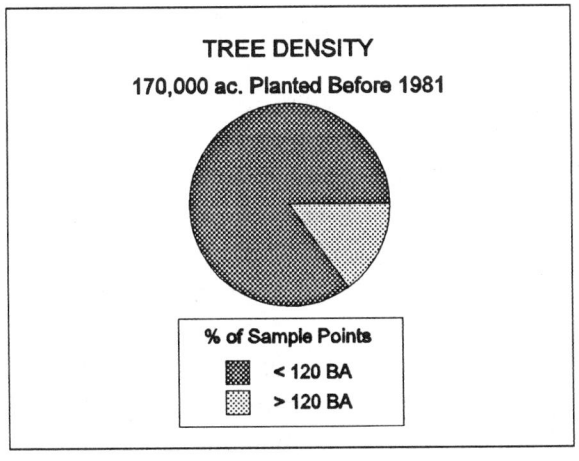

TREE DENSITY
170,000 ac. Planted Before 1981

% of Sample Points
■ < 120 BA
▨ > 120 BA

Methods and Discussion:

Individual sample points were installed in the field during forest inventory to sample conditions within a stratum. New programming was done to obtain point-level statistics shown in Appendix H.

Inter-tree competition is low in most areas as evidenced by several measures of density (basal area, number of trees, cover; see Appendix H) The breakpoint of 120 ft^2 was chosen as an indicator based on general observations of when pines experience bark beetle caused mortality. As crowns close and intertree competition increases, commercial thinnings will be possible if markets are favorable for small diameter material. The thinnings will lower density related mortality risk.

Question 11 - *What is the average plantation structure in older plantations?*

Answer: The average plantation structure (in 1991) was 23 years old, 277 trees per acre, 47 square feet of basal area per acre, tree height of 20 feet (1"+ dbh trees only), and a quadratic mean diameter (all trees) of 5.4 inches at breast height. See the first graph in Appendix G.

Methods and Discussion:

Individual sample points were installed in the field during forest inventory to sample conditions within a strata. Statistics shown in Appendix G were obtained for each stratum from inventory software (FIA or FVS) outputs, then acre-weighted averages were developed by forest type, then overall.. Note in the Appendix G graphic for the entire study area that the diameter class 5 to 10.9 inches is the one that characterizes the whole. It has the most density in basal area terms and is accumulating the most volume. Trees in that class will average about 10 inches in diameter by the year 2000. Also note in the Appendix C projection that the growth rate (for the period 1996 through 2005) is estimated at about 90 cubic feet per acre per year and rising.

Question 12 - *How variable are the older plantations?*

Answer: It depends on the statistic of interest and the scale of consideration.

Methods and Discussion: Consider variation in 3 ways:

Variation among forest types - There are differences in average age (18 to 26 years old), productivity (R-5 Site Class 2 to 4), species composition (4 to 7 tree species per stratum), and structure (180 to 430 tpa, 24 to 58 basal area per acre, 14 to 23 feet tree height, 3.1 to 5.7 qmd) among forest types.

The following table was developed from Appendices G and H:

Type	# of Sample Points	Age (yr)	Site (R-5 Site Class)	Tree Species per Stratum	Trees per Acre	Basal Area (ft²/ac)	Height of trees > 1" dbh (feet)	QMD of all trees (in)
Pacific Ponderosa Pine	244	24	3	5	339	56	23	5.4
Sierra Mixed Conifer	877	23	3/2	7	314	58	21	5.5
White Fir	567	26	3	7	243	47	21	5.7
Red Fir	472	18	3	5	431	26	14	3.1
Interior Ponderosa Pine	484	23	4	4	190	32	19	5.5
Jeffrey Pine	447	21	4	4	182	24	17	4.9
Entire Study Area	3091	23	3	6	277	47	20	5.4
Range across all sample points	n/a	n/a	n/a	0-7	0-700	0-140+	0-175	0-30+

Variation within a stratum - There is variation among cluster plots within an individual stratum. The Appendix G visualization is intended as an example of this variation. Notice the variation in cover in particular (upper right-hand perspective in the graphs). The visualization graphs were prepared from inventory data using software called *Stand Visualization System* and the *Forest Vegetation Simulator*. Species composition, density, and height are drawn to scale. The distribution of stems is random, assigned by the software.

Variation among sample points - There are 3,091 sample points of data providing the basis for characterization of older plantations. The range of variation among these sample points is displayed in Appendix H for several sample statistics. The variation among sample points is much larger than the variation in averages among forest types.

REFERENCES

Ayers. 1958. History of Timber Management in the California National Forests 1850 to 1937. Unpublished file report. USDA-FS, Washington, DC.

Buck. 1974. History of Division of Timber Management, U.S. Forest Service, Region 5, California. Unpublished file report. USDA Forest Service, San Francisco, CA.

Dunning, D. 1923. Some Results of Cutting in the Sierra Forests of California. USDA Department Bulletin No. 1176. Washington, D.C.

Eyre, F.H., editor. 1980. Forest cover Types of the United States and Canada. Society of American Foresters, Washington, D.C.

Fowells, H.A. and Duncan Dunning. 1948. A Survey of National Forest Planting in California Since 1930, third draft. Unpublished file report. USDA Forest Service, San Francisco, CA.

Helms, J.A. and Tappenier, J.C. 1995. Silvicultural Systems for the Sierra Nevada. in: SNEP Volume II. Davis, CA.

Hobbs, S.D., et. al. (editors). 1992. Reforestation Practices in Southwestern Oregon and Northern California. Forest Research Laboratory, Oregon State University, Corvallis, OR.

Levitan, Jack S.. 1991. The RAMPREP Timber Growth and Yield Model. Unpublished file report. USDA Forest Service, San Francisco, CA.

Mayer, K.E., and Laudenslayer, W.F., Jr. (editors). October, 1988. A Guide to Wildlife Habitats of California, California Department of Forestry and Fire Protection, Sacramento, CA.

Schubert, G.H., and Adams, R.S. 1971. Reforestation Practices for Conifers in California. State of California, Division of Forestry, Sacramento, CA.

USDA-Forest Service, December, 1983. Silviculture Systems for the Major Forest Types of the United States. Agriculture Handbook No. 445. Washington, D.C.

USDA-Forest Service, Region 5. 1956-1965. Annual Planting and Stand Improvement Report. Unpublished file report. USDA Forest Service, San Francisco, CA.

_____. 1966-1994. Annual Reforestation and Timber Stand Improvement Report. Unpublished file report. USDA Forest Service, San Francisco, CA.

_____. December, 1988. Final Environmental Impact Statement, Vegetation Management for Reforestation. San Francisco, CA.

_____. July, 1991. Reforestation Handbook. R-5 FSH 2409.26b. San Francisco, CA.

_____. December, 1994. Forestland and Resource Data Base, GIS and ORACLE Data Dictionary. Unpublished. On file at USDA Forest Service, Remote Sensing Lab, Sacramento, CA.

_____. June, 1995. R5 Stand Record System User's Guide. Unpublished file report. USDA Forest Service, San Francisco, CA.

_____. June, 1995. Forest Inventory and Analysis User's Guide. Unpublished file report. USDA Forest Service, Remote Sensing Lab, Sacramento, CA.

_____. January, 1995. Draft Environmental Impact Statement for Managing California Spotted Owl habitat in the Sierra Nevada, an Ecosystem Approach. San Francisco, CA.

Wykoff, Crookston, and Stage. 1982. User's Guide to the Stand Prognosis Model. USDA-FS Intermountain Forest and Range Experiment Station. General Technical Report INT-133. Ogden, UT.

APPENDIX A

Success Rate Calculations

Success Rate Calculations

source: Stand Record System

TABLE 1 OF 4											
CRITERIA FOR "ACRES STCKD"......CERTIFIED OR PROGRESSING TOWARD CERTIFIED OR >=**150 TPA**											
		1988		1989		1990		1991		1992	
Forest	District	ACRES PLNTD	ACRES STCKD	ACRES PLTD	ACRES STCKD	ACRES PLNTD	ACRES STCKD	ACRES PLNTD	ACRES STCKD	ACRES PLNTD	ACRES STCKD
MOD	53	0	0	161	161	0	0	62	62	84	84
	54	201	201	759	728	865	848	718	698	724	678
	55	423	214	124	108	38	38	282	282	566	566
	56	0	0	98	13	352	352	278	278	236	136
Subtotal		624	415	1142	1010	1255	1238	1340	1320	1610	1464
Percent Success			67		88		99		99		91
Overall Rate											91
LAS	51	138	67	1636	1507	973	899	930	850	1209	1098
	53	505	3	1165	947	2592	1731	1971	1238	2095	1373
	58	599	80	274	274	993	430	653	639	444	441
Subtotal		1242	150	3075	2728	4558	3060	3554	2727	3748	2912
Percent Success			12		89		67		77		78
Overall Rate											72
PLU	51	403	389	340	340	591	581	656	640	1022	1019
	52	0	0	3	3	626	567	570	486	415	364
	53	207	207	755	673	670	662	589	584	398	391
	54	48	48	92	67	139	132	335	309	247	238
	55	577	371	513	513	1915	1915	1604	1604	1573	1476
	56	274	267	395	383	301	259	472	442	579	487
Subtotal		1509	1282	2098	1979	4242	4116	4226	4065	4234	3975
Percent Success			85		94		97		96		94
Overall Rate											95
TAH	53	1122	1106	1586	1533	1549	1529	1160	1160	513	507
	54	596	592	499	499	911	911	730	730	778	769
	55	351	351	837	819	1003	981	490	487	909	828
	56	652	16	624	394	349	349	266	228	84	84

	57	329	329	287	225	282	281	276	276	292	53
Subtotal		3050	2394	3833	3470	4094	4051	2922	2881	2576	2241
Percent Success			78		91		99		99		87
Overall Rate											91
ELD	51	316	303	591	566	631	620	376	360	103	69
	53	631	620	840	799	690	689	293	244	282	280
	55	639	639	343	342	304	302	365	363	257	257
	56	1212	1212	1897	1869	1484	1484	546	514	370	344
Subtotal		2798	2774	3671	3576	3109	3095	1580	1481	1012	950
Percent Success			99		97		100		94		94
Overall Rate											98
STA	51	114	72	1008	960	76	66	1837	1343	1532	1249
	52	38	38	311	311	591	575	487	475	376	373
	53	385	318	318	265	175	142	301	275	0	0
	54	588	464	1024	850	764	683	876	636	797	771
Subtotal		1125	892	2661	2386	1606	1466	3501	2729	2705	2393
Percent Success			79		90		91		78		88
Overall Rate											85
INY	51	29	29	0	0	228	228	475	475	129	88
	52	97	97	251	251	258	185	0	0	204	162
Subtotal		126	126	251	251	486	413	475	475	333	250
Percent Success			100		100		85		100		75
Overall Rate											91
SIE	51	448	429	416	416	367	294	519	466	582	554
	53	470	383	757	669	1120	988	1020	887	961	918
	54	361	131	362	336	426	426	528	495	517	447
	55	312	305	496	492	531	529	448	427	557	508
Subtotal		1591	1248	2031	1913	2444	2237	2515	2275	2617	2427
Percent Success			78		94		92		90		93
Overall Rate											90
SEQ	51	306	206	454	356	865	478	561	461	684	571
	52	86	86	8	8	224	153	66	66	342	209
	53	593	551	299	229	210	197	241	212	1747	1735
	54	53	48	261	169	251	251	269	217	750	698

	56	267	239	478	469	652	545	613	424	922	376
Subtotal		1305	1130	1500	1231	2202	1624	1750	1380	4445	3589
Percent Success			87		82		74		79		81
Overall Rate											80
Bioregion Total		13370	10411	20262	18544	23996	21300	21863	19333	23280	20201
Percent Success			78		92		89		88		87
Total Acres Planted					102771		Total Acres Stocked				89789
Overall Rate 1988-1992											87
Overall Rate 1989-1992											89

		1988		1989		1990		1991		1992	
		ACRES PLNTD	ACRES STCKD	ACRES PLTD	ACRES STCKD	ACRES PLNTD	ACRES STCKD	ACRES PLNTD	ACRES STCKD	ACRES PLNTD	ACRES STCKD
MOD	53	0	0	161	161	0	0	62	62	84	84
	54	201	201	759	728	865	848	718	698	724	678
	55	423	326	124	108	38	38	282	282	566	566
	56	0	0	98	13	352	352	278	278	236	136
Subtotal		624	527	1142	1010	1255	1238	1340	1320	1610	1464
Percent Success			84		88		99		99		91
Overall Rate											93
LAS	51	138	67	1636	1507	973	899	930	850	1209	1098
	53	505	3	1165	947	2592	1744	1971	1243	2095	1373
	58	599	80	274	274	993	430	653	639	444	441
Subtotal		1242	150	3075	2728	4558	3073	3554	2732	3748	2912
Percent Success			12		89		67		77		78
Overall Rate											72
PLU	51	403	389	340	340	591	581	656	640	1022	1019
	52	0	0	3	3	626	567	570	486	415	364
	53	207	207	755	673	670	662	589	584	398	391
	54	48	48	92	67	139	132	335	309	247	238
	55	577	371	513	513	1915	1915	1604	1604	1573	1476
	56	274	267	395	383	301	259	472	442	579	487
Subtotal		1509	1282	2098	1979	4242	4116	4226	4065	4234	3975
Percent Success			85		94		97		96		94
Overall Rate											95
TAH	53	1122	1109	1586	1538	1549	1529	1160	1160	513	507
	54	596	592	499	499	911	911	730	730	778	769
	55	351	351	837	819	1003	992	490	487	909	828
	56	652	16	624	518	349	349	266	228	84	84
	57	329	329	287	225	282	281	276	276	292	53
Subtotal		3050	2397	3833	3599	4094	4062	2922	2881	2576	2241

TABLE 2 OF 4

CRITERIA FOR "ACRES STCKD"......CERTIFIED OR PROGRESSING TOWARD CERTIFIED OR >=*75 TPA*

547

Percent Success			79		94		99		99	87
Overall Rate										92
ELD	51	316	303	591	566	631	620	376	360	103	69
	53	631	620	840	799	690	689	293	244	282	280
	55	639	639	343	342	304	302	365	363	257	257
	56	1212	1212	1897	1887	1484	1484	546	514	370	344
Subtotal		2798	2774	3671	3594	3109	3095	1580	1481	1012	950
Percent Success			99		98		100		94	94
Overall Rate										98
STA	51	114	72	1008	960	76	66	1837	1373	1532	1376
	52	38	38	311	311	591	575	487	475	376	373
	53	385	318	318	265	175	142	301	301	0	0
	54	587	465	1024	850	764	683	875	635	797	771
Subtotal		1124	893	2661	2386	1606	1466	3500	2784	2705	2520
Percent Success			79		90		91		80	93
Overall Rate										87
INY	51	29	29	0	0	228	228	475	475	129	88
	52	97	97	251	251	258	185	0	0	204	162
Subtotal		126	126	251	251	486	413	475	475	333	250
Percent Success			100		100		85		100	75
Overall Rate										91
SIE	51	448	443	416	416	367	317	519	478	582	582
	53	470	383	757	669	1120	988	1020	899	961	918
	54	361	137	362	336	426	426	528	495	517	447
	55	312	305	496	492	531	529	448	448	557	508
Subtotal		1591	1268	2031	1913	2444	2260	2515	2320	2617	2455
Percent Success			80		94		92		92	94
Overall Rate										91
SEQ	51	306	217	454	361	865	491	561	461	684	571
	52	86	86	8	8	224	153	66	66	342	288
	53	593	551	299	233	210	205	241	222	1747	1743
	54	53	48	261	172	251	251	269	217	750	698
	56	267	239	478	469	652	545	613	424	922	376
Subtotal		1305	1141	1500	1243	2202	1645	1750	1390	4445	3676

Percent Success		87		83		75		79		83
Overall Rate										81
Bioregion Total	13369	10558	20262	18703	23996	21368	21862	19448	23280	20443
Percent Success		79		92		89		89		88
Total Acres Planted				102769	Total Acres Stocked					90520
Overall Rate 1988-1992										88
Overall Rate 1989-1992										89

549

		1988		1989		1990		1991		1992	
		ACRES PLNTD	ACRES STCKD	ACRES PLTD	ACRES STCKD	ACRES PLNTD	ACRES STCKD	ACRES PLNTD	ACRES STCKD	ACRES PLNTD	ACRES STCKD
MOD	53	0	0	0	0	0	0	0	0	0	0
	54	117	117	56	56	0	0	308	308	317	317
	55	0	0	0	0	0	0	0	0	0	0
	56	0	0	0	0	0	0	0	0	0	0
Subtotal		117	117	56	56	0	0	308	308	317	317
Percent Success			100		100		??		100		100
Overall Rate											100
LAS	51	0	0	0	0	0	0	0	0	0	0
	53	209	0	354	314	33	33	344	344	949	308
	58	0	0	0	0	0	0	7	0	0	0
Subtotal		209	0	354	314	33	33	351	344	949	308
Percent Success			0		89		100		98		32
Overall Rate											53
PLU	51	120	120	26	26	3	3	41	25	668	665
	52	0	0	0	0	0	0	12	12	203	203
	53	0	0	0	0	0	0	0	0	0	0
	54	0	0	0	0	0	0	0	0	12	12
	55	464	258	422	422	249	249	1365	1365	1434	1337
	56	0	0	0	0	0	0	0	0	12	12
Subtotal		584	378	448	448	252	252	1418	1402	2329	2229
Percent Success			65		100		100		99		96
Overall Rate											94
TAH	53	515	515	884	879	845	827	584	584	200	199
	54	47	47	0	0	0	0	0	0	0	0
	55	0	0	0	0	2	0	0	0	0	0
	56	0	0	20	20	0	0	8	8	0	0
	57	0	0	0	0	48	48	37	37	100	25
Subtotal		562	562	904	899	895	875	629	629	300	224

TABLE 3 OF 4 (*PLANTED AFTER WILDFIRE*)

CRITERIA FOR "ACRES STCKD"......CERTIFIED OR PROGRESSING TOWARD CERTIFIED OR >= *150 TPA*

Percent Success			100		99		98		100		75
Overall Rate											97
ELD	51	0	0	0	0	0	0	0	0	0	0
	53	0	0	0	0	2	2	0	0	0	0
	55	37	37	0	0	0	0	0	0	0	0
	56	0	0	0	0	0	0	0	0	0	0
Subtotal		37	37	0	0	2	2	0	0	0	0
Percent Success			100		??		100		??		??
Overall Rate											100
STA	51	26	26	837	789	0	0	1334	979	1174	905
	52	0	0	0	0	30	30	0	0	0	0
	53	0	0	0	0	0	0	0	0	0	0
	54	257	148	485	361	764	683	872	632	754	747
Subtotal		283	174	1322	1150	794	713	2206	1611	1928	1652
Percent Success			61		87		90		73		86
Overall Rate											81
INY	51	0	0	0	0	0	0	0	0	0	0
	52	56	56	258	185	0	0	0	0	0	0
Subtotal		56	56	258	185	0	0	0	0	0	0
Percent Success			100		72		??		??		??
Overall Rate											77
SIE	51	0	0	0	0	0	0	40	0	13	13
	53	0	0	0	0	5	4	35	32	74	42
	54	0	0	0	0	0	0	0	0	0	0
	55	0	0	0	0	0	0	0	0	0	0
Subtotal		0	0	0	0	5	4	75	32	87	55
Percent Success			??		??		80		43		63
Overall Rate											54
SEQ	51	33	33	5	0	15	0	144	125	15	15
	52	0	0	0	0	0	0	0	0	0	0
	53	12	12	4	0	0	0	176	163	1637	1637
	54	0	0	0	0	0	0	0	0	0	0
	56	65	65	98	98	409	409	0	0	13	10
Subtotal		110	110	107	98	424	409	320	288	1665	1662

Percent Success		100		92		96		90	100
Overall Rate									98
Bioregion Total	1958	1434	3449	3150	2405	2288	5307	4614	7575	6447
Percent Success		73		91		95		87	85
Total Acres Planted				20694	Total Acres Stocked				17933
Overall Rate 1988-1992									87
Overall Rate 1989-1992									88

552

TABLE 4 OF 4 *(PLANTED AFTER HARVEST)*											
CRITERIA FOR "ACRES STCKD"......CERTIFIED OR PROGRESSING TOWARD CERTIFIED OR >=**150 TPA**											
		1988		1989		1990		1991		1992	
		ACRES PLNTD	ACRES STCKD	ACRES PLTD	ACRES STCKD	ACRES PLNTD	ACRES STCKD	ACRES PLNTD	ACRES STCKD	ACRES PLNTD	ACRES STCKD
MOD	53	0	0	93	93	0	0	62	62	77	77
	54	10	10	116	116	650	650	304	286	148	148
	55	10	10	0	0	38	38	282	282	396	396
	56	0	0	5	5	0	0	227	227	199	99
Subtotal		20	20	214	214	688	688	875	857	820	720
Percent Success			100		100		100		98		88
Overall Rate											95
LAS	51	105	56	861	831	222	201	930	850	1200	1089
	53	30	0	160	80	37	21	88	74	74	74
	58	514	0	0	0	158	122	521	514	266	263
Subtotal		649	56	1021	911	417	344	1539	1438	1540	1426
Percent Success			9		89		82		93		93
Overall Rate											81
PLU	51	24	10	2	2	74	72	388	388	247	247
	52	0	0	3	3	18	4	513	448	212	161
	53	96	96	94	71	0	0	579	574	398	391
	54	0	0	0	0	35	28	296	270	196	187
	55	100	100	0	0	49	49	239	239	88	88
	56	149	146	15	8	264	256	400	370	480	418
Subtotal		369	352	114	84	440	409	2415	2289	1621	1492
Percent Success			95		74		93		95		92
Overall Rate											93
TAH	53	472	469	483	483	395	395	409	409	302	302
	54	470	466	18	18	118	118	730	730	766	757
	55	0	0	64	64	133	122	477	474	894	828
	56	532	0	43	43	90	90	258	220	41	41
	57	0	0	8	8	0	0	239	239	192	28
Subtotal		1474	935	616	616	736	725	2113	2072	2195	1956

Percent Success			63		100		99		98		89
Overall Rate											88
ELD	51	260	247	417	392	448	437	376	360	103	69
	53	0	0	58	58	94	94	254	222	257	257
	55	237	237	29	29	7	5	227	225	255	255
	56	228	228	14	14	73	73	546	514	370	344
Subtotal		725	712	518	493	622	609	1403	1321	985	925
Percent Success			98		95		98		94		94
Overall Rate											95
STA	51	0	0	0	0	17	17	503	364	358	344
	52	13	13	99	99	16	16	473	461	376	373
	53	0	0	0	0	0	0	301	275	0	0
	54	169	156	342	342	0	0	0	0	19	0
Subtotal		182	169	441	441	33	33	1277	1100	753	717
Percent Success			93		100		100		86		95
Overall Rate											92
INY	51	29	29	0	0	228	228	475	475	82	41
	52	41	41	251	251	0	0	0	0	204	162
Subtotal		70	70	251	251	228	228	475	475	286	203
Percent Success			100		100		100		100		71
Overall Rate											94
SIE	51	45	45	8	8	56	33	444	431	418	390
	53	331	268	59	59	205	205	737	658	698	698
	54	361	131	303	277	304	304	522	495	478	447
	55	93	93	212	212	99	99	407	386	365	326
Subtotal		830	537	582	556	664	641	2110	1970	1959	1861
Percent Success			65		96		97		93		95
Overall Rate											91
SEQ	51	114	69	335	313	493	350	356	284	585	493
	52	0	0	0	0	0	0	61	61	212	160
	53	253	253	9	9	97	92	59	43	110	98
	54	53	48	149	92	128	128	227	197	750	698
	56	43	30	82	82	0	0	538	402	909	366
Subtotal		463	400	575	496	718	570	1241	987	2566	1815

Percent Success		86		86		79		80		71
Overall Rate										77
Bioregion Total	4782	3251	4332	4062	4546	4247	13448	12509	12725	11115
Percent Success		68		94		93		93		87
Total Acres Planted				39833	Total Acres Stocked					35184
Overall Rate 1988-1992										88
Overall Rate 1989-1992										91

555

APPENDIX B

Status of Reforestation after Final Harvest

ANNUAL REFORESTATION AND TIMBER STAND IMPROVEMENT

ACCOMPLISHMENT REPORT

TABLE 22 - STATUS OF REFORESTATION AFTER FINAL HARVEST

REGION 05

FISCAL YEAR 1994

COLUMN NUMBER	1	2	3	4		5		6	
	FINAL HARVEST REPORTED IN 1988	ADJUSTMENTS TO DATE	REVISED FINAL HARVEST	ADEQUATELY STOCKED		NOT ADEQUATELY STOCKED		NOT ADEQUATELY STOCKED NO FURTHER TREATMENTS	
FOREST	ACRES	ACRES	ACRES	ACRES	%	ACRES	%	ACRES	%
01	0	0	0						
02	0	0	0						
03	3,768	-956	2,812	2,686	96	119	4	7	0
04	2,156	-1518	638	565	89	73	11	0	0
05	4,658	-804	3,854	3,596	93	258	7	0	0
06	11,137	-7,258	3,879	3,828	99	51	1	0	0
07	0	0	0						
08	4,346	+550	4,896	4,675	95	221	5	0	0
09	6,816	-5993	823	823	100	0	0	0	0
10	3,274	+71	3,345	3,276	98	69	2	0	0
11	0	+6,258	6,258	5,404	86	854	14	0	0
12	0	0	0						
13	2,258	-1,227	1,031	635	62	395	38	1	0
14	2,897	+4	2,901	2,901	100	0	0	0	0
15	0	+1,296	1,296	1,129	87	167	13	0	0
16	1,338	5,664	7,002	3,196	45	3,806 *	55	0	0
17	5,722	-958	4,764	4,363	92	389	8	12	0
18	7,944	-204	7,740	7,303	94	153	2	284	4
19	5	-5	0						
TOTAL	56,319	- 5,080	51,239	44,380	87	6,555	13	304	<1

* These acres are delayed for reforestation until herbicides can be used. Environmental documents are currently being prepared for site preparation, planting, and release. Hamm-Hasloe EIS has been signed and is through the NEPA process.

557

ANNUAL REFORESTATION AND TIMBER STAND IMPROVEMENT

ACCOMPLISHMENT REPORT

TABLE 22 - STATUS OF REFORESTATION AFTER FINAL HARVEST

REGION 05

FISCAL YEAR 1994

COLUMN NUMBER	1	2	3	4		5		6	
FOREST	FINAL HARVEST REPORTED IN 1989 ACRES	ADJUSTMENTS TO DATE ACRES	REVISED FINAL HARVEST ACRES	ADEQUATELY STOCKED ACRES	%	NOT ADEQUATELY STOCKED ACRES	%	NOT ADEQUATELY STOCKED NO FURTHER TREATMENTS ACRES	%
01	0	0	0						
02	0	0	0						
03	1,044	+501	1,545	1,409	91	134	9	2	0
04	1,808	-1254	554	471	85	83	15		
05	1,876	+1,862	3,738	3,415	91	323	9	0	0
06	17,897	-12,974	4,923	4,762	97	161	3	0	0
07	0		0						
08	36	+4,077	4,113	3,523	86	590	14		
09	0	867	867	846	98	21	2		
10	1,409	+1,578	2,987	2,790	93	197	7	0	0
11	0	+4,437	4,437	3,742	84	647	15	48	1
12	0		0						
13	302	+1,108	1,410	1,167	83	243	17	0	0
14	1,680	+1,192	2,872	2,865	100	7	0	0	0
15	1,499	+ 757	2,256	1,720	76	536	24	0	0
16	114	5,589	5,703	2,604	46	3,099 *	54	0	0
17	1,888	+404	2,292	2,113	92	179	8	0	0
18	1,226	+5,815	7,041	6,561	93	249	4	231	3
19	0	0							
TOTAL	30,779	13,959	44,738	37,988	85	6,469	14	281	1

* These acres are delayed for reforestation until herbicides can be used. Environmental documents are currently being prepared for site preparation, planting, and release. Herm-Harloe EIS has been signed and is through the NEPA process.

APPENDIX C

Projected Volume

559

SNEP STUDY AREA - PLANTATIONS PLANTED BEFORE 1981 - 170,000 ACRES

04-04-95 13:46:39

AVERAGE SUMMARY STATISTICS BY CYCLE

		START OF SIMULATION PERIOD						REMOVALS			AFTER TREATMENT						GROWTH THIS PERIOD			
		NO OF				DOM		TOTAL	MERCH	MERCH	NO OF	MERCH	MERCH				DOM	RES	PERIOD	ACCRE	MORT	MAI MERCH
YEAR	AGE	TREES	BA	SDI	CCF	HT	QMD	CU FT	CU FT	BD FT	TREES	CU FT	BD FT	BA	SDI	CCF	HT	QMD	YEARS	PER YEAR		CU FT
1991	23	278	48	106	37	34	5.4	625	471	1666									0	65	0	19
1995	27	276	61	131	44	39	6.2	846	663	2343									4	73	0	24
1996	28	276	64	137	46	41	6.5	918	727	2606									1	90	2	25
2005	37	269	101	196	64	52	8.3	1719	1471	5956									9	121	5	39
2015	47	257	141	256	79	64	10.1	2887	2598	11774									10	145	11	55
2025	57	240	179	306	92	75	12.8	4232	3917	19125									10	159	18	69
2035	67	222	212	346	102	84	13.4	5640	5315	27373									10	0	0	80

3,653 is linear interpolation
between these 2 numbers.

THE FOLLOWING STRATA WERE SUMMARIZED USING THE SORNEC VARIANT-

09E1	09E2	09E3	09F1	09F2
09R1	06M1	06M2	06M3	06E1
06E2	06E3	06R1		

THE FOLLOWING STRATA WERE SUMMARIZED USING THE WESSIN VARIANT-

11M1	11M2	11P1	11F1	11F2
11F3	11R1	11R2	11J1	11J2
11J3	17J1	17J2	17J3	17M1
17M2	17M3	17R1	17R2	03F1
03F2	03F3	03M1	03M2	03M3
03P2	03P3	03R1	16M1	16M2
16M3	16P1	16P2	16P3	16R1
16R2	04J1	04J2	04J3	15M2
15P1	15P2	15R1	13M1	13M2
13M3	13R1			

-FVS has different geographic variants (each with different growth coefficients). In this analysis, strata on the Modoc and Lassen National Forests were projected using the SORNEC variant of FVS, all other strata were projected using the WESSIN variant.

NOTE: Strata labels incorporate the national forest code, then the forest type code, then the age class code.

APPENDIX D

Land Area Table

LAND AREA TABLE

(NET FOREST SERVICE ACRES)

1991

Forest	Forest Land (7.6 million acres)				Non-Forest Land	TOTALS
	Natural Stocking	Plantations planted before 1981	Plantations planted from 1981-1991	Not stocked		
Modoc	1,095,000	35,000	22,200	17,900	624,200	1,794,300
Lassen	871,800	20,900	12,500	4,100	354,000	1,263,300
Plumas	952,400	18,600	25,300	35,800	220,400	1,252,500
Tahoe	604,300	30,900	28,200	500	153,300	817,200
Eldorado	475,400	12,900	10,900	1,100	103,900	604,200
Stanislaus	544,100	17,500	8,900	71,000	250,700	892,200
Inyo	948,300	1,600	1,000	200	980,000	1,931,100
Sierra	803,500	13,500	12,600	10,000	460,300	1,299,900
Sequoia	844,300	17,400	16,200	3,300	255,900	1,137,100
TOTALS	7,139,108	168,300	137,800	143,900	3,402,700	10,991,800
PERCENT OF FOREST-LAND	94%	2%	2%	2%		

APPENDIX E

Status of Plantation Inventories

Status of Plantation Inventories
Inventory Sample Design

FOREST /YEAR*	LIVE TREES			DEAD STANDING TREES					DOWN
	<1.0" DBH	1.0"-4.9" DBH	5.0"+ DBH	1.0"-4.9" DBH	5.0"+ DBH	5.0"-19.9" DBH	1.0"-19.9" DBH	20.0"+ DBH	10.0"+ **
MOD 1993	1/100 AC. FIXED	1/100 AC. FIXED	20 BAF PRISM				1/8 AC. FIXED	1/4 AC. FIXED	1/8 AC. FIXED
LAS 1993/94	"	"	"				1/8 AC. FIXED	1/4 AC. FIXED	1/8 AC. FIXED
PLU 1992	"	"	"	1/100 AC. FIXED	20 BAF PRISM				NO SAMPLE
TAH 1990	"	"	"	1/100 AC. FIXED	20 BAF PRISM				NO SAMPLE
ELD 1994	"	"	"				1/8 AC. FIXED	1/4 AC. FIXED	1/8 AC. FIXED
STA 1991	"	"	"	1/100 AC. FIXED	20 BAF PRISM				NO SAMPLE
INY 1994	"	"	"	1/100 AC. FIXED		1/8 AC. FIXED		1/4 AC. FIXED	1/8 AC. FIXED
SIE 1986	"	"	"		20 BAF PRISM				NO SAMPLE
SEQ 1990	"	"	"	1/100 AC. FIXED	20 BAF PRISM				NO SAMPLE

* Inventory Year   ** at the large end

Status of Plantation Inventories

Forest Type	Age Class	Strata	Forest	Acres	Years of Origin	Last Map Update *	Year Inventoried	# of Cluster Plots	# of Sample Points
			PLU	357	'72-'80	1992	1992	4	26
			STA	901	'71-'80	1992	1991	6	49
	1	P1X	SIE	1,116	'71-'80	1992	1986	2	10
			Sub-totals	2,374				12	85
			ELD	1,773	'61-'80	1992	1994	6	50
			STA	1,117	'61-'70	1992	1991	4	49
Pacific Ponderosa Pine	2	P2X	SIE	3,654	'30-'70	1992	1986	2	10
			Sub-total	6,544				12	109
			ELD	906	'49-'59	1992	1994	2	20
	3	P3X	STA	779	'46-'60	1992	1991	5	47
			Sub-total	1,685				7	67
Forest Type Totals				10,603				31	261

PLANTATION STRATA THAT HAVE BEEN INVENTORIED									
Forest Type	Age Class	Strata	Forest	Acres	Years of Origin	*Last Map Update	Year Inventoried	# of Cluster Plots	# of Sample Points
Sierran Mixed Conifer	1	M1X	LAS	3,691	'71-'80	1993	1994	11	76
			PLU	1,722	'71-'82	1992	1992	3	17
			TAH	5,432	'71-'80	1992	1990	8	40
			ELD	2,473	'71-'80	1992	1994	3	27
			STA	6,108	'71-'80	1992	1991	7	61
			SEQ	9,965	'71-'80	1992	1990	10	49
			Sub-totals	29,391				42	270
	2	M2X	LAS	12,355	'61-'70	1993	1994	8	58
			PLU	1,876	'47-'72	1992	1992	6	56
			TAH	16,209	'61-'70	1992	1990	8	40
			ELD	2,734	'61-'70	1992	1994	5	45
			STA	4,393	'61-'70	1992	1991	9	78
			SIE	6,260	'10-'70	1992	1986	5	24
			SEQ	4,292	'61-'70	1992	1990	7	33
			Sub-totals	48,119				48	334
	3	M3X	LAS	1,604	'36-'60	1993	1994	13	120
			TAH	1,225	'48-'60	1992	1990	8	40
			ELD	900	'40-'59	1992	1994	3	30
			STA	2,453	'51-'60	1992	1991	6	60
			SEQ	1,740	'32-'60	1992		5	23
			Sub-totals	7,922				35	273
Forest Type Totals				85,432				125	877

PLANTATION STRATA THAT HAVE BEEN INVENTORIED									
Forest Type	Age Class	Strata	Forest	Acres	Years of Origin	Last Map Update *	Year Inven- toried	# of Cluster Plots	# of Sample Points
Red Fir	1	R1X	MOD	64	'75-'76	1993	1993	3	29
			LAS	338	'62-'80	1993	1993	4	34
			PLU	218	'71-'80	1992	1992	8	76
			TAH	1,003	'71-'80	1992	1990	8	39
			ELD	429	'69-'80	1992	1994	8	69
			STA	783	'71-'80	1992	1991	6	55
			SIE	2,016	'50-'80	1992	1986	3	15
			SEQ	941	'62-'79	1992	1990	5	24
			Sub-totals	5,792				45	341
	2	R2X	PLU	333	'40-'70	1992	1992	7	47
			TAH	416	'62'-70	1992	1990	8	40
			STA	627	'50-'70	1992	1991	6	44
			Sub-total	1,376				21	131
Forest Type Totals				7,168				66	472

567

PLANTATION STRATA THAT HAVE BEEN INVENTORIED									
Forest Type	Age Class	Strata	Forest	Acres	Years of Origin	Last Map Update *	Year Inven-toried	# of Cluster Plots	# of Sample Points
White Fir (Eastside Mixed Conifer)	1	F1X	MOD	1,954	'71-'91	1993	1993	7	70
			PLU	1,342	'71-'82	1992	1992	12	120
			ELD	1,538	'71-'80	1992	1994	7	64
			Sub-totals	4,834				26	254
	2	F2X	MOD	641	'47-'70	1993	1993	11	101
			PLU	5,418	'61-'70	1992	1992	9	87
			ELD	862	'61-'69	1992	1994	3	27
			Sub-total	6,921				23	215
	3	F3X	PLU	791	'38-'60	1992	1992	8	78
			ELD	987	'40-'60	1992	1994	2	20
			Sub-total	1,778				10	98
Forest Type Totals				13,533				59	567

568

PLANTATION STRATA THAT HAVE BEEN INVENTORIED									
Forest Type	Age Class	Strata	Forest	Acres	Years of Origin	Last Map Update *	Year Inven-toried	# of Cluster Plots	# of Sample Points
Interior Ponderosa Pine	1	E1X	MOD	8,587	'70-'81	1993	1993	10	101
			LAS	821	'71-'80	1993	1994	3	30
			Sub-totals	9,408				13	131
	2	E2X	MOD	14,401	'61-'70	1993	1993	9	90
			LAS	4,128	'61-'70	1993	1994	12	104
			Sub-total	18,529				21	194
	3	E3X	MOD	9,396	'40-'60	1993	1993	10	100
			LAS	1,001	'36-'60	1993	1993	6	59
			Sub-total	10,397				16	159
Forest Type Totals				38,334				50	484

PLANTATION STRATA THAT HAVE BEEN INVENTORIED									
Forest Type	Age Class	Strata	Forest	Acres	Years of Origin	Last Map Update *	Year Inventoried	# of Cluster Plots	# of Sample Points
Jeffrey Pine	1	J1X	PLU	3,380	'71-'80	1992	1992	7	65
			TAH	3,706	'71-'80	1993	1990	8	39
			INY	1,223	'64-'74	1992	1994	9	45
			Sub-totals	8,309				24	149
	2	J2X	PLU	1,066	'61-'70	1992	1992	8	74
			TAH	2,162	'61-'70	1993	1990	8	40
			INY	141	'64-'69	1992	1994	8	40
			Sub-total	3,369				24	154
	3	J3X	PLU	1,451	'41-'60	1992	1992	7	70
			TAH	231	"58-'60	1993	1990	8	39
			INY	246	'52-'85	1992	1994	7	35
			Sub-total	1,928				22	144
Forest Type Totals				13,606				70	447
Inventoried Grand Total				168,676				401	3,108

PLANTATION STRATA THAT HAVE **NOT** BEEN INVENTORIED										
Forest Type	Age Class	Strata	Forest	Acres	Years of Origin **	Last Map Update *	Year Inven-toried	# of Cluster Plots	# of Sample Points
Pacific Ponderosa Pine	0	P0X	ELD	2,316	'82-'92	1992	No Inventory		
			STA	2,317	'81-'91	1992			
			SIE	3,536	'81-'91	1991			
			Sub-totals	8,169				0	0
Forest Type Totals				8,169				0	0
Sierran Mixed Conifer	0	M0X	LAS	5,261	'81-'92	1993	No Inventory		
			PLU	7,633	'81-'91	1992			
			TAH	22,814	'81-'94	1994			
			ELD	6,500	'81-'92	1992			
			STA	5,523	'81-'92	1992			
			SIE	8,737	'71-'91	1991			
			SEQ	14,235	'81-'93	1993			
			Sub-totals	70,703				0	0
Forest Type Totals				70,703				0	0

PLANTATION STRATA THAT HAVE **NOT** BEEN INVENTORIED									
Forest Type	Age Class	Strata	Forest	Acres	Years of Origin **	Last Map Update *	Year Inven-toried	# of Cluster Plots	# of Sample Points
Red Fir	0	R0X	LAS	1,230	'82-'93	1993	No Inventory		
			PLU	108	'85-'90	1992			
			TAH	1,077	'81-'92	1994			
			ELD	1,524	'81-'91	1992			
			STA	717	'81-'91	1992			
			SIE	2,139	'81-'91	1991			
			SEQ	1,284	'81-'93	1993			
			Sub-totals	8,079				0	0
Forest Type Totals				8,079				0	0
White Fir (Eastside Mixed Conifer)	0	F0X	MOD	1,719	'82-'92	1994	No Inventory		
			PLU	9,714	'81-'92	1992			
			ELD	8,550	'81-'91	1992			
			Sub-totals	19,983				0	0
Forest Type Totals				19,983				0	0
Interior Ponderosa Pine	0	E0X	MOD	20,434	'81-'94	1994	No Inventory		
			LAS	5,861	'81-'93	1993			
			Sub-totals	26,295				0	0
Forest Type Totals				26,295				0	0

PLANTATION STRATA THAT HAVE **NOT** BEEN INVENTORIED										
Forest Type	Age Class	Strata	Forest	Acres	Years of Origin **	Last Map Update *	Year Inven-toried	# of Cluster Plots	# of Sample Points
Jeffrey Pine	0	J0X	PLU	6,038	'81-'91	1992	No Inventory		
			TAH	3,421	'81-'92	1994			
			INY	1,048	'83-'92	1992			
			Sub-totals	10,507				0	0
Forest Type Totals				10,507				0	0
Not Inventoried Grand Total				143,736				0	0

* Forests updated plantation maps in the year indicated. The source imagery upon which plantation boundaries were drawn dates to 1991 (either ortho photos, color infrared photos, or spot 10 meter imagery). Instructions were to draw boundaries only for plantations where openings are visable on the 1991 imagery. Openings created after 1991 are not included. Plantation map coverage is complete through 1991 and incomplete from 1992 on.

** All acreage with origin prior to 1992 is accounted for because the imagery upon which plantation boundaries were drawn dates to 1991. The acreage accounting for origin after 1991 is a partial accounting. Only plantations where openings were created prior to 1992 with subsequent planting occured before year of update are included.

APPENDIX F

Wildlife Habitat Relationships Stages

Wildlife Habitat Relationship Stages [1]

Forest Type	Age Class	Strata	Forest	PLANTATION STRATA THAT HAVE BEEN INVENTORIED					
				ACRES BY HABITAT STAGE **					
				1X	2X	3P	3M	4P	4M
Pacific Ponderosa Pine	1	P1X	PLU		357				
			STA		901				
			SIE		1,116				
			Sub-totals	0	2,374	0	0	0	0
	2	P2X	ELD			1,773			
			STA		1,117				
			SIE			3,654			
			Sub-total	0	1,117	5,427	0	0	0
	3	P3X	ELD					906	
			STA			779			
			Sub-total	0	0	779	0	906	0
Forest Type Acre Totals by Stage				0	3,491	6,206	0	906	0

---

[1]Reference both Mayer, 1988 and USDA-FS, 1995.

				ACRES BY HABITAT STAGE					
Forest Type	Age Class	Strata	Forest	1X	2X	3P	3M	4P	4M
Sierran Mixed Conifer	1	M1X	LAS		3,691				
			PLU		1,722				
			TAH		5,432				
			ELD		2,473				
			STA			6,108			
			SEQ			9,965			
			Sub-totals	0	13,318	16,073	0	0	0
	2	M2X	LAS			12,355			
			PLU		1,876				
			TAH				16,209		
			ELD					2,734	
			STA			4,393			
			SIE			6,260			
			SEQ			4,292			
			Sub-total	0	1,876	27,300	16,209	2,734	0
	3	M3X	LAS					1,604	
			TAH				1,225		
			ELD						900
			STA					2,453	
			SEQ			1,740			
			Sub-total	0	0	1,740	1,225	4,057	900
Forest Type Acre Totals by Stage				0	15,194	45,113	17,434	6,791	900

PLANTATION STRATA THAT HAVE BEEN INVENTORIED

576

PLANTATION STRATA THAT HAVE BEEN INVENTORIED									
				ACRES BY HABITAT STAGE					
Forest Type	Age Class	Strata	Forest	1X	2X	3P	3M	4P	4M
Red Fir	1	R1X	MOD		64				
			LAS		338				
			PLU		218				
			TAH		1,003				
			ELD		429				
			STA		783				
			SIE		2,016				
			SEQ		941				
			Sub-totals	0	5,792	0	0	0	0
	2	R2X	PLU		333				
			TAH		416				
			STA		627				
			Sub-total	0	1,376	0	0	0	0
Forest Type Acre Totals by Stage				0	7,168	0	0	0	0

PLANTATION STRATA THAT HAVE BEEN INVENTORIED									
				ACRES BY HABITAT STAGE					
Forest Type	Age Class	Strata	Forest	1X	2X	3P	3M	4P	4M
White Fir (East-side Mixed Coni-fer)	1	F1X	MOD		1,954				
			PLU		1,342				
			ELD					1,538	
			Sub-totals	0	3,296	0	0	1,538	0
	2	F2X	MOD		641				
			PLU			5,418			
			ELD					862	
			Sub-total	0	641	5,418	0	862	0
	3	F3X	PLU			791			
			ELD		987				
			Sub-total	0	987	791	0	0	0
Forest Type Acre Totals by Stage				0	4,924	6,209	0	2,400	0

PLANTATION STRATA THAT HAVE BEEN INVENTORIED									
				ACRES BY HABITAT STAGE					
Forest Type	Age Class	Strata	Forest	1X	2X	3P	3M	4P	4M
Interior Ponderosa Pine	1	E1X	MOD		8,587				
			LAS			821			
			Sub-totals	0	8,587	821	0	0	0
	2	E2X	MOD		14,401				
			LAS			4,128			
			Sub-total	0	14,401	4,128	0	0	0
	3	E3X	MOD					9,396	
			LAS					1,001	
			Sub-total	0	0	0	0	10,397	0
Forest Type Acre Totals by Stage				0	22,988	4,949	0	10,397	0

PLANTATION STRATA THAT HAVE BEEN INVENTORIED

Forest Type	Age Class	Strata	Forest	1X	2X	3P	3M	4P	4M
Jeffrey Pine	1	J1X	PLU		3,380				
			TAH	3,706					
			INY					1,223	
			Sub-totals	3,706	3,380	0	0	1,223	0
	2	J2X	PLU			1,066			
			TAH			2,162			
			INY			141			
			Sub-total	0	0	3,369	0	0	0
	3	J3X	PLU			1,451			
			TAH			231			
			INY			246			
			Sub-total	0	0	1,928	0	0	0
Forest Type Totals				3,706	3,380	5,297	0	1,223	0
SNEP Study Area Totals				3,706	57,145	67,774	17,434	21,717	900

** Codes for size and cover (from USDA-FS, 1995):

Code	Size Class	DBH		Code	Closure Class
1	Seedling	< 1"		X	assigned to seedling or sapling size class
2	Sapling	1"-6"		P	Open Cover (less than 40%)
3	Pole	6"-11"		M	Moderate Cover (40%-69%)
4	Small Tree	11"-24"			

APPENDIX G

Current Plantation Condition Graphics

SPECIES CODES FOR APPENDIX G

CODE	SPECIES
DF	Douglas-fir
LP	Lodgepole pine
SP	Sugar pine
BO	Black oak
RF	Red fir
IC	Incense cedar
WF	White fir
JP	Jeffrey pine
PP	Ponderosa pine
ARPA9	Greenleaf manzanita
CECO2	Whitethorn
UG	Unidentified grass
CEVE3	Snowbrush
CEPR	Squaw carpet
ART5	Sage (woody shrub form)
CHR9	Rabbitbrush
RIB	Ribes - perennial shrub
RINE	Sierra currant
PRU2	Cherry
ARC5	Manzanita
CEIN3	Deerbrush
CHFO2	Bearclover

PLANTATION INVENTORY AVERAGES (ACRE WEIGHTED)
PLANTATION STRATA AGE CLASSES 1,2, AND 3 (>10 YRS OLD)

FOREST TYPE: **ENTIRE SNEP STUDY AREA**

NATIONAL FOREST OCCURRENCE: **MODOC, LASSEN, PLUMAS, TAHOE, ELDORADO, STANISLAUS, INYO, SIERRA, SEQUOIA**

SIZE: **170,000 ACRES**   AGE: **23**

SITE CLASS: **3**   HABITAT STAGE: **3X, 2X**

INVENTORY YEAR: **1991**
YEAR OF ORIGIN: **1968**

OF SAMPLE POINT CLUSTERS: **401**
OF SAMPLE POINTS: **3091**

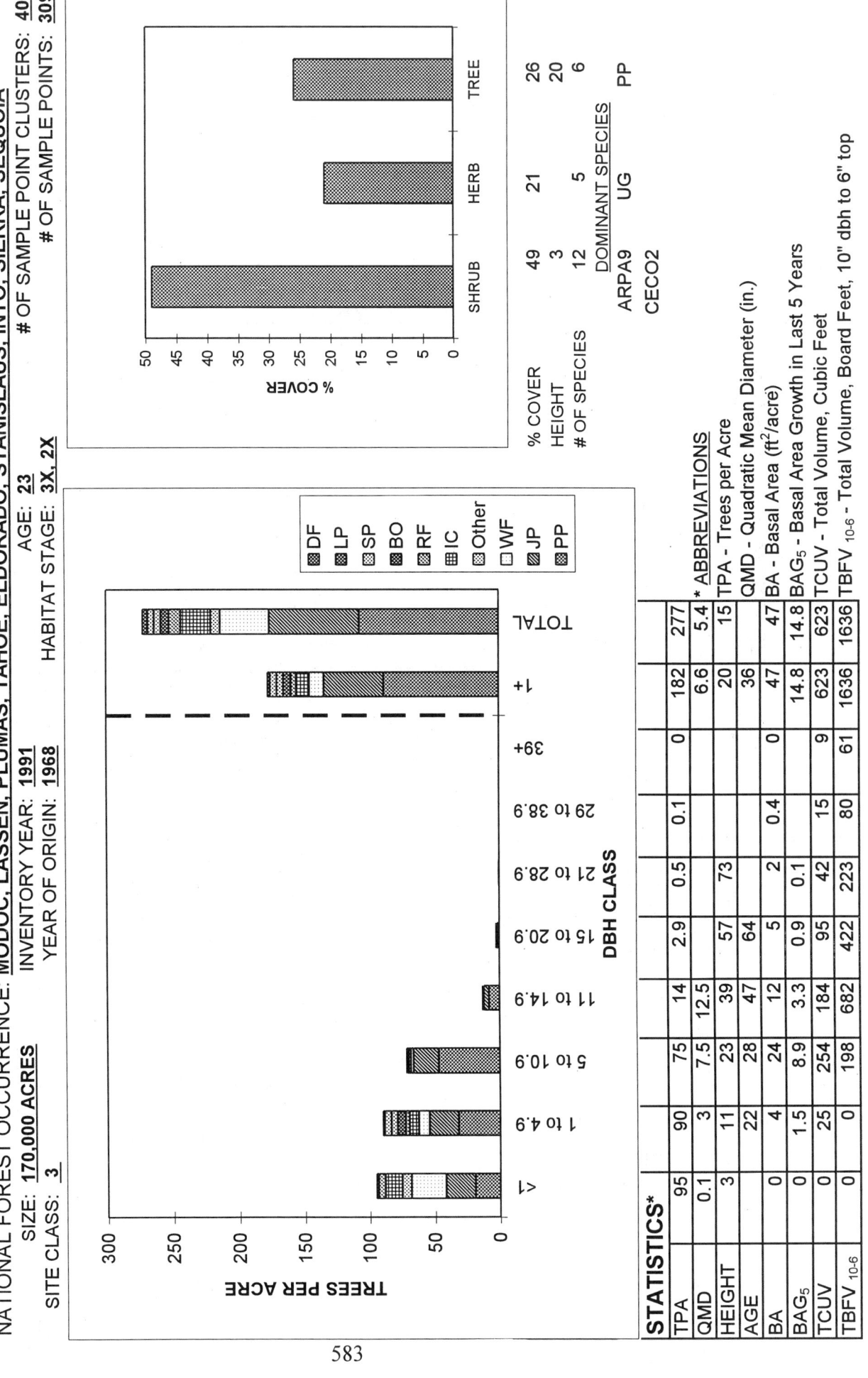

DOMINANT SPECIES

	ARPA9	UG	PP
	CECO2		
% COVER	49	21	26
HEIGHT	3	5	20
# OF SPECIES	12		6

STATISTICS*

	<1	1 to 4.9	5 to 10.9	11 to 14.9	15 to 20.9	21 to 28.9	29 to 38.9	39+	1+	TOTAL
TPA	95	90	75	14	2.9	0.5	0.1	0	182	277
QMD	0.1	3	7.5	12.5					6.6	5.4
HEIGHT	3	11	23	39	57	73			20	15
AGE	0	22	28	47	64				36	
BA	0	4	24	12	5	2	0.4	0	47	47
BAG5	0	1.5	8.9	3.3	0.9	0.1			14.8	14.8
TCUV	0	25	254	184	95	42	15	9	623	623
TBFV 10-6	0	0	198	682	422	223	80	61	1636	1636

* ABBREVIATIONS

TPA - Trees per Acre
QMD - Quadratic Mean Diameter (in.)
BA - Basal Area (ft²/acre)
BAG5 - Basal Area Growth in Last 5 Years
TCUV - Total Volume, Cubic Feet
TBFV 10-6 - Total Volume, Board Feet, 10" dbh to 6" top

583

PLANTATION INVENTORY AVERAGES (ACRE WEIGHTED)

PLANTATION STRATA AGE CLASSES 1,2, AND 3 (>10 YRS OLD)

FOREST TYPE: **PACIFIC PONDEROSA PINE**   NATIONAL FOREST OCCURRENCE: **PLUMAS, ELDORADO, STANISLAUS, SIERRA**

SIZE: **11,000 ACRES**	
SITE CLASS: **3**	

INVENTORY YEAR: **1989**   AGE: **24**

YEAR OF ORIGIN: **1965**   HABITAT STAGE: **3P, 2X**

OF SAMPLE POINT CLUSTERS: **31**

OF SAMPLE POINTS: **244**

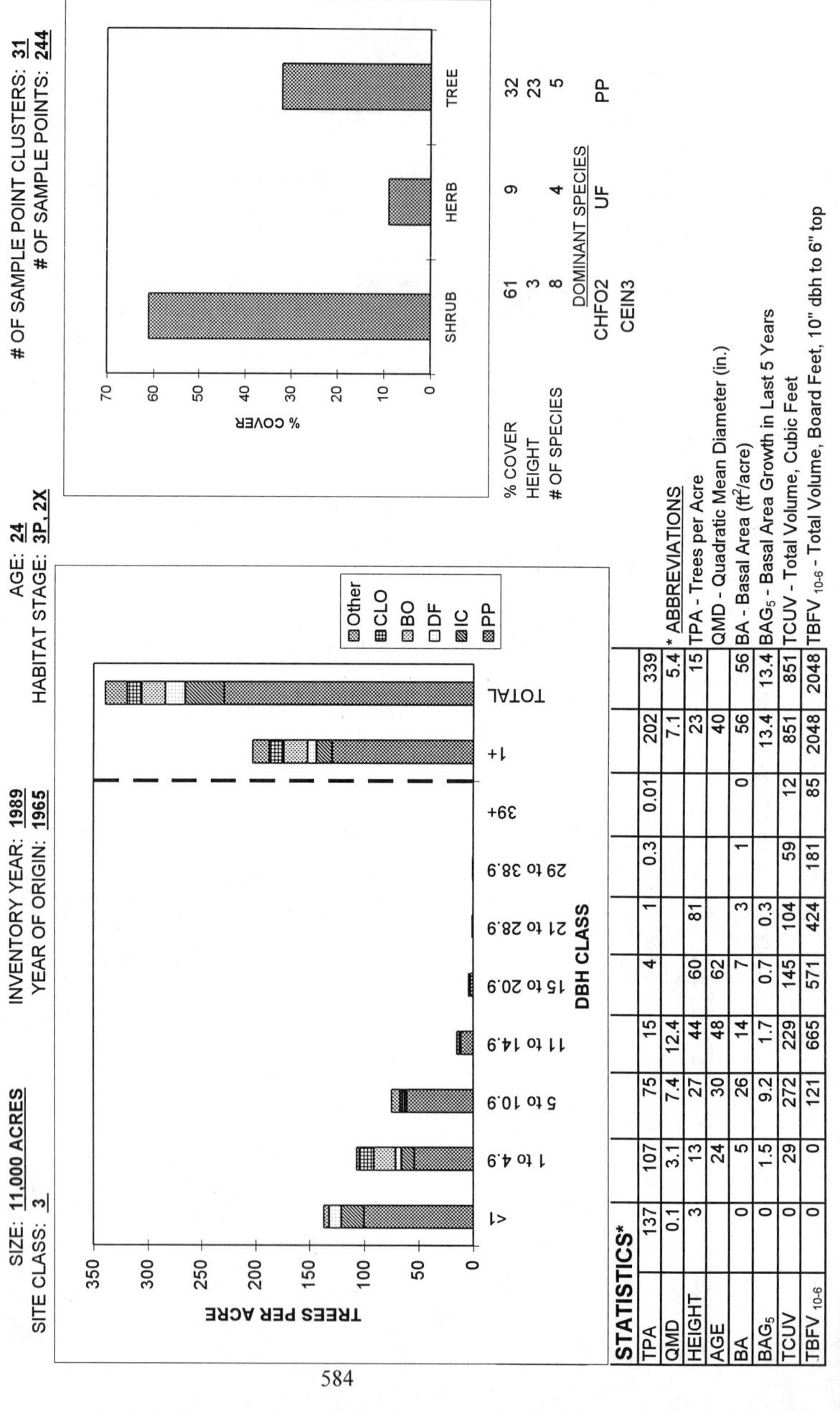

DOMINANT SPECIES

	% COVER	HEIGHT	# OF SPECIES
SHRUB	61	3	8
HERB	9		4
TREE	32	23	5

CHFO2	UF PP
CEIN3	

STATISTICS*

	<1	1 to 4.9	5 to 10.9	11 to 14.9	15 to 20.9	21 to 28.9	29 to 38.9	39+	1+	TOTAL
TPA	137	107	75	15	4	1	0.3	0.01	202	339
QMD	0.1	3.1	7.4	12.4					7.1	5.4
HEIGHT	3	13	27	44	60	81			23	15
AGE	0	24	30	48	62				40	
BA	0	5	26	14	7	3	1	0	56	56
BAG₅	0	1.5	9.2	1.7	0.7	0.3			13.4	13.4
TCUV	0	29	272	229	145	104	59	12	851	851
TBFV ₁₀₋₆	0	0	121	665	571	424	181	85	2048	2048

* ABBREVIATIONS

TPA - Trees per Acre

QMD - Quadratic Mean Diameter (in.)

BA - Basal Area (ft²/acre)

BAG₅ - Basal Area Growth in Last 5 Years

TCUV - Total Volume, Cubic Feet

TBFV ₁₀₋₆ - Total Volume, Board Feet, 10" dbh to 6" top

584

PLANTATION INVENTORY AVERAGES (ACRE WEIGHTED)
PLANTATION STRATA AGE CLASSES 1,2, AND 3 (>10 YRS OLD)

FOREST TYPE: **MIXED CONIFER**

NATIONAL FOREST OCCURRENCE: **LASSEN, PLUMAS, TAHOE, ELDORADO, STANISLAUS, SIERRA, SEQUOIA**

SIZE: **85,000 ACRES**   INVENTORY YEAR: **1991**   AGE: **23**   # OF SAMPLE POINT CLUSTERS: **125**

SITE CLASS: **3, 2**   YEAR OF ORIGIN: **1968**   HABITAT STAGE: **3P, 3M, 2X**   # OF SAMPLE POINTS: **877**

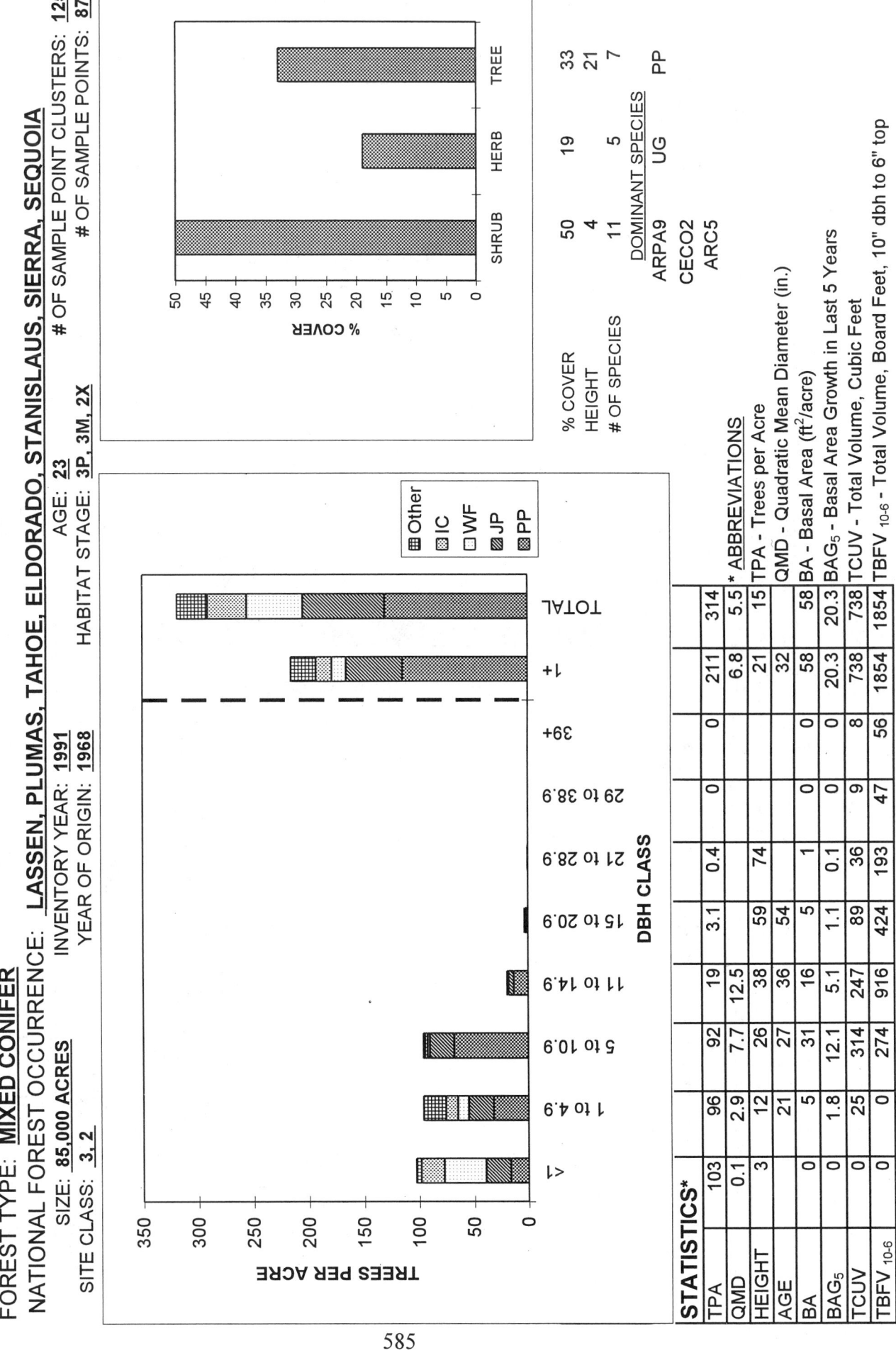

	% COVER	HEIGHT	# OF SPECIES
SHRUB	50	4	11
HERB	19		5
TREE	33	21	7

DOMINANT SPECIES

ARPA9	UG	PP
CECO2		
ARC5		

STATISTICS*

	<1	1 to 4.9	5 to 10.9	11 to 14.9	15 to 20.9	21 to 28.9	29 to 38.9	39+	1+	TOTAL
TPA	103	96	92	19	3.1	0.4	0	0	211	314
QMD	0.1	2.9	7.7	12.5					6.8	5.5
HEIGHT	3	12	26	38	59	74			21	15
AGE		21	27	36	54				32	
BA	0	5	31	16	5	1	0	0	58	58
BAG₅	0	1.8	12.1	5.1	1.1	0.1	0	0	20.3	20.3
TCUV	0	25	314	247	89	36	9	8	738	738
TBFV₁₀₋₆	0	0	274	916	424	193	47	56	1854	1854

* ABBREVIATIONS
TPA - Trees per Acre
QMD - Quadratic Mean Diameter (in.)
BA - Basal Area (ft²/acre)
BAG₅ - Basal Area Growth in Last 5 Years
TCUV - Total Volume, Cubic Feet
TBFV₁₀₋₆ - Total Volume, Board Feet, 10" dbh to 6" top

585

PLANTATION INVENTORY AVERAGES (ACRE WEIGHTED)
PLANTATION STRATA AGE CLASSES 1,2, AND 3 (>10 YRS OLD)

NATIONAL FOREST OCCURRENCE: **MODOC, PLUMAS, ELDORADO**

FOREST TYPE: **WHITE FIR**

SIZE: **14,000 ACRES**
SITE CLASS: **3**

INVENTORY YEAR: **1993**
YEAR OF ORIGIN: **1967**

AGE: **26**
HABITAT STAGE: **2X, 3P**

OF SAMPLE POINT CLUSTERS: **59**
OF SAMPLE POINTS: **567**

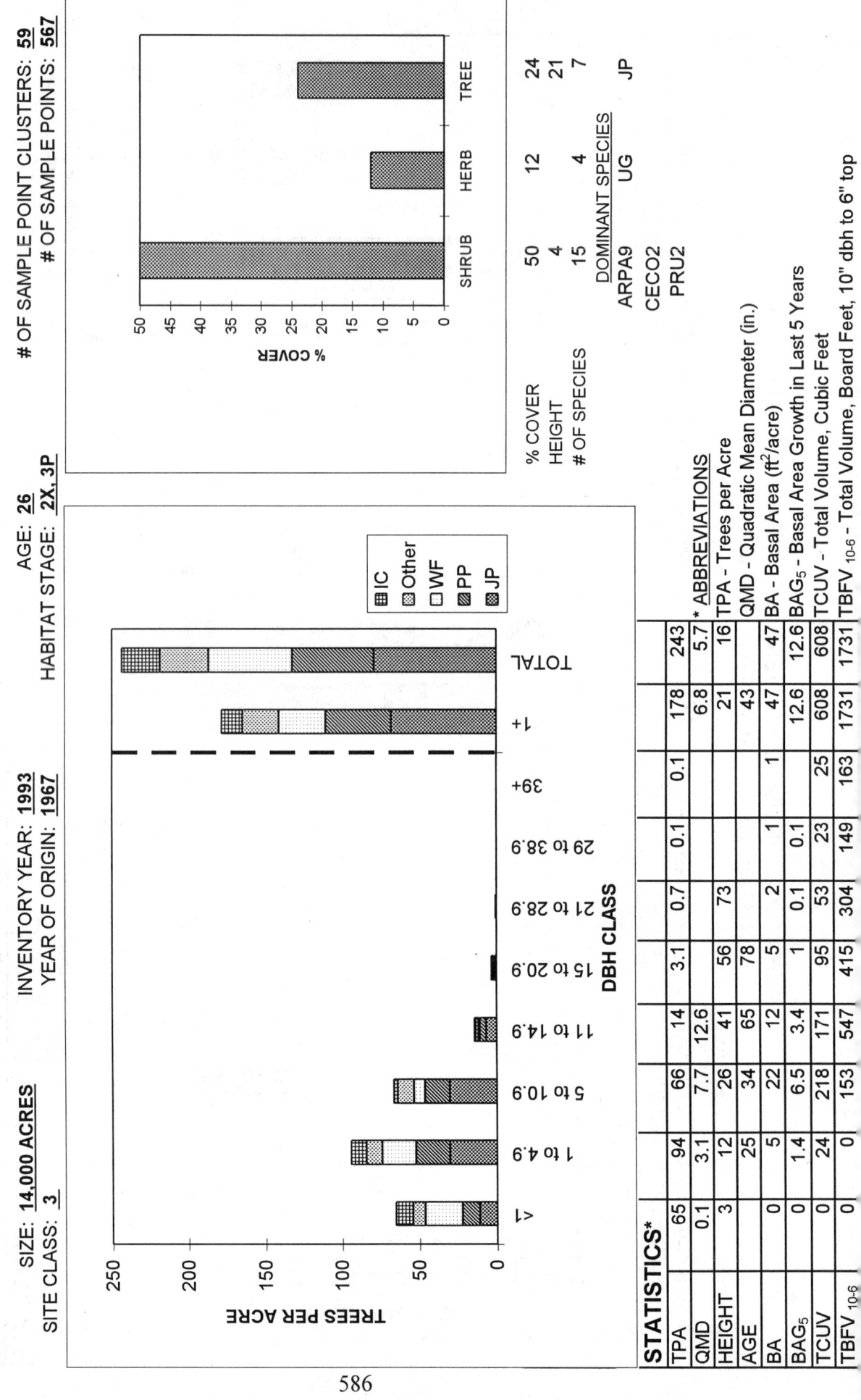

% COVER	50	12	24
HEIGHT	4	4	21
# OF SPECIES	15		7

DOMINANT SPECIES
ARPA9 UG JP
CECO2
PRU2

STATISTICS*		˅	1 to 4.9	5 to 10.9	11 to 14.9	15 to 20.9	21 to 28.9	29 to 38.9	39+	1+	TOTAL
TPA		65	94	66	14	3.1	0.7	0.1	0.1	178	243
QMD		0.1	3.1	7.7	12.6					6.8	5.7
HEIGHT		3	12	26	41	56	73			21	16
AGE		0	25	34	65	78				43	
BA		0	5	22	12	5	2	1	1	47	47
BAG₅		0	1.4	6.5	3.4	1	0.1	0.1		12.6	12.6
TCUV		0	24	218	171	95	53	23	25	608	608
TBFV₁₀₋₆		0	0	153	547	415	304	149	163	1731	1731

* ABBREVIATIONS
TPA - Trees per Acre
QMD - Quadratic Mean Diameter (in.)
BA - Basal Area (ft²/acre)
BAG₅ - Basal Area Growth in Last 5 Years
TCUV - Total Volume, Cubic Feet
TBFV₁₀₋₆ - Total Volume, Board Feet, 10" dbh to 6" top

586

PLANTATION INVENTORY AVERAGES (ACRE WEIGHTED)
PLANTATION STRATA AGE CLASSES 1,2, AND 3 (>10 YRS OLD)

FOREST TYPE: **RED FIR**

NATIONAL FOREST OCCURRENCE: **MODOC, LASSEN, PLUMAS, TAHOE, ELDORADO, STANISLAUS, SIERRA, SEQUOIA**

SIZE: **7,000 ACRES**

SITE CLASS: **3**

INVENTORY YEAR: **1990**   AGE: **18**

YEAR OF ORIGIN: **1972**   HABITAT STAGE: **2X**

OF SAMPLE POINT CLUSTERS: **66**

OF SAMPLE POINTS: **472**

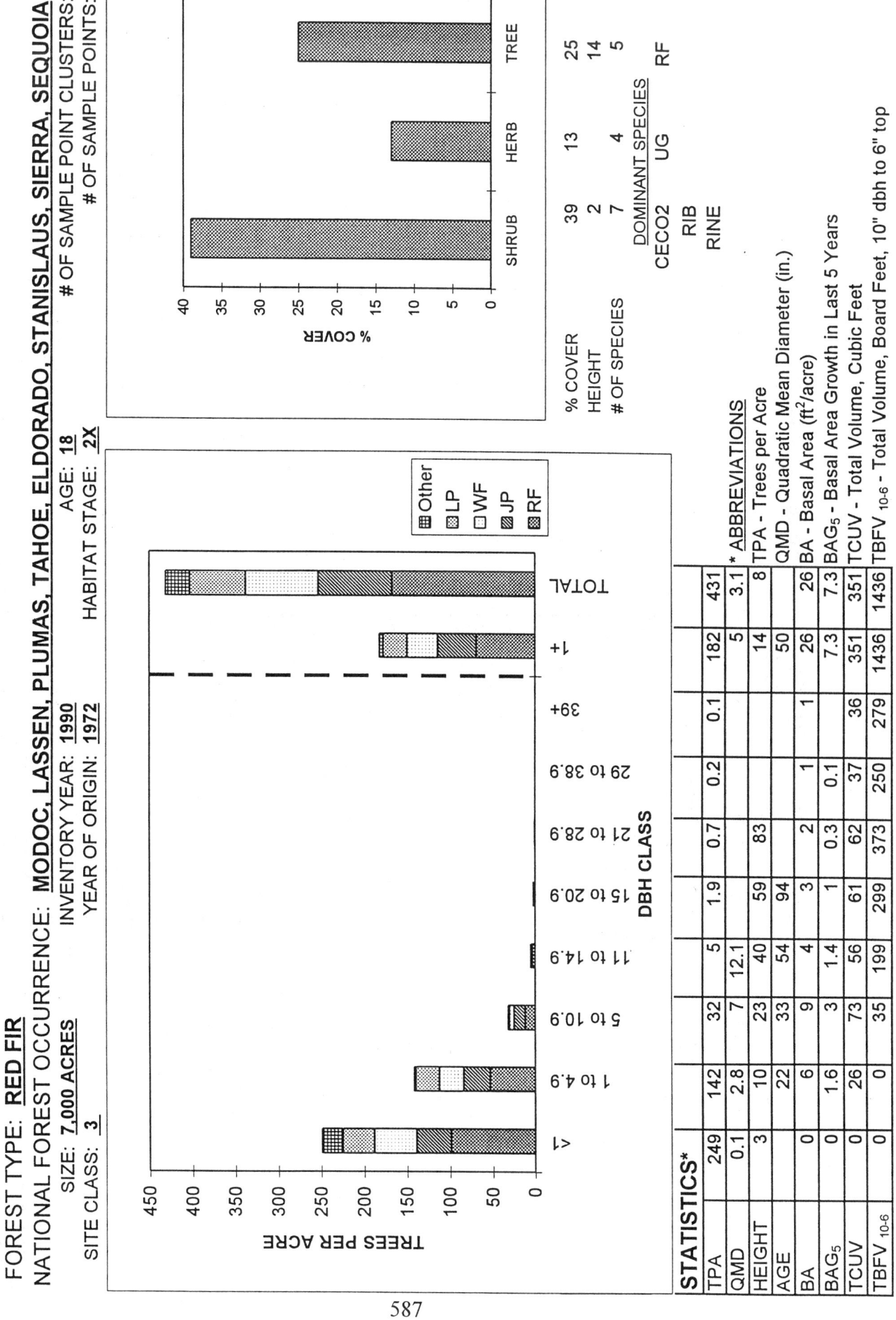

DOMINANT SPECIES

	SHRUB	HERB	TREE		
% COVER	39	13	25	CECO2	UG	RF
HEIGHT	2	4	14	RIB	
# OF SPECIES	7	4	5	RINE	

STATISTICS*

	<1	1 to 4.9	5 to 10.9	11 to 14.9	15 to 20.9	21 to 28.9	29 to 38.9	39+	1+	TOTAL
TPA	249	142	32	5	1.9	0.7	0.2	0.1	182	431
QMD	0.1	2.8	7	12.1					5	3.1
HEIGHT	3	10	23	40	59	83			14	8
AGE	22	33	54	94					50	
BA	0	6	9	4	3	2	1	1	26	26
BAG5	0	1.6	3	1.4	1	0.3	0.1		7.3	7.3
TCUV	0	26	73	56	61	62	37	36	351	351
TBFV 10-6	0	0	35	199	299	373	250	279	1436	1436

DBH CLASS

* ABBREVIATIONS

TPA - Trees per Acre

QMD - Quadratic Mean Diameter (in.)

BA - Basal Area (ft²/acre)

BAG5 - Basal Area Growth in Last 5 Years

TCUV - Total Volume, Cubic Feet

TBFV 10-6 - Total Volume, Board Feet, 10" dbh to 6" top

PLANTATION INVENTORY AVERAGES (ACRE WEIGHTED)
PLANTATION STRATA AGE CLASSES 1,2, AND 3 (>10 YRS OLD)

FOREST TYPE: **INTERIOR PONDEROSA PINE**   NATIONAL FOREST OCCURRENCE: **MODOC, LASSEN**

SIZE: **38,000 ACRES**   INVENTORY YEAR: **1993**   AGE: **23**   # OF SAMPLE POINT CLUSTERS: **50**

SITE CLASS: **4**   YEAR OF ORIGIN: **1970**   HABITAT STAGE: **2X, 4P**   # OF SAMPLE POINTS: **484**

% COVER	51	31	18
HEIGHT	3		19
# OF SPECIES	14	4	4

DOMINANT SPECIES		
ARPA9	UG	PP
CHR9		

STATISTICS*	<1	1 to 4.9	5 to 10.9	11 to 14.9	15 to 20.9	21 to 28.9	29 to 38.9	39+	1+	TOTAL
TPA	51	73	57	7	2.7	0.5	0.1	0	139	190
QMD	0.1	3.1	7.2	12.6					6.3	5.5
HEIGHT	3	11	23	41	56	70			19	15
AGE		22	28	66	80				37	
BA	0	4	17	6	4	1	0.3	0	32	32
BAG5	0	1.1	5.2	0.9	0.4	0.1	0.1		7.6	7.6
TCUV	0	28	218	105	94	39	10	1	494	494
TBFV 10-6	0	0	149	489	462	223	63	5	1391	1391

* ABBREVIATIONS
TPA - Trees per Acre
QMD - Quadratic Mean Diameter (in.)
BA - Basal Area (ft²/acre)
BAG5 - Basal Area Growth in Last 5 Years
TCUV - Total Volume, Cubic Feet
TBFV 10-6 - Total Volume, Board Feet, 10" dbh to 6" top

PLANTATION INVENTORY AVERAGES (ACRE WEIGHTED)
PLANTATION STRATA AGE CLASSES 1,2, AND 3 (>10 YRS OLD)

NATIONAL FOREST OCCURRENCE: **PLUMAS, TAHOE, INYO**

FOREST TYPE: **JEFFREY PINE**

SIZE: **14,000 ACRES**

SITE CLASS: **4**

INVENTORY YEAR: **1991**

YEAR OF ORIGIN: **1970**

AGE: **21**

HABITAT STAGE: **3P, 1X**

OF SAMPLE POINT CLUSTERS: **70**

OF SAMPLE POINTS: **447**

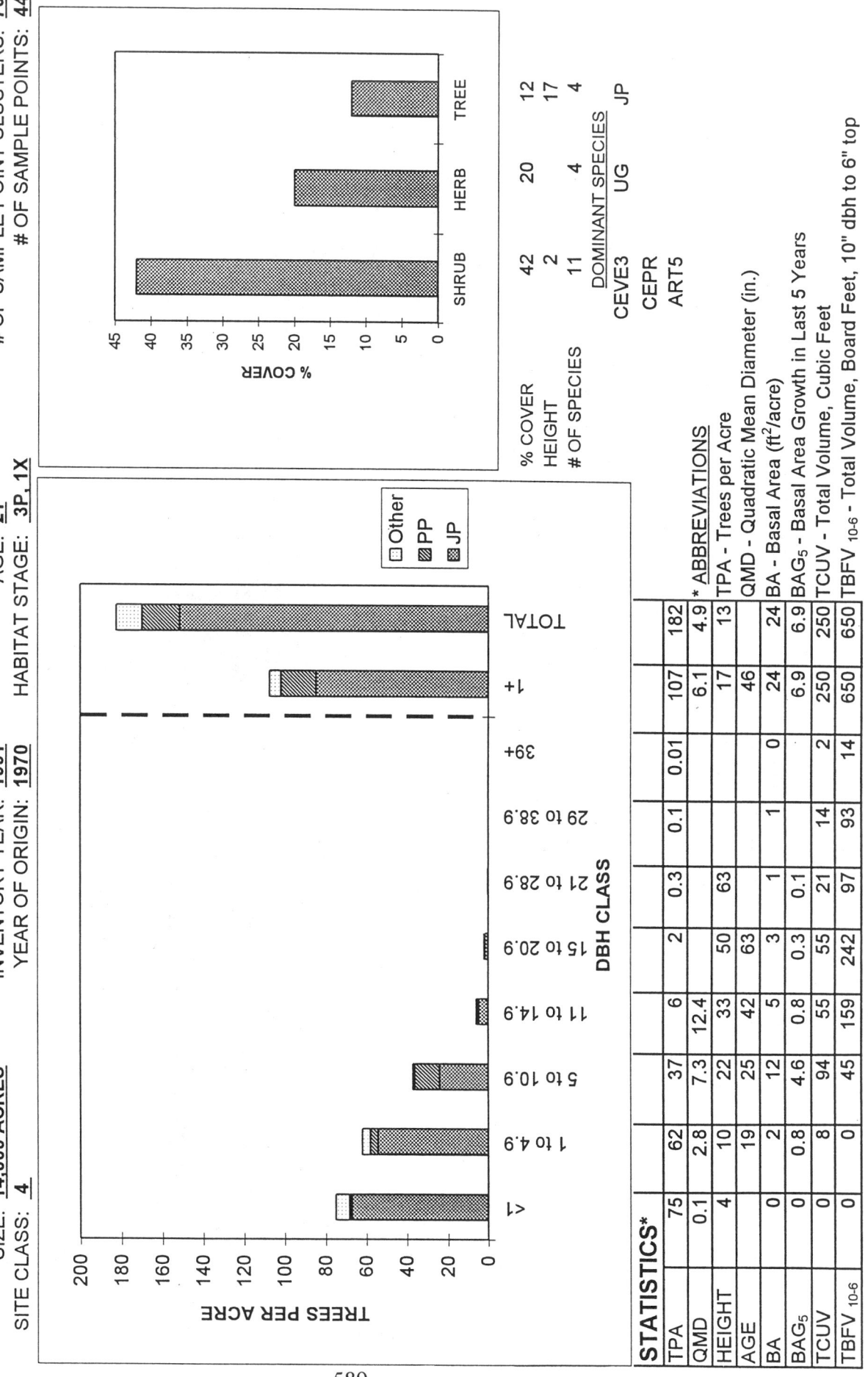

% COVER	42	20	12
HEIGHT	2		17
# OF SPECIES	11	4	4

DOMINANT SPECIES

CEVE3	UG	JP
CEPR		
ART5		

STATISTICS*

	<1	1 to 4.9	5 to 10.9	11 to 14.9	15 to 20.9	21 to 28.9	29 to 38.9	39+	1+	TOTAL
TPA	75	62	37	6	2	0.3	0.1	0.01	107	182
QMD	0.1	2.8	7.3	12.4					6.1	4.9
HEIGHT	4	10	22	33	50	63			17	13
AGE		19	25	42	63				46	
BA	0	2	12	5	3	1	1	0	24	24
BAG₅	0	0.8	4.6	0.8	0.3	0.1			6.9	6.9
TCUV	0	8	94	55	55	21	14	2	250	250
TBFV ₁₀₋₆	0	0	45	159	242	97	93	14	650	650

* ABBREVIATIONS

TPA - Trees per Acre

QMD - Quadratic Mean Diameter (in.)

BA - Basal Area (ft²/acre)

BAG₅ - Basal Area Growth in Last 5 Years

TCUV - Total Volume, Cubic Feet

TBFV ₁₀₋₆ - Total Volume, Board Feet, 10" dbh to 6" top

589

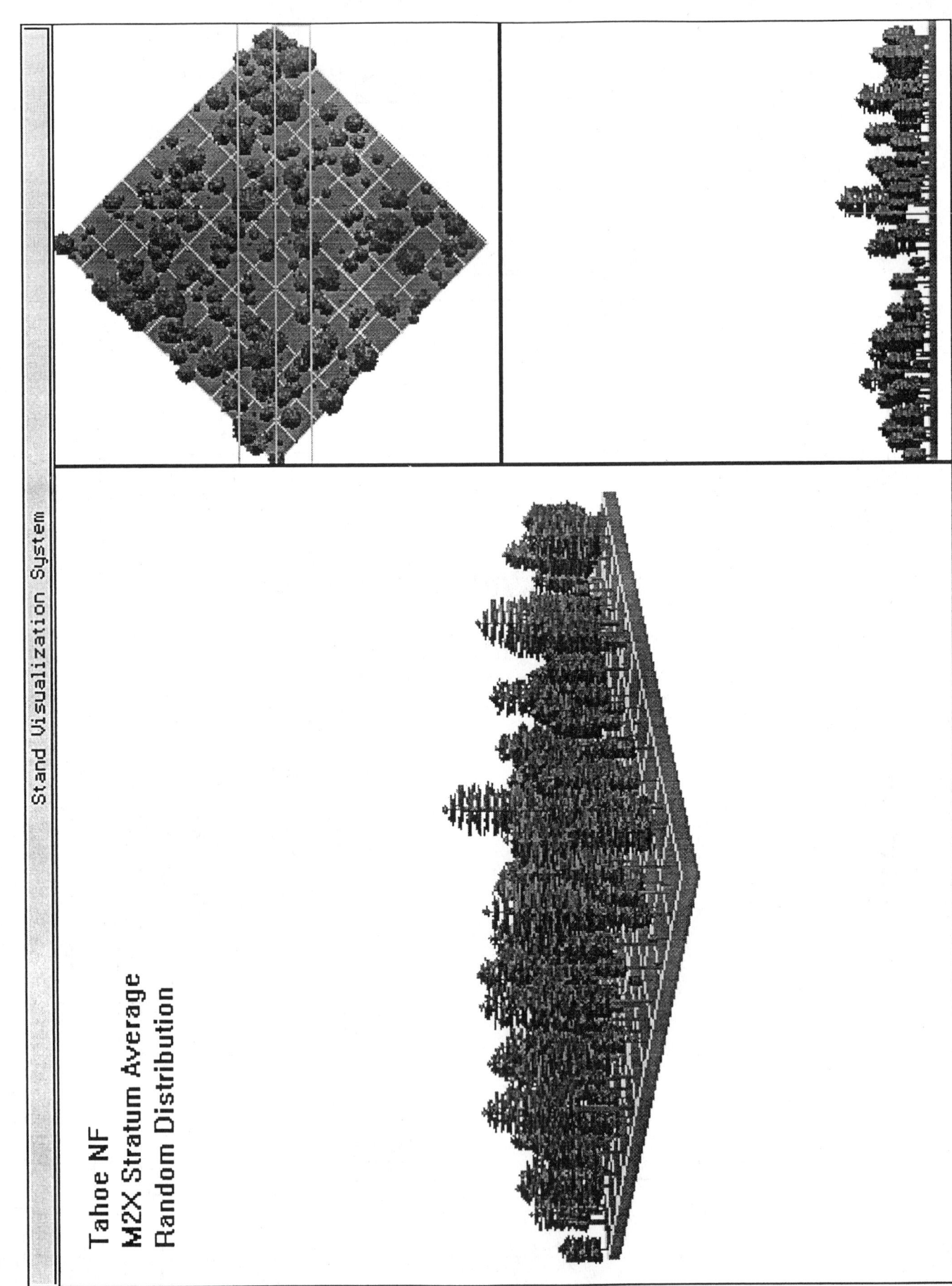

Stand Visualization System

Tahoe NF
M2X Stratum Average
Random Distribution

Stand Visualization System

Tahoe NF
M2X Strata
Cluster Plot 509
Random Distribution

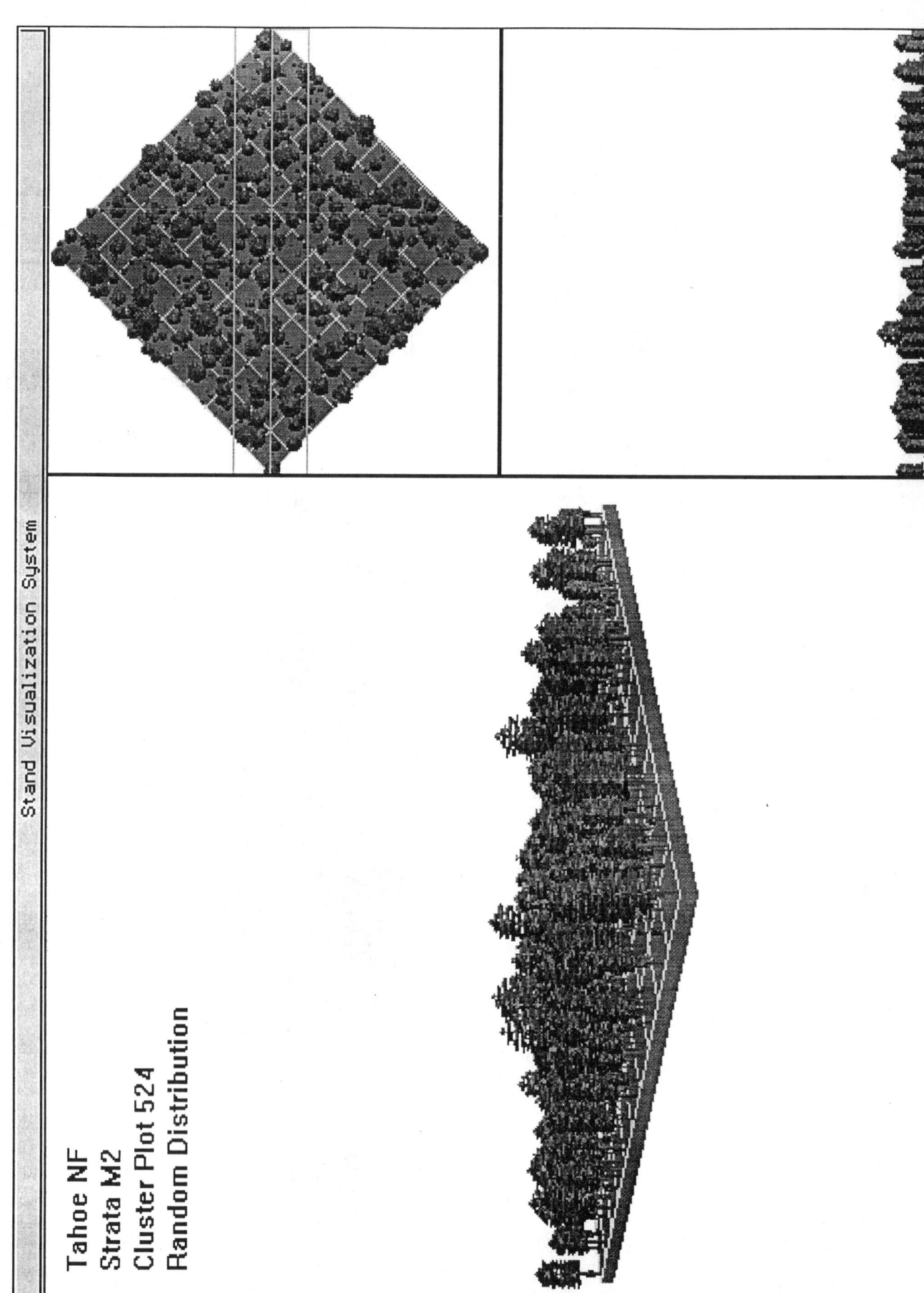

Stand Visualization System

Tahoe NF
Strata M2
Cluster Plot 524
Random Distribution

APPENDIX H

Variation Among Inventory
Sample Points

About 3,000 individual sample points of data have been collected on plantations planted prior to 1981. The graphs on the following pages are frequency diagrams for selected attributes. They are intended to convey how many of the 3,000 points contain particular values for particular attributes.

SNEP STUDY AREA

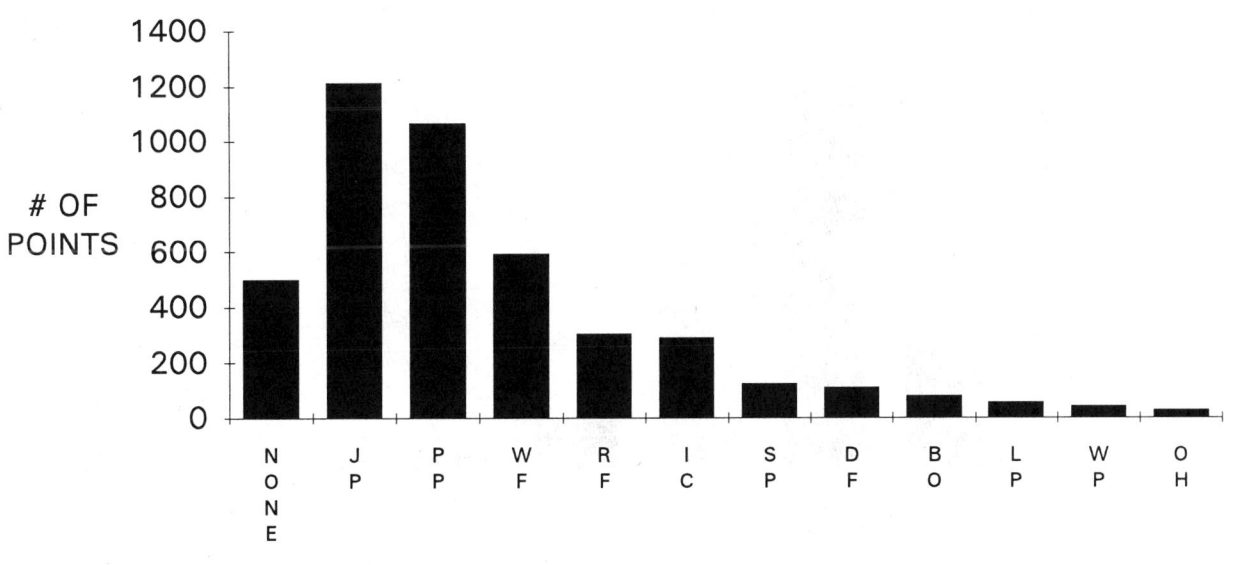

SNEP STUDY AREA

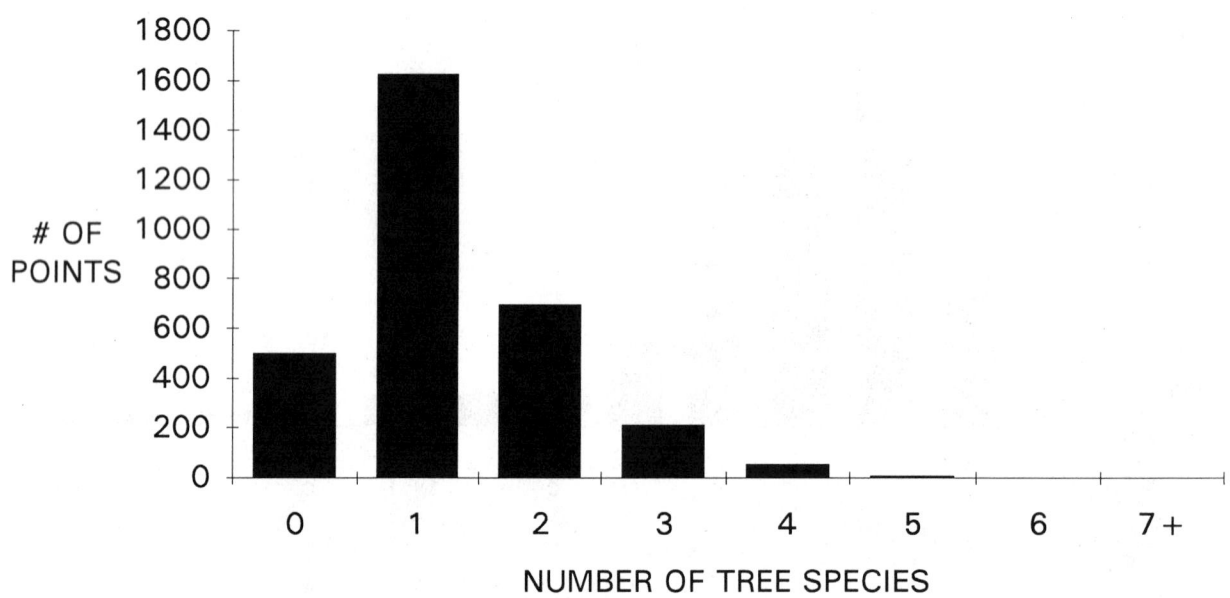

SNEP STUDY AREA
(EXCEPT SIERRA NF)

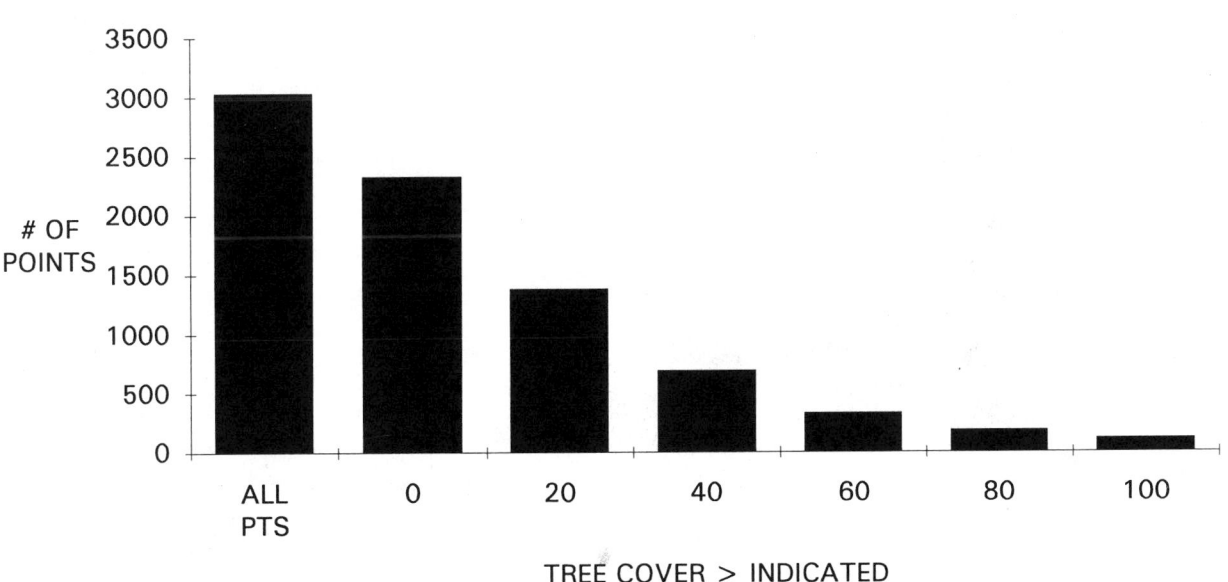

SNEP STUDY AREA

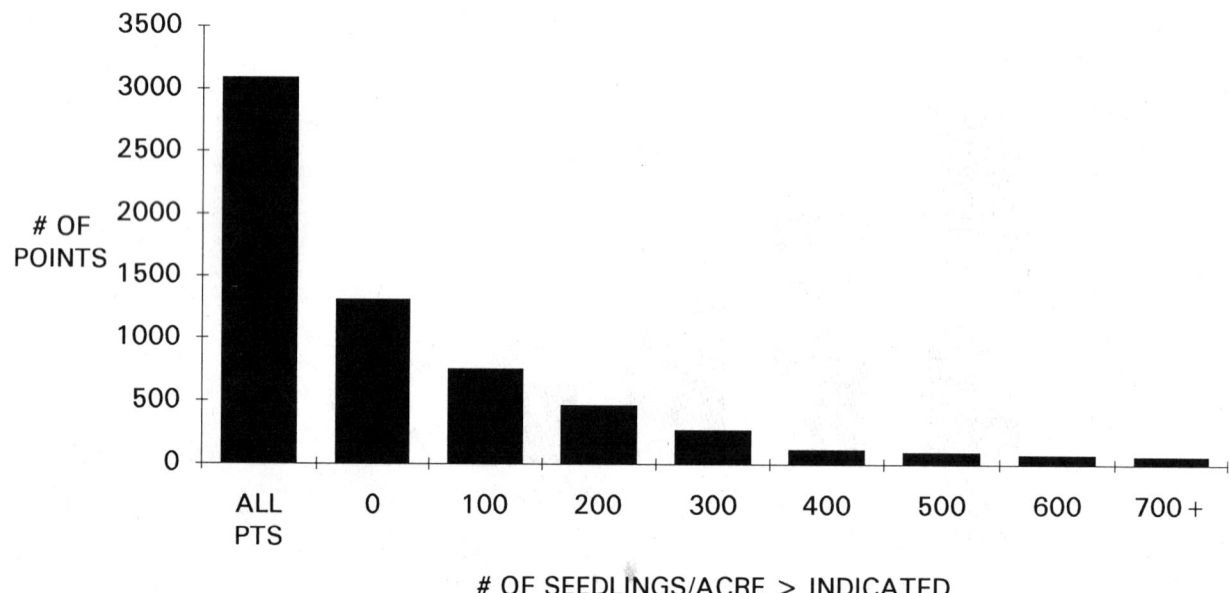

OF SEEDLINGS/ACRE > INDICATED

SNEP STUDY AREA

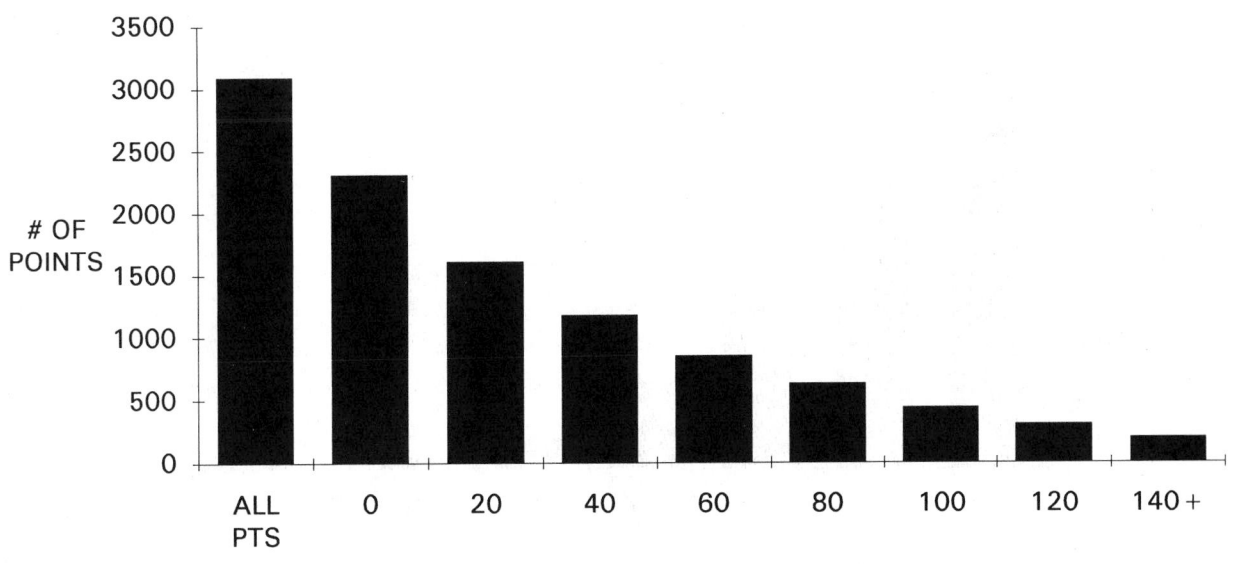

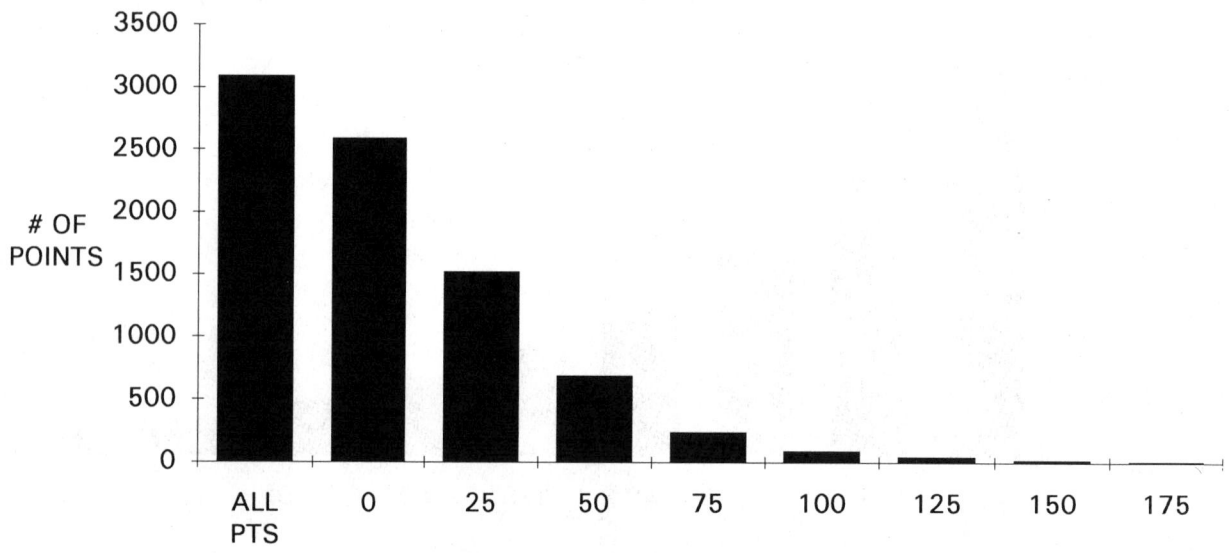

SNEP STUDY AREA

OF POINTS

TREES GREATER THAN INDICATED HEIGHT

SNEP STUDY AREA

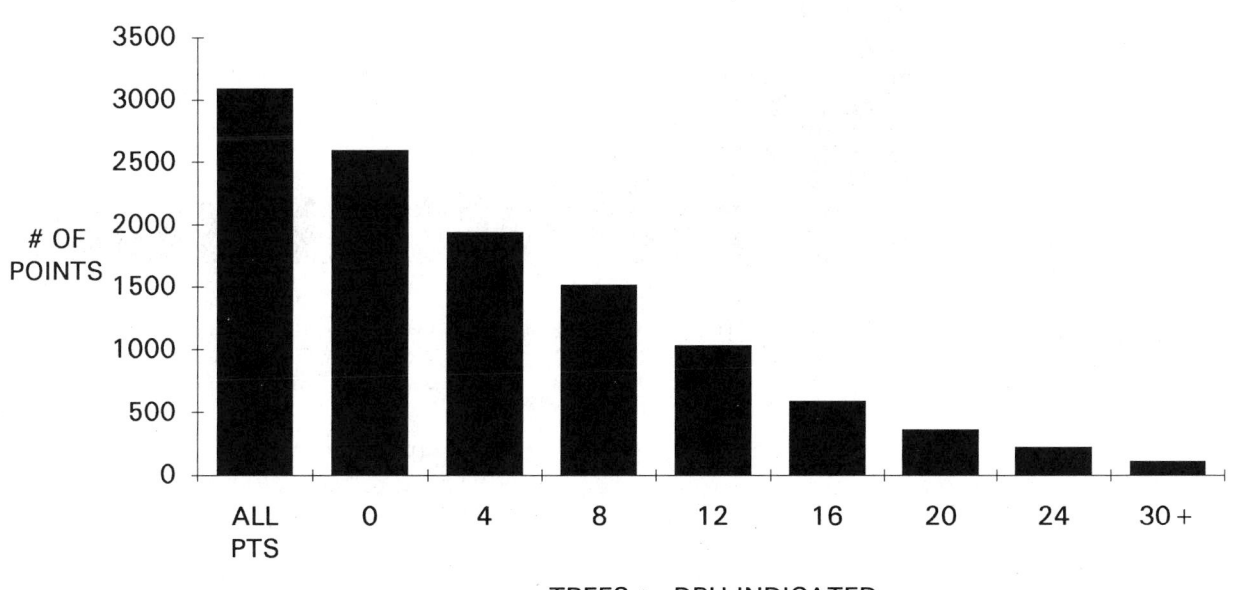

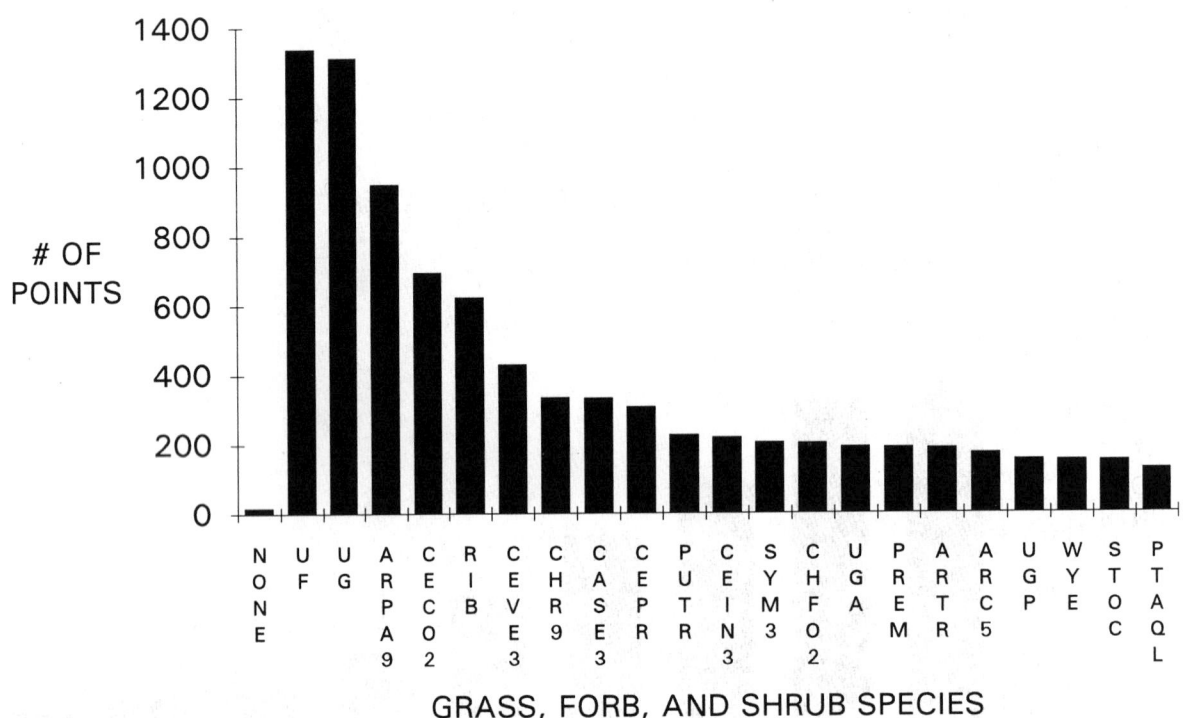

SNEP STUDY AREA

OF
POINTS

GRASS, FORB, AND SHRUB SPECIES

SNEP STUDY AREA

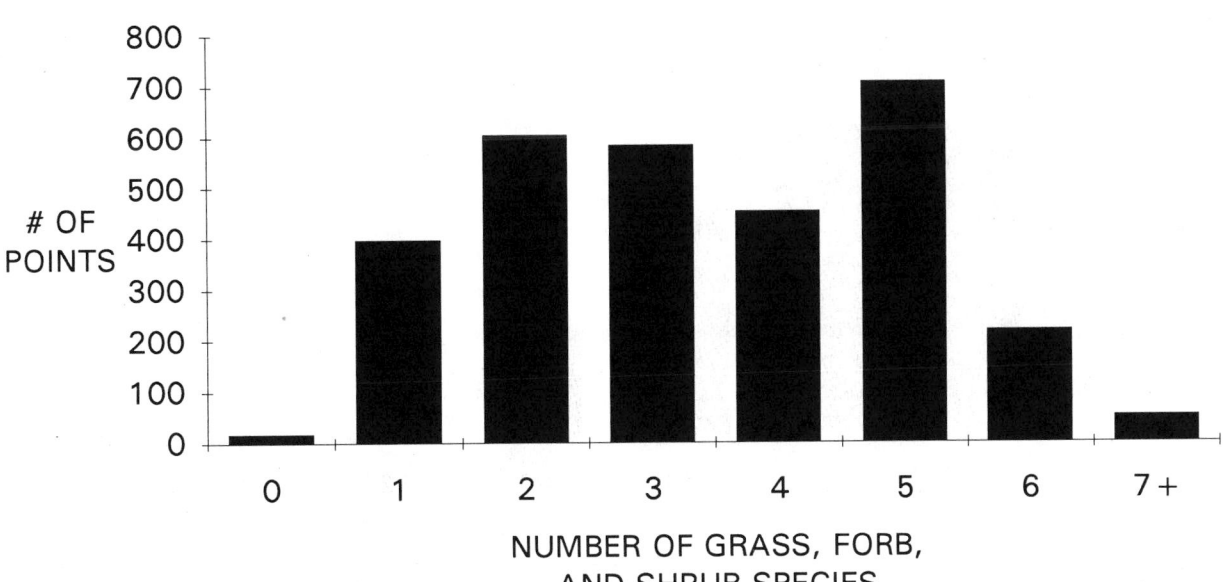

NUMBER OF GRASS, FORB,
AND SHRUB SPECIES

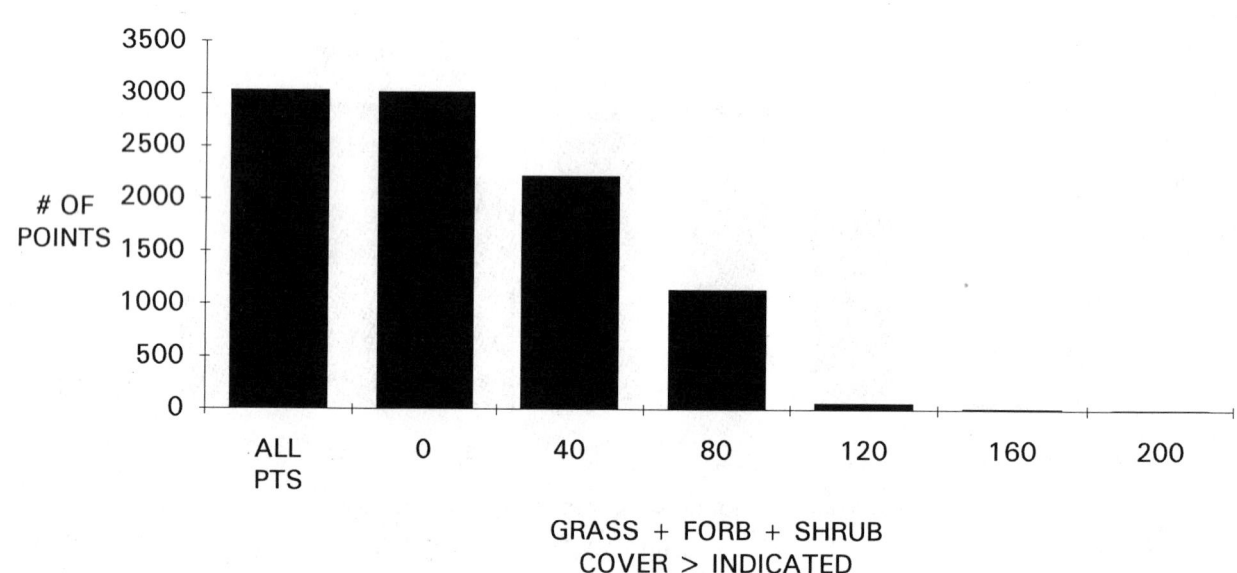

SNEP STUDY AREA
(EXCEPT SIERRA NF)

OF POINTS

GRASS + FORB + SHRUB
COVER > INDICATED

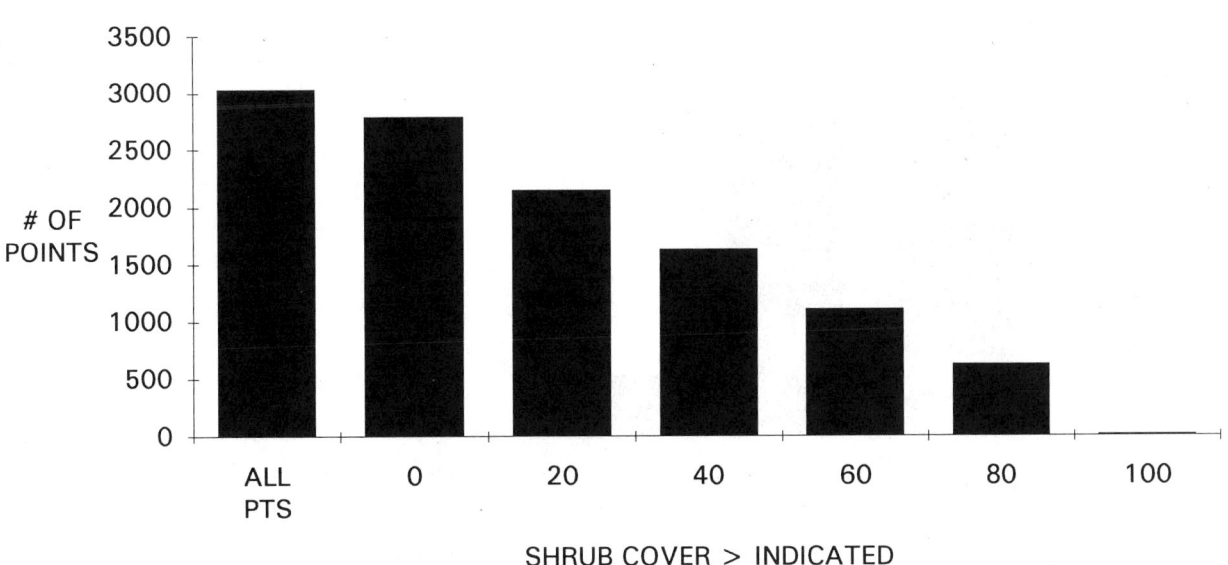

SNEP STUDY AREA
(EXCEPT SIERRA NF)

OF POINTS

SHRUB COVER > INDICATED

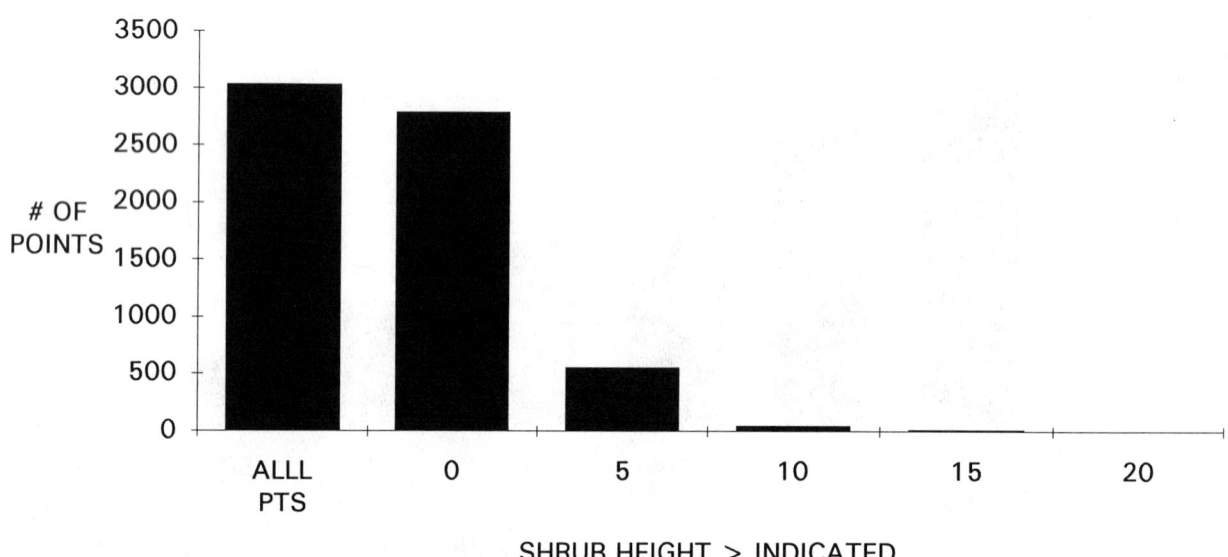

SNEP STUDY AREA
(EXCEPT SIERRA NF)

SNEP STUDY AREA
(EXCEPT SIERRA NF)

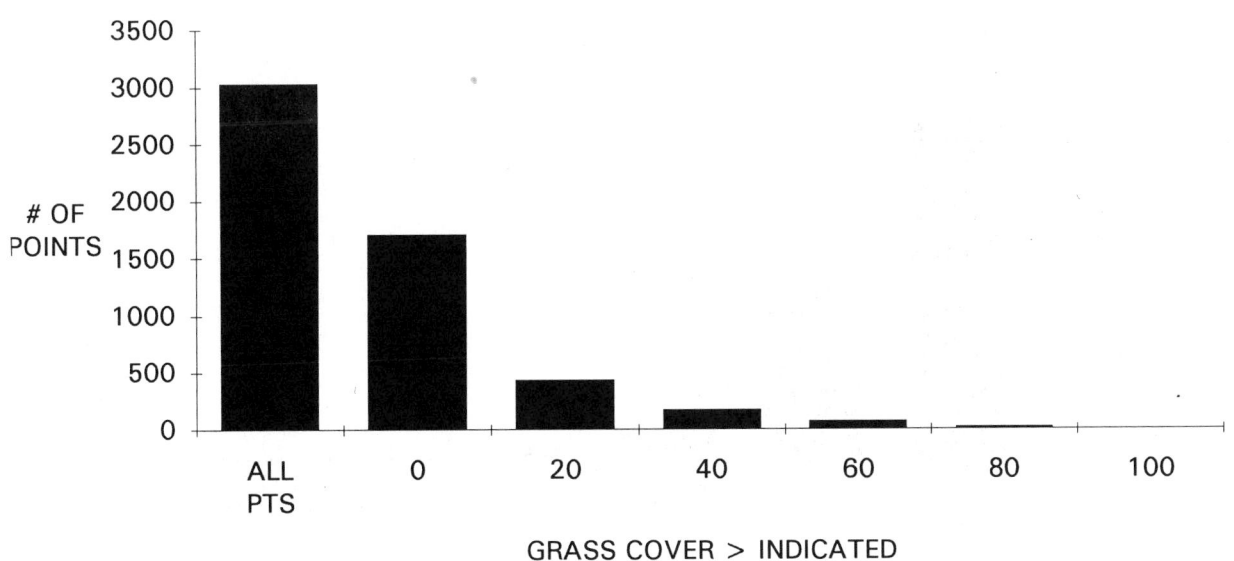

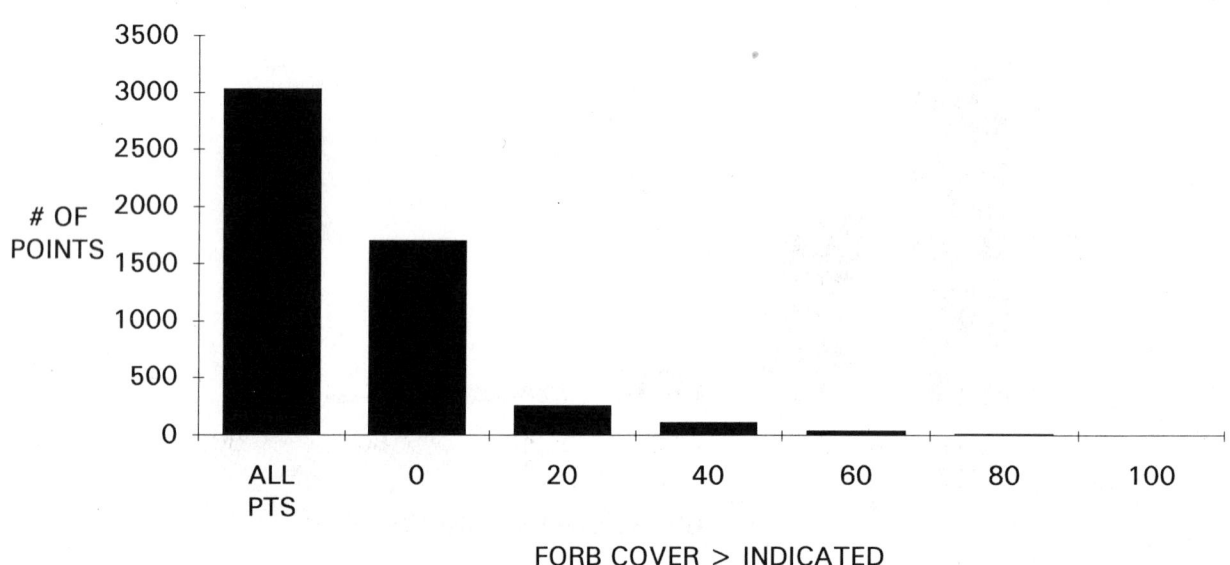

SNEP STUDY AREA
(EXCEPT SIERRA NF)

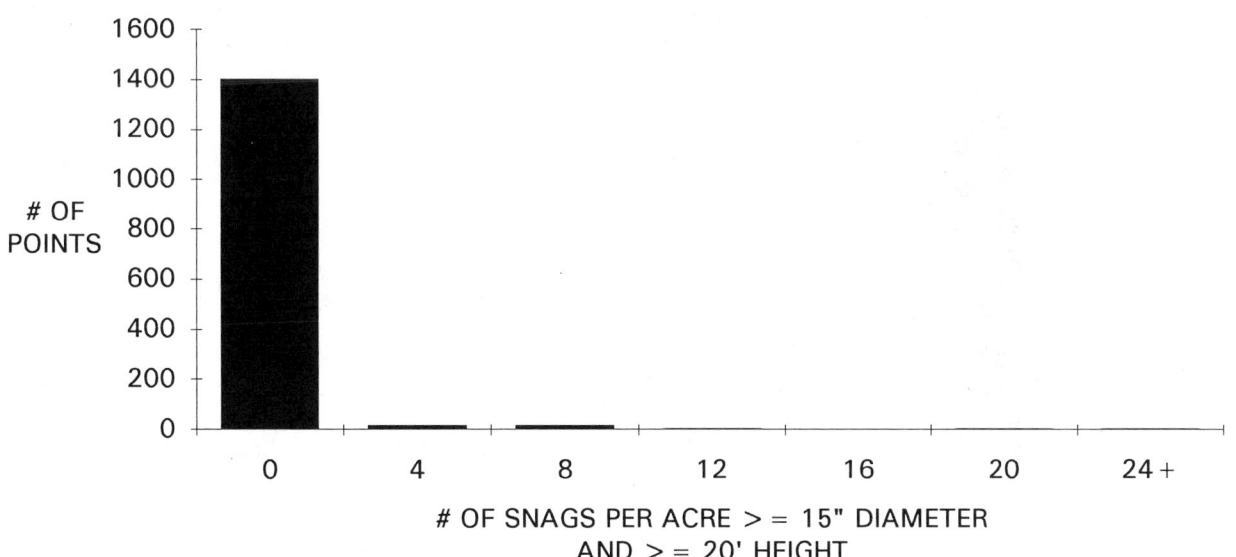

SNEP STUDY AREA
MODOC, LASSEN, ELDORADO, INYO NATIONAL FORESTS ONLY

OF
POINTS

OF SNAGS PER ACRE > = 15" DIAMETER
AND > = 20' HEIGHT

SNEP STUDY AREA
MODOC, LASSEN, ELDORADO, INYO NATIONAL FORESTS ONLY

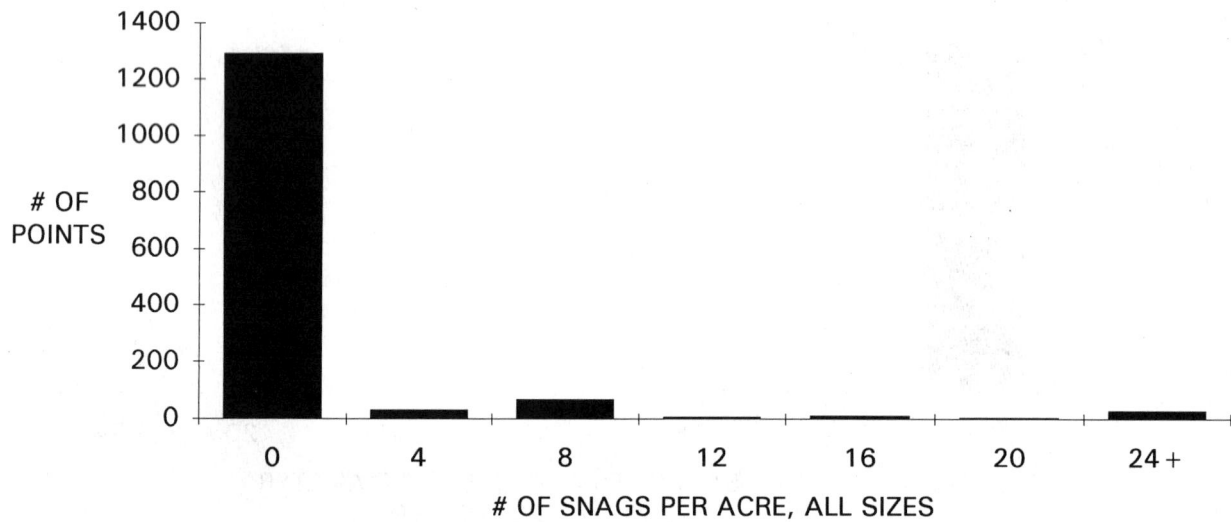

SNEP STUDY AREA
MODOC, LASSEN, ELDORADO, INYO NATIONAL FORESTS ONLY

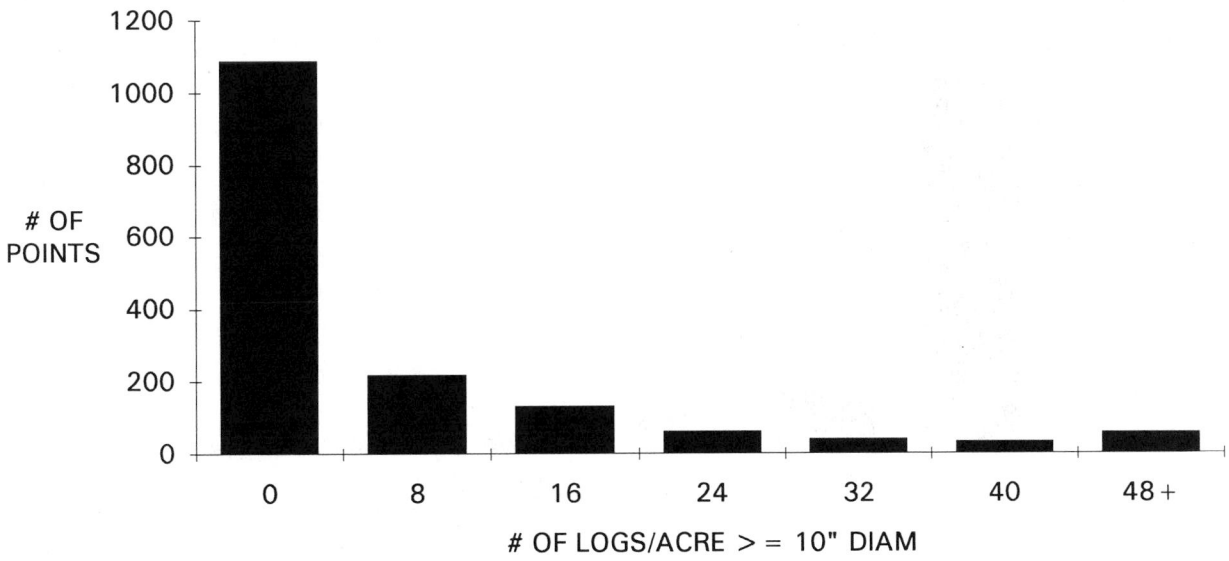

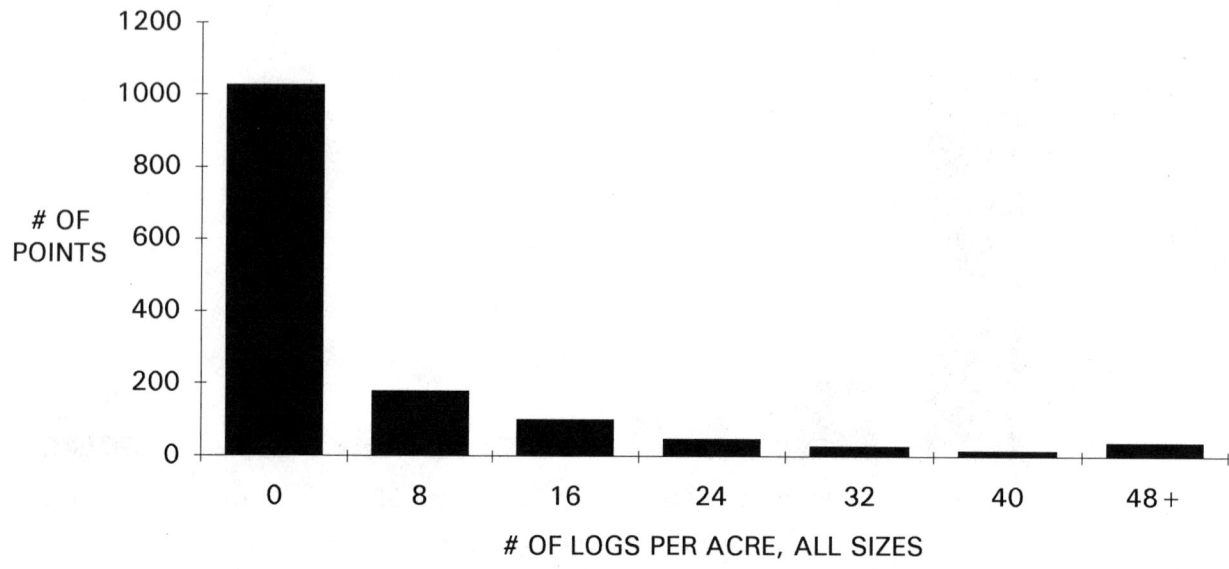

SNEP STUDY AREA
MODOC, LASSEN, ELDORADO, INYO NATIONAL FORESTS ONLY

OF LOGS PER ACRE, ALL SIZES

OF POINTS

APPENDIX I

Traditional Program Indicators

TRADITIONAL PROGRAM INDICATORS

<u>Reforestation Needs Report</u>

Reforestation needs have been assessed annually in a relatively consistent fashion since 1973. Records are on file at USDA Forest Service, San Francisco, California. The Needs Report estimates how much total acreage is in need of reforestation under the current national forest land and resource management plans and is used to monitor trends, and as a starting place for program planning and budget negotiations with Congress. Figure 1 displays the history of total reforestation needs for the SNEP Study Area.

Figure 1

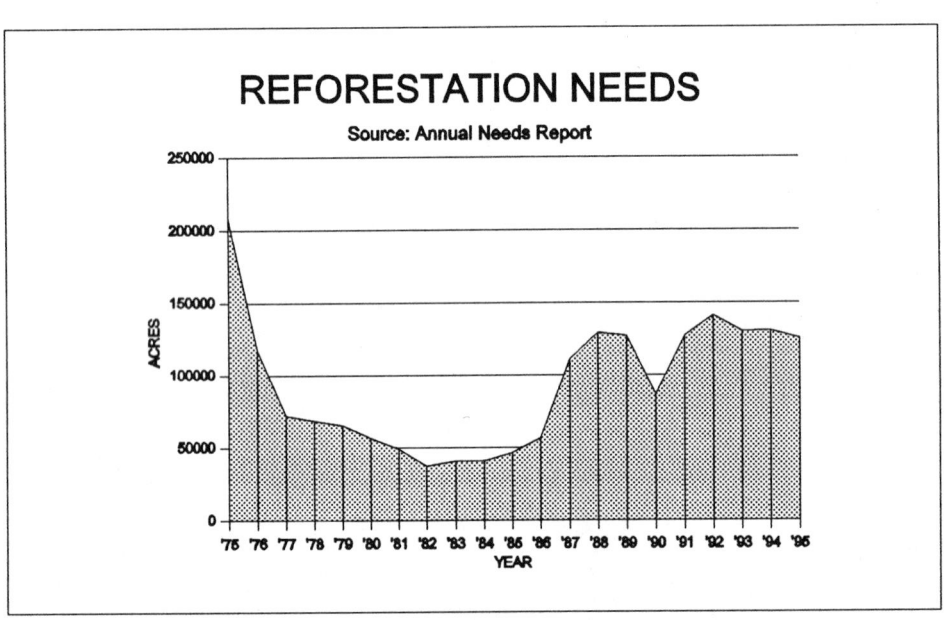

Needs estimates reflect a combination of management intent, levels of knowledge about the stocking conditions on the land base, planting rates, and trends in fire and harvest. Early 1970's estimates, reflective of management plans with most land considered suitable for timber production and many shrub covered areas lacking ground inventories, proved to be high. Subsequent improved inventories throughout the 1970's led to decisions to withdraw some areas from need, because either the lands were adequately stocked with trees or the lands did not qualify as suitable for timber production. In this same time period, planting rates exceeded the rate at which new areas were being created by fire or harvest. This combination led to the decline in need. Management plans in the early 1980's began to reflect a desire for increased harvest levels. Those increases happened in the late 1980's and, in combination with several large fires, caused needs to rise. Planting rates rose in respond to that need. 1990 is the year when the Needs Report was automated from stand records. The dip in that year is a reporting anomaly associated with that change.

Accomplishment Reports

Annual acreage treated has been reported and is on file (USDA-FS, 1956-1965; USDA-FS, 1966-1994) for the following reforestation activities for all or part of the period:

- Pre-treatment Examinations

- Site Preparation for Planting or Seeding

- Planting

- Seeding

- Site Preparation for Natural Regeneration

- Stocking/Survival Examinations

- Animal Damage Control

- Certification of Planting (seedling establishment)

- Certification of Seeding (seedling establishment)

- Certification of Natural Regeneration With Site Prep (seedling establishment)

- Certification of Natural Regeneration Without Site Prep (seedling establishment)

Using these reports, the intended indicator of success is a comparison between acres planted and certification of planting (establishment). The measure has never been reliable for these reasons:

- It compares different land areas. The areas planted in a given year are different than the ones being certified. The comparison would be valid if the annual planting amount was constant, as it was in the 1970's, but not since.

- Incentives to conduct and report planting operations are built in to the budget and management performance evaluation system. No such incentives exist for conducting certifications.

- Those that make the decisions to certify have a conservative bias. There is a tendency to withhold certification until the likelihood of tree persistence is virtually certain. Even low risks of fire, insect damage, animal damage, or dessication from moisture competition with competing vegetation are often viewed as cause to withhold certification.

Funding Levels

The primary source for reforestation funding is timber sale receipts retained for reforestation under the authority of the Knutson-Vandenberg Act of June 9, 1930 (46 Stat. 527; 16 U.S.C. 576-576b). A secondary source of funding for reforestation is annual appropriations from Congress. Total funding is declining because declining harvest levels have reduced available K-V funds; appropriations remain relatively constant, as displayed in Figure 2.

Figure 2

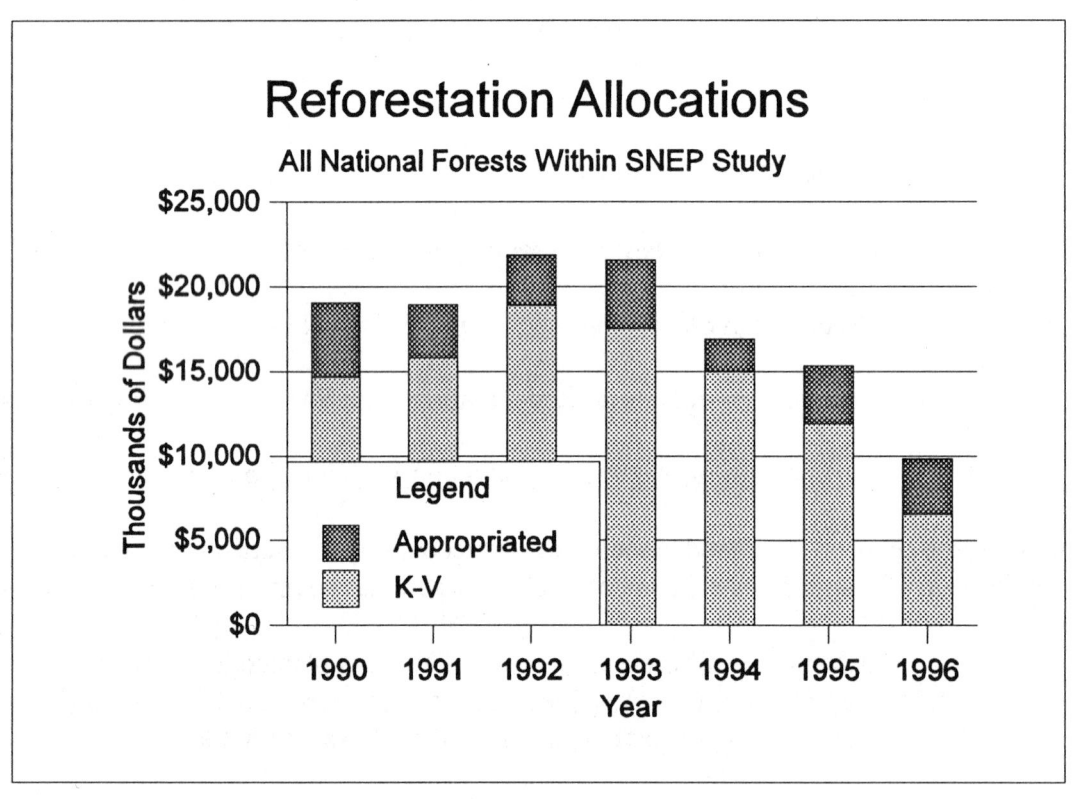

Unit Costs

The cost per unit of accomplishment is the primary management indicator of economic efficiency. Unit cost is calculated by dividing the funding level by the number of acres of *qualifying* accomplished activities. The activities that qualify are:

- Planting

- Seeding

- Site Preparation for Natural Regeneration

- Certification of Natural Regeneration Without Site Prep

The following activities are paid for with reforestation funds but accomplished acreage for these activities is not included in unit cost calculations:

- Pre-treatment Examinations

- Site Preparation for Planting or Seeding

- Stocking/Survival Examinations

- Animal Damage Control

- Certification of Planting

- Certification of Seeding

- Certification of Natural Regeneration With Site Prep

Figures 3-6 display current trends. Allocations are on a downward trend. Qualifying activity accomplishments are stable (Figure 4). Unit costs, therefore, are on a downward trend (Fugure 5). However, this has been achieved primarily by reducing the amount of site preparation (Figure 6), a non-qualifying activity. Decreasing the amount of site preparation will adversely affect the quantity of reforestation accomplished because some areas cannot be planted successfully without site preparation. For those areas that can be planted, reduced tree survival rates and increased release costs are expected.

Trends

Figure 3

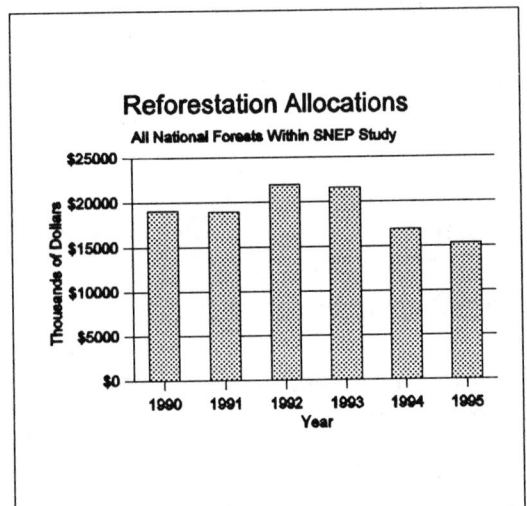

Figure 4

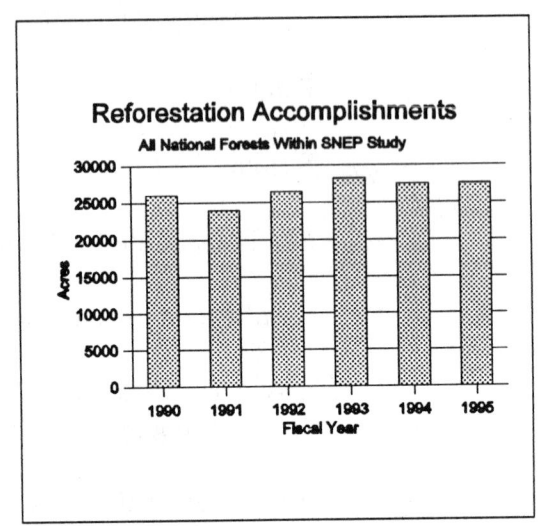

Figure 5

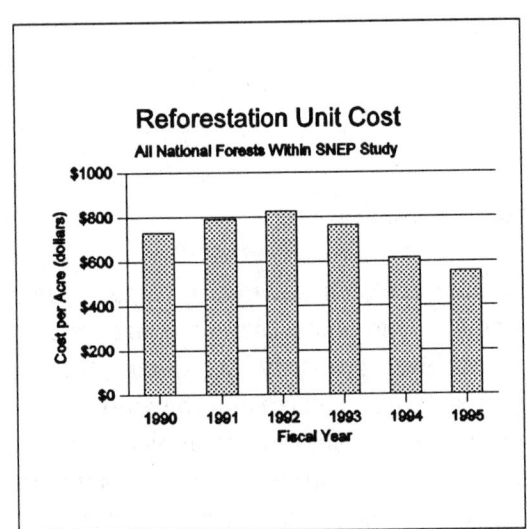

Figure 6

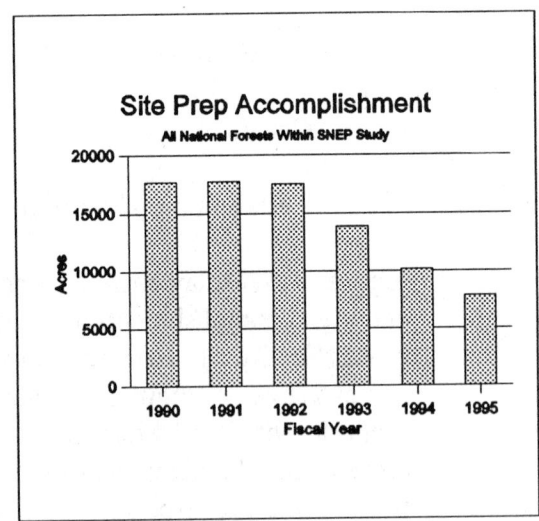

Tree Survival Report

Tree survival rates have been assessed at the end of the 1st and 3rd growing seasons for each land area planted since the Forest Service began operational planting (Fowells and Dunning, 1948). Records from 1980 forward are on file at USDA Forest Service, San Francisco, CA. Figures 7 and 8 summarize this information. Survival rates are used as a measure of efficiency. They convey little information about stocking success in plantations. Note that more shade tolerant species (firs) have lower survival rates than less tolerant species (pines), which is a result of their more restrictive physiologic requirements. Tradeoffs between survival rates and number of trees planted can be made to achieve the same stocking.. Cost is a driving factor in the decision regarding how many trees to plant.

Figure 7

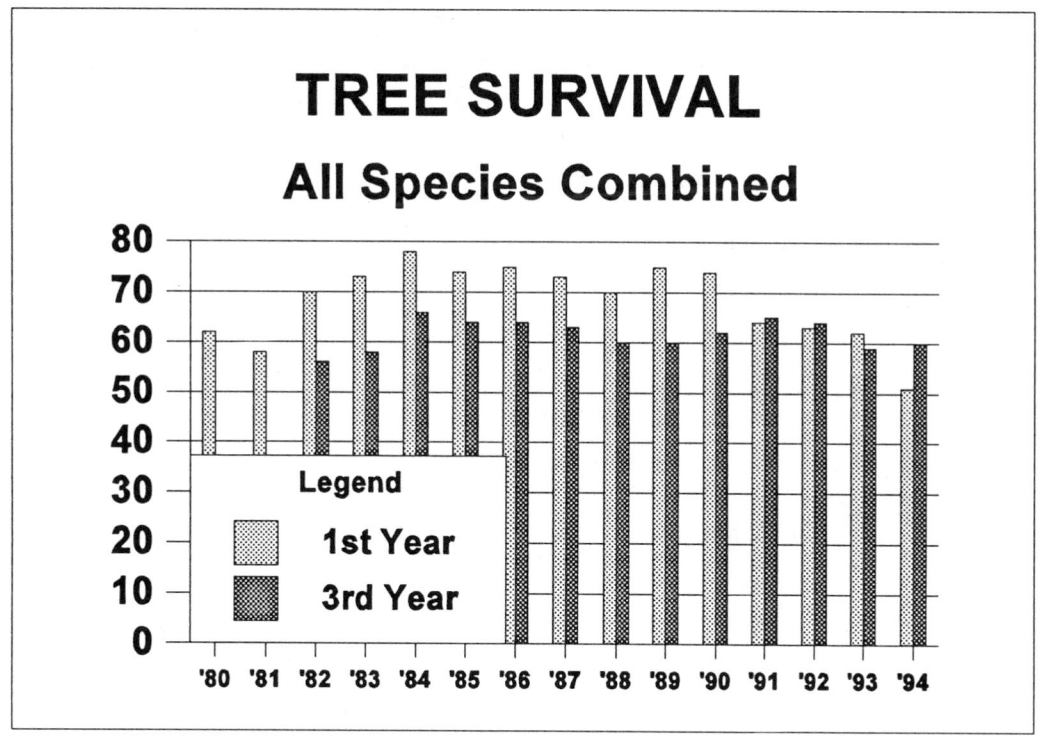

Figure 8

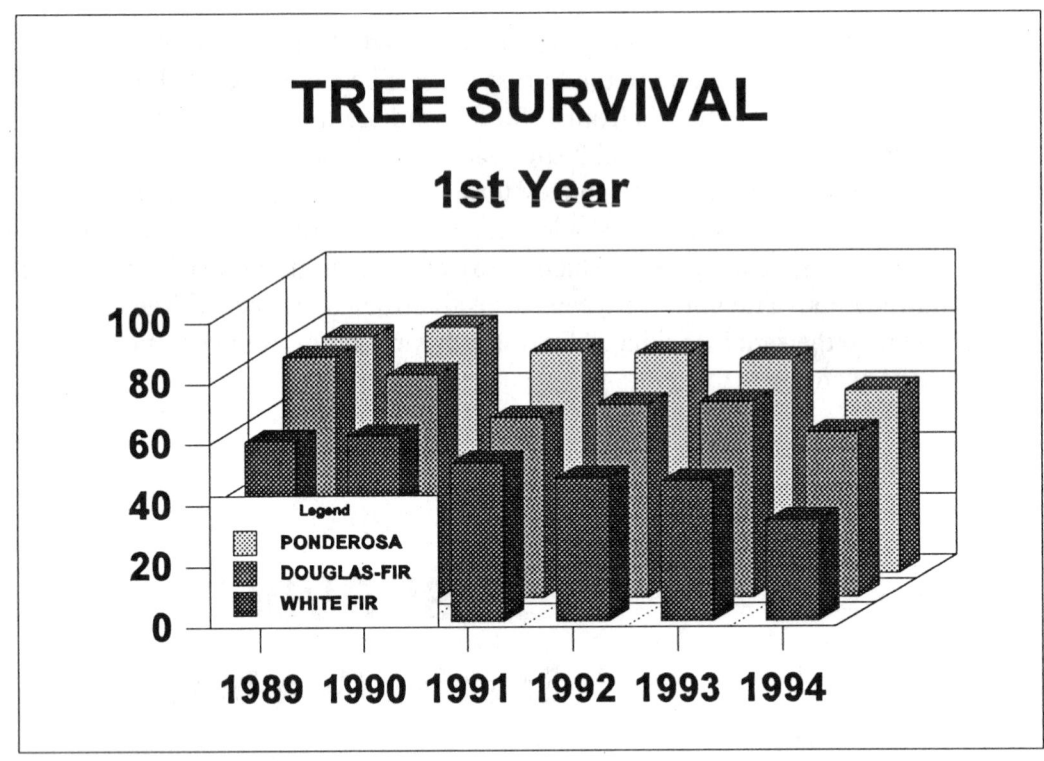

PHILIP M. McDONALD
USDA Forest Service
Pacific Southwest Forest and
   Range Experiment Station
Redding, California

JOHN C. TAPPEINER
USDI Forest and Rangeland Ecosystem
   Science Center
and
College of Forestry,
University of Oregon
Corvallis, Oregon

Silviculture-Ecology of Forest-Zone Hardwoods in the Sierra Nevada

Sierra Nevada Ecosystem Project: Final report to Congress, vol. III, *Assessments, Commissioned Reports, and Background Information.* Davis: University of California, Centers for Water and Wildland Resources, 1996.

621

Abstract

Although the principal hardwood species in the forest zone of the Sierra Nevada (California black oak, tanoak, Pacific madrone, and canyon live oak) are key components of many ecosystems, they have received comparatively little study. Currently they are underutilized and unmanaged. This paper brings together what is known on the silviculture-ecology of these species and weaves it into a framework that has value to the academician and the practitioner. With species amounts, utilization, adaptations, and ecology as background, seed production, regeneration, early seedling growth, root crown sprouts, growth of trees and stands, and epicormic branching are presented. Ten major points having management implications conclude the paper.

Key Words: Hardwoods, ecology, regeneration, vegetative propagation, growth

INTRODUCTION

Native hardwoods in the forest zone of California's Sierra Nevada constitute a major resource that currently has vast potential, but about which critical information is absent or fragmented. In old-growth stands, the hardwoods are decadent and dying, but little regeneration is present to replace them. Current artificial regeneration techniques are ineffective. In younger stands, tree density generally is too high, and tree growth is miniscule, but thinning guides by species and site quality are scarce. Oak acorns and Pacific madrone berries are recognized as being critical to wildlife, but the timing and magnitude of acorn and berry crops are poorly documented. The gain in water yield from deciduous hardwoods, relative to evergreen hardwoods and conifers, has been documented in northern and southeastern American stands, but no such studies are known for western hardwood stands.

Forest-zone hardwoods can be found throughout the Sierra Nevada and are an inherent part of many ecosystems. Until the hardwood component of these ecosystems is better understood, their management will be incomplete.

Research on the silviculture-ecology of forest-zone hardwoods in the Sierra Nevada of California has been scant. When knowledge from research in the Cascade Mountains of southwestern Oregon is included, several gaps are filled, but the overall research base remains small. Most of the work in both areas has been concentrated at a few locations where trials have been mostly case histories. If there is a strength, it is that most of the major components of hardwood silviculture have been examined, albeit not in depth. Another strength is that work in both California and Oregon, where replicated, has shown similar trends. Further, ecological and silvicultural findings on related species of Quercus in eastern North America show similarity to findings on western species of Quercus in several areas. The point is that the silvicultural concepts and principals presented here have support, but much more research is needed.

Because ecosystem management is likely to be the management paradigm for natural resources in the future, the material that follows needs to be put in perspective. Basically, the Sierra Nevada forest-zone hardwoods have never had a management philosophy because they were regarded as being largely uneconomical and something to be converted to pines and firs. McDonald and Huber (1994, 1995) have suggested that this is not realistic. The forest zone hardwoods have great worth when the total resource (wildlife, water, aesthetics, wood products) is assessed. Within the ecosystem management perspective, the role of silviculture and a viable hardwood timber processing industry is vital. Silviculturists will carry out the prescriptions needed to create, maintain, and even enhance desired assemblages of species, structures, and growth rates. The raw material derived from attaining these prescriptions will sustain a viable hardwood processing industry. Inherent to this vital role, however, is recognition that what is now known is not enough. New techniques must be tried, and new knowledge, particularly on a large area-long timeframe basis, must be developed. This paper presents what is known on the silviculture and ecology of forest-zone hardwoods in the Sierra Nevada.

SPECIES, OCCURRENCE, AND INVENTORY

Although California's indigenous hardwood resources can be divided into two basic groups: those that grow in the foothills and woodlands at lower elevations, and those that grow in the forest-zone at higher elevations, only those that grow in the forest zone are discussed here. And for them, only those that are the most abundant and have a fairly large natural range in the Sierra Nevada, are presented. These include tanoak (Lithocarpus densiflorus [Hook. & Arn.] Rehd.), California black oak (Quercus kelloggii Newb.), Pacific madrone (Arbutus menziesii Pursh), and canyon live oak (Quercus chrysolepis Liebm.). All of these species have an established history of utilization for wood products and other yields (Economic Development Administration 1968), and as food and raw material for human beings (Wolf 1945), especially Native Americans (Baumhoff 1963).

Seldom do these hardwood species, alone or together, occupy entire mountain sides. Most often they are found as single trees, in clumps or groves, or occupying a given aspect in areas of up to 100 acres. Exceptions can occur, however, where extensive cutting and burning of conifer associates has allowed hardwood species to dominate over much larger areas. Seldom do each of these species grow in pure stands; rarely are all of them found growing together. Only in the northern Sierra Nevada are tanoak, Pacific madrone, and California black oak associates, sometimes with scattered canyon live oak on poorer sites. In the southern Sierra Nevada, California black oak and canyon live oak may intermix occasionally, but usually grow alone. Canyon live oak is widespread throughout the Sierra Nevada, particularly on poor rocky sites and on south-facing walls of canyons where it often forms nearly pure stands. All of the hardwood species mentioned in this paper except Pacific madrone have a shrub form. In most instances, the shrub forms grow on poor or extremely poor sites and, in general, extend the specie's natural range to higher elevations. Shrub tanoak (Lithocarpus densiflorus var. echinoides) does this also, but is found on good sites, especially where moisture is plentiful.

Rarely are the hardwoods found without conifer associates. The most common are Douglas-fir (Pseudotsuga menziesii [Mirb.] Franco) and ponderosa pine (Pinus ponderosa Dougl. ex Laws var. ponderosa), with California white fir (Abies concolor var. lowiana [Gord.] Lemm.), incense-cedar (Libocedrus decurrens Torr.), and sugar pine (Pinus lambertiana Dougl.) less abundant.

Shrub species that associate with the hardwoods in the Sierra Nevada tend to be few and variable in number, primarily because of differences in tree density. Some common shrub genera include Arctostaphylos, Ceanothus, Rhamnus, Prunus, Castanopsis, and Adenostoma. Forbs and grasses, like the shrubs, vary tremendously beneath the hardwoods. They can be almost totally absent in the shade beneath dense stands, or quite diverse and abundant in more open stands.

The area in the Sierra Nevada clothed with forest-zone hardwoods totals 423,000 acres (Bolsinger 1988). Total growing stock volume of the principal forest-zone hardwood species in California in trees 5.0 inches in breast height diameter (dbh) and larger in 1985 was over 1.6 billion cubic feet with California black oak, canyon live oak, tanoak, and Pacific madrone constituting 92 percent of the total (table 1). This volume was split almost evenly between public and private land. Total sawtimber volume of the principal forest-zone hardwood species in the Sierra Nevada in trees 11.0 inches dbh and larger in 1985 was over 722 million cubic feet (table 1). Local volume tables for California black oak, Pacific madrone, and tanoak on a high site in northern California are available (McDonald 1978).

A major attribute of California hardwoods is that much of the sawtimber volume is in trees greater than 29 inches dbh. This is in strong contrast to hardwoods in the rest of the Nation where almost all trees in this size class have been harvested.

UTILIZATION

Although timber and wood products are generally thought to be a major use, a more detailed examination gives timber a low ranking. Currently, wildlife ranks first, followed by water, pleasing scenery, and wood products (McDonald and Huber 1995).

The hardwood forest environment, and especially its unique foodstuffs of acorns and berries has critical value for wildlife (McDonald and Huber 1994). At least 355 species in the western Sierra Nevada alone call this area "home" (Verner and Boss 1980). These include 26 species of amphibians, 27 reptiles, 208 birds, and 94 mammals.

Water is a major yield from the Sierra Nevada, and and one that is now reaching critical status in California. Current use in California is about 42 million acre feet of water annually with a predicted increase of 3.5 million acre feet by the year 2010 (California Department of Forestry and Fire Protection 1988). Increases are primarily for domestic and industrial use and to satisfy in-stream flow requirements. Much of the increase will have to come from the Sierra Nevada. Currently, 41 percent of total runoff in the state or over 32 million acre feet originate in the Sacramento and San Joaquin River Basins (California Department of Forestry and Fire Protection 1988).

Pleasing scenery is a major "yield" from the land and the colorful hardwood forests give accent to spring and contrast and beauty to the fall (Heady and Zinke 1978, Litton and McDonald 1980, McDonald and Whiteley 1972). Californians currently spend more than 100 million days each year recreating on forest land administered by state and federal governments (California Department of Forestry and Fire Protection 1988). This is predicted to increase, and a significant portion of it is expected to be in the Sierra Nevada.

Utilization of Sierra Nevada hardwoods for lumber and wood products began with the gold rush of 1849 and has continued to the present. Tannic acid for curing leather, crude lumber, charcoal, and fuelwood were the first uses. By the late 1880's high quality lumber for furniture, balconies, mantles, and flooring was being manufactured from California black oak. By the 1920's, a wealth of products were being manufactured from Sierra Nevada hardwoods. In addition to lumber, flooring, barrels, charcoal, and fuelwood, hardwoods were utilized for industrial timbers, crossties, novelties, pipes, bobbins and shuttles, and handles for tools. More recently, pallets, odor-free food storage units, veneer, and chips for pulp have been manufactured (Economic Development Corporation 1968, Huber and McDonald 1992). By 1994, no fixed, large-scale manufacturing industry existed. The only uses for Sierra Nevada hardwoods were for pulp chips and fuelwood. However, local "cottage" industries were springing up in the northern and central Sierra. They employed mini-mills and other modern machines to produce high-quality lumber for furniture, flooring, novelties, and other uses. Many new developments, among them the change in attitude on hardwoods from negative to positive, better estimates of the inventory base and resource value, cooperatives, better seasoning techniques, and a host of new marketing and promotional developments, suggest a revitalized hardwood industry with a solid future (McDonald and Huber 1994).

ADAPTATION AND ECOLOGY

Based on millions of years of adaptation through natural selection (Chaney 1925), the four major hardwood species in the Sierra Nevada are well adapted to changes in the environment. They ought to be--the fossil record reveals that they have lineage to the Mascall flora of the Miocene epoch of 12-26 million years ago. Consequently, they have survived such major geologic events as glaciation, volcanism, upthrusting, and subsidence. They also are well adapted to a broad range of more recent biotic agents and abiotic events (Cooper 1922, Keeley 1977, Kummerow 1973, Mooney and Dunn 1970). And the harsher the site, the better adapted they are. The adaptations are both morphological and physiological. Morphological features include special structures and coatings on leaves and stems to inhibit moisture loss, smooth upper-stem bark to facilitate the transport of water to the base of the tree via stemflow, an extensive deep-thrusting root system, capability to form a burl at an early age, and capacity to produce both an enormous amount of seed and large numbers of rapidly-growing root crown sprouts. The burl has at least two important functions: as a reproductive platform by virtue of its many dormant buds (from which sprouts arise), and as a food-storage organ. Physiological processes involve photosynthesis, transpiration, and respiration, which govern plant metabolism, energy intake, water losses, and eventually dominance potential (McDonald 1982).

The capability to internally monitor and control respiration is particularly worthwhile. Normally, plants respire excessively when internal moisture levels are low and internal temperatures become high. But these hardwoods have a built-in "fail-safe" mechanism that lowers respiration, even though temperatures may become quite high (Mooney and Dunn 1970). This keeps the plant from using all its energy reserves during the hot windy days of late summer. Equally important is that photosynthesis can take place at low internal moisture levels and that it can happen quickly after the onset of favorable conditions. Positive net photosythesis for an hour, early in the morning of a hot summer day, or for an hour in the early afternoon of a warm day in midwinter, provide energy inputs at opportune times.

The advantages gained from the adaptations above combine to give the species a special competitive advantage that takes the form of water wasting. The hardwood species discourage competition by using all the water in the soil without paying the price of high internal moisture stress, high respiration, and eventual death. Species that lack these adaptations succumb, because no water is left to support life functions.

A major limitation, however, is tree height--Sierra Nevada hardwoods do not grow as tall as conifer associates. Because of their shorter stature, the hardwoods need periodic disturbance to dominate. As Atzet and Martin (1992) noted "Disturbance brings change that helps maintain compositional, structural, and functional diversity, helps to select adapted, resilient individuals, and helps to dampen the effects of minor environmental oscillations and extremes. Change is an essential ingredient of healthy ecosystems." Sierra Nevada forest-zone hardwoods depend primarily on fire, logging, blow-down, insect devastation, or mass soil movement to provide the disturbed and temporarily vegetation-free ground needed for establishment (McDonald and others 1983). Continued absence of disturbance allows the conifers to overtop and eventually eliminate the hardwoods.

Fire is both a blessing and a curse for forest-zone hardwood species. On one hand, fire creates the necessary disturbance by killing the conifers. The hardwoods often are killed as well, but only aboveground. Belowground, they retain the capability to sprout and grow rapidly. On the other hand, the thin, poorly insulated bark provides little protection from heat. Just a little fire kills the trees to groundline. Once a hardwood stand is established, fire plainly is undesirable for scores of years.

SILVICULTURE

Seed Production

For the four primary hardwoods in the Sierra Nevada, the magnitude and periodicity of seed production are quite variable and dependent more on local conditions than on regional ones. For example, one study reported that abundant seed crops of California black oak were produced at 2- to 3- year intervals (Roy 1962). At the 2,500-foot elevation on the Challenge Experimental Forest in the northern Sierra Nevada, medium to bumper black oak seed crops were produced in 4 of 20 years. At the 2,800-foot elevation in south-central Shasta County, medium to bumper seed crops were borne on large trees in 4 of 8 years. At the 560-foot elevation in Shasta County, black oaks yielded sound acorns in 6 of 7 years. Of these, two each rated as bumper, medium, and light (McDonald 1990). Tanoak on the Challenge Experimental Forest produced 4 medium-heavy and 9 light-very light seed crops from 1958-1981. During the same period, Pacific madrone yielded 2 medium-heavy and 10 light-very light seed crops (McDonald (1992). Canyon live oak is reported to produce good seed crops every 2 to 4 years (Thornburgh 1990). The fecundity of the hardwood species, as noted by individual trees, is amazing. A 16-inch d.b.h. tanoak tree on the Challenge Experimental Forest had the equivalent of 1.1 million acorns per acre beneath it in a bumper seed year. The acorns were 79 percent sound (McDonald 1978). On the same site in a light seed year, a 15.7-inch d.b.h. Pacific madrone tree produced 107,640 berries or about 2.1 million seeds (McDonald 1978).

Regeneration

Exposure often is deadly to acorns on the ground, and only a few hours of sunlight slanting beneath a tree crown can kill the embryos. Freezing also kills the embryos in acorns that are not covered by leaves or other organic material. Deep duff and litter are ideal for germination and downward root penetration by young oak seedlings. However, any organic matter, which inevitably houses damping-off fungi and invertebrates such as slugs, is anathema to Pacific madrone seedlings. The best medium for this species is shaded, but bare mineral soil (McDonald and Tappeiner 1990, Pelton 1962).

Natural regeneration of the oaks (including tanoak) tends to be clumpy with large numbers beneath parent tree crowns and few elsewhere. After 6 to 12 years, tanoak seedlings tend to die back to the root crown, often for no obvious reason, and sprout from dormant buds on the burl (Tappeiner and McDonald 1984). Hence the seedlings become seedling-sprouts. Tanoak tends to accumulate more seedling-sprouts on the shady forest floor than other hardwood species. On a high site in the northern Sierra Nevada, young tanoaks reached a density of 6,000 per acre (McDonald 1978). Of the four major hardwood species, young Pacific madrone seedlings are the least abundant. They tend to be widely scattered with concentrations along the edges of dirt roads, at the base of overturned trees, and at other locations where the soil is both bare and shaded.

Artificial regeneration of the three oak species and Pacific madrone has shown them to be difficult to establish, and even harder to grow at an acceptable rate (McDonald 1978, Narog 1994). None of these species can be established in conventional sunlit plantations, even when fertilizer and water are provided the first year. Based on early results, McDonald (1990) noted the possibility that California black oak could be established in conventional plantations. However, when several of these plantations were revisited, tree form and development were not satisfactory. Consequently, direct seeding of germinated acorns or the planting of nursery-grown plugs gives adequate early survival, and perhaps even acceptable 10th-year survival, but growth is inconsistent and unreliable. Growth of black oak seedlings planted in the shade is unknown. The growth of planted and natural seedlings in shade has not been compared.

Early Seedling Growth

The mechanism and timing of very early seedling growth are a marvel of adaptation. Take California black oak as an example. The radicle is first to emerge from the acorn. Fueled by the abundant energy in the acorn, it grows downward for some time, often 10 to 20 days, before the epicotyl appears above ground (McDonald 1990). This process allows the seedling to get to and stay in a zone of available soil moisture, and in minimizing transpiration losses and herbivory. Black oak seedling roots commonly extend as deep as 30 inches the first growing season. Shoot length after one growing season is 6 to 8 inches, and probably does not begin to accelerate until root capacity is extensive enough to obtain adequate soil moisture. This may take years and in many instances, the seedling becomes overtopped by other vegetation. Continued overtopping almost always causes death.

The oak species and probably Pacific madrone form a rudimentary burl just below groundline and develop capability to produce sprouts at a young age. Dieback of the sprouts is common and the reproduction typically is made up of seedlings and seedling-sprouts. The seedling-sprouts, because of the burl, have higher odds for survival than the seedlings. Much information is available on age/height relationships of tanoak seedling-sprouts (Tappeiner and McDonald 1984) and on survival relationships of tanoak and madrone seedlings (Tappeiner and others 1986). The burl develops slowly and steadily with age, but height is indeterminate. At age 10, for example, tanoak seedling-sprouts in the northern Sierra Nevada might have a 0.5-inch diameter burl, four sprouts, and a sprout height of 20 inches. By age 40, the burl will be 2- to 3-inches in diameter, and be a clump of 4 to 6 stems, about 20 inches tall. Height of the seedlings and seedling-sprouts of the Sierra Nevada hardwoods noted here ranges up to 8 inches after the first growing season and up to 60 inches for older plants.

Root Crown Sprouts

All of the forest-zone hardwoods mentioned in this report produce both sprouts and seed. Species that have both reproductive modes have an obvious advantage over those that have only one. Sprouts, because of fast and robust growth, almost instantly reoccupy original sites. Seeds, through the action of disseminators, enable the species to occupy new areas. "It is not extravagance, but good investment for the oaks to provide subsistence for a continuing population of animal associates" (Grinnell 1936).

Root crown sprouts (as opposed to seedling-sprouts) are defined as those that originate from stumps larger than 2 inches in diameter. Such sprouts are the primary reproductive mode of the principal hardwoods. Examination of over 1,380 recently cut stumps in the northern Sierra Nevada revealed that almost all were of sprout origin. Plainly, most reproduction is by vegetative means (sprouts) with only one tree in hundreds originating from seed. This is consistent with the role of disturbance and the origin of stands.

Most root-crown sprouts develop from dormant buds on a burl that forms at or just below groundline. After cutting, burning, or other damage, sprouting is assured except for very old, moribund trees whose buds are occluded by thick bark. In fact, it is almost impossible to keep stumps of these hardwood species from sprouting. After the tree is killed above ground, the number of sprouts in the initial flush varies tremendously, but has been noted as being up to 1,400 on one large tanoak stump (Tappeiner and others 1990), and more than 300 on one 10-inch Pacific madrone stump (McDonald and Tappeiner 1990). Other sprouts originate from the top of the stump or on the vertical part of the stump between the top and the ground. These are called stool sprouts and are undesirable for several reasons. They are weakly attached to the stump, are peeled off by wind and snow, and are prone to heart rot at an early age. Leaving a low stump less than 8 inches tall promotes numerous, healthy, rot-free sprouts.

The size and vigor of the parent tree largely determines the number of sprouts and their height and crown spread. In general, stumps from larger trees produce a larger number of sprouts and more vigorous ones. Indeed, sprout height, clump width, clump area, leaf area, total above-ground biomass, and number of stems per clump 1 to 6 years after cutting, were statistically correlated with parent tree diameter at breast height before cutting or burning (Harrington and others 1984). Thus sprout clump size and total cover of sprout clumps can be predicted on a per acre basis and used to estimate competition, biomass, or other useful determinations.

Long ago, David Smith (1962) noted that "Vegetative reproduction obtained after clearcutting is usually superior to that resulting from partial cutting." This has proved true for the species denoted here. In a study on the Challenge Experimental Forest with California black oak, tanoak, and Pacific madrone, sprout clump dynamics were quantified in both a clearcutting and in a shelterwood where 50 percent of the stand basal area was removed (McDonald 1990). For all three species, more and vigorous sprouts were found in the clearcutting. Even shade-tolerant tanoak grew best in the clearcutting, probably because no roots of parent trees were utilizing site resources, particularly water. After 10 years, sprout clumps of California black oak in the clearcutting averaged 20 feet tall and about 10 feet wide (table 2). Clumps of tanoak sprouts in the clearcutting were about equally tall and wide; those of Pacific madrone were slightly taller (22 feet) after 10 years and were of equal width.

Given that sprouts are numerous and many die quickly, thinning at an early age seemed a likely technique to stimulate growth of selected stems. This was done on the Challenge Experimental Forest for California black oak, tanoak, and Pacific madrone, always leaving 3 or 4 sprouts well dispersed around the stump. Thinning was performed at ages 1 and 4. It proved difficult and ineffective at age 1 and yielded no gain in growth relative to unthinned sprouts at age 4 (McDonald 1978). Thinning sprout clumps before age 10 is not recommended. Results from thinning between age 10 and 30 are unknown but could prove beneficial.

Growth of Trees and Stands

Because disturbance, chiefly fire, is commonplace throughout the range of Sierra Nevada forest-zone hardwoods, and stand establishment is by root crown sprouts, most stands consist of clumps of sprouts, although many clumps have become single trees. These stands tend to be evenaged and quite dense. On a good site in northern California, trees in a 60-year-old mixed hardwood stand that were 3.5 inches in breast height diameter or larger, numbered 659 per acre and contained about 200 ft^2 of basal area per acre. They were growing at a rate of about 15 rings per inch.

Would the typically dense hardwood stands respond to thinning, and what was the best thinning technique? After trial and error, the consensus of foresters was "yes" they will respond to thinning, but only a "crown" thinning was practical. Crown thinning is where crowns of individual trees are provided growing space. A more traditional thinning technique would be to leave an even spacing of trees on each acre. For 60-year-old trees in the northern Sierra Nevada, a crown thinning of 40 to 50 percent with 100 to 125 ft^2 per acre retained, doubled the diameter growth rate after 8 years (McDonald 1980). On a stand basis, this amounted to growth of about 85 ft^3 per acre per year over the 8-year period. California black oak trees responded best when thinned to about 100 ft^2 per acre, and tanoak and Pacific madrone to about 125 ft^2 per acre--the latter two species needing a more shady environment.

Other findings of interest to silviculturists were that individual trees in a clump of up to four stems grew as well as if they were single trees. Consequently, clumps of up to four members can be retained with no reduction in growth. And when diameter growth was averaged for two of the wettest and two of the driest years and compared, the response was similar between wet and dry over a wide range of stand densities.

Tanoak and Pacific madrone rarely produce sprouts (called epicormic branches) along the bole, but California black oak does. Canyon live oak sprouts readily from the bole <u>and</u> the crown, particularly if the crown has only been scorched by fire. After a conifer-killing fire, logging, or a heavy thinning, large amounts of nutrients and water become available. The typically slow-growing and thin-crowned hardwood trees that remain do not have enough crown to utilize the extra site resources provided by the roots. These extra resources must be utilized in some way, so extra "crown" in the form of epicormic branches develops. Epicormic branching creates a dilemma for the forester. Stands of California black oak, for example, require thinning to increase growth and the production of acorns, but epicormic branches, which yield no acorns and constitute a serious lumber degrade, often result.

The crown thinning in the 60-year-old hardwood stands on the Challenge Experimental Forest created basal areas that ranged from 85 to 141 ft^2 per acre. These, plus trees in an unthinned control and those bordering small openings, were studied to quantify epicormic branching and to determine causal factors. In 1976 or 6 to 9 years after thinning, 2069 living and dead epicormic branches on 189 California black oak trees were observed. Statistically significant predictors of epicormic branching were position of tree in stand, cardinal direction of bole face, and bole segment (McDonald and Ritchie 1994). Number of epicormic branches increased with decreasing stand density, proximity to openings, on south and east bole faces, and with increasing distance above the stump.

630

These findings, together with the silvical characteristics noted earlier suggest that a series of crown thinnings be applied, beginning when the stand is as young as 20 years. The goal is to achieve rapid crown development, and wide-crowned trees that will in turn maximize growth and acorn production. This means applying a series of thinnings that provides some room each time for crown and root expansion.

MANAGEMENT IMPLICATIONS

The idea that native California hardwoods needed to be managed was stated over 30 years ago. Edwards (1957) and Roy (1962) denoted some silvicultural possibilities and made a few tentative management recommendations. Based on new silvicultural/ecological information, McDonald (1978) suggested that many benefits could be realized if natural resource managers in different disciplines worked together. Later Tappeiner and McDonald (1980), Plumb and McDonald (1981), and McDonald and Tappeiner (1987) suggested more detailed management recommendations based on an increasing amount of new ecological and silvicultural information. In 1994, McDonald and Huber noted that the extensive and complex hardwood ecosystems had value far beyond timber and wood products. They noted that on public land, wildlife, water, and pleasing scenery outranked wood products in terms of current and near-term use, and suggested an ecosystem management perspective for managing the hardwood resource. Later McDonald and Huber (1995) noted that on both private and public land, it will be silviculturists who maintain, manipulate, and create the ecological types and habitats desired by society. The art of hardwood silviculture should enjoy its finest hour.

The best of all these recommendations, plus some new ones from the preceding material, are denoted below.

o The forest-zone hardwood ecosystems in the Sierra Nevada are unique and special and worthy of being managed as such.

o Implicit in the inventory data is the fact that forest-zone hardwoods constitute a large, variable, and complex resource. Of extreme importance is that this resource is largely intact. Unlike softwoods, every hardwood age and size class is present, including large numbers of big, old-growth trees. Tree density also ranges widely--from one or two per acre to over 700 per acre. The wide variety of sizes and densities gives managers virtually unlimited opportunities to maintain, create, or sustain every habitat or ecological type that they should need. And when the conifer-hardwood mixtures are included, and they too are numerous and varied, the total number of habitats is huge and their variety and potential for management is virtually unlimited.

o The worth of forest-zone hardwoods may be manifest more in wildlife, water, and pleasing scenery than in wood products, but the wood products provide the raw material for industry, which in turn provides jobs and stability to rural America.

o Natural regeneration of California black oak, tanoak, Pacific madrone, and canyon live oak in an undisturbed setting is characterized more by a slow steady accumulation of seedlings rather than by large pulses of them.

o   Artificial regeneration in a conventional sunlit plantation is beset with problems, especially lack of consistent and reliable seedling growth. Partial shade appears to be mandatory, but how much and until when is unknown.

o   Propagation of root crown sprouts is the major regeneration method and until artificial regeneration techniques are perfected, vegetative propagation remains the best way of renewing hardwood stands.

o   Thinning of root crown sprouts is impractical through age 10, but after age 10 should stimulate growth on remaining sprouts. Retaining 3 to 4 of the most healthy sprouts evenly spaced around the circumference of the stump is necessary to maintain clump health.

o   Traditionally too-dense hardwood stands respond well to thinning. Diameter growth, for example, can be doubled relative to an uncut control.

o   Epicormic branches of California black oak are a major degrade under current log grading rules. These branches, although almost always present, can be minimized by a thinning regime that begins early and occurs often. The key is to create space into which crowns and roots can grow without becoming out of balance with each other.

o   Given that exposure promotes epicormic branching and that significantly more epicormics occur on trees at the edge of stands than on interior trees, the number of epicormic branches can be reduced by managing trees in larger aggregations.

REFERENCES

Atzet, Thomas; Martin, Robert E. 1992. **Natural disturbance regimes in the Klamath Province**. In: Kerner, Hannah M., ed. Proc. of the Symposium on Biodiversity of Northwestern California; 1991 October 28-30; Santa Rosa, CA. Rep. 29. Berkeley, CA: Wildland Resources Center, University of California; 40-48.

Bolsinger, Charles L. 1988. **The hardwoods of California's timberlands, woodlands, and savannas**. Resour. Bull. PNW-RB-148. Pacific Northwest Research Station, Forest Service, U.S. Department of Agriculture; 188 p.

Baumhoff, Martin A. 1963. **Ecological determinants of aboriginal California populations**. In: Publications in American Archeology and Ethnology. Volume XLIX. Berkeley, CA: University of California Press: 155-235.

California Department of Forestry and Fire Protection. 1988. **California's forests and rangelands: growing conflict over changing uses**. Sacramento, CA: 67-71.

Chaney, Ralph. W. 1925. **Studies on the fossil flora and fauna of the western United States. II. The Mascal Flora--its distribution and climatic relation**. Publication 349. Washington, DC: Carnegie Institution; 25-48.

Cooper, William S. 1922. **The broad sclerophyll vegetation of California. An ecological study of the chaparral and its related communities**. Publication 319. Washington, DC: Carnegie Institution; 119 p.

Economic Development Administration. 1968. **The Hoopa Valley Reservation hardwood study report**. Washington, DC: U.S. Department of Commerce; 162 p.

Edwards, Milton B. 1957. **California black oak--its management and economic possibilities**. Journal of Forestry 55: 506-510.

Grinnell, Joseph. 1936. **Up-hill planters.** The Condor 38: 80-82; March.

Harrington, T.B.; Tappeiner, J.C.; Walstad, J.D. 1984. **Predicting leaf area and biomass of 1- to 6-year-old tanoak and Pacific madrone sprout clumps in southwestern Oregon.** Can. J. For. Res. 14:: 209-213.

Heady, Harold F; Zinke, Paul J. 1978. **Vegetational changes in Yosemite Valley.** Occas. Pap. 5. Washington, DC: National Park Service, U.S. Department of Interior: 25 p.

Huber, Dean W.; McDonald, Philip M. 1992. **California's hardwood resource: history and reasons for lack of a sustained hardwood industry.** Gen. Tech. Rep. PSW-GTR-135. Pacific Southwest Forest and Range Experiment Station, Forest Service, U.S. Department of Agriculture; 14 p.

Keeley, Jon E. 1977. **Seed production, seed populations in soil, and seedling production after fire for two congeneric pairs of sprouting and nonsprouting chaparral shrubs.** Ecology 58: 820-829.

Kummerow, Jochen. 1973. **Comparative anatomy of sclerophylls of Mediterranean climatic areas.** In: di Castri, Francesco; Mooney, Harold A., eds. Mediterranean type ecosystems, origin and structure. New York: Springer-Verlag; 157-167.

Litton, R. Burton, Jr.; McDonald, Philip M. 1980. **Silviculture and visual resources.** In Proceedings 1979 Convention, Society of American Foresters; October 14-17, 1979. Boston, MA; 97-102.

McDonald, Philip M. 1978. **Silviculture-ecology of three native California hardwoods on high sites in north-central California.** Ph.D. dissertation. Corvallis: Oregon State Univ.; 309 p.

_____. 1980. **Growth of thinned and unthinned hardwood stands in the northern Sierra Nevada . . . preliminary findings.** Gen. Tech. Rep. PSW-44. Berkeley, CA: Pacific Southwest Forest and Range Experiment Station, Forest Service, U.S. Department of Agriculture; 119-127.

_____. 1982. **Adaptations of woody shrubs.** In: Hobbs, S.D.; Helgerson, O.T., eds. Proceedings of a workshop on Reforestation of Skeletal Soils; November 17-19; Medford, OR. Corvallis, OR: Forest Research Laboratory, Oregon State University; 21-29.

_____. 1990. **Quercus kelloggii Newb. California black oak.** In: Burns, Russell M.; Honkala, Barbara H., Tech. coords. Silvics of North America. Volume 2, Hardwoods. Agriculture Handbook 654. Washington, DC. p. 661-671.

_____. **Estimating seed crops of conifer and hardwood species.** Can. J. For. Res. 22: 832-838.

McDonald, Philip M.; Huber, Dean W. 1994. **California's hardwood resource: current status of the industry and an ecosystem management perspective.** Gen. Tech. Rep. PSW-GTR-153. Pacific Southwest Forest and Range Experiment Station, Forest Service, U.S. Department of Agriculture; 24 p.

_____. **California's hardwood resource: managing for wildlife, water, pleasing scenery, and wood products.** Gen. Tech. Rep. PSW-GTR-154. Pacific Southwest Forest and Range Experiment Station, Forest Service, U.S. Department of Agriculture; 23 p.

McDonald, Philip M.; Ritchie, Martin W. 1994. **Epicormic branching of California black oak: effect of stand and tree characteristics.** Northwest Science 68(1): 6-10.

McDonald, Philip M.; Tappeiner, John C.,II. 1987. **Silviculture, ecology, and management of tanoak in northern California.** In: Plumb, Timothy R.; Pillsbury, Norman H., tech. coords. Multiple-use management of California's hardwood resources; 1986 November 12-14; San Luis Obispo, CA. Gen. Tech.

Rep. PSW-100. Berkeley, CA: Pacific Southwest Forest and Range Experiment Station, Forest Service, U.S. Department of Agriculture; 64-70.

———. **Arbutus menziesii Pursh. Pacific madrone.** In: Burns, Russell M.; Honkala, Barbara H., Tech. coords. Silvics of North America. Volume 2, Hardwoods. Agriculture Handbook 654. Washington, DC. p. 124-132.

McDonald, Philip M.; Whiteley, Raymond V. 1972. **Logging a roadside stand to protect scenic values.** Journal of Forestry 70(2): 80-83.

McDonald, Philip M.; Minore, Don; Atzet, Tom. 1983. **Southwestern Oregon-Northern California hardwoods.** In: Burns, Russell M., tech. coord. Silvicultural systems for the major forest types of the United States. Agric. Handb. 445. Washington, D.C.: Forest Service, U.S. Department of Agriculture; 29-32.

Mooney, Harold A.; Dunn, E. Lloyd. 1970. **Convergent evolution of Mediterranean-climate evergreen sclerophyll shrubs.** Evolution 24: 292-303.

Narog, Marcia. Ecologist. Personal communication March 10, 1994.

Pelton, John. 1962. **Factors influencing survival and growth of a seedling population of Arbutus menziesii in California.** Madrono 16: 237-276.

Plumb, Timothy R.; McDonald, Philip M. 1981. **Oak management in California.** Gen. Tech. Rep. PSW-54. Pacific Southwest Forest and Range Experiment Station, Forest Service, U.S. Department of Agriculture; 11 p.

Roy, Douglass F. 1962. **California hardwoods: management practices and problems.** Journal of Forestry 60: 184-186.

Smith, David M. 1962. The practice of silviculture. Ed. 7. New York: John Wiley and Sons; 578 p.

Tappeiner, John C.,II; McDonald, Philip M. 1980. **Preliminary recommendations for managing California black oak in the Sierra Nevada.** Gen. Tech. Rep. PSW-44. Berkeley, CA: Pacific Southwest Forest and Range Experiment Station, Forest Service, U.S. Department of Agriculture; 107-111.

———. **Development of tanoak understories in conifer stands.** Can. J. For. Res. 14: 271-277.

Tappeiner, John C.,II; McDonald, Philip M.; Hughes, Thomas F. 1986. **Survival of tanoak (Lithocarpus densiflorus) and Pacific madrone (Arbutus menziesii seedlings in forests of southwestern Oregon.** New Forests 1: 43-55.

Tappeiner, John C.,II; McDonald, Philip M.; Roy, Douglass F. 1990. **Lithocarpus densiflorus (Hook. & Arn.) Rehd. Tanoak.** In: Burns, Russell M.; Honkala, Barbara H., Tech. coords. Silvics of North America. Volume 2, Hardwoods. Agriculture Handbook 654. Washington, DC. p. 417-425.

Thornburgh, Dale A. 1990. **Quercus chrysolepis Liebm. Canyon live oak.** In: Burns, Russell M.; Honkala, Barbara H., Tech. coords. Silvics of North America. Volume 2, Hardwoods. Agriculture Handbook 654. Washington, DC. p. 618-624.

Verner, Jared; Boss, Allan S. tech. coords. 1980. California wildlife and their habitats: western Sierra Nevada. Gen. Tech. Rep. PSW-37. Berkeley, CA: Pacific Southwest Forest and Range Experiment Station, Forest Service, U.S. Department of Agriculture: 439 p.

Wolf, C.B. 1945. **California wild tree crops.** Rancho Santa Ana Botanical Garden. Claremont, CA; 68 p.

Table 1. Growing stock and sawtimber volume for California black oak, tanoak, Pacific madrone, and canyon live oak in the Sierra Nevada, 1985[1]

Location	Growing stock	Sawtimber
	million ft^3	
National Forest and other Public land	830	353
Outside National Forests and Parks	810	369
Total	1740	722

[1]Extracted from Bolsinger 1988.

Table 2. Density, height, and width of California black oak sprouts for 10 years after cutting, Challenge Experimental Forest

Year	Sprouts per stump		Height		Crown width	
	Clear cut	Shelter wood	Clear cut	Shelter wood	Clear cut	Shelter wood
	number		ft.		ft.	
0	55+	28	-	-	-	-
2	55+	23	4	3	4	2
4	35	17	8	4	6	3
6	23	15	12	5	8	4
8	18	13	16	6	9	5
10	15	12	20	7	10	7

RICHARD B. STANDIFORD
Department of Environmental Science,
    Policy and Management
University of California
Berkeley, California

JULIA KLEIN
Department of Environmental Science,
    Policy and Management
University of California
Berkeley, California

BARRY GARRISON
California Department of Fish and Game
Sacramento, California

15

Sustainability of Sierra Nevada Hardwood Rangelands

Sierra Nevada Ecosystem Project: Final report to Congress, vol. III, Assessments, Commissioned Reports, and Background Information. Davis: University of California, Centers for Water and Wildland Resources, 1996.

637

ABSTRACT

Close to 800,000 acres of hardwood rangelands (also known as oak woodlands) in the Sierra Nevada have been converted to other land uses and vegetation types over the last 40 years, a decline of almost 16 percent. Major losses from 1945 through 1973 were from rangeland clearing for enhancement of forage production. Major losses since 1973 were from conversions to residential and industrial developments. Exurban migration represents the largest threat to continued sustainabiltiy of ecological functions on hardwood rangelands. This has increased fragmentation of habitat, conflicts between people with rural and urban value systems, predator problems, and soil and water erosion. At the individual stand or patch level, oak woodlands are much more stable than previously thought due to concerns about oak regeneration. Long-term trends reveal stand structures with recruitment into various size classes and increasing canopy density under typical livestock management practices. Technologies have been developed to carry out restoration of areas denuded of oaks in the past. Voluntary educational programs have made dramatic progress in accomplishing sustainable management practices by ranchers. It is less certain if the currently unregulated land use trends can be influenced by voluntary programs.

Keywords: hardwoods, rangelands, oaks

LIST OF TABLES

LIST OF FIGURES

California's oak woodlands, also known as hardwood rangelands, occupy over 10 million acres in the state (Bolsinger 1988; Greenwood et al.1993; Pacific Meridian Resources 1994). These oak woodland areas are characterized by an overstory canopy of hardwood tree species, predominantly in the oak genus (*Quercus spp.*), with an understory of annual grasses and occasional native perennial grasses. Approximately 30 percent of this acreage in in areas with less than 10 percent tree canopy cover. Griffin (1978), Bartolome (1987) Holmes (1990) and Allen et al.(1991) provide good ecological descriptions of these areas.

Since European settlement of California, oak woodlands have been managed primarily for livestock production. These areas have taken on a new importance because of the recognition that they have the richest wildlife species abundance of any habitat in the state, with over 300 vertebrate species relying at least partly on oak woodlands (Verner 1980; Barrett 1980; Garrison 1996). Other public values obtained from these areas include water quantity and quality, outdoor recreation, and aesthetics. California's oak woodlands are somewhat unique for western wildlands, with over 80 percent in private ownership (Greenwood et al. 1993).

There are 4.7 million acres of hardwood rangeland in the Sierra Nevada region. Table 1 shows the acreage by county and hardwood rangeland plant community (see next section for discussion of plant communities). Private ownership occurs on 85 percent of Sierra Nevada hardwood rangelands. These areas are concentrated in the western foothills of the Sierra Nevada extending from the xeric lower grasslands and savannahs of the central valley up to the more mesic higher elevation mixed hardwood and coniferous forests. The foothills form a belt from 20 to 30 miles wide and from 450 to 4500 feet in elevation along the eastern border of the central valley.

Conservation strategies for hardwood rangelands in the Sierra Nevada need to recognize the widespread extent of this broad habitat type, its importance for the economic livelihood of the region, and their important ecological values. This paper will assess the sustainability of hardwood rangelands in the Sierra Nevada. The definition of sustainable includes the following considerations:

- maintain ecosystem processes at multiple scales;
- maintain the existing diversity of biological organisms;
- maintain economic viability over the long-term.

Each of these items will be discussed in some detail below.

Table 1. Acreage of Sierra Nevada hardwood rangeland by county, vegetation type, and private ownership.

County	Thousand Acres				Pct. Private Ownership
	Blue oak[1]	Blue oak - foothill pine	Montane Hardwood	Total Hardwood Rangeland	
Shasta	71	212	4	287	97%
Tehama	285	332	17	634	83%
Butte	5	82	143	230	91%
Yuba	2	12	81	95	86%
Nevada	0	9	130	139	91%
Placer	5	0	100	105	90%
Eldorado	4	25	149	178	94%
Amador	38	79	61	178	97%
Calaveras	74	102	141	317	91%
Tuolumne	60	87	87	234	75%
Mariposa	130	80	89	299	88%
Madera	137	89	58	284	93%
Fresno	222	222	49	493	74%
Tulare	357	110	69	536	73%
Kern	657	26	38	721	78%
Sierra Totals	2047	1467	1216	4730	84%

[1] Includes trace amounts of valley oak woodland

CLASSIFICATION OF OAK WOODLANDS

A variety of systems have been used to classify oak woodlands in California. Table 2 provides a general cross-reference of these various classification systems. The distribution, density, and abundance of the various oak species, together with other tree, brush, and herbaceous species, forms the basis for evaluating the potential of a hardwood rangeland site for providing economic and ecologic utility. Although there are a number of different ways of classifying California's oak-dominated woodlands, the four vegetation types used in the California Wildlife Habitat Relationships System (CWHR) will be used in this discussion (Mayer and Laudenslayer 1988). The CWHR types for the Sierra Nevada hardwood rangelands are based on the dominant tree species, and include Valley Oak Woodland, Blue Oak Woodland, Blue Oak-Foothill Pine Woodland, and Montane Hardwood Forest. A brief description of each type is shown below. This material is excerpted from Garrison and Standiford (1996).

Table 2. Cross-reference for hardwood rangeland classification in the Sierra Nevada.

Allen et al. 1991	CALVEG	Griffin 1977	Munz and Keck 1973	Kuchler 1988	Eyre 1980	Mayer and Laudenslayer 1988
Blue Oak Series	Blue Oak	Foothill Woodland Blue Oak Phase	Foothill Woodland	Blue Oak - Digger Pine	Blue Oak - Digger Pine	Blue Oak Woodland
Blue Oak Series	Blue Oak - Digger Pine	Foothill Woodland Blue Oak Phase	Foothill Woodland	Blue Oak - Digger Pine	Blue Oak - Digger Pine	Blue Oak - Digger Pine
Interior Live Oak Series	***	Interior Live Oak Phase North Slope Phase	Foothill Woodland	***	***	Montane Hardwood
***	Canyon Live Oak	Blue Oak and Interior Live Oak Phases	Foothill Woodland	Sierran Montane Forest	Canyon Live Oak	Montane Hardwood Conifer and Montane Hardwood
Black Oak Series	Black Oak	Black Oak Phase	Foothill Woodland	Sierran Montane Forest	California Black Oak	Montane Hardwood Conifer and Montane Hardwood
Valley Oak Series	Valley Oak	Valley Oak Phase	Foothill Woodland	Valley Oak Savanna	***	Valley Oak Woodland
***	***	Riparian Forest	***	Riparian Forest	***	Valley Foothill Riparian
***	***	Northern Oak Woodland	Northern Oak Woodland	Oregon Oak	Oregon White Oak	Montane Hardwood

Valley Oak Woodland (from Garrison and Standiford 1996)

Vegetation Composition and Structure

These woodlands are dominated by valley oaks (*Quercus lobata*). Associated tree species in the Central Valley include California sycamore (*Platanus racemosa*), black walnut (*Juglans hindsii*), California boxelder (*Acer negundo*), Oregon ash (*Fraxinus latifolia*), interior live oak (*Q. wislizenii*), and blue oak (*Q. douglasii*). California black oak (*Q. kelloggii*) often occurs with valley oaks at higher elevations. At low elevations close to water, valley oak is associated with Fremont cottonwood (*Populus fremontii*) and tree willows (*Salix* spp.). Valley oak woodlands vary from open savannahs to closed canopy forests. Dense stands occur along natural drainages in deep soils. Tree density decreases as one moves from lowlands to uplands. The understory shrub layer can be dense along drainages and very sparse in uplands. Understory grasses and forbs are mostly introduced annuals. Mature valley oaks with well-developed crowns reach - maximum heights of 50-120 ft. The massive trunks and branches of mature trees dominate valley oak woodlands.

Ecological Processes

In many areas, there is little valley oak recruitment to replace mature tree losses due to both natural and human causes. This seems to be related to moisture competition with grasses and forbs, wild and domestic animals feeding on acorns and seedlings, and flood control projects. Fire

643

suppression has encouraged evergreen oak and pine invasion in upland valley oak sites. Valley oaks tolerate flooding and young trees will sprout when damaged by fire. Valley oak woodlands should be able to maintain themselves with natural disturbances such as fire and flooding. However, suppression of fire and flooding has adversely affected sustainability of valley oak woodlands.

Locational Characteristics

Valley oaks are found only in California. In the Sierra Nevada region, they occur in a patchy distribution adjacent to most major lowland valleys. Many valley oak woodlands occur as isolated stands in areas where surrounding habitats have been modified by agricultural, urban, and suburban activities. Annual grasslands, riparian forests, and other oak woodland types occur around valley oak woodlands. Conversion of valley oak woodlands to irrigated agricultural land uses has had the largest effect on the acreage decline of this type, currently estimated at less than 10 percent of its initial distribution. Valley oak communities generally occur on deep, well-drained alluvial soils of valleys and foothills below 2,400 feet, but may occur up to 5,600 feet as components of other vegetation types.

Blue Oak Woodland (from Garrison and Standiford 1996)

Vegetation Composition and Structure

Blue oak woodlands are highly variable with blue oak (*Q. douglasii*) comprising 80-100 percent of the trees present. Foothill pine (*Pinus sabiniana*), California buckeye (*Aesculus californica*), valley oak, interior live oak, canyon live oak (*Q. chrysolepis*), and California black oak are common associates of blue oak. The overstory of blue oak woodlands range from sparsely scattered trees on poor sites to nearly closed canopies on good quality sites . Annual grasses form most of the understory in open woodlands. Characteristic shrub species include poison-oak (*Toxicodendron diversilobum*), California coffeeberry (*Rhamnus californica*), and several species of Ceanothus and manzanita.

Ecological Processes

Blue oaks are relatively slow-growing, long-lived trees. Most blue oak stands exist as groups of medium to large trees with few or no young oaks, which may or may not indicate there is a regeneration problem. There is concern that in areas of poor regeneration, blue oak woodlands may be slowly changing into savannas and grasslands as trees die and are not replaced. Fires are an important environmental factor. Young, vigorous blue oaks can stump sprout readily, however, older, decadent trees cannot. Therefore, younger stands are more likely to regrow after fires. Poor blue oak recruitment from acorns occurs for several reasons. Introduced annual grasses out-compete blue oak seedlings for soil moisture. In addition, acorns and seedlings are eaten or damaged by insects, domestic livestock, and wildlife. Blue oak is also somewhat intolerant of shady conditions, and is unable to survive under dense overstory canopies. Disturbances with small openings may be needed for seedlings to survive and grow sufficiently to promote a broader age class distribution.

Locational Characteristics

Blue oak woodlands form a nearly continuous band along the Sierra Nevada-Cascade foothills of the Sacramento-San Joaquin Valley. Typically, blue oak woodlands are found below 3,000 to

4,000 feet, but this elevational threshold drops to around 2,000 feet in the northern range, and raises to around 5,000 feet in the southern range. At lower elevations on gentle slopes, blue oak woodlands typically occur as large blocks with highly variable canopy cover. On steeper ground, blue oak woodlands occur in small patches interspersed with other habitats such as annual grasslands, chaparral, riparian forests, and other types of oak woodlands. Blue oak woodlands occur on a wide range of soils, however, they are often shallow, rocky, infertile, but well-drained. There is considerable climatic variation with rainfall ranging from 10 to 60 inches annually.

Blue Oak-Foothill Pine Woodland (from Garrison and Standiford 1996)

Vegetation Composition and Structure
Foothill pine (formerly known as digger pine) and blue oak typically form most of the overstory of this highly variable community, with blue oak usually most abundant. Stands dominated by foothill pine have low blue oak density because of its shade intolerance. In the Sierra Nevada foothills, interior live oak and California buckeye are often associated with this type. Interior live oak becomes more abundant on steeper slopes, shallower soils, and at higher elevations. Shrub associates include several ceanothus and manzanita species, poison-oak and California redbud (*Cercis occidentalis*), and are usually clumped in areas of full sunlight. Blue oak-foothill pine woodlands have a diverse mix of hardwoods, conifers, and shrubs, and widely variable overstories. Foothill pine is taller and dominates the overstory.

Ecological Processes
Blue oak and foothill pine are relatively long-lived, but foothill pine tends to grow faster than blue oak. Fairly frequent fires historically occurred in this vegetation community. Regeneration is generally thought to be infrequent throughout California. Young, vigorous blue oaks sprout well, but older, more decadent trees do not. Therefore, younger stands are more likely to replace themselves after fires.

Locational Characteristics
Blue oak-foothill pine woodlands are found on steeper, dryer slopes with shallower soils than blue oak woodlands. At lower elevations on gentle slopes, these two communities intermix with grasslands. At higher elevations on steeper slopes, the communities are mixed with grasslands and shrublands. Riparian woodlands may bisect these mosaics along permanent and intermittent watercourses. Blue oak-foothill pine woodlands are found throughout the range of blue oak and form a nearly continuous band along the Sierra Nevada-Cascade foothills of the Sacramento-San Joaquin Valley, except for a gap in Tulare and southern Fresno counties. Elevation ranges from 500 feet in the north to 3000 feet in the south. This woodland type occurs on a variety of well-drained soils. Terrain is hilly and generally dry, and water is unavailable for much of the year.

Montane Hardwood Forest (from Garrison and Standiford 1996)

Vegetation Composition and Structure
Montane hardwood forests are perhaps the most variable of any California hardwood type. The dominant oak species vary by topography, soils, and elevation. Montane hardwood forests typically lack blue and valley oaks. The characteristic oaks are canyon live oak, interior live oak, California black oak, and Oregon white oak. Many areas of montane hardwood forest are located

on fairly productive forest soils, and are not truly "hardwood rangelands" but commercial hardwood forests under the jurisdiction of the California Forest Practices Act.

Canyon live oak often forms almost pure stands on steep canyon slopes and rocky ridgetops throughout the Sierra Nevada and Klamath Mountains. They have tremendously variable growth forms, ranging from shrubby forms with multiple trunks on rocky, steep slopes, to 60 to 70 foot tall trees on deeper soils in moister areas. California black oak tends to dominate on gentle topography at higher elevations. It grows to heights of 70 to 80 feet at maturity, with long, straight trunks in closed canopy situations. In open forests, California black oak has larger, spreading branches. Canyon live oak and California black oak are widely distributed and form the montane hardwood habitats throughout much of the Sierra Nevada. However, these two species are usually not associated with hardwood rangeland sites.

Interior live oak occurs with canyon live oak or alone on steep canyon slopes and rocky, steep slopes throughout the Sierra Nevada. It growth form varies much like canyon live oak. Both of these evergreen oaks have dense canopies. Oregon white oak dominates small amounts of montane hardwood types in the northern Sierra Nevada and Cascades. It grows to a height of 50 to 80 feet at maturity, with rounded crowns in open conditions and rather narrow crowns in closed conditions.

Associates of montane hardwood communities at higher elevation, good quality sites include ponderosa pine (*Pinus ponderosa*), Douglas-fir (*Pseudotsuga menziesii*), Pacific madrone (*Arbutus menziesii*), Jeffrey pine (*Pinus jeffreyii*), sugar pine (*Pinus lambertiana*), incense-cedar (*Calocedrus decurrens*), and white fir (*Abies concolor*). At lower elevations and poor sites with steep slopes, associates include foothill pine, knobcone pine, tanoak (*Lithocarpus densiflorus*), and Pacific madrone. Blue oak and valley oak can be associates at lower elevations. Understory shrub species include poison-oak, Ceanothus, manzanita, mountain-mahogany, coffeeberry, wild currant (*Ribes spp.*), and mountain misery. Forbs and grasses are not as prevalent as on lower elevation hardwood rangeland types. Montane hardwoods have a pronounced hardwood tree layer with poorly developed shrub and herbaceous layers.

Ecological Processes

Since oaks of montane hardwood communities are long-lived and slow-growing, the community is rather stable and persistent. Initial tree establishment is by acorn. Once established, the four dominant oaks, canyon live, interior live, California black, and Oregon white, can sprout vigorously from stumps, allowing rapid re-establishment after a fire. Frequent fires over relatively small areas result in a variety of age classes across the landscape. The large number of hardwood and conifer species allows this type to occupy many environments and locations. The general inaccessibility of these habitats have protected them from many of the human-induced disturbances such as intensive agricultural, residential and commercial development, grazing, and wood cutting. Montane hardwoods occur over a wide elevational range. Surrounding habitats include conifer-dominated types, chaparral types, blue oak and valley oak woodlands, and annual grasslands.

Physical Characteristics

Slopes range from gentle to steep. Soils are mostly rocky, coarse, and poorly developed. However, relatively large California black oak stands occur in mountain valleys on alluvial soils. Exposures tend to be south, west, and east, while conifers tend to dominant on northern exposures. Climates are typically Mediterranean but extremely variable given the wide distribution of this type. Average summer temperatures are moderate, while average winter temperatures range from near freezing to the mid-40's$^{\circ}$F. Snow occurs in the winter at higher elevations, but does not remain as long as on adjacent conifer-dominated habitats.

SPATIAL AND TEMPORAL ASPECTS OF SUSTAINABILITY

Landscape-Level Sustainability

Over the long term, pollen analysis shows shifts in distribution of oak stands along altitudinal gradients. Approximately 10,000 years ago, oaks became a significant component of the Sierra Nevada montane forest according to pollen record analysis (Byrne et al. 1991). Prior to 10,000 years ago, persistent snowpacks into early summer may have minimized the importance of drought and caused dominance of dense coniferous forest types; fire seemed to be relatively rare from 12-10,000 years ago at these montane elevations. Increasing drought stress and more intense fires caused a relatively quick compositional change to a ponderosa pine-black oak woodland beginning 10,000 years ago; these open woodlands may have persisted from 10-5,000 years ago. During this period, the pollen record indicates that the oaks were associated with understory species which are characteristic of open, seasonally dry regions. Most of the oak trees located at the upper elevational limit of oaks were black oak and shrubs such as *Quercus vaccinifolia* (huckleberry oak). Roughly 5,000 years ago, oaks were replaced by pines and firs in the montane forest. The relatively larger existence of oaks in the Sierran montane forest from 10-5,000 years ago may be attributed to both more intense summer drought and increased fire intensity during this period at the montane forest elevation.

Viewed from a statewide scale, California's hardwood rangelands have decreased by over one million acres in the last 40 years (Bolsinger 1988). Major losses from 1945 through 1973 were from rangeland clearing for enhancement of forage production. Major losses since 1973 were from conversions to residential and industrial developments.

At a regional or watershed scale, certain parts of the hardwood rangelands have decreased due to rapid urban expansion (Doak 1989), firewood harvesting (Standiford et al. 1996), range improvement practices (Bolsinger 1988), and conversion to intensive agriculture (Mayer et al. 1985). This has caused increased fragmentation of habitat, increased conflicts between people with rural and urban value systems, predator problems, and soil and water erosion. No factor has had a more noticeable effect on shaping the oak community than urban development (Doak 1989). Urban expansion is most acute in the foothills of the Sierra, particularly from Nevada and Yuba counties southward to Fresno county. Blue oak and valley oak have been most affected (Holmes, 1990). The effect of spatial and temporal change on the acreage of hardwood rangeland habitat in the Sierra Nevada region are shown below in Table 3. Over a 40 year period, over 800,000 acres of hardwood land in the Sierra Nevada have been lost, representing almost 16 percent of the total acreage that existed 40 years ago.

Table 3. 40 year percent change in hardwood habitat by county in the Sierra Nevada region (from Bolsinger 1988).

County	40 yr. pct. change
Shasta	+7%
Tehama	-23%
Butte	-9%
Yuba	-18%
Nevada	-18%
Placer	-32%
Eldorado	+2%
Amador	-28%
Calaveras	-29%
Tuolumne	-42%
Mariposa	-21%
Madera	-13%
Fresno	-19%
Tulare	-2%
Kern	-15%
Sierra Totals	-16%

Oaks are desirable for firewood and have been harvested from hardwood rangelands for hundreds of years. Spanish missionaries were the first Europeans to harvest oak fuelwood. Gold and quicksilver miners later utilized oaks for shaft supports (Rossi 1980). By 1900, oaks were employed for commercial charcoal production and cleared for orchard plantations (Holmes 1990). Firewood harvest on hardwood rangelands (Doak and Stewart 1985) escalated in the mid-1970's, driven by high prices of alternative energy sources. Despite this trend, there was no historical assessment of the acreage and volume of firewood harvested on hardwood rangelands. To address the current impact of firewood harvest on hardwood rangelands, California Department of Forestry and Fire Protection personnel conducted annual aerial monitoring of firewood harvesting trends from 1988 through 1992. Surveyors estimated acreage, intensity, and location of harvest sites. Table 4 shows the compares the Sierra Nevada region to the entire state (Standiford et al. 1996). The aerial monitoring showed significant regional impacts from firewood harvesting in Shasta and Tehama counties. Although they have less than 10 percent of the state's hardwood rangeland, 50 percent of the total cords were harvested in these two counties (Standiford et al. 1996).

Table 4. General summary statistics of CDF aerial monitoring of firewood harvesting on hardwood rangelands over a 4-year period (Fall 1988 to Fall 1992).

Firewood Harvest Characteristics	Sierra Nevada Hardwood Rangelands	Total State Hardwood Rangelands
Estimated Cords Harvested	256,661	278,924
Acres	22,860	24,714
Precut crown cover	57%	58%
Postcut crown cover	17%	18%
Number of harvests	87	120
Annual percent acres harvested	0.12%	0.06%

Clearing oak woodlands for range improvement has historically altered the structure and extent of oak savannahs (Bartolome 1987). Mayer et al. (1985) attribute the decline in oak communities to "range modification" programs which usually involve conversion of the oak woodland to another vegetation type. Often this technique involved herbicides and controlled burning or mechanical removal, piling and burning to clear out the vegetation in order to reduce fire hazards or improve forage and watershed production (Holmes 1990). These practices have greatly reduced the distribution of oaks in northern California, particularly in the Sierra foothills (Rossi 1980).

Stand Level Sustainability Considerations

From the period 1932 to 1992, the canopy density and basal area of blue oak woodlands at the stand level has increased under typical livestock grazing practices, and fire exclusion policies (Holzman 1993). This indicates that if conversion does not occur, oak stands are fairly stable to increasing over a moderately long period, despite the publicized problem of lack of natural regeneration (Muick and Bartolome 1986; Bolsinger 1988; Swiecki and Bernhardt 1993). Holzman (1993) found that over the 60 year period of the study of blue oak communities in both the coast ranges and the Sierra Nevada foothills, mean oak basal area increased due to residual tree growth and recruitment of new individuals. The number of blue oak trees was stable or increased on most study sites. The quantity of foothill pine individuals significantly decreased while the number of interior live oak trees increased. At some sites interior live oak increased into the blue oak cover types suggesting that regionally the live oaks are encroaching into the deciduous oak communities. Despite this stand level stability, the most dramatic and significant alteration to the blue oak communities is the decrease of blue oak woodlands due to development. More than 20% of the plots in the blue oak study sites were converted to other land uses, primarily residential subdivisions (Holzman 1993).

In a study of 708 sites within the foothill woodlands, Davis (1995) quantified changes in tree cover and density of foothill woodland vegetation from 1940 to 1988 and found that: 1) on a statewide basis, tree and total woody cover in foothill woodlands seem relatively stable; 2) cover dynamics vary from site to site and do not reveal landscape level pattens except at large physiographic and climatic region levels; and 3) locally, woody cover is more dynamic than has been previously suggested. Tree cover increased at 45% of the sites and decreased at 42% of the sites. Tree cover decreased by more than 20% in 16% of the samples while tree cover increased by at least 12% in 17% of the sites. They conclude that decreases in tree cover at some sites is counterbalanced by increases at others. Thus, while large changes occur within individual sites, the overall cover of blue oaks remained relatively constant from 1940 to 1988. The authors caution, however, that the 48 year study interval may not be sufficiently long to detect the predicted decline in oak cover given present recruitment rates. An alternative explanation postulated by Davis (1995) is that blue oak demography is more dynamic than assumed; therefore, existing age and size structure information do not accurately predict future demographic changes.

Pollen analysis studies document the dynamics of hardwood rangeland composition over a very long-term period (Byrne et al. 1991). In general, hardwood rangelands showed a long-term period of relatively stable oak densities under the period of use by Native Americans. Following introduction of livestock grazing by Europeans, and clearing practices for intensive agriculture approximately 150 years ago, oak densities declined dramatically. Exotic annuals first show up in the pollen record at this same time. Since this initial exploitation of the oak resource in this early settlement period, oak cover on hardwood rangelands has increased dramatically. This is attributed to fire exclusion policies of the last 50 years, and the preponderance of low intensity, extensive management practices associated with ranching uses.

SUSTAINING ECOSYSTEM PROCESSES

With the introduction of domestic livestock and exotic annuals during the Spanish mission days, hardwood rangeland ecosystems have changed dramatically. The herbaceous layer has changed from a perennial layer to an annual layer (Crampton 1974). Fire intervals have increased dramatically and fire intensity has also increased (McClaren and Bartolome 1989). The overstory layer, if not converted to another land use, has generally increased (Holzman and Allen-Diaz 1991). Soil moisture late in the growing season has decreased, and bulk density has increased due compaction from higher herbivore densities (Gordon et al. 1989). Riparian zones are now less dense and diverse (Tietje et al. 1991). A general summary of the changes in ecosystem inputs from pre-settlement conditions to the current time are shown below (Table 5). The effect of these changes on ecosystem processes are discussed in more detail below.

Table 5. Comparison of Sierra Nevada oak woodland conditions before and after European settlement.

Pre-European Settlement Conditions	Changes in Ecosystems Inputs
Perennial herbaceous layer	Exotic annual invasion
Regular fire interval	Long fire interval and increase intensity
More open overstory layer	Overstory layer of unconverted stands has increased
Soil moisture higher, later into growing season	Soil moisture late in growing season decreased
Lower soil bulk density	Increased soil bulk density
Snags, large woody debris	Snags, woody debris cleaned up in typical management activities
Denser, more diverse riparian zone	Riparian zones less dense and diverse
Lower herbivore densities	Higher herbivore density, primarily domestic livestock

Herbaceous Composition

The pre-European herbaceous community consisted primarily of native perennial bunchgrasses such as purple stipa, pine blue-grass, blue wildrye, California brome, California melic, prairie junegress and California oatgrass (Crampton 1974). Perennial forbs such as Brodiaea and various legumes were also a part of the native oak community understory species (Holmes 1990). The native understory species were displaced by alien annuals from primarily Europe, Asia, Africa and South America upon the arrival of the European settlers. This displacement occurred in four distinct waves (Burcham 1970): 1) Wild Oat, 1845-1855; 2) Wild Barley and filaree, 1855-1870; 3) Yellow starthistle, bromes, other barleys, 1870; 4) medusahead, 1900. Soft chess, now the most widespread annual (Bartolome 1987) became abundant in the late 1890s.

Oak Canopy and Forage Production Processes

The oak canopy has an effect on forage production, composition, and quality that varies around the state depending on precipitation, oak species, and amount of oak canopy cover. Oaks compete with the forage understory for both sunlight and moisture, and alter the nutrient status of the site because of the deep-rooting of of oaks and nutrient cycling from litter fall.

Oak removal was historically recommended as a means of increasing forage production on hardwood rangelands (George et al.). For the deciduous blue oak, most studies have demonstrated increased forage production following tree removal on areas previously containing over 25% canopy cover and receiving over 20 inches of rain (Kay 1987; Jansen 1987). Conversely, where there is less than 20 inches of rain, areas with low blue oak canopy (less than

651

25 percent cover) consistently had higher forage yields than adjacent open areas (Holland and Morton 1980; Frost and McDougald 1989). In areas with moderate blue oak canopy cover (25 to 60 percent), there was a variable canopy effect on forage production (McClaren and Bartolome 1989a). Figure 1 shows how moderate blue oak canopy (50%) affects seasonal forage production in different rainfall areas of the state.

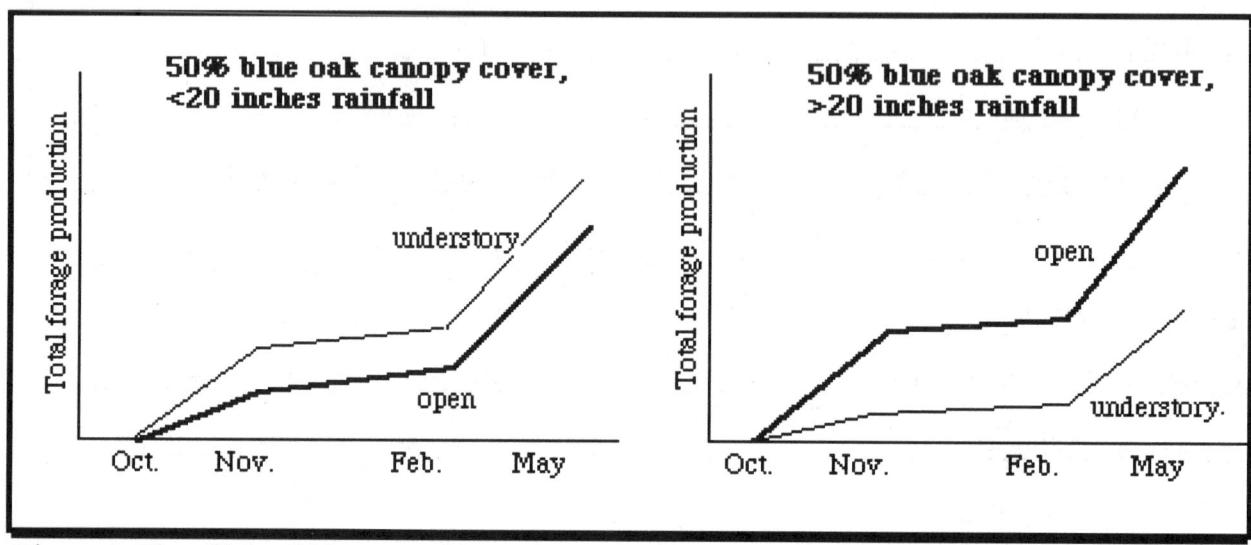

Figure 1. The effect of 50 percent blue oak canopy cover on seasonal forage production compared with open annual grasslands in two rainfall zones.

Blue oak, in the southern and central portion of its range, provides green forage earlier (with adequate rainfall) and in higher quantities (15 to 100% greater) compared to the forage in open areas (Holland 1980; Frost and McDougald 1989; Ratliff et al. 1991); the difference in forage quality and quantity (though not necessarily timing of initial growth) may be even more pronounced during drought due to the shading provided by tree canopies and the consequent reduction in moisture loss through evapotranspiration (Frost and McDougald 1989).

In evergreen live oak stands, with leaves that shade forage growth during the winter and early spring months, the few studies which have been carried out show a larger competitive effect of oaks on forage production (Ratliff et al. 1991). In general, live oaks stands with over 25 percent canopy cover will have lower forage growth than cleared areas. One study in the Southern Sierra Nevada foothills, however, showed that in drought years, live oak shading helped conserve soil moisture, resulting in higher forage production than on open sites (Frost and McDougald 1989).

Table 6 below summarizes the results of research studies of the relationship between oak canopy and forage production.

Table 6. The effect of oak canopy on hardwood rangeland forage production (note: a "+" indicates that forage production is enhanced by oak canopy, and a "–" indicates that forage production is inhibited by oak canopy)

Species Group	Canopy Cover	Winter Forage Production	Spring Forage Production
Live oaks	Scattered (<10% cover)	– / +	– / +
	Sparse (10 - 25% cover)	– / +	– / +
	Moderate (25 - 60% cover)	–	–
	Dense (over 60% cover)	–	–
Deciduous oaks	Scattered (<10% cover)	+	+
	Sparse (10 - 25% cover)	+	+
	Moderate (25 - 60% cover)	– / +	– / +
	Dense (over 60% cover)	–	–

The increase in forage production beneath blue oak canopies, or in areas previously beneath blue oak canopies, is attributed, in part, to increased soil fertility due to leaf fall and decomposition (Jackson et al. 1990; Frost and Edinger 1991; Firestone 1995). Enhanced soil fertility also improved forage quality beneath blue oaks or where blue oaks were removed. However, since the nutrient input from leaf liter ceases after tree removal, forage production increases will be temporary, until soil fertility gradually declines to similar levels as adjacent open areas. Long term studies have found it may take 15 years for this nutrient effect from oak cover to dissipate after tree removal (Kay 1987).

Oak canopies also have an effect on forage species composition. Studies have found that understories of both blue and live oak stands favor later successional herbaceous species such as wild oats, soft chess and ripgut brome. Clovers, annual fescues, filaree, soft chess, and foxtail fescue account for more of the total herbage biomass in open areas than under oak canopy (Ratliff et al. 1991; Holland 1980).

In general, managers of livestock enterprises on hardwood rangelands should consider the following general guidelines when managing their oaks (Standiford and Tinnin 1996):

- There is of little or no value in removing blue oaks in areas with less than 20 inches of annual precipitation;
- On areas with over 20 inches of annual rainfall, thinning oaks where the canopy exceeds 50 percent will have the greatest effect on forage production;
- In areas thinned for forage enhancement, residual tree canopies of 25 to 35 percent are able to maintain soil fertility and wildlife habitat, and minimize erosion processes; and
- Tree removal activities should always be planned considering all values of the trees, including wildlife habitat, soil stability, etc. in addition to the possible forage production benefits.

Soil Processes and Nutrient Cycling

In an investigation of soil associated characteristics under different tree species canopy and in open grassland sites, Frost and Edinger (1991) found higher organic carbon levels, greater cation exchange capacity, lower bulk density and greater concentrations of some nutrients (at a soil depth of 0-5 cm) under blue oak canopies than in open grassland. Organic matter input from blue oak leaf litter primarily accounts for this finding; leaching of nutrients from rainwater drip may also make a significant contribution. The soil conditions beneath interior live oak and blue oak are similar; shading from the evergreen canopy, therefore, is thought to primarily account for the reduced total annual herbage production under interior live oaks under moderate environmental conditions (Frost and Edinger 1991). This may at least partially account for the higher production under blue oak canopies as compared to open grassland sites in the central Sierra foothills. Upon removal of overstory blue oak species, there is a gradual decline to levels comparable to the open grassland (Holland 1980; Kay 1987). Frost and Edinger (1991) attribute this to the store of nutrients in blue oak litter which is gradually depleted over time.

Comparison of soil moisture relationships in hardwood rangelands with perennial grasses has soil moisture until later in the growing season than hardwood rangelands with annual grasses (Gordon et al. 1989). This difference in soil moisture may at least partially explain some of the observed lack of sapling recruitment in oak woodlands. Evaluation of hardwood rangeland soil bulk density shows that areas with livestock grazing have a higher bulk density than ungrazed areas.

Working in the foothills of the Sierra Nevada, Jackson et al. (1990) found that soils under blue oak canopies have higher nitrogen turnover rates and inorganic nitrogen contents than surrounding open grassland soils due primarily to the higher nitrogen content from mineralization of oak leaf litter. There was no difference in soil water potential between the understory and the open grassland. The increased fertility under the blue oak canopy did not result in enhanced forage productivity; however, blue oaks do maintain a reservoir of soil organic nitrogen that could be rapidly depleted if the oaks were removed.

Grazing Processes

Livestock grazing has had a major impact on the oak woodlands of California's Sierra Nevada. By 1880, Spanish coastal missions had acquired approximately four million sheep and nearly 1 million cattle (Holmes 1990) fostering a large demand for forage and oak browse. This high grazing demand has largely persisted, particularly affecting blue oak, black oak and valley oak. In addition to grazing by cattle and sheep, hogs and rodents have been important browsers of oaks. Feral hogs consume acorns while rodents such as ground squirrels and pocket gophers utilize large quantities of acorns and seedlings; this is perhaps due to removal of rodent predators and the introduction of food sources such as oats and filaree (Holmes 1990).

Grazing has both positive and negative effects on hardwood rangeland sustainability. Some of the positive effects of livestock grazing include:

- Reduced moisture competition between oaks and herbaceous material (Hall et al. 1992);
- Reduced transpirational surface area in seedlings, and may help conserve moisture late in the growing season (Welker and Menke 1990);
- Habitat for rodents who consume acorns and young seedlings may be reduced;

- Fuel ladders are eliminated, reducing the probability of crown fires in grazed woodlands;

Some of the negative effects of livestock grazing are shown below:

- Livestock and other grazing animals consume oak seedlings and acorns (Swiecki and Bernhardt 1993; Adams et al. 1992 ; Hall et al. 1992);
- Grazing may increase soil compaction, making root growth for developing oak seedlings more difficult (Gordon et al. 1989);
- Soil organic matter may be reduced.

Oak Regeneration and Recruitment Processes

One of the key concerns that landowners, policy makers, and the public have about the state's hardwood rangelands is whether there is adequate oak regeneration to sustain current woodlands and savannas. Several surveys of oak regeneration (Bolsinger 1988; Muick and Bartolome 1987; Standiford et al. 1991; Swiecki) have shown a shortage of trees in the sapling size class for certain species (especially blue oak, Engelmann oak, and valley oak) in certain regions of the state (sites at low elevation, on south- and west-facing slopes, on shallow soils, with excessive populations of natural or domesticated herbivores). If this shortage of small trees continues over time, then the oak stands may gradually be lost as natural mortality factors or tree removal take their toll on the large, dominant trees in the stand, and woodlands convert to other vegetation types such as brushfields or grasslands.

Deciduous oak regeneration was locally abundant prior to 1900. Present stand structure suggests that oak regeneration was more frequent in the past. However, deciduous oaks have reproduced poorly in the past 50 years (Griffin 1978). While seedlings become established, few develop into saplings. Live oaks, whose seedlings may be more resistant to grazing and browsing, have produced saplings with more success than have deciduous oaks over the past few decades. Pocket gophers, a significant seedling predator, may prefer deciduous oak roots to those of live oaks. Much of the failure of deciduous oak seedling establishment may be attributed to acorns and seedling damage by cattle, deer, rodents and insects (Griffin 1978).

According to demographic studies and experimental research, most extant blue oak populations are dominated by older individuals; current recruitment levels are insufficient to maintain the present distribution of blue oak (Davis 1995; Swiecki and Bernhardt 1993). Valley and blue oak are not regenerating in sufficient numbers to maintain existing stands (Muick and Bartolome 1986). However, the causes and mechanisms, which seem to vary according to species, region and site, are still under investigation (Bartolome 1987).

Current research indicates that present recruitment of blue oaks may arise from a gap mechanism by which an understory seedling bank persists until a moderate stand disturbance (such as clearing, fire or natural tree mortality) occurs, after which sapling recruitment proceeds (Swiecki and Bernhardt 1993). Natural blue oak regeneration is thus a multiple step process which requires many years for completion. When grazing pressures and plant competition are minimal (such as along along roadsides beyond pastures) or where micro-habitat is favorable, pioneer establishment of blue oaks in open sites can occur. However, the seedling bank-gap-sapling recruitment mechanism, or seedling advance regeneration, seems to be the most pervasive mode of natural blue oak recruitment and regeneration. Undisturbed sites with moderate to dense oak canopies are unlikely sites for sapling recruitment. Since there are various steps and life history stages involved in the seedling advance regeneration mechanism, several variables differentially affect regeneration at different temporal stages of the recruitment process.

Swiecki and Bernhardt (1993) evaluated the status of stand level blue oak regeneration and examined how management tools, environmental factors and site history affect blue oak sapling recruitment at 15 different blue oak-dominated locations. Saplings (basal diameter of 1 cm or greater and a dbh of 3 cm or less) were found on 15.3% of the plots; the majority of these grew from seedlings as opposed to sprouts from cut stumps. Based on observed mortality and sapling recruitment, 13 out of 15 sites had a net loss in blue oak density and canopy cover. These results differ from the earlier discussions on stand level stability and shows the need for long-term regeneration monitoring. Statistical analysis showed variables such as topographic position, browsing intensity, recent canopy gaps and clearings, and total overstory and shrub cover, were associated with sapling recruitment at most of the study locations. Insolation, soil water holding capacity, and repeated fire were important at some locations.

Swiecki and Bernhardt (1993) propose the following recommendations to enhance blue oak recruitment: 1) minimize understory shrub clearing in blue oak communities; 2) reduce the intensity and duration of browsing pressure on woody vegetation; 3) employ fire to manipulate understory vegetation so as to favor recruitment; 4) leave intact at least 20% overstory canopy cover within 0.1 ha unit of regeneration sites; 5) following gap creation, minimize livestock use until blue oak saplings are taller than browse level; 6) minimize "potentially adverse impacts" in sites near the limits of blue oak range.

Valley oak has experienced inadequate regeneration since the last century (Griffin 1973; Bernhardt and Swiecki 1991; and Danielsen and Halverson 1991). While seedlings establish, few develop into saplings. Alien annual grasses, which make less water available to oaks than native perennial grasses, may be one cause of this effect.

Stump sprouting has been widely observed in most oak woodland species. Studies have shown a high probability of achieving stump sprouting for blue and live oak species. This observation reduces the concern that a lack of sapling trees once suggested (McCreary et al. 1991; Standiford et al. 1996).

Figure 2 below shows a decision key for hardwood range landowners and managers to use to assess oak regeneration (Standiford and Tinnin 1996). This shows that there are several questions to be raised in considering the process of oak regeneration (Bartolome et al. 1987). First, there needs to be an assessment of the current stand structure and whether this is consistent with the objective for the stand. Secondly, the health and vigor of the existing trees need to be assessed to determine if recruitment of small trees is needed to replace future tree mortality. Thirdly, the number of seedling and sapling trees should be evaluated. In areas with tree mortality, seedlings and saplings will be needed to replace tree mortality. When overstory tree density is below the desired level for management objectives, seedlings and sapling trees will be needed to increase tree density.

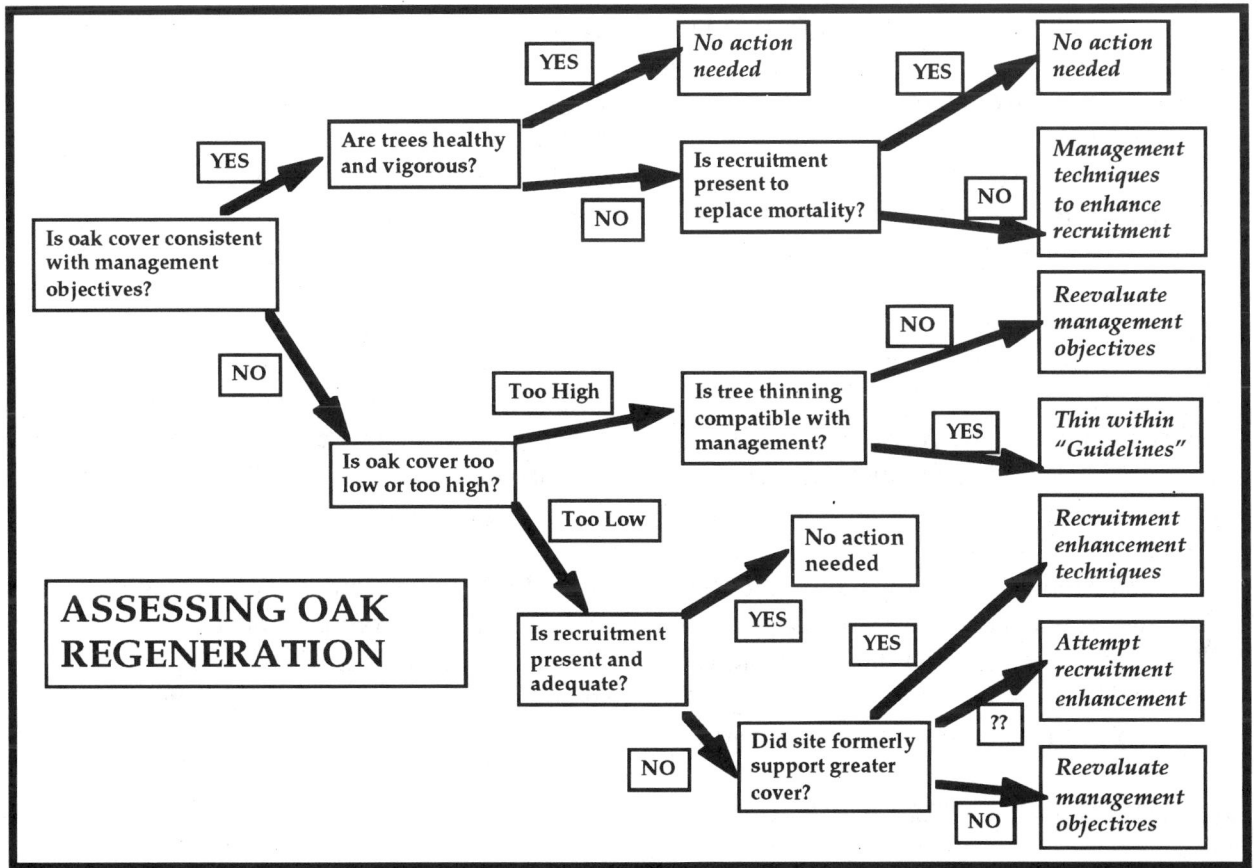

Figure 2. Decision key for evaluating oak regeneration on hardwood rangeland.

Oak restoration and planting (from McCreary 1996)

On areas that have been determined to have a "regeneration problem," it may be necessary to establish more oaks. Planting acorns or seedlings may be necessary where recruitment is inadequate to maintain oak cover on a long-term basis. However, the same factors which limit natural oak regeneration can make it difficult to successfully artificially regenerate native oaks. In general, substantial care must be taken to plant, protect and maintain young oaks in the field to ensure success. While there are many approaches for establishing oaks, the procedures described below have proved successful for a variety of oaks in a variety of environments.

Direct Seeding Acorns

Acorns should be collected fairly near the planting site, or from a very similar environment. Acorns can be collected directly from the trees or from the ground beneath. Generally, the healthiest acorns are those collected from the tree branches, since acorns that fall to the ground can dry out and be damaged - especially if they lie exposed for more than a few days during hot, dry weather. Acorns should be collected in early fall, when they begin to turn from green to brown and are starting to fall to the ground. Acorns should be placed in cold storage at temperatures just above freezing. Acorns collected from the trees can be placed directly in the refrigerator, while those collected from the ground should be soaked in water for several hours before storage. Those that float should be discarded.

Acorns can be directly planted from early November (after the first rains have soaked the soil) until early March. However, it's generally better to plant the acorns early in the season since research has shown that the earlier they are placed in the ground, the earlier they start to grow a root system. Plant the acorns one-half to one inch deep with the germinated root tip pointing down. Place ungerminated acorns on their sides in the holes and cover with soil.

Planting Seedlings

An alternative oak restoration effort is to use containerized or bare root seedlings. Seedlings are preferred in areas of high animal depredation on directly sown acorns. Seedlings may also give a substantial head start over directly sown acorns. However, seedlings are much more expensive to procure and plant. Containerized oak seedlings can also become "pot bound" if held too long. Seedlings should be planted between December and February, when the soil is wet, but not frozen.

Recent studies have shown that augering 1-2 foot holes below planting spots can help seedlings grow faster by breaking up hard, compacted ground and promoting deeper root development. Site preparation must include control of annual grasses and forbs using mulches, mechanical means, or herbicides. Placing a slow-release fertilizer tablet a few inches below and to the side of the root has increased initial seedling growth.

Riparian Management Processes

Although little of the state's water supply originates on hardwood rangelands in the Sierra Nevada, virtually all of it flows through riparian zones on hardwood rangelands (CDF 1988). Also, most of the state's major reservoirs are located on hardwood rangelands. Riparian zones provide important habitat for wildlife and aquatic organisms. Hardwood rangeland management has an impact on water quality and wildlife and fisheries habitat. Little basic research has been completed on the hydrological processes on hardwood rangelands, although several studies in the Sierra Nevada been initiated (IHRMP 1994). It has been shown that removal of up to one-third of the oak canopy has little effect on water quality and yield in one regional study (Epifanio et al. 1991). New efforts have been started to develop rangeland management practices to minimize erosion as part of the state's water quality management plan (Humiston 1995).

Fire Ecology Processes

Fire is a natural part of California's oak woodland ecosystem as well as an important management tool since Native Americans first inhabited these areas. Fire plays a role in the development of oak woodland stand structure, oak regeneration processes, the development of habitat for wildlife, nutrient cycling, and economic uses of oak woodlands for domestic livestock. The ecological effects of fire will vary depending on the frequency of fires, the season and intensity of the fires, and the size of patches that occur from fire-induced mortality of mature trees. Adjacent vegetation types, such as chaparral and montane forests, influence fire effects in oak woodlands. Recent increases in the acreage of stand destroying fires in oak woodlands resulting from decades of attempting to exclude fire from our wildland areas, points to our need to

658

develop strategies in which fire is included in management activities in order to sustain the economic and ecological values of our oak woodlands.

Fire Frequency

Because of the long period of human habitation of oak woodlands, it is extremely difficult to separate the "natural" role of fire from the human use of fire as a management tool. Lightning fires have helped shape oak woodlands. Lightning-caused fires originate from major storms coming northward from Mexico. It is speculated that decades may pass between major lightning-caused fire events in oak woodlands (Griffin, 1977). Oak woodlands are extremely well adapted to hot summer fires (Mooney, 1977). Mature oaks can survive regular low intensity ground fires, and most woodland oak species have the capacity for young seedlings and saplings to resprout after being top-killed by fire.

Native Americans made frequent use of fire in their stewardship of oak woodlands (Holmes 1990). There are numerous accounts of burning by Native Americans in woodlands to enhance habitat for game species, to improve access for hunting and gathering of acorns, and to maintain plant materials in an appropriate growth form for crafts (Jepson 1910; Cooper 1922). However, it is almost impossible to document the frequency, intensity, and extent of burning by Native Americans from existing fire ecology studies.

The first European settlers in oak woodlands continued to use fire as a management practice to keep stands open for livestock production and to encourage forage production. Surveys indicated oak woodland burning intervals of 8 to 15 years by ranchers (Sampson 1944). Local prescribed burning associations were set up in various locations around the state, where neighbors came together annually to help conduct burns in the highest priority areas.

The use of burning as a management tool to mimic the effects of nature ceased on the state's conifer forest lands in the early part of the century. However, ranchers continued the extensive use of prescribed burning until the 1950s. At that time, the use of fire in oak woodlands declined, driven by negative urban attitudes towards fire, increasing housing density in rural areas of the state, concerns about liability from escaped prescribed fires, and air quality concerns. Fire suppression became the standard management strategy on oak woodlands, as it had become decades earlier on conifer lands.

One of the few studies of fire frequency on Sierra Nevada hardwood rangelands was carried out by McClaren and Bartolome (1989) in Central Sierra oak woodlands. Figure 3 shows the fire history in one sample area at the University of California's Sierra Foothill Research and Extension Center. Fire frequency in these foothill oak forests was around 25 years prior to settlement by Europeans in the mid-1800s. After settlement by Europeans, the use of fire as a management tool can be observed, with a fire frequency of about every 7 years. No fires were observed from 1950 until the mid-1980s, when fire suppression was the dominant practice.

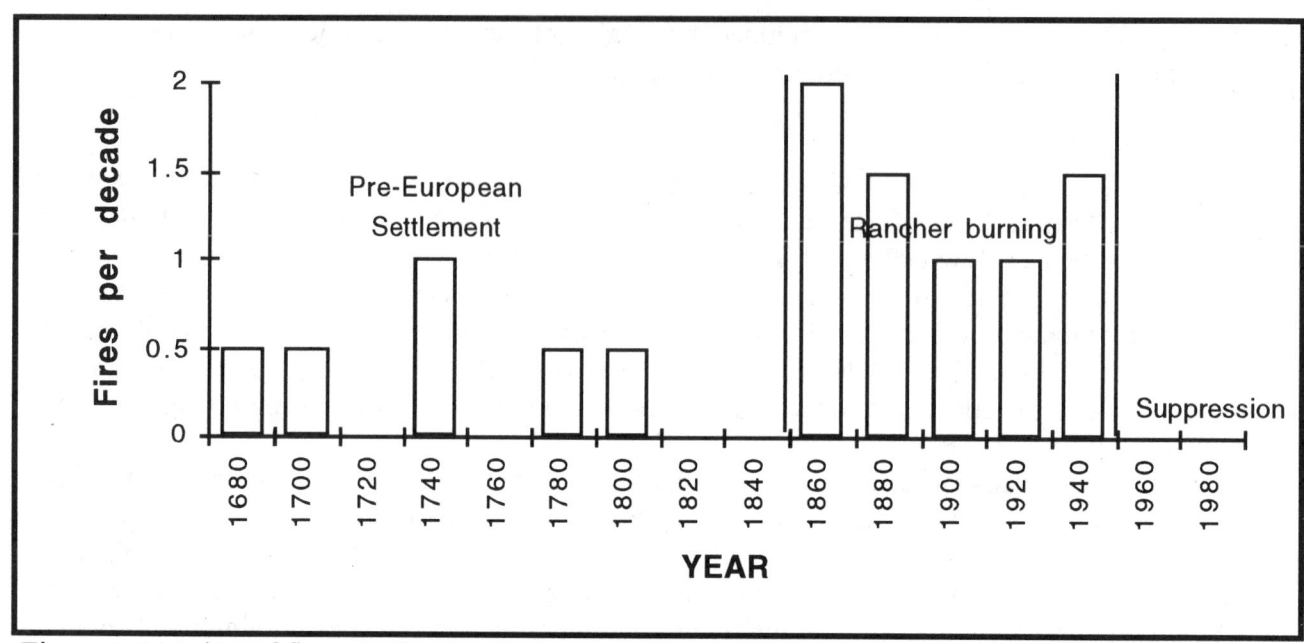

Figure 3. Number of fires per decade for a sample blue oak stand at the Sierra Foothill Research and Extension Center -- 1680 to 1983.

Effects of Fire On Oak Woodland Sustainability

Higher fire frequencies in the past may have created conditions more conducive for oak regeneration. McClaren and Bartolome (1989) compared oak stand age structure with fire history, and showed that oak recruitment was associated with fire events. Most oak recruitment in their Central Sierra study area occurred during periods of high fire frequency in the 1880s to 1940s. Oak recruitment has been rare since fire suppression.

The factors leading to enhanced oak regeneration from higher fire frequencies are not entirely clear. Allen-Diaz and Bartolome (1992) looked at blue oak seedling establishment and mortality with the treatments of grazing and prescribed burning in coastal areas of hardwood rangelands. Neither of these treatments significantly affected oak seedling density nor the probability of mortality when compared to unburned and ungrazed areas, suggesting that seedling establishment is compatible with grazing and fire.

Perhaps the importance of fire on oak regeneration is explained by the enhanced postfire oak sprout growth documented by Bartolome and McClaren (1989). They concluded that in areas of moderate grazing with fire intervals of around 7 years, seedlings taking up to 18 to 20 years to exceed the livestock browse line (around 5 feet) would survive to become saplings and persist in the stand. In heavily grazed areas, only those trees that exceeded the browse line in 10 to 13 years would be recruited. Other factors affecting oak regeneration which would be influenced by the timing of fire events include: the seedbed for acorns; the competition for moisture from herbaceous species; and the habitat for wildlife species that feed on acorns and seedlings.

Fire also kills diseases and pests, such as the Filbert Weevil (*Cucurlio occidentalis*) and the Filbert Worm (*Melissopus latiferreanus*), which can infest the acorn crop (Lewis 1991). Fire also reduces fuel ladders under oak canopies preventing high intensity crown fires.

Wildlife Habitat and Biodiversity Processes

California's hardwood rangelands provide habitat for over 300 vertebrate wildlife species; more than 2000 plant species; and an estimated 5000 species of insects. Figure 4 graphically shows the diversity of vertebrate wildlife species predicted for each of the five major hardwood rangeland habitat types (including coastal oak woodlands). The management and long-term sustainability of California's hardwood rangeland habitats will best be served if ecological components and their inter-relationships are recognized and addressed by owners and managers.

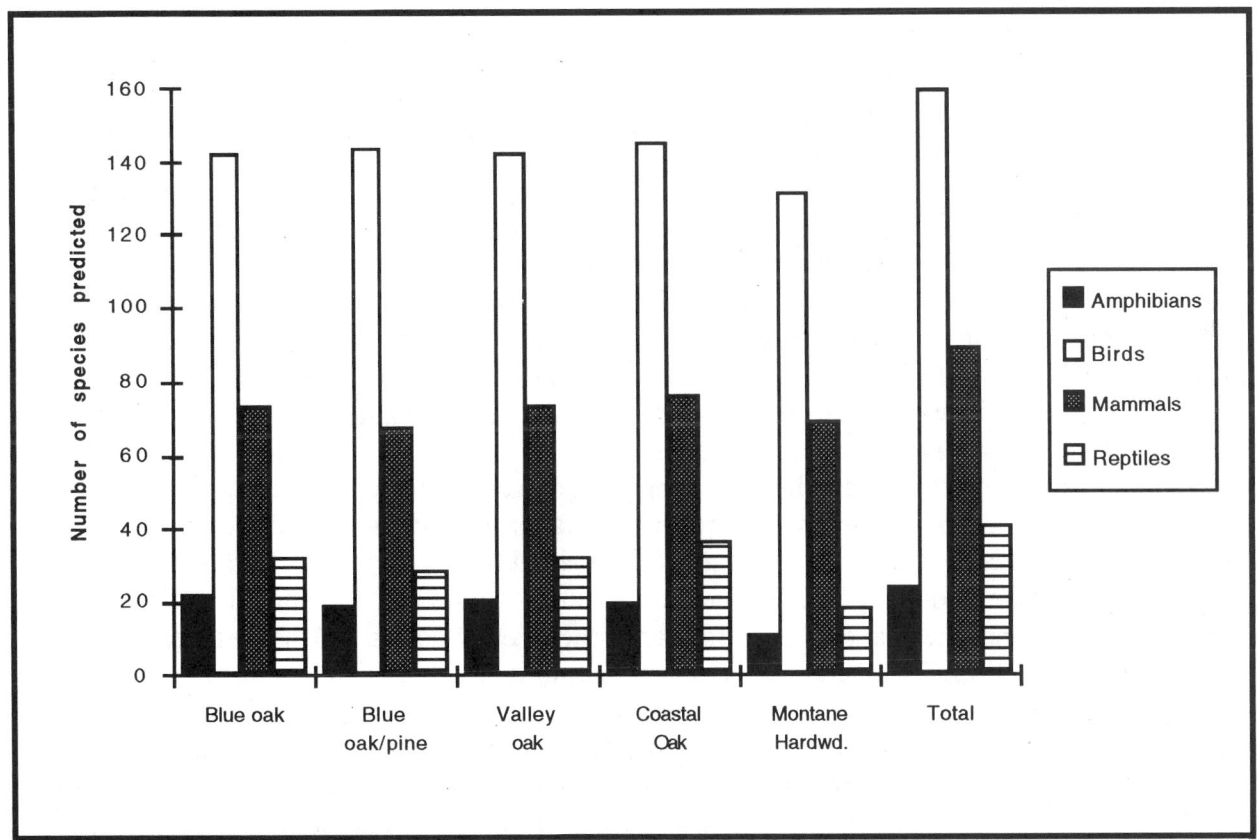

Figure 4. Numbers of amphibians, birds, mammals, and reptiles predicted to occur in the five California hardwood rangeland habitats by Version 5.0 of the California Wildlife Habitat Relationships System (CWHR). This list only includes those species in the CWHR System that are predicted to use one or more tree size and canopy cover classes for breeding, feeding, and/or cover.

Wildlife are abundant inhabitants of the oak woodlands; the persistence of this varied wildlife can only be assured by maintaining the diverse habitats contained within the Sierra Nevada oak woodlands. Oak woodlands provide habitat for many wildlife species which depend on the oak trees, shrubs, grasses, forbs, seeds, fruits, insects and other components of the oak woodland system. Much of the wildlife diversity is directly related to the vegetation diversity of trees, shrubs, logs, leaf litter, grasses, forbs and other habitat components (Block 1990). Changes in one of these components (such as alteration in tree density through urbanization or fuelwood removal) changes other factors (light regime, shrub layer, leaf litter, etc.).

In a 3 year study of non-game wildlife populations at the Sierra Foothill Research and Extension Center, Block and Morrison (1990) found 113 bird species (at least 60 of which bred at the site), including 43 year-round residents, 11 winter residents which bred elsewhere, 17 breeding species which wintered elsewhere, 21 migrant birds and 21 incidental species (Block 1990). Much of the bird species diversity is directly related to the plant diversity in the Sierra oak woodlands. For example, Hutton's vireo, orange-crowned warbler, and Wilson's warbler are closely associated with interior live oak. Birds such as the white-breasted nuthatch and western bluebird are closely associated with blue oak (Block 1990). Wintering and migrant birds rely on the woodland resource for survival. Moreover, the specific habitats utilized by the birds change seasonally. For example, many resident birds obtained insects from foliage of blue and interior live oaks during the breeding season and were restricted to live oaks when the blue oaks had shed their leaves.

Block and Morrison (1990) recorded five small mammal species, including the brush mouse, pinyon mouse, deer mouse, dusky-footed woodrats and ornate shrews. They found low numbers of small mammals in their study sites and hypothesized that the indictment of small mammals as a major cause of poor white oak regeneration is premature.

Block and Morrison (1990) found one amphibian species (the California slender salamander) and three reptile species (the western fence lizard, western skink and the southern alligator lizard) in their Sierra Nevada sites. Distribution of the California slender salamander was limited to interior live oak stands, while western fence lizard and the southern alligator lizard and western skink are found in both live and blue oak stands.

Favorable hardwood rangeland habitats supply food, water, and cover to sustain wildlife species. Each habitat element provides unique niches, favoring particular wildlife species. Conversely, the absence of a particular element in a habitat may limit species diversity. Examples of elements of a hardwood rangeland habitat that are important to consider include riparian zones, vernal pools, wetlands, dead and downed logs and other woody debris, brush piles, snags, rock outcroppings, and cliffs. Figure 5 gives the relative number of wildlife species that are predicted to use various elements found on hardwood rangelands.

Riparian habitat elements are used by almost 90 percent of all hardwood rangeland wildlife species, illustrating the importance of conserving this habitat element where present. Over one-third of all bird species on hardwood rangelands make use of snags, suggesting that management strategies maintaining an appropriate number of snags will result in greater wildlife species diversity. Downed woody debris from fallen limbs or dead trees, provide an extremely valuable habitat for most reptiles and amphibians, as well as for many bird species. Oak woodland management for wildlife must include these trees as well as trees in various stages of vigor in order to maintain critical wildlife habitat (Block and Morrison 1990). Mid-elevation hardwood rangeland habitats, with several oak species, vertical diversity in vegetation structure, and diverse riparian zones, have the richest diversity of wildlife (Motroni et al. 1991).

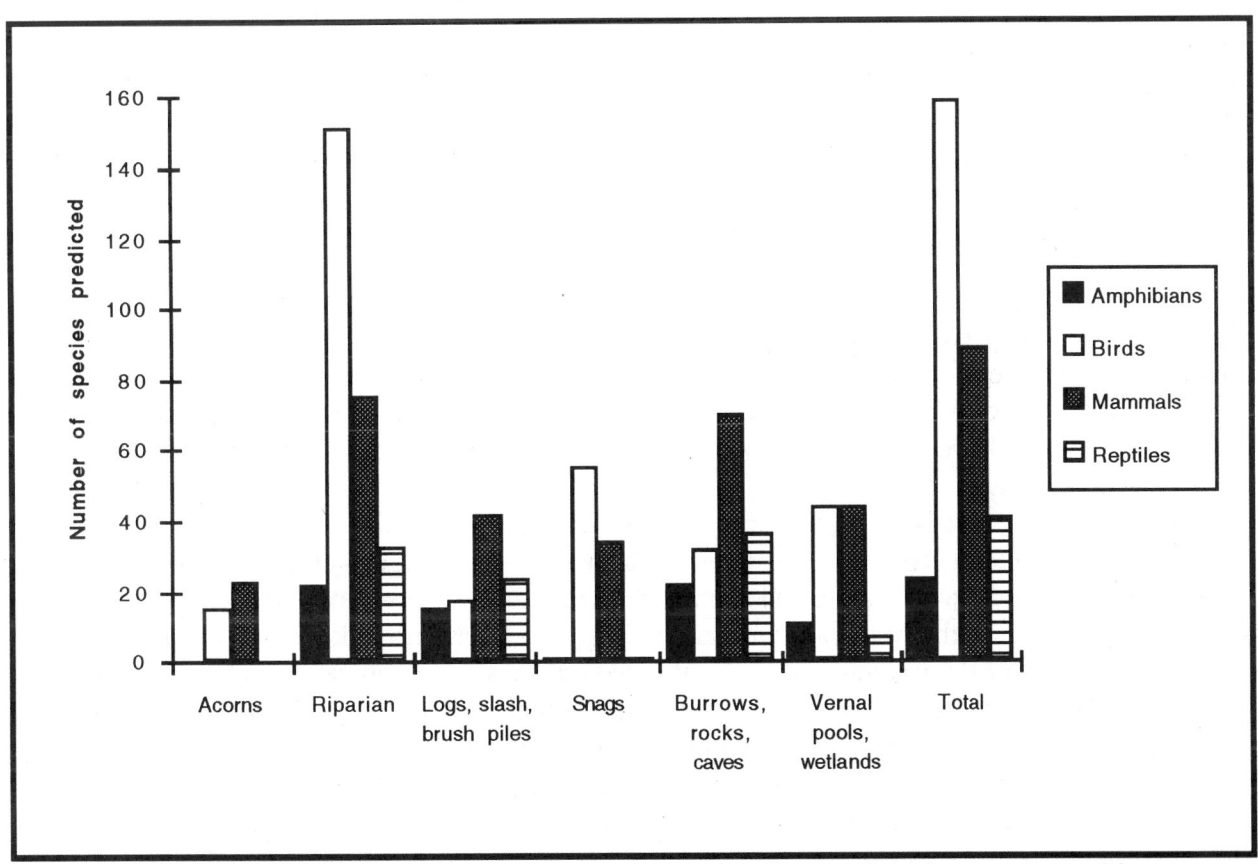

Figure 5. Number of amphibians, birds, mammals, and reptiles predicted to use several important habitat elements of California hardwood rangeland habitats by Version 5.0 of the California Wildlife Habitat Relationships System (CWHR). This list includes those species in the CWHR System that are predicted to use one or more of these elements for breeding, feeding, and/or cover.

With this background on factors influencing biodiversity on hardwood rangelands, and the spatial and temporal trends for these habitats, the threats to continued high biodiversity include: 1) fragmentation of large blocks of extensively managed hardwood rangelands; 2) reduction in important habitat elements such as snags, woody debris, and diverse riparian zones; and 3) increasing interface with urban areas, bringing household pets, humans, and fire suppression policies into contact with hardwood rangeland habitats. These threats to biodiversity can be reduced by encouraging cluster development and conservation of connecting corridors between large hardwood rangeland habitat blocks (Giusti and Tinnin 1993).

MAINTAIN ECONOMIC VIABILITY AND UTILIZATION OF HARDWOOD RANGELANDS

Hardwood rangelands have been important to humans living in the Sierra Nevada for centuries. For the most part, traditional management practices utilized by Native Americans and then by the ranching community, were able to maintain large blocks of habitat that supported ecosystem processes at a variety of scales. Recent trends in human use, however, is leading to conversion of lands to residential and industrial uses as people leave the major urban areas of the state to seek the aesthetic and amenity values of hardwood rangelands. Some of the economic and utilization issues facing hardwood rangelands in the Sierra Nevada are discussed below.

Stewardship by Native Americans

The original human inhabitants of Sierra Nevada hardwood rangelands were Native Americans. Acorns were the dietary staple and sustained their cultures that lived among the oak woodlands (Pavlik et al. 1991). Virtually all tribes west of the Sierra harvested acorns for food. Acorns are estimated to have been the primary diet for more than 3/4 of all Native Americans in California; black oak was the preferred species in many regions (McCarthy 1993). Each tribe had special mechanisms for acorn gathering, storing, hulling, drying leaching, pounding and cooking. The bark roots, wood, small branches and galls of oaks were also utilized.

Acorns were second to salt among the most frequently traded foods among Native Americans. The trade in acorns flowed from west to east with, for example, Miwoks gathering black oak acorns from the western Sierra and trading with the Mono Lake Paiute for pinyon pine nuts (Pavlik et al. 1991); trading across elevational zones was also common (McCarthy 1993). Territorial claims of tribes, villages, families and individuals were often based on the distribution of acorn-producing oak groves. The finding that many cultural traditions and celebrations focused on the oaks attests to the central role oaks played in their lives. Aside from providing sustenance and goods for barter, oaks and acorns were also employed as medicines and dyes.

The use of fire and burning was the most prevalent and effective management tool native Californian people utilized to manage the oaks and the acorn crop (McCarthy 1993). Low-intensity fires were also used to promote oak growth while avoiding damage from high intensity fires, and helped keep prized oaks from being dominated by conifer species. Many village sites were found to be located near mature black oak stands

Economic Viability of Hardwood Rangelands

Since the 1800s, hardwood rangelands in the Sierra Nevada have been used mainly for domestic livestock products. Dramatic annual fluctuations in livestock markets, coupled with risk from forage shortages due to high variability in annual rainfall, has made many livestock operations marginal. Figure 6 shows the range of fluctuation for several of these factors (Doak and Stewart 1986; USDA various years). Another risk to maintenance of extensively managed livestock operations are the high opportunity cost from suburban developments or intensive agricultural products such as wine grapes. Uncertainty about federal grazing policies, where many hardwood rangeland operators lease summer forage, also hinders economic viability of hardwood rangeland enterprises. Low profitability and high risk has accelerated conversion of extensively managed private ranches to suburban developments.

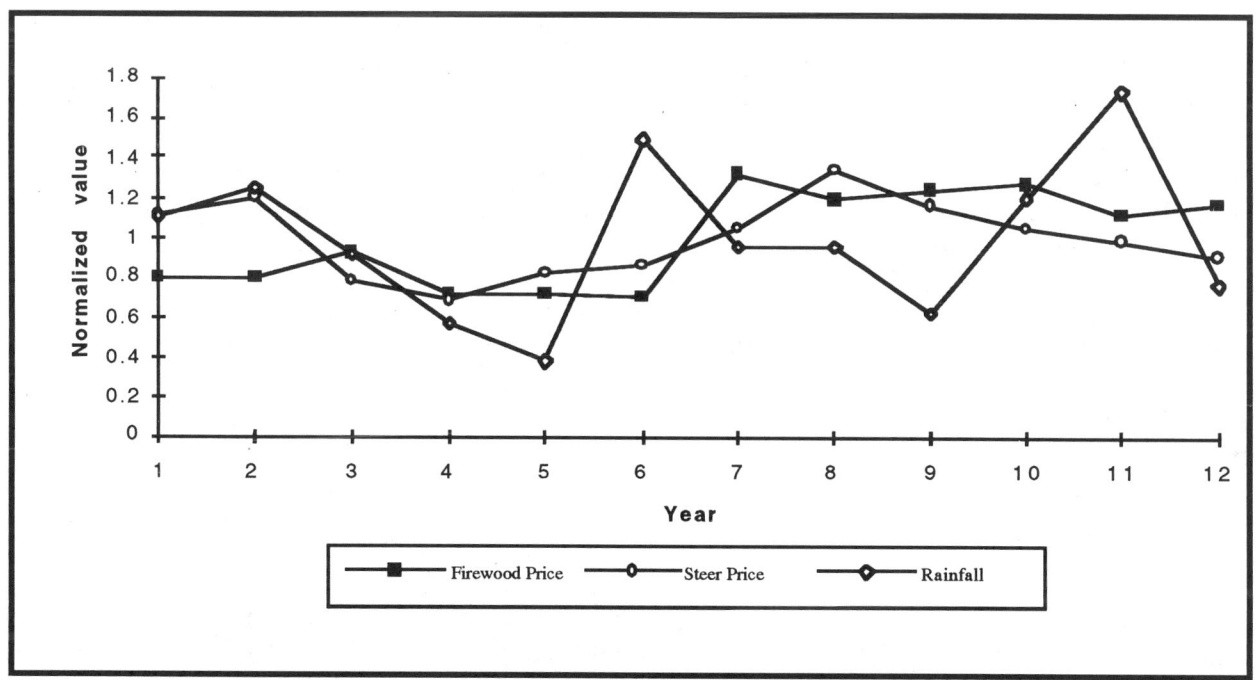

Figure 6. 12 year trends in steer and firewood prices, and annual rainfall, for a southern Sierra Nevada hardwood rangeland area (lines are normalized, so that 1.0 is the mean value over the 12 year period).

Traditional efforts to increase profitability of hardwood rangelands have focused almost exclusively on enhancing forage production through removal of the oaks. This simplification of the ranch ecosystems did pay short term dividends in improved forage yields, but the same risk from fluctuating product markets and weather variability continued to make ranching a low profitability enterprise.

New markets have developed in the last 20 years for the oak trees on hardwood rangelands for firewood and as habitat for commercial hunting enterprises. This diversified economic portfolio has helped to enhance the economic sustainability of hardwood rangelands by spreading risk out over several enterprises, increasing overall returns per acre, and providing an economic incentive to conserve more diverse hardwood rangeland ownerships.

A study was initiated to study the effects of these new markets for firewood and hunting on hardwood rangelands (Standiford and Howitt 1990; Standiford and Howitt 1993). Firewood production, livestock production, and commercial hunting were incorporated into a multi-product objective function to model the optimal oak canopy levels of hardwood range owners over time.

Effect of hunting on total financial return

Total ranch profitability is one of the most important factors impacting conversion of hardwood rangelands to subdivisions and other more urbanized uses of the resource, and away from the large expanses of extensively managed open space that characterizes most hardwood range operations. The hypothesis is that hunting and firewood harvesting offers a broadened market base for hardwood range managers and improved economic returns to the land, which may help to reduce conversions.

665

Figure 7 shows the net present value per acre (NPV) over a 12 year period for a hardwood range site with 750 cubic feet per acre. This figure shows the major impact that hunting has on the total economic value of hardwood range management. On a poor forage-producing site, NPV is increased by 142 percent with hunting (from $51 to $123 per acre), and hunting is the dominant economic value on the site. On a high quality forage-producing site, hunting increases the NPV by 59 percent (from $138 to $221 per acre), although cattle production remains the dominant economic value on this site. This figure shows the relatively minor contribution that firewood harvesting makes to the total economic value of the operation.

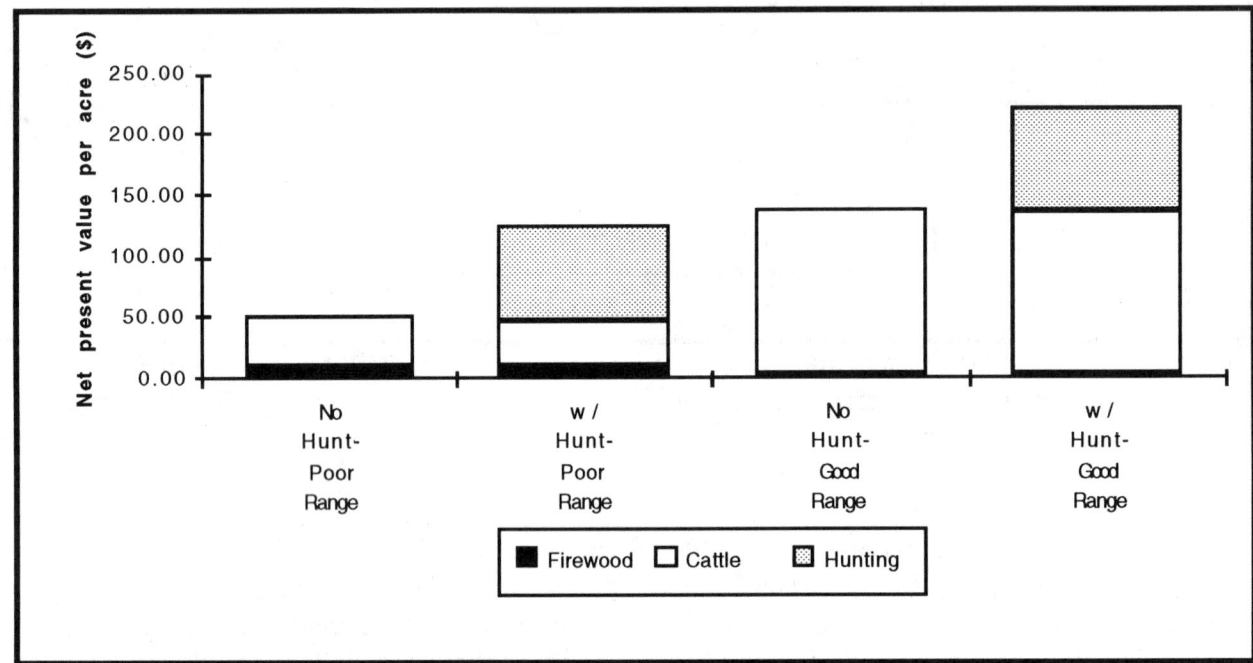

Figure 7. Effect of hunting on net present value of a 1000 acre hardwood rangeland site with 750 cubic feet per acre, and poor forage-producing capacity (poor range) or high forage-producing capacity (good range).

Effecting of hunting on firewood harvest

Figure 8 shows the cumulative firewood harvest over a 12 year period on a low productivity range site. Less oak firewood harvesting occurs when hunting value is received. This indicates that the marginal decrease in hunting revenue due to oak canopy changes is greater than the marginal revenue from the firewood harvest. Hunting apparently provides an incentive for hardwood range managers to conserve oak trees. The optimum decision is for no firewood harvesting to occur over a on areas with less than 500 cubic feet per acre of oak wood volume (about 6 cords). The marginal cost of harvesting firewood exceeds the market price at these levels. This is consistent with the low levels of firewood harvesting reported above. Ranch managers are not likely to completely clear their oaks for forage enhancement because the marginal revenue of the added forage is less than the marginal cost of cutting trees.

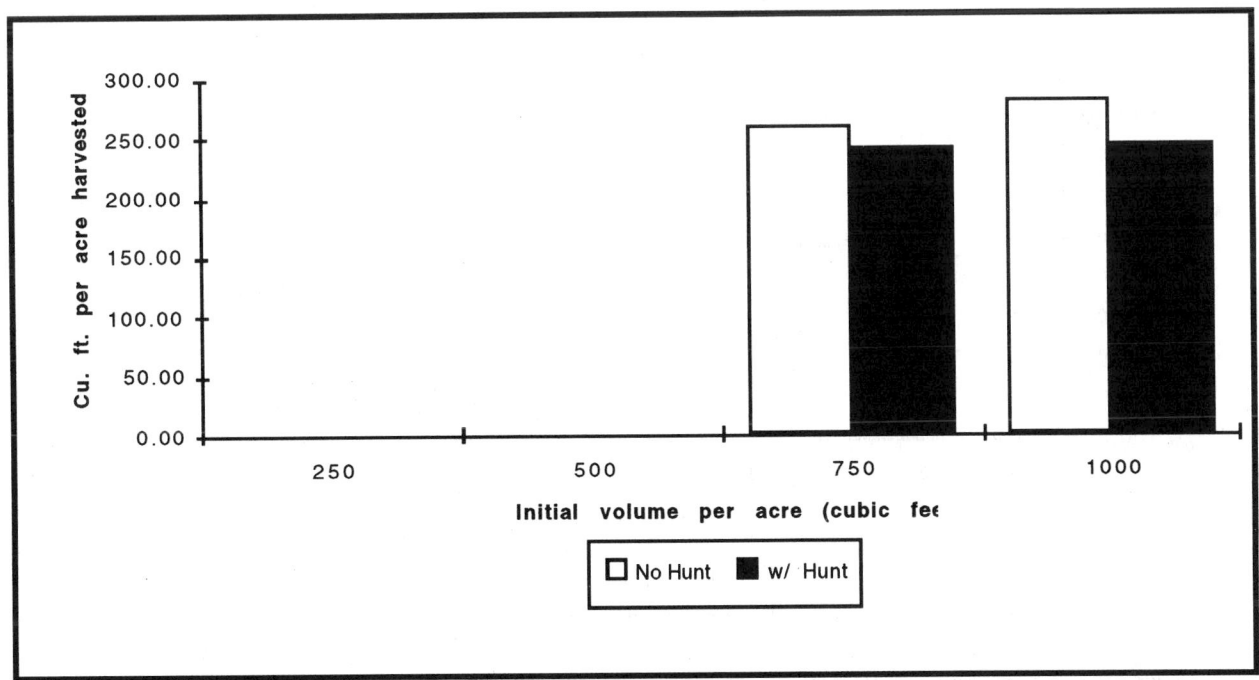

Figure 8. Predicted total firewood harvested over 12 years for hardwood rangelands with and without hunting enterprises.

Effect of Hunting on Livestock Density

Figure 9 shows the optimum number of cow-calf pairs on a 1000 acre hardwood rangeland parcel with oak crown canopy cover levels ranging from 25 to 80 percent. As crown cover increases, livestock density decreases. Livestock density is lower on areas with hunting, due to allocation of some of the forage base to wildlife species, and also labor and management constraints. Decreased livestock use helps reduce risk from fluctuating livestock markets and poor forage years, and may relieve pressure on important resources such as oak regeneration and riparian zones.

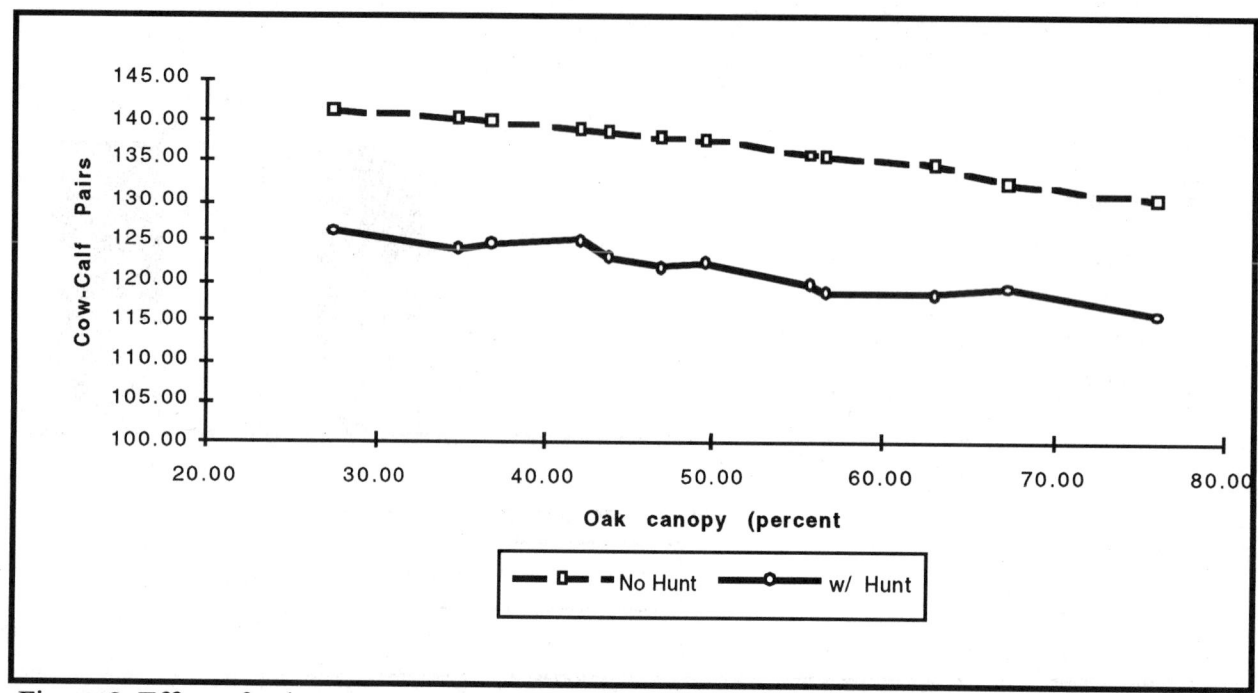

Figure 9. Effect of oak canopy cover and commercial hunting enterprises on optimum cow-calf pairs on a 1000 acre hardwood rangeland parcel.

Interest in hardwood rangeland conservation raises the question as to whether current private markets will provide adequate oak cover to meet perceived public needs. With new markets for recreational hunting on private lands, preliminary results indicate that these markets may provide some incentive for hardwood rangeland managers to reduce tree harvesting levels. This research indicates that it is unlikely that any level of firewood harvesting will occur on oak stands with low volumes per acre. The hunting enterprise reduces intensity of livestock use, decreasing pressure to enhance the forage base with tree harvest. There is no economic incentive to clear dense oak stands for improvement for livestock use based on the current range of revenues and costs.

New Markets

Wood Products and Specialty Forest Products
Throughout history, rangeland hardwoods have been utilized for fuelwood. The spreading, highly-branched tree form of most rangeland hardwoods creates numerous grain deviations making them a low quality tree for other wood products by standard log and lumber grading rules. There are numerous limitations to the utilization of rangeland hardwoods for other wood products (Shelly et al. 1996):

- low proportion of stem to branch wood,
- unknown or poorly understood wood properties, and
- unproven product performance.

Little scientific research has been performed on the wood properties of most California hardwood species because of the lack of a strong commercial interest. The exceptions are California black oak, tanoak and madrone. These are primarily timberland species but they can also be found in some rangeland regions. In certain situations, rangeland hardwoods may be a viable resource for local needs or specialty products. Availability and quality concerns make it unlikely that any rangeland hardwoods could supply a commodity market; however, based on wood properties and characteristics, successful niche markets are possible. Local products made by artisans, woodworkers and hobbyists prove that high value products can be made, however special manufacturing techniques and innovative marketing strategies may be required to do it economically.

Hardwood forests are also a resource for many products that are not primarily based on processing the wood. Numerous enterprises have developed across the country that are based on gathering plant materials from the forest for a wide variety of uses. Several examples of collected materials that have found established markets are:

- Wild mushrooms
- Berries and wild fruit
- Acorns, nuts, and seeds
- Decorative branches and other plant materials for floral displays
- Bark, leaves, and roots for flavoring, medicinal, or pharmaceutical uses
- Wild plants for nursery stock
- Basket making and weaving supplies
- Plant materials for natural dyes

Typical characteristics of these enterprises are that they are usually small, labor intensive, cottage industries with few equipment needs and low capital costs. All forms of marketing can be found, from roadside stands, direct sales to wholesale/retail vendors, or to catalog ventures.

Markets for Amenity Values

Historically, the market value of hardwood rangelands for subdivision near urban areas has exceeded their value for amenities and ecological functions. The recent human population increase in hardwood rangelands, however, has raised the potential values of woodland amenities to a point where they are often a financially viable alternative to land development (Scott 1996). Landowners may find that woodland conservation provides the best financial scenario, especially if they own woodlands with high conservation value. However, land owners outside of the suburban fringe may find that their properties are not increasing in development potential and are unlikely to be considered woodland open space.

Woodlands provide a large component of the quality-of-life sought by many relocating industries, and the relatively low cost of industrial sites in these woodlands is equally appealing. Woodland owners along the wildland urban interface often find that their management options track public demand for specific values. If woodland conversions trigger a public demand for amenity protection, the solutions typically must be found on private lands. Open space easements, and other deed restrictions provide financial, tax, or development incentives for the voluntary maintenance of public amenity values on private lands.

CONSERVATION POLICY ISSUES

A series of policy instruments to conserve hardwood rangelands have evolved in California and throughout the Sierra Nevada region against the backdrop of the ecological and economic factors described above. A variety of interest groups have expressed concerns about oak woodlands to the California State Board of Forestry (BOF), the state regulatory and policy-making body responsible for forest and rangelands. Three incidents hastened the development of a state hardwood policy by the BOF (IHRMP 1992): 1) Monterey and Santa Clara counties petitioned the BOF to classify oaks as commercial species regulated under the Forest Practice Act because of concerns over hardwood harvesting; 2) a 1,000 acre Timber Harvest Plan (THP) in the Northern Sierra requested removal of most black oaks in a critical migratory deer corridor; and 3) the increase in the number of new biomass power plants had the possibility of severely impacting hardwoods on commercial and non-commercial lands. In response to these issues, the BOF asked the University of California (UC), the California Department of Forestry and Fire Protection (CDF), and the California Department of Fish and Game (CDF&G) to develop a program of research, education, and monitoring on conservation of hardwood rangelands (Passof and Bartolome 1985). This program is known as the Integrated Hardwood Range Management Program (IHRMP).

With the development of the IHRMP, the BOF adopted a *Resolution on Hardwoods* on February 3, 1987. This resolution concluded that although the BOF had the authority and obligation under the Forest Practice Act (California Legislature 1980) to protect the hardwood resource, it was premature to declare hardwoods "commercial," which would immediately invoke Forest Practice Act regulations on hardwood rangelands. An intensive educational program, problem-focused research, and frequent monitoring of the resource was felt to be the most effective way to work with landowners and local governments to resolve hardwood issues. The IHRMP was the mechanism expected to accomplish the goals of this non-regulatory program. This policy has continued up to the present.

The IHRMP's mission is stated as follows:

> *"To maintain, and where possible expand, the acreage of California's hardwood range resource to provide wildlife habitat, recreational opportunities, wood and livestock products, high quality water supply, and aesthetic value."*

The initial goals and direction of the IHRMP were driven by statewide concerns about regeneration, wildlife habitat, and conversion pressure (IHRMP 1988), and were focused at a stand or single property level. As understanding of the ecological processes on these lands have increased, IHRMP goals have broadened to include multi-ownership, landscape level considerations (IHRMP 1992). The current goals of the IHRMP are to:

* Develop methods to sustain hardwood rangeland ecosystems and landscapes;
* Maintain wildlife habitat on hardwood rangelands;
* Restore degraded hardwood rangelands;
* Ensure land use planning uses available information to conserve hardwood rangeland ecosystems;
* Maintain economically viable hardwood rangelands;
* Maintain statewide information base about trends, conditions, and extent of hardwood rangelands; and
* Help focus public awareness about the importance of hardwood rangeland habitats

The IHRMP has funded 66 research studies over ten years, which in turn has stimulated additional research on various aspects of hardwood rangelands. Specific areas investigated with IHRMP funding include: oak regeneration (20 projects); wildlife habitat (11 projects); soil, water and land use issues (10 projects); hardwood rangeland management strategies (10 projects); and monitoring trends and status of hardwood rangelands (15 projects). This research has been conducted by investigators in UC, the California State University, private universities, and private research and consulting firms. These research studies, resulting in over 150 new scientific articles, contribute to the base of understanding of the ecological and managerial processes extent on hardwood rangelands (IHRMP 1992). Research results have been disseminated in IHRMP-sponsored symposia and workshops and incorporated directly into educational documents and newsletters.

An important aspect of the development of educational programs is to characterize the demographics of the various audiences that have on impact on hardwood rangelands (Huntsinger and Fortmann 1990; McClaran and Bartolome 1985; Day 1987; Pillsbury and Oxford 1987; Whittington and Tietje 1993). A wide variety of educational programs have been developed for the diverse audiences affecting hardwood rangelands.

Surveys were implemented to evaluate the effectiveness of education as a conservation policy. A survey comparing participants in IHRMP educational program to the population at large showed that ranchers, resource managers, conservation groups, and consultants, though diverse, have a strong set of shared values (Stewart 1991). Natural beauty and maintenance of wildlife diversity were the two most important values of hardwood rangelands to all audiences surveyed. Cooperative Extension (CE) has had some contact regarding oak woodland issues with 49 percent of the ranchers in the state, and 69 percent of the resource managers. Of those who attended various IHRMP educational workshops, 74 percent of the ranchers and 70 percent of the resource managers had some follow-up discussions with CE about oaks. Individuals who participated in IHRMP educational programs were more likely to carry out oak enhancing management activities than non-participants.

The attitudes and management practices of hardwood rangeland owners were evaluated in 1985, just prior to the intensive educational outreach of the IHRMP (Huntsinger and Fortmann 1990). This same survey was repeated in 1992 to discern trends that resulted from the expanded educational programs (Huntsinger 1992). This showed that 18 percent of hardwood rangeland properties had been sold in the seven year period, indicating that education must be an on-going process because of high ownership turnover. Livestock grazing was still the dominant hardwood range land use after seven years, occurring on 67 percent of all acres. The percentage of large parcel owners relying on livestock grazing as their major source of income declined from 70 percent in 1985 to 50 percent in 1992. Following the seven year period of intensive educational outreach, oaks were more valued by landowners for wildlife habitat, soil protection, enhancement of property values, and for browse and mast production. The number of large owners selling firewood decreased from 40 percent in 1985 to 23 percent in 1992. The number of large landowners who cut living trees for forage enhancement declined from 58 percent in 1985 to 38 percent in the seven year period. During this same time period, the number of owners who conducted wildlife habitat improvements increased from 56 percent of the large landowners to 64 percent. Owners who received advice from CE or other public advisory services were more likely to carry out oak promoting practices (protect sprouts, maintain fixed oak canopy levels, thin softwoods to promote oak growth, planting oaks). Strong attitudes against regulation of hardwood rangelands continued in the majority of all ownership classes.

Local Policy Initiatives

In May, 1993, the BOF held hardwood hearings to evaluate the effectiveness of seven years of research and education as an approach to hardwood rangeland conservation. These hearings showed strong support for the continuation of research, outreach, and monitoring, and revealed a high diversity of threats facing hardwood rangelands throughout the state. Within the Sierra Nevada region, firewood harvesting was recognized to be a concern only in the northern Sacramento Valley, while conversion to subdivisions was important in the central Sierra Nevada (IHRMP 1994). These findings confirmed that statewide regulations would not be able to effectively address the wide diversity of conservation issues. The BOF decided to intensify its outreach to local governments, and encourage their participation in local policy development with the assistance of the IHRMP. Following a period of outreach, the Board will evaluate progress by local governments in providing policies which protect hardwood rangelands, and determine where statewide policies might be needed to address continuing problems.

The IHRMP has worked closely with local governments to encourage the development of local policies to conserve hardwood rangelands. Within the Sierra Nevada region, 13 of the 15 counties have adopted or started the process of adopting local hardwood rangeland conservation strategies in response to the BOF resolution. The strategies followed fall into three general categories, namely: county voluntary guidelines; land use planning; and tree harvesting ordinances. Table 7 describes the type of county policy for the Sierra Nevada region. Each of these are discussed below.

County Voluntary Guidelines

At the 1993 BOF Hardwood Hearings, Tehama County political and agricultural leaders volunteered to initiate a broad-based effort to address concerns about widespread firewood harvest on hardwood rangelands in their county. This resulted in the appointment of a county oak committee composed of various resource agencies, environmental groups, and agricultural groups. They developed a set of voluntary oak retention guidelines to maintain economic viability of grazing and ecological values of hardwood rangelands. This set of guidelines was passed by the county Board of Supervisors, and mailed to all landowners in the county (Gaertner 1995). With this county effort as a successful pilot project, several other counties began to develop voluntary guidelines. There are currently 10 counties in the Sierra Nevada region in various stages of developing voluntary guidelines. The leadership for drafting guidelines varied in different areas, and included the local chapter of the California Cattleman's Association, the County Board of Supervisors, the County Planning Department, the Agricultural Commissioner's Office, and the Resource Conservation District. Each effort addresses important local issues, and include education and monitoring. For example, several of the voluntary guidelines in the northern Sacramento Valley addressed impacts from firewood harvest, while biomass harvest, fire protection, and soil erosion were important issues addressed in southern Sierra guidelines. Most of the guidelines also have general recommendations on urban development patterns.

General Planning Process

The county General Plan sets policies governing land use. The California Oak Foundation, working with the BOF, put together sample language on the importance of oak woodlands for the General Plan and mailed this to all county planning departments. Only three counties in the Sierra Nevada are using some part of the land use planning process to address oak conservation issues. This approach has been more widely used in the Central Coast and southern California regions of the state. (Tietje and Berlund 1995). Within the Sierra Nevada, Tuolumne County has an especially innovative open space conservation strategy, in which they prioritize various habitats, and establish priorities for maintaining open space on the basis of the relative sensitivity of the habitat in the county. Landscape-based goals are established to link open space habitats together through corridors (Peck 1993)

Ordinances

Only one county in the Sierra Nevada region has utilized a tree ordinance as a mechanism to protect oaks. Ordinances create a regulatory environment at the county or city level, and usually involve a permitting process for the removal of any tree over a certain size class, and mitigation standards where tree removal is allowed. Tree ordinances are more common in Bay Area and Southern California counties. Most tree ordinances have focused on the single tree rather than at a broad habitat scale. CDF has developed an educational book on tree ordinances which describes the importance of setting objectives for an area prior to writing an ordinance, and monitoring whether the objectives have been accomplished (Bernhardt and Swiecki 1991). This book has been distributed to all counties in the state.

Table 7. Type of county hardwood rangeland policy being developed in the Sierra Nevada region.

Sierra Nevada County	Voluntary Guidelines	Ordinances	Land Use Planning Process
Shasta	x		
Tehama	x		
Butte	x		
Yuba			
Nevada			
Placer		x	
Eldorado			x
Amador	x		
Calaveras	x		
Tuolumne	x		x
Mariposa	x		
Madera	x		
Fresno	x		
Tulare			x
Kern	x		

Conclusion

Important information has been developed on the ecology and sustainable management of hardwood rangelands through activities of the IHRMP. Sociological and biological monitoring shows that diverse audiences have accepted and acted on educational information. A large number of counties have started the process of adopting local conservation strategies to conserve hardwood rangelands. It is quite clear, that education and research have played a major role in conserving hardwood rangelands. Major accomplishments have been made in the more rural areas of the state, where livestock and natural resource management are the predominant land use. Where individual landowners have the ability to implement management activities that affect large acreages, education and research has contributed to decisions that favor conservation of hardwood rangelands.

However, for much of the Sierra Nevada region, conversion of hardwood rangelands to urban or suburban land use is having the largest impact on sustainability of resource values. Educational materials developed on hardwood rangeland conservation in land use planning have been widely accepted by professionals working in the land use arena. However, very little progress has been made in incorporating these educational materials into successful land use plans adopted by the county government. Since conversion to residential and industrial uses is ultimately is a land use decision, it is a political process involving action by elected officials with input from different constituencies. The political and economic forces vary greatly in different parts of the Sierra Nevada. Since "success" in this area involves multiple individuals agreeing on a political course of action, this issue will present the largest challenge for a research and education strategy. It needs to be evaluated very carefully over the next several years to determine if education and research alone are sufficient to sustain the ecological values of hardwood rangelands.

BIBLIOGRAPHY

Adams, T.E., P.B. Sands, W.H. Weitkamp, and N.K. McDougald. 1992. Oak seedling establishment on California rangelands. Journal of Range Management 45(1):93-98.

Allen-Diaz, B.H. and J.W. Bartolome. 1992. Survival of *Quercus douglasii (Fagaceae)* seedlings under the influence of fire and grazing. Madrono 39(1): 47-53.

Allen, B. H., B. A. Holzman, and R. R. Evett. 1991. A classification system for California's hardwood rangelands. Hilgardia 59(2):1-45.

Barbour, M.G. and J. Major, eds. 1988. Terrestrial Vegetation of California. California Native Plant Society, Special Publication, Number 9.

Barrett, R. H. 1980. Mammals of California oak habitats -- management implications. *in* Proceedings of the Symposium on the Ecology, Management, and Utilization of California Oaks, June 26-28, 1979. USDA Forest Service General Technical Report PSW-44:275-291.

Bartolome. J.W., P.C. Muick, and M.P. McClaren. 1987. Natural regeneration of Californian hardwoods. In: Proc. symp. on multiple-use management of California's hardwood resources; 1986 San Luis Obispo, Calif. USDA Forest Service, Pacific Southwest Forest and Range Exp. Station, Berkeley, California. Gen Tech. Rep. PSW-100:26-31.

Bartolome, J.W. 1987. California annual grassland and oak savannah. Rangelands 9(3) 122-125.

Bernhardt, E. A. and T. J. Swiecki. 1991. Guidelines for developing and evaluating tree ordinances. report to California Dept. of Forestry and Fire Protection Urban Forestry Program. 76 p.

Bernhardt, Elizabeth A. and Tedmund J. Swiecki, 1991. Minimum input techniques for valley oak restocking. USDA Forest Service Gen Tech. Rep. PSW-126: 2-8.

Bolsinger, C. L. 1988. The hardwoods of California's timberlands, woodlands, and savannas. USDA Forest Service Pacific Northwest Research Station Resource Bulletin PNW-RB-148. 149 p.

Block, W.M. 1990. Geographic variation in foraging ecologies of breeding and nonbreeeding birds in oak woodlands. Studies in Avian Biology 13:264-269.

Block, William M. and Michael Morrison, 1990. Wildlife diversity of the central Sierra foothills. California Agriculture. March-April 19-22.

Block, W. M., M. L. Morrison, and J. Verner. 1990. Wildlife and oak woodland interdependence. Fremontia 18:72-76.

Burcham, L.T. 1970. Ecological significance of alien plants in California grasslands. In: Proceedings of the Association of American Geographers. Vol. 2. p36-39.

Byrne, R., E. Edlund, and S. Mensing. 1991. Holocene changes in the distribution and abundance of oaks in: Proc. Symp. Oak Woodlands and Hardwood Rangeland Management. USFS Gen. Tech. Rep. PSW-126:182-188.

California Legislature. 1980. Z'Berg-Nejedly Forest Practice Act of 1973; Division 4, Chapter 8, Public Resources Code.

CDF (California Department of Forestry and Fire Protection). 1988. California's forests and rangelands: growing conflicts over changing uses. Forest and Rangeland Resource Assessment Program, Sacramento, CA.

Cooper, W.S. 1922. The broad-sclerophyll vegetation of California. Carnegie Inst. Wash. Pub. 319. 124 pp.

Danielsen, Karen C. and William L. Halvorson, 1991. Valley oak seedling growth associated with selected grass species. In USDA Forest Service Gen. Tech. Rep. PSW-126: 9-11.

Davis, F. W. 1995. Vegetation change in blue oak and blue oak/foothill pine woodland. Report to California Department of Forestry and Fire Protection. Contract 8CA06673. 34 p.

Day, N. 1987. Study of urban attitudes towards oak trees. Report by Polaris to the California Dept. of Forestry and Fire Protection.

Doak, S.C. and W. Stewart. 1986. A model of economic forces affecting California's hardwood resource: monitoring and policy implications. Report submitted to the Forest and Rangeland Assessment Program, California Department of Forestry and Fires Protection, in partial fulfillment of contract #8CA42151.

Doak, S. C. 1989. Modeling patterns of land use and ownership. final report to California Department of Forestry and Fire Protection. Contract no. 8CA63967.

Epifanio, C. R., M. J. Singer, X. Huang. 1991. Hydrologic impacts of oak harvesting and evaluation of the modified universal soil loss equation. in: Proc. Symp. Oak Woodlands and Hardwood Rangeland Management. USFS Ge. Tech. Rep. PSW-126:189-193.

Eyre, F.H. 1980. Forest Cover Types of the United States and Canada. Society of American Foresters, Washington, DC.

Firestone, M. K. 1995. Nutrient cycling in managed oak woodland-grass ecosystem. final report to the Integrated Hardwood Range Management Program. 56 p.

Frost, W.E. and N.K McDougald. 1989. Tree canopy effects on herbaceous production of annual rangeland during drought. Journal of Range Management 42: 281-283.

Frost, W.E. and S.B. Edinger. 1991. Effects of tree canopies on soil characteristics of annual rangeland. Journal of Range Management. 44(3):286-288.

Gaertner, 1995. Local action to conserve California's oak woodlands. in Newsletter of Integrated Hardwood Range Management Program. Quercus 3(1):1-7.

Garrison, B. 1996. Vertebrate Wildlife Species and Habitat Associations. in: Standiford, R. B. and P. Tinnin. 1996. Guidelines for managing California's hardwood rangelands. U.C. Division of Agriculture and Natural Resources Publication (in press).

Garrison, B. and R.B. Standiford. 1996. Chapter 2: Oaks and Habitats of the Hardwood Rangeland. in: Standiford, R. B. and P. Tinnin. 1996. Guidelines for managing California's hardwood rangelands. U.C. Division of Agriculture and Natural Resources Publication (in press).

George. M. 1987. Management of hardwood range: a historical review. Range Science Report 12, Agronomy and Range Science, U.C. Davis. 15 pp.

Griffin, J.R. 1973. Valley oaks- the end of an era? Fremontia.1:5-9.

Giusti, G.A, and P.J. Tinnin. 1993. A planner's guide for oak woodlands. Publication of the Integrated Hardwood Range Management Program, Univ. of Calif., Berkeley, 104 pp.

Gordon, D. R., J. M. Welker, J. W. Menke, and K. J. Rice. 1989. Competition for soil water between annual plants and blue oak seedlings. Oecologia 79(4):533-541.

Greenwood, G. B., R. K. Marose, J. M. Stenback. 1993. Extent and ownership of California's hardwood rangelands. prepared for Strategic Planning Program, California Dept. of Forestry and Fire Protection unpublished report.

Hall, L. M., M. R. George, D. D. McCreary, T. E. Adams. 1992. Effects of cattle grazing on blue oak seedling damage and survival. J. Range Manage. 45(5):503-506.

Holland, V.L. 1980. Effect of blue on rangeland forage production in central California. In: Proceedings of the Symposium on the Ecology, Management and Utilization of California Oaks. General Technical Report PSW-44. Pacific Southwest Forest and Range Experiment Station, Forest Service, USDA. p. 314-318.

Holland, V.L. and J. Morton. 1980. Effect of blue oak on nutritional quality of rangeland forage in central California. In: T.R. Plumb. Proc. symp. on the ecology, management, and utilization of California oaks; 1979 June 26-28; Claremont, California. USDA Forest Service, Pacific Southwest Forest and Range Exp. Station, Berkeley, California. General Technical Report PSW-44:319-322.

Holmes, Tyson H. 1990. Botanical trends in Northern California Oak Woodland. Rangelands 12(1): 3-7.

Holzman, Barbara Ann. 1993. Vegetation change in California's blue oak woodlands 1932-1992. Ph.d dissertation. University of California, Berkeley.

Holzman, B. A. and B. H. Allen-Diaz. 1991. Vegetation change in blue oak woodlands in California. in: Proc. Symp. Oak Woodlands and Hardwood Rangeland Management. USFS Gen. Tech. Rep. PSW-126:189-193.

Humiston, Glenda. 1995. California Rangeland Water Quality ManagementPlan. State Water Resources Control Board, Sacramento, CA. 75 pgs.

Huntsinger, L. and L. P. Fortmann. 1990. California's privately owned oak woodlands: Owners, use, and management. J. Range Manage. 42(3):147-152.

Huntsinger, L. 1992. Impacts of education: Preliminary results of a follow-up survey. in: Integrated Hardwood Range Management Program Fifth Progress Report. pp. 19-27.

IHRMP. 1988. Integrated hardwood range management program: First progress report. Berkeley, CA. 25 pp.

IHRMP. 1992. Integrated hardwood range management program: Fifth progress report. Berkeley, CA. 47 pp.

IHRMP. 1994. Integrated hardwood range management program: Sixth progress report. Berkeley, CA. 37 pp.

Jackson, L.E., R.B. Strauss, M.K. Firestone and J.W. Bartolome, 1990. Influence of tree canopies on grassland productivity and nitrogen dynamics in deciduous oak savanna. Agriculture, Ecosystems and Environment. 32: 89-105.

Jansen, H.C. 1987. The effect of blue oak removal on herbaceous production on a foothill site in the northern Sierra Nevada. In: Proceedings of the Symposium on Multiple-Use Management of California's Hardwood Resources. General Technical Report PSW-100. Pacific Southwest Forest and Range Experiment Station, Forest Service, USDA. p. 343-350.

Jepson, W.L. 1910. The silva of California. Univ. of Calif. Mem., Vol. 2. 480 pp.

Kay, B.L. 1987. Long-term effects of blue oak removal on forage production, forage quality, soil and oak regeneration. In: Proc. symp. on multiple-use management of California's hardwood resources; 1986 San Luis Obispo, Calif. USDA Forest Service, Pacific

Southwest Forest and Range Exp. Station, Berkeley, California. Gen Tech. Rep. PSW-100:351-357.

Kuchler, A.W. 1988. The Map of Natural Vegetation of California. Dept.Geography. University of Kansas. in : Barbour, M.G. and J. Major, eds. 1988. Terrestrial Vegetation of California. California Native Plant Society, Special Publication, Number 9.

Lewis, V. 1991. The temporal and spatial distribution of filbert weevil invfested acorns in an oak woodland in Marin County, California. in: Proc. Symp. Oak Woodlands and Hardwood Rangeland Management. USFS Ge. Tech. Rep. PSW-126:156-160.

Mayer, K.E. and W.F. Laudenslayer, Jr. eds. 1988. A Guide to Wildlife Habitats of California. California Dept. of Forestry and Fire Protection, Sacramento.

Mayer, K. E., P. C. Passof, C. Bolsinger, W. W. Grenfall, and H. Slack. 1985. Status of the hardwood resource of California: A report to the Board of Forestry. California Dept. of Forestry and Fire Protection, Sacramento, CA. 126 pp.

McCarthy, Helen, 1993. Managing Oaks and the Acorn Crop. In Before the Wilderness: Environmental Management by Native Californians. Ed. Thomas C. Blackburn and Cat Anderson. A Ballena Press. Menlo Park: 213-228.

McClaren, M.P. and J.W. Bartolome. 1989. Fire-related recruitment in stagnant *Quercus douglasii* populations. Canadian Journal of Forest Research 19: 580-585.

McClaren, M.P. and J.W. Bartolome. 1989a. Effect of *Quercus douglasii* (*Fagaceae*) on herbaceous understory along a rainfall gradient. Madrono 36:141-153.

McClaran, M. P. and J. W. Bartolome. 1985. The importance of oaks to ranchers in California foothill woodlands. Rangelands 7:158-161.

McCreary, D.D. 1996. Chapter 9: Sustainable management of hardwood rangelands: Regeneration and stand structure considerations. in: Standiford, R. B. and P. Tinnin. 1996. Guidelines for managing California's hardwood rangelands. U.C. Division of Agriculture and Natural Resources Publication (in press).

McCreary, D. D., W. D. Tietje, R. H. Schmidt, R. Gross, W. H. Willoughby, B. L. Weitkamp, and F. L. Bell. 1991. Stump sprouting of blue oaks. in: Proc. Symp. Oak Woodlands and Hardwood Rangeland Management. USFS Gen. Tech. Rep. PSW-126:64.

Mooney, H.A. (ed.). 1977. Convergent evolution in Chile and California Mediterranean climate ecosystems. Dowden, Hutchinson and Ross, Inc., Stroudsberg, Pennsylvania.

Motroni, R S., D.A. Airola, R.K. Marose, and N.D. Tosta. 1991. Using wildlife species richness to identify land protection priorities in California's hardwood rangelands. in: Proc. Symp. Oak Woodlands and Hardwood Rangeland Management. USFS Gen. Tech. Rep. PSW-126:110-119.

Muick, P.C. and J. R. Bartolome. 1987. An assessment of natural regeneration of oaks in California. Report submitted to the Forest and Rangeland Assessment Program, California Department of Forestry and Fires Protection, in partial fulfillment of contract #8CA42136. 101 pp.

Munz, P.A. and D.D. Keck. 1973. A California with Supplement. University of California Press, Berkeley.

Pacific Meridian Resources. 1994. California hardwood rangeland monitoring final report. prepared for Strategic Planning Program, California Dept. of Forestry and Fire Protection unpublished report.

Passof, P. C. and J. W. Bartolome. 1985. An integrated hardwood range management program. University of California Wildland Resources Center Report No. 6. 18 p.

Pavlik, Bruce, Pamela Muick, Sharon Johnson and Marjorie Popper.1991. Oaks of California. Cachuma Press.

Peck, S. 1993. Tuolumne county wildlife project mitigates development impacts. in Newsletter of Integrated Hardwood Range Management Program. Quercus 1(1):6-7.

Pillsbury, N. H. and J. K. Oxford. 1987. The hardwood management issue: county perceptions of use, change, problems, and regulation. In: Proc. Symp. Multiple-Sue Management of California's Hardwood Resources. USFS Gen, Tech. Rep. PSW-100:404-410.

Ratliff, R.D., D.A. Duncan, and S.E. Westfall. 1988. Influence of overstory type on herbage production on California annual grassland range. Abstr. 41st Meeting Soc. Range Manage. Corpus Christi, Texas. No. 12.

Ratliff, Raymond D., Don Duncan and Stanley E. Westfall. 1991. California oak-woodland overstory species affect herbage understory: management implications. Journal of Range Management 44(4): 306-310.

Rossi, R.S. 1980. History of the cultural influences on the distribution and reproduction of oaks in California. In: Proceedings of the Symposium of Ecology, Management, and Utilization of California Oaks. Claremont, California. USDA Forest Serv. Gen. Tech. Rep. PSW-44:7-18.

Sampson, A.W. 1944. Plant succession on burned chaparral lands in northern California. California Agr. Exp. Stn. Bull. No. 685.

Standiford, R.B., N. K. McDougald, R. Phillips, A. Nelson. 1991. South Sierra oak regeneration survey. California Agriculture 45(2):12-14.

Standiford, R. B. and P. Tinnin. 1996. Guidelines for managing California's hardwood rangelands. U.C. Division of Agriculture and Natural Resources Publication (in press).

Standiford, R.B. and R.E. Howitt. 1990. Solving empirical bioeconomic models: a rangeland management application. American Journal of Agricultural Economics May, 1992:421-433.

Standiford, R.B. and R.E. Howitt. 1993. Multiple use management of California's hardwood rangelands. Journal of Range Management 46:176-181.

Standiford, R.B., D. McCreary, S. Gaertner, L. Forero. 1996. Sustainability of firewood harvesting on hardwood rangelands. (in press) accepted for publication in California Agriculture.

Stewart, W. 1991. Monitoring values and practices of oak woodland decision makers on the urban fringe. in: Proc. Symp. Oak Woodlands and Hardwood Rangeland Management. USFS Gen. Tech. Rep. PSW-126:174-181.

Swiecki, T. J. and E. A. Bernhardt. 1993. Factors affecting blue oak sapling recruitment and regeneration. report to California Dept. of Forestry and Fire Protection Strategic Planning Program. Contract no, 8CA17358.

Scott, T. 1996. Chapter 7: Open Space and Private Land Opportunities for Hardwood Rangeland Conservation. in: Standiford, R. B. and P. Tinnin. 1996. Guidelines for managing California's hardwood rangelands. U.C. Division of Agriculture and Natural Resources Publication (in press).

Shelly, J., W. Tietje, D. McCreary. 1996. Chapter 8: Resource Evaluation for Forest Products. in: Standiford, R. B. and P. Tinnin. 1996. Guidelines for managing California's hardwood rangelands. U.C. Division of Agriculture and Natural Resources Publication (in press).

Swiecki, Tedmund J. and Elizabeth A. Bernhardt. 1993. Factors affecting blue oak sapling recruitment and regeneration. prepared for California Department of Forestry and Fire Protection Strategic Planning Program.

Tietje, W. D., R. H. Barrett, E. B. Kleinfelder, and B. T. Carre. 1991. Wildlife diversity in valley-foothill riparian habitat: North central versus central coast California. In: Proc. Symp. Oak Woodlands and Hardwood Rangeland Management. USFS Gen, Tech. Rep. PSW-100:120-125.

Tietje, W. D. and T. Berlund. 1995. Land-use planning in oak woodland. in Newsletter of Integrated Hardwood Range Management Program. Quercus 3(2):1-9.

USDA (U.S. Dept. of Agric.). various years. Livestock and meat prices and markets. Federal-State Market News Service.

Verner, J. 1980. Birds of California oak habitats -- management implications. Pp. 246-264 *in* Proceedings of the Symposium on the Ecology, Management, and Utilization of California Oaks, June 26-28, 1979. USDA Forest Service General Technical Report PSW-44.

Welker, J.M. and J.W. Menke. 1990. The influence of simulated browsing on tissue water relations, growth and survival of *Quercus douglasii* (Hook and Arn.) seedlings under slow and rapid rates of soil drought. Functional Ecology 1990(4):807-817.

Whittington, J. and W. D. Tietje. 1993. Oak management in California municipalities. California Agriculture 46(2).

CRAIG M. OLSON
Department of Environmental Science,
    Policy, and Management
University of California
Berkeley, California

JOHN A. HELMS
Department of Environmental Science,
    Policy, and Management
University of California
Berkeley, California

16

Forest Growth and Stand Structure at Blodgett Forest Research Station 1933-95

Sierra Nevada Ecosystem Project: Final report to Congress, vol. III, *Assessments, Commissioned Reports, and Background Information*. Davis: University of California, Centers for Water and Wildland Resources, 1996.

681

A. INTRODUCTION

This report summarizes results of analyses of data collected at Blodgett Forest Research Station (hereafter referred to as the Forest) from 1933 to 1995. This data set represents the longest existing set of time-series information on the effects of alternative silvicultural treatments on stand growth and development of mixed conifer forests. As such, it can be used as a benchmark in evaluating the likely consequences of alternative scenarios for the management of Sierran Forests on forest sites of similar productivity. The first part of this report describes the nature of the Forest and its management since its inception in 1933, and the second compares the effects of alternative silvicultural treatments on growth, yield, and stand structure, regeneration, and fuel accumulation.

B. Blodgett Forest and its Compartment Structure

The University of California at Berkeley's 3,000 ac Blodgett Forest Research Station is managed by the Department of Environmental Science, Policy, and Management, College of Natural Resources. It is located in the Sierran mixed conifer type (Guide to Wildlife Habitat in California, Mayer and Laudenslayer 1988) on the west side of the Sierra Nevada between 3900 and 4800 feet, near Georgetown, California, along the Georgetown Divide. Most of the Forest was acquired as a gift in 1933 from the Michigan-California Lumber Company. In 1963, an inholding of 160 ac was purchased from the Bacchi family.

Prior to the turn of the century some trees were probably taken from the Forest during the gold rush and to construct the Georgetown Ditch which was built to transport water from Loon Lake and Pilot Creek to Georgetown. Just at or after the turn of the century, logging began in earnest using narrow gauge railroad with access and ground skidding by cable steam engines. Nearly the entire area was harvested. In approximately three different entries, 1900, 1908, and 1913, probably the majority of timber volume was removed from the Forest and much of the forest was burned to reduce logging slash.

The Forest is managed to provide opportunities for research, teaching and demonstration. As the Forest developed from primarily brushfields to vigorous young-growth stands, the research program broadened from studies on regeneration to all aspects of forest ecology and management. Since the late 1950s, literally hundreds of research projects have been conducted and reported (See Bibliography of Publications Based on Blodgett Forest Research, Nov. 1993, 49 p.). Since 1957, an annual timber harvest has been tailored to develop a continuing series of age classes and diverse stand structures for research. The timber sales are conducted in a manner equivalent to that used by a private forest landowner. Currently, timber harvest plans are submitted to and approved by the California Department of Forestry and Fire Protection. Timber sales are advertized regionally and logs are offered and sold to the highest bidder. The actual logging is contracted separately to a licensed timber operator.

The Forest has 109 compartments dedicated to various management schemes designed to provide a diversity of stand structures (Figures 1a and 1b). In general there are five broad

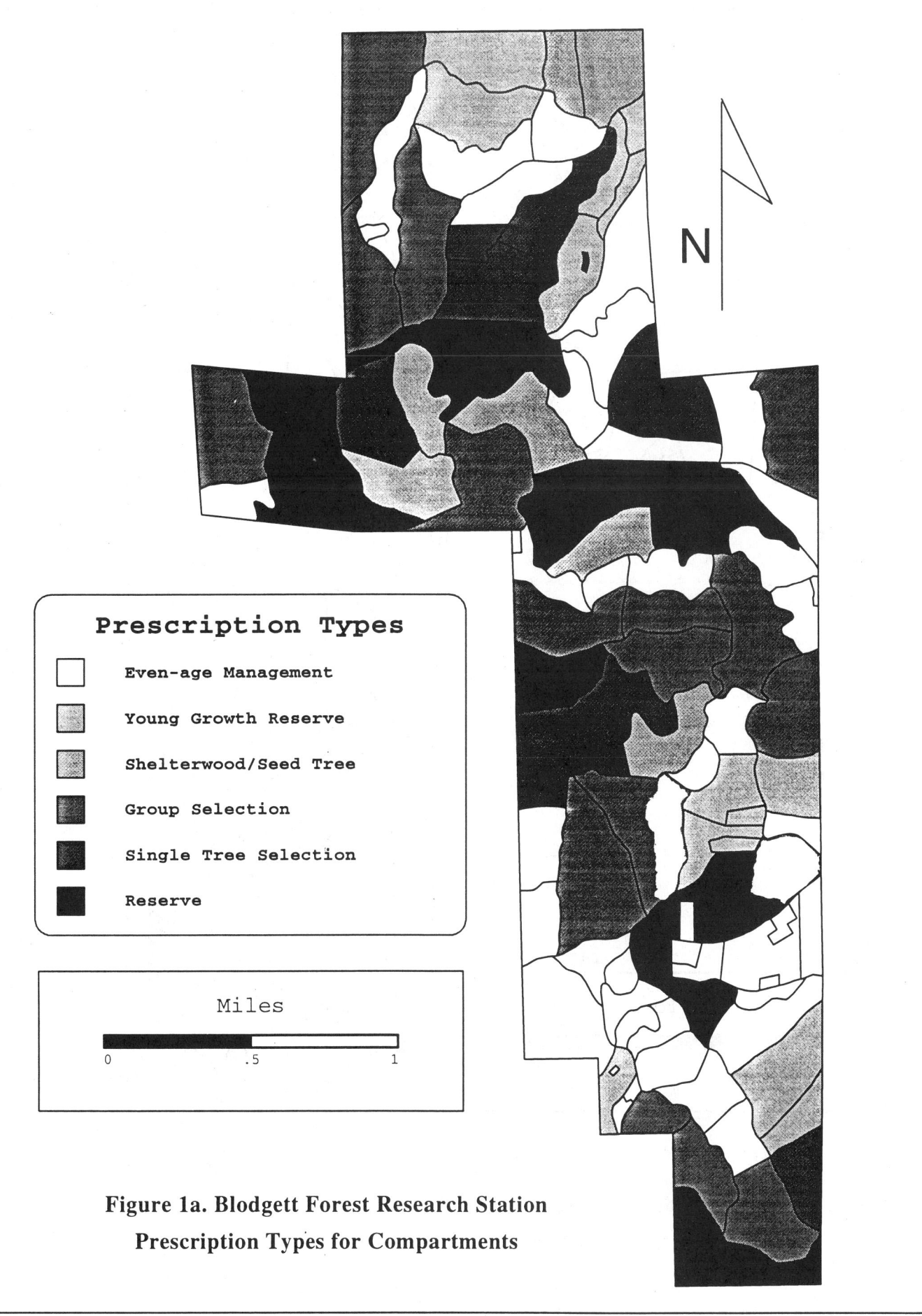

Prescription Types

☐ Even-age Management

▨ Young Growth Reserve

▨ Shelterwood/Seed Tree

▨ Group Selection

▨ Single Tree Selection

■ Reserve

Miles

0   .5   1

Figure 1a. Blodgett Forest Research Station
Prescription Types for Compartments

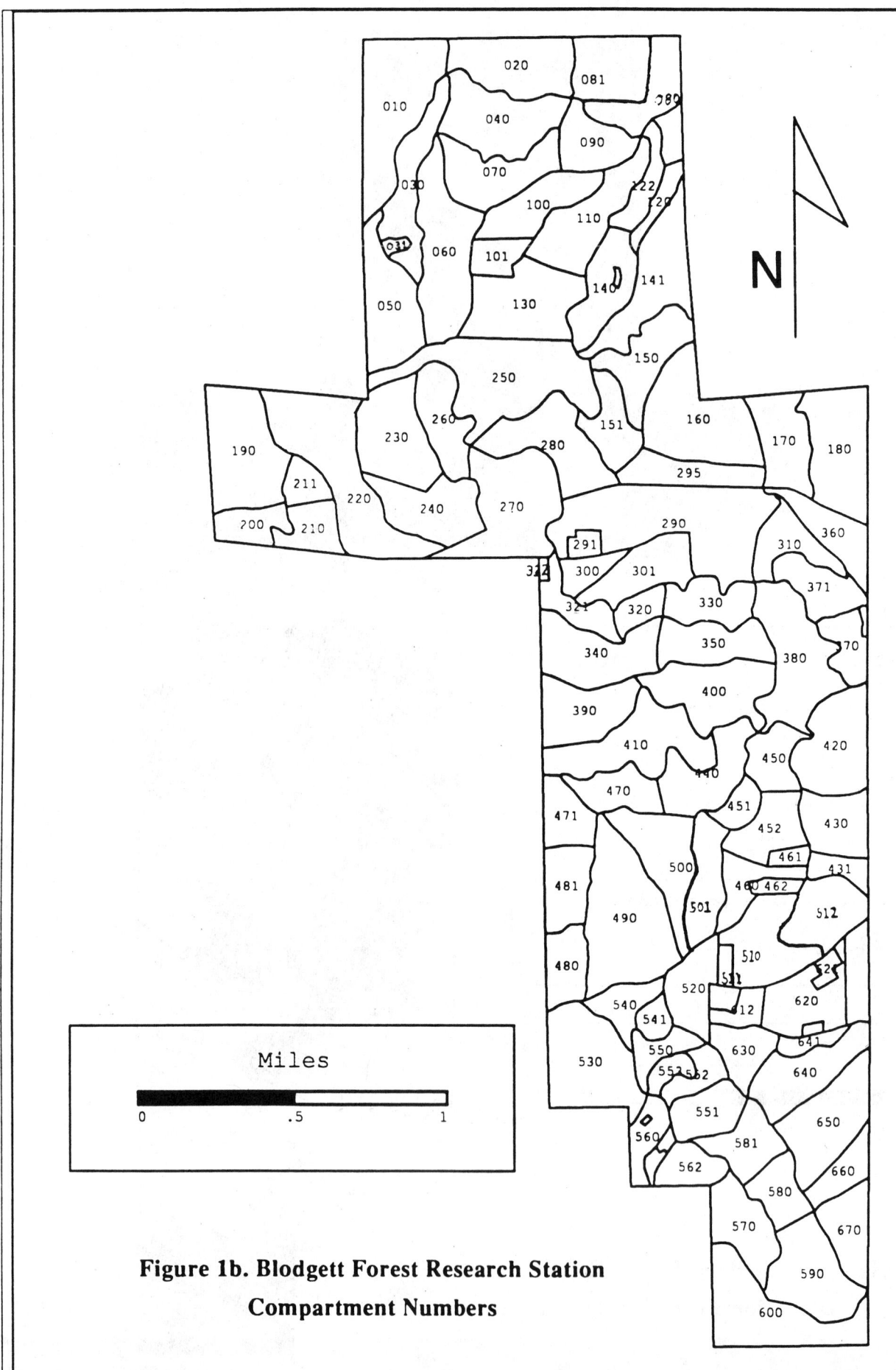

Figure 1b. Blodgett Forest Research Station Compartment Numbers

categories: uneven-aged management, even-aged management, administrative reserve, ecological or old-growth reserve, and research reserve. Within each of these categories there are one to several different management prescriptions as set forth in the Forest's guiding document "Policy for Use of Blodgett Forest Research Station, June 1, 1987 (editorial revisions April 5, 1989)".

1) <u>Uneven-aged Management</u> There are approximately 1086 acres in 26 compartments assigned to uneven-aged management. There are two regeneration methods -- group selection and single-tree slection. The desired residual stand structure has been defined as having a diminution quotient of 1.2 and a growing stock level of 120 to 180 sq ft /ac and maximum tree diameter of 30-36 inches.

   a) <u>Group selection</u> Fourteen compartments (734 ac, Table 1) have been assigned to group selection. One- to two-ac groups comprising 10-15 percent of the area within each compartment are removed with a cutting cycle of approximately 10 years. Two entries have been made in most compartments in the 1970s, 1980s, and 1990s. In addition, compartments 50 and 420 had entries in the late 1950s and early 1960s. Competing vegetation has been controlled using cattle grazing, herbicide application, and mechanical removal.

Table 1. Group selection compartments and number of acres.

Compartment #	Acres
10	58.7
50	44.5
60	56.2
180	49.4
190	53.7
270	56.9
340	41.3
350	30.9
380	55.6
400	41.9
420	43.2
490	72.3
500	40.2
562	17.3
570	30.3
590	42.0
Total	734.4

   b) <u>Single-tree selection</u> Eight compartments (318 ac, Table 2) have been assigned to single-tree selection. Single trees or very small groups of less than 0.2 ac are removed with a cutting cycle of approximately 10 years. Most compartments have had two entries in the 1970s and 1980s. In compartments 160, 230, 420, and 500 three entries have been made beginning in the late 1950s.

Competing vegetation has been controlled by cattle grazing and occasional herbicide application.

Table 2. Single-tree selection compartments and number of acres.

Compartment #	Acres
101	11.7
110	42.0
130	50.0
160	56.8
230	44.5
410	49.4
470	21.0
471	19.2
670	22.9
Total	317.5

2) Even-aged Management   There are approximately 1,045 acres in compartments assigned to even-aged management. Three regeneration methods are used: shelterwood, seed-tree, and clearcutting. The expected rotation age is 60 to 90 years with the longer rotation providing a vegetation structure with larger trees.

a) Shelterwood   Applied to four compartments (97 ac, Table 3). In each case, a residual stand of about 15 trees per acre totalling approximately 50 ft^2/ac basal area is used to provide shelter and seed for regeneration. The residual stand is removed in approximately 8-10 years, that is, after the establishment of the new stand.

Table 3. Shelterwood compartments, acres within each compartment, and the year harvested.

Compartment #	Acres	Year Harvested
80	20.5	1973 prep*, 1986 seed[+], 1994 overwood[x]
81	33.2	1973 prep, 1986 seed
280	43.3	1979 seed, 1986 overwood
Total	97.0	

* The prepartory step is used to prepare the shelter-seed trees to be wind firm and large crown seed producers.
[+] The seed step removes the majority of the trees leaving the shelter-seed trees.
[x] After a new stand is established under the shelter-seed trees the shelter-seed trees or overwood are removed (in approximately 8-10 years).

b) Seed-tree   Applied to one compartment (Table 4). A preparatory partial harvest was done to isolate the intended seed trees to encourage wind firmness. At final harvest, five to six well-distributed trees per acre of good form, representing the appropriate species mix, were retained to provide seed. The seed trees were cut after establishment of regeneration, usually about 7 years. Based upon a regeneration analysis additional seedlings were planted to augment natural regeneration.

Table 4. Seed tree compartments, size, and year harvested.

Compartment #	Acres	Year Harvested
301	27.8	1983 seed[+], 1986 overwood[*]

[+] The seed step removes the majority of the trees leaving the seed trees.
[x] After a new stand is established under the seed trees the seed trees or overwood are removed (in approximately 3-5 years).

c) Clearcutting Forty nine compartments (864 ac, Table 5) are designated to the clearcutting regeneration method. In the year after harvest, the compartments are planted to a stocking of at least 340 seedlings per acre, targeting an even distribution in the number of seedlings for each of the five major native conifers. Hardwoods (pricipally oak and tanoak) are regenerated by coppice.

Table 5. Clearcutting compartments, acres within each compartment, and the year harvested.

Compartment #	Acres	Year Harvested
30	34.0	
31	3.7	65
70	39.6	
90	25.9	
100	27.8	
141	45.1	90
150	32.7	
151	22.9	82
170	32.1	
200	18.5	80
295	22.9	
320	10.5	
321	17.3	80
322	1.2	80
330	22.2	91
360	21.6	84
370	16.7	84
371	22.5	85
372	1.0	84
431	9.9	88
450	20.3	
451	9.3	69
480	19.2	91
481	20.4	75
501	24.0	86,87
511	4.9	83

512	31.0	93
530	54.9	
540	16.1	
541	7.4	
550	11.7	
551	21.6	
552	12.4	
553*	7.4	85
560	13.6	84
561*	1.2	68
563*	3.1	78
564	0.6	83
580	20.4	
581*	22.9	69
611*	5.6	64
612*	10.5	78
620*	29.0	85
621	4.3	88
622	1.2	88
623	11.5	
624	10.0	90
640*	34.0	85
641*	7.4	77
Total	864.0	

* Converted from brushfields

3) <u>Ecological or Old Growth Reserve</u>   There are approximately 349 acres in 12 compartments set aside as ecological or old growth reserves (Table 6).

Table 6. Ecological or old growth reserve compartments and number of acres.

Compartment #	Acres
210	15.4
220	61.8
221	1.0
290*	96.4
291	4.9
300	9.9
310	22.8
390*	32.8
510*	35.1
521	3.0
600	48.2
630	17.9
Total	349.2

*Principally old growth; the remainder are 70-80 year old young growth

4) <u>Administrative Reserve</u>   There are approximately 125 acres in five compartments set aside as administrative reserves to protect visual and cultural values as well as structures and other physical improvements (Table 7).

Table 7. Administrative reserve compartments and number of acres.

Compartment #	Acres
142	1.0
211	10.5
250	85.2
291	4.9
520	22.9
Total	124.5

5) <u>Young Growth Reserve</u>   There are 355 acres in 15 compartments assigned as young growth reserves (Table 8). Young growth reserves are intended to be harvested 90 years after they are regenerated. Following harvest the compartments will be regenerated to an appropriate mix of the six principle tree species. During the rotation no silvicultural activites, such as thinning or herbicide use, will occur.

Table 8. Young growth reserve compartments and number of acres.

Compartment #	Acres
20	41.4
40	44.5
120	7.4
121	6.8
122	14.8
140	31.1
240	37.7
260	30.2
430	26.6
452	25.3
460	17.3
461	4.9
462	6.2
650	45.7
660	14.8
Total	354.7

Soils

There are four main soil types found within Blodgett Forest. Three of the soil types, Musick, Holland, and Bighill, are developing in place on granite parent material. The four type, Cohasset, is developing in place on andesite parent material. Each can be characterized as well drained sandy-loam that are 3 to 6 feet with low to moderate erosion hazard rating on slopes less than 30 percent (California Code of Regulations, Title 14). Exposed mineral soil on slopes over 30 Percent is subject to high hazard for sheet and surface rill erosion. There are three other soil types that occur within the forest - Jocal, Aquecept, and Crozier. The major soil types have the capacity to grow the principal conifers of the area (excluding incense-cedar) to 90-100 feet in 50 years and are considered Dunning (1942) Site I.

Climate

The climate at Blodgett Forest is characterized by cool wet winters and warm dry summers. The mean annual precipatation from 1962 to 1995 was 62.3 inches, 78 percent of which falls in the five months, November to March (Table 9). The maximum annual precipatation during that period was 108.7 inches in 1981-1982 and the minimum was 26.6 inches in 1976-1977. During the winter about 35 percent of the precipitation falls as snow, averaging about 100 inches per year. The average minimum temperature in January over the period was 33°F and the average maximum temperature in July is 83 °F. Frosts can occur in any month but are rare from June to September.

Table 9. Average maximum and average minimum temperature (°F) and average precipitation (inches) at the BFRS weather station 1962 to 1995[1].

Month	Average Maximum °F	Average Minimum °F	Average Precipitation (inches)
January	46	33	11.14
February	48	33	9.30
March	50	34	9.21
April	56	37	5.14
May	67	45	2.03
June	75	52	0.83
July	83	59	0.34
August	83	59	0.33
September	76	54	1.19
October	64	46	3.93
November	50	37	8.53
December	46	33	10.37

C. Forest Inventory

Over the years as forest condition and management objectives have changed, various methods have been used to assess vegetation on the Forest. Today, there is a forestwide

---

[1] From: Schurr, F.G. 1995. Unpublished Report. Blodgett Forest Research Station, Georgetown, CA.

Forest Growth and Stand Structure at BFRS
1933-1994

system of permanent plots and a variety of resources (timber, regeneration, ground cover, fuel, and wildlife) are monitored on a continuing basis. Initially, there was a single plot established by George Sudworth in 1899, and this was followed by four forestwide inventories in 1934, 1946, 1955, and 1973.

1) Sudworth's 1899 Plot
Within George Sudworth's field records written in 1899 (U.C. Forestry Library) is a short note describing the stocking of a plot that is now within Blodgett Forest. He measured one 1/4-ac plot listing the diameters of all trees by species (Figure 2a,b). His description reads:

> "Average height of all very near 150 ft. Clear 30-35 ft. Average number of logs = 6. Abundant reproduction of all species 1 - 12 years old. Low (illegible word) Rosaceous shrub forms close ground cover in main; tree seedlings about margins of plot -- dense. All fire marked 15-years back. Average conditions for region. Humus 1 1/2 in. deep. Soil sandy loam with rock."

This plot represents a stand of 108 trees per acre having a surprisingly high total basal area of 930 ft^2/ac. This density is more than double the approximately 400 ft^2/ac shown for high site land in Dunning and Reineke's (1933) yield tables for 150-year-old young-growth mixed conifer in the Sierra. The proportion of basal area by species in Sudworth's plot was white fir 48.5%, ponderosa pine 19.4%, incense-cedar 13.1%, sugar pine 9.9%, and Douglas-fir 9.1%. The largest eight trees per acre, those between 48 to 54 inches dbh, were all white fir and ponderosa pine, but all five species were represented in diameters greater than 44 inches. Apparently there were no trees between 10 and 16 inches dbh. There was only one standing dead tree on the plot, a 23-inch dbh white fir. Using local volume tables the volume for the plot was 55,380 bd.ft. or 221,520 bd.ft./ac.

If these data represent average conditions, the original stands on the Forest must have been very dense with many large, old trees. However, Sudworth documented conditions on typical timber stands but he did not report the actual area occupied by commercial timber stands. One might have expected that the dense canopy plus the occurrence of fire and grazing would have resulted in little ground cover or regeneration, however Sudworth reports abundant regeneration.

2) 1900 to 1933
The area that is now Blodgett Forest was owned by several private individuals and companies during this period. The area was extensively logged by ground skidding cables from steam engines with railroad access and other means. The University of California has no inventory or harvest records from this period and perhaps none exist.

Figure 2a. 1899 DBH Distribution by Species

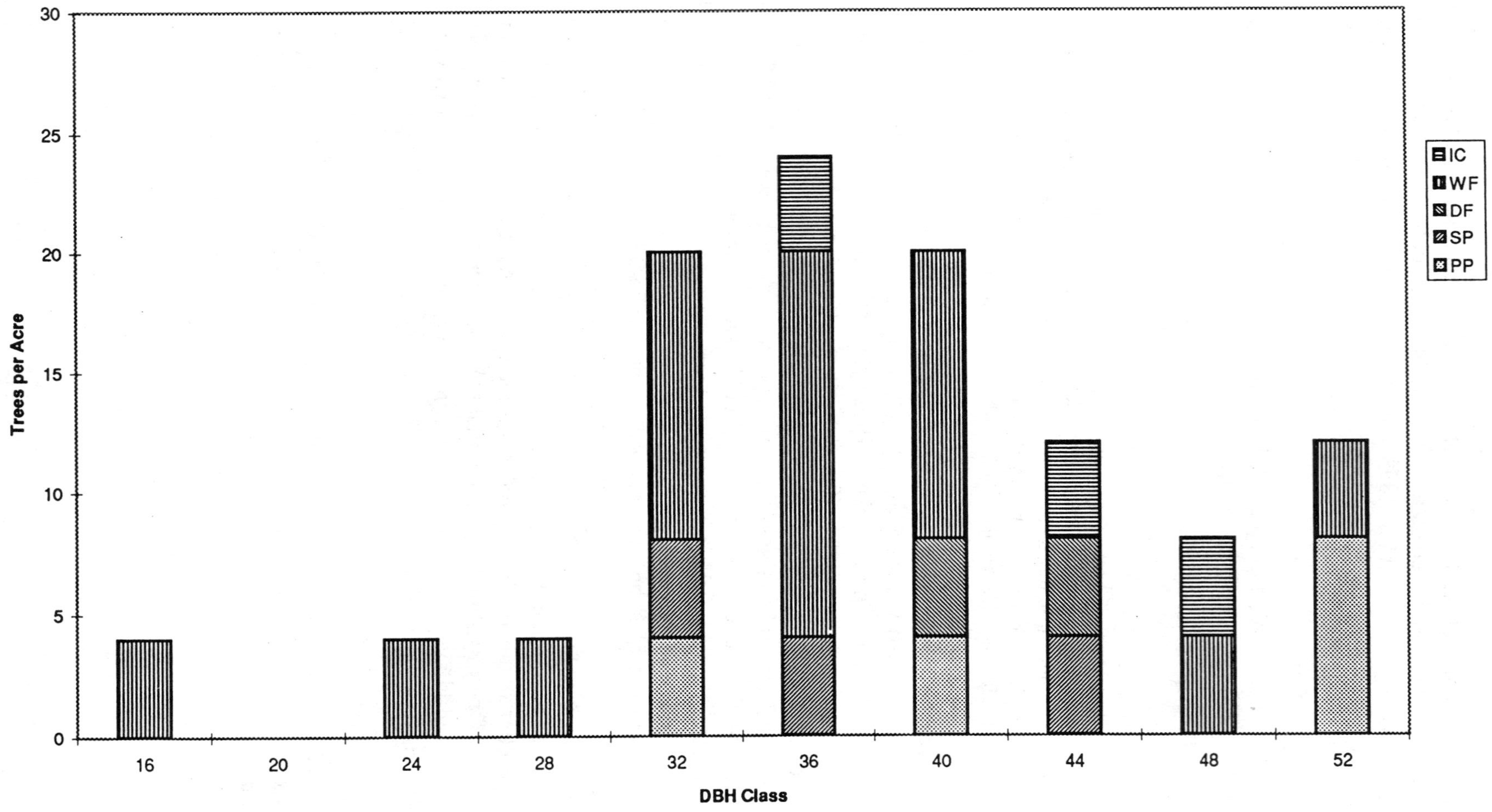

Forest Growth and Stand Structure at BFRS
1933-1994

Figure 2b. 1899 Basal Area (sq.ft.) by Species on one 1/4 acre plot in BFRS

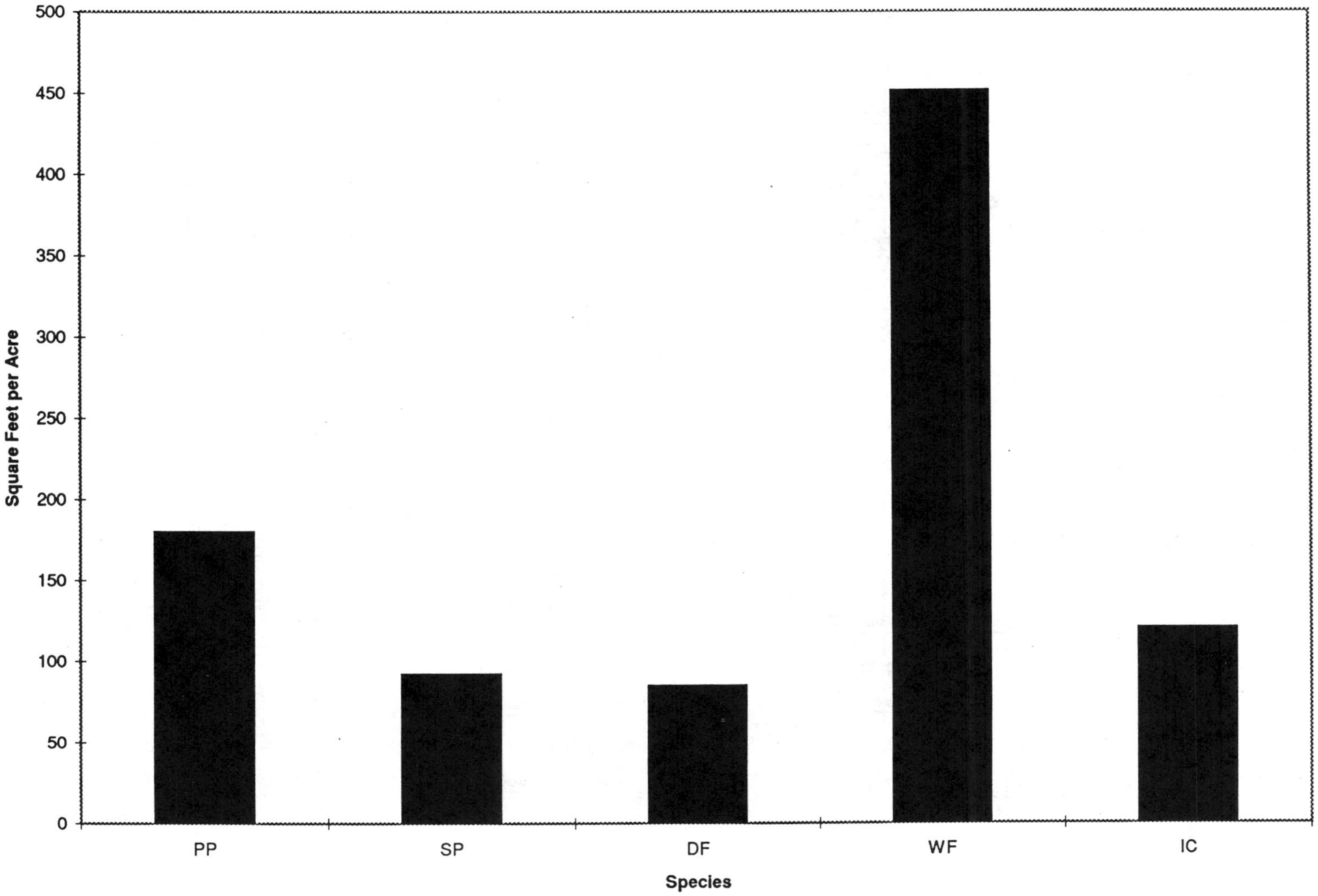

693

3) 1934 to 1956

The first measurements done by the School of Forestry were plots installed by Professor Percy Barr in 1933 to study growth and yield of high density young ponderosa pine. In 1934-35, 1946, and 1955 under the direction of Barr, surveys of young growth were conducted on those areas not covered by brush or in residual old growth (1934 and 1955 inventory summaries are shown in Table 9). These restocking surveys consisted of a strip inventory (5% in 1934 and 1955, and 10 % in 1946) of trees greater than 6 inches dbh. By 1933, 2,060 acres (75.5%) of the Forest were in young growth, 588 acres (21.5%) were in brush and 82 acres (3.0%) were in residual old growth (Fig. 3).

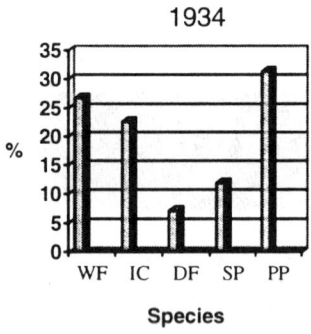

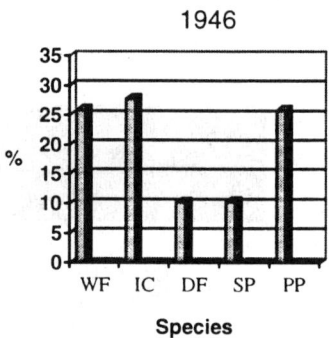

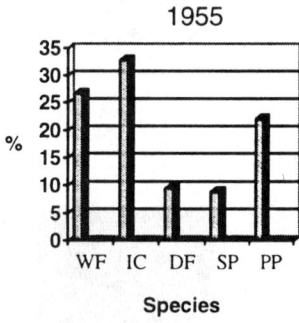

Figure 3. Percent species composition for number of trees greater than 8 inches dbh for the 5 principal conifer species in 1934, 1946, and 1955.

We can see in Figure 3 that the proportion of stems greater than 8 inches of sugar pine and ponderosa pine was declining in Blodgett Forest during the period from 1934 to 1955 while the proportion of incense-cedar and Douglas-fir was increasing. Such a shift is probably due to the differential survival of the more shade tolerant species in the understory. We would conjecture that the pines in the overstory were not dying but rather that understory incense-cedar and white fir were surviving and growing into the 8 inch class at a greater rate than the pines.

4) 1957-1973

In 1957, Michigan-California Lumber Company exercised part of their option, reserved at the time of their donation to UC, to remove all trees on the Forest greater than 24 in dbh. This resulted in 1.26 MM bf being harvested on several 40-acre units on the eastern boundary of the forest. At this time, access was still limited to the summer months when the only road, leading to a CCC-constructed house, was trafficable. However, the young growth had reached merchantable size and this, together with previously unmerchantable old growth, created an opportunity for the University to conduct timber sales that would raise the necessary capital to permit management of the property. A basic road system was devised and the Forest was divided into an initial set of compartments. Annual timber sales were commenced and the proceeds used to construct an internal net of roads, to build structures, and to provide electric power that would provide the necessary support for research. Over time, the compartment structure was refined and in the mid 1960s, a preliminary management plan was developed in which the Forest was divided into compartments allocated to even- and uneven-aged management with ecological reserves.

In 1973 there was a stratified random sample inventory of the entire Forest designed to give a forestwide estimate of stocking, growth, and volume (see Table 9). This inventory was not designed to give accurate estimates by compartment.

5) 1974 to 1994

The first system of permanent, comprehensive forest inventory plots was started in 1974 and completed by 1980. The original plot system (those located in uneven-aged compartments in 1974 and 1975) consisted of 1/20 acre circular plots located on 3 chain intervals along N-S and E-W transects. Transects were located randomly until 20 plots were located within a compartment. Since 1975, the inventory system has been modified to a 6-chain grid of 1/10 acre plots. [Compartments that were inventoried in 1974 and 1975 were reinventoried using the current system, locating the grid to correspond to the location of the original plots as much as possible]. There are approximately 700 1/10 acre plots forestwide. On even-age regenerated compartments, the number of plots was quadrupled (3-chain grid) to assess regeneration stocking and growth using plots 1/100 ac in size. In 1994, nearly half of the plots on the Forest were remeasured. A projected total volume has been estimated for the Forest as of 1994 (Table 9).

There have been four distinctly different inventory systems used at Blodgett each of which involved considerably different designs. The inventories of 1934 to 1955 used a systematic strip method in areas of reproduction. The inventory of 1973 used a stratified random design of the entire forest. The inventory of 1974 and 1975 used random location of 1..'0th acre circular plots in the uneven-aged management units. The inventory 1976 to present used systematic location of 1/10th acre plots on a 6-chain grid. These plots are permanent plots intended for periodic remeasurement.

D. GROWTH and DEVELOPMENT

Measurements on the Forest, beginning with Sudworth's 1899 single plot through successive inventories to the end of the summer in 1994, permit a unique comparison of stand dynamics and growth under alternative systems of management. In particular, comparisons can be made between even- and uneven-aged compartments in terms of age and size structure (height and diameter) and species distribution. The extensive nature of the forest inventories enables relatively precise estimates to be made of volume growth by species on a forestwide basis. By selecting compartments, within each system of management, having similar silvicultural prescriptions it is possible to evaluate the effect of choice of management system on growth, yield, and establishment of regeneration.

The following series of tables presents results from inventory data and harvest records. Table 10 depicts the results of forestwide inventories showing how volume per acre has changed over time since the entire forest was cut over at the beginning of the century. Inventories in 1934 and 1955 did not include brush areas and old growth forest areas within Blodgett, which represented 588 and 82 acres, respectively.

It should be noted that inventory volume is the gross volume measured and does not include deduction for defect or breakage while harvest volume reported is the net volume which is the gross volume minus defect volume and breakage. Current experience at Blodgett suggests that net volume is 5 - 8 percent less than gross volume. This makes growth estimates of compartments where there has been harvest somewhat conservative.

Table 10. Forest-wide inventories 1934 to 1994

Year	Acres	MBF	MBF/Acre
1934	2061[+]	26,183	12.70
1955	2061[+]	37,816	18.35
1973	2817*	63,941	22.68
1994[x]	2817*	82,467	29.27

[+] Area excluding old growth and brushfields - Total Forest area = 2731 acres

* Area excluding roads - Total Forest area = 2895 acres

[x] Volume estimated prior to 1994 harvest

Table 11 summarizes the volume harvested from the forest for period between inventory summaries.

Table 11. Harvest volumes during periods between inventories, 1933-1994.

Harvest Period	Harvest Volume (MBF)
1934-1956	0
1957-1973	27,700*
1974-1994	39,757

* There was no harvest from 1959-1961

Tables 10 and 11 show that, since 1934, the Forest has increased in stocking from 26,183 MBF (12.7 MBF/ac) to 82,467 MBF (29.27 MBF/ac). This growth occurred despite the fact that over the 37-year period from 1957 to 1994, 67.4 MMBF was harvested. In terms of growth, from 1934 to 1955, when no harvests occurred, average growth was 269 bd ft/ac/yr; from 1955 to 1973, growth averaged 787 bd ft/ac/yr; and from 1974 to 1994, growth averaged 986 bd ft/ac/yr. In 1994 the reserve compartment area was 424 acres and had 24,434 MBF or 57.7 MBF/ac. If we exclude the reserve compartments from volume estimates then the average 1994 volume on the 2,393 acres is 24.0 MBF/ac and growth for the 38 year period 1955 to 1994 was 868 bf/ac/yr; including the reserve compartments the growth for the period was 894 bf/ac/yr. This indicates that growth increased as stocking increased, and that the Forest is capable of sustaining a growth of over 800 bd ft/ac/yr. Over the past 39-year period, harvests are equivalent to approximately 68.7% of growth, consequently growing stock on the Forest is steadily increasing despite harvesting approximately 1.775 MBF per year. In addition, average diameter on the forest is increasing to include 30- to 40-inch trees and small and large harvest units have created a patchwork of age classes, thus forest structure is becoming more diverse.

Timber harvest volume by species from the Forest for 1957 to 1994 is shown in Figure 4. Many of the high and low levels in harvest volume is a result of accommodating research projects. The Figure shows large volumes harvested in 1966-67 which were associated with the financing of the purchase of the Bacchi Property inholding. The period from 1984 to 1986 had increased harvest in order to accommodate several clearcut research projects. About 40 percent of the volume harvested consists of ponderosa pine and sugar pine and the bulk of the remainder (33 percent) consists of white fir. "Other" harvest species shown in Figure 4 includes hardwoods (primarily black oak) and undifferentiated fuelwood harvest.

Figure 4. Net Volume of Timber Harvest (Mbf)

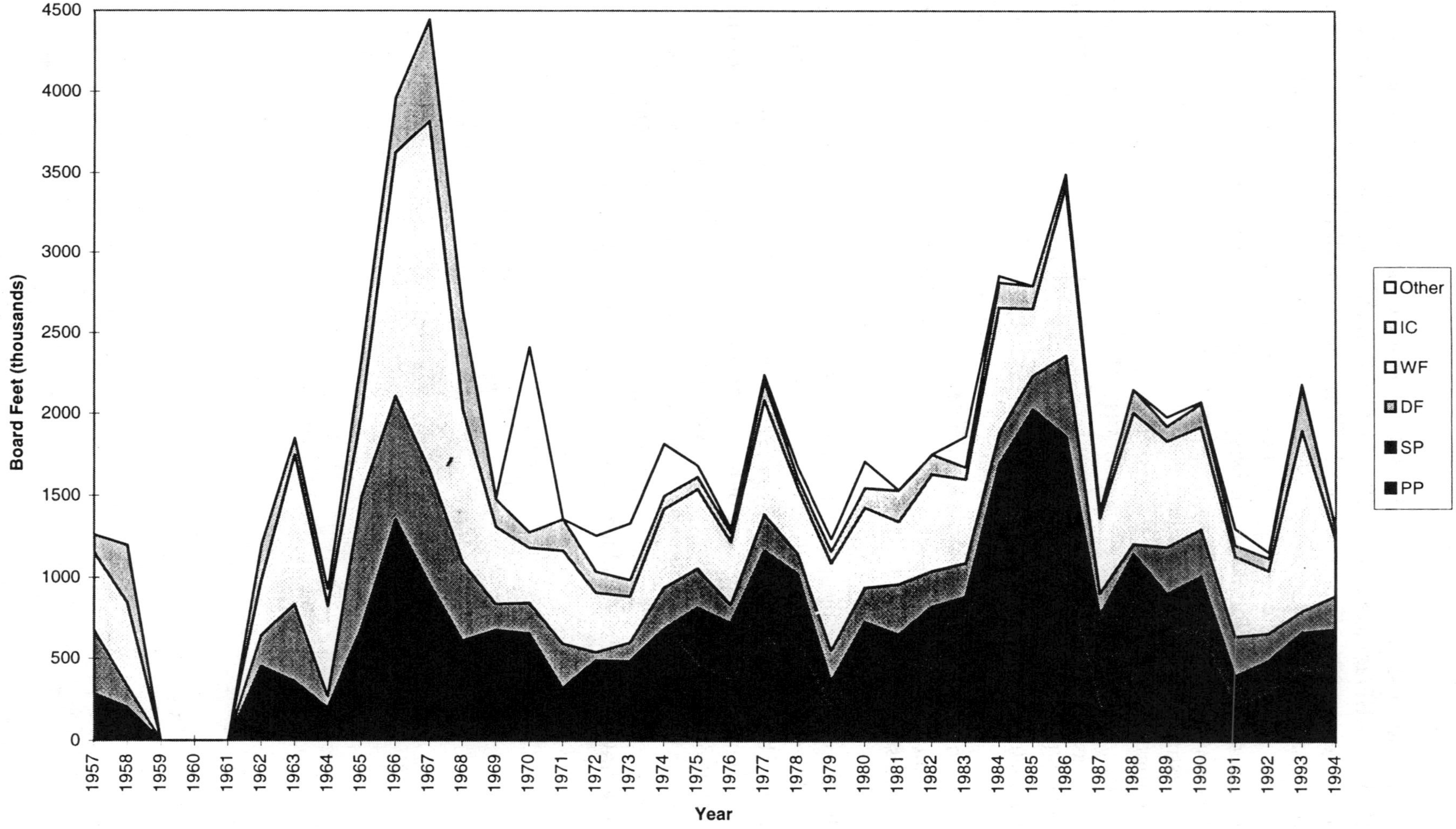

Other
IC
WF
DF
SP
PP

Board Feet (thousands)

Year

4500
4000
3500
3000
2500
2000
1500
1000
500
0

1957
1958
1959
1960
1961
1962
1963
1964
1965
1966
1967
1968
1969
1970
1971
1972
1973
1974
1975
1976
1977
1978
1979
1980
1981
1982
1983
1984
1985
1986
1987
1988
1989
1990
1991
1992
1993
1994

Forest Growth and Stand Structure at BFRS
1933-1994

Comparison of Even- and Uneven-Aged Silvicultural Prescriptions

To compare the effects of even- and uneven-aged systems on forest productivity, compartments have been chosen within each silvicultural treatment (totaling approximately 1/4 of the Forest) that have had similar history of inventories and harvesting entries from approximately 1974 (Tables 12, 13 and 14). Gross growth per acre per year (G+H/Yrs) is computed by subtracting the inventory volume at time one from that of time two, adding any volume cut in the intervening period, and then dividing by the total time period in years. Mortality, defect, and breakage was ignored as a component of gross growth.

Harvest volume is the scaled net volume removed from the compartments prorated over the entire comparment areas, while inventory volume is the gross volume estimated from the system of permanent plots within the compartment. Ideally, harvest volume, as a proportion of total compartment volume within group cut compartments, would be the same as the proportion of permanent plots harvested. This is not likely to be the case and the estimated gross growth per acre may be significantly different from the true gross growth.

Table 12. Comparison of **board foot growth** (Scribner MBF) and harvest on selected compartments.

Group Selection Compartments 270 and 380 (112.5 acres)

Year	# plots	PP	SP	DF	WF	IC	BO	Other	Total	G+H/Yrs
74-75 Inv	32	3.09	1.46	1.97	4.52	0.72	2.98		14.75	
Harvests		3.30	2.44	1.30	3.41	0.79		0.20	11.43	
94 Inv	34	5.91	3.66	4.25	7.01	1.60	2.64	0.12	25.17	1.09

Single-tree Selection Compartments 160 and 410 (106.2 acres)

Year	# plots	PP	SP	DF	WF	IC	BO	Other	Total	G+H/Yrs
80 Inv	22	6.46	4.40	4.21	4.31	0.41	2.67	0.03	23.15	
Harvests		2.24	1.03	.98	1.96	0.13			6.34	
94 Inv	27	7.95	3.68	4.84	6.41	0.69	2.67		27.19	0.71

Even-aged, thinned from below - Compartments 40, 90, 120, and 140 (108.9 acres)

Year	#plots	PP	SP	DF	WF	IC	BO	Other	Total	G+H/Yrs
76-78 Inv	33	6.81	1.52	1.44	4.96	2.94	2.37	0.23	20.27	
Harvests		2.26	0.78	0.71	1.03	0.47			5.25	
94 Inv	33	8.19	1.78	3.62	9.58	3.66	2.69	0.60	30.12	0.89

Even-aged with overstory removal - Compartments 30, 70, 100, 530 (156.2 acres)

Year	#plots	PP	SP	DF	WF	IC	BO	Other	Total	G+H/Yrs
77-78 Inv	46	4.45	1.00	2.23	3.21	3.45	4.13	0.07	18.55	
Harvests		4.21	0.93	1.35	1.79	1.18		0.05	9.51	
94 Inv	53	2.79	1.92	2.60	3.63	3.28	1.58		15.78	0.40

Even-aged, Clearcut - Compartment 481 (20.4 acres)

Year	#plots	PP	SP	DF	WF	IC	BO	Other	Total	G+H/Yrs
75 Harv		6.01	1.75	5.38	5.45	0.57		0.78	19.95	
89 Inv	18	2.07		0.42	0.01		0.10		2.60	0.19

Even-aged, Clearcut - Compartment 321 (17.3 acres)

Year	#plots	PP	SP	DF	WF	IC	BO	Other	Total	G+H/Yrs
80 Harv		2.65	7.95	8.12	2.99	1.24	2.67	0.25	25.88	
94 Inv	5	0.59						0.99	1.58	0.11

Reserve (Uncut) - Compartments 20 and 220 (103.2 acres)

Year	#plots	PP	SP	DF	WF	IC	BO	Other	Total	G+H/Yrs
76 Inv	28	10.93	1.08	8.39	6.93	6.57	2.90	0.02	36.81	
94 Inv	29	20.23	2.72	16.91	11.78	9.78	2.41	0.12	63.96	1.51

Reserve (Uncut) - Compartments 290 and 600 (144.6 acres)

Year	#plots	PP	SP	DF	WF	IC	BO	Other	Total	G+H/Yrs
81 Inv	25	13.08	6.36	3.46	8.50	3.99	0.82	0.19	36.40	
94 Inv	35	16.60	5.40	9.71	13.12	4.40	1.00	0.40	50.63	1.09

Table 13. Comparison of **cubic foot growth** and harvest on selected compartments.

Group Selection Compartments 270 and 380 (112.5 acres)

Year	PP	SP	DF	WF	IC	BO	Other	Total	G+H/Yrs
74-75 Inv	609	287	477	1122	273	666	7	3441	
Harvests	658	551	328	843	303		107	2790	
94 Inv	903	610	859	1475	505	588	48	4987	216.8

Single-tree Selection Compartments 160 and 410 (106.2 acres)

Year	PP	SP	DF	WF	IC	BO	Other	Total	G+H/Yrs
80 Inv	1193	807	954	946	317	772	17	5088	
Harvests	441	188	224	469	115			1301	
94 Inv	1263	614	1094	1296	371	746	13	5503	122.5

Even-aged, thinned from below - Compartments 40, 90, 120, and 140 (108.9 acres)

Year	PP	SP	DF	WF	IC	BO	Other	Total	G+H/Yrs
76-78 Inv	1126	265	378	1054	1029	631	205	4688	
Harvests	371	132	193	237	164			1097	
94 Inv	1191	290	799	1658	1068	674	219	5905	136.1

Even-aged with overstory removal - Compartments 30, 70, 100, 530 (156.2 acres)

Year	PP	SP	DF	WF	IC	BO	Other	Total	G+H/Yrs
77-78 Inv	802	185	531	686	970	965	103	4242	
Harvests	763	180	328	412	325	.	71	2080	
94 Inv	464	352	572	690	897	372		3348	69.8

Even-aged, Clearcut - Compartment 481 (20.4 acres)

Year	PP	SP	DF	WF	IC	BO	Other	Total	G+H/Yrs
75 Harv	781	273	800	852	116		430	3253	
89 Inv	682	80	165	17	27	110		1081	77.2

Even-aged, Clearcut - Compartment 321 (17.3 acres)

Year	PP	SP	DF	WF	IC	BO	Other	Total	G+H/Yrs
80 Harv	345	1240	1208	469	252	647	139	4300	
94 Inv	751		82	87	12		377	1309	93.5

Reserve (Uncut) - Compartments 20 and 220 (103.2 acres)

Year	PP	SP	DF	WF	IC	BO	Other	Total	G+H/Yrs
76 Inv	1895	204	1605	1292	1548	586	140	7271	
94 Inv	2912	442	2848	1846	2003	491	223	10764	194.1

Reserve (Uncut) - Compartments 290 and 600 (144.6 acres)

Year	PP	SP	DF	WF	IC	BO	Other	Total	G+H/Yrs
81 Inv	2151	1061	670	1443	763	293	181	6560	
94 Inv	2412	852	1456	2066	945	331	219	8281	132.3

Table 14. Comparison of **basal area growth** (ft^2/ac) and harvest on selected compartments.

Group Selection Compartments 270 and 380 (112.5 acres)

Year	PP	SP	DF	WF	IC	BO	Other	Total	G+H/Yrs
74-75 Inv	23	10	20	49	26	20	1	149	
Harvests	25	24	14	37	27		4	132	
94 Inv	25	18	29	57	35	18	2	184	8.36

Single-tree Selection Compartments 160 and 410 (106.2 acres)

Year	PP	SP	DF	WF	IC	BO	Other	Total	G+H/Yrs
80 Inv	40	28	37	36	27	27	1	195	
Harvests	15	6	9	19	10			59	
94 Inv	36	20	41	46	31	25	1	200	4.53

Even-aged, thinned from below - Compartments 40, 90, 120, and 140 (108.9 acres)

Year	PP	SP	DF	WF	IC	BO	Other	Total	G+H/Yrs
76-78 Inv	35	9	16	42	65	21	11	199	
Harvests	12	4	8	10	11			45	
94 Inv	31	9	30	54	67	22	10	224	3.86

Even-aged with overstory removal - Compartments 30, 70, 100, 530 (156.2 acres)

Year	PP	SP	DF	WF	IC	BO	Other	Total	G+H/Yrs
77-78 Inv	28	7	21	26	60	30	6	178	
Harvests	27	7	13	17	20		4	88	
94 Inv	15	12	21	25	59	12		143	3.12

Even-aged, Clearcut - Compartment 481 (20.4 acres)

Year	PP	SP	DF	WF	IC	BO	Other	Total	G+H/Yrs
75 Harv	18	7	20	25	7		17	93	
89 Inv	88	9	24	3	5	6		135	9.64

Even-aged, Clearcut - Compartment 321 (17.3 acres)

Year	PP	SP	DF	WF	IC	BO	Other	Total	G+H/Yrs
80 Harv	8	33	30	14	14	21	6	125	
94 Inv	71		8	14	2		30	125	8.93

Reserve (Uncut) - Compartments 20 and 220 (103.2 acres)

Year	PP	SP	DF	WF	IC	BO	Other	Total	G+H/Yrs
76 Inv	59	7	51	43	84	16	8	268	
94 Inv	75	13	75	55	95	14	12	339	3.91

Reserve (Uncut) - Compartments 290 and 600 (144.6 acres)

Year	PP	SP	DF	WF	IC	BO	Other	Total	G+H/Yrs
81 Inv	68	31	20	45	45	10	15	235	
94 Inv	70	23	37	61	55	12	9	267	2.46

Tables 12-14 show that:

1) The reserve (uncut) stands are growing at the rate of 132 to 194 ft^3/ac/year (1,090 to 1,510 bd ft/ac/yr and 2.5 to 3.9 ft^2/ac/yr basal area). These stands have a current stocking of 267 to 339 ft^2/ac and a volume of 8,281 to 10,764 ft^3/ac. Growth percent, based on cubic volume growth for the period 1974 to 1994, is 2.0 to 2.7 percent. Normal yield table values (Dunning and Reineke 1933) for basal area and volume for young growth mixed conifer forests (age 80 yr and site index 100) are 321 ft^2/ac and 18,600 ft^3/ac. The relatively low growth of reserved stands compared with normal yield table values is probably due to a number of reasons. Sites chosen by Dunning and Reineke as a basis for their normal yield tables had an incense-cedar component of approximately 5 percent whereas the proportion of slower growing cedar on the Forest is about 30 percent. In addition Dunning and Reineke's plots did not include black oak as does Blodgett. Another major reason for stands on the Forest appearing to have lower volume than those in normal yield tables is that board foot volumes in Dunning and Reineke are based on International rule which provides estimates of volume that are about 20 percent higher than those estimated using Scribner rule which is now commonly used in the Sierra and on Blodgett Forest.

2) Stands managed under group selection, in which the stands have been cut using small groups and with trees between the groups being thinned from below, show a growth rate of 216 ft^3/ac/yr which is similar to the better set of reserve stands. Absolute growth in group selection areas, similar to even-aged areas, is likely to be comparatively low due to the time necessary for regeneration in the harvested groups to develop substantial volume. Growth efficiency in terms of cubic volume is a high 6.3 percent which is undoubtedly associated with higher individual tree growth at a stocking level that is half that of the reserve stands. Also, the two group selection compartments considered here had relatively low stocking in 1974 (149 ft^2/ac). This, coupled with the amount of basal area removed between 1974 and the present (132 ft^2/ac) is likely to have contributed substantially to the relatively high stand increment (8.4 ft^2/ac/yr).

3) Stands managed under single tree selection show a growth rate of 123 ft^3/ac/yr and growth efficiency in terms of cubic volume growth is 2.5 percent. Both of these values are substantially lower than for group selection. This difference is probably mostly associated with the level of harvest in the group selection stands being double that in the single tree selection stands. This has the effect of lowering the value of "growth + harvest" over the period.

4) Stands managed under the even-aged system are divided into three groups: a) those that have received thinnings from below and have not yet been clearcut, b) those that have received thinnings featuring thinning from above and not yet been clearcut, and c) those that have been clearfelled and regenerated. Table 13 shows, not surprisingly, that stands thinned from below under an even-aged system are

performing similarly to those managed under single tree selection. Stands having overstory removal are growing at a lower rate due probably to the time needed to transfer growth potential to the smaller, younger, and possibly initially partially suppressed trees in this transition to an even-aged structure. Those stands that were clearcut and replanted naturally have lower growth over the period due to the lesser growth in even-aged stands during the regeneration and stand closure stage relative to stands that are fully stocked. However, growth in diameter and height of trees on the planted stands in the Forest are greater than that shown in Oliver and Powers (1978) tables for unmanaged ponderosa pine plantations. In general, computer simulations indicate that average volume increment from clearfelling and planting coupled with weeding and precommercial will equal or exceed other management styles, but group selection and thinning from below (CT and STS) can also show good growth efficiency and comparable productivity over an entire rotation.

E. Regeneration

Regeneration surveys (including both natural regeneration and planted seedlings) were carried out Forestwide in 1994 and summarized for each of the following management types: group selection, single tree selection, even-aged and thinned from below, even-aged with overstory removal, even-aged and clearcut, and reserve.

a) Seedlings (0 to 4.5 ft tall)

The total number of seedlings forestwide, disregarding recent clearcuts, ranged from 1,381 /ac within young growth reserves to 3,321 /ac in commercially thinned stands (Table 15).

Table 15. Number of seedlings per acre by species and managment type.

Management	PP	SP	DF	WF	IC	BO	HW	SW	Total
	----------------------------Seedlings per Acre----------------------------								
Group Selection	140	170	98	398	423	1525	121	0	2875
Single Tree	355	90	138	379	445	1271	140	0	2818
O'story Removal	139	43	166	334	546	1456	123	0	2807
Even-age, thinned	68	45	189	482	450	1637	447	3	3321
Y-G Reserve	6	36	53	369	142	272	478	25	1381
O-G Reserve	26	50	200	647	1185	479	612	82	3281

i) Managed Compartments

The most abundant species in all treatment areas is California black oak which constituted from 49 to 53 percent of all seedlings. The next most abundant were the shade-tolerant species incense-cedar (14 to 19 percent) and white fir (12 to 15 percent). The more intolerant ponderosa and sugar pines combined constituted only 1 to 13 percent (average 9 percent) of all species and Douglas-fir 3 to 6 percent. Given that the desirable number of seedlings needed for management is approximately 300/ac, in all management types there is more than adequate numbers of each species for maintaining stands with the proportion of species existing in the original stand.

ii) Reserves

Table 15 shows that the reserve compartments differ markedly in the total number of seedlings, 1,381 in the young-growth reserve and 3,281 in the old growth reserve. This is due to differences in stand structure where the former is composed of a more closed canopy, and the latter contains some larger old growth trees and gaps in the canopy. The young-growth reserves have seedlings of white fir, black oak, and other hardwoods (principally tanoak) as the most abundant species (27, 20, and 35 percent, respectively) whereas the most abundant species in the old growth reserves are incense-cedar (28 percent) and white fir (22 percent). The other notable difference in the reserve compartments compared to managed compartments is the higher proportion of other hardwoods (23 percent vs. 7 percent in the young growth compartments) and the presence of other softwoods (2 percent vs. virtually none in young-growth reserves).

Observations show that planted regeneration under shelterwoods, group selection, and clearcutting, often being planted two year old seedings, grows much more rapidly than natural regeneration.

Figure 5 shows the relative abundance of seedlings by species and management type. Incense-cedar and white fir are consistently well represented, having no less than 10 percent each, of all seedlings for all management types.

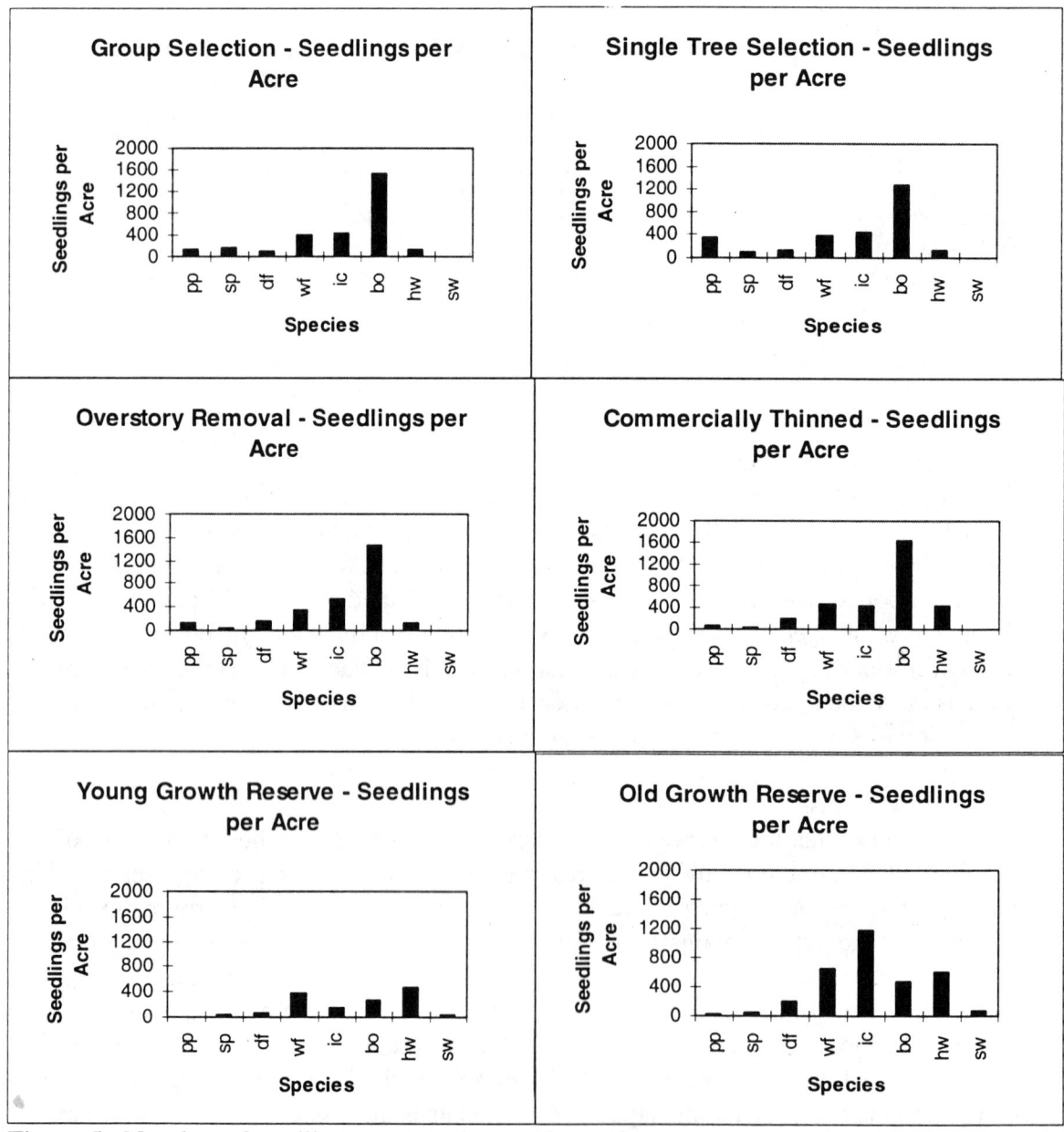

Figure 5. Number of seedlings per acre by species and management type.

b) Saplings (0.0 - 4.0 in dbh)

As shown in Table 16, the total number of saplings ranged from 155 in the even-aged, overstory removal compartments, to 277 in the single tree selection areas.

Table 16. Number of saplings per acre by species and managment type.

Management	PP	SP	DF	WF	IC	BO	HW	SW	Total
			--------------------------Saplings per Acre--------------------------						
Group Selection	8	2	19	83	63	2	64	0	241
Single Tree	22	2	26	112	100	5	10	0	277
O'story Removal	7	10	10	49	44	10	23	2	155
Even-aged Thin	0	3	50	58	55	37	26	0	229
Y-G Reserve	8	3	19	108	53	3	47	6	247
O-G Reserve	3	9	6	85	79	0	26	9	217

i) Managed compartments

The most abundant species in this size class of regeneration were white fir (25 to 40 percent) and incense-cedar (24 to 36 percent). Together, these two species constituted 65 percent of all saplings in all managed compartments combined. Other hardwoods were 14 percent of the total (4 to 27 percent), Douglas-fir 12 percent (6 to 22 percent), and the more intolerant sugar and ponderosa pines combined were 6 to 11 percent). In marked contrast to the situation in the seedlings size class, California black oak saplings constituted only 6 percent of the total (1 to 16 percent), indicating high mortality and browsing in comparison with conifer species.

ii) Reserves

The most abundant species in the reserve compartments were white fir (42 percent) and incense-cedar (28 percent). California black oak saplings were almost non-existant, and Douglas-fir and the pines each constituted 5 percent of the total. Unlike the case with seedlings, the distributions of saplings by species in the young growth and old growth reserves were quite similar.

The distribution of saplings by treatment type is shown in Figure 6.

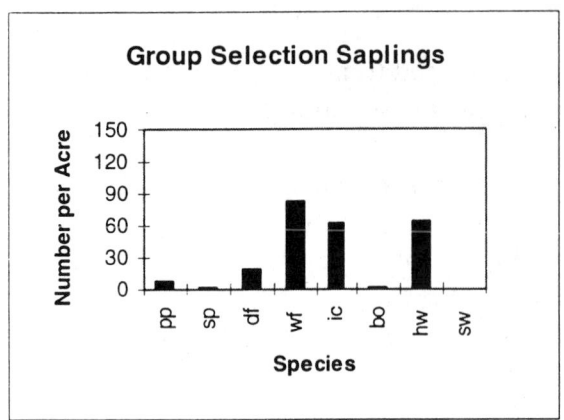

Group Selection Saplings

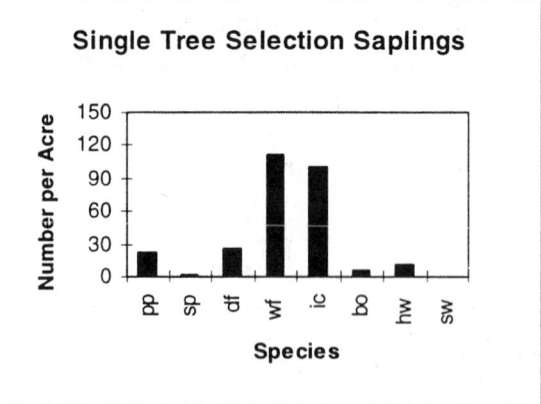

Single Tree Selection Saplings

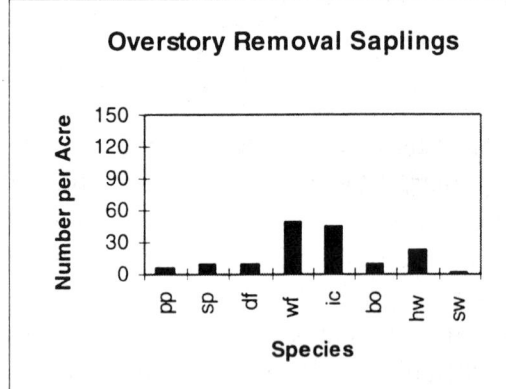

Overstory Removal Saplings

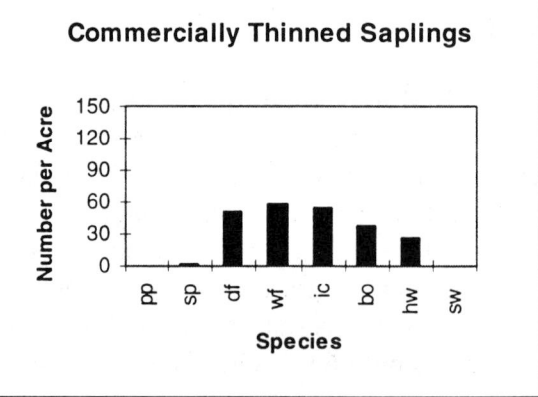

Commercially Thinned Saplings

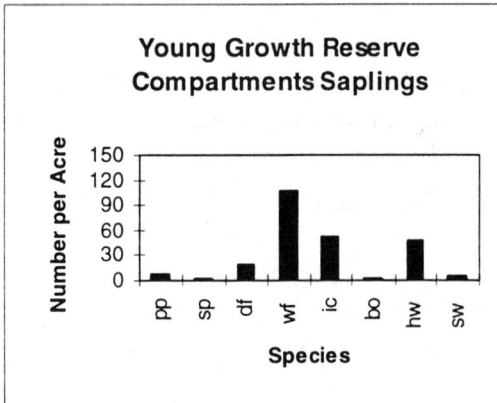

Young Growth Reserve Compartments Saplings

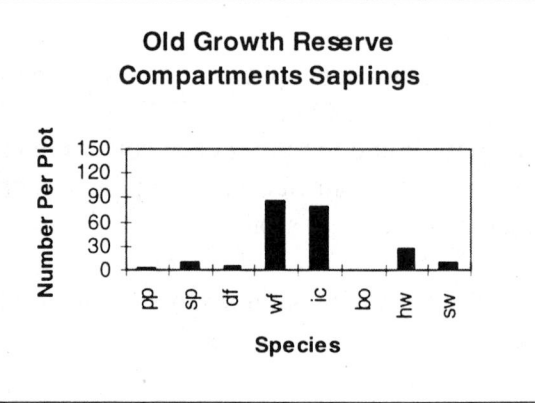

Old Growth Reserve Compartments Saplings

Figure 6. Number of saplings per acre by species and management type.

F. Regeneration in Groups as a function of Distance from Edge

A survey was made of the effect of edge of residual stand on the growth of regeneration within the group. Seven groups were evaluated in 1994 that were comparable in slope and aspect. They were all harvested between 1982 and 1986. All groups had received site preparation after harvesting and were planted to mixed conifer species. Natural regeneration occurred in all groups and the differences in growth of these two types of regeneration are mostly separated by dividing the regeneration into size classes.

Figure 7 shows the abundance of seedlings a) less than 3 feet tall, and b) greater than 3 feet tall as a function of distance from the edge. Both diagrams show, as would be expected, fewer numbers of regeneration close to the edge of the stand, particularly in terms of the taller regeneration which shows the competitive effects of edge trees. The smaller-sized regeneration shows the greatest number in the zone 17 to 33 feet from the edge which probably is associated with favorable microclimate and increased seed fall -- particularly partial shade and lower evaporative stress. As distance from the edge increases, the smaller-sized regeneration become less frequent towards the center of the group. The larger-sized regeneration shows uniform abundance from a distance of 33 to 92 feet from the edge. The variability in numbers of saplings from 117 to 167 feet from the edge and near the center of the group is due to a rapid decline in sample size and no trend should be deduced from this portion of the data.

In Figure 7 it can be seen that the shade-tolerant incense-cedar has highest numbers of small-sized   (< 3 ft tall) regeneration in the shaded micro-environment provided by the edge trees. White fir, surprisingly, does not show this same trend. The intolerant ponderosa pine shows relatively uniform abundance of small-sized regeneration with increasing distance from the edge, however the number of larger-sized saplings (> 3 ft tall) increases markedly with increasing distance from the edge.

Based upon the number of seedlings and saplings found of each species it appears there is sufficient stocking of all species to meet any likely target species mix. Thinning activities can be tailored to produce the desired mix.

Given edge trees of approximately 100 ft tall, it can be concluded that:
1) the close edge of approximately 1/4 to 1/3 of tree height is unfavorable to the establishment of regeneration of all species except perhaps for California black oak and sugar pine.

2) group diameter greater than of one tree height is sufficient to obtain adequate numbers of regeneration of all species.

3) to obtain greatest numbers of large regeneration of ponderosa pine, group diameter should be a minimum of two tree heights.

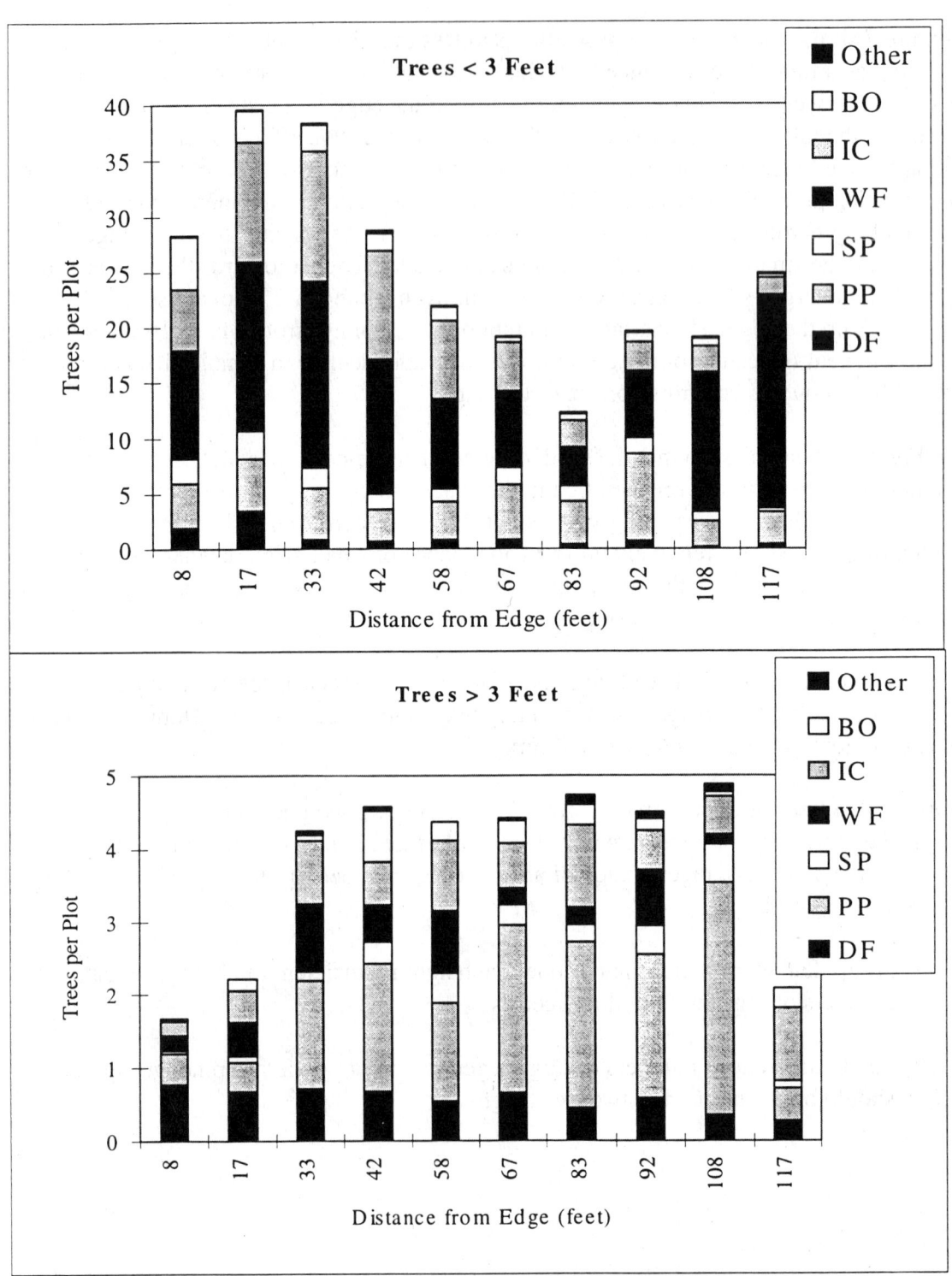

Figure 7. Number of seedlings less than 3 feet tall and seedlings greater than 3 feet tall per plot (1/200 acre) by distance from group edge (feet) for Douglas-fir (DF), ponderosa pine (PP), sugar pine (SP), white fir (WF), incense-cedar (IC), California black oak (BO), and all other tree species (Other).

G. Diameter Distribution

The distribution of breat height diameters of trees in a stand gives an indication of the structural diversity of the stand. Since tree diameters are well correlated to tree heights, the diameter distribution provides information on both horizontal and vertical distribution. This structure is important to wildlife and is an indication of survival of trees in the various age classes. An examination of tree diameters in Blodgett shows how the different management schemes affect structure (Table 17 and Figures 8 to 11).

We can see from Figures 8 to 11 that management has resulted in a classic J-shaped distribution, except for clearcut compartments. The management or silvicultural activities at Blodgett removes trees greater than 40 inches in diameter, eliminating the largest classes. The uneven-aged and commercial thinning compartments all had increases in the larger size classes while the overstory removal compartments had a reduction in the larger classes, as would be expected. Comparing the results of these different management approaches in 1994, we see that both the uneven-aged methods resulted in a distinctly J-shaped distribution with considerable numbers of larger trees (more than 3 trees per acre greater than 30 inches). The two thinning strategies, commercial thinning and overstory removal, produced a more linear distribution of diameters. This is result is expected as the uneven-aged managed stands need a considerable number of stems for future recruitment into the larger diameter classes, while the thinning approaches intend to concentrate volume growth on the residual, larger trees for future clear felling.

Table 17. Number of trees per acre by diameter class (in.) by management type in Blodgett Forest Research Station and for 8 plots measured by Sudworth in 1899 in the mid-Sierra mixed conifer.

Diameter Range (in.)	Sudworth Old Growth	Single-Tree Selection		Group Selection		Commercial Thinning		Overstory Removal		Clearcut	Old Growth Reserve		Young Growth Reserve	
	1899	80	94	74-76	94	76-78	94	77-78	93-94	89,94	80,81	94	76	94
	----------------------------------Inventory Years---------------------													
	-------------------------------------Trees per Acre--------------------													
10-15	4.5	51.4	57.8	26.6	42.4	50.8	59.7	45.2	61.7	19.7	47.5	47.6	47.5	59.8
15-20	8.5	23.2	21.9	15.9	23.2	16.6	24.8	17.2	21.7	2.37	26.7	25.3	26.8	27.6
20-25	10.0	13.2	13.3	5.31	13.5	8.23	15.2	9.35	6.79	0	10	15.6	23.6	23.3
25-30	15.5	6.82	7.04	1.56	7.06	3.23	7.27	5.87	4.34	0	9.17	6.18	8.93	12.8
30-35	15.5	1.36	2.59	0.31	2.65	1.77	3.03	2.61	1.89	0	2.92	8.24	2.86	9.66
35-40	12.0	0	1.11	0.31	0.59	0.61	1.52	0.43	0.75	0	2.08	2.06	1.79	2.36
40-45	11.0	0	0	0	0.29	0.3	0	0.43	0	0	2.08	2.35	0.71	1.97
45-50	10.5	0	0	0	0	0	0	0	0	0	0.83	0.59	0	0
50-55	6.5	0	0	0	0	0	0	0.22	0	0	0	0.29	0.36	0
55-60	3.5	0	0	0	0	0	0	0	0	0	0.83	0.29	0	0.34
50-65	1.0	0	0	0	0	0	0	0	0	0	0	0	0	0
65-70	1.5	0	0	0	0	0	0	0	0	0	0	0.29	0	0
70+	1.5	0	0	0	0	0	0	0	0	0	0	0	0	0
Total	101.5	95.98	103.74	49.99	89.69	81.54	111.52	81.31	97.17	22.07	102.11	108.79	112.55	137.83

Diameter Range	Sudworth Old Growth	Single-Tree Selection		Group Selection		Commercial Thinning		Overstory Removal		Clearcut	Old Growth Reserve		Young Growth Reserve	
	1899	80	94	74-76	94	76-78	94	77-78	93-94	89,94	80,81	94	76	94
	--------------------------------------Trees per Acre------------------------													
>10"	101.5	96.0	103.7	50.0	89.7	81.5	111.5	81.3	97.2	22.1	102.1	108.8	112.6	137.8
>20"	88.5	21.4	24.1	7.5	24.1	14.1	27.0	18.9	13.8	0	27.9	35.9	38.2	50.4
>30"	62.5	1.4	3.7	0.6	3.5	2.7	4.6	3.7	2.6	0	8.8	14.1	5.7	14.3
>40"	35.5	0	0	0	0.3	0.3	0	0.7	0	0	3.8	3.8	1.07	2.3

712

Forest Growth and Stand Structure at BFRS 1933-1995

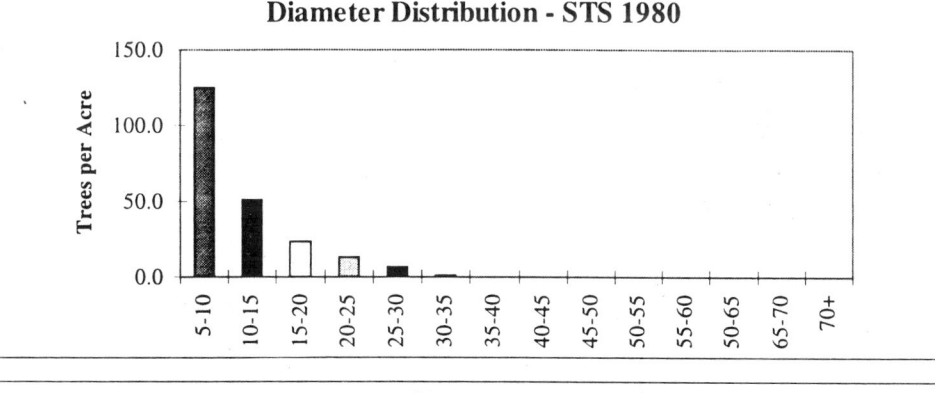

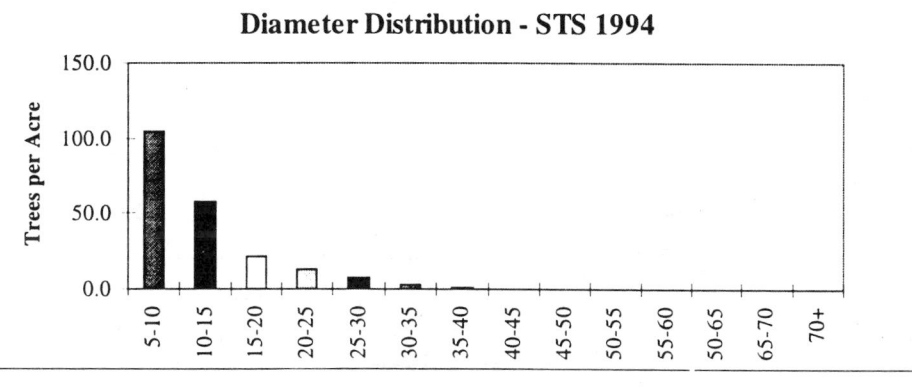

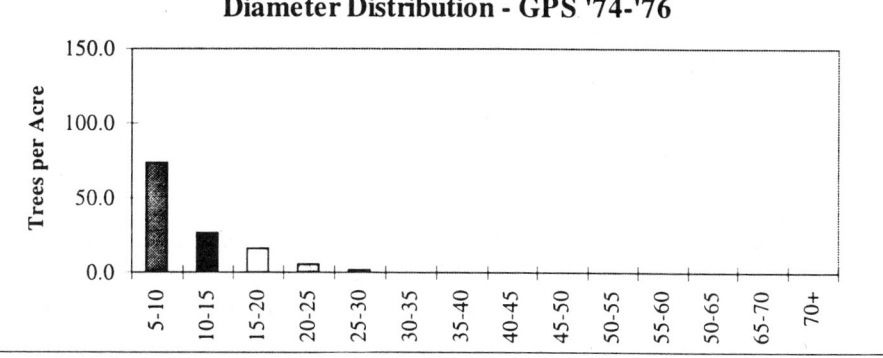

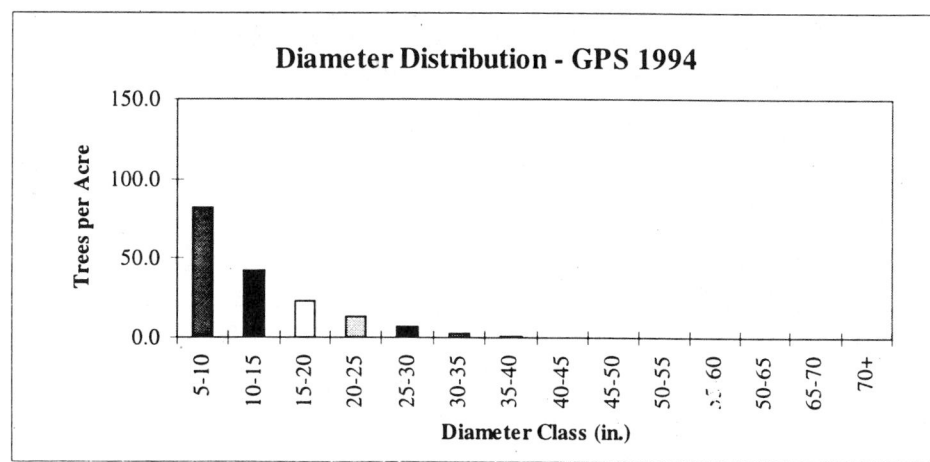

Figure 8. Trees per acre by diameter class for selected single-tree selection (STS) and group selection (GPS) compartments at BFRS by year.

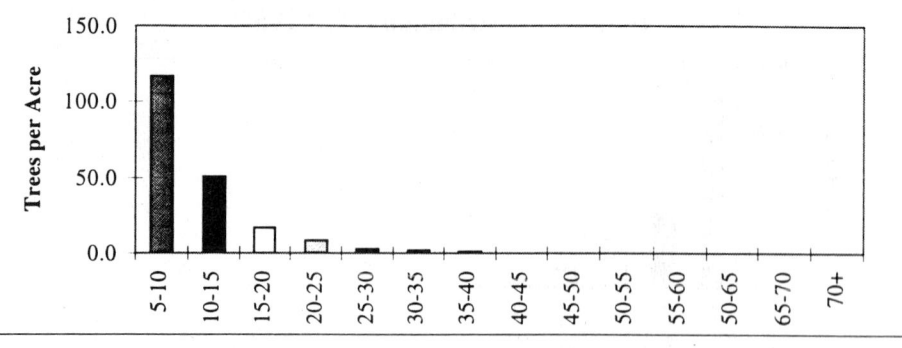

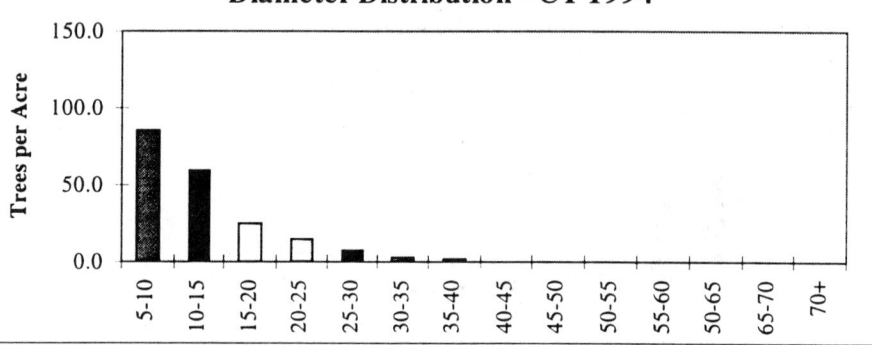

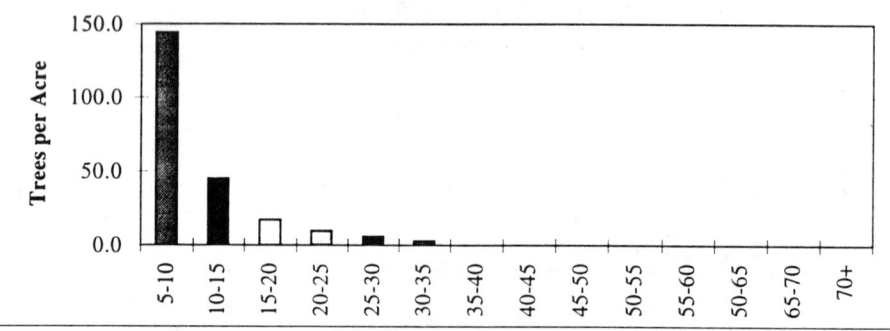

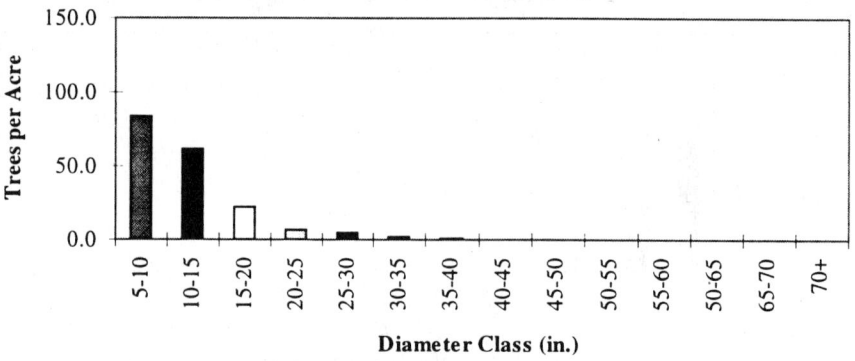

Figure 9. Trees per acre by diameter class for selected commercial thinning (CT) and overstory removal (OR) compartments at BFRS by year.

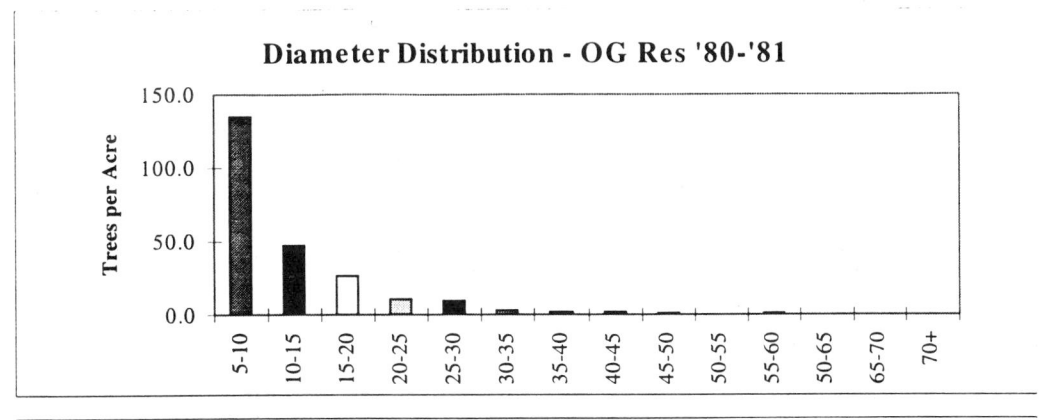

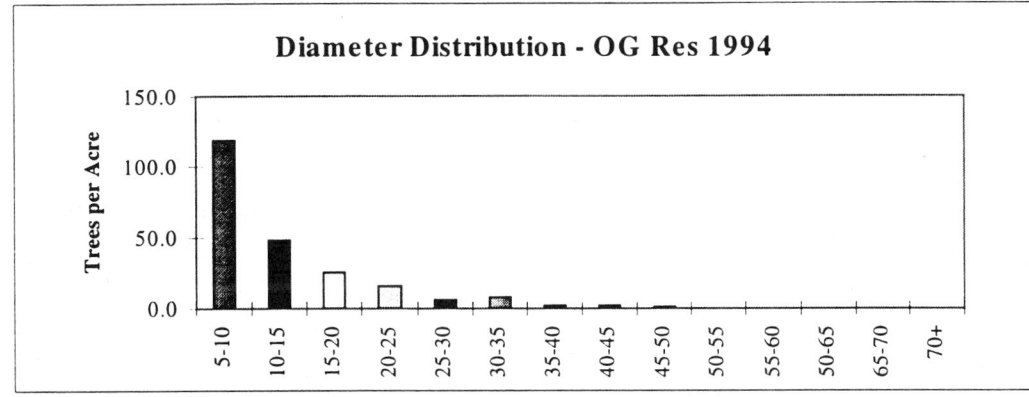

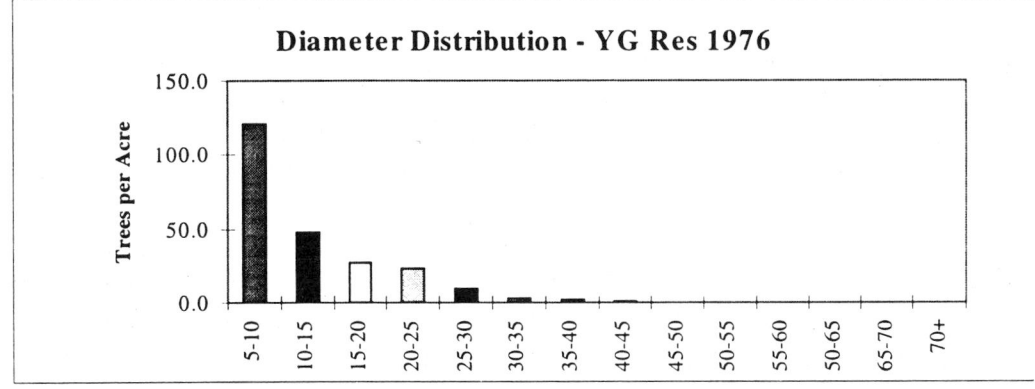

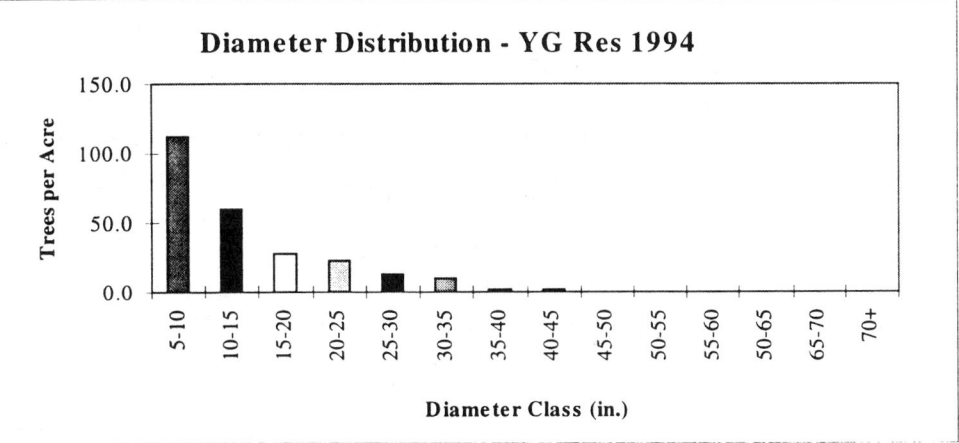

Figure 10. Trees per acre by diameter class for selected old growth reserve (OG Res) and young growth reserve (YG Res) compartments at BFRS by year.

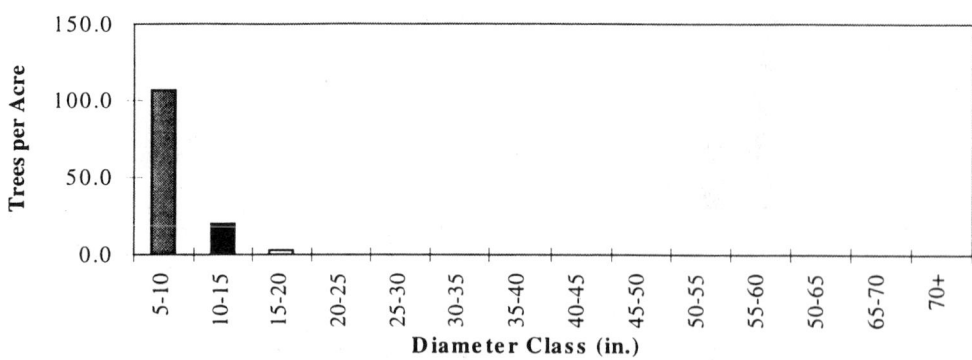

Diameter Distribution - 14 yr old Clearcut

Figure 11. Trees per acre by diameter class for selected clearcut compartments at BFRS by year.

One issue facing forest managers today is the management, protection, and restoration of late seral old growth forests. We know from early reconnaisances of the Sierran region that much of the forests were late seral with wide open stands of large trees (McKelvey and Johnston 1992). If we are to reconstruct these late seral forests then we must have some idea as to their structure and target such structure for it is unlikely that we could ever let natural forces in the absence of pre 1850 fire regimes reconstruct these stands.

Comparing the distribution of diameters found by Sudworth (1899) to those measured at Blodgett we see a marked difference (Figures 8-12). Sudoworth measured diameters of trees greater than 11 inches on 1/4 acre plots (Table 17). He took some 50 plots throughout the Sierra, and eight of these were in the mixed conifer in the mid-Sierra.

The plots Sudworth measured at the turn of the century had few small trees while at Blodgett there are nearly 100 trees per acre just in the 5 to 10 inch class and nearly 50 trees in the 10-15 inch class. Sudworth's plots averaged more than 60 trees per acre greater than 30 inches in diameter. So these stands had many large trees, few small trees, and an open forest floor. This is a large difference in structure that will not be easy to duplicate through management. In the reserve stands, though they are adding trees to the larger diameter classes, there are no mechanisms for eliminating the abundant small trees. As well, the uneven-aged managed compartments require maintenance of a considerable proportion of small trees for recruitment into the larger classes, so neither of these strategies will come close to approximating the stands of the turn of the century for perhaps a hundred years. An examination of eight plots measured by Sudworth in 1899 in the mid-Sierra mixed conifer (Figure 12) shows that the average number of trees per acre greater than 11 inches was 101 (Table 17) and the average number of trees per acre greater than 30 inches was 63. These plots had an average of 720 sqft/ac basal area and a quadratic mean diameter of 38.9 inches for trees greater than 11 inches diameter.

Perhaps biomass thinning of 5 to 10 inch DBH trees in commercially thinned stands could result in stands that approach the size distribution of the plots measured by Sudworth in about 30 to 40 years. Free to grow trees on high site lands can add 4 inches in DBH per decade.

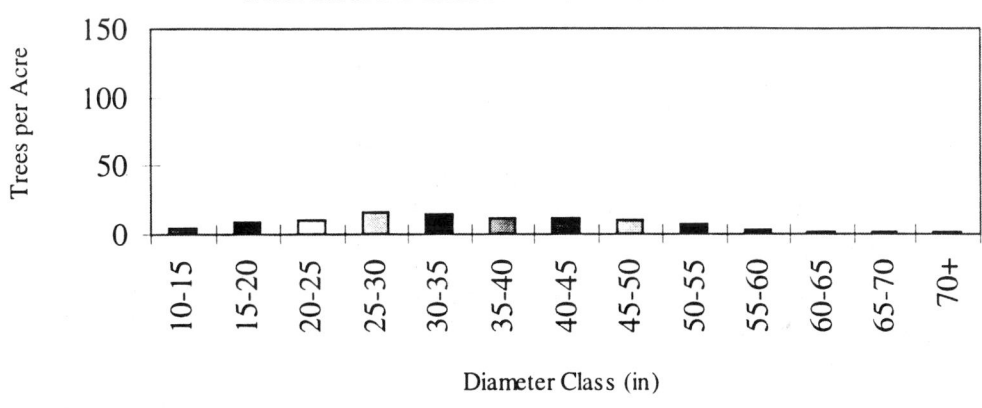

Figure 12. Trees per acre by diameter class for eight 1/4-acre plots measured by Sudworth in the mid-Sierra mixed conifer in 1899.

H. Snags

Standing snags were recorded in Blodgett Forest as part of the permanent plot inventory system since 1976. For each standing dead tree recorded on a plot the species, dbh, height, bark condition, time since death, and presence of bird nesting cavities. Table 18 shows the average number of snags greater than 4.5 inches at breast height per acre, the average diameter at breast height, and the average height of the snags by treatment type for selected compartments in 1994 (Compartment 481 was measured in 1989, 14 years after clearcutting). Management practices at BFRS do not include the making of snags. The snags observed on the permanent inventory plots occur naturally or are a result of harvest damage.

We can see in Table 18 that even though most snags were retained during harvest in the clearcut units, they had the lowest number per acre (6.5/ac) compared to the other treatments.

The young growth reserve compartments had the highest snag density (64.7/ac) as these stands are going through the stem exclusion phase. The old growth reserve compartment (C290) has a more diverse structure and less competitive pressure resulting in lower snag density (44.8/ac). Incense-cedar represents about half of all snags in the compartments shown in Table 18.

Table 18. Snag densities per acre (tpa), average snag diameter (dbh), and average snag height (tht) by treatment for the BFRS in 1994.

	Acres		PP	SP	DF	WF	IC	BO	TO	Oth	Tot
Group Selection	107	tpa	1.2	2.0	1.4	8.9	6.1	2.3			22.1
Comps 270 and 380		dbh	9.0	12.5	11.0	12.1	9.5	18.3			11.8
		tht	41.8	34.5	28.3	38.4	20.8	27.1			31.6
Single Tree Selection	113	tpa	2.0	1.8	1.2	6.7	21.2	12.0		1.4	46.4
Comps 160 and 410		dbh	9.6	13.0	16.3	10.8	6.0	8.4		22.5	8.5
		tht	33.5	44.6	18.2	33.8	20.8	35.4		13.8	28.2
Commercial Thin	106	tpa	3.4	0.7	0.3	6.9	9.1	2.5	1.6	0.9	25.5
Comps 40, 90, 120,		dbh	13.1	7.4	14.1	8.0	8.9	11.2	9.1	6.5	9.4
and 140		tht	23.3	29.3	11.0	37.8	25.4	35.5	24.4	18.0	29.1
Overstory Removal	152	tpa		0.3	0.5	3.2	12.6	1.4	0.6	0.8	19.5
Comps 30, 70, 100,		dbh		5.4	4.5	9.5	6.9	10.4	5.6	6.6	7.7
and 530		tht		20.0	41.8	39.8	22.8	26.1	12.8	25.8	26.1
Clearcut		tpa	0.3	1.2	0.3	3.3	0.5	1.0			6.5
C321 1994	17	dbh	4.6	3.8		8.8	19.7	11.9			8.9
C481 1989	20	tht	18.0	13.0		13.9	25.0	33.5			18.6
YG Reserve	99	tpa	4.6		1.8	8.5	41.2	0.6	7.3		64.0
Comps 20 and 220		dbh	11.3		8.7	12.8	7.8	39.3	5.6		8.8
		tht	34.6		35.7	55.8	29.7	28.5	33.9		34.3
OG Reserve	93	tpa	2.0	3.4	1.3	9.5	13.4	0.9		1.3	31.7
Comp 290		dbh	12.1	18.5	8.0	10.7	7.2	13.0		6.6	10.0
		tht	43.7	67.9	28.6	33.1	24.7	52.3		25.6	34.1

All snags greater than 4.5 inches DBH were recorded on permanent inventory plots. However, Cunningham et al. (1985) report that snags should be at least 33 cm (13 in.) at breast height and 6 m (20 ft.) tall with at least 40 percent bark cover to be suitable for wildlife nesting. Balda (1975) suggests that suggests that densities of such snags should be at least 6.5/ha (2.6/ac) to maintain cavity nesting birds at natural levels in Arizona ponderosa pine forests. Reynolds et al. (1985) also suggests 6.5 snags per hectare for nesting birds, but defines snags as those greater than 20 cm (7.9 in.) and greater than 2.6 m (8.6 ft.) tall in Colorado forests. In Figure 13 we can see that small diameter snags represent the greatest proportion of all snags. Table 19 shows the number of snags greater than 8 inches DBH and greater than 12 inches DBH by treatment type.

Only the overstory removal and clearcut treatments resulted in fewer snags per acre, ones greater 12 inches DBH, than is recommended in other studies. We would surmise that overstory removal tends to remove trees likely to become snags, especially the larger ones, thus resulting in few large snags. Clearcut areas on the other hand leave no trees for large snag recruitment. Even if numerous large snags are left during logging, snag attrition will result in fewer snags over time. Morrison and Raphael (1993) found that 67 percent of the snags in unburned Sierran forests fell in a ten year period. Recruitment for that same period was greater than attrition and they found a net increase in snag density over the ten year period 1978 to 1988.

Table 19. Number of snags per acre greater than 8 inches DBH and greater than 12 inches DBH by treatment type at BFRS in 1994.

Treatment	Number Snags per Acre > 8 inches DBH	Number Snags per Acre > 12 inches DBH
Group Selection	13.4	8.0
Single Tree Selection	17.0	7.3
Commercial Thinning	11.0	5.9
Overstory Removal	5.9	1.9
14 Year Old Clearcut	2.7	0.9
Young Growth Reserve	23.9	11.6
Old Growth Reserve	15.5	7.7

There are a large number of snags per acre less than 12 inches DBH in all but the clearcut compartments. Looking back at Section G of this report we see that the distribution of live trees is similar to that the dead snags, but there about 5 to 10 times as many live trees as dead standing ones.

Since the group selection compartments have only been entered 2-3 times the majority of the area has been treated much the same as the single tree selection area and we would expect similar numbers of snags per acre. However, we see very few snags in the 4.5 to 8 inch class in the group selection compartments. If we look back at page 31 we see that in the mid 1970s the group selection compartments, for whatever reason, had relatively few trees per acre in the 5-10 inch category, providing few trees as recruitment for snags in the small size class in the mid 1990s.

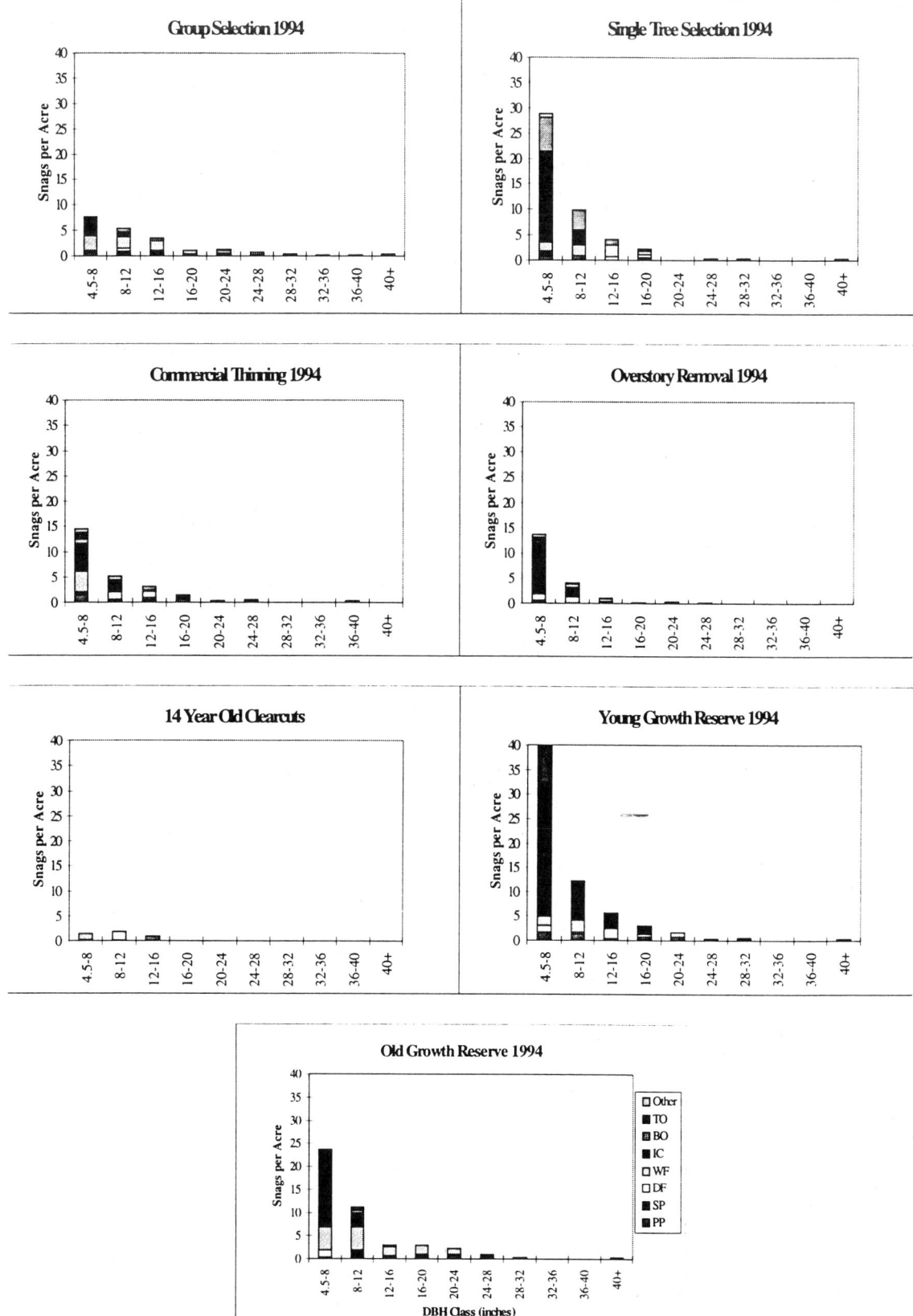

Figure 13. Snags per acre by DBH size class by treatment type at BFRS.

I. Fuels

Tables 20 and 21 show that the amount of light and heavy fuels in any given treatment area depends primarily on management or silvicultural method. Clearcutting and planting resulted in 1/3 less fuel than other treatments. The least amount of fuels were removed in the individual tree selection method compared to the other partial harvest methods. All treatments retained adequate amounts of duff layer needed for soil protection. As expected, both young-growth and old-growth reserve areas had the most amount of fuel material, however except for clearcut and planting, the differences were small. Understandably, overstory removal compartments had significantly less material greater than 10 inches in diameter compared to the other "thinning" and uneven-aged management compartments, as the intent of overstory removal is to capture mortality, thereby removing material greater than 10 inches in diameter that would otherwise be deposited on the forest floor.

These impacts on fuels were made without a deliberate intent to achieve particular fuel conditions. And over the years, the amount of fuels removed in preparation for planting in clearcut and group selection areas have become less, recognizing their value in preventing soil surface movement and providing habitat. With the identification of specific goals of retaining medium to light fuels on site, quite different results of fuel retention could be obtained.

Table 20. Sample size, (n) fuel depth in inches, and standard error by fuel type and management type[1].

Mgmt*	n	Duff Depth	SE	Litter Depth	SE	Woody Fuel Depth	SE
		--------		Inches		--------	
GPS	211	1.66	0.29	1.39	0.18	6.51	1.77
ITS	86	2.06	0.35	1.34	0.17	5.66	1.23
OR	110	1.37	0.26	1.16	0.14	4.95	0.68
CC	21	1.32	0.31	2.07	0.27	4.63	0.84
CT	167	1.71	0.46	1.64	0.39	7.22	2.71
OG	60	2.43	0.42	1.00	0.13	4.81	0.84
YG	99	2.08	0.42	1.86	0.31	5.81	1.53
Avg.	-	1.78	0.36	1.46	0.23	6.06	1.62

Table 21. Fuel weight in tons per acre and standard error (SE) for duff and woody fuel diameter class in inches and by rotten (R) and sound (S) by management type[1].

Mgmt*	Duff	SE	0-.25	SE	0.25-1.0	SE	1.0-3.0	SE	>3.0	R3-10	R11-20	R >20	S3-10	S11-20	S>20	Total
									--------Tons/Acre--------							
GPS	19.57	3.45	0.32	0.06	1.81	0.26	3.27	0.66	12.36	1.09	2.66	2.11	2.71	1.77	1.29	37.34
ITS	24.29	4.15	0.25	0.04	1.68	0.23	3.30	0.69	13.47	1.77	3.43	0.76	3.29	2.56	1.66	42.99
OR	16.11	3.07	0.25	0.04	3.45	0.26	3.41	0.69	7.64	1.36	1.62	0.00	3.01	1.64	0.00	30.86
CC	15.54	3.65	0.11	0.04	0.96	0.32	1.47	0.67	4.36	1.46	0.63	1.55	0.73	0.00	0.00	22.44
CT	20.17	5.46	0.25	0.07	1.63	0.58	2.16	0.92	14.02	1.82	4.09	2.60	3.00	1.58	1.10	38.23
OG	28.71	5.01	0.59	0.06	2.60	0.26	2.29	0.44	13.02	0.74	2.47	2.62	2.60	1.79	2.65	47.21
YG	24.52	4.96	0.29	0.06	1.82	0.38	1.90	0.55	11.76	1.90	1.81	2.30	2.81	2.94	0.00	40.29
Avg	21.00	4.25	0.30	0.06	2.04	0.35	2.74	0.70	11.92	1.46	2.73	1.81	2.83	1.91	1.01	37.99

*Management types: GPS=Group selection, ITS=Individual tree selection, OR=Overstory removal, CC=Clearcut, CT=Commercially thinned, OG=Old growth reserve, YG=Young growth reserve

---

[1] From: Gregoire, R. 1995. Unpublished Report. Blodgett Forest Research Station, Georgetown, CA.

Forest Growth and Stand Structure at BFRS 1933-1995

723

J. Shrubs and Forbs

Over the past 30 years of management of Blodgett Forest, the understory vegetation on many compartments has been manipulated to provide a temporary advantage to regenerating conifers. Treatments have included underburning, herbicide applications, grazing, hand weeding, mechanical cutting, and mixtures of treatments. For the past 20 years, records have been kept on the amount of ground cover vegetation present on the Forest.

Vegetation treatment in any particular year may have only covered a portion of a compartment to meet research or management objectives. Therefore, treatments in successive years were conducted to treat additional untreated areas within a compartment rather than to re-treat previously treated areas.

Understory vegetation was recorded by species for each permanent plot within the Forest. Table 22 shows mean understory vegetation percent cover by management type and by compartment. Shrubs represented 12 percent cover forest wide. Four species, each nearly equally represented, comprised 62 percent of the total shrub cover, deerbrush (*Ceanothus integerrimus*), greenleaf manzanita (*Arctostaphylos patula*), bush chinquapin (*Castanopsis sempervirens*), and tanoak (*Lithocarpus densiflorus*). Table 22 shows the results of remeasurements in 1993-1994 showing the average amount of ground cover by silvicultural treatment and method of control of ground vegetation.

Table 22. Mean shrub, herb, and total cover (percent), basal area (ft^2), year of last harvest, vegetation treatment and year, and number of plots by compartment management type and compartment number for compartments measured from 1992 to 1994.

	Comp.	Last Harvest	Vegetation Treatment* and Year	# Plots	Shrubs	Herbs	Total Cover	Basal Area
					----------Cover (%)----------			ft^2/ac
Group Selection								
	50	84	H 89,86,84,83	10	18.2	2.0	20.2	211
	60	89	H 92,90	14	1.1	2.3	3.4	197
	180	86	H 89	11	1.5	1.1	2.6	201
	260	76	-	9	21.7	1.6	23.3	214
	270	87	G, H 89	19	3.9	0.3	4.2	218
	350	92	G	8	0.0	0.0	0.0	288
	380	85	G, H 91,89	15	7.2	3.1	10.3	150
	420	92	G, H 84	12	10.0	4.4	14.4	174
	490	93	G	21	25.5	11.1	36.6	171
	570	88	G, H 82	9	1.1	0.0	1.1	206
	590	87	G, H 91	9	20.3	1.7	22.0	201
Weighted Average							13.7	197.4
Single Tree Selection								
	110	82	H 87,84	13	0.8	4.5	5.3	187
	160	83	-	16	16.9	3.4	20.3	204
	230	93	-	13	9.7	8.3	18.0	226
	295	91	-	8	3.1	0.0	3.1	218
	410	86	G, H92,87	11	1.1	0.5	1.6	195
	470	89	G	7	2.9	0.7	3.6	208
	471	91	G, H 91	5	0.0	0.0	0.0	185
	670	85	G, H 91	5	18.0	6.0	24.0	175
Weighted Average							10.4	202.3
Commercial Thinning								
	40	85	-	12	10.3	0.6	10.9	220
	90	85	-	8	4.8	2.5	7.3	225
	120	80	-	3	33.0	18.3	51.3	200
	121	80	-	3	40.7	3.6	44.3	226
	122	80	-	2	23.5	2.0	25.5	266
	140	85	-	10	12.9	13.2	26.1	223
	580	85	G	6	37.8	3.9	41.7	226
Weighted Average							23.6	223.5
Overstory Removal								
	30	81	-	13	21.5	4.9	26.4	193
	70	89 (90 pct)	-	8	3.1	0.0	3.1	168
	100	84	H 88	9	4.9	5.4	10.3	146
	170	86	B 82	10	11.8	2.0	13.8	191
	530	81	G, H 90	23	3.0	0.9	3.9	175
	540	87	G, H 90	4	33.8	15.0	48.8	150
	552	84	G	2	33.0	18.5	51.5	144
Weighted Average							14.3	173.8
Clearcut								
	321	80	G,H83,82, W 83,82,81	5	9.6	0.6	10.2	125
	560	84	G, H 90,86	3	11.7	0.0	11.7	216
Weighted Average							10.8	159.1
Young Growth Reserve								
	20	84	-	9	5.6	0.0	5.6	364
	220	13	-	20	3.1	1.7	4.8	322
	520	66	G	7	4.3	11.3	15.6	343
	630	-	G	4	12.5	0.0	12.5	279
	650	85	G, W 75	12	68.4	0.2	68.6	140
Weighted Average							23.6	314.3
Old Growth Reserve								
	290	-	-	27	9.8	2.3	12.1	292
	390	-	-	7	0.0	0.0	0.0	323
	600	-	-	8	24.4	0.6	25.0	216
Weighted Average							12.5	282.7
Shelterwood								
	440	87	G	11	2.2	3.7	5.9	259

B= burned; G= grazed; H= herbicide application; W= Mechanical weeding; - = No treatment
*Vegetation treatments often covered only a portion of a compartment in order to meet research objectives

Table 23. Control of understory vegetation under different silvicultural regimes (data from 44 compartments)

	Understory Cover (%)		
	Shrubs	Herbs	Total
No Shrub Treatment			
Group	21.7	1.6	23.3
Single Tree	11.4	4.4	15.8
Thinning	23.3	6.3	29.6
Reserve	6.0	1.5	7.5
Herbicide			
Group	6.2	1.8	7.9
Single Tree	0.8	4.5	5.3
O'Removal	4.9	5.4	10.3
Grazing			
Group	18.5	8.0	26.5
Single Tree	2.9	0.7	3.6
O' Removal	33.0	18.5	51.5
Shelterwood	2.2	3.7	5.9
Grazing + Herbicide			
Group	7.7	1.9	9.2
Single Tree	4.9	1.7	6.6
O'Removal	7.6	3.0	7.2
Underburning			
O'Removal	11.8	2.0	13.8

Table 23 shows that without any treatment, the amount of understory vegetation in managed compartments is approximately 16 to 30 %. This amount of cover can be compared with the level of approximately 30 % which is the threshold level above which growth of conifer saplings is markedly reduced (Oliver 1984). The relatively low level of 7.5 % cover in untreated reserve compartments is due to their having high stocking levels of 290 to 360 ft^2/ac. The effectiveness of herbicides is shown by compartments with this treatment having understory vegetation cover of between 5 and 10 %. As might be expected, cattle grazing results in the most variable amount of control with cover ranging from 4 to 52 %. The use of a combination of grazing plus spot herbicide kept understory cover to 7 to 9 %. Underburning, with average ground cover of 14 % was not as effective as other methods of control (except grazing) but still satisfactory. It should be noted that, in all methods of shrub and herb control, substantial amounts of understory vegetation have been retained. The management goal in vegetation control is not to eliminate all ground cover but to reduce it below a 20 to 30 % level.

K. Discussion and Conclusions

The permanent plot system and silvicultural practices in Blodgett Forest Research Station were not established or applied in a manner designed to test hypotheses and draw inferences. For example, residual stocking levels, choice of thinning prescriptions, conditions of fuels, or regeneration characteristics, all vary among compartments due to differences in past history and existing stand conditions. Consequently, in applying each cutting method on several compartments, variable stand conditions among compartments necessitates differences in treatment specifications. This makes it is impossible to make precise, quantitative statements on the effects of silvicultural treatments on stand characteristics. The problem is made more complex when attempting to compare the effects of alternative silvicultural approaches, forestwide. In addition, the Forest has only been managed for approximately half of a 60- to 70-year rotation; consequently it is too early to draw definitive conclusions. However, some limited general observations on stand growth and development can be made based upon 60-years of harvest and inventory records and time-series measurements on permanent plots for 20 years.

Extrapolation from Blodgett Forest to broad areas of the Sierra Nevada
Care must be taken in generalizing from data obtained from Blodgett Forest and in extrapaolating to other parts of the Sierra. All silvicultural methods used at Blodgett may be applied throughout the Sierra. However, the results, particularly of growth, must be extrapolated to other areas with caution because Blodgett Forest: 1) is located on high site quality land (Site Class IA and I (Dunning 1942) capable of producing at least 165 ft^3/ac/yr), 2) is on relatively flat ground (no cable yarding required), 3) has relatively small compartments (less than 90 acres), and 4) has a high degree of technical competence and supervision of silvicultural activities. In the Sierra Nevada, approximately 7 % of private forest industry lands (196,000 ac) and 3 % of public lands (222,000 ac) are of similar site quality (Hiserote *et al.* 1986, Colclasure *et al.* 1986, and Lloyd *et al.* 1986). Consequently, results from Blodgett Forest are directly applicable to perhaps 420,000 acres in the Sierra. Considering just those lands sufficiently productive in the Sierra Nevada to warrant active forest management (Site Quality III and above), Sites I and Ia lands represent 9 % of the total forest area (7 % of National Forest lands and 14 % of private industrial lands). On lands that are less productive and steeper than Blodgett Forest, stands will respond more slowly to treatment, silvicultural operations will be more difficult to apply, and overall volume production and economic return will be lower and less cost effective.

1. Overall Conclusions
Because the whole Forest was heavily cut-over between the turn of the century and 1927, three overall conclusions are:
   a) in the space of 21 years from 1934 to 1955, unmanaged, cutover, relatively poorly stocked, but highly productive sites can gain in board foot volume at a rate of 1.8 % per year.
   b) forest development over the next 37 year period from 1956 to 1993 supported an active timber harvest in which about 68% of the growth was removed while, at the same time, al'owing the forest to build up growing stock while increasing stand vigor and health. Board foot volume accrued at 2.7% per year during this period.
   c) the use of a variety of silvicultural harvesting and regeneration methods has demonstrated that a wide diversity of stand structural types can be developed.

2. Timber management

- Forest Practice Rules - Blodgett Forest is managed in a similar manner to lands managed by small private landowners. Taxes are paid, timber harvest plans prepared and submitted to the State for approval, and all standards of the State forest practice rules are met or exceeded. All operations, maintenance, and salaries of Blodgett Forest personnel are funded from revenue obtained from timber sales.

- Growth - Forestwide, from 1934 to 1994, the average volume increased from 12,700 bd ft/ac to 29,270 bd ft/ac (24,000 bd ft/ac excluding reserve compartments).
  Over the 39-year period 1955-1994, over the 2,895 ac Forest:
  a) total volume harvested averaged 1,775,000 bd ft/yr.
  b) approximately 69 % of growth was harvested.
  c) standing volume increased from 18,350 bd ft/ac to 29,270 bd ft/ac.
  d) an average of 614 bd ft/ac/yr was logged.
  e) including reserve compartments (424 acres), growth plus harvest averaged 894 bdft/ac/yr.
  f) excluding reserve compartments, growth plus harvest was 868 bf/ac/yr.
  g) over the last 10 to 15 years, well stocked 70- to 100-year-old stands (>200 ft^2/ac) are growing at the rate of nearly 1,000 bd ft/ac/yr.
  h) long-term productivity appears to be relatively independent of cutting method as long as there is sufficient stocking that is relatively free to grow.

- Retention of Pines - Successive forestwide inventories in 1933, 1946, and 1957 (before any harvesting was done) show that, as stands go through the stem exclusion phase, sugar pine and ponderosa pine combined decline from 40 to 30 percent of all stems. They did not survive as well as the more shade tolerant incense-cedar and white fir. Inventories since 1957 show that, except in areas clearcut and planted, pine seedlings and saplings in the Forest are fewer in number compared to the more shade tolerant white fir and incense-cedar. Also, the naturally-regenerated pine does not seem to be surviving well into the sapling stage. Under natural conditions, pines are probably maintained in mixed conifer stands by frequent, low intensity fires which reduce the number of competing shade-tolerant species. In single-tree and group selection managed stands where wildfires are suppressed, the retention of pines in the overstory seems possible through substantial investments in selective precommercial and commercial thinnings, vegetation management, selective harvesting, and prescribed burning.

- Choice of Group Size - Current planning is tending to favor the use of either group or single tree selection systems for regenerating mixed conifer stands. A major issue is how to determine optimal group size. There are engineering issues of the space needed to fall and yard in a safe manner while minimizing damage to residual trees. Silviculturally, groups size should be chosen such that the microclimate created favors the shade tolerance characteristics of the desired mix of regenerating trees, shrubs or grasses. Experience at Blodgett has shown that reduced growth occurs in groups near the stand edge. Towards the center of .5 to 1.5 acre groups, growth of intolerant pine regeneration is greater than that of fir and cedar. Naturally regenerated or planted shade tolerant species will be favored near the stand edge or in groups of small size.

- Snags - Group and single tree selection methods and commercial thinning can retain and recruit snags of sufficient size at or above levels necessary for cavity nesting wildlife. In carrying out clearcutting or overstory removal, all existing snags are retained at harvest except those constituting a hazard to personnel. However, 10-years after harvest, most of these snags have fallen due to natural decay processes. Past prescriptions for clearcutting and overstory removal have not retained large live trees to become snag replacements.

- Fuels - In managing mixed conifer stands, the choice of treatments and the manner of their application affects the distribution of light, medium and large dead woody material. This material has value for wildlife habitat, nutrition, soil cover, and to protect against soil erosion. This material also constitutes fuel and contributes to fire hazard. Knowledge is needed, therefore, on the extent to which alternative silvicultural treatments affect the quantity of this material. A major difficulty in evaluating treatment effects is that standards of silvicultural practice change over time. In particular, clearcutting, site preparation, and planting conducted in the early 1980s removed, by design, considerably more dead and down woody fuel compared with other silvicultural methods. Currently, post harvest site treatment practices are designed to leave the medium to large woody material which is now recognized as desirable for wildlife habitat and to protect the surface soil from erosion.

- Cattle grazing and herbicides can be effective in reducing shrub competition with conifers. Cattle grazing produces highly variable reduction in shrub competition. Certain shrub species are very thoroughly controlled, such as deerbrush (*Ceanothus integerrimus*), while other shrubs, such as the unpalatable gooseberry (*Ribes spp*), are not controlled at all. Herbicide use, being more target specific, is more consistently effective in reducing shrub and hardwood competition to specified levels.

- Shrubs are effectively suppressed to a level of less than 12% when conifer crowns form a closed canopy and basal areas reach approximately 250 ft^2/ac.

3. Sierran Issues and Alternative Management Scenarios

- Biodiversity. The compartment design on the 2,895-acre Forest has resulted in a diverse landscape consisting of a mosaic of age classes, stand structures, and species composition. The Forest has allocated approximately 1,052 acres to uneven-aged management, approximately 985 acres to even-aged management (including 125 acres of shelterwood and seed tree regeneration), approximately 355 acres to young growth reserves (gradually, over 90 years, clearfell and plant, no other management), and approximately 349 acres to no-cut ecological reserve. Such an allocation provides a spectrum of habitats from early seral (newly clearcut) to mid seral (reserve compartments) while at the same time over 600 bf/ac/yr has been harvested forestwide over the last 37 years. The Forest provides, therefore, an indication of what might be obtainable on a landscape basis where the management goal was to provide diversity of stand structures to attain forest health, diversity of wildlife habitat, and sustainable timber yields.

- Fire Hazard Reduction. Since wildfire suppression policies were introduced earlier in the century, there has been a significant accumulation of dead, woody fuels in Sierran forests. On Blodgett Forest there is most dead, woody fuel accumulation in the unmanaged reserve and uneven-aged managed stands, and less in clearcut and planted areas and overstory removal compartments. Small diameter trees in both managed and reserve stands provide ladder fuels that could allow fires to reach tree crowns. These ladder fuels were less common in those areas of late seral stands at the turn of the century due to the paucity of small diameter trees. In these stands, it is conjectured that wildfires were commonly restricted to ground fires of low intensity.

There has been no experience at Blodgett Forest in the creation or management of late-seral, low fire hazard areas because of the small size of the Forest and because sufficient time has not elapsed for the development of very large-sized trees. Experience suggests, however, that fuel management and stand structures can be developed, in time, using a combination of thinning and underburning that would reduce the likelihood of catastrophic wildfires.

- Pre-EuroAmerican Stand Conditions
The USDA Forest Service and other groups are developing plans having the goal of returning much of the the Sierra Nevada to within the range of "pre-Euro-American conditions". These conditions have not been identified in terms of species composition, age classes, or stand structures. The best descriptions of stand conditions in the 1800s are those of John Muir, plots established by Sudworth in 1899 - 1901, and early photographs such as those evaluated by Gruell (1994). Although these descriptions may not be "average" they are representative of at least a portion of the Sierra Nevada that consisted of open, park-like conditions and late-seral stage stands. In addition to these stands, the Sierra is most likely to have had mosaics of stands of varying age class, density, and species composition.
An examination of Sudworth's field notes, describing eight 0.25-ac plots measured in 1899 in the mixed conifer type in or near Blodgett Forest, showed that there was an average of 101 trees per acre greater than 11 inches dbh and 63 trees per acre greater than 30 inches dbh. Average basal area stocking was 720 ft^2/ac. Stands were uneven-sized but not necessarily uneven-aged, and there was limited regeneration.

There has been no direct experience at Blodgett Forest that provides a silvicultural prescription on how to produce late-seral stage stands having attributes similar to "pre-EuroAmerican" conditions. Experience at Blodgett suggests, however, that it is possible, on high site quality lands, to accelerate the growth of well-spaced trees to create stands having elements of a late seral condition (i.e. mosaics of large, well-spaced trees, gaps containing smaller trees and shrubs, large snags and downed woody material, and multi-layered canopies). Silvicultural prescription could favor a sufficient pine component by thinning and underburning. Experience suggests that, on productive sites, such stands can be developed from bare ground in 100 to 150 years. Similar approaches could be taken on sites of lower productivity, however the time taken to obtain stands having elements of late-seral structure would be longer.

L. Acknowledgments

Over the years many people have been involved in the design of inventories and other data collection efforts and numerous people have participated in the data collection. We would like to especially thank Robert C. Heald, Forest Manager since the mid-1970s, for designing, facilitating, and managing the inventory and data collection over the last, nearly 20 years. Percy Barr designed the inventories of 1934 to 1955; Ken Stumpf and Lee C. Wensel designed the inventory of 1973; and, Robert C. Heald designed the current permanent plot inventory system which began in 1975. Weather records were summarized for the forest by Heald in 1976, Scott Holman and Heald in 1989, and Frieder Schurr in 1995. Ryan Gregoire summarized the fuels data in 1994. Scott Holman originally designed the database where all inventory data is compiled. Since its development Roger Church and then Tara Barrett, the database managers, have improved on its utility. We are indebted to all these people for their efforts. And finally, besides designing and analyzing data, Bob Heald, Frieder Schurr, and Tara Barrett helped immeasureably in the development of this report by clarifying, retrieving, and critiquing all aspects of the analysis and interpretation of results.

M. Literature Cited

Balda, R.P. 1975. The relationship of secondary cavity nesters to snag densities in western coniferous forests. USDA For. Serv. Reg. 3, Wildlife Habitat Tech. Bull. 1, 37 p.

Colclasure, P., J. Moen, and C.L.Bolsinger. 1986. Timber resource statistics for the Northern Interior Resource Area of California. USDA Forest Service Resource Bulletin PNW-135.

Cunningham, J.B., R.P. Balda, and W.S. Gand. 1980. Selection and use of snags by secondary cavity-nesting birds in the ponderosa pine forest. USDA For. Serv. Research Paper RM-222.

Dunning, D. 1942. Calif. For. & Range Exp. Sta. Note 28

Dunning, D. and L.H. Reineke. 1933. Preliminary yield tables for second growth stands in the California pine region. USDA Technical Bulletin 354, 23 p.

Davis, L.S.; R.J. Lilieholm; T.M. Barrett; and, K. Arha. 1993. Bibliography of Publications Based on Blodgett Forest Research. Blodgett Forest Research Station, Department of Forestry and Resource Mangement, University of California, Berkeley, 49 p.

Gruell, G.E. 1994. Understanding Sierra Nevada Forests. California Forest Products Commission, Sacramento, CA, 31 p.

Heald, R.C. 1989. Policy for use of Blodgett Forest Research Station. Unpublished Report on file at University of California, Blodgett Forest Research Station, Georgetown, CA, 18 p.

Hiserote, B.A., J. Moen, and C.L.Bolsinger. 1986. Timber resource statistics for the San Joaquin and southern California Resource Areas. USDA Forest Service Resource Bulletin PNW-132.

Lloyd, J.D., J. Moen, and C.L.Bolsinger. 1986. Timber resource statistics for the Sacramento resource area of California. USDA Forest Service Resource Bulletin PNW-134.

Mayer, K.E. and W.F. Landenslayer, Jr. (Eds.). 1988. A guide to Wildlife Habitats of California. California Dept. Of Forestry and Fire Protection, Resources Agency, Sacramento, CA.

McKelvey, K.S. and J.D. Johnston. 1992. Historical perspectives on forests of the Sierra Nevada and the Transverse Ranges of southern California: Forest conditions at the turn of the century. In: The California Spotted Owl: A Technical Assessment of Is Current Status. USDA Forest Service, Pacific Southwest Research Station, General Technical Report PSW-GTR-133, pp.225-246.

Morrison, M.L. and M.G. Raphael. 1993. Modeling the dynamic of snags. Ecological Applications 3(2): 322-330.

Oliver, W.W. 1984. Brush reduces growth of thinned ponderosa pine in northern California. USDA For. Serv. Res. Paper PSW-172, 7p.

Oliver, W.W. and R.F. Powers. 1978. Growth models for ponderosa pine: I. Yield of unthinned plantations in northern California. USDA For. Serv. Res. Paper PSW-133, 21p.

Reynolds, R.T., B.D. Linkhart, and J. Jeanson. 1985. Characteristics of snags and trees containing cavities in a Colorado conifer forest. USDA For. Serv. Research Note RM-455.

Sudworth, G. B. 1899. Personal field notes, Notebook No. 3. University of California, Berkeley, Biosciences Library.

University of California, Berkeley, Department of Forestry and Resource Management. 1989. Policy for Use of Blodgett Forest Research Station. June 1, 1987, revised April 5, 1989, University of California, Department of Forestry and Resource Management, Berkeley.

DEAN URBAN
School of the Environment
Duke University
Durham, North Carolina

CAROL MILLER
Graduate Degree Program in Ecology
Colorado State University
Fort Collins, Colorado

17

Modeling Sierran Forests: Capabilities and Prospectus for Gap Models

Sierra Nevada Ecosystem Project: Final report to Congress, vol. III, *Assessments, Commissioned Reports, and Background Information.* Davis: University of California, Centers for Water and Wildland Resources, 1996.

733

Introduction

This paper responds to the desire of the Sierra Nevada Ecosystem Project (SNEP) to address current capabilities for projecting Sierran forest ecosystems into an uncertain future, relying on available modeling techniques. Here we present an overview of the forest gap model ZELIG as implemented for Sierran forests, emphasizing specific concerns of SNEP but putting these into the context of our overall goals for the Sierra Nevada and elsewhere. This overview is divided into several parts: a short history and lineage of gap models; our efforts to date in the Sierra Nevada as part of the National Park Service's (now NBS) Global Change Research Program. We should emphasize that, as the NBS program is not scheduled for completion until after 1996, this report describes "work in progress." We close with a final prospectus as to our capabilities in the near-term future and how our efforts can be reconciled with other modeling approaches.

Background

Gap models (Shugart and West 1980) simulate forest dynamics as the manifestation of tree-by-tree demographic processes: establishment, growth in a competitive milieu, and mortality. Relative to other tree-based models, gap models make the simplifying assumption that at a small spatial scale the environment can be considered relatively homogeneous in the horizontal dimension and that trees within this area mutually influence each other. Thus, a gap model simulates a small model plot corresponding to the zone of influence of a canopy-dominant tree (or conversely, the gap one creates when it dies). The history and philosophy of gap models is detailed by Shugart (1984) and Botkin (1993); Urban and Shugart (1992) have traced the lineage of several variant models and illustrate recent trends in these models.

Gap models share a logic that distinguishes them from many other forest simulators, in that trees do not interact directly with each other; neither do trees react to an extrinsically specified environmental context. Rather, individual trees influence their environment (*e.g.*, through leaf area), and the collective influences of many trees define the environmental context of the model plot. This collective environment then influences individual trees (*e.g.*, through shading). Thus, gap models are unique in that the trees generate their own environmental context during the course of the simulation.

Gap models also share a common logic in the implementation of the demographic processes of establishment, growth, and mortality. Each of these is specified as a maximum potential that could be achieved under optimal conditions; that is, optimal establishment rate, optimal annual diameter increment, or optimal longevity. These potentials are then reduced to reflect suboptimal environmental conditions on the plot (shading, drought, cold temperature, lack of fertility). Thus, as the environmental conditions of the plot change through time, the trees respond dynamically to these changing conditions. Because the influence of each tree on its environment depends on its species and size (the models use species-specific allometric relationships to simulate leaf area, height, and biomass of various tree components), and because the response of each tree to its environment may also vary with size (shading by taller trees, allometric N demand) or by species (shade tolerance, drought tolerance, temperature response, tissue chemistry and N demand), gap models are especially powerful in simulating mixed-age, mixed-species stands.

Because of the logic of the implementation of tree demographics, gap models have also been especially appealing as tools for exploring the consequences of novel environmental conditions, including climatic variability (Solomon 1986, Pastor and Post 1988, Urban *et al.* 1993, among others) and management activities (Aber *et al.* 1979; Smith *et al.* 1981; Hansen *et al.* 1995). This capability to explore novel environmental conditions, including unprecedented management tactics, affords gap models an important advantage over models tightly calibrated to measured field conditions, such as stand yield models based on regressions. Such regression-based models are by their structure restricted to an empirical domain dictated by the data used to construct the model. Because the NBS research program is a global change program concerned primarily with anticipating forest response to novel environmental conditions, the use of a gap model was clearly recommended.

The original gap models (Botkin *et al.* 1972, Shugart and West 1977) made a variety of assumptions to simplify model parameterization. These included simple schemes for estimating allometric relationships (*e.g.*, the height-diameter curve) and initial growth rates. These early models also simulated the physical environment in rather simple ways (*e.g.*, the soil water balance, soil fertility). More recently, the models have shown a tendency to become much more data-intensive and to incorporate increasingly sophisticated submodels of the physical environment (reviewed in Urban *et al.* 1991, Urban and Shugart 1992).

Some of these trends are easily illustrated with the current Sierra Nevada implementation of the gap model ZELIG (Urban *et al., in prep.*)

ZELIG version FACET 3.1: the Sierran Model

ZELIG is a second-generation gap model in the sense that it retains much of the philosophy and logic of its parent models (JABOWA and FORET), but it has been completely rewritten with new algorithms and parameterizations. ZELIG is especially configured for spatial applications (Smith and Urban 1988, Urban and Smith 1989, Urban *et al.* 1991, Weishampel *et al.* 1992, Urban and Shugart 1992). This model, unlike other gap models, is implemented as a grid of model plots; trees on adjacent grid cells may influence each other through shading. ZELIG also serves as the framework for model-based comparisons among a variety of forest ecosystems under contrasting environmental regimes (Lauenroth *et al.* 1993), and also for comparisons between grasslands and forests (Coffin and Urban 1993). The model is currently implemented or under testing in the Oregon Cascades (Urban *et al.* 1993; Hansen *et al., in press*), the Olympics (N. Zolbrod, U. Washington, thesis *in prep.*), the White Mountains of New Hampshire (Schwarz 1993, Schwarz *et al.* 1994), the southern Appalachians in North Carolina (K. Allen, Duke University, master's thesis *in prep.*), and in the Sierra Nevada (Urban *et al., in prep*; Miller and Urban, *in prep.*).

The Sierran implementation of ZELIG has been developed under the NBS's Sierra Nevada Global Change Program. The major projects contributing to this research program are represented in Figure 1, and our modeling effort has served to help integrate these various studies. The overall concern of this program is anthropogenic environmental change; specific concerns are the role of the water balance as this might be altered under climatic change, and fire regimes as these might respond to changing climate and also to changing fire management practices. These foci reflect our consensus that soil moisture and fire are primary constraints on Sierran forest ecosystems.

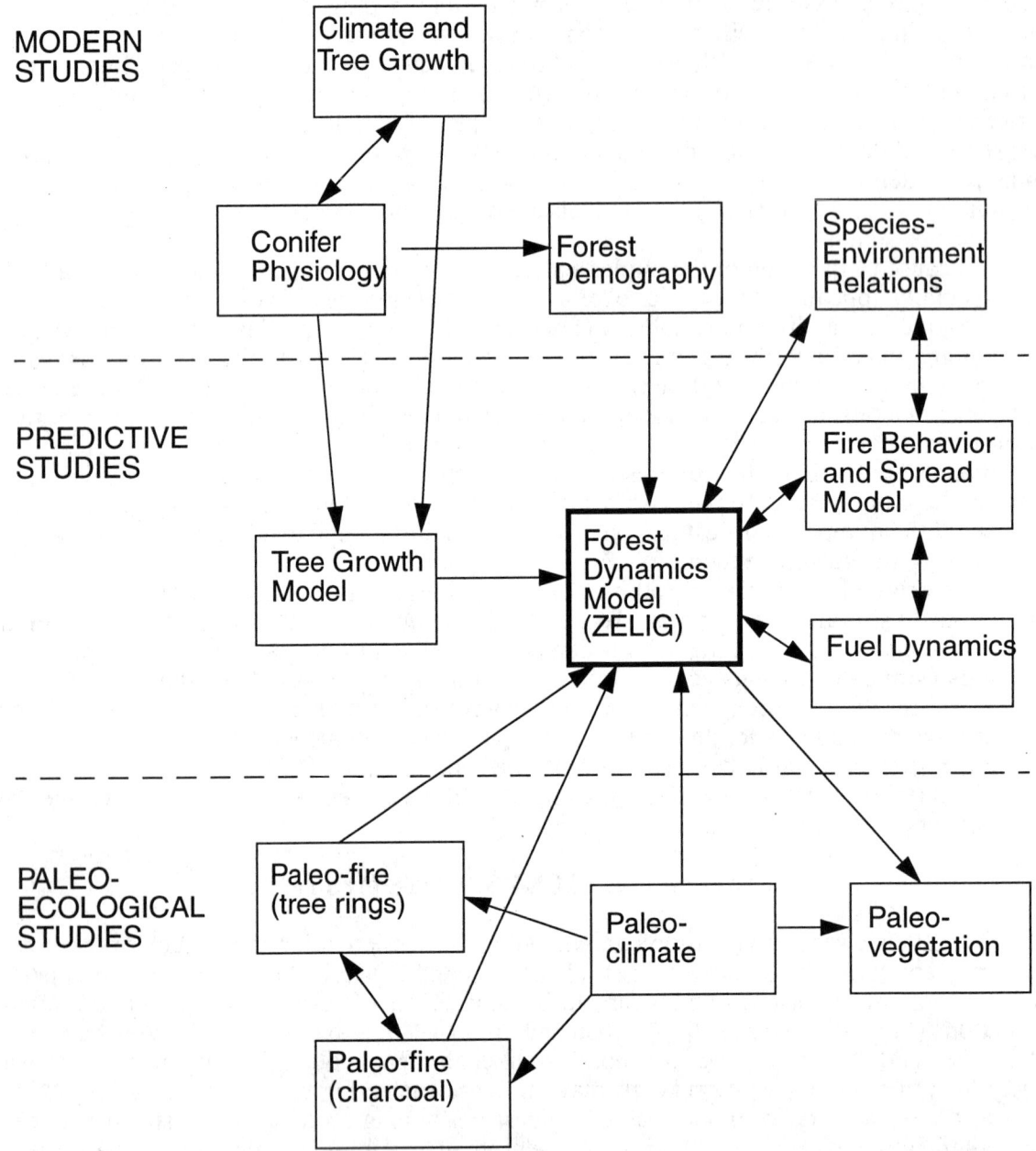

Figure 1. The relationships among studies within the Sierra Nevada Global Change Research Program (redrawn from Stephenson and Parsons 1993). Boxes represent individual studies and arrows represent some of the major linkages.

Our approach to modeling Sierran forests has been to develop model components (especially a soil moisture model and a fire model) that are sufficiently general and robust that, once developed and verified for our primary study site (Sequoia National Park), could be implemented readily at other Sierran sites (especially Yosemite), or indeed, in another region. This is in keeping with the general ZELIG philosophy: the same code is being used at all study sites in various regions of the United States.

Our strategy in model development has been to incorporate as much local data and expertise as possible, and to encode these as algorithms that are as general and site-independent as possible. The initial version of the model is then benchmarked and further tested to ensure it is robust. Current efforts are geared toward further refinements in response to our initial model tests.

Current Status

The ZELIG model itself is largely free of internal site-specific parameters. Rather, the model is driven by two parameter files: a *site* file and a *species* file. The site file includes climate and soils data. The Sierran model is a FACET variant of ZELIG, which means that the model is designed to simulate a site (model grid) at any elevation or topographic position (slope, aspect). The model corrects climate internally for topography using locally estimated lapse rates and established models. Thus, ZELIG requires as input data, mean monthly minimum and maximum temperature, precipitation, and the interannual variability (standard deviation) in these. Lapse rates are used to adjust temperatures and precipitation for elevation (Running *et al.* 1987, Daly *et al.* 1994), and temperature is used to fractionate precipitation into snow *versus* rain. Temperatures and precipitation are used in conjunction with latitude, slope, and aspect, and elevation to predict solar radiation (Bonan 1989, Nikolov and Zeller 1992). Soils are defined in terms water-holding capacity for each of any number of layers; water-holding capacity is itself estimated from the depth and texture of each layer (Cosby *et al.* 1984).

The species driver file includes parameters that define potential growth rates, environmental tolerances, and allometric relationships of each species. In contrast to early gap models which estimated some of these parameters without data, ZELIG is rather data-intensive: Sierran allometries are based on hundreds to tens of thousands of individual trees. Growth rates are calibrated to local tree growth measurements where available, or adjusted to stand-level data as necessary for data-poor species. Parameters are constrained to be consistent with known autecology (Minore 1979) and local data.

The Soil Water Balance. Much of our effort to date has focused on the soil water balance as a primary constraint on forests directly, and indirectly through its effect on the fire regime. The current model simulates the water balance as the difference in water demand (energy supply) and water supply. Water demand depends on radiation and temperature, using a Priestley-Taylor estimate of potential evapotranspiration (PET; Bonan 1989). Demand thus varies with elevation (via temperature lapse rates) and topographic position (relative radiation). Water supply depends on water input (precipitation plus snowmelt) and water storage (mostly a function of soil depth for these sandy soils). The forest canopy influences the water balance though interception and by effecting the depth distribution of transpiration (which depends on fine root density per soil layer). Thus, the water balance is responsive to static (*in situ*) constraints such as topography and soil, as well as to dynamic constraints that might be expected to change under greenhouse scenarios, especially temperature and precipitation. Importantly, we have taken special care to ensure that this model can simulate water relations under a broad range of environmental conditions, both within the Sierra and at other study sites in other parts of the country.

The Fire Regime. The ZELIG fire model represents a new advance in fire modeling as it integrates fire, climate and forest pattern. Although other gap models have incorporated fire, this model is unique because it simulates a climatically sensitive fire regime and a spatially heterogeneous fuel bed. A schematic of the fire model is shown in Figure 2.

Climate is coupled to the fire regime through ZELIG's soil water balance, from which a proxy for fuel moisture is computed. Thus, fuel moisture is dynamic; it changes from year to year, throughout the fire season, and reflects current canopy conditions. This approach provides a means for investigating the influence of climate on the fire regime, and is a critical improvement over other gap models where fuel moisture is treated as a constant parameter.

Fuel loads are coupled to tree-level information, and therefore reflect current plot conditions. Whereas other gap models have assumed a constant accumulation rate for a given forest type (Kercher and Axelrod 1984, Keane et al. 1990), our model accumulates fuels according to tree-level allometries, with annual rates calibrated to data from a long-term fuel

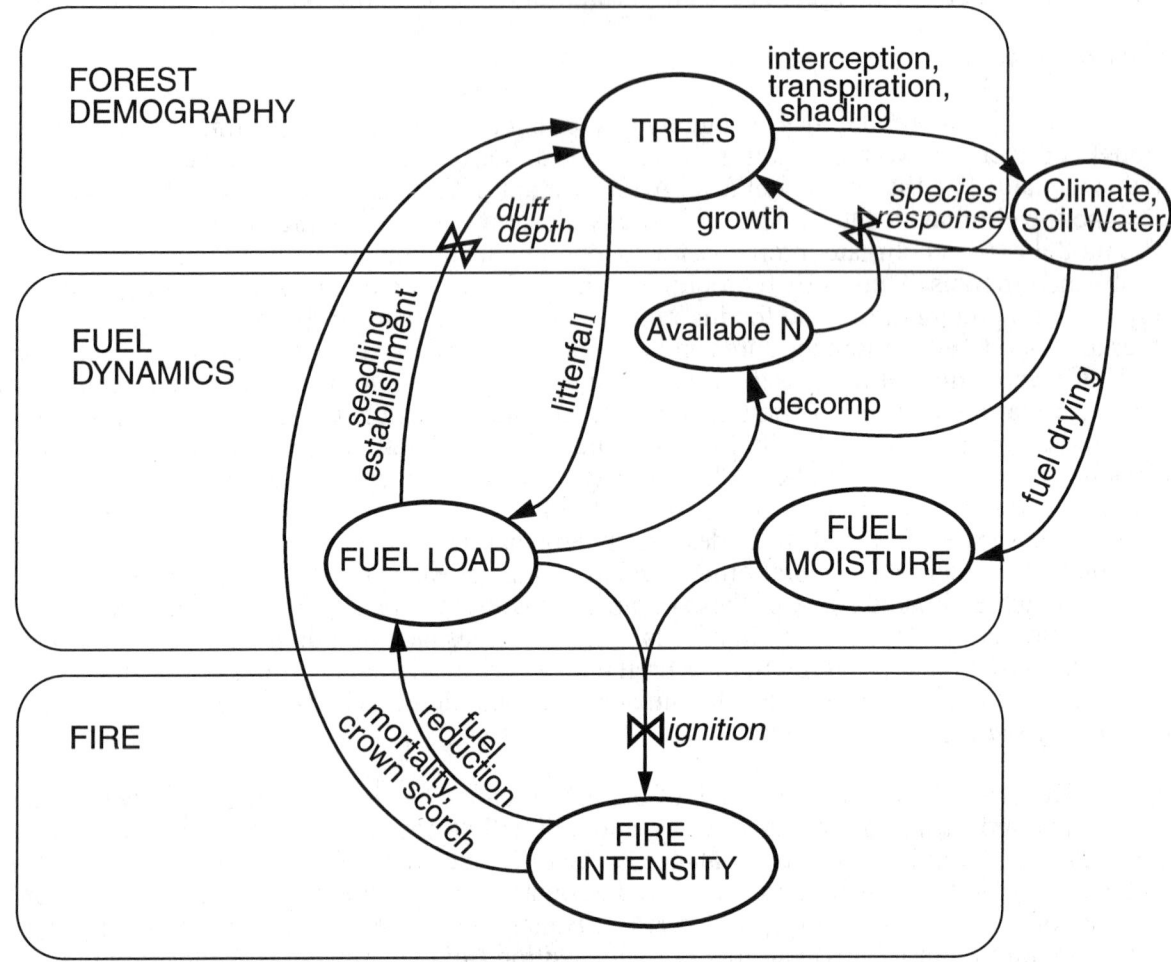

Figure 2. Schematic of the fire model in ZELIG version 3. Fuel loads relfect forest condition because litterfall is a function of tree-level allometries. Fuel moisture is computed from the soil water balance, thus coupling fire with climate. Fire frequency is internally generated by the model, with fire occurrence and fire intensity being functions of fuel moisture and fuel load. Implementation of the model on a raster grid enables the generation of spatial heterogeneity within the simulated stand.

study (van Wagtendonk, National Biological Service, *unpub. data*). A portion of each tree's foliage and branches fall each year as litterfall. Also, when a tree dies, its biomass is added to the fuel bed. Thus, the fuel loading on each plot reflects the size and species of trees on that plot, is sensitive to temporal changes in forest structure and composition, and is not constrained by an assumed accumulation rate for a particular "forest type."

Fuel loads and fuel moisture act together to define the intensity, severity, size and frequency of fires. First, the year and month of a potential fire event are determined probabilistically from user inputs. Fire intensity is then calculated (Rothermel 1972) for each plot, according to both the fuel load and fuel moisture on that plot. For those plots (if any) where the computed fire intensity exceeds an assumed threshold, fire effects (fuel reduction, crown scorch, tree mortality) are calculated according to known regression equations (Brown *et al.* 1985, Ryan and Reinhardt 1988, Van Wagner 1973). In addition to these direct fire effects, an important influence of fire in the model is its indirect effect on seedling establishment and species composition. Establishment success for some species is constrained by the depth of the forest floor, or duff layer; this layer is substantially reduced when a fire occurs.

The spread of fire is not explicitly simulated; fire does not travel from cell to cell in a contagious fashion (this feature may be included in a future version, however). Even so, the spatial structure of the model allows fire to affect only those plots that are "burnable" (*i.e.*, those plots that are both dry enough and have sufficient fuel loading). From this, fire size can be estimated as the number of burnable plots. Note that at wet sites, potential fire starts may be common, but burnable plots, and therefore actual fires, will be rare. In this way, climatic factors can influence fire frequency.

Capabilities and Domain of Applicability

The benchmarked version of the Sierran model does an adequate job of reproducing the gross distribution of the major tree species with respect to environmental gradients (Figure 3). This version is less satisfactory in reproducing successional trends in species abundance; we are currently working to improve this aspect of the model. We have not yet attempted to apply the model to subalpine forests or sites near treeline, as we are not confident that our model can simulate the extreme physical regimes of these sites. The model also does not apply to low-elevation savannah and chaparral, nor to grass- or shrub-dominated vegetation. While these latter cases are perhaps within the realm of possibility for gap models (Burton and Urban 1989, Coffin and Urban 1993), we feel these are beyond the scope of our Sierran project.

Within the scope of our efforts, both the water balance and fire model seem remarkably robust. The soil moisture model behaves well over an elevation gradient spanning 4000 m relief (Figure 4); the model also responds appropriately to variations in soil properties and topographic exposure. We are currently working to improve the manner in which the model distinguishes topsoil from deep-soil water relations, a concern borne of our interest in the role of topsoil moisture in governing seedling dynamics.

The fire model successfully reproduces empirical relationships among fire frequency, fire magnitude, and fire severity as these are governed by fuel loads and fuel moisture (*e.g.*, Figure 5). The model also reproduces elevational trends in the fire regime as inferred from fire-scar data. One of the model's greatest potentials is its ability to generate a dynamic and detailed "map" of fuels that can be used to interface with a landscape fire spread model such as FARSITE (Finney 1994). In contrast to models such as FARSITE, which rely on homogeneous "average" fuelbed conditions assigned by forest cover type, our fire model can provide information on the spatial heterogeneity of fuels as generated by gap dynamics. Currently, the model only treats dead and down fuels, and so is best suited for simulating low intensity surface fire regimes. We plan to add live fuels to augment the model's ability to simulate other types of fire regimes.

Our preliminary testing of the model in Sequoia National Park, as well as initial tests in other study sites suggests that there are no algorithmic limits to implementing this model throughout the Sierra Nevada and into the Cascade Range. For example, we feel the fire model should be applicable to other forest ecosystems, and we plan to extend the model northward from the Sierra along this latitudinal gradient. Between the Sierran and Pacific Northwestern versions of ZELIG, we currently have preliminary species parameters for all common western conifer tree species. The physical submodels (radiation, water balance) are sufficiently general to span this area as well. Some aspects of the model still require site-specific data for implementation; necessary data include soil depth and texture (which vary at all spatial scales) as well as species silvics and growth rates (which differ regionally in response to genetic variation). We suspect that species data could be collated through a concerted effort, especially focusing on Forest Service data used to calibrate local variants of the FVS model (WESSIN). Data on soils are typically not available at a level of resolution appropriate to our modeling efforts, but some simple assignments might be made from coarse-resolution soils maps such as the STATSGO database. Finally, our modeling effort would require stand-level data for local verification of the simulator--a data requirement not restricted to gap models but required for any model that is to be used for predictive applications.

739

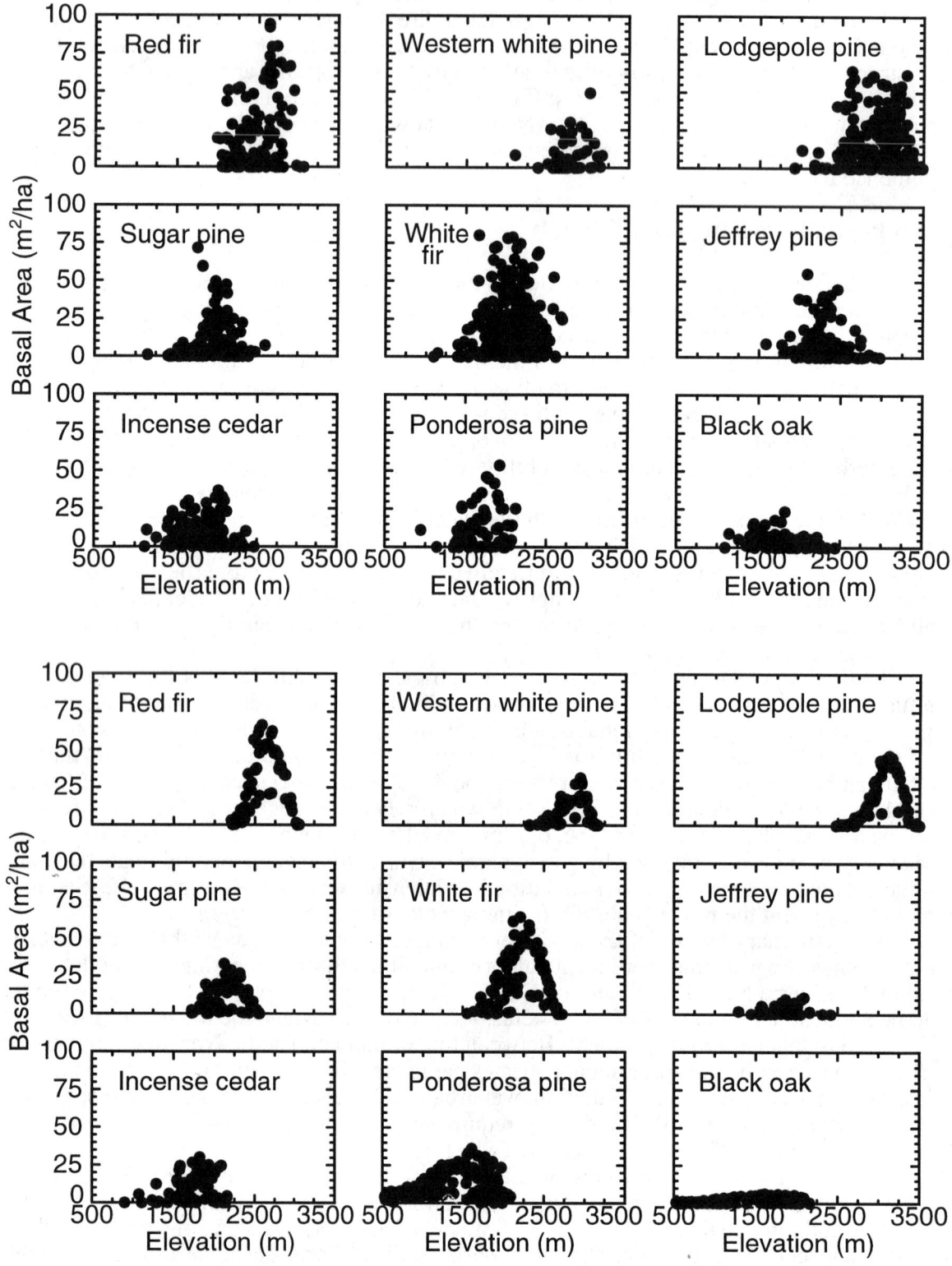

Figure 3. Distributions of common trees species, based on 599 sample quadrats (top panels) and as simulated with the Sierran version of ZELIG (bottom panels; as 300 100-plot grids).

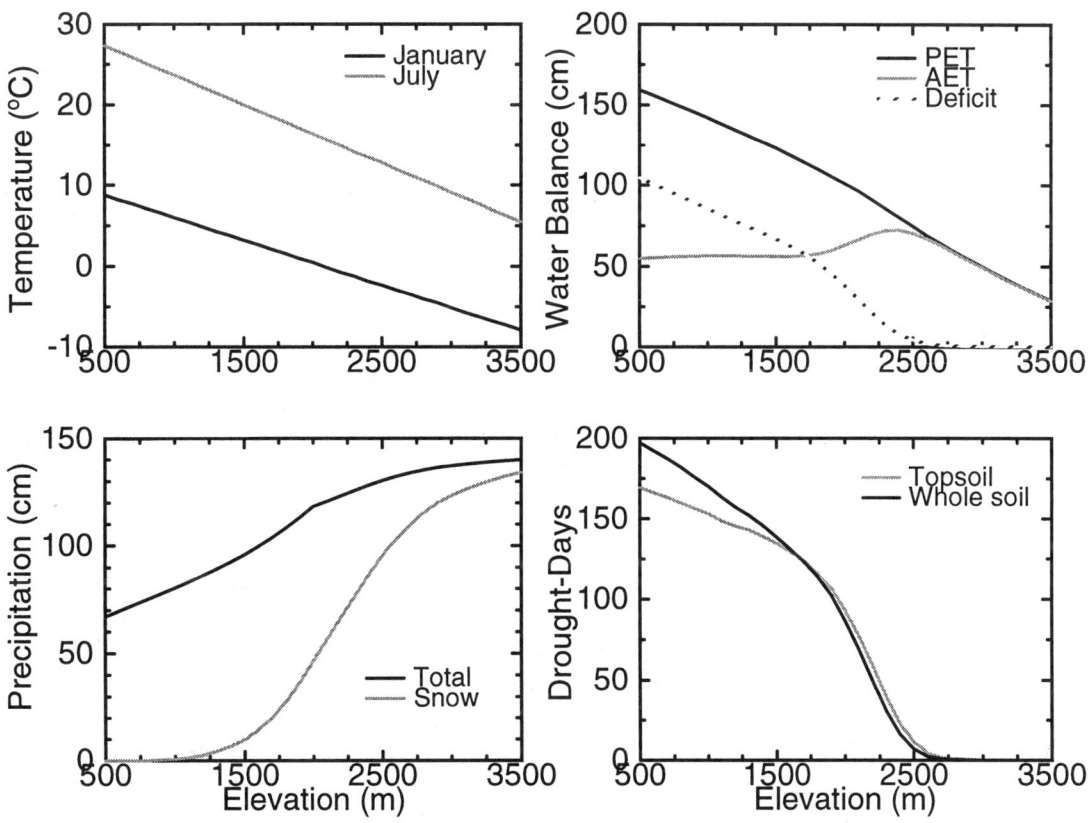

Figure 4. Components of the water balance in Sequoia National Park (39.6°N, 115.6°W, as simulated with the soil moisture model in ZELIG version 3.

Prospectus

The ZELIG family of models was designed to be general while retaining the flexibility for application-specific extensions. An especially pertinent example of this has been the modification of the PNW version of ZELIG for applications concerned with timber management (Garman *et al.* 1992; Hansen *et al.* 1993, 1995). This extension involved incorporating empirical equations to estimate timber volume (ZELIG already includes local taper equations, so this was rather straightforward), and more substantially, adding a user interface that allows extremely sophisticated timber management tactics via an "event scheduler." This interface (Garman *et al.* 1992) was specifically designed to examine alternative silvicultural practices such as green-tree retention and highly selective cuts specified as any combination of diameter limits and species selection. Because ZELIG simulates individual trees on a grid of model plots, this approach is especially appropriate for exploring single-tree or small-group selection strategies. The model is configured to respond to the removal of single trees on a given plot or groups of trees from multiple grid cells (adjacent or otherwise). The PNW version of the model has also been extended to make predictions about wildlife habitat availability, by incorporating statistical (discriminant function) models that assign each grid cell as "habitat" or "not habitat" for a suite of forest birds; this model has been used to examine trade-offs between alternative silvicultural options (retention level and rotation length) and wildlife habitat diversity (Hansen *et al.* 1995).

The ZELIG model also gains flexibility from its modular structure. Thus, if a specific application argues for an alternative model formulation, this new function can simply be substituted into the code. For example, the model now uses allometric relationships that do not

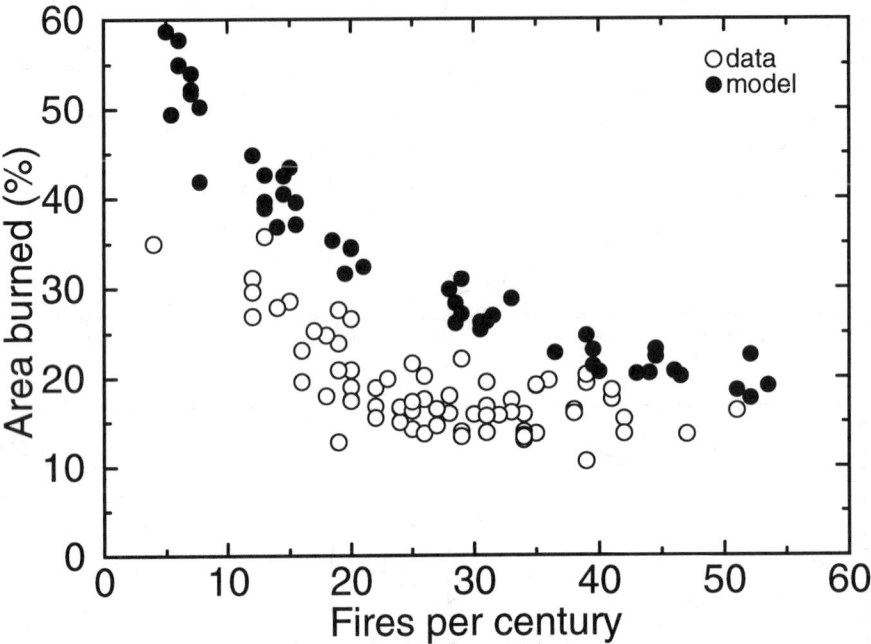

Figure 5. Average area burned related to fire frequency. Open circles represent mean values from fire scar data from five giant dequoia groves; area burned is the percent of sample trees within a site that recorded the same fire (Swetnam 1993). Filled circles are mean values from simulations usiong site descriptions from the fire scar study; area burned is the percent of model plots that had fire intensities greater than 90 kWm^{-1}. Fire magnitude tends to be underestimated by fire scars and overestimated by the logic used in the model (which does not simulate contagion effects), and so the discrepancy between model output and data is as expected.

vary across sites. In particular, trees do not grow taller on more mesic sites (or in thinner stands) as data typically show. Yet it would be a simple change to the code to substitute a function that included soil moisture as an additional argument to influence tree height (see Harrison and Shugart 1991 for an example of site-dependent allometries in a gap model). At a larger scale, Garman *et al.* (1995) have calculated allometries for western tree species, with the allometries adjusted for different regions of each species range (*e.g.,* Coast Range *versus* the Cascades); these allometries are now used in the PNW version of ZELIG (Hansen *et al.* 1995).

The flexibility of the ZELIG model greatly facilitates any efforts to reconcile the gap model with other modeling approaches. For example, the gap model could be parameterized (and perhaps incorporate alternative functions) to make it empirically consistent with FVS models, simply by using the same data to estimate parameters for each model. The two approaches would remain conceptually different, but at least in this case discrepancies in output from the two models could be attributed to these more fundamental differences instead of to data problems.

Conclusion

With respect to the mission of SNEP, one inescapable conclusion emerges: there is no model currently available that meets the needs of SNEP. Because it was designed to address many of the same issues as SNEP faces, the Sierran version of ZELIG clearly would meet many of these needs. Moreover, other extensions to the model concerned with forest management could be extended to Sierran systems, increasing the model's utility even further. But the model is still under testing and it would be premature to attempt to apply it in predictive applications under conditions outside its current domain.

Literature Cited

Aber, J.D., D.B. Botkin, and J.M. Melillo. 1979. Predicting the effects of differing harvest regimes on productivity and yield in northern hardwoods. Can. J. For. Res. 9:10-14.

Bonan, G.B. 1989. A computer model of the solar radiation, soil moisture, and soil thermal regimes in boreal forests. Ecol. Model. 45:275-306.

Botkin, D.B. 1993. Forest dynamics: an ecological model. Oxford University Press, Oxford.

Botkin, D.B., J.F. Janak, and J.R. Wallis. 1972. Some ecological consequences of a computer model of forest growth. J. Ecology 60:849-873.

Brown, J.K., M.A. Marsden, K.C. Ryan, and E.D. Reinhardt. 1985. Predicting duff and woody fuel consumed by prescribed fire in the northern Rocky Mountains. USDA Forest Service Research Paper INT-337.

Daly, C., R.P. Neilson, and D.L. Phillips. 1994. A digital topographic model for distributing precipitation over mountainous terrain. J. Appl. Meteor. 33:140-158.

Burton, P.J., and D.L. Urban. 1989. Enhanced simulation of early secondary forest succession by incorporation of multiple lifeform interaction and dispersal. Studies in Plant Ecology 18:47-49.

Coffin, D.P., and D.L. Urban. 1993. Implications of natural-history traits to ecosystem dynamics: comparison of a grassland and forest. Ecol. Model. 67:147-178.

Cosby, B.J., G.M. Hornberger, R.B. Clapp, and T.R. Ginn. 1984. A statistical analysis of the relationships of soil moisture characteristics to the physical properties of soils. Wat. Resour. Res. 20:682-690.

Finney, M.A. 1994. Modeling the spread and behavior of prescribed natural fires. Pages 138-143 in Proceedings of the 12th Conference on Fire and Forest Meteorology. Jekyll Island, Georgia.

Garman, S.L., A.J. Hansen, D.L. Urban, and P.F. Lee. 1992. Alternative silvicultural practices and diversity of animal habitat in western Oregon: a computer simulation approach. Pages 777-781 in P. Luker (ed.), Proceedings of the 1992 Summer Simulation Conference. Soc. for Computer Simulation, Reno, Nevada.

Garman, S.L., S.A. Acker, J.L. Ohmann, and T.A. Spies. 1995. Asymptotic height- diameter equations for twenty-four tree species in western Oregon. Res. Paper 10. Forest Research Laboratory, Oregon State University, Corvallis, OR.

Hansen, A.J., S.L. Garman, B. Marks, and D.L. Urban. 1993. An approach for managing vertebrate diversity across multiple-use landscapes. Ecol. Applic. 3:481-496.

Hansen, A.J., S.L. Garman, J.F. Weigand, D.L. Urban, W.C. McComb, and M.G. Raphael. 1995. Ecological and economic effects of alternative silvicultural regimes in the Pacific Northwest: a simulation experiment. Ecol. Applic. 5:535-554.

Harrison, E.A. and H.H. Shugart. 1991. Evaluating performance of an Appalachian oak forest dynamics model. Vegetatio 86:1-13.

Keane, R.E., S.F. Arno, and J.K. Brown. 1990. Simulating cumulative fire effects in ponderosa pine/Douglas-fir forests. Ecology 71:189-203.

Kercher, J.R., and M.C. Axelrod. 1984. A process model of fire ecology and succession in mixed-conifer forest. Ecology 65:1725-1742.

Lauenroth, W.K., D.L. Urban, D.P. Coffin, W.J. Parton, H.H. Shugart, T.B. Kirchner, and T.M. Smith. 1993. Modeling vegetation structure-ecosystem process interactions across sites and biomes. Ecol. Model. 67:49-80.

Miller, C., and D.L. Urban. A model of the interactions among climate, fire and forest pattern in the Sierra Nevada. (*in prep.*)

Minore, D. 1979. Comparative autecological characteristics of northwestern tree species --a literature review. GTR PNW-87. PNW Forest and Range Experiment Station, Portland, Oregon.

Nikolov, N.T., and K.F. Zeller. 1992. A solar radiation algorithm for ecosystem dynamic models. Ecol. Model. 61:149-168.

Pastor, J., and W.M. Post. 1988. Response of northern forests to CO_2-induced climate change. Nature 334:55-58.

Rothermel, R.C. 1972 A mathematical model for predicting fire spread in wildland fuels. USDA Forest Service Research Paper INT-115, 40 p.

Running, S.W., R.R. Nemani, and R.D. Hungerford. 1987. Extrapolation of synoptic meteorological data in mountainous terrain and its use for simulating forest evapotranspiration and photosynthesis. Can. J. For. Res. 17:472-483.

Ryan, K.C., and E.D. Reinhardt. 1988. Predicting postfire mortality of seven western conifers. Canadian Journal of Forest Research 18:1291-1297.

Schwarz, P. 1993. A suite of software tools for managing a large parallel programming project. Tech. Rep. 129, Cornell Theory Center, Ithaca, NY.

Schwarz, P.A., D.L. Urban, and D.A. Weinstein. 1994. Partitioning the importance of abiotic constraints and biotic processes in generating vegetation pattern on landscapes. 9th Annual U.S. Landscape Ecology symposium, Tucson.

Shugart, H.H., and D.C. West. 1977. Development of an Appalachian deciduous forest succession model and its application to assessment of the impact of the chestnut blight. J. Environ. Manage. 5:161-170.
Shugart, H.H., and D.C. West. 1980. Forest succession models. BioScience 30:308-313.

Smith, T.M., H.H. Shugart, and D.C. West. 1981. The use of forest simulation models to integrate timber harvest and nongame bird habitat management. Proc. North Amer. Wildl. and Nat. Resource Conf. 46:501-510.

Smith, T.M., and D.L. Urban. 1988. Scale and resolution of forest structural pattern. Vegetatio 74:143-150.

Solomon, A.M. 1986. Transient response of forests to CO_2-induced climate change: simulation experiments in eastern North America. Oecologia 68:567-579.

Stephenson,N.L., and D.J. Parsons. 1993. A research program for predicting the effects of climatic change on the Sierra Nevada. Pages 93-109 in S.D. Veirs, Jr., T.J. Stohlgren and C. Schonewald-Cox (eds.), Proceedings of the Fourth Conference on research in California's national parks. Transactions and Proceedings Series 9. U.S. Department of the Interior, National Park Service.

Swetnam, T.W. 1993. Fire history and climate change in giant sequoia groves. Science 262:885-889.

Urban, D.L., and T.M. Smith. 1989. Microhabitat pattern and the structure of forest bird communities. American Naturalist 133:811-829.

Urban, D.L., G.B. Bonan, T.M. Smith, and H.H. Shugart. 1991. Spatial applications of gap models. For. Ecol. and Manage. 42:95-110.

Urban, D.L., M.E. Harmon, and C.B. Halpern. 1993. Potential response of Pacific Northwestern forests to climatic change: effects of stand age and initial composition. Climatic Change 23:247-266.

Urban, D.L., and H.H. Shugart. 1992. Individual-based models of forest succession. Pages 249-292 in D.C. Glenn-Lewin, R.K. Peet, and T.T. Veblen (eds.), Plant succession: theory and prediction. Chapman and Hall, London.

Urban, D.L., C. Miller, N. Stephenson, and D. Graber. The physical template and biotic mechanisms of gradient response in forests of the Sierra Nevada. (*in prep.*)

Van Wagner, C.E. 1973. Height of crown scorch in forest fires. Canadian Journal of Forest Research. 3:373-378.

Weishampel, J.F., D.L. Urban, H.H. Shugart, and J.B. Smith, Jr. 1992. Semivariograms from a forest transect gap model compared with remotely sensed data. J. Veg. Science 3:521-526.

FRANK W. DAVIS
Institute for Computational Earth System
 Science
University of California
Santa Barbara, California

18

Comparison of Late Seral / Old Growth Maps from SNEP Versus the Sierra Biodiversity Institute

Sierra Nevada Ecosystem Project: Final report to Congress, vol. III, *Assessments, Commissioned Reports, and Background Information*. Davis: University of California, Centers for Water and Wildland Resources, 1996.

745

BACKGROUND

The Sierra Biodiversity Institute (SBI) produced a map of Late Seral/Old Growth Forest in the Sierra Nevada from 1990 Thematic Mapper (TM) satellite data. TM data with a spatial resolution of 0.125 ha were classified into 2 classes (LSOG vs. non-LSOG) based on spectral properties of a large set of sites that were visited in the field and were assigned to LSOG or other land cover classes. Effort focused on mapping late seral conditions in the westside, montane mixed conifer forest type. The final map, which covers both public and private lands, was produced at 1 ha (2.47 ac) resolution.

SNEP's LSOG database consists of maps and data sheets produced based on expert opinion of resource specialists from the USDA Forest Service, the National Park Service, and other state and federal land owners. The database was prepared for public lands only and provides a landscape-level representation of forest composition and structure with an average polygon size of around 1000 ha (2500 ac). Each polygon is assigned a dominant vegetation type and an overall LSOG ranking of 0 to 5 based on the extent and structural features of forest patches within the polygon as well as recent management history. Langley (1995) examined the accuracy of the ratings of forest patches within mixed conifer polygons and found considerable variation in forest structure at the local and patch level.

Because they were prepared at different spatial resolution using different data sources, classification rules, and mapping procedures, SBI and SNEP offer two alternative and somewhat complementary views of the distribution and extent of late seral forest in the Sierra Nevada. The former is spatially consistent and fine-grained but thematically coarse in the sense that it simply classifies each forested grid cell as LSOG or non-LSOG. In contrast, SNEP's LSOG map is somewhat inconsistent in source information and mapping method, spatially coarse-grained, but each map polygon contains richer descriptive data pertaining to forest structure, composition, and management history.

The purpose of this exercise is to compare SBI and SNEP maps of LSOG forest. *The objective is not to assess the statistical accuracy of either product, nor to endorse one or the other map.* Rather, it is simply to document differences in mapped LSOG area, illustrate spatial patterns of agreement or disagreement between the maps, and to provide possible explanations for those patterns.

Study Area and Methods

SBI and SNEP LSOG maps were compared over the national forests and national parks of the western slopes of the Sierra Nevada and the Lake Tahoe Basin. Inyo, Toiyabe, and Modoc National Forests were not included.

For the analysis, we generated 1 ha grids of SNEP forest type and LSOG rank, and overlaid those grids with the SGI map to create 3-way contingency tables of type, rank, and SBI class. Input data from SNEP included seventeen land cover types, but only six montane conifer forest types were considered in subsequent data analyses: Jeffrey Pine, Upper Montane Red Fir, Montane Mixed Conifer, White Fir, and Eastside Pine/Pine-Fir.

The total area of LSOG polygons assigned to these types is 2,459,121 ha (table 1). Upper Montane Red Fir and Montane Mixed Conifer types comprise 88% of this area (table 1).

The study area was divided into northern and southern sectors in order to test for any systematic effects related to latitudinal gradients in environmental factors, forest structure and composition, or land management. The northern sector included the Eldorado, Tahoe, Plumas, and a portion of the Lassen National Forests, as well as the Lake Tahoe Basin. The southern sector included the Stanislaus, Sierra, and Sequoia National Forests as well as Yosemite and Sequoia/Kings Canyon National Parks. The Jeffrey Pine type is distributed mainly in the southern sector, and White Fir and Eastside Pine types are predominantly in the northern sector. Red Fir and Mixed Conifer types are well represented in both sectors (table 1).

Results

Jeffrey Pine Forest

Of 130,000 ha in this type, 7.7% was ranked by SNEP as Rank 4 or 5, and 58% as Rank 3. Roughly 10% of SBI cells in this type were classified as LSOG. There is very low association of SNEP polygon rank and SBI LSOG status: for example, only 16% of the area in Rank 3 or Rank 4 polygons is also mapped as LSOG by SBI (Table 2). This may be due in part to the low density and crown cover of many late successional Jeffrey Pine stands on thin soils of ridges and outcrops. Although this condition generally led to lower ratings by the SNEP mapping team, it is more likely that open stands with large trees would be given a high ranking by SNEP than by SBI, because such stands would be spectrally unlike the denser and more closed stands that were used by SBI to train their spectral classifier.

Upper Montane Red Fir Forest

This type is roughly equally distributed between northern and southern sectors and totals 624,700 ha. In the north, 15% of the area in this type was assigned by SNEP a rank of 4 or 5, compared to 35% in the south. SBI indicates a similar pattern, with 14% of the area of the type in the north classified as LSOG versus 23% in the south. The fraction of polygon classified as LSOG by SBI is positively correlated with SNEP's LSOG rank, but the association appears stronger in the north than the south (table 2). Over the entire region, the fraction of SBI pixels is around 10% for rank 1 and rank 2 polygons, and around 30% for higher ranking polygons. Given the closed nature of both mid and late seral stands of Red fir, one might predict that it would be difficult to spectrally discriminate among the higher ranks using TM data. There is no obvious explanation for the better association of SBI and SNEP ratings in the northern Sierra. Perhaps it is related to management history and the stronger contrast among stands of different rank on national forests compared to those on national park lands, or to the more open structure of Red fir stands in the southern Sierra.

Montane Mixed Conifer Forest

This forest type was mapped over more than 1.5 million hectares. In the north, 13% of the area was assigned to rank 4 or rank 5, compared to 16% of the area in the south. Twenty percent of the total area was classified by SBI as LSOG. Overall, the fraction of area in SBI LSOG increases steadily as SNEP LSOG rank increases (table 2, figure 1). For example, less than 3% of the area in rank 1 polygons is classified as SBI LSOG compared to 61% in rank 5. This relationship is similar in both northern and southern sectors (table 2). The association of SBI LSOG and SNEP rank is much stronger for this widespread type than any other forest types, as one would predict given that SBI's mapping effort concentrated specifically on Sierran Mixed Conifer Forest. SNEP's mapping and classification approach also tended to emphasize this forest type.

Close to one million hectares or nearly two-thirds of the area of Montane Mixed Conifer type was rated by SNEP as rank 2 or 3. Thus based on absolute area, considerably more SBI LSOG occurs in lower ranking SNEP polygons than in higher ranking polygons. Specifically, SBI classified 168,236 ha within SNEP rank 2 and rank 3 polygons as LSOG, compared to 114,136 ha in rank 4 and rank 5 polygons. This discrepancy could be related to SBI's finer resolution mapping, which would be more likely to detect small patches of late seral forest in landscapes of predominantly early or mid-seral conditions. The spatial pattern of SNEP rank and SBI class suggests that this is often the case but that there are also large contiguous areas where the mapping systems disagree (figure 2).

White Fir Forest

Nearly all of the mapped extent of this type occurs in the northern sector (table 1). Seventy percent of the area was rated by SNEP as rank 2 or 3, compared to 11% in rank 4 or 5. SBI also classified 11% of the area as LSOG, but there is little relationship between SBI class and SNEP rank for this type. As with the Upper Montane Red Fire Forest Type, the closed nature of regenerating stands of this type make it difficult to spectrally discriminate seral stages.

Eastside Pine/White Fir-Pine Forest

Of the nearly 122,000 ha mapped to this type, only 8% of the areas was rated by SNEP as rank 4 or rank 5, a number quite close to the 9% classified by SBI as LSOG. The relationship between SNEP rank and SBI class is not strong, with less than 3% of the area in polygons of rank 1 or 2 classified is LSOG, compared to 14% for rank 4 and 7% for rank 5.

General Observations

If one classifies SNEP polygons or rank 4 and 5 as areas of late seral/old growth conditions, then one obtains quite comparable estimates of LSOG area by forest type using SBI versus SNEP data. However, there is only modest association between the two representations in the actual *location* of LSOG conditions. Association is highest for the Montane Mixed Conifer Type, such that one could predict with fair success the rank of the SNEP polygon based on the proportion of the polygon mapped by SBI as LSOG forest. Association between SNEP and SBI representations of LSOG distribution is relatively low for the remaining types. Spatial patterns of disagreement indicate both local and landscape scale differences between the two representations. With the exception of Upper Montane Red Fir Forest, regional differences in the relationship between SNEP and SBI maps are not pronounced.

There are many possible explanations for the observed low to moderate degree of association between SBI and SNEP. Perhaps most importantly, the comparison points out that LSOG forests in the Sierra Nevada are not easy to define or map. Structural and compositional traits of LSOG stands vary widely among community types and environments. The spatial pattern of Sierran LSOG forest is complex and often manifested as a very fine scale mosaic pattern, making estimates of LSOG location and extent highly sensitive to the spatial resolution of the image data and/or the minimum mapping unit used to portray LSOG conditions. From a methodological perspective, the two overriding differences between the SBI and SNEP LSOG maps appear to be the large difference in the spatial resolution of mapping and SBI's use of TM imagery versus SNEP's use of air photos and expert opinion.

751

Tables

Table 1. Mapped extent of six major forest types on the western slopes of the Sierra Nevada, as classified and mapped by SNEP's LSOG assessment team. The fractional distribution of the types among subregions and among SBI's mapped LSOG (SBI=1) and non-LSOG (SBI=0) is also tabulated. For example, of the total area mapped by SNEP as Montane mixed conifer, 56.51% falls in the northern sector of the study region. Over the entire region, 19.01% of the area mapped by SNEP as Montane mixed conifer was classified by SBI as LSOG (12.71% + 7.30%).

Table 2. Relationship between SNEP LSOG rank and SBI LSOG as a function of forest type and region. Region 1 is the northern sector and Region 2 the southern sector. Cell values are the percent of area classified by SBI as LSOG for each combination of region, forest type, and LSOG rank. For example, 33.2% of the area in the northern Sierra that was mapped by SNEP as Rank 3 Montane mixed conifer was classified by SBI as LSOG. The final column is the percent of total area of the type in each region that was classified by SBI as LSOG.

TABLE 1

	NORTH				SOUTH				Total Area (ha)	Grand Total
	Area (ha)	$SBI=0$	$SBI=1$	Subtotal	Area (ha)	$SBI=0$	$SBI=1$	Subtotal		
Jeffrey Pine	6686	4.29%	0.87%	5.15%	123033	84.75%	10.10%	94.85%	129719	100.00%
Upper Montane Red Fir	299682	41.24%	6.73%	47.97%	325021	39.84%	12.18%	52.03%	624703	100.00%
Montane Mixed Conifer	867855	43.80%	12.71%	56.51%	667799	36.18%	7.30%	43.49%	1535654	100.00%
White Fir	42554	82.24%	8.00%	90.24%	4601	8.69%	1.07%	9.76%	47155	100.00%
Eastside White Fir/Fir-Pine	117979	90.20%	6.59%	96.79%	3911	3.09%	0.11%	3.21%	121890	100.00%
Total									2459121	

753

TABLE 2

Type	Region	SNEP LSOG RANK						ALL
		0	1	2	3	4	5	
Jeffrey Pine	1	16.4%	25.0%		16.6%	19.9%	16.8%	17%
	2	0.0%	2.0%	10.8%	16.5%	16.7%		10.6%
	All	16.4%	2.0%	10.8%	16.5%	16.9%		11.0%
Upper Montane Red Fir	1		5.4%	8.6%	19.6%	20.1%	54.5%	14.0%
	2		11.0%	10.0%	28.4%	38.1%	25.4%	23.4%
	All		8.8%	9.1%	24.0%	31.4%	28.1%	18.9%
Montane Mixed Conifer	1	4.9%	8.7%	13.3%	33.2%	49.2%	62.1%	22.5%
	2	0.5%	1.0%	5.9%	20.7%	48.0%	61.2%	16.8%
	All	2.8%	5.0%	10.6%	27.3%	48.7%	61.4%	20.0%
White Fir	1	19.7%	3.5%	2.7%	16.6%	6.2%		8.9%
	2	6.1%			16.9%		19.8%	11.0%
	All	19.7%	4.5%	2.7%	16.6%	6.2%	19.8%	9.1%
Eastside Pine/Pine-Fir	1		2.8%	1.3%	10.5%	14.1%	13.8%	6.8%
	2		0.0%				6.8%	3.6%
	All		2.6%	1.3%	10.5%	14.1%	7.3%	6.7%

754

Figures

Figure 1. Barplot showing the relative amount of Montane mixed conifer forest type as a function of SNEP rank and SBI LSOG.The height of the each bar is proportional to the area in that LSOG rank. The dark shaded portion of the bar indicates the fraction of that SNEP rank that was classified by SBI as LSOG. Thus, most Montane mixed conifer was assigned a rank of 2 or 3. The proportion of area classified by SBI as LSOG increases steadily with rank. However, the absolute area in SBI LSOG in ranks 2 and 3 exceeds that in ranks 4 and 5.

Figure 2. Spatial patterns of co-occurence of SNEP forest ranking and SBI LSOG for Eldorado, Stanislaus, and Tahoe National Forests.

Figure 1

Sheet1 Chart 1

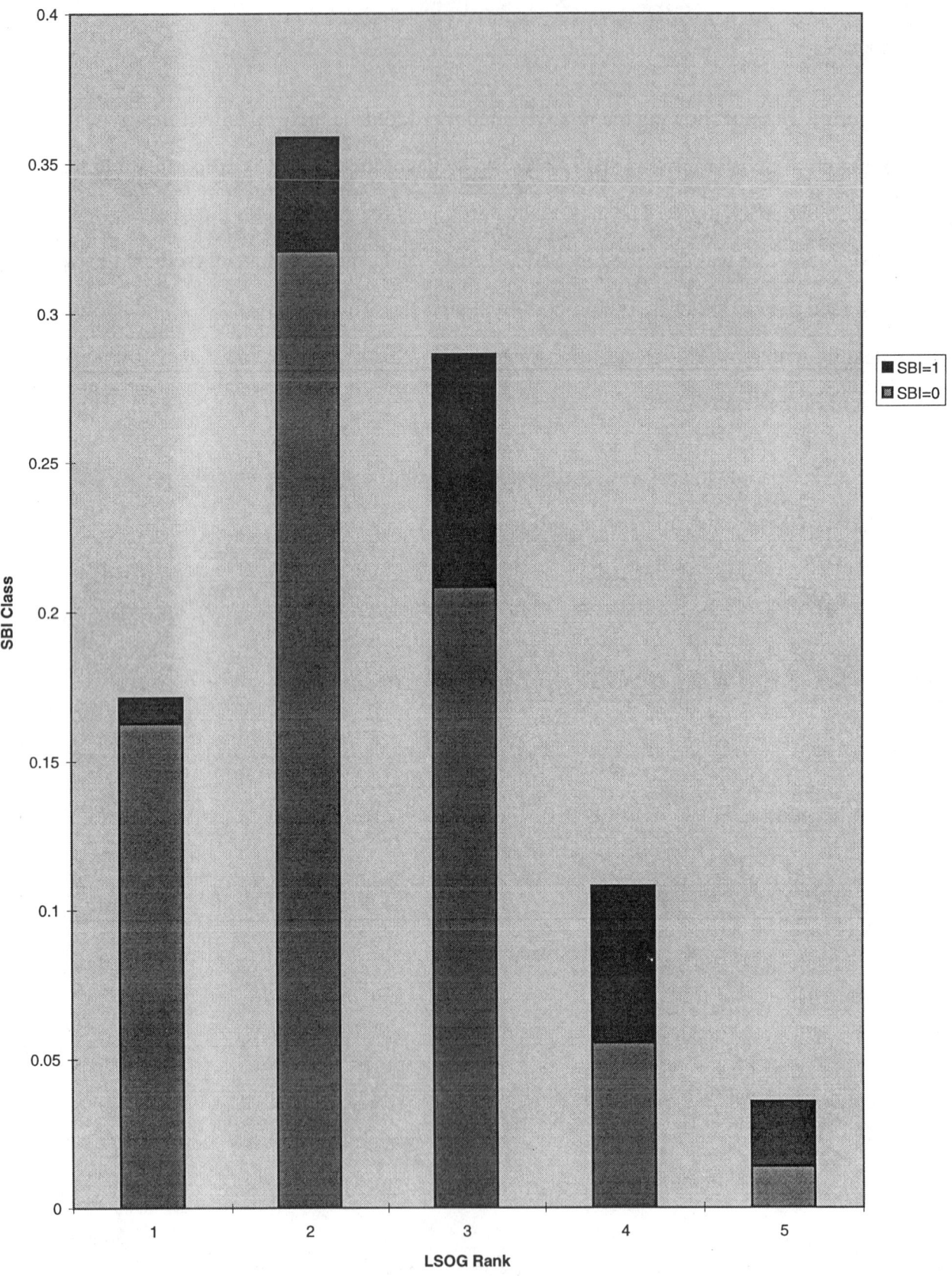

756

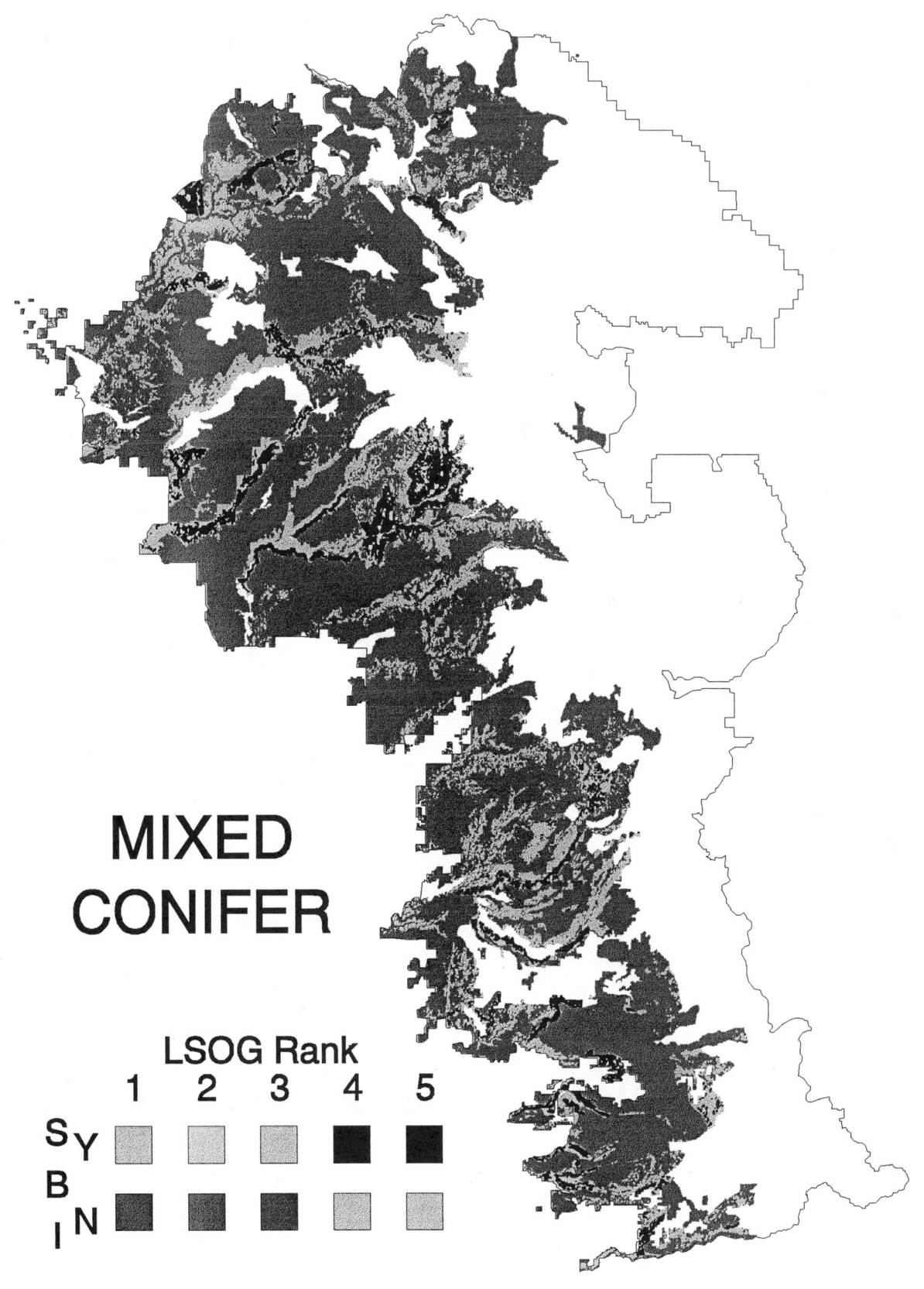

MIXED
CONIFER

LSOG Rank

	1	2	3	4	5
S Y					
B N					
I					

DAVID SAPSIS
California Department of Forestry and Fire
  Protection
Fire and Resource Assessment Project
Sacramento, California

BERNI BAHRO
U.S. Forest Service
El Dorado National Forest
Placerville, California

JAMES SPERO
California Department of Forestry and Fire
  Protection
Fire and Resource Assessment Project
Sacramento, California

JOHN GABRIEL
Sierra Nevada Ecosystem Project GIS
  Laboratory
University of California
Davis, California

RUSSELL JONES
Sierra Nevada Ecosystem Project GIS
  Laboratory
University of California
Davis, California

GREGORY GREENWOOD
California Department of Forestry and Fire
  Protection
Fire and Resource Assessment Project
Sacramento, California

19

An Assessment of Current Risks, Fuels, and Potential Fire Behavior in the Sierra Nevada

Sierra Nevada Ecosystem Project: Final report to Congress, vol. III, Assessments, Commissioned Reports, and Background Information. Davis: University of California, Centers for Water and Wildland Resources, 1996.

759

ABSTRACT

In this paper we examine the relative occurrence of large fires (risk), extent and pattern of fuel characteristics, and associated extreme fire behavior potential that currently exists for the Sierra Nevada Ecosystem core study area. The pattern of large fires (greater than 300 acres) was analyzed based on the spatial features of fuel type, population density, and weather zone. All three of these factors were found to be important in determining the size and likelihood of large fires. Risk as measured by the frequency, or return interval, of fires greater than 300 acres shows significant variation across the study area. Expected return intervals for such large fires range from greater than 10,000 years (i.e., extremely low risk) in high elevation, fuel discontinuous areas, to between 10 and 150 years in grass/brush fuel complexes coincident with zones of high ignitions, and long fire weather seasons. Fuels were mapped based on vegetation classifications for the region, and indicate a large percentage of the study area as having relatively high loads of surface fuels, particularly in the low- to mid-elevation western edge of the study area. Most of the shrub, pine/oak/grass, and pine/mixed conifer zones represent fuels with high associated hazard. This finding is supported by an analysis of potential fire behavior under severe fire weather. We found that for the SNEP area east of Sacramento, over half of the fuel covered landscape would support flame lengths in excess of 8 feet when burned under adverse conditions. This level of extreme fire behavior carries with it difficulty of control and likely undesirable effects on ecological and social resources in the Sierra.

INTRODUCTION

Much of the concerns regarding impending threats to the social and biological integrity of the Sierra Nevada are focused on fire and its capacity to do damage. In this light, an assessment of current conditions regarding fire risks, fuels, and hazard associated with extreme fire behavior are requisite to understanding why and where fire related problems exist in the Sierra. That is, to understand how fire might impact elements in Sierran ecosystems, we must understand where fires can be expected to occur, and should they occur how they might be expected to behave. In this paper we provide a spatial analysis of the probability of large fire occurrence (risk), fuel conditions, and how these fuels translate to hazard when burning under extreme environmental conditions likely to support large fires. In addition to providing base inputs into a larger regional scenario model (Sessions et al. 1996), these maps have inherent value as stand-alone products: explicit spatial delineation of current extent and magnitude of fire risk and hazard in the Sierras.

RISK

This procedure produces a map of the SNEP study area that shows the expected annual frequency of large (300+ acres) fires on a grid made up of 10 acre cells. Fire frequency is based upon ignition history, ratio of large fires to ignitions, and three point estimates of fire size (mean fire size) from the distribution of fire sizes in nine strata. Strata are based on life form, weather zone, and population density class.

Data

The CDF Strategic Planning Program provided State and National Forest fire point data to the SNEP team, which added additional fire point locations based on data provided by the National Park Service. The combined GIS fire point coverage has the following attributes:

1. Life form (Grass, Brush, Timber, Red Fir)
2. Weather Zone (1-5)
3. Population density class (Low, Medium, High)
4. Size of fire
5. Year of fire

Life Form - Fire behavior conditions can be markedly different in grass, brush, timber and Red Fir. Fires spread fastest in grass fuels because of the high surface to volume ratios. In brush, fires are hotter and may be more difficult to attack directly. Timber fires have the potential for crown fire conflagrations that can require multi-agency suppression efforts. Fire behavior at higher elevations may be less severe, such as in the Red Fir belt.

Weather Zone - Along with fuels, weather is a key driving factor in large fires. The SNEP study area includes five National Weather Service fire weather zones. Regional climatology, such as mean temperature, average relative humidity in summer, and wind patterns could affect the rate of large fires.

Population Density - Intermixed areas of urbanization and wildland could affect the rate at which large fires occur, and their ultimate extent. To some degree, fuel continuity is broken by the presence of roads and ornamental vegetation, affording more tactical advantages for fire suppression forces. Roads also provide accessibility for ground fire suppression resources. Detection and response can be rapid, with greater proximity to local suppression. In contrast, lower population density in the Sierra often means relatively remote locations, difficult terrain, limited road access, and more topographically diverse landscapes (e.g., steeper slopes).

The fire point data set is compiled from the following sources:

Source:	Period
CDF (Emergency Activity Reporting System)	1981-93
USFS (National Interagency Fire Management Integrated Database)	1970-93
NPS (converted from perimeter data)	SEKI: 1921-93
	YOSE: 1931-93

The combined data used in this analysis consists of 39,986 fire records from the period 1981-93. Of these fire records, 303 (0.76%) are large, which we defined for the purposes of the analysis as at least 300 acres in size. The CDF fire data records are origin points of vegetation fires geographically located as section (public land survey) centroids. The USFS data is similar, but after 1985 is referenced by latitude and longitude. For USFS and CDF data, any overlapping points (falling in the exact same location, i.e., section centroids) were redistributed randomly over the section. These data were used to generate a stratified set of landscape elements based on their occurrence of fires at least 300 acres in size (Table 1).

Table 1. Strata definitions for SNEP large fire analysis.

Stratum	Lifeform	Population	Wx_Zone	Fires_all	Fires_big	p_big
1	Grass/Brush	Low	North	4,829	39	0.008076
2	Grass/Brush	Not Low	North	2,191	10	0.004564
3	Grass/Brush	Low	South	2,808	66	0.023504
4	Grass/Brush	Not Low	South	760	14	0.018421
5	Timber	Low	North	13,321	64	0.004804
6	Timber	Not Low	North	7,299	23	0.003151
7	Timber	Low	South	5,433	74	0.01362
8	Timber	Not Low	South	1,407	7	0.004975
9	Red Fir	Low	South	937	6	0.006403

To derive Table 1, we looked at the percentage of large fires within 1) life forms; 2) population density classes; and 3) weather zones (Table 2).

Table 2. Fire size data by life form, population, and weather zone.

	Fires_all	Fires_big	p_big
Life Form			
Grass	4,808	45	0.94
Brush	5,780	84	1.45
Timber	27,251	166	0.61
Red Fir	1,938	6	0.31
Population			
Low	28,306	249	0.88
Medium	5,743	25	0.44
High	5,937	29	0.49
Wx_Zone			
Redding	8,015	59	0.74
Reno	4,756	23	0.48
Riverside	246	4	1.63
Sac	15,870	54	0.34
Fresno	11,099	163	1.47

Life Form (vegetation): We combined the grass and brush fire data, which have large relatively high percentages of large to total fires (0.94% and 1.45%), when compared to either Timber (0.61%) or Red Fir (0.31%). We did not combine the Timber and Red Fir because the percentages in Red Fir appear substantially lower than in Timber.

The vegetation data used to define Life Form follows:

National Parks: Vegetation coverage themes from each National Park (USDI Park Service records)

State Lands: Fire Management Analysis Zone (FMAZ) National Fire Danger Rating System fuel model (CDF records)

USFS R-5:   Determined from fuel model associated with each fire or from vegetation code ("org_cover") associated with each fire. Red Fir codes determined by overlay with USDA Forest Service vegetation strata information. (USFS Region 5 Remote Sensing Laboratory records).

Records that were not coded from the above information were overlayed on the statewide CALVEG database (about 7,400 out of 59,000+ records).

Population: Population density was determined by the FMAZ coverage, and is a rough approximation of the degree of structure protection effort needed during fire suppression. All

763

USFS population density was coded as Low. Population density classes collapse into two categories based on observations that the proportion of large fires in low population density (0.88%) is almost twice the proportion in high population density (0.45%) or medium population density (0.49%).

Weather: Weather Zone stratification was determined from National Weather Service Fire Weather Zones. We combined the Riverside and Fresno weather zones, in which the rate of large fires is clearly greater, and the remaining weather zones (Redding, Reno and Sacramento) in which the rate of large fires is much less. The more southerly located zones of Riverside and Fresno may be reflecting relatively drier and/or windier conditions.

Analysis

We calculated the average of the lowest 75%, middle 20% and upper 5% of fire sizes in each stratum. These averages can be thought of as having probabilities of .75, .2 and .05, respectively. These probabilities are used to determine the average annual frequency of large fires in each Section. The expected annual frequency for a large fire is calculated as the product of:

- the annual rate of ignition (total fires/year)
- the proportion of large fires (large fires/total fires)
- fire size probability (.75, .20, .05)

For example, if the rate of ignition is 0.5, the fire is in Stratum 1, and we want to know the rate of large fires for fires in the bottom 75% of the fire size distribution:

rate (fires)	*times*	*p(large)*	*times*	*p(window size)*	*equals*	*rate(879 acre fire)*
0.5	*	.008076	*	.75	=	.003028

Table 3 shows the data passed to the SNEP Geographic Information System. Listed to the right of each stratum number is the proportion, or probability, that a fire will be at least 300 acres in size, followed by the average fire size of the smallest 75%, middle 20% and top 5% of fire sizes in the data which comprise each stratum.

In the example, a large fire of 879 acres (Table 3 Stratum 1-next page) would have an annual frequency of about .003.

Expected Frequency of Large Fires

The data in Table 3 were used to develop a cumulative large fire probability grid. There are three "windows" (areas of analysis) for each of the 9 strata, for a total of 27 windows. For each stratum, we centered three moving windows (corresponding to the three large fire sizes) on each 10 acre cell, allocating to each cell within the windows the product of rate of ignition for the section, ratio of large fire to ignitions for the stratum associated with the section, and probability associated with the window (.75, .2, .05). When this procedure was completed for all nine strata,

Table 3. Probability and window size for large fire spatial analysis.

		p and Window Size (acres)		
Stratum	p(big)	p_size=0.75	p_size=0.2	p_size=0.05
1	0.008076	879	8,227	89,419
2	0.004564	659	32,780	6,400
3	0.023504	652	2,108	9,920
4	0.018421	533	5,444	25,932
5	0.004804	1,108	7,978	39,707
6	0.003151	882	9,087	18,000
7	0.01362	957	4,721	14,608
8	0.004975	420	588	630
9	0.006403	420	618	704

the probabilities were summed for each cell. Therefore, each cell location on the grid represents the summation of probabilities associated with at least 3, and as many as all 27 windows (Vol 1 Chapter 8). This figure presents the inverse of these occurrences, corresponding to the estimated fire return interval (in years) that correspond to these annual frequencies. The data are presented this way because it is easier to interpret relative large fire occurrence based on intervals as opposed to fractional rates on a per year basis.

The fire return intervals for each cell were grouped into six classes, ranging from an average of 10 to 150 years in areas of highest risk, to less greater than 10,000 years in areas of lowest risk (Figure 1). Much of the front country and Sierra Foothills falls into the highest risk category, while high elevation areas of sparse, discontinuous fuels show significantly lower rates of large fire incidence. Areas where the fuels are dominated by grasses and brush tended to have a higher incidence of large fires. An area of concentrated large fire risk is evident in the area to the Northeast of Sacramento, where all elements used in the analysis (fuel type, weather zone, and population density) tended to support large fire occurrence.

Discussion

The relatively short time span of the underlying data (13 years) has both advantages and drawbacks. On the plus side, these data are perhaps more reliable for describing current and near term future risk. The downside is that a paucity of fire incidence over substantial areas in the data period could translate into unreasonably low fire frequency estimates for these areas. One should assume that actual fire frequency in areas where fires were scarce in the data period may be higher than the map indicates. Additionally, the reader is cautioned in interpreting the classification of specific areas on the map. In that the model used to estimate the fire frequency is based on

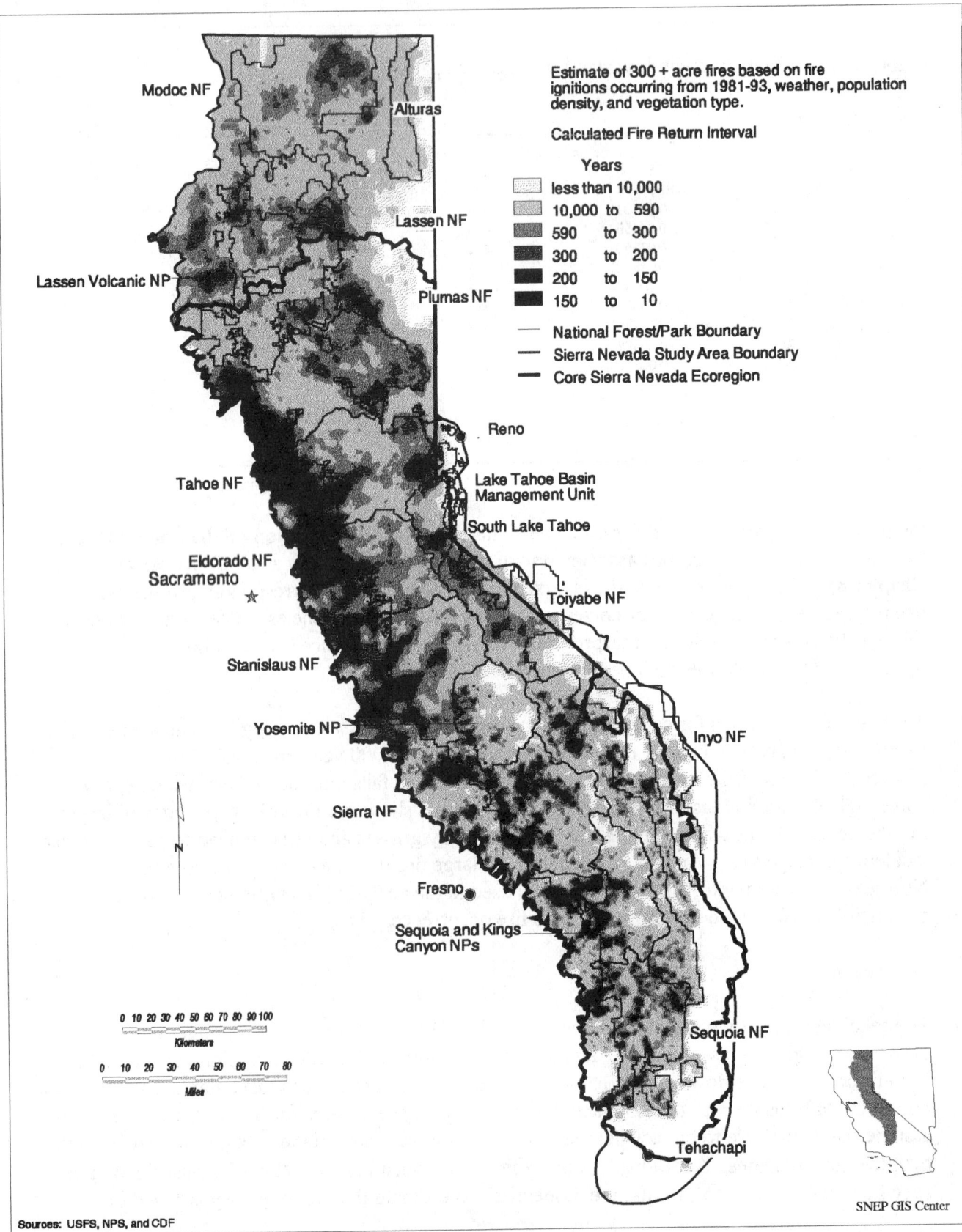

Estimate of 300 + acre fires based on fire
ignitions occurring from 1981-93, weather, population
density, and vegetation type.

Calculated Fire Return Interval

Years

	less than 10,000
	10,000 to 590
	590 to 300
	300 to 200
	200 to 150
	150 to 10

—— National Forest/Park Boundary
—— Sierra Nevada Study Area Boundary
—— Core Sierra Nevada Ecoregion

Modoc NF

Alturas

Lassen NF

Lassen Volcanic NP

Plumas NF

Reno

Tahoe NF

Lake Tahoe Basin
Management Unit

South Lake Tahoe

Eldorado NF
Sacramento

Toiyabe NF

Stanislaus NF

Yosemite NP

Inyo NF

Sierra NF

Fresno

Sequoia and Kings
Canyon NPs

Sequoia NF

Tehachapi

N

0 10 20 30 40 50 60 70 80 90 100
Kilometers

0 10 20 30 40 50 60 70 80
Miles

SNEP GIS Center

Sources: USFS, NPS, and CDF

766

combined strata definitions, actual fire frequency for a particular area may be different than actual fire frequency due to averaging from other areas of like strata. However, we are confident that the relative frequency and regional trends evinced by the map are a reflection of actual likelihood of large fire, and are hence useful information in interpreting risk across the study area.

As is evident from the map, areas at the western fringe of the study area have higher probabilities of large fire. These areas correspond to areas of greater fine fuel concentration, more open stands and hence greater wind penetration to the surface, and higher levels of population resulting in greater sources of ignition. The low lying areas also have longer fire seasons where environmental conditions conducive to fire spread persist for longer periods than the higher elevation areas of the Sierra Nevada. These findings are similar to those of McKelvey and Busse (1996) who found a very strong influence of elevation on 20th Century fire occurrence for National Forest lands. Although the data used to generate this map was limited in temporal extent, it is evident that large fires are prevalent on lower areas and river corridors where a large influence of human use is evident. Further, open stands of grass and brush likely influence early fire progression, thus limiting the effectiveness of initial attack efforts, and contribute to the incidence of relatively large fires. The north-south relationship for fire weather needs further exploration, but given the relative prevalence of high fire danger weather throughout the state during summer months, it appears that fire risk is predominantly a function of interactions between fuel and ignition factors, all of which tend to increase as one moves down slope along the western front of the range.

FUELS

Fuels provide the energy source for fire, and characteristics associated with fuels strongly influence fire risk and behavior. Any classification of fuels implicitly assumes to characterize material as it burns (Hornby 1935). Thus, fuel models are really only interpretable when coupled with a fire behavior model that generates predictions of fire behavior using information about those fuels. As vegetation provides the basis for fuels, it is not surprising that fuel characteristics are often well correlated with vegetation composition and structure. A characterization of fuels in the SNEP study area not only provides the basis for estimating potential fire behavior under conditions favorable for large fires to occur, but also in conjunction with other vegetation data allow for refinement of potential vegetation/fuel modifications designed to reduce fire hazard.

To estimate fire behavior we must have information on three sets of variables: fuels, weather, and topography (Rothermel 1983). In the sense that we wanted to generate site-specific estimates of fire behavior, we needed fuel models that correspond with the use BEHAVE, the standardized model for site-specific fire behavior prediction in the United States (Andrews 1986). Consequently, the first step in generating fire hazard information is to define the kinds of fuel models represented in the Sierra Nevada. Although a group of 13 standard fuel models has been established to describe many fuel complexes common throughout North America (Anderson 1982), the BEHAVE program allows the user to develop custom models to better represent actual fuel conditions than when using only the standard models (Burgan and Rothermel 1984).

We used a combination of standard and custom models to describe the fuels in the Sierra Nevada (Table 4). A complete description of fuel characteristics associated with these models can be found in Appendix A. It should be noted that in as much as fuel models are really only relevant in how they describe a system's capacity to burn, they consequently may appear to be fundamentally different that what they are describing. What is important to remember is that it is the reality of the output of the fire behavior prediction system that is important, whereby the fuel model, weather information, and topography interact to produce estimates of rates of spread, flame length, etc. (Rothermel 1983).

Table 4. Descriptions of fuel models used in classifying lands in the Sierra Nevada Ecosystem Project (SNEP) core study area.

FUEL MODEL #	DESCRIPTION
1	SHORT GRASS; common open grassland and woodlands.
2	TIMBER/GRASS Pine/, juniper and sagebrush woodlands.
4	CHAPARRAL; older decadent chamise/sclerophylous shrubs.
5	BRUSH; low shrubs and soft chaparral
6	DORMANT BRUSH; intermediate montane shrubs
8	TIMBER LITTER-- LIGHT; hardwoods, lodgepole pine, red fir
9	TIMBER LITTER -- MODERATE; dense white fir; underburned mixed conifer
10	TIMBER LITTER -- HEAVY; pine/mixed conifer with understory
12	SLASH--MODERATE; pine/mixed conifer with intermediate activity fuels
13	SLASH --HEAVY; pine/mixed conifer with very high loads of activity fuels
14	BURNED/PLANTATION; recently burned areas or immature plantations
16	CUSTOM PINE/MIXED CONIFER; litter with understory and activity fuels
18	CUSTOM SPARSE FIR; open jeffrey pine and true fir
20	CUSTOM RED FIR; Dense red fir with limited activity fuels
23	CUSTOM DENSE FIR; Dense mixed conifer/fir with understory and activity fuels
26	CUSTOM SIERRAN CHAPARRAL; intermediate between model 4 and 6.

Two key assumptions are important to recognize in this fuel modeling approach. One is that fire behavior related to a given fuel type (as represented by a fuel model) is actually a distribution of outputs based on the range of environmental conditions that the fuel may be exposed to while burning. A given fuel model will produce a wide range fire behavior outputs when modeled using the natural variation in fuel moistures, windspeeds, etc. The variation in accuracy of a fuel model across this distribution can lead to poor predictions when fuels are mapped for assessment under conditions that are not assumed by the mapper, or when the mapper is forced to choose from an alternative set of fuel models (Salazar 1987). Implicit in the fuel model mapping in this effort was the need to characterize fire behavior under a range of conditions -- from average fire weather where most ignitions take place, to extreme weather conditions under which large damaging fires are most likely to occur (Srauss et al. 1989).

We consequently employed a two-stage fuel modeling approach, where fuels were classified over the entire SNEP region assuming average weather conditions and using standard fuel models; and a second, more refined fuel modeling approach to reflect expectant fire behavior under extreme conditions. As most fires occur under the former, while most acres are burned under the latter conditions, both strategies have merit based on what element of the fire environment is at issue. The regional fuel map and the extreme fire behavior map both support an assessment of fire hazard in the Sierra Nevada where fuels form the basis of this hazard. Additionally, as fuels are the element in the fire environment most under the capacity for mitigation by management activities, these hazard maps indicate where this management might best be directed. However, in that land managers are really concerned with the effects of fire, and not the fire itself *per se*, hazard is only one part of a set of information required to make decisions on managing the land for desirable outcomes.

The second key assumption, related to the first, is that these fuel models only reflect surface fuels, and consequently only are relevant in their effect on surface fire spread. Although there are good relationships established between surface fire and propagation of crown fire in forested systems (Van Wagner 1977 and 1993, Alexander 1988), the fuel models themselves say nothing about crown fuels/fire, despite this being an important spread mechanism under severe conditions. This assumption underscores the need to understand what kinds of conditions, as well as what kinds of fire behavior indices are of concern in any analysis of fire hazard. As the estimates of fire behavior under extreme conditions carry with them expectations for initiation of crowning and spotting, it is incumbent upon the models to reflect the changes in fire potential relating to these mechanisms of fire spread not explicit in BEHAVE. That is, as fire weather gets more extreme, so does the potential for fire behavior mechanisms outside the explicit purview of the basic fire spread model. Our efforts to model surface fire spread must bear this in mind (Rothermel 1991).

Data and Methods

As stated, fuels often show a high degree of correspondence with vegetation. For example, where we have mature red fir, we can generally characterize the nature of the fuel complex. Using this relationship, we made use of the best available data on plant composition and structure for areas within the SNEP study area. For areas within the boundaries of the National Forest system, we used their strata coverage in the USFS CalVeg database. This classification was used because we perceived it as having the greatest utility in terms of vegetation structure information relevant to fuels, while providing complete coverage on National Forests lands. The strata database is actually an aggregation of the calveg label classification of vegetation type/size/density used for modeling forest growth and yield. In areas where non-productive lands lacked a strata label, or there were insufficient numbers of inventory plots to assign a strata label, we fell back on using the general vegetation type information in the calveg label to determine an appropriate fuel model. This coverage has been recently developed by USFS Region 5, and a summary of the techniques used to generate this coverage can be found in the Forest Inventory and Analysis Users Guide (USFS 1994).

Although a quality assessment of this data set is outside the scope of this report, it should be noted that this coverage was used as the basis for determining fuels on private lands within Forest boundaries where it existed, and consequently does not have representative inventory plots from these private lands. Consequently, although the same general procedure was employed whereby statistically valid samples of inventory plots were used to determine strata definitions, none of the plots were on private inholdings. A correspondingly lower level of accuracy likely accompanies the vegetation descriptions on these lands.

Using information based on ground surveys, field experience, and input from individual National Forests, the strata coverage was converted to fuel models using a crosswalk. In that the groupings of the calveg labels into strata labels were different forest by forest, and that actual strata-fuels relationships differed as well, each national forest was assigned its own crosswalk. An example crosswalk for the Eldorado National Forest is shown in Table 5. Although most crosswalks were quite similar, we chose to provide the opportunity for forest-specific interpretations of fuels derived from the vegetation inventory database.

TABLE 5. Vegetation-Fuel Model crosswalk for the Eldorado National Forest. "Regional Fuel Model" refers to fire behavior associated with normal fire weather, while "Extreme Fuel Model" refers to behavior associated with extreme fire weather conditions. Refer to Table 4 and Appendix A for fuel model descriptions.

Vegetation Classification USFS strata/calveg:	Regional Fuel Model	Extreme Fuel Model
A3S, A3P, A3N, A3G H3X, AC__, CH__, QC__, QO__	8	8
A1X, F0X, F1X, F2X, M0X, M1X, M2X, P0X, P1X, P2X, R0X, R1X	14	14
F3G, F3N, F3X, F4G, F4N	9	23
F3P, F3S, F4S	9	18
FNO	5	5
PNO, MNO	5	26
M3G, M3N, M3P, M3S, M3X, M4G, M4N, M4P, M4S, P3G, P3N, P3P, P3S	10	16
R3G, R3N, R3P, R3S, R4G, R4N, R4P, R4S	8	20
XNO, CC__	4	26
BS__	2	2
HG__, HJ__	1	1
BA__, WA__	0	0

Where the SNEP core study area was not covered by the CalVeg strata classification, two additional databases were used to define fuels. In the case of Yosemite and Sequoia/Kings Canyon National Parks, fuel model themes for use within the BEHAVE program have already been developed, and consequently where simply clipped out and placed into the fuels coverage. That is, these two National Parks had already developed fuel model maps, and we used them without any changes. In that both of these coverages have been used as the basis for fire spread modeling using FARSITE (Finney 1996), a spatial refinement of the BEHAVE model, it was assumed that the quality of these coverages was sufficient for our analysis.

The remaining areas not covered were mapped using the GAP analysis database as the basis for information regarding vegetation structure (Davis and Stoms 1996). These areas included private lands outside the Park/Forest boundaries, as well as large inholding areas within Forest administrative boundaries. We used the primary wildlife habitat relationship attribute ('WHR1') within this data set, to develop a similar vegetation/fuel model crosswalk as was used with the strata coverage (Table 6). Again, although a quality assessment of these data is beyond our scope here, it should be noted how the accuracy and precision of these data compare to the rest of the mapping effort. The minimum mapping unit of the GAP polygon coverage is roughly two orders of magnitude greater than the strata coverage, and there is no size and density information accompanying the WHR vegetation type classification. Consequently, we believe that although the GAP data does provide a means for assessing vegetation community type, it is less than an ideal coverage of vegetation in regard to classifying fuels. Without being able to further refine vegetation structure, we assumed that one crosswalk for all GAP-fuel models was sufficient for the entire SNEP area (Table 6).

One additional rectification was made to the fuels coverage, oweing to recent stand history that would likely affect fuel characteristics. Recent wildfire was used to reflect fuel complex changes that would not otherwise be accounted for in the base vegetation data. For areas on the National Forests, fire perimeter data created by the CALOWL EIS team, was used to delineate recent burned areas (USDA 1995). All fires less than 15 years old and greater than 100 acres in size were overlaid and assumed to be unique plantation polygons. Where data were available, large fires (>300 acres) on private land that burned in shrub and forest types were treated in a similar fashion. Fires occurring on grassland type fuels were assumed to result in no change in fuel model type. The intent of this procedure was to reflect the inherently low flammability and reduced fire hazard associated with plantations and new shrub regrowth (see Appendix A, model 14).

Results and Discussion

Putting all four sources of fuels information together results in a Regional Fuel Model Map for the Sierra Nevada (See Vol 1 Chapter 8). Of the approximately 18 million acres within the SNEP core study area, 25% of the area lacked basic vegetation data from which to derive fuels information. These areas were located primarily north of the Lassen National forest, and on the eastern edge of the study area. Neither Gap nor National Forest mapping projects extend to these areas.

TABLE 6. Vegetation-Fuel Model crosswalk for SNEP private lands using the GAP vegetation database (Davis and Stoms, 1996). "Regional Fuel Model" refers to fire behavior associated with normal fire weather, while "Extreme Fuel Model" refers to behavior associated with extreme fire weather conditions. Refer to Table 1 and Appendix A for fuel model descriptions.

Vegetation Classification GAP whr1:	Regional Fuel Model	Extreme Fuel Model
ADS, ASP, LPN, MHW, MRI, RFR, SCN, VRI	8	8
BOP, JUN, PJN, SGB	2	2
AGS, BOW, DSC, JST, PGS, VOW, WTM	1	1
CRC	4	26
LSG	5	5
DFR, EPN, JPN, WFR	9	23
CPC, MHC, PPN, SMC	10	16
BAR, LAC, OVN, RIV CRP, URB	0	0

Of the remaining areas, 11% is dominated by grass fuels (model 1), with an equal amount in mature shrub types (models 4, 5, and 6). Both of these fuel types are located predominantly in the western zone of the study area in the Sierra foothills. The balance of the landscape (53% or approx. 9.5 million acres) are dominated by forest types spanning the range from recently burned areas and plantations (model 14) through hardwood forests, to dense pine mixed conifer areas, to areas with significant levels of logging slash (models 12 and 13). The most abundant forested fuel type is the heavy pine/mixed conifer type (model 10) occupying 16%, or 2.8 M acres, followed by the lodgepole/red fir/ subapline type (model 8) occupying 14% (2.5 M acres). A sizeable percentage of the study area (11% or 1.9 M acres) is also occupied by the pine/grass type (model 2).

The regional picture of fire hazard reflected by this fuel map indicates a very high percentage of the low- to mid-elevation woodland and forest zone to be in a high hazard condition, capable of extreme fire behavior (including spotting) when burning under adverse weather conditions. This finding is supported in the more complex custom fuel modeling for extreme fire behavior that follows.

As is evident, there are significant scale related differences resulting from the different source vegetation data. Areas within the forest boundaries exhibit a finer grain, pixel-like character, while those adjacent private lands reflect the larger GAP vegetation polygons that they were derived from. Apart from any assessment of accuracy, it is evident that the precision within the Forest boundaries is greater than that of the adjacent lands, and any use of these data for subsequent analysis should be aware of this difference.

A portion of the region is mapped for fuels for prediction of extreme fire behavior, and is shown in Sessions et al. (1996) for the Eldorado National Forest and surrounding areas. This map depicts fuel models used to predict fire behavior under extreme environmental conditions. Of the approximately 1.46 M acres covered by this map, 15% (146,000 acres) are grass fuels, 6% (95,000 acres) are mature shrub dominated fuels, and 10 (150,000 acres) are non-fuel types (water, barren, agriculture, etc.). The remaining acres are all in forested fuel types, with the largest proportion again as heavy pine/mixed conifer (model 16) occupying 36% (531,000 acres). The pine-grass type also has a significant coverage of 9% (138,000 acres). The remaining forest types are relatively evenly distributed amongst dense fir (model 23), sparse fir (model 18) and red fir (model 20), each occupying approximately 3-6% of the land base, or roughly 50 - 95,000 acres. Finally, there is 4% (58,000 acres as recently burned areas or young plantations) 40% of which is a result of the 1992 Cleveland Fire apparent in the middle right of the figure.

These fuel type distributions correspond relatively well with the regional fuel classification, and indicate that when one considers that model 2, 16 and to a lesser extent model 23, as being high hazard forest fuels where surface fuel characteristics coupled with high canopy density and a high preponderance of ladder fuels either from understory development or immature conifer cohorts, that roughly one half of the land base supports fuel and vegetation characteristics that indicate high crown fire potential. Although the fuel models are only useful in predicting surface fire behavior, it must be understood that the vast majority of crown fire behavior activity in California is strongly linked to surface fire intensity, and any effective treatment of this problem implies surface fuel treatments in addition to stand density modifications (Alexander 1988, Sapsis and Martin 1994).

Another interesting aspect of the pattern of extreme fuels across the land is made apparent when comparing Forest Service lands with adjacent state lands. Although not all private inholdings within the forest are reflected, there is roughly a 50-50 split in land ownership for the Eldorado/private lands map. The vast majority of grass and pine/grass fuels occurs on private land, while the vast majority of the densely forested fuel types lie within the National Forest. Along the western margin of the National forest there is a mixture of brush, dense conifer, and low elevation hardwood/conifer that presents a particular hazard when juxtaposed with urbanization of this area. Almost universally, the ecotone between the brush/hardwood and the pine belt supports high hazard surface fuels, extensive mid-story vertical fuels (i.e., ladder fuels), and crown densities sufficient for dependent crown fire development (Van Wagner 1977, Alexander 1988). These features contribute to making this area of particular concern in the event of fires occurring during extreme weather.

EXTREME FIRE BEHAVIOR

In as much as most acres currently being affected by wildfires are by fires exhibiting high rates of spread and other characteristics associated with extreme fire behavior, we recognize the need to estimate quantifiable descriptors of fire behavior likely in the event of severe wildfire. Although the occurrence of environmental conditions associated with extreme fire weather are different throughout the SNEP area, and are reflected in different rates of burning, the relationship between fire weather, fire behavior, and adverse impacts on resources is common across the range. That is, extreme fire behavior always occurs under conditions that will support such fire behavior, and these kinds of fires tend to be difficult to bring under control. Further, these kinds of fires are likely to generate the greatest degree of fire effects on resources -- tree mortality, soil erosion, etc. Consequently, it is highly desirable from an assessment standpoint to be able to estimate fire behavior under those conditions that are likely to result in large damaging fires, i.e., those occurring under extreme fire weather.

Data and Methods

Fire behavior estimates were made using the BEHAVE computer program (Andrews 1986). We chose to describe fire behavior in terms of flame length for a number of reasons. Although this measure represents only one index of fire behavior, we chose to use it as a general indicator of fire behavior in that it gives information that is generally understandable to the average person, and has been used to infer both difficulty of control and ecological effects. Specifically, suppression tactics and fire induced mortality on conifers have been directly related to flame length (Albini 1976, Ryan and Reinhardt 1988). Additionally, surface fire flame length is an important consideration in conditions leading to initiation of crown fire (Van Wagner 1977).

Inputs required to generate estimates of flame length within BEHAVE are fuels (models), weather (fuel moistures and windspeed) and slope. Using the fuel models defined previously we linked weather and slope information into classes, ran individual BEHAVE runs for each discrete combination, then linked the outputs back to those grid cells having the appropriate combinations of fuel, weather and slope class.

We assumed that estimates of extreme fire behavior based on wind and slope driven frontal fire behavior (i.e., maximum possible outputs where wind and slope work in parallel) would offer the best single estimate of potential fire behavior, as head fires dominate the burn distribution. As extreme fire behavior is almost unilaterally associated with high winds where much of the slope effect is dampened and actual fire spread is driven by overhead wind driven spotting, we chose to work solely on identifying likely surface fire estimates for the heading front, then make inferences regarding crown fire initiation (Sessions et al. 1996).

Slope influences on fire behavior were assessed by using the digital elevation model (DEM) in the GIS database to separate the landscape into grids of less than 40% and greater than 40%, and ran individual fuel model/weather scenarios at 20% and 60% slope to estimate midpoints for these classes.

Weather inputs were generated using National Fire Danger Rating System (NFDRS) methodology for sorting weather data based on danger rating indices of fire behavior. We used the pcFIRDAT and pcSEASON computer programs to sort historic weather station data based on the 97% worst weather as indicated by the distribution of the Burning Index (BI) (CDF 1994). These programs are derivatives of the FIRE FAMILY group of programs developed in by the US Forest Service (Main et al . 1982). The BI is a danger rating index related to both rate of spread and energy release, and hence serves as the closest analog to flame length when viewed as a predictor of potential fire behavior (Deeming et al. 1977). Each daily reading of weather inputs from a station translates to an estimated BI, which are then summed into a cumulative distribution that can be sorted. As extreme fire weather is often considered to occur during the worst 3% of cases, we choose this as the cutoff point in the distribution. Although all estimates of extreme weather were based on 2 pm readings, usually associated with peak daily severity, fire weather patterns associated with large scale, high intensity fires commonly occur during sustained period of high fire danger where similar readings are sustained for longer periods of time. Thus, the "worst-case" design of the NFDRS system can be though of as compatible with the objective of determining appropriate weather conditions supporting extreme fires.

The DEM was also used to separate out two aspect classes -- a northeast and a southwest class, from which adjustments to the base weather data were made. Additional adjustments based on vegetation type were also included to incorporate elevational changes in weather as it deviated from the location of the representative weather station. For instance, Red Fir occurs at significantly higher elevations than the Bald Mountain weather station used to assess fire weather for the Eldorado National Forest area, and consequently should reflect higher fuel moistures than that estimated for vegetation types near the elevation of the station. Although a variety of means were available to do this, we relied on expert judgement and experience in the forest to make these adjustments. The final modifications to the weather data concerned the effect of stand structure on windspeed. The data coming out of the fire weather records reflects measurements taken at 20 feet above the surface, and BEHAVE requires mid-flame estimates for this factor. We used the adjustment table based on 20 ft wind, fuel model and canopy cover (Albini and Baughman 1979). An example of the base weather inputs and vegetation/fuel model adjustments in shown in Table 7.

Results and Discussion

Flame length estimates for the Eldorado National Forest and surrounding private lands span the spectrum from less than 2 feet in high elevation red fir/lodgepole pine types, to greater than 18 feet the low elevation chaparral types (Figure 2). We broke the flame length outputs into 4 feet increments for the black and white figure shown here, whereas a more precise rendering of this information can be found in 2 ft increments and in color, in Sessions et al. (1996). Both figures indicate the significant extent of extreme fire behavior potential that exists in this region.

Of the 1.46 million acres depicted, 10% is covered by non-fuel, hence has no representative flame length. The largest flame length class is the 8-12 ft. category, covering 40% of the land area. The vast majority of this class is found in the lower elevation transition zone from grey pine/oak/brush through the body of the pine/mixed conifer zone up to about 5,000 ft elevation (Figure 2). As was stated previously, fire behavior in this class indicated a high resistance to control, and a high capacity for resource damage.

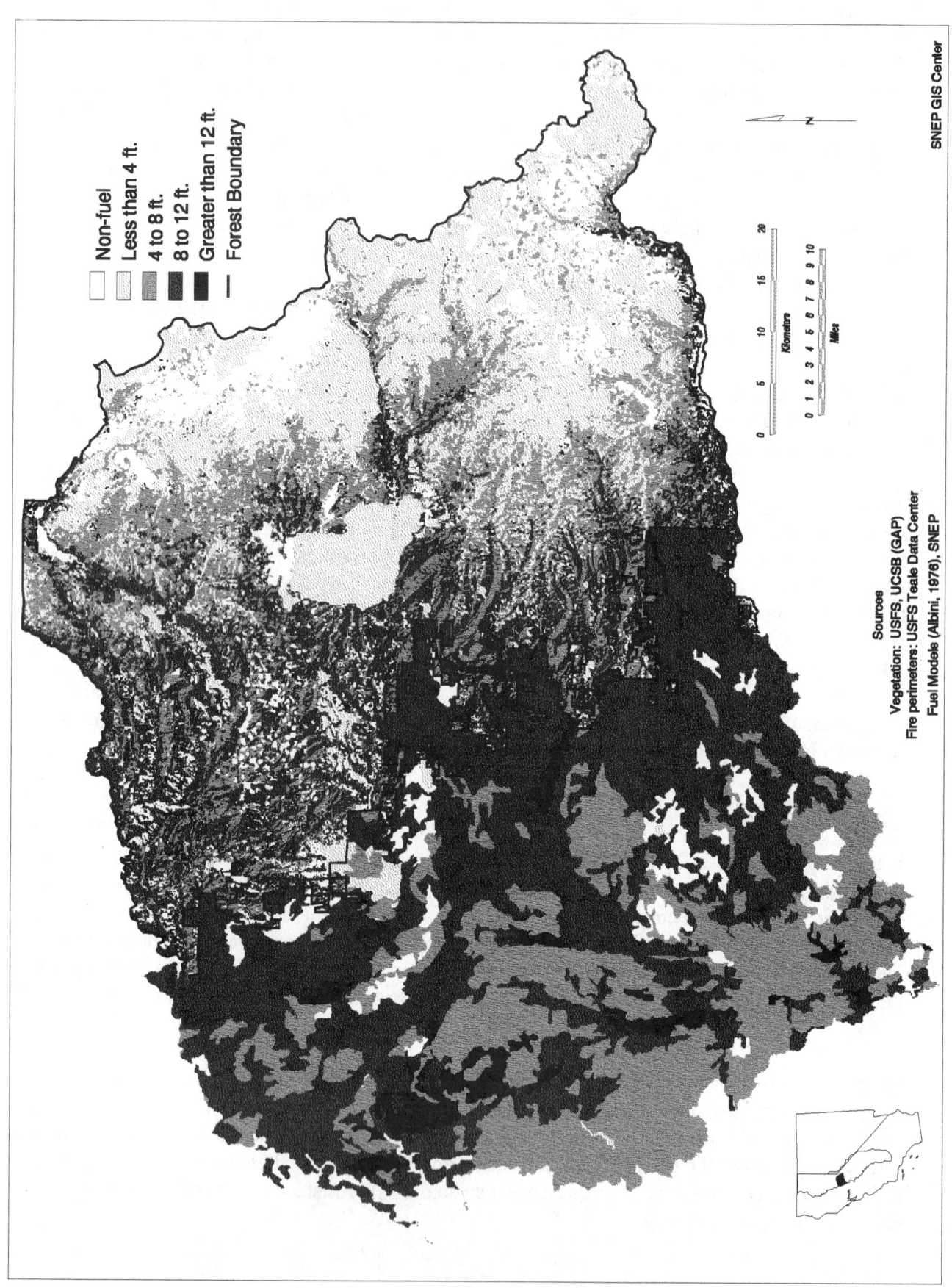

Non-fuel
Less than 4 ft.
4 to 8 ft.
8 to 12 ft.
Greater than 12 ft.
Forest Boundary

Kilometers
0   5   10   15   20
0 1 2 3 4 5 6 7 8 9 10
Miles

N

Sources
Vegetation: USFS, UCSB (GAP)
Fire perimeters: USFS Teale Data Center
Fuel Models (Albini, 1976), SNEP

SNEP GIS Center

776

Table 7. Environmental inputs used for fire behavior calculations on the Eldorado National Forest and surrounding areas. These environmental parameters correspond with model input requirements when using the BEHAVE fire prediction model.

Base Inputs

1hr fuel moisture:	3%
10hr fuel moisture:	4%
100 hr fuel moisture:	5%
live woody fuel moisture:	70%
live herb fuel moisture:	30%
Wind:	6 mph
Wind Vector:	0 degrees offset from slope

Adjustments :

All alpine (A strata) types:
+2% dead fuel moisture
+1 mph south slopes
-2 mph north slopes

Red Fir (R strata) types:
    all except X
+3% dead fuel moistures
-3 mph on north slopes
    X (plantation)
+2% dead fuel moistures

Dense Fir (F strata) types:
    N, G, and 3X classes
+1% dead fuel moistures, -2 mph on south slopes
+2% dead fuel moistures -4 mph on north slopes
+30% live fuel moistures

Sparse Fir
    S, P classes
+1% dead fuel moistures, +1 mph on south slopes
+2% dead fuel moistures -1 mph on north slopes

Fir Plantations and FNO   No Change

Dense Pine (P strata) and
Mixed Conifer (M strata) types:
    N, G, 3X
+1% dead fuel moisture
-1 mph on south slopes
-2 mph on north slopes

Sparse Pine and Mixed-
Conifer types:
    S, P
+ 1 mph on south slopes, - 1 mph on north slopes

Pine and mixed Conifer
Plantations and PNO, MNO   No Change

All GAP and non-Timber strata: No Change

When we superimpose this coverage onto development patterns, urban-interface issues such as human health and safety and potential housing loss become apparent.

The next most abundant flame length class is the 4-8 ft. grouping covering 29% of the land base. An additional 5% of the area --mostly areas covered by brush fuels-- is expected to support flame lengths greater than 12 ft. Hence, fully three-quarters of this area is expected to burn with flame lengths greater than 4 feet when burning under severe fire conditions. Only 15% of the area supports predictions of flame lengths less than 4 feet.

Clearly, the 45% (632,000 acres) that is estimated to burn with than 8 foot or greater flames presents a high potential for stand replacing fire, whether through crown fire or through other mechanisms of tree mortality. Additionally, the 8 % in the 6-8 foot class represents areas of lesser but still significant potential for large, damaging fires. Thus, when non-fuel areas are accounted for, more than half the landscape fuel covered landscape is expected to demonstrate extreme fire behavior if burning under severe weather.

These findings indicate that not only are crown fires expected to occur under these conditions, certain spatially limited fuel modifications (e.g., fuel breaks) may offer only limited utility as a tactical point of control for wildfire suppression (Sessions et al. 1996, Van Wagtendonk 1996, Weatherspoon and Skinner 1996). Thus, the only significant means by which large area mitigation of extreme fire behavior and potential for reduced resource damage lies with area based treatment methods.

When coupled with the information presented on risk here and in McKelvey and Busse (1996), these findings on hazard present a significant issue of concern for Sierra Nevada Ecosystems. Although findings on fire size and abundance indicate no trends in increasing amounts of fire in the Sierra (Erman and Jones 1996) what we may be seeing is an increase in fire severity resulting from stand and fuel condition changes resulting from harvesting and fire suppression. Further, with clear climate induced responses and an uncertain future in regard to incidence of severe fire weather, the prospects for fire related damage from extreme wildfire loom large. Fuel conditions in much of the Sierra Nevada support the potential for large fires exhibiting extreme fire behavior with likely undesirable effects. Future management of the region would be well served to understand this, and make hazard reduction an objective in any land management strategy.

ACKNOWLEDGMENTS

The authors wish to thank the significant contributions of Karen Gabriel and all of the members of the SNEP GIS laboratory for their dedicated efforts and commitment to seeing this project through to completion. Without their selfless efforts, this paper would never have come to pass. We would also like to thank members of CDF and USFS fire management staff for valuable contributions to the vegetation/fuels classifications, and help in determining appropriate weather data for fire behavior analysis.

LITERATURE CITED

Albini, F.A. 1976. Estimating wildfire behavior and effects. General Technical Report INT-30. Ogden UT: U. S. Department of Agriculture, Forest Service, Intermountain Forest and Range Experiment Station. 92 p.

Albini, F.A., and R.G. Baughman. 1979. Estimating windspeeds for predicting wildland fire behavior. Research Paper INT-221. Ogden UT: U. S. Department of Agriculture, Forest Service, Intermountain Forest and Range Experiment Station. 12 p.

Alexander, M.E. 1988. Help with making crown fire assessments.. pp. 147-156 In: Protecting homes from wildfire in the intermountain west -- Proceedings of a workshop, Oct. 6-8, 1987. General Technical Report INT-251. Ogden UT: U. S. Department of Agriculture, Forest Service, Intermountain Forest and Range Experiment Station.

Anderson, H.E. 1982. Aids to determining fuel models for estimating fire behavior. General Technical Report INT-122. Ogden UT: U. S. Department of Agriculture, Forest Service, Intermountain Forest and Range Experiment Station. 22 p.

Andrews, P.A. BEHAVE: fire behavior prediction and fuel modeling system --BURN subsystem Part 1. General Technical Report INT-194. Ogden UT: U. S. Department of Agriculture, Forest Service, Intermountain Forest and Range Experiment Station. 130 p.

Burgan, R.E., and R.C. Rothermel. 1984. BEHAVE: fire behavior prediction and fuel modeling system --FUEL subsystem. General Technical Report INT-167. Ogden UT: U. S. Department of Agriculture, Forest Service, Intermountain Forest and Range Experiment Station. 126 p.

California Department of Forestry and Fire Protection (CDF). 1994. PcFIREDAT/pcSEASON Users Guide. Sacramento, CA. 45 p.

Davis, F., and D. M. Stoms. 1996. Sierran vegetation: A GAP analysis. In *Sierra Nevada Ecosystem Project: Final Report to Congress*, vol II, chap. 25. Davis: University of California, Centers for Water and Wildland Resources.

Deeming, J.E., R.E. Burgan, and J.D. Cohen. 1978. The national fire danger rating system -- 1978. Gen. Tech. Rep. INT-39. Ogden UT. USDA Forest Service, Intermountain Forest and Range Experiment Station. 63 p.

Erman, D. C., and R. Jones. 1996. Fire frequency analysis of the Sierra Nevada. In *Sierra Nevada Ecosystem Project: Final Report to Congress*, vol II, chap. . Davis: University of California, Centers for Water and Wildland Resources.

Finney, M.A. 1996. FARSITE Fire Area Simulator v. 2.0 -- Users Guide and Technical Documentation. Systems for Environmental Management, Missoula, MT. 116 p.

Hornby, L.G. 1935. Fuel type mapping in Region 1. *Journal of Forestry* 33(1):67-72.

Main, W.A., R.J. Straub, and D.M. Paananen. 1982. FIREFAMILY: Fire planning with historic weather data. General Technical Report NC-73. St. Paul MN: U. S. Department of Agriculture, Forest Service, North Central Forest and Range Experiment Station. 31 p.

McKelvey, K.S., and K.K. Busse. 1996. Twentieth-century fire patterns on forest service lands. In *Sierra Nevada Ecosystem Project: Final Report to Congress*, vol II, chap. 44. Davis: University of California, Centers for Water and Wildland Resources.

Rothermel, R.C. 1983. How to predict the spread and intensity of forest and range fires. General Technical Report INT-143. Ogden UT: U. S. Department of Agriculture, Forest Service, Intermountain Forest and Range Experiment Station. 161 p.

_____. 1991. Predicting behavior and size of crown fire in the Northern Rocky Mountains. Research Paper INT-438. Ogden UT: U. S. Department of Agriculture, Forest Service, Intermountain Forest and Range Experiment Station. 46 p.

Ryan, K.C., and E.D. Reinhardt. 1988. Predicting postfire mortality of seven western conifers. *Canadian Journal of Forest Research* 18:1291-1297.

Salazar, L.A. 1987. Matching fuel model sets: national fire danger rating system and fire behavior prediction system. pp. 63-70 In: Proceedings of the 9th Conference on Fire and Forest Meteorology. San Diego, CA. April 21-24, 1987. American Meteorological Society, Bethesda, MD.

Sapsis, D.B., and R.E. Martin. 1994. Fire, the landscape, and diversity: a framework for managing wildlands. pp. 270-278 IN: Proceedings of the 12th conference on fire and forest meteorology, October 26-28, 1993, Jekyll Island, Georgia. Society of American Foresters.

Sessions, J., K.N. Johnson, D. Sapsis, B. Bahro, and J. Gabriel. 1996. Simulating forest growth, fire effects, timber harvest, and watershed disturbance in the federal forests of the Sierra Nevada. In *Sierra Nevada Ecosystem Project: Final Report to Congress*, vol II, chap. . Davis: University of California, Centers for Water and Wildland Resources.

Struass, D. , L. Bednar, and R. Mees. 1989. Do one percent of forest fires cause ninety-nine percent of the damage? *Forest Science* 35:319-328.

USDA Forest Service. 1994. Forest Inventory and Analysis Users Guide. U.S. Department of Agriculture, Forest Service, Region 5. San Francisco, CA.

Van Wagner, C.E. 1977. Conditions for the start and spread of crownfire. *Canadian Journal of Forest Research* 18:818-820.

————. 1993. Prediction of crown fire behavior in two stands of jack pine. *Canadian Journal of Forest Research* 23:442-449.

Van Wagtendonk, J.W. 1996. Use of a deterministic fire growth model to test fuel treatments. In *Sierra Nevada Ecosystem Project: Final Report to Congress*, vol II, chap. 46. Davis: University of California, Centers for Water and Wildland Resources.

Weatherspoon, C.P. and C. N. Skinner. 1996. Landscape level strategies for forest fuel management. In *Sierra Nevada Ecosystem Project: Final Report to Congress*, vol II, chap. 60. Davis: University of California, Centers for Water and Wildland Resources.

Appendix A. Fuel model descrpitions used in classifying fuel characteristics and fire behavior modeling for the Sierra Nevada Ecosystem Project Study Area. Fuel Model numbers less than 1 through 13 reflect standard models used nationwide (Albini 1976), while fuel model numbers greater than 13 reflect custom models developed specifically for this study. Heat of combustion for all fuel models is assumed to be 8,000 BTU/lb. Interested readers wishing to understand the nature of these fuel characteristics, and how they affect fire behavior, are directed to Rothermel (1983), Burgan and Rothermel (1984) and Burgan (1987).

Fuel Model 1 -- Short Grass
Loading (t/a)/surface-to-volume ratios (1/ft):
1hr   0.74/3500
10hr
100hr
live
Depth (ft): 1.0
Moisture of Extinction(%): 12

Fuel Model 2 -- Timber, Grass and Understory
Loading (t/a)/surface-to-volume ratios (1/ft)
1hr   2.00/3000
10hr   1.00/109
100hr   0.50/30
live   0.50/1500
Depth (ft.):   1.0
Moisture of Extinction (%): 15

Fuel Model 4 -- Chaparral
Loading (t/a)/surface-to-volume ratios (1/ft)
1hr   5.01/2,000
10hr   4.01/109
100hr   2.00/30
live   5.01/1,500
Depth (ft.):   6.0
Moisture of Extinction (%): 20

Fuel Model 5 -- Brush
Loading (t/a)/surface-to-volume ratios (1/ft)
1hr   1.00/2,000
10hr   0.50/109
100hr
live   2.00/1,500
Depth (ft.):   2.0
Moisture of Extinction (%): 20

Appendix A (cont.):

Fuel Model 6 -- Dormant Brush
Loading (t/a)/surface-to-volume ratios (1/ft)
- 1hr   1.50/1,750
- 10hr   2.50/109
- 100hr   2.00/30
- live

Depth (ft.):   2.5

Moisture of Extinction (%): 25

Fuel Model 8 -- Closed Timber Litter/Hardwood Forest
Loading (t/a)/surface-to-volume ratios (1/ft)
- 1hr   1.50/2,000
- 10hr   1.00/109
- 100hr   2.50/30
- live

Depth (ft.):   0.2

Moisture of Extinction (%): 30

Fuel Model 9 -- Hardwood Litter
Loading (t/a)/surface-to-volume ratios (1/ft)
- 1hr   2.92/2,000
- 10hr   0.41/109
- 100hr   0.15/30
- live

Depth (ft.):   0.2

Moisture of Extinction (%): 25

Fuel Model 10 -- Timber and Understory
Loading (t/a)/surface-to-volume ratios (1/ft)
- 1hr   3.01/2,000
- 10hr   2.00/109
- 100hr   5.01/30
- live   2.00/1,500

Depth (ft.):   1.0

Moisture of Extinction (%): 25

Fuel Model 11 --Light Logging Slash
     Loading (t/a)/surface-to-volume ratios (1/ft)
          1hr   1.50/1,500
          10hr   4.51/109
          100hr 5.51/30
          live
     Depth (ft.):   1.0
     Moisture of Extinction (%): 15

Fuel Model 12 -- Medium Logging Slash
     Loading (t/a)/surface-to-volume ratios (1/ft)
          1hr   4.01/1,500
          10hr   14.03/109
          100hr 16.53/30
          live
     Depth (ft.):   2.3
     Moisture of Extinction (%): 20

Fuel Model 13 -- Heavy Logging Slash
     Loading (t/a)/surface-to-volume ratios (1/ft)
          1hr   7.01/1,500
          10hr   23.04/109
          100hr 28.05/30
          live
     Depth (ft.):   3.0
     Moisture of Extinction (%): 25

Fuel Model 14 -- Plantations/Young Brush
     Loading (t/a)/surface-to-volume ratios (1/ft)
          1hr   1.00/2,000
          10hr   0.50/109
          100hr
          live   2.00/1,500
     Depth (ft.):   0.2
     Moisture of Extinction (%): 25

Appendix A (cont.)

Fuel Model 16 -- Mixed Conifer/Pine -- Heavy
Loading (t/a)/surface-to-volume ratios (1/ft)

1hr	3.00/2,000
10hr	2.00/109
100hr	3.00/30
live	2.00/1,500

Depth (ft.):   1.5

Moisture of Extinction (%): 25

Fuel Model 18 -- Mixed Conifer/FIr Low Density
Loading (t/a)/surface-to-volume ratios (1/ft)

1hr	0.80/2,000
10hr	0.50/109
100hr	2.00/30
live	1.50/1,500

Depth (ft.):   1.5

Moisture of Extinction (%): 25

Fuel Model 20 -- Red Fir
Loading (t/a)/surface-to-volume ratios (1/ft)

1hr	2.00/2,000
10hr	0.41/109
100hr	
live	

Depth (ft.):   0.25

Moisture of Extinction (%): 25

Fuel Model 23 -- Mixed Conifer/Fir -- High Density
Loading (t/a)/surface-to-volume ratios (1/ft)

1hr	2.00/2,000
10hr	1.50/109
100hr	3.00/30
live	2.00/1,500

Depth (ft.):   1.3

Moisture of Extinction (%): 25

Appendix A (cont.)

Fuel Model 26 Sierran Chaparral
    Loading (t/a)/surface-to-volume ratios (1/ft)
        1hr   2.70/2,000
        10hr   2.70/109
        100hr 1.80/30
        live   3.6/1,500
    Depth (ft.):   3.6
    Moisture of Extinction (%): 25

REBECCA T. RICHARDS
Department of Agronomy and
    Range Science
University of California
Davis, California
now with
Department of Sociology
University of Montana
Missoula, Montana

20

Special Forest Product Harvesting in the Sierra Nevada

Sierra Nevada Ecosystem Project: Final report to Congress, vol. III, Assessments, Commissioned Reports, and Background Information. Davis: University of California, Centers for Water and Wildland Resources, 1996.

787

TABLE OF CONTENTS

ABSTRACT

Special forest products have historically been gathered in the Sierra Nevada for food, medicine, and other household and occupational purposes. Collection of special forest products continues in the Sierra Nevada today for many of these same uses. However, new uses for and values toward special forest products have developed. The most frequently collected and most economically valuable products are in decline while many "minor" products are either emerging or increasing. Some of these products may be intensely valued by particular sociocultural user groups even disproportionately in relation to both the amounts harvested, economic value received, and ecological impacts on the landscape. Conversely, the collection of other special forest products may have unanticipated ecological or socioeconomic consequences depending on past, present, and future conditions of removal, including harvesting pressure. Management options for special forest products include adequate support for special forest product management programs; consistent regionwide reporting of administrative data from these programs; collection of ecological plant association data on key products; and the collection, linkage, and monitoring of administrative, ecological, and sociocultural and economic data as part of forest management systems.

KEYWORDS: Forests and forest lands, ethnobiology, biodiversity, resource administration, special forest products.

LIST OF FIGURES

793

INTRODUCTION

The Issue

Special forest products are also referred to as "miscellaneous", "minor", "nonconvertible", or "nontimber" products. In categorizing the products gathered or collected from U.S. national forests, the USDA Forest Service (Forest Service) has defined special forest products as those resources "sold, gathered, or collected from the National Forest System. There are four lists: Plants, Animals, Minerals, and Aquatic Resources" (USDA Forest Service 1994). More narrowly, the Forest Service has defined special forest products as those products constituting or deriving from "trees, shrubs, forbs, non-vascular plants, fungi and micro-organisms that live in forest or grassland ecosystems" (USDA Forest Service 1995). In this assessment, the broad definition was considered for data parameters while the more narrow vegetative definition was used as the assessment focus.

Use of special forest products is diverse, including "aromatics; berries and wild fruits; chips, shavings, excelsior, sawdust, bark, and pine straw; cones and seeds; cooking wood, smoke wood, and flavorwood; decorative wood; forest botanicals as flavorings, medicinals, and pharmaceuticals; greenery and other floral products; honey; mushrooms; nuts; recreation and wildlife; specialty wood products; syrup; and weaving and dyeing materials" (USDA Forest Service 1993, 7). Broadly speaking, however, special forest product use generally falls under five general areas: food, herbs, medicinals, decoratives and specialty items" (USDA Forest Service 1995). All past and potential uses of special forest products were considered in this assessment.

Importance of Special Forest Products

In the northern coastal forests, central Cascades, and western Rockies, the special forest product industry is well-developed. It has been estimated that the floral green and Christmas ornamental trade alone generated almost $130 million in product sales in 1989 while the 3.94 million pounds in wild edible mushrooms gathered in 1992 provided an estimated 10,400 harvesters with just over $20 million in income (Schlosser and Blatner 1994). The economic value of the special forest product industry in the Sierra Nevada is unknown but its potential worth might be compared to not only the economic value of the Pacific Northwest special forest product industry but relative to that of the Sierra Nevada wood product industry as well, e.g., Forest Service revenue sharing to schools and counties in 1991-92 in Sierra Nevada counties totaled just under $31.7 million and about 15,400 workers were employed full-time in logging, sawmilling, and wood remanufacturing (Wildland Resources Center 1994). [1]

Consumer demand for special forest products is characterized by seasonal market dynamics. The Bureau of Land Management (BLM), which administers extensive public forest land in western Oregon and Washington, notes that consumer demand for many special forest products such as cedar boughs seasonally fluctuates, while other products such as chip and cull logs are cyclic according to the market price (USDI Bureau of Land Management 1993). Consumer demand for minor products is also differentiated by regional variation. In western Oregon, consumer demand for minor products increases the

---

[1] Sierra Nevada counties included Shasta, Tehama, Lassen, Plumas, Sierra, Butte, Yuba, Nevada, Placer, ElDorado, Amador, Calaveras, Alpine, Tuolumne, Mariposa, Madera, Fresno, Tulare, and Kern.

796

further south one goes in the state with most BLM forest product consumers seeking firewood (USDI Bureau of Land Management 1993). Finally, harvester demand for special forest products varies by ethnicity. In northern California and southwestern Oregon, Southeast Asians represent at least half the number of wild mushroom harvesters (Richards and Creasy in press) while on the eastside, Hispanics appear to dominate the cutting of juniper floral green in eastern Oregon and Caucasians control lichen rock removal (Richards in press).

However, much is unknown about the special forest product industry, even in the Pacific Northwest where the floral green segment alone is a million dollar enterprise (Schlosser, Blatner, and Zamora 1992). Although expansion of the special forest product industry may provide critical jobs in many rural Northwest communities, these jobs are typically accompanied by low wages and "few if any" benefits so that the rural development benefits of the industry may offer only mixed blessings (Schlosser and Blatner 1994). Little socioeconomic information has been collected about the value of special forest products to the landowner, the income which people earn in the special forest product industry, and the distribution channels for plants collected in the "other edible and medicinal" segment of the industry (Schlosser and Blatner 1994). In addition, gathering conflicts between traditional, recreational, and commercial harvesters have resulted since ethnic diversity within the special forest product industries has increased and different social values attributed to various products have diverged (Richards and Creasy in press).

Finally, very little systematic ecological data collection has been applied to special

forest product assessment and management. The most complete assessment to date has

focused on the floral green segment of the industry and has concluded that product

availability and quality are greatly influenced by forest management practices. Floral

green and "more traditional" forest product production is reported to be greatest with

intermediate stand practices, uneven-aged management, and other partial cutting

approaches while other "specific" floral green plants may actually increase under clearcut,

seed tree, and shelterwood regeneration techniques (Schlosser and Blatner 1994). This

assessment has been possible because the types and amounts of specific floral green

plants have been documented (Schlosser, Blatner, and Zamora 1992). Such information

on special forest products is currently lacking for the Sierra Nevada forests.

<u>Public Perceptions, and Special Forest Products</u>

For centuries, Native American tribes gathered various plants on the slopes and in

the foothills of the Sierra Nevada for medicinal, ornamental, religious, and culinary uses.

Their past and present collection of many native plants and their environmental

management to enhance production have been well recorded (Blackburn and Anderson

1993). Nevertheless, as a Miwok ethnobotanical guide to Indian Grinding Rock State

Park notes, while many native Californians still use plants in the traditional ways:

it has become very difficult to do so. The botany of California has changed

drastically since the arrival of the Spanish in the 1700s. The meadow area before

you, surrounding the huge, centuries old valley oaks is a good example.

Introduced European plants, such as annual grasses and yellow star thistle, have successfully invaded, and for the most part replaced, perennial grasses and other native vegetation. This type of invasion is quite common throughout California. Additionally, pollution of soil, water, and air, loss of plant habitat to development, gathering restrictions on public and prviate lands, and the loss of knowledge as the culture was suppressed by Euroamerican settlers, all make living in the traditional ways today extremely difficult (Harrison 1991, 21).

In contrast, plant collection by non-Native Americans from the Sierra Nevada has received surprisingly little documentation. Spanish residents of the coast considered the range formidable and avoided it. Until the discovery of gold in 1849, only a few hardy travellers made any Sierra Nevada crossings. After the gold rush, the non-Native American inhabitants of the Sierra Nevada depended on mining, logging, and ranching, all of which relied on well-organized camps and well-supplied mule-trains, railroads, and subsequently, trucks, for sustenance. Public perceptions about the daily necessity of miner's grub, the chuck wagon, and the logging camp messhall are probably more accurate historic facts about survival in the Sierra Nevada than are any romanticized assumptions about the wilderness foraging skills of most early settlers, who were often unfamiliar with the terrain and plants (Marks 1994). Nevertheless, miners and settlers alike relied on many native California plants for medicinal aid and a seasonal respite from daily diet (Westrich 1989).

With the railroads and improved roads, the recreational industry of the Sierra Nevada slowly grew around the establishment of early resorts and summer homes (Storer and Usinger 1963). Since the late 1940s, urban development has expanded throughout

799

the foothills and the recreational industry is well established in the high country. All of these developments have depended on supplies imported from outside the Sierra Nevada in exchange for timber, gold, and other traditional resource exports, and more recently, in situ amenity values. Hence, throughout the post-1849 period, special forest product harvesting has not played a significant economic role for non-Native American residents of the Sierra Nevada. This is in marked contrast to the coastal mountain communities of southwestern Oregon and northwestern California where special forest product gathering has not only been a subsistence but an important economic activity since at least the middle part of this century (Robbins 1988; Kunkler 1975; Richards in press).

Despite the fact that special forest product harvesting has not played a major economic role in the non-Native American settlement of the Sierra Nevada, it has nonetheless been an important cultural activity in for Sierra Nevada community life since ethnicity and different community traditions have played an important role in what products have been gathered. Despite its relative unimportance as a historic economic activity, special forest product harvesting may present future development opportunities for not only Sierra Nevada rural residents (Mater Engineering 1993), but for commercial harvesters outside the Sierra Nevada who might shift some of their current harvesting from the Pacific Northwest and northwestern California (Richards and Creasy, in press) to the Sierra Nevada.

Sierra Nevada Ecosystems and Special Forest Products

The physical features, climatic factors, and forest community types of the Sierra Nevada play the major role in determining what products are gathered and in what amounts. Special forest products are gathered in the Sierra because of natural supply first and foremost. Because ecological conditions in Sierra Nevada forests differ greatly from those in the Pacific Northwest, a particular product like bolete (*Boletus* spp.) mushrooms may be gathered from a Sierra Nevada forest in August even if market demand is greater for another species of mushrooms such as chantrelle (*Cantharellus* spp.) or matsutake (*Tricholoma magnivelare*) mushrooms, which do not generally grow in the Sierra Nevada. Other special forest products like morel (*Morchella* spp.) mushrooms do occur in both Pacific Northwest and Sierra Nevada forests but may not grow in abundance. Anecdotal reports indicate that the drier climate and lower latitudes of the Sierra Nevada generally constrain the supply and season for morels relative to the Northwest forests. Mushroom pickers claim that for the Sierra Nevada, morel production is greatest, and most commercially viable, only following fire. These ecological and economic interactions play important roles, when seasonal and regional fluctuations in market demands (especially in expanding markets) coincide with natural production. Hence, future harvesting pressure for particular special forest products may increase in the Sierra Nevada, as illustrated by the case of morel collection following the Cleveland Fire of 1992 on the Eldorado National Forest. When such events do occur, both public and private forest mangers have to increasingly consider special forest product production in administering different ecosystem management practices and implementing or controlling different disturbance regimes like fire or timber harvest. Despite the fact that special forest product harvesting is illegal in national parks, national park managers also need to understand what products occur within park boundaries and which may be subject to periodic harvesting pressure, especially where supply may not warrant gathering. Documenting which products are most frequently collected and in what amounts is therefore the most critical initial step toward assessing the ecosystem management implications of special forest product harvesting in the Sierra Nevada.

KEY QUESTIONS

In the spring of 1994, I proposed to document which special forest products are harvested from the Sierra Nevada and in what amounts study by surveying national forests in the Sierra Nevada on special forest product use. In June 1994, the Sierra Nevada Ecosystem Project (SNEP) Coordinating Committee requested that a special forest product database also be developed for the Camp Creek watershed on the Eldorado National Forest as a special watershed-based case. Following funding in August 1994, my initial fieldwork indicated that little if no special forest product collection occurred in the Camp Creek watershed except for firewood. In October 1994, the SNEP Coordinating Committee redirected the final assessment to focus on the Eldorado National Forest as a case study of special forest product use and to generally survey the other Sierra Nevada national forests. Assessment goals were to ascertain regional current and historic trends and to identify concerns and issues in special forest product use. Because other SNEP projects were focused on Native American issues, the assessment was limited to nonNative American special forest product uses. Within the limited scope of the case study and the general survey of the national forests, the key questions which were addressed in the final assessment were:

1. What has been the historic pattern of nonNative American special forest product collection?

2. What special forest products are currently collected from the Sierra Nevada national forests?

3. What are the trends in current special forest product policy and management and do they affect special forest product collection?

4. How can information from this assessment inform policy choices for ecological sustainability of special forest products and the implications of those choices for ecological, social, and economic conditions?

BACKGROUND

One of the most important gaps in our existing records about special forest product harvesting in the Sierra Nevada is the extent to which plants and other products have been collected by non-Native Americans since 1849. Few historical records note nontimber forest product collection, and the few which do primarily concern food and medicines. Similarly, little if any information exists about the state of current special forest product harvesting in the Sierra Nevada. This assessment is to the best of my knowledge the first attempt to systematically describe historic and current patterns of special forest product harvesting in the Sierra Nevada forests.

<u>What is Known About Special Forest Products in the Sierra Nevada</u>

Plants were gathered by early California settlers for enjoyment, medicine, food, and household use. Wild flowers were picked for bouquets just as they are today. However, settlers also gathered various plants that grow wild in the Sierra Nevada high country and foothills. These plants were eaten as food, employed in work and household chores, and used as medicines for internal ailments, snakebites, lice treatments, poison oak or rheumatism balms, wound poultices, and many other ailments.

Although they were new to California, settlers often recognized native California species from eastern North American or European related species which provided old remedies. Some settlers subscribed to the tradition of herbal medicine known as the Doctrine of Signatures, which holds that

> every single medicinal plant on the face of Mother Earth comes bearing a sort of 'signed statement' as it were, which plainly reveals its potential uses to whoever takes the time to read it. So it goes with Barberry. Its golden wood (from which the pious Spaniards used to fashion crucifixes) is quite plainly its signature. It's the yellowest of golden yellows; yellow is the tint of jaundiced flesh; hence, here's an herb meant to treat an ailing liver (Westrich 1989).

Others read or heard of the teachings of the well known apothecary, Nicholas Culpepper, whose herbal teachings were widely known (Westrich 1989). Some settlers also learned new uses for the new, unfamiliar species from their Native American or Spanish neighbors. A representative list of these native California plants is shown in table 1 (from Westrich 1989; Storer and Usinger 1963 and referenced from Hickman 1993).

Table 1

Some Native California Plants Gathered from the Sierra Nevada by Settlers

Common Name	Scientific Name	Major Product Use
Alder	*Alnus* spp	Medicine
Angelica	*Angelica* spp.	Medicine
Arrowhead or wapato	*Sagittaria latifolia*	Food
Barberry or Oregon grape	*Berberis repens*	Medicine
Bearberry	*Arctostayphylos uva-ursi*	Medicine
Blackberries	*Rubus* spp.	Food
Bluecurls	*Trichostema* spp.	Tea
Bracken fern	*Pteridium aquilinum*	Medicine
California laurel	*Umbellularia californica*	Insecticide, tea
Canchalagua	*Centaurium venustum*	Medicine
Cascara or buckthorn	*Rhamnus purshiana*	Medicine
Cattail	*Typha latifolia*	Bandages, diapers
Clover	*Trifolium* spp.	Medicine
Cow parsnip	*Heracleum lanatum*	Medicine
Gray or foothill pine	*Pinus sabiniana*	Tea
Elderberry	*Sambucus* spp.	Food
Figwort	*Scrophularia* spp.	Balm
Gooseberry	*Ribes* spp.	Food
Gumplant or tarweed	*Grindelia* spp.	Medicine
Horsetail rush	*Equisetum* spp.	Medicine
Hound's tongue	*Cynoglossum* spp.	Medicine
Juniper	*Juniperus* spp.	Medicine
Larkspur	*Delphinium* spp.	Lice treatment
Milkweed	*Asclepius* spp.	Medicine
Miner's lettuce	*Montia perfoliata*	Greens
Mint	*Mentha arvensis*	Tea
Mountain bee plant	*Cleome serrulata*	Bee attractant
Mountain pennyroyal	*Monardella odoratissima*	Tea
Mugwort or wormwood	*Artemisia* spp.	Medicine
Oregon ash	*Fraxinus latifolia*	Medicine
Pigweed	*Chenopodium* spp.	Greens
Plantain	*Plantago* spp.	Poultice
Sage	*Salvia* spp.	Medicine
Serviceberry	*Amelanchier alnifolia*	Food
Sierra plum	*Prunus subcordata*	Food
Soap plant or amole	*Chlorogalum omeridianum*	Soap
Toyon	*Heteromeles arbutifolia*	Christmas green
Tule or bullrush	*Scirpus acutus*	Thatch
Western raspberry	*Rubus leucodermis*	Food
Wild grape	*Vitis californica*	Food
Wild onions	*Allium* spp.	Food
Wild rose	*Rosa* spp.	Medicine
Wild strawberry	*Fragaria californica*	Food
Willow	*Salix* spp.	Medicine
Yarrow	*Achillea* spp.	Poultice
Yerba santa	*Eriodictyon californicum*	Tobacco, medicine

In addition to the native plants, settlers also gathered nonnative, introduced plants. Some of these are shown in table 2 (from Westrich 1989; Storer and Usinger 1963 as referenced from Hickman 1993).

Table 2
Some Nonnative California Plants Gathered from the Sierra Nevada by Settlers

Common Name	Scientific Name	Major Product Use
Chicory	*Cichorium intybus*	Medicine
Curly dock	*Rumex crispus*	Medicine
Fennel	*Foeniculum vulgare*	Medicine
Groundsel	*Senecio vulgaris*	Medicine
Mallow	*Malva* spp.	Medicine
Milk thistle	*Silybum marianum*	Medicine
Mustard	*Brassica nigra*	Medicine
Nettle	*Urtica dioica*	Medicine
Queen Anne's lace	*Daucus carota*	Medicine
Shepherd's purse	*Capsella bursa-pastoris*	Medicine
Storkbill	*Erodium cicutarium*	Medicine
Sweet clover	*Melilotus* spp.	Medicine
Teasel	*Dipsacus* spp.	Medicine

Even before the gold rush of 1849, native California plants were collected not only for household use but for commercial sale. The Sierra Nevada foothill plant chia (*Salvia columbariae*), which is also widespread throughout coastal California chaparral, was valued for its seeds as both food and medicine. By 1849, chia seeds were selling by Los Angeles traders for as much as eight dollars a pound (Westrich 1989), a fortune by today's standards and certainly comparable to the twenty-six dollars a pound for which fresh morel mushrooms were being sold in Berkeley in May, 1995!

Other native California plants were valued by American settlers as much as the Spaniards and Native Americans. Such was the case of the common Sierra Nevada

806

foothill soap plant (*Chlorogalum pomeridianum)* which Kentucky journalist Edwin

Bryant, who came to California before the gold rush, enthusiastically mentioned:

"The botany and flora of California are rich, and will hereafter form a fruitful

field of discovery to the naturalists", wrote Bryant. "There are numerous plants

reported to possess extraordinary medical virtues. The 'soap plant' (Amole) is

one which appears to be among the most serviceable. The root, which is the

saponaceous portion of the plant, resembles the onion, but possess the quality of

cleansing linen equal to any 'oleic soap' manufactured by my friends Cornwall &

Brother of Louisville, Ky" (Westrich 1989, 8).

In some cases, native plants actually did prove commercially valuable. Barter and

trade in medicinal herbs was a common practice among Spanish Californians (Westrich

1989) and some plants in particular were important commercial products. A good

example is canchalagua (*Centaurium venustum*). Growing from Plumas County

southward and common in and near Yosemite Valley, canchalagua is

unmentioned in modern herbals but was once the talk of California, an old stand-

by cure-all to the Indians, the prized panacea of every Spaniard's household, often

found hanging in bunches from the hacienda rafters. Here was a commodity in

great demand, often coveted, always sought, sometimes traded--even begged for

and sent all the way to the Polynesian Islands, where it was eagerly awaited by

Spaniards and Americans living in that distant land. Edwin Bryant noted that

Californians viewed Calchalagua as "an antidote for all the diseases to which they

are subject , but in particular for cases of fever and ague" (Westrich 1989, 23).

807

During the gold rush, wild plants, some of which are also native to the Sierra Nevada, were collected on the trail to California, often by women whose responsibility it was to keep the family healthy.

Many herbs and roots were gathered as the overlanders came upon them during their journey. If the time of year was right, herbs such as the mullein plant were collected and made into candy and tea to ward off the bitter winter cold. Horsemint and catnip were gathered by rivers and used for stomach complaints. In late fall, dried sunflower stalks were gathered and used to supplement the fuel supply. In early spring and summer there might be yellow tansy mustard (*Thelesperma trifidum*), pigweed (*Amaranthus*), and peppergrass (*Lepidium montanum*) to gather and cook for greens (Wittmann 1994, 55).

Men, too, collected plants both on the trail and after arrival in California, particularly for medicinal purposes and most commonly, from all accounts, when women were not available to gather.

In the case of injury or illness, prospectors searched out and collected medicinal plants. Soft turpentine from pine trees was used to coat cuts and wounds. Spruce bark tea became a popular anti-dyspeptic and scurvy treatment...(Marks 1994, 237).

Such an early California male collector was Sutter's Fort resident, Heinrich Lienhard. Lienhard was a Swiss immigrant who traveled to California in 1846 and wrote lengthy descriptions of his experiences. His notes illustrate the dependency of early miners on their Sierra Nevada foothill flora for medical relief:

Once when Thomen stopped on his way back from the mines, ... he was so sick that I made him a tea brewed from the roots of the California Ash. He believe it would cure him, and it did make him well (Westrich 1989, 95).

Native Sierra Nevada plants were particularly valued as dietary supplements by early Sierra Nevada settlers, who even used the needles of the gray, foothill or digger pine (*Pinus sabiniana*) to combat scurvy.

The settlers also visited the Digger Pine now and again for a store of its stiff gray-green needles from which to make a medicinal tea, an infusion reputed to prevent scurvy and/or serve as a mild diuretic. Insofar as it furnished leaves for this potion, the Digger Pine was no different than any other California pines or spruces or firs; they all had needles that served this purpose well. This was a fact which many miners, living in mortal fear of scurvy, were quick to take to heart. One such adventurer made a point of mentioning his first needle tea in a journal he penned about life in the California mines. "Had this evening spruce or fir tea for the first time," he wrote. "Some use it daily as a preventative of scurvy. It had to me not a very pleasant taste but think it is healthy. It makes a colorless tea, looks like water" (Westrich 1989, 38-39).

While some native plants were gathered for necessary medical uses, other plants were often collected as a welcome, even joyous escape from the hardships of daily pioneer life. In his 1846 diary, Lienhard wrote that on his long anticipated trip to Sutter's Fort he became distracted by gathering wild blackberries.

It was not long before the road swung toward the left and curved past a clump of willow on the bank of the American Fork where I saw some blackberry vines. Hungry for fresh fruit, I stopped long enough to pick a handful of these luscious berries. Unfortunately, they stained my best suit, which I was wearing in honor of the occasion; it took me a long time and a considerable amount of scrubbing with cold water dipped out of the river to get it clean again. But the fruit was unbelievably delicious (Westrich 1989, 14-15).

While blackberries are widely reported to have been gathered, other wild foods were also collected from the Sierra Nevada by early settlers. For example, "black" raspberries and wild strawberries were gathered from the forests above Placerville, as witnessed by the name of the general area known as Strawberry where early Placerville residents went every spring to pick wild strawberries (Denis O'Rourke Witcher, Museum Director, Eldorado County, personal communication, 16 June 1995).

Angloamerican settlers were not the only newcomers to California to collect native plants from the Sierra Nevada. Newspaper articles from the 1800s mention that the Chinese and Italians gathered wild mushrooms from the Sierra Nevada (Denis O'Rourke Witcher, personal communication, June 16, 1995). The Chinese also cultivated native California arrowhead (*Sagittaria latifolia*) on the islands of the Sacramento and San Joaquin delta and "ate the tubers under the name of tule potato" (Storer and Usinger 1963, 66).

Although early settlers did not gather many of the staple plant foods which Native Americans used (such as acorns), they did harvest some native plants which Native

Americans also valued. The result was sometimes conflict as Mary Stuart Bailey, a

pioneer woman in Amador County noted in her 1852 diary:

> Weather charming. Went out today to gather grapes to eat. Very fine. The
>
> stream on which we are is dry, rightly named Dry Creek. Went to gather grapes
>
> before the Indians got them all. Gathered about a bushel and intend drying some
>
> (Myers 1980, 90-91).

The native resources of the Sierra Nevada were not only valued for medicine and

food by the early settlers but for many other uses. Firewood was obviously cut and

gathered, and settler livelihoods depended on being able to cut posts and rails for fences

and corrals and to shape working implements and household utensils from roundwood.

The winter holidays depended on Christmas trees and bough greenery. Masonry for

fireplaces and even cabins required the collection of local rocks. While many such forest

resources were undoubtedly collected, few have been documented. Nevertheless, as the

legacy for native food and medicinal plants indicates, California settlers undoubtedly

depended on many special forest products both familiar and unknown to us today.

Data Limitations and Information Needs

Special forest product collection continues in the Sierra Nevada today but by a

wide range of consumers. Some harvesting is for incidental use while other gathering is

carried out for commercial, cultural, or recreational purposes. Anecdotal evidence

indicates that considerable ethnic and regional variation exists in what products are

collected and by whom. It appears that some historical patterns of special forest product

continue while others have changed. For example, residents' dependence on Sierra

Nevada plants for medicinal purposes has obviously declined since the 1800s but it has not disappeared. While some individuals may gather medicinal plants in the Sierra for their personal use just as miners and settlers did a century and a half ago, most medicinal plants are more likely to be gathered by herbalists who conduct plant tours or offer seminars and workshops. The degree to which commercial harvest of native Sierra plants for the herbal or pharmaceutical market occurs is unknown since, as other researchers have noted, data on these industries are extremely difficult to obtain (Schlosser and Blatner 1994).[2]

Changes in special forest product harvesting would not be unexpected given the land tenure shifts in the Sierra Nevada and the growth of population in California since 1849. It is well documented that the loss of control over their native lands to private landowners and public agencies has contributed to the limitations on Native American forest product collection (e.g., Blackburn and Anderson 1993). However, it is not clear to what extent land consolidation in the Sierra Nevada and the expansion and diversity of California's residential population may have also constrained special forest product collection by nonNative Americans. Although product collection probably occurs on small private tracts, such collection is unlikely to be significant in temporal and spatial terms on the larger landscape. Similarly, while small-scale collection may be culturally important, it is unlikely to have great commercial impact on Sierra Nevada communities if it is confined to household or incidental use.

---

[2] Several calls were made to Bay Area and Los Angeles companies which specialize in developing pharmaceutical products from known medicinal herbs and forest plants, but data could not be obtained.

The collection of products from large areas of public and private land, however, may be significant today in ways that forest product collection of yesteryear was not. This has long been recognized by the Forest Service which has issued permits to individuals seeking to gather forest products since the turn of the century. Hence, permit trends may reflect cultural and social patterns of special forest product harvesting, which in turn may have both direct and indirect social and ecological impacts on Sierra Nevada forests. These potential social and ecological trends have in part been recognized by past and existing forest management policies, which have attempted to address minor product harvesting through regulation.

Conflicting policies for special forest product management on national forest lands extends to the Forest Reserve Act of 1891 and the Forest Management Act of 1897. The 1891 preservation act mandated the protection of forest resources while the 1897 act insured their availability to the greatest number of people possible. In attempting to specify how the Forest Service should uphold the two acts and the conflicting principles of preservation and use, Gifford Pinchot, first national forester of the Forest Service, issued *The Use Book* of 1905 (published in 1906) in which he instructed that

> The timber, water, pasture, mineral, and other resources of the forest reserves are for the use of the people. They may be obtained under reasonable conditions without delay. Legitimate improvements and business enterprises are encouraged. Forest reserves are open to all persons for all lawful purposes. Persons who wish to make any use of the resources of a forest reserve for which a permit is required should consult the nearest forest office (USDA Forest Service 1906, 11).

813

In establishing the permit system, the Forest Service was obliged to recognize the

legal claims of those with title to lands within the forest reserves but was also given the

jurisdiction to grant special privileges in the form of "applications for permission to

occupy or use lands, resources, or products of a forest reserve" including "the purchases

of sand, clay, gravel, hay, and other forest reserve products" (USDA Forest Service 1906,

27-28). As a designated "special privilege," forest product permits could be issued

"unless otherwise specifically fixed by regulation" and "may be granted by the Forester

for any term consistent with forest reserve interests" (USDA Forest Service 1906, 29). In

issuing the permit, the Forester (later the ranger or district ranger) was expected to charge

reasonably for the permit and to submit all payments to the "Special Fiscal Agent,

Washington D.C." or the national office. Finally, in administering permits, forest officers

were reminded by Pinchot that they were

> servants of the people. They must answer all inquiries concerning reserve
>
> methods fully and cheerfully, and be at least as prompt and courteous in the
>
> conduct of reserve business as they would in private business.. Information should
>
> be given tactfully, by advice, and not by offensive warnings (USDA Forest
>
> Service 1906, 18).

However, when tact and information fail and permit violations occur, "all forest officers

are directed to be vigilant in discovering violations of forest reserve laws and regulations

and diligent in arresting offenders" (USDA Forest Service 1906, 92).

Little has changed since the turn of the century. District rangers are still charged

with carrying out these competing policies of serving the public, enforcing the law, and returning the receipts to Washington, D.C. Because the districts are not allowed to retain the receipts for administering special forest product permits, few financial resources exist to administer special forest product management. Currently, permits special forest products are written out by hand rather than entered on computer. Hence, no automated databases currently exist to systematically track and analyze types and amounts of products harvested. Permit records are maintained at both the district and the forest level in order to account for permit receipts to the national office. Thus, permits are stored only until annual audits are completed and then discarded.

Because of the limitations of the national forest permit system for nontimber products, our current knowledge of special forest product gathering is limited not only by the lack of historical records but by current constraints on available data. In California, large private corporations like Georgia Pacific also issue permits for the collection of special forest products, but these are not maintained in an automated database and often do not designate the particular product for which the permit is requested. Most Georgia Pacific permits are issued only for hunting and fishing, and in the last decade fewer than 20 have been written for collection of special forest products like cones or mushrooms. In addition, only employees and customers are allowed to cut firewood (Angie Pasazza, Resource Department, Georgia Pacific Corporation, 28 June 1995).

Given these data limitations and information needs, this assessment aimed to systematically analyze current special forest product permit records for national forests in the Sierra Nevada. Trends in types and amounts of special forest products gathered and special interests and concerns about collection were examined.

Given these data limitations and information needs, this assessment aimed to systematically analyze current special forest product permit records for national forests in the Sierra Nevada. Trends in types and amounts of special forest products gathered and special interests and concerns about collection were examined.

METHODS

Because historic trends in special forest product harvesting appear to have shifted in the last century, this assessment aimed to provide descriptive quantitative and qualitative data for current trends in special forest product collection, particularly by different cultural user groups, across the Sierra Nevada and, especially, from the national forests. It also aimed to examine special concerns and interests as reflected in the case study of the Eldorado National Forest.

Sierra Nevada National Forest Survey Data

In August 1994, I developed a brief electronic mail (DG) questionnaire that was revised and distributed by cooperators in the Region 6 office in September[5] and sent to the nine Sierra Nevada national forests.[4] The questionnaire requested special forest product permit summary data and anecdotal concerns and information concerning special forest productsAggregate annual data for specific measures were sought including measures on the types of product permitted, the amounts for which the permit was issued, and the fees charged for the permit . Qualitative comments were also requested on the

---

[5] I would like to especially thank Brian Stone and Anne Bradley for their help.
[4] The nine forests were the Modoc, Lassen, Plumas, Tahoe, Eldorado, Stanislaus, Sierra, Sequoia, and Inyo National Forests.

sociocultural characteristics of permittees and specific concerns about special forest product collection.

Since permits are maintained on a fiscal year (1 October through 30 September) basis, data were requested for the previous four fiscal years (1990 through 1993) since most permit records are saved for a maximum of four years. Because the questionnaire was sent at the peak of fire season and at the start of a new fiscal year, data were not requested for 1994. Forest personnel were asked to complete and return the questionnaire to the regional office by the end of October.

By November 1994 most forests had responded and by January 1995, eight responses had been received.[6] Several forests delegated the data collection to their ranger district offices and others returned questionnaires directly from the forest supervisor's office. Quantitative permit data were compiled from those forests submitting district-level data in a forest-wide summary and all data were entered and analyzed in a database program (Microsoft Access). Qualitative comments about sociocultural user groups and patterns of harvest were reviewed and trends and concerns were summarized.

Limitations and Assumptions of the National Forest Survey

In general, record information is vital for virtually all phases of program evaluation and impact assessment. However, while record information may be adequate for routine administrative functioning, it may not necessarily be sufficiently accurate for program monitoring (Burstein and Freeman 1985). This caveat is even more significant given the fact that the aggregate permit records were obtained indirectly via survey

---

[6] Responses were received from all the forests except the Inyo National Forest.

817

questionnaire. Thus, several limitations exist in using permit records as a measure of special forest product collection activity in the national forests of the Sierra Nevada.

First, permits are only issued to those individuals who take the trouble to seek them and do not reflect unpermitted gathering. The degree to which forest users comply with national forest regulations to secure a permit for special forest product collection is unknown.

Second, it must be assumed that the permit data reported in the survey reflect all the permit records from every district in every forest. Because permits are usually issued and regulated from the district office, forests for which incomplete district data were received may not be adequately represented or missing districts may not have issued special forest product permits.

Third, both types and amounts of special forest products vary by code and unit of measure. For example, biomass may reflect green or dry biomass and may otherwise be reported as cull logs or saw logs. In addition, biomass permits may be issued in units of tons, cubic feet, cunits, or even pickup loads. Much of the challenge in compiling the permit record data for the eight Sierra Nevada forests was in tracking the different categories for any given product and its unit of measure.

Fourth, even though a permit may be issued for an amount as large as 500 tons, it is not necessarily the case that 500 tons was actually harvested. Similarly, no data are available to determine whether any permitted amounts of a product were exceeded.

Finally, different forest personnel encounter different aspects of managing special forest product use so that information gaps often exist. Many permits are issued through the district or forest timber management office via the reception desk. However, specific concerns about ecological impacts for any given product may be raised to the forest botanist, ecologist, or archaeologist rather than the office which maintains or issues the permit records. Because of the number of office networks and functions, information concerning special forest product use may not be transmitted to those completing the survey questionnaire for the regional office.

Special forest product permits are issued according to national forest boundaries and usually, for only select areas within each forest. For example, firewood collection may be allowed only in areas where timber has been harvested and only for dead and down logs. In addition to this spatial variation within the forest, collection areas may vary temporally from year to year. Even if individual collection maps (often attached to a product permit) were available for the years studied, the limitations of time and funding would not allow for such data to be collected. Furthermore, one would have to assume that permittees collect in only designated areas, which may or may not be true for any given product on any given forest.

Finally, special forest products are generally assessed by forest community habitat type rather than by watershed drainage boundaries (Schlosser and Blatner 1994). Hence, it is not possible to systematically extrapolate from the data used for this study to the watershed level. Because habitat types shift from north to south, trends in special forest product harvesting can be characterized from the national forest data by gross boundaries of north, central, and south Sierra Nevada subregions. Patterns in collection trends are reflected in the data for the subregional scale of the Sierra Nevada. National forest boundaries often overlap in terms of ecological community types and gathering practices so that subregional differences become more apparent as the boundaries are aggregated into larger ecological and institutional units.

Because data were only available for a very narrow, four-year period at most, it is not possible to extrapolate to previous years of special forest product gathering in the Sierra Nevada. The limitations of such a narrow window are many given the cycles of drought and flood characteristic of the region and given the rapid pattern of settlement and resulting environmental changes in the last century and a half. Despite these limitations, it should be stressed that this survey is the first systematic compilation and analysis of special forest products across national forests for the Sierra Nevada. As a result, it provides initial baseline data of what products are being collected and by whom for the region.

Eldorado National Forest Case Study Data

For the Eldorado National Forest case study, numerous forest and district personnel cooperated in providing both quantitative and qualitative information.[7] Where the permit survey for the Sierra Forest provided only aggregated permit data, individual permit data were obtained for fiscal years 1991 through 1993 and entered into a database (Mircosoft Access). These data generally included the name and address of the permittee and the type, amount, and price (fee) of the product for which the permit was issued.[8]

---

[7] Thanks are extended to Rex Baumback, Bob Jessen, Susan Yasuda, Barbara Rabinsky, Mike Foster, Bonnie Tolbert, Vicki Ethier, Annette Parsons, Joanne Fites, and all the others who helped from the Eldorado National Forest.
[8] For the sake of confidentiality, permittee names and addresses were not analyzed and hence not reported.

Specific measures used from these data included type, amount, and price of product and geographic affiliation of the permittee. Permittee affiliation was obtained by coding permit addresses as to geographic affiliation, i.e., local, regional (Sacramento or Bay Area), or extraregional (North Coast, South Coast, and by state if out of state).

District and forest personnel most frequently reported public and management concerns about mushroom collection on the forest. To identify the nature of these concerns and issues, all public comment letters (n=28 excluding 27 identical form letters) were analyzed, and specific ecological and social concerns were identified from the letters. These concerns were compiled as a coding sheet based on standard content analysis procedures as described in Krippendorff (1980) and Holsti (1969). The letters were then coded by three independent judges, all graduate students of ecology at UC Davis, as to the presence or absence of the concerns. The use of three independent judges is consistent with established content analysis methodology (McCullough 1993). Coded responses were then assigned a single response based on the rating for which a minimum of two out of the three judges agreed. Concerns were then tabulated and graphically analyzed for frequency. In addition, the addresses of the letter writers (n=55 including form letters) were coded for geographical regional affiliation, and the regional affiliations of the letter writers were compared with those of the mushroom permittees on the forest.

In addition to the content analysis of public comment letters, a local commercial mushroom picker who has actively worked with the Eldorado National Forest in developing its wild mushroom policy provided field assistance and background information. Finally, internet messages by representatives of North American

Mycological Society groups provided additional contextual information for understanding wild mushroom harvesting on the Eldorado National Forest.

Limitations and Assumptions of the Eldorado Case Study

The limitations and assumptions of permit data for the regional, aggregate permit data also exist for the Eldorado National Forest individual permit data. These include the assumptions about compliance, completeness, uniformity, and internal validity described above. Individual records were obtained directly from the supervisor's office so that any measure error introduced by obtaining data by survey was avoided. In addition, the qualitative data provided by numerous forest personnel in different functions contribute to completeness and internal validity. However, the problems of compliance and uniformity remain.

Because of geographic location, different user groups may use one particular national forest in ways unique to that forest so that generalizing to the rest of the national forests in the Sierra Nevada is limited. Thus, the Eldorado case study is most limited in its external validity. However, qualitative data provided by the regional survey contribute to the general comparisons for sociocultural user groups and special forest product concerns on the Eldorado National Forest. In addition, the Eldorado case study provides valuable information on at least one commercially valuable special forest product, wild mushrooms, which are gathered annually from western forests as a multimillion industry (Schlosser and Blatner 1994). Thus, this initial assessment is a significant first step in establishing baseline data for future monitoring of special forest product collection in the

Sierra Nevada and for evaluating current management of existing products susceptible to harvesting pressure.

Supplemental Special Forest Product Use Interviews

A limited number of supplemental special forest product use interviews were conducted in conjunction with the Eldorado National Forest case study and the general survey of national forests in the Sierra Nevada. Because of the historical importance of medicinal and food plants and the perception that different commercial and ethnic uses of special forest products in the Sierra now exist, ethnic herbal and pharmaceutical companies and businesses were contacted by phone or through interviews to determine to what extent these enterprises were distribution outlets for special forest products from the Sierra Nevada. In addition, University of California Cooperative Extension (UCCE) personnel who actively worked with different ethnic groups in the central Sierra Nevada counties were interviewed and contributed data to this assessment.[3] These interviews supplemented the review of literature concerning special forest product use in the Sierra Nevada. Data obtained from these sources are referenced throughout this report.

---

[3] The assistance of Sua Yang, Maria Hernandez, Joanne Sutherlin, Aaron Nelson, and Joanne Ikeda is gratefully acknowledged.

RESULTS

National Forest Survey

A wide range of special forest product permits were issued by the national forests of the Sierra Nevada for the four-year period beginning in fiscal year 1990. The quantities of products collected varied greatly, but the units of measure for which the permits were written were exceedingly diverse from forest to forest and even district to district (table 3). Hence, it is not possible to aggregate the total amount of special forest products collected for the time period of the study.

Table 3
Total Amount of Special Forest Products for Which Permits were Issued from National Forests in the Sierra Nevada FY90-FY93

Forest	*Academic Plants*	Plants
Eldorado	Total	14

Forest	*Bark*	Pickup Loads	Pounds	Lin Ft
Tahoe		2	0	0
Sierra		4	300	0
Sequoia		0	0	2000
	Total	6	300	2000

Forest	*Bees*	Colonies	Site
Tahoe	Total	300	1

Forest	*Biomass*	Tons	MBF	Pickup Loads
Modoc		83721	0	0
Lassen		0	4378	0
Plumas		8345	0	0
Tahoe		0	0	2
Sierra		0	2250	0
Sequoia		1900	0	0
	Total	93966	6628	2

Forest	*Boughs*	Tons	Pieces	Cords	Cu Ft	Lin Ft
Modoc		1	0	0	0	0
Lassen		34	0	0	0	0
Plumas		1726	0	0	0	169
Tahoe		17.5	1000	18	0	8000
Eldorado		0	0	0	2896	183
Sierra		1	645	0	1534	0
Sequoia		0	0	0	6700	1000
	Total	1779.5	1645	18	11130	9352

Forest	Christmas Trees	Trees	Lin Ft
Modoc		3719	0
Lassen		38911	0
Plumas		36484	0
Tahoe		4280	0
Eldorado		0	6895
Sierra		1975	160
Sequoia		3490	0
	Total	88859	7055

Forest	Cones	Tons	Bushels	Pieces	Sacks
Lassen		220	515	0	0
Plumas		0	0	4341	0
Tahoe		101.5	0	33100	0
Eldorado		0	0	0	771
Sierra		0	0	65000	0
Sequoia		4	0	1000	7
	Total	325.5	515	103441	778

Forest	Ferns	Sacks	Pieces
Tahoe		4	0
Sierra		0	2522
	Total	4	2522

Forest	Firewood	Cords
Modoc		42828
Lassen		46630
Plumas		58389
Tahoe		11071
Eldorado		50755
Stanislaus		45240
Sierra		45559
Sequoia		23118
	Total	323590

Forest	Native American Plants	Unreported
Tahoe		0
Sierra	Total	0

Forest	Ladybugs	Unreported
Tahoe		0
Eldorado		0
	Total	0

Forest	Lichen	Tons	Cu Ft
Modoc		0	6000
Plumas	Total	500	6000

Forest	Manzanita	Cubic Feet	Tons	Lin Ft	Pieces
Modoc		1000	0	0	0
Tahoe		0	4.5	4000	0
Eldorado		0	0	0	2660
Sierra		0	0	0	0
Sequoia		1200	0	21500	0
	Total	2200	4.5	25500	2660

Forest	Mistletoe	Cu Ft
Sequoia	Total	20

Forest	Moss	Pounds
Tahoe		26
Sequoia		67
	Total	93

Forest	Mushrooms	Days	Month	Season
Lassen		1	0	0
Eldorado		0	0	49
Stanislaus		35	2	0
	Total	36	2	49

Forest	Needles	Pounds
Sierra	Total	1038

Forest	Rock	Tons
Sierra	Total	1

Forest	Roundwood	Pieces	MBF	Lin Ft	Cords	Tons
Lassen		1100	10	0	0	0
Tahoe		455	0	1188	2	0
Eldorado		2015	27	0	0	0
Sierra		18568	0	0	0	1
Sequoia		11051	0	0	0	0
	Total	33189	37	1188	2	1

Forest	Sawdust	Tons
Sierra	Total	3

Forest	Seeds	Pounds
Tahoe	Total	600

Forest	Specialty Wood Parts	Pieces	Tons	Cords	Cu Ft
Lassen		200	2	0	0
Tahoe		300	0.75	52	0
Eldorado		440	0	0	0
Sequoia		0	0	0	200
	Total	940	2.75	52	200

Forest	Transplants	Pieces
Lassen		0
Plumas		84
Tahoe		132
Eldorado		100
Sierra		566
	Total	882

In addition to widely varying units of measures, fee structures by which forests and districts charged for special forest product permits also differed greatly. Some permits were issued for free use and others were issued for a fee. Fees in turn could vary depending on the unit of measure, the year, and whether the permit was being issued to an individual or a nonprofit organization. For example, Christmas tree permits could be issued for free use or could be charged $1 per ft or anywhere from $1 to $10 for a whole tree depending on the permittee, the unit of measure, and the district or forest permit policy.

Because of a consistent unit of measure, dollar amounts for the total number of fees charged can be aggregated. For the four-year period of the study, $3,347,634 was collected in permit fees for special forest products from the eight national forests in the survey. Of this amount, 61% was charged for firewood, 20% was charged for Christmas trees, and 16% was charged for biomass. The remaining 3% of total fees was charged for all other special forest products (table 4).

In addition to widely varying units of measures, fee structures by which forests and districts charged for special forest product permits also differed greatly. Some permits were issued for free use and others were issued for a fee. Fees in turn could vary depending on the unit of measure, the year, and whether the permit was being issued to an individual or a nonprofit organization. For example, Christmas tree permits could be issued for free use or could be charged $1 per ft or anywhere from $1 to $10 for a whole tree depending on the permittee, the unit of measure, and the district or forest permit policy.

Because of a consistent unit of measure, dollar amounts for the total number of fees charged can be aggregated. For the four-year period of the study, $3,347,634 was collected in permit fees for special forest products from the eight national forests in the survey. Of this amount, 61% was charged for firewood, 20% was charged for Christmas trees, and 16% was charged for biomass. The remaining 3% of total fees was charged for all other special forest products (table 4).

Table 4
Total Fees and Total Number of Permits Issued by National Forests in the Sierra Nevada
FY90-FY93

Product	Total Fee ($)	Total Permits (n)	Fee-to-Permit Ratio ($:n)
Firewood	2,043,613	97,249	21
Christmas trees	680,622	68,697	10
Biomass	545,231	150	3,635
Cones	63,574	96	662
Roundwood	4,084	206	20
Boughs	3,455	252	14
Manzanita	2,112	49	43
Lichen	1,225	12	102
Specialty wood	1,061	23	46
Mushrooms	1,040	67	16
Transplants	790	47	1,681
Bees	330	4	83
Bark	140	20	7
Ferns	140	2	70
Seeds	105	13	8
Moss	72	3	24
Ladybugs	30	10	3
Mistletoe	10	1	10
Academic plants	0	14	0
Native American plants	0	8	0
Needles	0	6	0
Rock	0	1	0
Sawdust	0	3	0
Total	3,347,634	166,933	20

The minor proportion of fees collected for special forest products other than firewood, Christmas trees, and biomass is reflected in the total number of permits issued for the same period. Because a permit must be obtained not only to collect an initial amount of product but also to collect additional amounts of product once the maximum amount has been collected, permits do not proportionally represent mutually exclusive permittees. In other words, a single permittee may have been issued multiple permits and many or few such permittees may be represented in the total number of permits. Although the total number of permits does not represent the total number of permittees harvesting products, it is a measure of collection activity and hence, with limitations, of amounts harvested. Thus, the total number of permits should be directly correlated with the sum total of permit fees collected for that product. This is the case since the most frequently permitted products, firewood and Christmas trees, together represent 99% of the total number of permits issued (58% and 41% respectively) and 81% of the sum total of fees charged (table 4).

The economic value of permitted special forest products should be reflected in the fee-to-permit ratio since permits represent the amount which each collector can harvest. The fee-to-permit ratio illustrates the value of many "minor" special forest products despite the fact that together, they are worth less than 3% of the total amount of fees for the four-year period (table 4). Biomass is the most valuable product since each permit issued during the period was worth $3,635 of the total amount of product. However, other products such as transplants, cones, lichen, bees, ferns, specialty wood products, manzanita, and moss are all worth more than the mean fee-to-permit ratio of $20.

Firewood is just above average with a fee-to-permit ratio of $21 and Christmas trees are well under average with a fee-to-permit ratio of only $10.

Although the fee and permit aggregate data indicate that firewood, Christmas trees, and biomass are the dominant special forest products collected in the Sierra Nevada, these aggregate data alone do not represent either the sociocultural significance of many minor products nor their economic value to particular individuals, groups, or communities who may rely on these products as a main or supplemental livelihood. The $78,168 in fees for these minor special forest products does not represent the income earned from directly selling the products or from adding further value to them through various production and distribution channels. In addition, the 837 permits issued for these products do not represent the total number of permit requests for *other* products for which permits were not issued. The sum total of permits also does not reflect the amount of unpermitted collection that may have occurred during this period. Finally, all three measures, i.e., amount of fees, number of permits, and fee-to-permit ratio, best represent previous demand rather than present or future demand for special forest products across the Sierra Nevada.

Such representation requires both temporal and spatial data. Temporal trends in demand for products are indicated by the trends in the number of permits issued for each product over the four year period. Spatial trends in demand are indicated by the concentration in the total number of permits issued for each product by each national forest for the period. Products are considered in order of the total amount of fees collected for the four-year period (table 4) and for the national forests reporting data (table 3). These two measures are considered in the context of qualitative accounts of special forest product harvesting reported in the national forest survey and in interviews.

Firewood

Firewood permits have generally declined on the national forests of the Sierra Nevada since 1990 (figure 1). The greatest amount of firewood has been harvested in the northcentral Sierra Nevada forests including the Lassen, Plumas, Eldorado, and the Stanislaus and in the southern Sierra Nevada on the Sequoia (figure 2). The least amount of firewood has been collected from the Modoc, Tahoe, and Sierra. On all the forests, firewood is cut for both commercial and household use. From north to south, firewood collection patterns vary.

On the Modoc National Forest, primarily local residents cut firewood. Personal use is limited to 10 cords per household and is allowed all year except when fire conditions are high and soil moisture conditions may cause resource damage. To protect wildlife habitat, no snags except juniper (*Juniperus* spp.) and lodgepole pine (*Pinus contorta*) may be cut and wood removal is allowed in designated areas only. In addition to juniper and lodgepole, species harvested include ponderosa pine (*Pinus ponderosa*), white fir (*Abies concolor*) and incense cedar (*Libocedrus decurrens*). Small commercial permits range from 10 to 25 cords maximum with no more than 5 permits or 125 cords allowed per permittee in a given year. On the Lassen National Forest, 10 cords are allowed per household for domestic use. Numerous violations of firewood cutting regulations have been reported. These include cutting wood without a permit, exceeding diameter limits, exceeding the allowable quantities for personal use, cutting live trees,

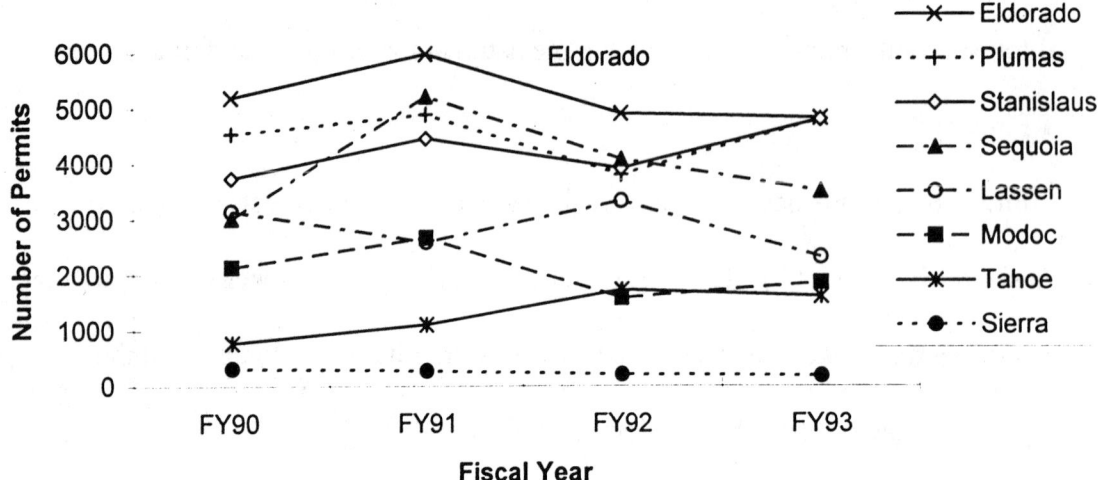

Figure 1
Trends in Firewood Permits by National Forest FY90-FY93

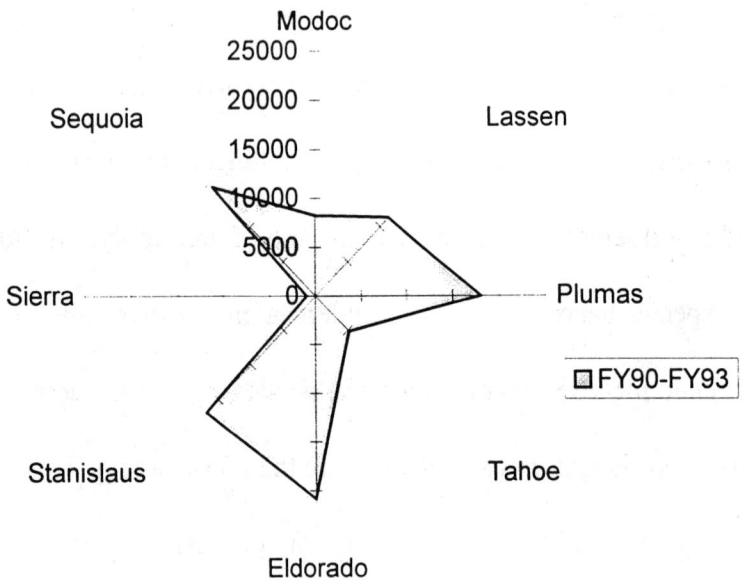

Figure 2
Total Number of Permits for Firewood by National Forest FY90-FY93

and cutting standing hardwood. Conflicts with local Native Americans were noted. As one employee is reported to have said:

For years, it has been part of their culture to collect and sell wood for the public. Whole families live off this. The Forest Service keeps careful track of 'them' to make sure no one family gets more than 10 cords, no matter how many are in the [extended tribal] family.

On the Eldorado National Forest, almost all firewood is from cull logging decks. Most wood is harvested by local loggers and commercial firewood cutters although some collection, including illegal cutting, occurs for personal use. Commercial firewood may also be sold as pulp, cull, or fuel logs as well as for firewood. Species harvested include hardwoods such black oak (*Quercus kelloggii*), madrone (*Arbutus menziesii*) and manzanita (*Arctostaphylos* spp.) as well as ponderosa pine, incense cedar and white fir. Because firewood can only be collected from dead and down trees and in designated areas, firewood cutting on the Eldorado has declined since 1988 with the reduction in logging. This trend appears to be the case for the other Sierra national forests as well.

Unlike the other Sierra forests, firewood permits on the Sequoia are sold by the cord on a bid basis so prices and amounts vary by permittee. Firewood is collected primarily for heating local homes, particularly since many of the local communities do not have natural gas and would have to depend on relatively expensive propone fuel or electricity to heat their homes if firewood was not available.

<u>Christmas Trees</u>

Despite the large number of Christmas trees harvested from seven of the national forests in the Sierra Nevada, only the three northern forests have each issued more than 25 permits in the last four years (figure 3; see also table 3). The Modoc, Lassen, and Plumas National Forests have all issued thousands of Christmas tree permits in this period (figure 4). The remaining central and southern forests have all sold several thousand trees each but issued fewer than 24 permits on each forest for the same period (figure 4; see also table 3).

The greatest number of permits has been issued by the Plumas National Forest. On the Plumas, Christmas trees have been sold from the clearing limits along roads as part of road maintenance. Christmas tree permits are issued to nonprofit groups like schools and local fire departments for annual fund raising sales. On the Lassen, most Christmas tree permits are purchased by private individuals, nonprofit organizations, and small commercial cutters from the area. Nonprofit groups buy trees at the reduced rate of $1 while small commercial trees range from $0.90 to $3.90 per tree. On the Modoc, a maximum of two trees is permitted per household and each tree requires a permit. Commercial cutting is not allowed, and all trees must be 6 in diameter with stumps no greater than 12 in high. Cutting is allowed anywhere on the forest except within prohibited wood cutting areas, tree plantations, and within 200 ft of campgrounds and roads. Permittees are generally local residents.

On the central and southern forests where only a few permits have been issued, most permittees are nonprofit organizations and commercial cutters. On the Eldorado,

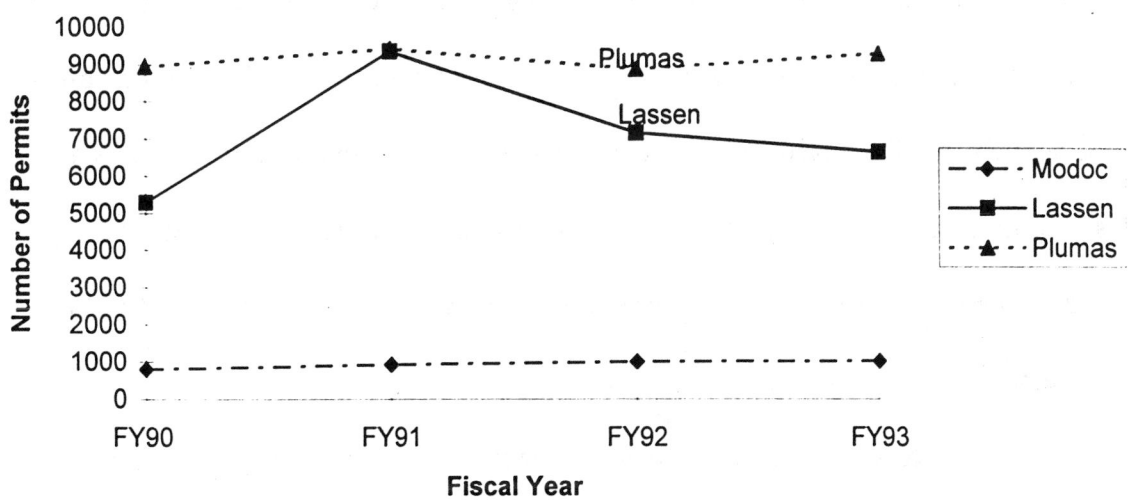

Figure 3
Trends in Christmas Tree Permits by National Forest FY90-FY93

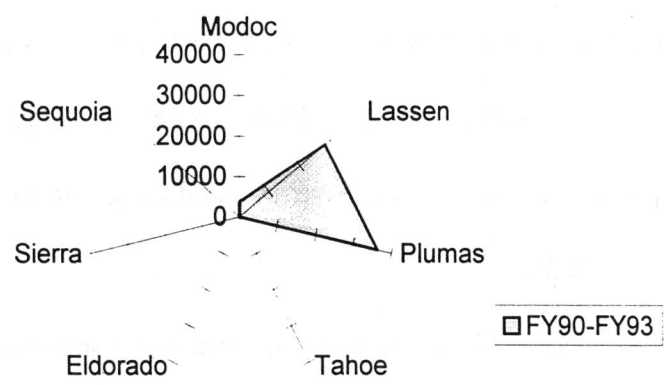

Figure 4
Total Number of Permits for Christmas Trees (n >25) by National Forest FY90-FY93

most permits are issued in logging slash areas, which are declining in number. Some Christmas tree cutting is also done to thin sapling stands. Permit prices vary by the linear foot from $0.30 for red fir (*Abies magnifica*), $0.20 for white fir, and $0.10 for all other species. On the Sierra National Forest, only a few free-use, administrative permits are issued per year to local nonprofit groups including one for the local town tree on one district. Few permits are issued because of silvicultural reasons and time constraints. One employee noted that

> folks are very selective about the trees they want. They are doing us a
> favor of sorts by helping us thin stands that would otherwise be thinned
> through service contracts.

On the Sequoia, Christmas tree permits are sold on contracts subject to sealed bids.

Biomass

The sale of biomass permits has been somewhat erratic over the last four years as the cogeneration plant demand for wood chips has been relatively volatile (figure 5; see also table 3). The two northern forests, the Modoc, Lassen, and Plumas, have not only issued the largest number of permits but have also sold the greatest amount of biomass (figure 6; see also table 3).

On the Lassen National Forest, local landowners and small logging operators remove dead biomass from thinning operations, which are cleared for fire hazard reduction, and as salvage. Most biomass is shipped to local cogeneration plants. On the Modoc, cull logs are sold to Oregon and California logging companies as dry biomass. Some districts have issued free permits for thinning salvage biomass, and other districts

836

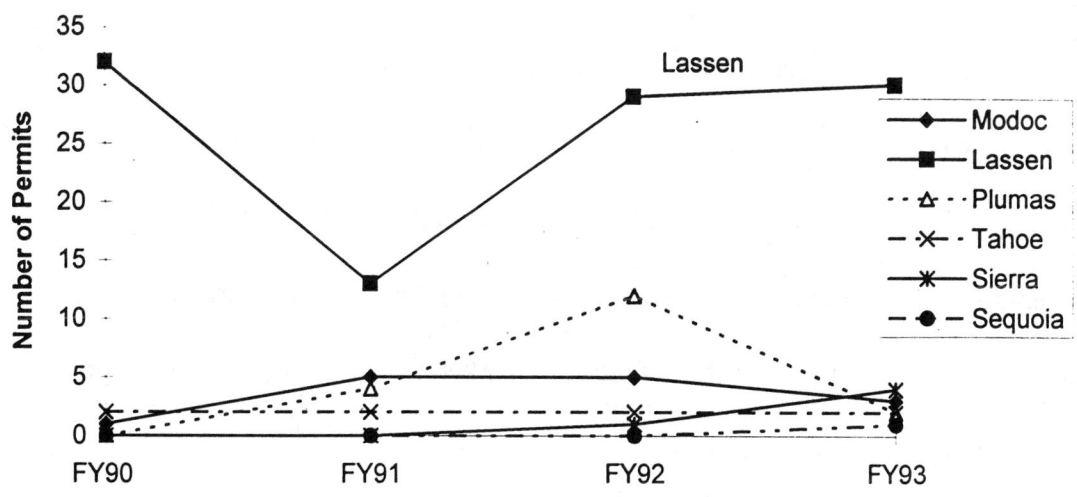

Figure 5
Trends in Biomass Permits by National Forest FY90-FY93

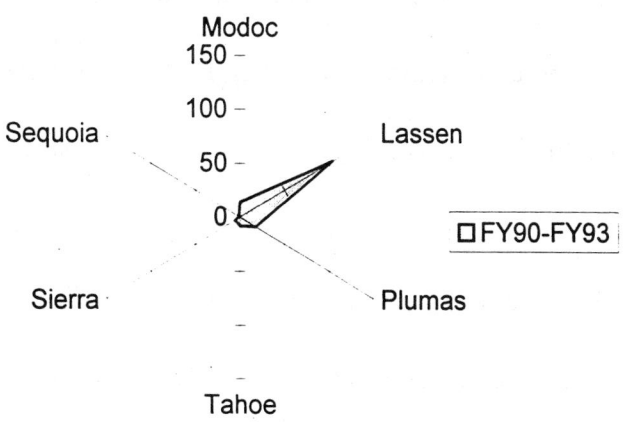

Figure 6
Total Number of Permits for Biomass by National Forest FY90-FY93

have issued thinning service contracts for green biomass, which has been sold as fuel to a local cogeneration plant.

To the south, the Stanislaus National Forest does "not consider biomass to be a special forest product" and did not report biomass permits. On the Sierra National Forest, local contractors buy cull log decks and thinning material as biomass for local cogeneration plants. Some districts would like to accelerate issuing biomass permits to accomplish fuel reduction projects, but the chip market has fallen because four local cogeneration plants closed in 1994.

Cones

While not as economically significant in terms of a net fees as firewood, Christmas trees, and biomass, cones are high in fee-to-permit value (see table 4). In general, permits to gather cones have declined in recent years except on the Sierra National Forest where sugar pine (*Pinus lambertiana*) cone collecting has become commercially more important (figure 7). In general, cones are more important as a minor special forest product on the central forests of the Sierra Nevada (figure 8; see also table 3).

On the Sierra National Forest, most permittees, including local public schools, collect cones for resale. A commercial cone buyer places ads in the local papers to solicit cones for purchase. The Sierra sells cones at $0.01 a piece for 4,000 cones per permit. Sugar pine cones are the most commonly gathered. Cones can only be picked from the ground. Some local residents also collect cones for decorative crafts. On the Sequoia,

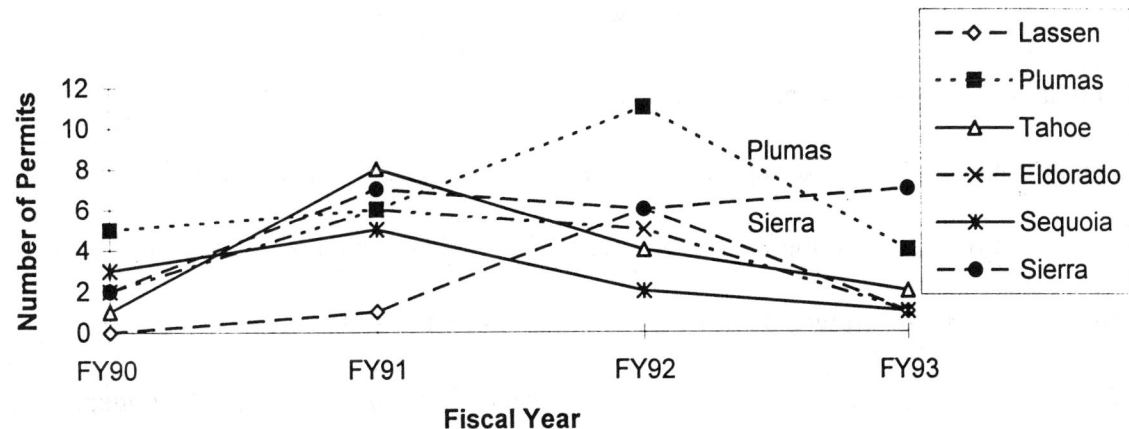

Figure 7
Trends in Cone Permits by National Forest FY90-FY93

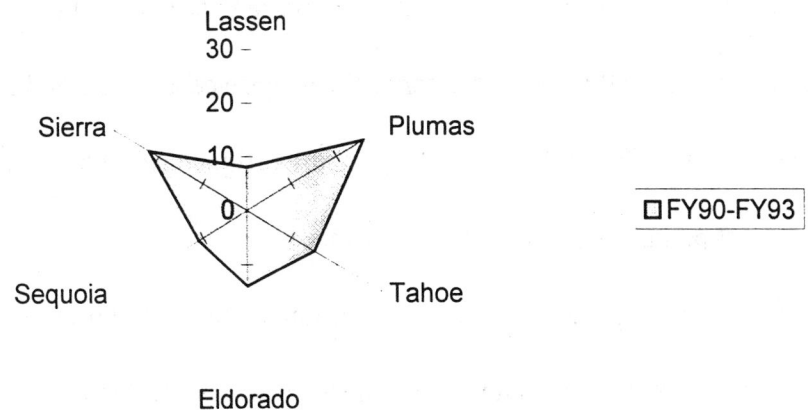

Figure 8
Total Number of Permits for Cones by National Forest FY90-FY93

National Forest, dry cones are collected for Christmas wreaths, and green sequoia (*Sequoiadendron giganteum*) cones are also gathered for resale for seed germination. Although the Stanislaus did not report any permits for cones, the forest does receive "an estimated three or four requests a year for decorative pine cones, which we sell for $1 per 100 lb bag. Actual amounts collected are probably far less than the $10 minimum charge." On the Eldorado, sugar pine cones are the most commonly gathered cones.

To the north, permittees on the Lassen National Forest collect cones for buyers from southern Oregon who then sell them to florists and wreathmakers. On the Lassen, Plumas, and Tahoe forests, local craftspeople also collect cones, particularly lodgepole pine cones, for decorative products such as wreaths.

Roundwood

Roundwood consists of posts, poles, and rails. In general, roundwood permits are limited in number. On the Sierra National Forest, roundwood permits were once in demand but they have declined substantially (figure 9; see also table 3). Most roundwood permits are issued by the Sierra, primarily for incense cedar posts and rails for a state historical park and Native American roundhouses (figure 10). On both the Sierra and Sequoia, post permits are also sold for fencing.

To the north, posts and rails on the Eldorado National Forest are cut from thinning areas principally by ranchers and home improvement users. On the Lassen, posts and poles are collected mainly from dead lodgepole pine and incense cedar trees for fences, corrals, and woodsheds. Problems have been reported with illegal cutting, slash

840

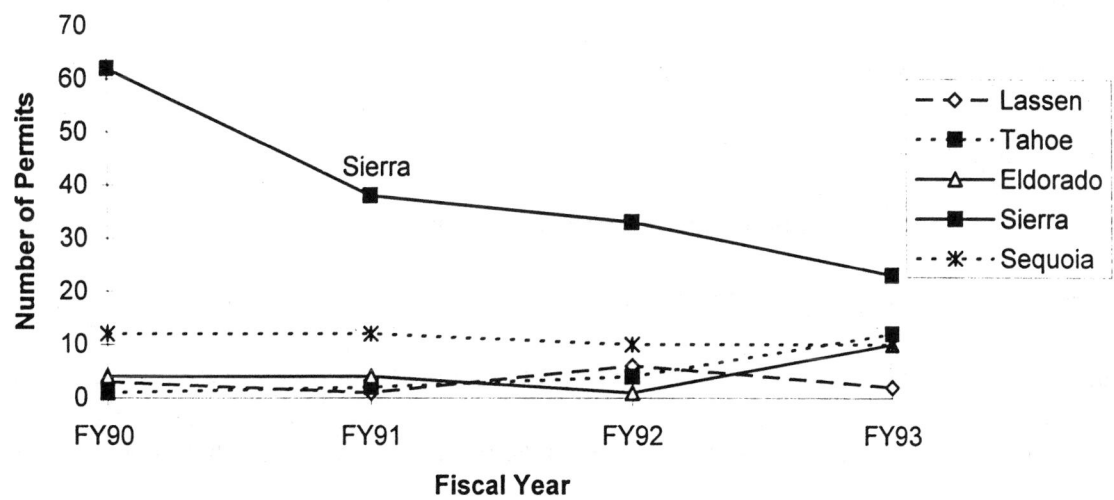

Figure 9
Trends in Roundwood Permits by National Forest FY90-FY93

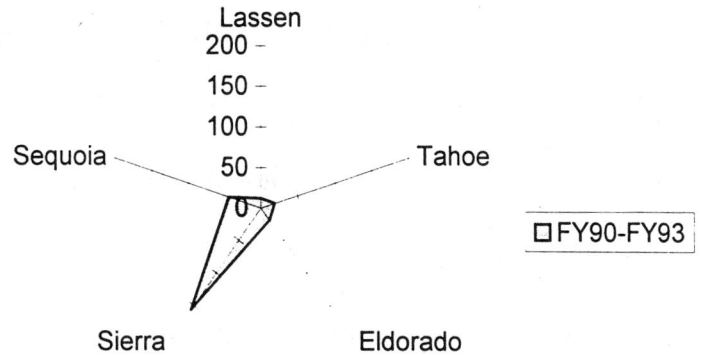

Figure 10
Total Number of Permits for Roundwood by National Forest FY90-FY93

accumulation, and vehicle ruts in wet meadow areas. On the Plumas, incense cedar posts can only be taken from dead and down trees.

Boughs

Unlike cone permits which are issued throughout the Sierra Nevada, bough permits are primarily requested on the northcentral forests and mainly for white fir and incense cedar limbs. Trends in bough permits are mixed (figure 11). On the Sierra, Tahoe, and Modoc National Forests, bough permits have increased while elsewhere in the Sierra Nevada, they have declined. The greatest number of bough permits has been sold by the Plumas National Forest (figure 12; see also table 3). However, little information about bough collecting on the Plumas was reported.

On the adjoining Tahoe National Forest, evergreen boughs are collected for wreaths and some are sold wholesale by a local family business. On the Lassen, bough cutters from southern Oregon buy permits for boughs, which they resell to commercial florists and wreathmakers. Overcutting of incense cedar limbs has been in a problem in the past so permits are strictly limited and monitored, and references from permittees are required. A few permits for juniper boughs are also sold primarily to nonlocal residents on the Modoc. Permit requests for dogwood (*Cornus* spp.) boughs are also reported to have increased on the Plumas, Lassen, Tahoe, and Eldorado National Forests.

Further south, boughs are collected for both commercial and private use on both the Sierra and the Sequoia National Forests. On the Sierra, permits for boughs are sold primarily to nonprofit organizations such as schools. Some permits for incense cedar boughs have also been bought by a private contractor who is trying to expand his supply

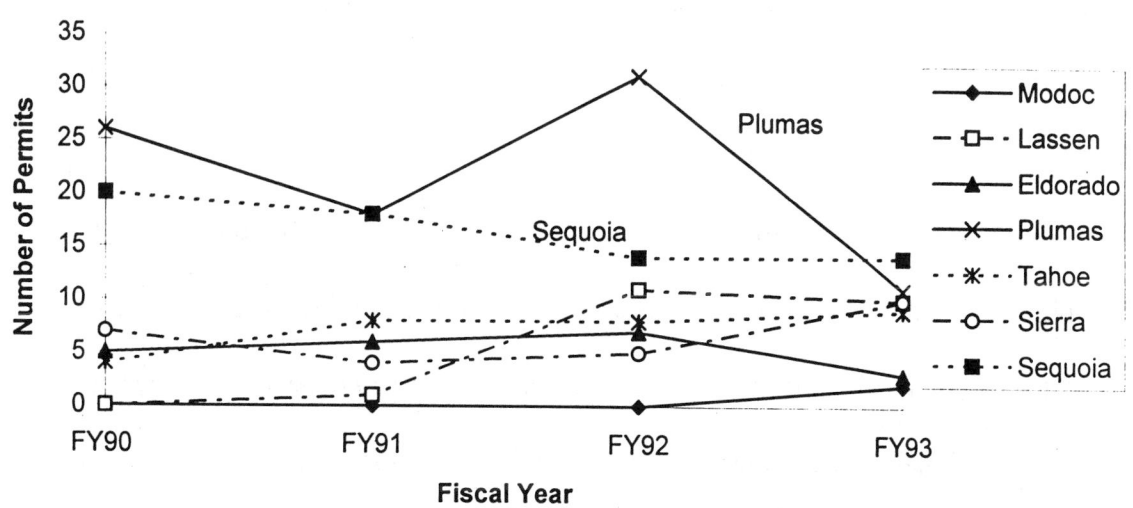

Figure 11
Trends in Bough Permits by National Forest FY90-FY93

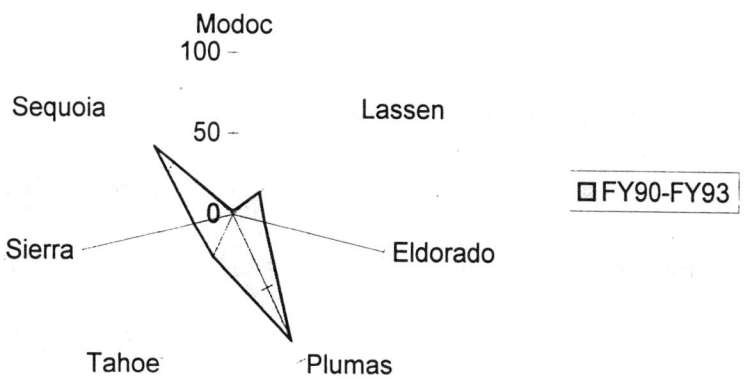

Figure 12
Total Number of Permits for Boughs by National Forest FY90-FY93

sources. In the past, he has mainly bought boughs from forests in southern California, but reportedly "the supply is getting scarce and restrictions on collection are becoming burdensome."

Manzanita

Manzanita boughs are collected primarily for pet bird perches and for floral displays. Trends have been erratic since few permits in general are written specifically for manzanita branch collection (figure 13). Most permits have been issued by the Sequoia National Forest, primarily to one individual who makes a part-time job out of collecting and selling the material to pet and bird stores (figure 14; see also table 3). Elsewhere on the Eldorado, Tahoe, Plumas, and Modoc National Forests, manzanita branches are also collected by local craftspeople for their own business or resale elsewhere. Manzanita is also cut for firewood.

Mushrooms

Over 50 permits have been issued for mushroom collection on three national forests in the Sierra Nevada, but almost all have been written in only one year so annual comparisons are not possible. Most of these permits were issued on the Eldorado and Stanislaus National Forests for morel (*Morchella* spp.) mushrooms during the spring following the wildfires of 1993 (figure 15; see also table 3). In addition, the Eldorado did not begin requiring permits for wild mushrooms until 1993. The 1993 permit allowed a maximum limit of 50 pounds of mushrooms for the annual (fiscal year) season. The Stanislaus National Forest issued daily, weekly, monthly, and seasonal permits.

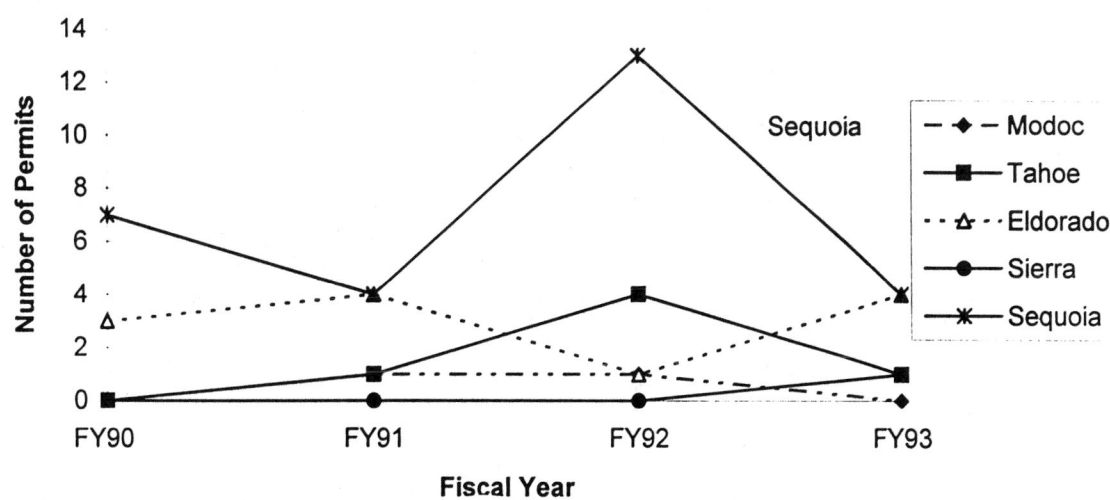

Figure 13
Trends in Manzanita Permits by National Forest FY90-FY93

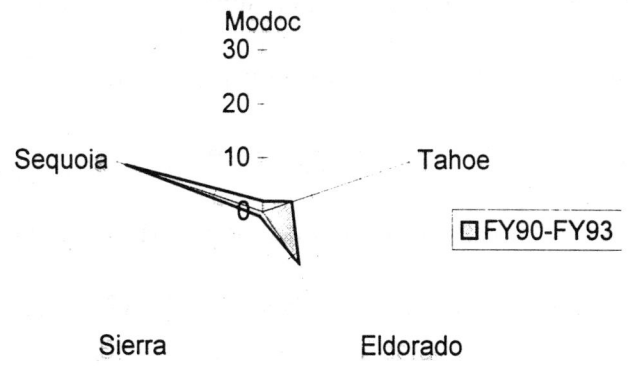

Figure 14
Total Number of Permits for Manzanita by National Forest FY90-FY93

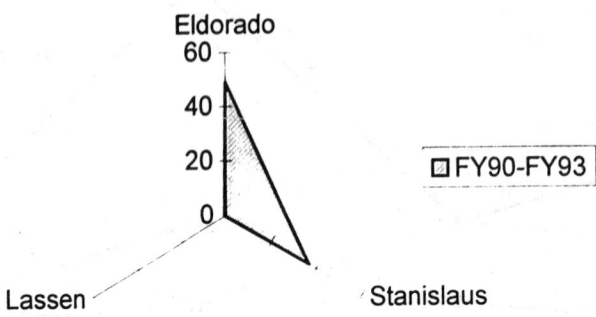

Figure 15
Total Number of Permits for Mushrooms by National Forest FY90-FY93

The northern forests have also reported interest in wild mushroom collection.

Requests for matsutake (*Tricholoma magnivelare*) mushroom permits have been reported

from the Modoc, Lassen, and Plumas National Forests, and requests for puffball

mushrooms (*Lycoperdon* spp.) have been noted on the Modoc. Because of the increase in

morel mushroom gathering on private land following the 1993 Fountain Fire, the Lassen

expects mushroom collection to increase substantially following wildfires there.

TheTahoe National Forest also reports that people collect mushrooms, especially morels,

for personal use although no permits are issued. Both the Eldorado and Tahoe National

Forests report that some gatherers may also be commercially selling morels harvested

from national forest lands.

Other Minor Products

Permits for the remaining special forest products from table 3 numbered fewer than a dozen for the four-year period. With such a small number of permits, trend patterns over the period cannot be accurately assessed. However, aggregate totals do indicate some regional trends for several products. These include stumps, burls, root wads, and other specialty wood products which are generally sold to small local businesses. Most of these specialty wood products have been collected primarily on the northern forests, especially on the Tahoe National Forest where pitch stumps, manzanita burls, and incense cedar root wads are collected for decorative wood products (figure 16). On the Sequoia National Forest, pine knots are gathered for wood carvings and on the Lassen, burls are often collected by nonprofit organizations for large-scale barbeque cooking for fund-raisers and for manufactured specialty products like burl tables.

Transplants for home and commercial landscaping are also collected from national forest lands in the Sierra Nevada. Most permits have been issued by the Plumas and Sierra forests for landscape purposes (figure 17). On the Lassen National Forest, transplants have been dug to revegetate the landscape around government buildings. On the Plumas, a local resident is issued a permit and guidelines for digging transplants for his native species nursery. On the Eldorado National Forest, commercial harvesters collect juniper, white pine (*Pinus monticola*), and lodgepole pine for bonzai trees.

Other minor products are collected from a few national forests. Bark from dead trees and laying at the base of trees is gathered for landscaping purposes from the Tahoe, Sierra, and Sequoia National Forests. On the Sierra, permits for lodgepole pine and

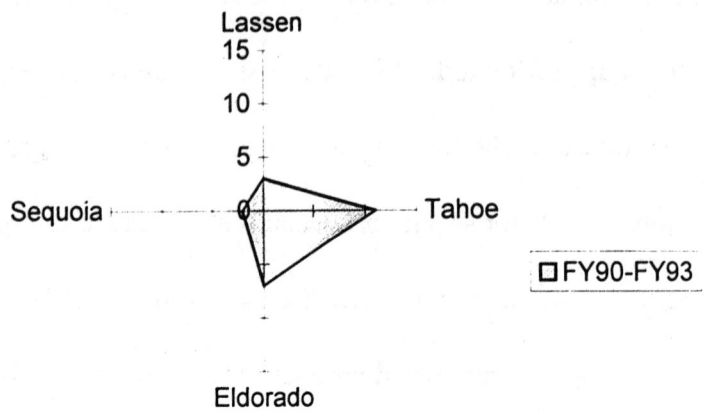

Figure 16
Total Number of Permits for Specialty Wood by National Forest FY90-FY93

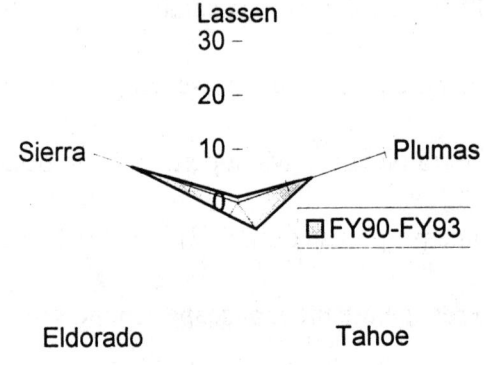

Figure 17
Total Number of Permits for Transplants by National Forest FY90-FY93

848

incense cedar bark are also issued for traditional Native American structures.

Bees, presumably honeybees (*Apis mellifera*), are collected from the Tahoe National Forest, but little information about bee collection was reported. Permits for the common garden variety ladybug beetle (*Hippodamia convergens*) have also been issued on the Tahoe, and additional requests for ladybug permits have been reported by the Eldorado and Stanislaus National Forests. Collectors claim that ladybugs are harvested from the Plumas and Lassen National Forests. Ladybugs usually congregate in canyons and along streams with openings and pine trees, and collectors take the insects from the same site several times in a season. Collections occur in the fall and late spring and are generally done by hand. The ladybugs are then transported and put in cold storage before being sold. A large number of the insects reportedly die because they are stored too long or under inappropriate conditions. While the Tahoe National Forest does not permit the actual collection of the insects, it does issue a permit for the operation of the commercial ladybug enterprise on national forest land.

Permits have been issued by the Tahoe and Sierra National Forests for "fiddeheads" or bracken ferns (*Pteridium aquilinum*). On the Tahoe, fiddlehead collection has occurred for many years. Most collectors are Asian and come in the spring to collect the ferns when they have just emerged in the "fiddlehead" stage. The ferns are picked just below the head, steamed, and eaten as food. Some of the ferns are resold to restaurants, and others are gathered only for private household use. Collectors take as many bags as they can fill. On the Sierra National Forest, most collectors are Southeast Asians, especially the Hmong, who collect ferns each May for ceremonial banquets. Both the Tahoe and the Sierra National Forests report that collectors come in large numbers and "collect wherever they want, including non-Forest Service lands as well as private lots. They don't understand they need a permit."

In addition to ferns, both lichen and moss collection has been permitted in several national forests of the Sierra Nevada. In the northern Sierra, lichens are gathered on the Modoc, Lassen, and Plumas National Forests. On the Modoc and the Lassen, lichen is collected on basalt or "flat" rock for resale to the Bay area. On the Modoc and the Plumas forests, lichen is also gathered for the dry floral market. Little was reported about moss collection, but permits to gather moss have been issued by the Tahoe and Sequoia National Forests. Mistletoe has been collected by permit on the Sequoia as well.

Sawdust and native seeds have also been collected by permit on the Sierra and Tahoe National Forests for landscaping and restoration purposes respectively. Quartz crystals are reportedly gathered from the Tahoe and Eldorado National Forests as well. Permits for river rock and decomposed granite have also been issued on the Sierra National Forest.

Permits for pine needles, primarily for decorative purposes and Native American basket weaving, have been issued on the Plumas, Stanislaus, and Sierra National Forests. The Modoc, Plumas, Tahoe, and Sierra National Forests all report that many native plants are gathered both by permit and without permit by Native Americans for basket weaving, medicines, and food. In addition, the Plumas National Forest has reported increased permit requests for beargrass (*Xerophyllum tenax*), a Native American basket weaving material, from commercial collectors.

<u>Eldorado National Forest Case Study</u>

Permits for special forest products on the Eldorado National Forest were primarily

issued for firewood collection during the fiscal period of 1991 through 1993. Of the total

number of permits (N=459), 72% were issued for firewood. The remaining permits were

written for a variety of special forest products, most of which were mushrooms (figure

18).

Individuals obtaining special forest products from the Eldorado National Forest

during the three-year period were primarily local residents. Of the 459 permittees, 68%

were local residents (figure 19). These were followed by permittees from the Sacramento

and Bay areas respectively. A smaller number of permittees were from areas of

California north of the Eldorado National Forest and from out of state, including Oregon,

Nevada, and Utah.

Regional affiliation varied according to the particular product for which the permit

was written. All the permits for Christmas trees on the Eldorado National Forest were

issued to local residents. Similarly, most firewood permits were written for local

residents (figure 20). Roundwood permits were also issued primarily to local people. In

contrast, permits for boughs (figure 21) and cones (figure 22), were issued to individuals

from the northern part of the state or out of state. Because most boughs and cones are

used in the Christmas floral green industry, it is not surprising that most of these permits

went to areas such as northern California and Oregon where the floral green industry is

well developed. In contrast to bough and cone permits, most mushroom permits were

issued to individuals from the Bay area (figure 23). The remaining special forest product

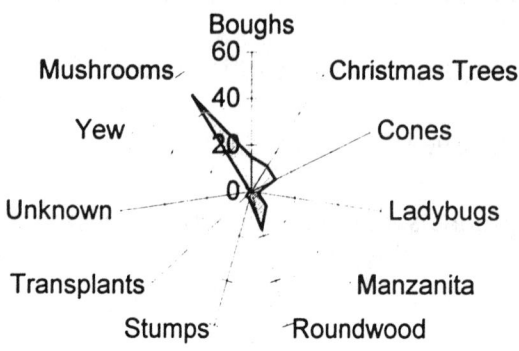

Figure 18
Distribution of Special Forest Product Permits (Excluding Firewood) Issued by the
Eldorado National Forest FY91-FY93

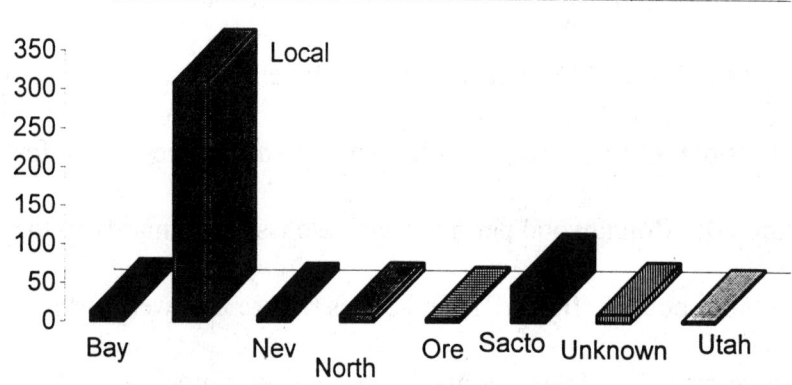

Figure 19
Regional Affiliation of Permittees of Special Forest Products on the Eldorado National
Forest FY91-FY93

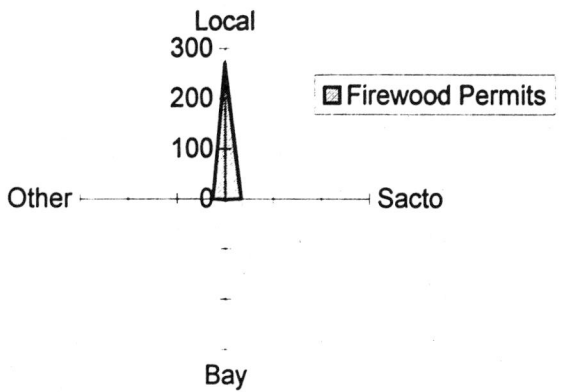

Figure 20
Regional Affiliation of Individuals with Firewood Permits on the Eldorado National
Forest FY91-FY93

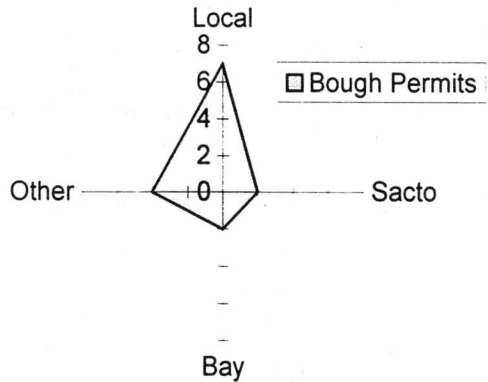

Figure 21
Regional Affiliation of Individuals with Bough Permits on the Eldorado National Forest
FY91-FY93

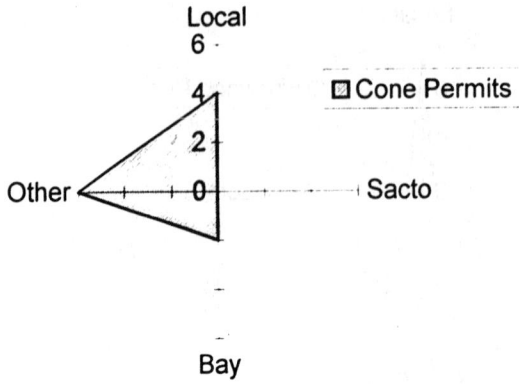

Figure 22
Regional Affiliation of Individuals with Cone Permits on the Eldorado National Forest
FY91-FY93

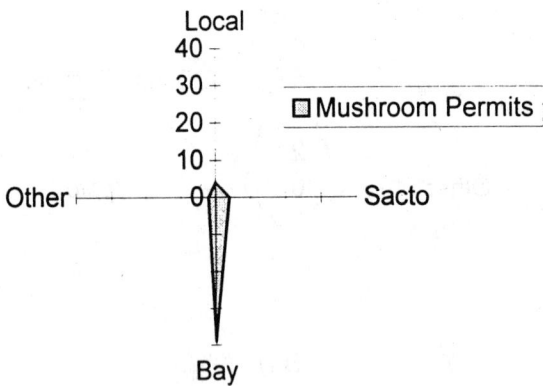

Figure 23
Regional Affiliation of Individuals with Mushroom Permits on the Eldorado National
Forest FY91-FY93

permits were too few in number to adequately represent the regional affiliation of the permittees.

Concerns about Special Forest Products on the Eldorado National Forest

Interviews with forest and district personnel indicated that a wide variety of concerns existed about both the direct and indirect effects of special forest product harvesting. The major product harvested was firewood, and some personnel said that they believed illegal cutting was increasing because of the decline in timber harvest since 1984 and hence a reduction in designated wood cutting areas on the forest. Illegal fuelwood cutting was considered especially problematic in the black oak belt on the ridgetops close to the roads. Some illegal ladybug collection had also been documented, and the jurisdictional ambiguity of permitting the enterprise but not the product was of administrative concern.

Several concerns about wildlife existed in conjunction with special forest product permitting policy on the forest. Permits for porcupine (*Erethizon dorsatum*) quills have been requested by both Native American and non-native American basket makers, and there was uncertainty as to how such requests should be considered. In addition, grey squirrel (*Sciurus griseus*) harvest was considered a major impact as a result of Southeast Asian hunting although licensing and monitoring of squirrel hunting was the jurisdiction of the California Department of Fish and Game. There were also accounts that Asian harvesters were cutting willows for basket making without a permit. In general, however, the greatest controversy related to special forest products concerned the harvest of wild mushrooms on the forest.

Wild Mushroom Harvesting on the Eldorado National Forest

After the Cleveland Fire of 1993, numerous requests were received by the Eldorado National Forest for permits to harvest morel mushrooms the following spring. Morels typically fruit in abundance following wildfire, in part perhaps because the formation of sclerotia may be induced as a result of root mortality from severe disturbance (Miller, Torres, and McClean 1994). Because the Cleveland Fire had occurred in a steep area heavily checkerboarded with private timber company land, forest personnel were concerned about the possibility of large numbers of mushroom pickers inducing further soil erosion and creating conflicts with private landowners. In addition, little information is known about the role of morels in the recovery of a forest ecosystem following a fire. Some forest biologists were concerned about losing the ecological nutrient-cycling function of fungi if the harvesting pressure on morels in the burn area became too great. As a result, $20 permits were sold for personal collection of a maximum of 50 lb of mushrooms for the season and for only certain designated areas within the Cleveland Fire burn area. To minimize the impact of monitoring the harvest, morel gathering elsewhere in the forest was prohibited.

Because of the public interest in the morel harvest, a letter was issued by the acting forest supervisor on 22 February 1994 requesting public comment on the implementation of the Eldorado National Forest's mushroom harvesting policy. Well over half of those responding during the public comment period were from the Bay area (figure 24). This regional representation of letter writers directly correlates with the

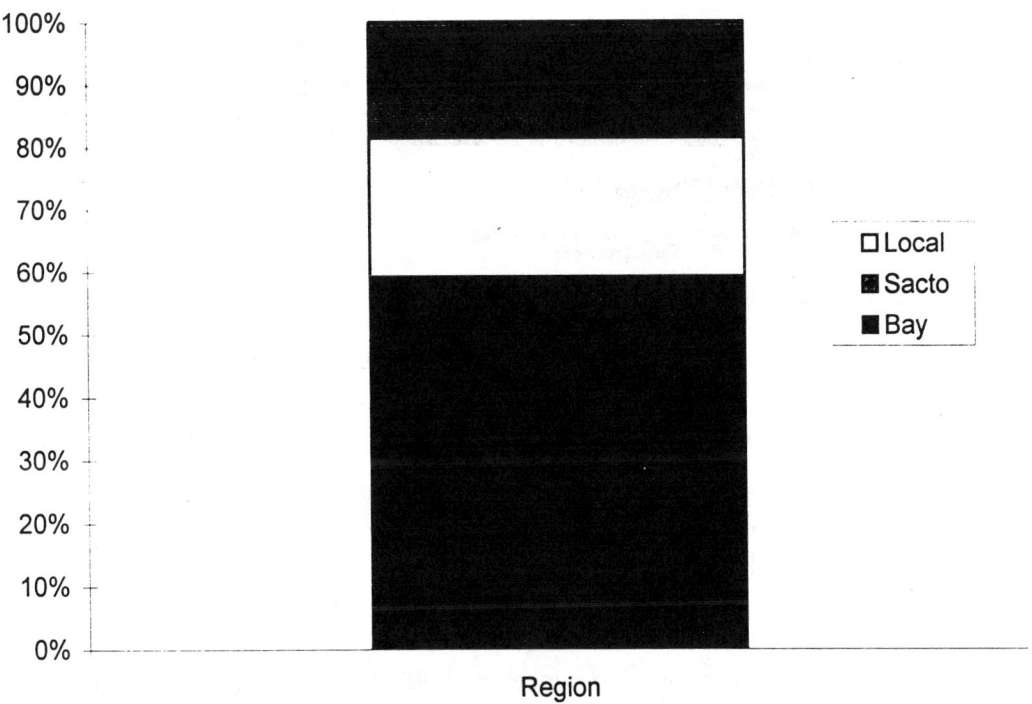

Figure 24
Regional Affiliation of Individuals Writing Public Comment Letters on the 1994
Eldorado National Forest Mushroom Harvesting Policy

geographic origin of the mushroom permittees, the majority of whom were also from the

Bay area (figure 23).

The letter writers represented several non mutually exclusive social roles (figure

25). Just under half were mushroom society members and/or individual letter writers

only. Only 4% identified themselves as environmentalists, 14% identified themselves as

conscientious forest users, and 39% represented themselves as experienced mushroom

pickers, and 11% indicated they were mushroom experts. In contrast, 18% indicated that

they were proponents of the timber industry.

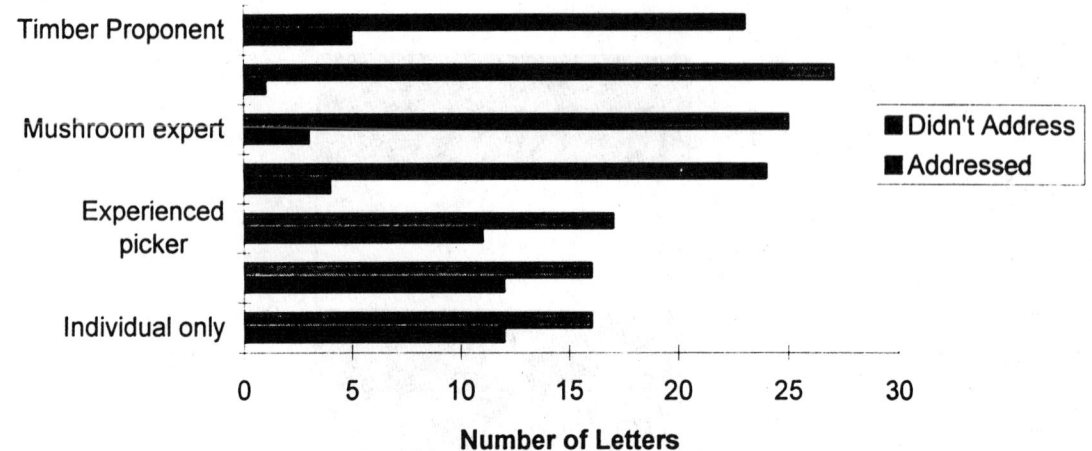

Figure 25
Social Roles Assumed in Public Comment Letters on the 1994 Eldorado National Forest
Mushroom Harvesting Policy

Relatively few letters addressed concerns about surface impact to the soil (18%)

and impacts on other users (4%) . As shown in figure 26, most letters addressed possible

risks to morel regeneration following harvest (64%) with many of the letters claiming that

overharvesting did not pose a serious problem for future regeneration of the species.

Other writers referred to both the recreational (32%) and monitoring (29%) benefits of

allowing mushroom harvesting, and many wrote that they thought a greater amount of

mushrooms should be collected for a lower fee. This was reflected in the fact that half

(50%) of the letters criticized the forest's mushroom management policy as too restrictive

(figure 27). The second most frequent criticism was that pickers were overregulated

(39%). About one-third of the letter writers indicated that they thought the Eldorado

National Forest's mushroom management policy was a waste of taxpayer's money while

only 14% claimed that they thought some form of mushroom monitoring was necessary

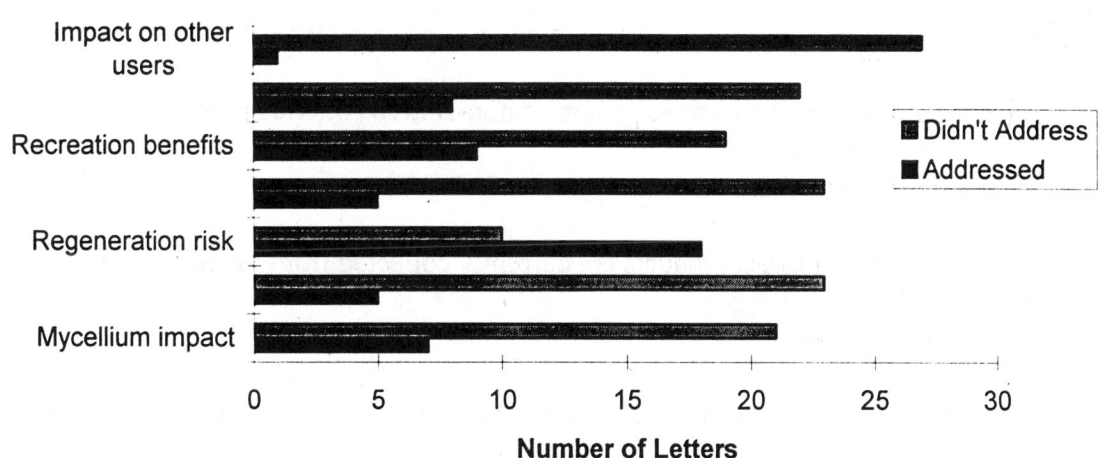

Figure 26
Concerns about Personal Mushroom Harvesting in Public Comment Letters on the 1994 Eldorado National Forest Mushroom Harvesting Policy

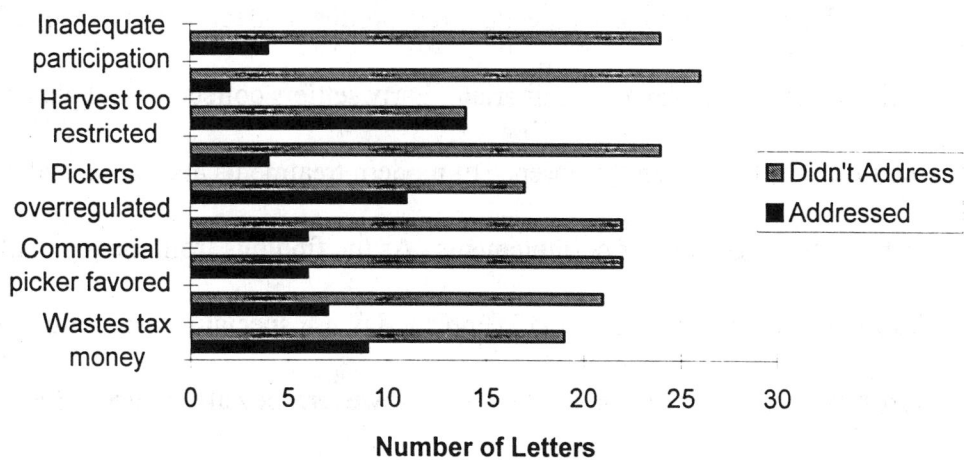

Figure 27
Concerns about Mushroom Management in Public Comment Letter on the 1994 Eldorado National Forest Mushroom Harvesting Policy

CONCLUSIONS

Through a review of the literature and from the national forest survey and the
Eldorado National Forest case study, this assessment addressed three key questions:

1. What has been the historic pattern of non-Native American special forest
   product collection?

2. What special forest products are currently collected from the Sierra Nevada
   national forests?

3. What are the trends in current special forest product policy and management
   and how do they affect special forest product collection?

In addressing these questions, findings from this assessment provide baseline data for
policy development toward the ecological, social, and economic sustainability of special
forest products.

Patterns of Special Forest Product Collection

Historical patterns of special forest product collection in the Sierra Nevada by
early settlers were primarily utilitarian. Early settlers collected wild plants to supplement
their diets, heal them in the absence of modern treatments and cures, and serve their labor
as household fuel and work implements. As the findings from the regional survey and the
Eldorado case study demonstrate, people today use special forest products from the Sierra
forests for some of these same purposes. However, they also collect forest resources for
very different reasons than their forebears did a century and a half ago. This general
finding is supported by interviews with botanists, biologists, timber management officers
and other personnel on all eight of the Sierra Nevada national forests which responded to

the survey. They are also supported by data and observations from cooperative extension personnel, mushroom collectors, medicinal plant distributors, and many others contacted for this assessment.[9] These views all inform the interpretations and conclusions presented here.

It should be stressed that these interpretations are often speculative at best given the paucity of data and the difficulty in obtaining confirmatory information from a wide range of sources. Nevertheless, the intent of this study was to provide a broad, regional description of special forest product collection in the Sierra Nevada, including historic, contemporary, and future trends. While speculative, it is the intent of this discussion to present the opportunities which special forest products hold for the Sierra as well as the limited knowledge we currently have of real conditions.

Fuelwood

Of the greatest historic and contemporary importance are the special forest products collected in the Sierra Nevada for fuelwood. The collection of firewood continues to be the most economically significant and most frequently harvested special forest product from the region today. As the permit data for the Eldorado National Forest indicate, the most frequent demand for firewood in the Sierra Nevada is from local residents. However, in recent years, firewood collection appears to have declined. Because most firewood collection is limited to areas in which logging or thinning has already occurred, mountain communities may experience increased future firewood

---

[9] I would like to thank Tom Ratcliff, Beth Corbin, Linnea Hansen, Kathy van Zuuk, Mike Foster, Tom Beck, Joanna Clines, Steve Anderson, Scott Jackson, Andy Dyer, John Russmore, Kevin Fort, Tuo Lee Xiong, and many others who aided this assessment.

restrictions on national forest fuelwood collection as timber harvests decline. A 1986

report indicates that mountain region residents comprise less than 5% of the total

population of California but use well over half of the firewood since

> (t)hey have large heating requirements, alternative heating fuels are expensive,
>
> and relatively inexpensive firewood can be collected from the National Forests
>
> and from some private land. For most of these residents, heating with firewood
>
> makes good financial sense (Doak and Stewart 1986).

The legal alternative for those seeking firewood at a relatively low cost is to

replace national forest fuelwood with either increased purchases or harvests of firewood

from private lands. If private land should also become more unavailable to firewood

cutting, the current problems with illegal harvest of fuelwood from national forests might

accelerate, especially if Forest Service monitoring and enforcement were reduced.

In recent years, technological and forest management changes have created

markets for new fuelwood products like biomass for wood chip energy production. In

1986, there were 72 biomass projects in California using forest or mill residues for power

generation. Of these, 66 were cogeneration plants (Doak and Stewart 1986). Since 1986,

some of these plants have failed and others have been close to closing. At the same time,

new plants have been activated. Because the collection of biomass is directly related to

the market for cogeneration plant energy, biomass harvest has been erratic. The uncertain

market for biomass fuel has posed management problems for the Sierra national forests

which have come to depend on biomass removal as a no-cost fire-prevention and forest

health thinning tool. On the Lassen National Forest where the greatest amount of biomass has been harvested, contractors may have to be paid to thin forest stands in lieu of buying permits for biomass if the local cogeneration plants shut down. Similar concerns are expressed in the south on the Sequoia and Stanislaus National Forests.

In the north, the Modoc National Forest has not only relied on biomass removal as a fire prevention strategy but as a means of improving wildlife habitat on juniper woodlands as well. Collector interest in harvesting juniper for biomass fuel as well as for fences, firewood, and ornamental wood working has apparently increased. Demand has been stimulated by the chip market for local cogeneration plants including a new plant in Klamath Falls, Oregon. Chip harvesting has accelerated on private land with ranchers receiving $10 per acre for juniper removal. Juniper removal on the forest could reduce the current juniper cover from over 60% to about 40% for improved wildlife habitat. Juniper is currently removed by hydraulic shears at ground level, but different harvesting methods are being explored. Leaving boughs and limbs on the ground may be more important since recent data indicate whole juniper tree removal can result in an undesirable net export of plant nutrients from the juniper grassland ecosystem (Miller and Rose 1995).

Christmas Trees, Floral Greens, and Dry Floral Ornamentals

Historically, Christmas trees were undoubtedly harvested from the Sierra Nevada by early Euro-American settlers. In terms of net fee receipts, Christmas trees are currently the second most important economic product from the national forests from the region. However, permit demand has not dramatically increased relative to market demand from the population growth in the state. Several factors may contribute to this phenomenon.

Only the northern forests of the Sierra Nevada continue to issue large numbers of

Christmas tree permits to individuals while permit numbers on Christmas tree cutting

have increasingly been restricted by the central and southern forests. This is illustrated by

the Eldorado National Forest where permits for Christmas trees have been increasingly

limited to nonprofit organizations since the private "choose-and-cut" operations were

established in the region in the early 1950s. To avoid competition with commercial

growers, forests like the Eldorado have restricted the numbers of Christmas tree permits

and the conditions under which they are issued. With the continued growth in the private

Christmas tree industry, it is unlikely that permit numbers on the national forests will

increase. The Christmas tree harvest will likely decline even on the northern forests as

small, private "choose-and-cut" operations continue to presumably expand. Because

Christmas tree cutting may also serve as a thinning tool, these restrictions further

constrain another forest fuel load management option, particularly as many observers

note, there is not much market for small trees.

Of emerging importance in the Sierra Nevada is the collection of floral products

not supplied in large quantities from private lands. These include cones, boughs, and

mistletoe for Christmas floral greenery, manzanita branches for floral arrangements, and

lichen and moss for the dry floral industry. An emerging market for dogwood boughs for

floral displays is indicated by the increased number of permit requests on many forests.

While trends in the harvest of these floral products appear too erratic to determine

whether demand for floral products from the Sierra Nevada is expanding, it does appear

that the floral industry plays a significant economic role for a limited number of community residents and out-of-area commercial harvesters in the region. As the permit data for the Eldorado National Forest indicate, nonlocal harvesters collect more floral products from the Sierra Nevada than any other group of products, except wild mushrooms. It is unlikely that the floral industry as a whole will diminish. Floral greens have been commercially harvested from the Pacific Northwest since at least the 1930s (Robbins 1988). Moss has been marketed in the decorative trade since at least 1902 (Nelson and Carpenter 1965), and lichens have been popular as Christmas decorations for centuries in Scandinavia where they have been imported from the United States since 1935 (Llano 1948).

At this point in time, harvesting for the floral trade in the Sierra Nevada appears to be limited and poorly positioned to compete with that of the Pacific Northwest. Ecological conditions, especially moisture, constrain the type and amount of typical floral green products available in the Sierra Nevada. It is also likely that the special forest product floral industry in the Sierra will be limited by the same or similar economic factors which constrain the growth of the industry east of the Cascades and in the western Rockies. These factors include lower product prices to harvesters, certain permit restrictions, and a lack of investment capital and market development (Schlosser and Blatner 1994). Nevertheless, it appears that the northern forests of the Sierra are already becoming linked to the Pacific Northwest floral industry through cone, bough, and lichen collection. In addition, the increase in number of permit requests for beargrass, a major component of the Pacific Northwest floral industry, indicates that the industry in the northern forests may be poised for limited expansion and integration.

In the southern forests of the Sierra Nevada, the floral industry appears to be indigenous and currently weakly developed. This may be changing as the southern Sierra forests may be absorbing some of the harvesting pressure from the forests further south where increasing restrictions may be shifting demand northward. At least one community in the southern Sierra has explored expanding local economic opportunities by either collecting wild plants and/or cultivating wild plants for the trade (e.g., Mater Engineering 1993). In addition, unique products such as sequoia cones and large amounts of other desirable products not found in quantity elsewhere, such as sugar pine cones, may allow the floral industry in the southern Sierra Nevada to expand. The southern forests may also be well positioned for an expansion of the trade because of their proximity to southern California markets and because of the available labor pool of experienced special forest product collectors.

Ethnic diversity within the floral special forest products industry is likely to continue to increase. Hispanic and Southeast Asian harvesters increasingly engage in commercial special forest product harvesting of juniper boughs, wild mushrooms, and other plants throughout the Pacific Northwest (Richards in press). These groups appear to have extended harvesting to the northern national forests of the Sierra Nevada. Many of these harvesters are California residents (Richards and Creasy in press), and it is not unlikely that these groups will exert increased pressure to collect floral plant products in all the forests of the Sierra Nevada if market conditions develop.

Wild Edible Plants

While wild edible plant foods were important dietary supplements a century and a half ago, they do not appear to be widely collected by non-Native Americans in the Sierra Nevada today. Permits are not currently issued by national forests in the Sierra Nevada for wild edible plants except wild mushrooms and ferns. [10] Permits are not currently required to gather food such as blackberries, wild grapes, and wild strawberries. Few reports have noted berry or grape picking or the digging of roots such as wild onions, arrowhead, or other plants (see table 1). However, the numerous publications written for backpackers or "survivalists" who are interested in wild plant foraging attests to the interest of an unknown population who may still collect historically important food plants in the region (see, for example. Elias and Dykeman 1990 who describe many wild edible plants which grow in the Sierra Nevada). Currently, the demand for wild edible plants by "foragers" in the Sierra Nevada is unknown. Similarly, any future demand for a wild edible plant industry in the Sierra is unpredictable.

Although few records exist about settler or Native American consumption of wild mushrooms, there are reports that Native Americans harvested morels and other species in California (Blackburn and Anderson 1993). Wild mushrooms have also been gathered for many years by immigrants and settlers. Several members of ranching families who graze cattle on the Sierra and Stanislaus National Forests indicate that their families have long picked morels and continue to do so today. On the Eldorado National Forest, an

---

[10] Pinon (*Pinus edulis*) cone seeds ("pinons") are collected on the east side of the Tahoe National Forest, but permits were not reported. Pinon permits may also be issued on the Inyo National Forest, which is not represented in the survey.

experienced mushroom picker reports that elderly Italian American men continue a long tradition of gathering *porcini* or bolete (*Boletus* spp.) mushrooms as well as Caesar amanita (*Amanita caesariana*) mushrooms from the forest. This observation is supported in a letter to the Eldorado National Forest with an enclosed photograph copied from the Placerville *Mountain Democrat* of an overall-clad gentleman drying bolete mushrooms in 1915.

Despite historical local use, most demand for wild mushrooms today is from urban, nonlocal wild mushroom afficionados, especially members of wild mushroom clubs and societies. These collectors harvest wild mushrooms, primarily morels, from only a few forests in the Sierra Nevada and particularly, following a major wildfire. Findings from the content analysis of the public comment letters to the Eldorado National Forest indicate that wild mushroom collecting is a highly valued activity by these harvesters and one in which they maintain an intense interest.[11] The current harvesting of wild mushrooms in the Sierra Nevada appears to primarily consist of both traditional and newly emerging recreational harvesting for personal use. Although commercial harvest of wild mushrooms has not yet become a major activity in the Sierra Nevada, it may periodically increase following a series of future wildfires.

---

[11] This has also been recently demonstrated by the Internet postings on 9 February 1995 by North American Wild Mushroom Association members soliciting input to the public comment period on the special forest product draft management strategy plan from the Forest Service national office.

In contrast, fiddlehead fern collection is dominated solely by Asian harvesters who apparently collect for both personal and commercial use.[12] Permit numbers are very low, but the intensive harvesting in the spring by a particular ethnic group makes fern collection a particularly salient feature of the special forest product industry in the Sierra Nevada. Since bracken fern can be an invasive weed in conifer plantations, encouraging fiddlehead collection in plantations may serve a positive silvicultural management function for forests in the Sierra.

Fern harvesting reflects the growing ethnic diversity of the national forest users of the Sierra Nevada. Studies indicate that 44% of Hmong housewives in San Joaquin, Merced, and Fresno counties reported that someone in their home hunted animals and brought them home to eat. Deer (*Odocoileus hemionus*) was most frequently hunted, followed by squirrel and pheasant (*Phasianus* spp.) (Ikeda et al. 1991). Similar trends are reported for the Mien and other Southeast Asians living in the Central Valley. On the Sequoia National Forest, wildlife poaching by Southeast Asian harvesters has occurred with a recent capture of about 50 pond turtles (*Clemmys marmorata*), a category two sensitive species and a Southeast Asian banquet delicacy. Since Southeast Asian populations are among the most rapidly increasing in central California, the trend in fern collecting, hunting, and other forms of forest resource use is likely to increase, particularly in the central and southern Sierra Nevada forests, in the future.

---

[12] In northeastern North America, settlers and Native Americans alike have eaten ostrich fern fiddleheads (*Matteuccia struthiopteris*) for generations (von Aderkas 1984) and in western Washington, bracken fern fiddleheads have provided starch and fiber in the diet of native tribal people there (Norton 1979).

Wild Medicinal Plants

Medicinal wild plants were historically collected to supplement pioneer diets. Today, permits are not generally requested nor required for the collection of medicinal wild plants from national forests in the Sierra Nevada. Nevertheless, a few reports indicate that some collection of medicinal plants is occurring in the region today. An emerging commercial herbal market may play a more significant role in special forest product gathering in the Sierra Nevada in years to come. A growing consumer interest in alternative herbal medicine is demonstrated by the growth of the Herb Research Foundation, whose mission includes conducting and supporting quality research on medicinal plants, promoting the informed use of herbs in preventive medicine, and supporting the development of herbs as cash crops. Interest in herbal medicine is also indicated by a wide array of books, including publications devoted to the harvesting of wild medicinal plants (Castleman 1991, Moore 1993). Several herbal medicine practitioners already gather plants from the Tahoe National Forest. The growth of California herbal products like a local Sacramento enterprise which produces an herbal "anti-allergy" cookie from imported *Ephedra* spp.(also known as Mormon tea) is an indication that a future market may exist in the herbal industry for wild plants from the Sierra Nevada (Philp 1995). Demand for medicinal plants from the Sierra may increase, particularly in the northern and central forests where communities like Nevada City and Truckee attract those seeking alternative lifestyles.

The ethnic use of wild medicinal plants may expand in the Sierra Nevada. Mexican herbal medicine shops (*botanicas*) are common in the valley cities like Fresno where a major U.S. distributor of Mexican botanical herbs, Vida Mex, is located. According to the distribution list provided by the company, 240 products are available to botanicas. Of these, 30 are purchased from the United States, 174 are supplied from Mexico, and the remainder come from all over the world. Of these 240 products, many are plants listed in table 1 and grow in the Sierra Nevada. These include *cola de caballo* or horsetail rush (*Equisetum* spp.), *bolsa de pastor* or shepherd's purse (*Capsella bursa-pastoris*) chia (*Salvia columbariae*) *enebro* or juniper berries (*Juniperus* spp.) *estafiate* or mugwort (*Artemisia* spp.), *gordolobo* or mullein (*Verbascum thapsus*), *hojas de fresno* or ash leaves (*Fraxinus* spp.), *llanten* or plantain (*Plantago* spp.), *milerana* or yarrow (*Achillea* spp.), *mirto* or California laurel (*Umbellularia californica*), *ortiga* or nettle (Urtica spp.), *poleo* or pennyroyal (*Monardella* spp.), *raiz angelica* or angelica (*Angelica* spp.), *salvia* or sage (*Salvia* spp.), and *uva ursi* or bearberry (*Arctostaphylos uva-ursi*). The extent to which Mexican Americans and other Hispanic groups in California buy products from botanicas or gather medicinal plants in the wild for either commercial or personal use is unknown. However, the expected increase in the Hispanic population and the large demand for medicinal plants by Hispanics in the state may mean that the market for some medicinal plants may be supplied to some extent by collection for either personal or commercial use from the Sierra Nevada in the years to come.

Given the historical importance of several of the wild medicinal plants which grow in the Sierra Nevada, potential demand may yet emerge for certain plants unexpectedly in the future. Canchalagua (*Centaurium venustum*) was hailed as a miracle drug by nineteenth century Californians. Pacific yew (*Taxus brevifolia*) is the source of natural taxol which emerged as a cancer-treatment drug in the 1980s and grows in limited numbers in the forests of the Sierra Nevada. Similarly, a future plant may yet be found in the Sierra Nevada to meet the needs for new pharmaceutical compounds (Bates 1985). Should such a plant be located in considerable quantities, global data indicate that the value of such a single species would be worth over $203 million (Farnsworth and Soejarto 1985).

Finally, the monitoring of any potential growth in the demand for wild medicinal plants by the national forests in the Sierra Nevada will be all the more important given the fact that some historically important medicinal plants may include sensitive or endangered species. For example, of the plants listed in table 1, several groups may include rare or endangered species, namely, *Angelica callii, Trichostema ovatum, Trifolium bolanderi, T. lemmonii, T. macilentum* var. *dedeckerae, Ribes menziesii* var. *ixoderne, R. tuberense, Delphinium recurvatum, Monardella stebbinsii, Chenopodium simplex, Chlorogalum grandiflorum, Scirpus subterminalis, S. elementis,* and *Allium sanbornii* var. *sanbornii* and var. *congdonii* (Skinner and Pavlik 1994).

<u>Woodworking, Landscaping and Restoration</u>

The harvest of roundwood, including posts, poles, and rails, was historically necessary for ranching, mining, and logging, the main economic occupations of the Sierra Nevada. In recent years, demand for roundwood has appeared to decline. Like firewood, the harvest of roundwood products is generally restricted to collection areas designated after timber harvest or thinning. However, demand for roundwood may also be decreasing because of alternative fencing and building materials.

Home decorating, landscaping, and revegetation trends have recently provided markets for specialty wood carvings, bark mulch, landscape rock, transplants, and native seed. While these products do not appear to be extensively collected on the basis of permit numbers, demand may be considerable and future collection pressure may increase. Specialty wood carvings appear to be a limited but important economic opportunity for those in mountain communities who can successfully market their handicrafts. Trends in community interest in value-added wood working also appears to be increasing with small-scale furniture or cabinetry efforts reported on the Modoc and Sierra National Forests.

Mineral resources are often permitted under mineral law and are not generally reported as a special forest product. Tons of lichen-covered flat rock have been annually removed for years from the BLM district of Susanville for the urban landscape market (Richards forthcoming). With the expansion of the urban landscaping industry in California, demand may increase for rocks of different types from Sierra national forests. Rock removal and its associated impacts from archaeological, riparian, or sensitive plant areas may be particularly problematic in the future.

Transplants for gardens and collections are also a concern on many forests. Some report problems with live plant collectors digging lady slipper orchids (*Cypripedium* spp.), most of which are sensitive or endangered species. Bonzai tree transplants are also considered problematic. Although some forests have issued bonzai permits, the number of permits has been restricted since the number of plants with classic bonzai landscaping value is limited.

Although the number of permits issued for native seed collection for shrub and grass restoration projects has been low, the demand for native seed is expected to grow on several forests. The northern forests have seen an increase in native seed collection, especially bitterbrush (*Purshia tridentata*) for range and forest rehabilitation. Commercial native seed is a profitable industry in the Great Basin with commercial collectors earning $8 a pound on average for bitterbrush seed (Richards forthcoming). While commercial seed collection is not generally permitted on national forests in the Sierra Nevada, demand for commercial seed permits may increase in the future, particularly in years when widespread wildfires require extensive revegetation seedings and seed collection is profitable. Most seed is presently collected and germinated by the Forest Service, but several forests report increasing private and public partnerships in restoration seed collections and plantings. Some also note that seed collections may be limited to one forest and then planted on many other forests so that a regional gap exists in adhering to the Forest Service guidelines of the Regional Native Seed Species Policy of 1995 for collecting and using native seed for revegetation.

Trends in Special Forest Product Policy and Management

In general, this assessment indicates that public demand for special forest product collection will probably not decline in the near future in the Sierra Nevada. The permitted supply of some products like Christmas trees and firewood is expected to decline even as demand remains steady or increases. In addition, the permitted supply of a diverse group of other products, both old and new, is increasing under current special forest product policy. Demand for special forest products is likely to become more complex as personal use diversifies with the growing ethnic and urban population and the accompanying shifts in cultural values. At the same time, commercial use may become more extensive with local and out-of-region harvesters often competing for the same products. Native American concerns about special forest products are reported to be increasing on several forests, particularly the Plumas, Sierra, and Tahoe National Forests. Traditional Native American basket weaving and medicinal plants are seen as particularly vulnerable to overharvesting pressure by commercial collectors. These problems are not unique to the Sierra Nevada but exist in forest regions outside the Sierra Nevada as well (Richards and Creasy in press).

Some forests report that special forest product requests and concerns will become more numerous and diverse as the American public turns to its national forests not only to make a living but for cultural alternatives and social experiences like medicinal herb interpretive tours and specialized morel collecting trips of the mushroom societies. The biggest constraint to managing this expansion in special forest product gathering is forest system funding since permit fee receipts continue to be forwarded directly to the Treasury in Washington, D.C. as they have been since 1906. Funding for special forest product management and monitoring continues to decrease on the national forests as the population continues to increase and demands for natural resources grow.

Funding constraints are recognized in the special forest products draft management strategy plan recently released by the national office (U.S. Forest Service 1995). The plan also acknowledges that existing policies are "vague, confusing, and incomplete" especially in terms of units of measure, pricing, and administration of commercial and noncommercial harvests. While not "establishing resource policy", the management plan outlines six major goals for national forests to meet, namely to

1.   Link forest land management to the needs of the people, including technical assistance to rural communities and sensitivity to the traditional religious beliefs of American Indians;

2.   Integrate special forest product resources into ecosystem management, including maintenance of biodiversity;

3.   Identify international, national, regional, and local policies that influence special forest product resources, including the national and regional directives and guides in managing products;

4.   Integrate special forest product species into inventorying, monitoring, and research activities across functional boundaries, including better database and geographic information systems (GIS) vegetation information;

5.   Develop biological models of species distribution and productivity that can be linked with economic and market probability models, including better databases for buying, processing, and selling of nontimber commodities;

6.   Provide for and engage in interagency technology transfer across boundaries, including interagency workshops and international exchanges (U.S. Forest Service 1995).

This assessment has indicated that the first step in meeting some of these goals for the Sierra Nevada is to develop improved special forest product databases. Without consistent and currently updated data, it will be extremely difficult to address the questions that remain to be answered, especially whether economic and biological models can be developed to better understand supply and demand cycles for special forest products within the ecological constraints of their distribution and growth requirements. In addition, better databases are needed to assess to what extent the economic needs of rural communities and the different cultural values of special forest product user groups conflict and whether special forest product demand can be met not only by the national forests but by private lands. Without a systematic database for better inventorying and monitoring special forest products harvested in the Sierra Nevada it will not be possible to determine whether certain special forest products are sustainable in terms of fulfilling economic needs, cultural values, and ecosystem functions. For example, data currently available from several agencies may exist that could be linked to indicate whether biomass removal can be both an economic product and a fire management tool while improving wildlife habitat and maintaining long term ecosystem health through continued nutrient cycling. Similarly, while the public may view the removal of river rock and wild transplants as benign, and even as positive "natural" landscaping. data may be tracked to identify the extent to which such collection methods impact the watersheds and plant communities of the Sierra. As the case study of the Eldorado National Forest mushroom policy illustrates, a particular social group's interest in a product may result in that product being culturally disproportionate significant relative to its actual economic value or its ecological contribution on any given forest. Conversely, the role of socioeconomic needs for certain special forest products like firewood, including insecure land tenure or access, and their resulting ecological and land management impacts are not as well studied in western North America as they have been overseas (see Belsky 1994; Peluso 1992; Ireson 1991).

Such a database will need to be developed in the context of new and emerging uses and values in relation to special forest products if these resources are to be managed for a large number of different user groups. Thus, the role of special forest products in the management of Sierra Nevada ecosystems may be more complex than many scientists and laypeople realize. A regional database of special forest products to track vegetative and socioeconomic information would go a very long ways toward explaining that complexity. This will only be possible when forests are adequately funded to maintain management programs; administrative data from these program are reported consistently regionwide; ecological plant association data include special forest products; and administrative, ecological, and sociocultural and economic data are collected, linked, and monitored as part of the forest management system.[13]

---

[13] I would like to thank Judy Jernstedt and two annoymous reviewers for helpful comments on an earlier draft of this report.

REFERENCES

Bates, D. M. 1985. Plant utilization: patterns and prospects. *Economic Botany* 39 (3):241-65.

Belsky, J. M. 1994. Soil conservation and poverty: Lessons from upland Indonesia. *Society and Natural Resources* 7:429-43.

Blackburn, T. C. and K. Anderson, eds. 1993. *Before the wilderness: Environmental management by native Californians.* Menlo Park, California: Ballena Press.

Burstein, L. and H. E. Freeman. 1985. Perspectives on data collection in evaluations. Pp. 15-32 in *Collecting evaluation data: Problems and solutions*, eds. L. Burstein, H. E. Freeman, and P. H. Rossi. Beverly Hills, California: Sage Publications.

Castleman, M. 1991. *The Healing Herbs: The Ultimate Guide to the Curative Power of Nature's Medicines.* Emmaus, Pennsylvania: Rodale Press.

Doak, S. C. and B. Stewart. 1986. *A model of economic forces affecting California's hardwood resource: Monitoring and policy implicatons* California Department of Forestry. Sacramento, California: California Department of Forestry.

Elias, T. S. and P. A Dykeman. 1990. *Edible wild plants: A north american field buide.* New York, New York: Sterling Publishing Company.

Farnsworth, N. R. and D. D. Soejarto. 1985. Potential consequences of plant extinction in the United States on the current and future availability of prescription drugs. *Economic Botany* 39 (3):231-40.

Harrison, W. 1991. *Bountiful land: A guide to the Miwok plant trail.* Indian Grinding Rock State Historic Park: Chaw'se Association.

Hickman, J. C. 1993. *The Jepson manual: Higher plants of California.* Berkeley: University of California Press.

Holsti, O. R. 1969. *Content analysis for the social sciences and humanities.* Reading, Massachusetts: Addison-Wesley.

Ikeda, J. P. et.al. 1991. Food habits of the Hmong living in central California. *Journal of Nutrition Education* 23 (4):168-75.

Ireson, C. 1991. Women's forest work in Laos. *Society and Natural Resources* 4:23-36.

Krippendorff, K. 1980. *Content analysis: An introduction to its methodology.* Beverly Hills, California: Sage Publications.

Kunkler, A. 1975. *Hardscrabble: A narrative of the California hill country.* Reno: University of Nevada Press.

Llano, G. A. 1948. Economic uses of lichens. *Economic Botany* 2:15-45.

Marks, P. C. 1994. *Precious dust: The saga of the western gold rush.* New York, New York: Harper Collins West.

Mater Engineering. 1993. *North Fork value-added and special forest products market reserarch project.* Unpublished file report to the North Fork Ranger District, Sierra National Forest.

McCullough, L. Leisure themes in international advertising: A content analysis. *Journal of Leisure Research* 25 (4):380-8.

Miller, R. E. and J. A. Rose. 1995. Historic expansion of *Juniperus occidentalis* (western juniper) in southeastern Oregon. *Great Basin Naturalist* 55 (1):37-45.

Miller, S. L., P. Torres, and T. M. McClean. 1994. Persistence of basidiospores and sclerotia of ectomycorrhizal fungi and *Morchella* in soil. *Mycologia* 86(1):89-95.

Moore, M. 1993. *Medicinal plants of the Pacific West.* Santa Fe, New Mexico: Red Crane Books.

Myers, S. L. 1980. *Ho for California! Women's overland diaries from the Huntingdon Library.* San Marino, California: Henry E. Huntingdon Library and Art Gallery.

Nelson, T. C. and I. W. Carpenter. 1965. The use of moss in the decorative industry. *Economic Botany* 19 (1):70.

Norton, H. H. 1979. Evidence for bracken fern as a food for aboriginal people of western Washington. *Economic Botany* 33 (4):384-96.

Peluso, N. 1992. *Rich forests, poor people: Resource control and resistance in Java.* Berkeley: University of California Press.

Philp, T. 1995. A cookie to fight allergies? Claim goes unchecked. *Sacramento Bee*, A1, A18.

Richards, R. T. *A socioeconomic study of wild mushroom harvesting in the Klamath bioregion.* Unpublished final report to the Siskiyou and Klamath National Forests.

————In press. Alternative products on public rangelands. *Sustaining Rangeland Ecosystems Symposium Proceedings* . Corvallis, Oregon: Oregon State University.

Richards, R. T. and M. Creasy. In press. Ethnic diversity, resource attachment, and ecosystem management: Matsutake mushroom harvesting in the Klamath bioregion. *Society and Natural Resources.*

Robbins, W. G. 1988. *Hard times in Paradise: Coos Bay, Oregon, 1850-1986.* Seattle: University of Washington Press.

Schlosser, W. E. and K. A. Blatner. 1994. *Special forest products: An eastside perspective.* Final Report: Eastside Forest Ecosystem Management Assessment Team .

Schlosser, W. E., K. A. Blatner, and B. Zamora. 1992. Pacific Northwest forest lands potential for floral greenery production. *Northwest Science* 66:44-55.

Skinner, M. W. and B. M. Pavlik (eds.). 1994. California native plant society's inventory of rare and endangered vascular plants of California. 5th ed. Sacramento, California: California Native Plant Society.

Storer, T. I. and R. L. Usinger. 1963. *Sierra Nevada Natural History*. Berkeley, California: University of California Press.

USDA Forest Service. 1906. *The use book: Regulations and instructions for the use of the national forest reserves.* Washington, D.C: Government Printing Office.

―――. 1993. *Income opportunities in special forest products: Self-help suggestions for rural entrepreneurs* Margaret G. Thomas and David R. Shumann. USDA Forest Service Agriculture Information Bulletin 666. Washington, D.C.

―――. 1994. *List of special forest products.* Unpublished file report. Washington, D.C.

―――. 1995. *Special forest products: A national strategy.* Unpublished file report. Washington, D.C.

USDI Bureau of Land Management. 1993. *Managing special forest products in Oregon and Washington* U.S. Department of the Interior. BLM Task Force Final Report. Portland, Oregon.

von Aderkas, P. 1984. Economic history of ostrich fern, *Matteuccia struthiopteris*, the edible fiddlehead. *Economic Botany* 38 (1):14-23.

Westrich, L. 1989. *California herbal remedies.* Houston, Texas: Gulf Publishing Company.

Wildland Resources Center. 1994. *Conserving the California spotted owl: Impacts of interim policies and implications for the long-term.* Report 33. Davis, California.

Wittman, C. 1994. Herbs along the Oregon Trail: Pioneer women and their medicine. *The Herb Quarterly* (64):52-56.

PAUL R. MILLER
Forest Service
USDA Pacific Southwest Research Station
Riverside, California

21

Biological Effects of Air Pollution in the Sierra Nevada

Sierra Nevada Ecosystem Project: Final report to Congress, vol. III, *Assessments, Commissioned Reports, and Background Information.* Davis: University of California, Centers for Water and Wildland Resources, 1996.

Cahill and others (SNEP) have described the nature and extent of air pollution in the Sierra Nevada in another section of this report. The purpose of this section is to examine two topics of concern under the broad subject of biological effects of air pollutants in the Sierra Nevada. The first topic of primary concern is ozone transported to the western slope of the Sierra from upwind urban areas and its effect on sensitive tree species. The second topic is the simultaneous deposition and accumulation of nitrogen compounds in relation to ecosystem processes. The principal regions of concern are the middle and southern portions of the western slope of the Range because the combined pollutant loads from the San Francisco Bay Area and urban centers of the San Joaquin Valley present the maximum chronic exposure to ozone in this region. At present there is no such evidence of photochemical pollutant transport to eastern Sierra Nevada forests.

Annual measurements since 1991 of the crown health of ponderosa pine (*Pinus ponderosa* Dougl. ex Laws) and Jeffrey pine (*Pinus jeffreyi* Grev. and Balf.) from Lassen Volcanic National Park southward to Mountain Home State Park show an increasing level of chronic ozone injury from north to south. The amount injury is also influenced by the nearness of forest stands to the Valley, elevation and terrain position. Trees on upper slopes and ridge lines tend to show the most damage. Within stands the dominant and codominant trees are less injured than intermediate or suppressed trees which have more intense competition for light, water and nutrients. There is also a species difference in ozone sensitivity.

Ponderosa and Jeffrey pine are the most sensitive species to ozone and accumulated needle injury is easily detectable on older needle whorls as a chlorotic mottle. On the other hand black oak (*Quercus kellogii*) shows injury symptoms to foliage only in years with abundant soil moisture and average ozone exposure. The decreasing order of sensitivity for other conifers is white fir (*Abies concolor*), incense cedar (*Calocedrus decurrens*) and, sugar pine (*P. lambertiana*). Foliage symptoms are rarely seen on these species in the Sierras. The chronic ozone injury to ponderosa and Jeffrey pine interacts with other stresses, in particular periodic drought, to make them more vulnerable to bark beetle attack.

Each drought year causes the length of needles formed in those years to be progressively shorter because water deficits diminish photosynthesis and limit growth. Low stomatal conductance in dry summers reduces ozone uptake and ozone injury. When the drought is broken the recovery from drought is hampered by the diminished surface area of photosynthetically active needle tissue in shorter one-year-old and older needle whorls formed during the drought. Even though the newest needles formed in the first growing season following a resumption of adequate precipitation attain a more nominal length, higher stomatal conductance increases ozone flux to old and new needles further diminishing the ability of sensitive trees to recover from the drought. Chronic ozone injury symptoms appear on older needle whorls and they drop to the forest floor. Ozone and drought interact to influence the competitive ability of ponderosa and Jeffrey pines in mixed conifer stands. The intensity of this interaction is related to frequency of 2-3 year drought periods.

Fire exclusion favors the reproduction and growth of white fir and incense cedar and limits the regeneration of ponderosa and Jeffrey pine because the latter require a mineral seedbed to become established. Further reductions in competitive ability of ponderosa and Jeffrey pines due to ozone stress, exacerbates the conversion to stands with more fir and cedar. The development of live fuel ladders of understory fir and cedar which may lead to a higher frequency of destructive crown fires, i.e., old growth trees of all species of species are more likely to be eliminated.

If present concentrations of ozone persist for many years into the future the Sequoia-Kings Canyon National Park (SEKI) and the Sequoia National Forest (SNF) will be the most affected regions. The rate of decline in dominance of ozone-injured ponderosa and Jeffrey pine will depend upon the frequency of droughts and associated bark beetle-caused mortality. Because there is a wide range of ozone sensitivity within these species the effect will be selection for those genotypes which are more resistant to ozone, and a loss of within-species diversity.

If ozone air quality improves it is expected that the crown condition (vigor) of ponderosa and Jeffrey pines will improve as shown in the San Bernardino National Forest (SBNF) between 1974 and 1989. If ozone air quality worsens the level of tree injury now present in SEKI and SNF will spread northward. Conditions will worsen in SEKI and SNF. Managed forests may require repeated salvage cuts as happened in the SBNF in the 1960's and 1970's.

Another potential biological effect of air pollution is the dry deposition of nitrogen to forests. Nitrogen is present in photochemical smog along with ozone in the form of nitric acid and nitrogen dioxide gases, and fine particles comprised of nitrate and ammonium salts. Direct effects on foliage are not present as a result of exposure but nitrogen accumulated from dry deposition has been shown to increase the rate of litter decomposition and in the most polluted portions of the SBNF a state of nitrogen saturation may exist today. The nitrogen content of water from watersheds in the San Gabriel mountains exceeds Federal standards for drinking water. The Sierra Nevada is still a sink for nitrogen deposited from the atmosphere but a combination of time and increased deposition rates may lead to altered nutrient cycling and eventually nitrogen saturation.

Literature Review

Western Slope of the Sierra Nevada Mountains

Air quality issues for the Sierra Nevada have been referred to in the context of effects on air quality related values in Wilderness because of the stipulations of the Clean Air Act and 1977 Amendments. Peterson and others (1993) have provided a guide for evaluating effects on air quality related values in Sierra Nevada Class I Wilderness areas. The purpose of this review is to examine air pollution effects for west-side ecosystems without respect to Clean Air Act designation.

Detection of ozone injury symptoms to ponderosa and Jeffrey pines in the Sierra Nevada (Miller and Millecan 1971) and subsequent surveys by the USDA, Forest Service, Forest Pest Management using 52 trend plots (Pronos and Vogler 1981, Allison 1982, 1984a, 1984b) provided the earliest data describing the extent of ozone, injury and the early trends of the severity of injury. For example, Pronos and Vogler (1981) reported that between 1977 and 1980 the general trend was an increase in the amount of ozone symptoms present on pine foliage. Peterson and others (1991) sampled crown condition and derived basal area growth trends from cores collected from ponderosa pines at sites in seven Federal administrative units (National Forests and National Parks) located from north to south in the Sierra Nevada including Tahoe National Forest, Eldorado National Forest, Stanislaus National Forest, Yosemite National Park, Sierra National Forest, Sequoia-Kings Canyon National Park, and Sequoia National Forest. In July-August 1987, four symptomatic and four asymptomatic sites were visited in each unit and only sites with ponderosa pines greater than 50 yr old were selected for sampling. The symptomatic plots generally indicated increasing levels of chronic ozone injury (reduced numbers of annual needle whorls retained and chlorotic mottle symptoms on younger age classes of needles) from north to south.

Peterson and others (1991) documented the regional nature of the ozone pollution problem originating primarily from the San Joaquin Valley Air Basin (SJVAB), as well as the San Francisco Bay Air Basin further to the west. The study found no evidence of recent large-scale growth changes in ponderosa pine in the Sierra Nevada mountains; however the frequency of trees with recent declines of growth did increase in the southernmost units. Since these units have the highest levels of ozone (and more chlorotic mottle symptoms on needles of younger age classes) it was postulated from the weight of the evidence that ozone is one of the contributing factors to decline in basal area growth. Other factors limiting tree growth in this region include periodic drought, brush competition and high levels of tree stocking.

Another tree ring analysis and crown injury study was focused on Jeffrey pines in Sequoia-Kings Canyon National Park (Peterson and others 1989). This study suggested that decreases of radial growth of large, dominant Jeffrey pines growing on xeric sites (thin soils, low moisture holding capacity) and exposed to direct upslope transport of ozone, amounted to as much as 11 percent less in recent years relative to adjacent trees without symptoms.

Both permanent plots and cruise surveys have been employed in Sequoia, Kings Canyon (SEKI) (Wallner and Fong 1982 ; Warner and others 1982, and Yosemite (YOSE) National Parks to determine the spatial distribution and temporal changes of injury to ponderosa and Jeffrey pine within the Parks (Duriscoe and Stolte 1989). Comparisons of the same trees at 28 plots between 1980-82 and 1984-85 in SEKI showed increases of ozone injury to many trees and increases of the total number of trees with ozone injury. Ozone injury was found to decrease with increasing elevation of plots. The highest levels of tree injury in the Marble Fork drainage of the Kaweah River at approximately 1800 m elevation were associated with hourly averages of ozone frequently peaking at 80 to 100 ppb, but seldom exceeding 120 ppb.

A cruise survey in 1986 evaluated 3120 ponderosa or Jeffrey pines in SEKI and YOSE for ozone injury (Duriscoe and Stolte 1989) . More than one-third of these trees were found to have some level of chlorotic mottle. At SEKI symptomatic trees comprised 39% of the sample (574 out of 1470) and at YOSE they comprised 29% (479 out of 1650). Ponderosa pines were generally more severely injured than Jeffrey pines. The Forest Pest Management (FPM) score (low score equals high injury) was 3.09 for ponderosa and 3.62 for Jeffrey (Pronos and others 1978). These cruise surveys identified the spatial distribution of injury in SEKI and YOSE, and indicated trees in drainages nearest the San Joaquin Valley were most injured.

In SEKI field plot observations of seedling health and mortality in natural giant sequoia (*Sequoiadendron giganteum* Bucch.) groves from 1983 to 1986 showed that emergent seedlings in moist microhabitats had ozone-induced foliar symptoms. Seedling numbers were reduced drastically from drought and other abiotic factors during this period (Miller and others 1994). A variable such as ozone that could injure seedling foliage sufficiently to reduce root growth immediately after germination could increase vulnerability to late summer drought. Following fumigation giant sequoia seedlings developed chlorotic mottle following exposure to both ambient ozone concentrations and 1.5 X ambient ozone in open top chambers during the 8-10 weeks following germination (Miller and others 1994). Significant differences in light compensation point, net assimilation at light saturation, and dark respiration were found between seedlings in charcoal filtered air treatments and 1.5 X ambient ozone treatments (Grulke and others 1989). One interpretation of these results is that ozone has the potential to be a new selection pressure during the regeneration phase of giant sequoia, possibly reducing genetic diversity.

The Lake Tahoe Basin is located at the northern end of the Sierra Nevada sampling transect (near the Eldorado National Forest) (Peterson and others 1991). Because it is an isolated air basin the air quality situation is distinct from other Sierra Nevada sites, and air pollution trends there are likely to be more related to local control measures and less to regional (SJVAB) measures. In 1987 a survey of 24 randomly selected plots in the basin included a total of 360 trees of which 105 (29.2 %) had some level of foliar injury (Pedersen 1989). Seventeen of these plots had FPM injury scores (Pronos and others 1978) that fell in the slight injury category. Of 190 trees in 16 cruise plots that extended observations to the east outside the basin, 21.6 % had injury--less than in the basin.

The Forest Ozone Response Study (FOREST)

Ozone injury index (OII) Changes by General Location and by Individual Plot Between Years from 1991 to 1993.

Annually since 1991 the ozone injury has been determined for 1700 trees in approximately 33 individual plots located from Lassen Volcanic National Park in the northern Sierra Nevada to Mountain Home State Park in the southern Sierra Nevada, including three plots in the SBNF by the FOREST interagency task group (Guthrey and others 1993 and 1994).

Changes in the calculated ozone injury index (OII) between years for the 1991 to 1993 period are represented as means for about 50 trees in each of three plots at each location in Table 1. Trees that died during this period were not included in the comparison. A higher mean value indicates more injury since the index varies for 0 (no injury from ozone) to 100 (the most severe ozone injury). So far the actual range of OII observations is from 5.4 at Lassen Volcanic National Park to 65.7 in the western district of the San Bernardino National Forest. The subjective meaning of these OII values is a trace of injury or very slight injury at Lassen Volcanic National to a high moderate or low severe amount of injury at the San Bernardino site (Schilling and others 1995).

To evaluate the OII changes between 1991 and 1993, the paired t-test was used to determine if changes were significant (Table 1). All t-statistics are presented and a t-value of at least .05 or smaller was judged to be necessary before significant differences could be claimed. Accordingly, the majority of changes between 1991-1992 and 1992-1993 were decreases indicating some improvement in crown condition. The exceptions in 1991-1992 were Jerseydale and Barton Flats which both increased slightly. In 1992-1993 only Mountain Home State Park showed an increase compared to five sites with no change and six sites with a decrease in OII. Mather and Wawona in Yosemite (YOSE) had low OII scores in 1991 and have continued to decrease in the last two years.

Table 1. OII Changes from 1991 to 1993 at 33 Sierra Nevada Plots Listed in North to South Order and Three San Bernardino Mountain Pine Plots.

Plot Name	1991 Mean	t stat.	1992 Mean	t stat.	1993 Mean
Manzan. Lake (LV)	---	---	2	.03	1(-)
WhiteCloud	15	.18	14	.95	14
Sly Park	18	.29	16	.04	14(-)
5 mi LC	16	.06	14(-)	.31	15
Mather (YOSE)	11	.03	8(-)	.002	5(-)
Jersey Dale	15	.0005	22(+)	.51	23
Wawona (YOSE)	12	.08	10	0	3(-)
Shaver Lake	9	.78	10	.22	11
Grant Gr. (SEKI)	26	.02	24(-)	.27	23
Giant For. (SEKI)	29	0	25(-)	.01	23(-)
Mtn. Home	21	0	13(-)	0	18(+)
Barton Flats	29	0	34(+)	.01	32(-)

Annual Changes in the Proportion of Trees with Ozone Injury Symptoms at Each Location From 1991 to 1993.

The smallest proportion of symptomatic trees was seen at Manzanita Lake (.187) and the most at Barton Flats (1.00), using 1993 data as an example (Table 2). From year-to-year, significant decreases in numbers of trees at each location with ozone injury symptoms occurred at Mather, Wawona, and Mountain Home in 1992 and Wawona in 1993. Increases were seen at Jerseydale in 1992 and Mountain Home in 1993. The stability of this count at most plots is the prevailing condition.

Table 2. Changes in proportion of trees with foliar symptoms of ozone in 1991, 1992, and 1993 at Sierra Nevada and San Bernardino Mountain Pine Plots.

Location Name	1991 Mean	t stat.	1992 Mean	t stat.	1993 Mean
Manzan. Lake (LV)	---	---	.200	.29	.187
WhiteCloud	.701	.47	.673	.49	.653
Sly Park	.628	.39	.590	.37	.533
5 mi LC	.620	.87	.624	.14	.678
Mather (YOSE)	.520	0	.300(-)	.78	.313
Jersey Dale	.538	.001	.742(+)	.10	.835
Wawona (YOSE)	.490	0	.317(-)	0	.159(-)
Shaver Lake	.514	.41	.469	.001	.655
Grant Gr. (SEKI)	.946	.74	.953	.08	.913
Giant For. (SEKI)	.924	.37	.903	.64	.890
Mtn. Home	.806	0	.535(-)	.0002	.721(+)
Barton Flats	.976	.32	.992	.08	1.000

Distribution of OII Across Crown Position Classes (CPC) for all Plots in 1993 and Changes of Ranking at all Locations in 1991-1993.

Table 3 shows that for one sample year, 1993, Dominant (D) and Open Grown (OG) trees have generally lower OII's than Co-Dominant (CD), Intermediate (I), and Suppressed (S) trees. Table 4 represents a larger aggregation of these data, a summary of 1991, 1992 and 1993 which also shows significant differences in OII between crown position classes but changes in the ranking from year to year.

Table 3. Average OII in 1993 in relation to crown position class, including all trees in all plots.

	Crown Position Class				
	D	CD	I	S	OG
Number of Trees	308	661	500	105	110
Average OII	10.50	15.50	16.80	15.54	11.55

Table 4. Ranking of OII in Relation to Crown Position Class (CPC) in 1991, 1992 and 1993 at all plots.

CPC	1991		CPC	1992		CPC	1993	
OG	14.35	a	D	12.05	a	D	10.50	a
D	15.45	a	OG	12.20	ab	OG	11.55	ab
S	17.59	ab	S	14.25	abc	CD	15.50	bc
CD	17.79	ab	CD	17.07	bc	S	15.54	bc
I	19.57	b	I	18.57	c	I	16.80	bc

Effects of Pollutant Mixtures

The California Air Resources Board has published annual summaries of research sponsored by the Board to assess acidic deposition effects in the Sierra Nevada (California Air Resources Board 1983,1994) in compliance with two consecutive programs approved by the State legislature. A major theme of this work is the assessment of wet and dry deposition of sulfur and nitrogen species and their effects on geologic substrates (rocks and soils), surface waters, and aquatic biota. Critical assessments of this major body of research are in progress by subject matter experts. This task is enormous and complex. This important work will be published by the California Air Resources and will be a much more comprehensive product than could be attempted in the present document, however, the following paragraphs will discuss some research that relates to direct effects of sulfur and nitrogen compounds on the foliage of pines, and on possible accumulative effects on the mixed conifer ecosystems of the Sierra Nevada.

Investigations of the possible combined effects of sulfur dioxide and ozone were completed in the region just northeast of Bakersfield in a two-year period (Taylor and others 1986). Both ozone and sulfur dioxide were measured continuously at Bakersfield (Oildale), at Democrat Springs, Fire Guard Station in the lower Kern Canyon (oak woodland) and at Shirley Meadow (mixed conifer forest). Daily ozone peaks at Bakersfield and Shirley Meadow were similar in magnitude but sulfur dioxide was never detectable at Shirley Meadow and only detectable on rare occasions at Democrat Springs. Sulfate levels in pine needle tissue was not elevated at Shirley Meadow and there was no evidence to suggest anything except ozone injury to foliage of sensitive ponderosa and Jeffrey pines. Controlled fumigations of pine seedlings in open-top chambers using mixtures of ozone and sulfur dioxide did indicate an enhancement of foliar injury by the mixture of ozone and sulfur dioxide.

Seedling exposures to simulated acid rain and ozone were carried out with ponderosa pine for a three year period at Whitaker Forest, an experimental site in the southern Sierra Nevada. This experiment was part of the Electric Power Research Institute research program entitled: Response of Plants to Integrated Stress (ROPIS). The experimental design included acid rain (pH 3.5, 4.4, 5.3), ozone (CF, NF, NF150, AA), two levels of dry deposition (90 % and 60% filtration), and two levels of soil moisture availability (adequate and drought stressed). After 2 consecutive years of exposure the preliminary results suggested no effect from acid rain treatments, a much greater effect of ozone on adequately watered seedlings, and an interaction between 60% particle filtration and ozone resulting in more ozone injury (Temple and others 1992).

These results appear to be consistent with the appearance of mature ponderosa pines near the Whitaker Forest site, but seedling responses can not be offered as a complete substitute for data from mature trees. Seedlings are characterized by higher physiological rates and higher growth rates than mature trees.

Accumulative Effects of Nitrogen on Ecosystem Processes

Although there is an absence of direct effects of wet or dry acidic deposition on foliage and above-ground processes there is still the possibility that a gradual degradation of forest ecosystems may be developing through cumulative impacts on soils. Mechanisms for cumulative impact may include accelerated soil acidification (Reuss and Johnson, 1986), trace metal accumulation (Smith, 1990), and nitrogen saturation (Aber et al 1989). The nitrogen saturation hypothesis will be discussed in greater detail because nitrogen accumulation appears to be a distinct characteristic of California wildlands, which are traditionally nitrogen-limited, exposed to photochemical smog.

A detailed study of the gaseous and particulate species of sulfur and nitrogen was done in a rural area in the Kern River Canyon east of Bakersfield, and two urban areas including Martinez and San Jose (John, et al, 1984). The oxides of nitrogen were present at higher concentrations than sulfur oxides at all sites. Levels of NO_3^- and NH_4^+ washed from foliage and litter of ponderosa and Jeffrey pines at ten sites across an O_3 gradient in the San Bernardino mountains were highly correlated (R=0.73 to 0.82) with average hourly ozone concentrations. Deposition of sulfur also followed the same pattern (Fenn and Bytnerowicz 1993).

The nitrogen content of ponderosa pine litter was positively correlated with litter decomposition rates in the SBNF (Fenn and Dunn 1989). The same was true of litter decomposition rates of sugar pine and incense cedar; also, ponderosa pine foliage exhibiting severe ozone damage at high pollution plots abscised 2-4 years earlier than foliage from low pollution plots. Nitrogen availability in the litter layer is affected indirectly by the rate of ozone-induced litter fall, as well as the nitrogen content of needle tissue. The amount of litter fall was greatest from trees with moderate amounts of crown injury (Arkly and Glauser 1980), as compared to severely injured and uninjured trees. Therefore, the total amount of nitrogen varies with litter depth and can be expected to be quite variable over the landscape depending on amounts of crown injury from tree to tree. From ozone injured trees the litter has a higher proportion of needles from younger whorls inherently higher in nitrogen content (and lower in Ca content). This undoubtedly contributes to the increased nitrogen content of litter at plots in the western portions of the San Bernardino mountains (Fenn and Dunn 1989).

The continued accumulation of nitrogen in forest ecosystems, leading to nitrogen saturation, has important ecological effects including: soil acidification, cation depletion due to excess nitrate and cation leaching losses, nutrient imbalances, changes in plant communities as a result of the competitive advantage of nitrophilous species, decreased mycorrhizal symbiosis and increased drought stress (Aber and others 1989, Schulze 1989, Skeffington and Wilson 1988). Decreased run-off water quality due to high nitrate concentrations is another product of nitrogen saturation already demonstrated in Europe (Hauhs and others 1989), the eastern United States (Stoddard 1994), and in stream-flow from the San Gabriel mountains in southern California (Riggan and others 1985).

Summary

An assessment of the impact of air pollution on Sierra Nevada, west-side mixed conifer forests includes both the present evidence for chronic injury to sensitive species by ozone, and the possible accumulative effects of nitrogen deposition from the atmosphere. The reaction of ponderosa and Jeffrey pines and companion species in the mixed conifer type to ozone and nitrogen deposition is determined by complex interactions of both abiotic and biotic disturbance elements. In the future it is necessary to include climate warming as one of the driving variables.

Literature Cited

Aber, J.D., K.J. Nadelhoffer, P. Steudler, and J.M. Melillo 1989. Nitrogen saturation in northern forest ecosystems:Excess nitrogen from fossil fuel combustion may stress the biosphere. *Bioscience* 39:378-386.

Allison, J.R. 1982. *Evaluation of ozone injury on the Stanislaus National Forest*. USDA. For. Serv. Pac. SW Region, Forest Pest Management Report 82-07, 7pp.

Allison, J.R. 1984a. *An evaluation of ozone injury to pines on the Eldorado National Forest*. USDA. For. Serv. Pac SW Region, Forest Pest Management Report 84-16, 10pp.

Allison, J.R. 1984b. *An evaluation of ozone injury to pines on the Tahoe National Forest*. USDA. For. Serv. Pac. SW Region, Forest Pest Management Report 84-30, 10pp.

Arkley, R.J.; R. Glauser 1980. Effects of oxidant air pollution on pine litterfall and the forest floor. In *Proc symp Effects of*

Air Pollutants on Mediterranean and Temperate Forest Ecosystems. USDA, Forest Service, Gen. Tech. Rep. PSW-43, 249 pp.

Cahill, T. and others (SNEP document)

California Air Resources Board. 1983. *First Annual Report to the Governor and the Legislature on the Air Resource Board's Research and Monitoring Program.* Sacramento, CA.

California Air Resources Board. 1994. *Annual Report to the Governor and the Legislature of the Atmospheric Acidity Protection Program.* Sacramento, CA. 86 pp.

Duriscoe, D.M. and K.W. Stolte. 1989. Photochemical oxidant injury to ponderosa (*Pinus ponderosa Dougl.* ex Laws) and Jeffrey pine (*Pinus jeffreyi Grev. and Balf.*) in the national parks of the Sierra Nevada of California. In *Effects of air Pollution on Western Forests,* Edited by R.K. Olson and A.S. Lefohn, Transactions Series No.16, Air and Waste Management Association, Pittsburgh, pp 261-278

Fenn, M.E. and P.H. Dunn. 1989. Litter decomposition across an air pollution gradient in the San Bernardino Mountains. *Soil Society of America Journal* 53:1560-1567.

Fenn, M.E. and A. Bytnerowicz. 1993. Dry deposition of nitrogen and sulfur in the San Bernardino National Forest in southern California. *Environmental Pollution* 81:277-285.

Grulke, N.E., P.R. Miller, R.D. Wilborn, and S. Hahn. 1989. Photosynthetic response of giant sequoia seedlings and rooted branchlets of mature foliage to ozone fumigation. In *Effects of air Pollution on Western Forests,* Edited by R.K. Olson and A.S. Lefohn, Transactions Series No.16, Air and Waste Management Association, Pittsburgh, pp 429-422.

Guthrey, R., S. Schilling, and P.R. Miller. 1993. *Initial Progress Report of an Interagency Forest Monitoring Project: Forest Ozone REsponse STudy (FOREST).* USDA Forest Service, Pacific Southwest Research Station, Riverside, CA. 42 pp.

Guthrey, R., S. Schilling, and P.R. Miller. 1994. *Second Progress Report of an Interagency Forest Monitoring Project: Forest Ozone REsponse STudy (FOREST).* USDA Forest Service, Pacific Southwest Research Station, Riverside, CA. 22 pp.

Hauhs, M., K. Rost-Seibert, G. Raben, T. Paces, and B. Vigerust. 1989. Summary of European Data. In *The role of nitrogen in the acidification of soils and surface waters,* Edited by J.L. Malanchuk and J. Nilsson, Nordic Council of Ministers, Copenhagen, Miljorapport 10.

John, W., S.M. Wall, J.J. Weselowski. 1984. *Assessment of dry deposition in California*. California Air Resources Board, Final Report No. A1-156-32.

Miller P.R., A.A. Millecan. 1971. Extent of oxidant air pollution damage to some pines and other conifers in California. *Plant Disease Reporter* 55: 555-559.

Miller, P.R., N.E. Grulke, K.W. Stolte. 1994. Effects of air pollution on giant sequoia ecosystems. USDA, Forest Service, Gen. Tech. Rep., PSW-15, pp 90-98.

Pedersen, B.S. 1989. Ozone injury Jeffrey and ponderosa pines surrounding Lake Tahoe, California and Nevada. In *Effects of Air Pollution on Western Forests*, Edited by R.K. Olson and A.S. Lefhon, Transactions Series No.16, Air and Waste Management Association, Pittsburgh, pp 279-292.

Peterson, D.L., M.J. Arbaugh, L.J. Robinson. 1989. Ozone injury and growth trends of ponderosa pine in the Sierra Nevada. In *Effects of air Pollution on Western Forests,* Edited by R.K. Olson and A.S. Lefohn, Transactions Series No.16, Air and Waste Management Association, Pittsburgh, pp 293-308.

Peterson, D.L., M.J. Arbaugh, and L.J. Robinson. 1991. Regional growth changes in ozone-stressed ponderosa pine (*Pinus ponderosa*) in the Sierra Nevada, California, USA. *Holocene* 1:50-61.

Peterson, D.L.; D.L. Schmoldt, J.M. Eilers, R.W. Fisher, and R.D. Doty. 1993. *Guidelines for Evaluating Air Pollution Impacts on Class I Wilderness Areas in California*. General Technical Report PSW-GTR-136. USDA, Forest Service, Pacific Southwest Research Station, Albany, CA. pp. 34.

Pronos, J., D.R. Vogler, R.S. Smith. 1978. *An evaluation of ozone injury to pines in the southern Sierra Nevada*. USDA Forest Service, Pacific Southwest Region, Forest Pest Management, Report 78-1, 13pp.

Pronos, J. and D.R. Vogler. 1981. *Assessment of ozone injury to pines in the southern Sierra Nevada*, 1979/1980. Forest Pest Management Report 81-20. 13pp

Reuss, J.O., D.W. Johnson. 1986. *Acid deposition and the acidification of soils and waters*. Springer-Verlag, New York, 119 pp.

Riggan, P.J., R.N. Lockwood,and E.N. Lopez. 1985. Deposition and processing of airborne nitrogen pollutants in Mediterranean-type ecosystems of southern California. *Environmental Science and Technology* 19: 781-789.

Schulze, E.D. 1989. Air pollution and forest decline in a spruce (*Picea abies*) forest. *Science* 244:776-783.

Schilling, S.L., R. Guthrey, and P.R. Miller. 1995. *Comparison of 1991 to 1995 ozone injury indexes at Sierra Nevada and San Bernardino mountain sites. Third Progress Report of the Forest Ozone Response Study.* USDA, Forest Service, Pacific Southwest Research Station. Riverside, CA. 9pp.

Skeffington, R.A., and E.J. Wilson. 1988. Excess nitrogen deposition: Issues for consideration. *Environmental Pollution* 54:159-184.

Smith, W.H. 1990. *Air pollution and forests: Interactions between air contaminants and forest ecosystems.* ed. 2, Springer-Verlag, New York.

Stoddard, J.L. 1994. Long-term changes in watershed retention of nitrogen: Its causes and aquatic consequences. In *Environmental Chemistry of Lakes and Reservoirs,* Edited by L.A. Baker, Advances in Chemistry Series No. 237, American Chemical Society, Washington, D. C., pp. 223-284.

Temple, P.J., G.H. Riechers, and P.R. Miller. 1992. Foliar injury responses of ponderosa pine seedlings to ozone, wet and dry acidic deposition, and drought. *Environmental and Experimental Botany* 32:101-113.

Taylor, O.C., P.R. Miller, A.L. Page, and L.J. Lund. 1986. *Effect of ozone and sulfur dioxide mixtures on forest vegetation of the southern Sierra Nevada.* Final Report, California Air Resources Board Contract No. A0-135-03. Sacramento, CA.

Wallner, D.W., and M. Fong. 1982. *Survey Report,* National Park Service, Three Rivers, California.

Warner, T.E., D.W. Wallner, and D.R. Vogler. 1982. Ozone injury to ponderosa and Jeffrey pines in Sequoia-Kings Canyon National Parks. In *Proc. Conf. on Research in California's National Parks,* Edited by van Riper, C., L.D. Whittig, M.L. Murphy, Univ. Calif. Davis, CA pp 1-7.

JOHN W. MENKE
Department of Agronomy and
    Range Science
University of California
Davis, California

CATHERINE DAVIS
University of California
Davis, California

PETER BEESLEY
Agronomy and Range Science
University of California
Davis, California

22

Rangeland Assessment

Sierra Nevada Ecosystem Project: Final report to Congress, vol. III, *Assessments, Commissioned Reports, and Background Information*. Davis: University of California, Centers for Water and Wildland Resources, 1996.

List of Tables

ABSTRACT

This public rangeland/livestock grazing assessment includes a post-1905 history of livestock use on 10 National Forests of the Sierra Nevada and Modoc Plateau, a compilation of plant species indicators of livestock grazing effects, an assessment of grazing effects on sagebrush-steppe and mountain meadow rangelands, and a case study on correlation of meadow and riparian conditions in the Sierra Nevada.

While this assessment spans 5 decades of monitoring, it is important to recognize that although substantial reductions in livestock grazing intensity have occurred, most ranges were stocked above carrying capacity until very recently. A key indicator of improved condition that we have observed is an increase in native perennial grass composition on some upland sagebrush-steppe rangelands. A key indicator of declining condition is the continued cheatgrass invasion of many uplands. Based on the historical evidence of abuse of California mountain meadows during the post-Gold Rush Era, the recolonization by native plants, low abundance of non-native weeds, and the soil protection being provided by herbaceous vegetation as indicated by 4-5 decades of range monitoring data is significant. Considering past heavy grazing in northeastern California, the eastern Sierra in the Carson City and Tahoe environs, and lands of the Mother Lode nearest Sacramento, it is not surprising that the Modoc, Plumas, Tahoe, Eldorado and Toiyabe Forests are continuing to lag a bit in recovery since their meadows were probably most impacted during the early days following settlement. The declining abundance of grass species on mountain meadows of the Sierra National Forest and the low abundance of grass species on mountain meadows of the Sequoia National Forest during the 4-5 decade monitoring period is a biodiversity concern.

In a case study we investigated the potential for using long-term condition and trend monitoring data to indicate nearby riparian stream functionality. Using aggregated Parker transect data to the genus level, the lifeform categories of grasses, legumes, sedges, rushes, and forbs, and the raw data of bare soil exposure, litter and non-native species present currently and over the last 5 decades, we were able to predict 11-12 of 13 functioning-at-risk riparian/stream trend directions correctly. As used in the assessments developed here, variable dynamics indicating sedge to grass ratio changes without compensation of rushes, invasion or retreat of weedy forbs, reductions in abundance of late seral grasses such as Deschampsia and Glyceria species, radical fluctuation in clover composition, and 'red-flag' indicators like more than 7-10% bare soil exposure sometime in the meadow's 40-50 year history, were adequate to make the predictions.

Keywords: forage, grasses and grasslands, history, livestock, meadows, rangelands, riparian vegetation, communities, grazing, livestock management, range management, restoration, indicator plant species

INTRODUCTION

Rangeland ecosystem assessment includes bio-physical, ecological, managerial, and socio-economic components. As livestock grazing animals gather forage from the range vegetation, plant species are differentially affected depending on the season and the intensity of grazing, and the frequency of repeated grazing events. When plant species are differentially affected the plant community species composition changes. As the animals move from place to place they trample soils, redistribute nutrients and seeds, and modify vegetation fuel loading levels thereby affecting other processes such as forage productivity, wildfire intensity or even potential for fire occurrence, and wildlife habitat values.

Livestock and range managers have opportunities to use animal herding practices, water developments, fencing, scientifically-designed grazing systems, and many other approaches to enhance forage productivity, wildlife habitat and water quality, and reduce many of the possible negative or potentially non-sustainable grazing effects. Some members of the public have come to expect more products, watershed and aesthetic values from rangelands or at least less visible resource degradation. Therefore more cooperation between ranchers using the public land and agency land managers will be required to alleviate these problems where possible with reasonable effort. Cooperation here refers to ranchers and agency managers doing their best to understand undesirable grazing impacts and jointly having a commitment to stopping them wherever feasible. It does not mean a continuation of trust with no penalties for poor performance on either side.

Implementation of sustainable stewardship programs takes time, costs money and must have an educational component. It takes a commitment to collect and use existing knowledge. Unlike many problems facing society, adequate knowledge and skills exist to assess rangeland site specific problems and prescribe solutions. However, local land managers and rancher permittees may not possess the necessary information to make sustainable rangeland management decisions. The key point is that they must acquire this information and then cooperate as defined above. We feel there is a major realignment of responsibility needed in agencies and Land Grant Universities to develop, extend and use new or newly acquired but applicable old information. Within land management agencies this is a call for coordination between those closest to the ground with their place-based knowledge and those higher up in the bureaucracy with their systems-based knowledge.

Unlike other resource uses of public lands, rancher permittees annually use designated grazing allotments as part of their business enterprises under 10-year renewable grazing permits. These contractual arrangements have existed for many decades in most cases, and unlike timber sales or mining claims they are not expected to end or be periodic unless non-sustainable resource impacts occur that cannot be managed. Since the determination of non-sustainability is difficult where a use causes small but cumulative degradative effects over many years, it behooves both parties to use many sensitive indicators of problems to alleviate them before they become irreversible impacts. The purpose of this rangeland assessment is to determine whether, where, how and why non-sustainable ecological impacts are occurring. There is a further temporal aspect to this assessment, that is, if non-sustainable impacts have occurred, when did they occur or are they on-going?

We know that the Sierra Nevada and Modoc Plateau rangelands were abusively grazed and impacted by non-sustainable livestock grazing prior to 1905 (Kinney's report on past conditions of rangelands in another Sierra Nevada Ecosystem Project report). Later in this assessment we review the post-1905 grazing history of Sierra Nevada and Modoc Plateau rangelands since the establishment of public land management agencies; much overgrazing has occurred since 1905 as well. Knowledge needed to judge what is sustainable rangeland management has increased greatly over the past 50 years and especially over the last 20 years. The guidelines or standards by which managers should judge sustainability of range management activities are relatively well understood.

Beginning on the eastern edge of the Sacramento and San Joaquin valleys, low elevation Sierra foothill annual grasslands, blue oak/foothill pine savannas, and interior liveoak/blue oak woodlands, which are largely in private ownership, produce forages utilized by livestock and many wildlife animals. These areas are also where some of the most rapidly developing housing subdivisions in the state of California continue to occur. Where available, fall and spring acorn mast and browse forage production from oak trees and shrubs complement diets of herbivores. As nutritional quality of annual herbaceous forages from grasses and forbs decline in late spring each year, migratory wildlife animals and livestock benefit from moving up in elevation, using forage plants with later phenological development, typically on public lands.

Grazing permits on public and private mountain rangeland provide high protein, green forage during summer that is critical to the seasonal forage supply for rancher permittees. Recreational pack-and-saddle stock also use high elevation subalpine and alpine meadow and riparian areas in summer. In fall, big game hunters, often with pack animals, use mountain rangelands to harvest mule deer, black bear, and limited numbers of bighorn sheep. High-elevation summer range is critical habitat for these game species and other wildlife, especially for mule deer rearing young on nutritious foods in close proximity to riparian vegetation which provides fawn hiding cover from predators and humans.

The status of blue oak/foothill pine savannas and blue oak/interior liveoak woodlands is assessed in a separate report (by Standiford in this Sierra Nevada Ecosystem Project document). For nearly 10 years resource managers, scientists and the public have been concerned about inadequate oak tree regeneration in this foothill region of the Sierra. Unhealthy age-class structures, indicated by poor recruitment of seedlings, have been well studied. The combination of mortality factors including land development, fuelwood cutting, livestock grazing, competition from exotic annual grasses for soil water, fire, and other causes have led to many concerns. Much progress has been made in management policies to maintain the oak component in these foothill woodlands, but housing development continues to reduce the contribution of oak trees to foothill ecosystem function.

In mid-elevation west-slope mixed conifer forests, livestock foraging areas are limited to 'stringer meadows', riparian areas, brushfields, and 'transitional range' where even-age forest management activities or wildfires have produced temporary (7-15 years) forage resources in clearcuts, burned areas, or along roadsides seeded with grasses. Plantation grazing by cattle or sheep is sometimes used to reduce grass and shrub competition with conifer seedlings. Recreational pack-and-saddle stock use of foothill and mid-elevation rangeland is low because vistas are limited, temperatures in summer are often unfavorably hot, and the attractive elements of lakes and streams are infrequent in closed-canopy mixed conifer forest. Private land ownership limits access to much of the foothill oak woodland and annual grassland savanna rangelands.

East-side pine forests, pinyon/juniper, and sagebrush-steppe and bitterbrush upland ranges, especially common on the Modoc Plateau and east slope Sierra, provide open vistas but distances from metropolitan centers often limit pack-and-saddle stock use in these areas. Many of these rangelands are administered by the Bureau of Land Management (BLM) and provide critical mule deer and pronghorn antelope winter range, sage grouse habitats, important wetland and waterfowl habitat, as well as complementary spring and fall livestock grazing. In general, pack-and-saddle stock use increases with elevation and scenic quality and is greatest in subalpine and alpine wilderness areas on National Forest and National Park lands in the southern Sierra. 'Primary range' for livestock grazing in the Sierra Nevada and Warner Mountains occurs mainly on wet and mesic subalpine and alpine meadows on public lands including many wilderness areas, and developed meadows/irrigated pastures on private lands.

Much is known about pre-1905 changes in land, vegetation and herbivore use of Sierra and Modoc Plateau rangelands, but little information has been collated and summarized previously. This task has now been done in the report by Kinney. Some past vegetative changes, including sagebrush density increases and cheatgrass (Bromus tectorum) invasion, have led to conditions that are very resistant to restoration, while other situations such as damaged riparian systems present great opportunities for aquatic habitat restoration. By identifying these diverse situations and their likelihood for rehabilitation, society can choose policies for future public rangeland management and encourage improved land stewardship. Where possible in this assessment we will identify research, technology, and manager/rancher training needs.

Since the early to mid-1950's the Forest Service has been gathering a range condition and trend database (Parker C&T transect) to help determine changes in range plant communities and soil stability (Table 1). As part of this assessment we have collated much of this data for 10 National Forests including the Modoc, Lassen, Plumas, Eldorado, Tahoe, Toiyabe, Stanislaus, Sierra, Sequoia, and Inyo National Forests. Most of the transects for Meadow and Sagebrush range types (Table 2) which had been read multiple times were put into a database (Oracle) to facilitate summarization and analysis. These two range types are the most important to assess change since they provide the primary range forage source on Sierran and Modoc Plateau grazing allotments and are less likely to be confounded by plant successional processes unrelated to grazing. For example, range trends in Conifer range types may be solely due to tree growth and development (natural succession) and not grazing. Additionally, only the Meadow and Sagebrush range types have enough readings in recent decades to make strong trend interpretations.

The general decline in number of readings per decade (Table 1) is primarily a reflection of a Forest Service-wide decision to not continue to use the Parker Three-Step Range Condition and Trend monitoring method while searching for another method. Problems with interpretation of frequency data in the small 3/4-inch loop sampling frame, and lack of a direct relationship between frequency and canopy cover by species led to its abandonment. Experience from Forest Service Region 4 was brought to Region 5 in a training exercise in the mid-1980s. During this meeting replacement of the Parker Method by frequency sampling in larger quadrats was suggested for range trend monitoring. Since that time the Region 5 Range Handbook never got revised and a new range condition monitoring method was not adopted or promoted. Inadequate budgets also limited monitoring efforts. A further problem has been that recent hires have not been range trained and thus there has been few personnel to facilitate adequate monitoring. For lack of an alternative, on some Forests with experienced range conservationists, Parker transects have been re-read more regularly. Long-term continunity in the collection of monitoring data is critical. Without documentation of patterns of long-term changes, management decisions are much less certain to be the best for good land stewardship.

Alternative monitoring methods such as the Toe-Point Method have been used for years to supplement Parker transects in order to monitor range types not typically included in the permanent Parker transects such as annual grassland, oak woodlands and transitory range, or on key areas of allotments which did not have Parker transects. Many range conservationists have used the Toe-Point Method to estimate carrying capacity. Newer methods, such as nested-rooted frequency analysis (Region 4 approach) have been shown to be more sensitive to range condition trend but, again, inadequate formal adoption has led to a large gap in range condition monitoring information for the Sierra Nevada and Modoc Plateau rangelands. Since these other methods have had variable application by National Forests and do not cover a long period, we used the older condition and trend data.

Two National Forests in northern California, the Modoc and Klamath, have used the Region 1 ECODATA computer programs and collection of vegetation sampling methods which were developed from an ecosystem approach. These procedures were originally designed to aid in vegetation classification, but secondary uses to relate ecological status to carrying capacity and range condition trend may be a primary value. Since plant communities are the primary unit of vegetation, description of the plant species canopy cover is necessary to classify units of range vegetation. Frequency data alone does not allow classification. Without a range vegetation classification, it is impossible to define desired future condition or potential natural plant communties. A critical need is to get range vegetation classified on all allotments. Secondly, a range condition monitoring method needs to be adopted and training needs to begin as soon as possible. We recommend that a concerted effort be made to link past range condition monitoring data to whatever new method is chosen. Superimposing some of the new plots on top of some of the Parker Transects is one way make this linkage. This is being done already on the Klamath National Forest.

We re-read 24 Meadow Parker transects on 7 National Forests in summer 1995 in cooperation with local National Forest range specialists to strengthen the database and test for correlations with nearby riparian and stream conditions. As will be described in more detail below, we evaluated stream riparian conditions near these 24 transects and conducted multivariate canonical correspondence analysis (Jongman et al. 1987) of the paired stream/riparian data with the 1995 Parker transect data. If the transect data were correlated with the stream/riparian condition data it would be possible to estimate riparian conditions more widely in the Sierra and Modoc Plateau on grazing allotments using the Forest Service Parker Transect database which we have compiled. This analysis also allowed us to evaluate recent changes in livestock management and various riparian restoration efforts in 24 site-specific cases since that information was also gathered for the analysis. We include one extensive Appendix table summarizing the transect data for these 24 sites so readers of this report can make their own interpretation of the data if they desire.

To summarize, this assessment includes a history of livestock grazing on 10 National Forests with a focus on numbers of livestock grazed since 1905 or the establishment of the Forest Service (covering the period following the Kinney report to the present). We have gathered together an extensive database of Forest Service condition and trend data for Meadow and Sagebrush range types for permanent transects that have been repeatedly read over the last 5 decades on 10 National Forests. We are using a small sample of this database in conjunction with data we collected in summer 1995 on 24 grazing allotments or units on 7 National Forests to determine whether correlations exist between meadow status and stream/riparian functionality.

The data we have used could be considered as a pseudo-random selection of wet and mesic (moist) meadow and sagebrush-steppe sites in that we chose which transects would be used solely on the basis of the frequency of past re-reading as well as whether each transect was wholly within one plant community type. Some of the transects were inappropriately located originally and crossed two or more plant communities thereby not providing useful information-- these transects were rejected from our sample if they happened to become candidates. In all cases we are using the data to help determine whether sustainable range management is occurring on public rangelands in the Sierra Nevada and Modoc Plateau. We have referenced literature where scientists have studied range condition trends and hypothesized reasons for these changes.

Finally, we have also prepared a major section on plant indicators of livestock grazing effects. We are including this section following the history section since it forms the basis for which we judge change due to livestock grazing. Some readers may want to skip over this technical section to the ecological and biophysical rangeland assessment sections which follow. From the beginning of the field of range science, range managers have used vegetation species composition and soil cover as two primary indicators of vegetation change and stability of grazed ecosystems. We believe this is the most important information range managers can use to detect short-term changes which eventually result in long-term changes and sometimes serious problems for management if undetected for an extended period of time. Botanists and ecologists alike use species presence to indicate resource use impacts. We prepared draft plant indicator material and then circulated it among agency resource specialists to refine this section of the report. Its purpose is to provide information which range managers can and should use to determine shorter term indicators of vegetation and range stability changes. One clear need arises from this effort--greater plant identification skills are essential for resource specialists doing rangeland monitoring and assessments.

POST-1905 HISTORY OF LIVESTOCK GRAZING ON NATIONAL FOREST LAND

The objective of this section of the assessment is to discuss the grazing history of the Sierra Nevada and Modoc Plateau as it relates to the condition of rangelands in the SNEP study area today. For this reason, not only are stock numbers and season of use discussed, but also changes in allotment size and number, range improvement projects and manipulation of the vegetation. In addition indirect influences on range management, such as socio-economic conditions and priorities of management, will be discussed where they have significantly affected rangeland management. Citations in this section are in the text and refer to specific National Forest unpublished documents.

Livestock were introduced into the Sierra in the mid 1700s following settlement by the Spanish. However, grazing was not a significant impact on the majority of the range until the period following the Gold Rush. It was not until the formation of the Forest Service following 1905 that livestock numbers began to be recorded. The primary sources of information used in this paper are the US Forest Service, individual Range Allotment Files (2210 files). Where available the grazing history was collected per allotment, the allotment being the unit of Forest Service land allotted to a permittee. Where this information was incomplete, grazing information at the Ranger District or Forest level was used.

Qualitative livestock stocking history is presented for six regions of the Sierra Nevada and Modoc Plateau as follows: 1) the Modoc Plateau and Warner Mountains, 2) Northern Sierra, 3) Sierra Foothills, 4) Central and Southern Sierra, 5) High Sierra, and 6) Eastern Sierra. These regions are ecologically distinct, and because of their distinct ecology and topography, ranching operations and livestock management have developed differently. This section of the assessment addresses the following points for each of these areas: 1) The change in stocking rate of livestock indicating times of highest use and reasons why, 2) changes in allotment size and number of allotments, reasons for these changes and effects, and changes in stocking rate and impacts on the land, 3) changes in type of livestock grazed and reasons for changes related to impact on the land, and 4) trends in range improvement or enhancement practices.

Fire has perhaps had the largest effect on the landscape and ecology of Sierra Nevada rangeland. As it related to livestock, fire had its greatest effect from 1880-1910 when sheepherders apparently set large brush fires every fall as they left the public lands. Miners also used fire extensively in the Sierra to expose the surface geology in looking for gold and silver. These fires opened vast areas of the western montane slopes and foothill areas for what came to be called 'transitory range' grazing. Due to the suppression of fire from 1920-present, these areas closed in with brush or denser forests thus becoming uneconomical and unproductive for livestock forage. Since wildfires still occur, transitory range continues to be created, but on a much more limited scale, never attaining the size of the areas opened to grazing as in the past. It was this human activity that led to the explosion of mule and black-tailed deer populations in the Sierra Nevada and Modoc Plateau range and forest lands.

During the World Wars I and II increased livestock use occurred on National Forests and other public lands throughout the West, often without regard to appropriate stocking rates, thus causing overuse from 1914-1920 and again from 1939-1946. During World War I the demand for wool and mutton was higher so sheep use was high, while during World War II cattle use was increased. The foot-and-mouth disease epidemic of 1924 had a severe effect on the Stanislaus National Forest grazing program, where all livestock for the 1924-25 season were slaughtered. Use was permanently reduced after that time. This event indirectly affected the surrounding forests by making use during that time go up slightly to offset this loss in capacity. This event also affected the eastern Sierra because of the closure of the Sonora Pass area to sheep, thus reducing transient use by this herbivore.

Modoc Plateau and Warner Mountains

The Modoc National Forest was established in 1903, except for 323,000 acres of the Doublehead Ranger District which was added in 1920. Until 1934 (Taylor Grazing Act) very little attention was given to grazing carrying capacity limits. From 1934-46 much information was collected about range condition and many changes were proposed to bring management more in line with range carrying capacities (i.e. sustainable use for livestock). However, significant reductions in actual use did not occur in many cases until the 1950-60 period. It was also during this time that large scale vegetation manipulation projects occurred. From 1960-70, many changes in allotment sizes took place, eliminating many of the 'uneconomical allotments' (see discussion below), and this affected overall use. It was not until the 1980s and 1990s, however, that reductions in use began to bring use into balance with forage production capacity.

The 1880-1934 period: Most livestock grazing in California was largely unregulated before the establishment of the National Forests. Prior to the establishment of the Modoc Forest in 1903, the entire area was subjected to extremely heavy use by transient cattle and sheep, in addition to the use obtained by local livestock owners. This transient use reached the point where attendant range depletion was jeopardizing the local livestock economy. Primarily for protection of the local industry, the Modoc National Forest was created. However, the ranges had been so seriously depleted by that time from a protracted series of drought years between 1917 and 1935, and by over-stocking during the war years 1916-19, they have never satisfactorily recovered. A major factor in this response has been the invasion of cheatgrass following the loss of native perennial grasses. This change in composition is discussed elsewhere in this assessment.

During this time the main emphasis of Forest Service management was to maintain the local livestock economy. There is much evidence that Forest Service personnel were aware of depleted and degenerating rangeland conditions but they would not take any action to alleviate grazing pressure if it would jeopardize a rancher's livelihood. The following quote expresses this: "The proper thing to do is to reduce the number of stock to meet forage conditions. This we have been planning to do for several years, but because of ... the precarious condition of all the stockmen concerned we feel that it is a most inopportune time to make reductions" (from the 1933 Annual Grazing Report, Modoc National Forest). More evidence that Forest Service personnel were aware of the over-use of the range are the exclosure plots set up to monitor meadow and bunchgrass types, and a quote from the 1924 Annual Grazing Report for the Modoc National Forest that states: "The meadows are too closely fed, there is not much reseeding on the range, and browse, especially in the southwestern portion of the allotment is becoming too closely fed, and some of it killed. May 1st is really too early to feed the lower part of the area ... But the demand makes it difficult to refuse stockmen the use of the range till a later date." It is clear that too little emphasis was given to animal distribution control, an option to improve management without reducing numbers.

World War I demands for food and fiber caused use to increase from 1914 to the mid 1920s. Any reductions during this time were due to the economic climate, for example: "Probably the heaviest adjustment in livestock (both cattle and sheep) came about during the period of 1918-1923, due to over-capitalization and moving transient livestock out of the NW corner of the Forest" (from Tucker Allotment Management Plan, Doublehead Ranger District, Modoc National Forest). Also during this time allotments were large and many of them were 'community allotments' with several permittees, thus making monitoring of use more difficult, which resulted in higher use. The only limiting factor to use during this time was the lack of watering sources for stock, thus areas close to water sources were depleted while remote areas were lightly used.

The Warner Mountains are some of the most productive rangeland on the Modoc National Forest and they were not limited by water sources. Thus they were more easily exploited, and by a larger number of smaller livestock operations. Use of the Warner Mountains was not reduced during the period from 1920-1940, so as not to jeopardize the operations of these smaller ranchers. After 1924, reductions in permitted livestock outside the Warner's brought much of the range on the Modoc National Forest into better balance (Reasons for Trends in Permitted Use, 1920 report, Modoc National Forest).

The 1934-1950 period: In most cases overall livestock use was not reduced significantly until 1934 when new carrying capacities were calculated following the passage of the Taylor Grazing Act. The most drastic reductions were made from 1935-39: "Cattle were reduced 39%, and sheep 28% since 1934... Season adjustments account for about 40% of the total reduction in use, while actual cuts in numbers of stock accounted for the other 60%.". Stocking rates went up during the World War II years from 1939-46, but they were still in most cases half of the pre-1920 stocking rates. It was also during this time that many of the larger community allotments were split into smaller allotments, and many allotments changed livestock class from sheep to cattle due mostly to economic reasons (Modoc National Forest history reports).

According to the 1944, Forest Summary, Range Allotment Analysis, Modoc National Forest, many major range improvements were implemented during the 1934-1944 period, the majority being water sources for stock, making more upland areas available for grazing. There was much emphasis on expanding viable range acreage: "20,000 acres are recommended for reseeding, these include meadows, sage flats or former meadows, aspen basins etc... 15,000 acres of eroded bottom land are recommended for gully plugs, and erosion dams, ... 10,000 acres are recommended for water spreading and irrigation, ... 20,000 acres of sagebrush land are recommended for clearing, (provided current trials are successful)".

Though extensive manipulation of vegetation was proposed, Forest Service personnel were aware of the limitations of their range as indicated in the following quotation: "... in areas of extreme depletion, lower value species such as members of the Brassicaceae and <u>Polygonum</u> species were recommended for stabilizing soil". Sagebrush eradication was only proposed where silver sagebrush (<u>Artemisia cana</u>) was invading meadows or where <u>Artemisia tridentata</u> ssp. <u>wyomingensis</u> was increasing in density on bunchgrass (sagebrush-steppe) range. At the time there was no concern given to potential natural communities, thus reseeded mixtures were all exotics including: the wheatgrasses <u>Agropyron cristatum</u>, <u>A</u>. <u>dasystachyum</u>, <u>A</u>. <u>intermedium</u>, common timothy (<u>Phleum pratensis</u>), smooth brome (<u>Bromus inermis</u>), etc. In retrospect, this was fortunate because today we know that seeding with non-local gene pools of native species could have done more harm than seeding exotics. None of these exotic grasses have become invasive or problem species since that time. Willows and aspens were often eradicated. Economical forage production was the primary objective.

The 1950-1970 period: During this time more permanent reductions in numbers of livestock occurred on most allotments, even on the Warner Mountain Ranger District. Seasons were also reduced in most cases, and many of the 'uneconomical' allotments were abandoned. This period was also a time when many sheep allotments were being converted to cattle, thus creating more 'uneconomical' allotments, since cattle could not utilize much of the area sheep had previously used. It was also during this time that many resource enhancement projects were implemented. For example, on the Willow Creek allotment: 53 acres plowed and drilled with wheatgrasses and perennial ryegrass (<u>Lolium perenne</u>), 25 acres sprayed to eliminate sagebrush, 1.5 miles of water spreading ditch around the seeded area (Willow Creek Allotment Management Plan, Big Valley Ranger District, Modoc National Forest). These projects caused fluctuations in use, for example, non-use during reseeding or after a burn, and increased use after clearing of sagebrush and reseeding. At this time broadcast seeding after large burns became more economical and thus more common. In most cases, where use went up it was because of recombination of allotments, or due to enhancement projects.

The 1970-1980 period: Livestock use was mostly static during this time but many allotment boundaries changed. Many of the smaller allotments were combined or were deemed uneconomical as more ranchers quit the livestock business. It was during this time that the Forest Service began to take a more ecologically oriented approach to range management. Monitoring of range use and condition was more common. More resource protection projects such as exclosures in riparian areas, riparian pastures, and rest-rotation systems of grazing were done. However, on many allotments actual use still exceeded the carrying capacity.

The 1980-present period: Actual use began to drop again in the 1990s, due in part to reductions by the Forest Service in numbers and season of use, more allotments being closed or placed in rest-rotation systems of grazing, and drought effects. The 'Riparian Initiative' of the Forest Service also greatly changed the current management since the riparian areas had always been the areas which received highest use. The abuse had been recognized but was not acted on until the 1980s: "General forage conditions on most ranges on the Warner Mountain and Big Valley Ranger Districts are improving slightly, or at least are remaining static. Exceptions are ... drainages, meadows, watering places and other natural concentration areas. These heavily used areas appear to continue to decline though not at an alarming rate..." (1944, Forest Summary, Range Allotment Analysis, Modoc National Forest). Since 1980, many resource protection projects were implemented, from check dams, to riparian exclosures, bank stabilization projects, etc. These have tended to immediately decrease livestock use, with the possible long-term consequences of increasing forage and thus use in the future.

Northern Sierra

The Northern Sierra area includes the montane portions of the Lassen, Plumas and Tahoe National Forests. Given that we were able to gather more information for the Lassen National Forest, many of the references will be to this Forest. These areas were established as National Forests in 1908, along with most of the Sierran Forests. Highest livestock use was prior to that time, the majority being from transient sheep grazing. Use remained high until after the 1920s. From 1928-1939, when use was lowered, allotments were made smaller, and more allotments were converted to cattle. From 1939 through the 1940s use went up again due to World War II. From 1950-1970 use was greatly reduced when many uneconomic allotments were dropped or combined. Since 1970 use has declined, partly due to a change in management focus from livestock production to resource protection.

The 1880-1928 period: As stated above this was the time of highest livestock use. The following quotation is applicable to the whole Sierra: "By 1880 there were 5,727,000 sheep in California ... after this time their numbers began to decline because of poor range conditions and later controls on the herding of sheep on public lands. Forest vegetation [primarily brush since most herbaceous forage was consumed by livestock] was affected through burning by herders and the consumption and trampling of vegetation by sheep" (The Effects of Humans on the Sierra Nevada Mixed Conifer Forest, report by Jim Johnston, Lassen National Forest). The Lassen National Forest received a large amount of transient use even after 1908, since it was a driveway for sheep to the northeast: "Driveways account for 5% of sheep grazing on this Forest, since it is located to receive travel from Nevada, northeastern California and Oregon ... Taking it along with other sheep travel it amounts to 25% of the total sheep grazing. The appraisal of 1922 gave a figure of 10,211 cow-months in excess of the current 54,150 cow-month's and 70,408 sheep-months in excess of the current 30,606 sheep-months... The feed close to water is practically gone and that in outlying districts is limited" (1909 Annual Grazing Report, Lassen National Forest). On most allotments the highest use occurred by the early 1920s, but on the whole reductions in use were not mandated by the Forest Service until 1934.

The 1928-1949 period: Use started to decrease in the mid to late 1920s, but not until 1934 did the Forest Service make significant reductions in numbers and seasons. "By 1915 the U.S.F.S. fixed the allotment lines, but major changes in the broad patterns of grazing did not occur until the early 1940s" (History of Tahoe National Forest 1840-1940: A Cultural Resources Overview History, Tahoe National Forest). "Reductions have brought the actual use down to a point near the present estimate which is a little under the 1934 grazing survey figures" (1946 Annual Report, Lassen National Forest). It was recognized that range conditions were in a degraded state: "There are 64 allotments on the Forest now, with few considered in good condition" (1946 Annual Report, Lassen National Forest). Emphasis however was still on maximizing use of rangeland. In the 1940 Statistical Report for the Lassen National Forest, the following work was proposed: recommend reseeding--620 acres; rodent control--60,000 acres;

re-treatment rodent control--80,000 acres and recommended new rodent control-- 112,100 acres. Rodent control, mostly for gophers in meadows, attests to the drying and declining condition of meadows.

While in 1934 only 5,500 acres of rangeland were reported overgrazed, in 1940, 19,000 acres were reported. The lack of concern was evident in the statement: "As a whole, we do not feel greatly alarmed over our overgrazed areas as we are holding them in check in spite of most adverse weather conditions" (1934 Annual Grazing Report, Lassen National Forest). Much of the rangeland on the forests in the northern Sierra and southern Cascades is in timbered areas. With the harvesting of timber much temporary rangeland was created following 1940: "Our large reductions for the next 10 years are on account of lands that will be cut over by 1944 ... if the sheep grazing experiment turns out as satisfactorily as we feel it will, we should be able to take care of the sheep as the lands are cut over" (1934 Annual Grazing Report, Lassen National Forest). There was little clearing of brush to open areas for grazing during the 1928-1949 period. From 1941-1946 use went up due to World War II, but it was still lower than in the 1920s.

The 1950-1970 period: Both animal numbers and season of use were reduced soon after 1950 due to the realization that areas were over-stocked and to the growing encroachment of brush, both on montane slopes and in meadow areas: "A direct result of the grazing is the widespread appearance of sagebrush. Spraying was applied in the 1940s, and 1950s on sagebrush" (1946 Annual Grazing Report, Lassen National Forest). In response to this increase in brush, many clearing, burning and spraying projects were undertaken: "Considerable range improvements have been made on the Forest, but many more are needed to facilitate proper management. Fences and water development are those most required. The same is true of range resource development with the emphasis on water spreading, rodent control and some reseeding" (1946 Annual Grazing Report, Lassen National Forest). Changes were made in the allotments as a result of the vegetation changes: "In general the east side ranges are economical... A number of the west side ranges ... are considered as non-usable. Pine reproduction and brush make several other allotments marginal. Boundary changes are necessary in many cases to bring allotments to an economic size; these changes are chiefly on the west side" (1946 Annual Grazing Report, Lassen National Forest). During this period, most seasons were shortened, numbers reduced, allotments were dropped, and others were combined usually with a reduction in use.

The 1970-present period: The process of recombining and eliminating uneconomical allotments continued during this time. From 1970-80, use did not vary greatly, many sheep ranges changed to cattle or dropped out. In the 1980s use was again reduced, this time due to a change in management emphasis, which actually started in the 1970s. Concern over resource protection began to govern range use. Again, the 'Riparian Initiative' and several other Forest Service programs shifted emphasis to the protection and conservation of riparian areas. With this change in emphasis many exclosures, riparian pastures, erosion control structures, and replanting of riparian species occurred.

Sierra Foothills

National Forest ranges in the Sierra Foothills are primarily 'transitory ranges' on the west slope of the Sierra with limited lower-elevation annual grasslands and oak woodlands. They are primarily used during the winter months, for short periods during the spring and early summer, and sometimes in conifer plantation grazing programs. These areas, especially in the central Sierra received heavy use from 1870-1900 because of their close proximity to mining communities. They were also affected by the early sheepherders, not so much by direct grazing pressures as by the fires sheepherders set. From 1900-1930, the Forest Service continued to stock these areas at a fairly high rate. In the 1940s use on these areas decreased due to allotment closures and reduced numbers and season. From 1950 to 1970, use was again reduced and many areas were closed. In the 1980s and 1990s use was further reduced due to the cumulative effect of years of fire suppression and the resultant increase in brush and urban development.

The 1870-1900 period: These areas were first grazed in the spring and fall by sheep when the large bands numbering up to 6 million were driven from the San Joaquin Valley up to the high Sierra. Again, the sheepherders' fires impacted the foothills more than grazing. "Some herders developed the practice of setting fires to clear underbrush in order to increase forage the following year... Once a fire was set however there was no method of controlling the destruction..." (Basque 'Tramp herders' on Forbidden Ground: Early Grazing Controversies in California's National Reserves, Forest Service). The number of acres burned during this time was quite extensive: "While no records were kept...the largest percentage of the most destructive fires in the mountains of California were caused by sheepmen during the 30 years preceding the establishment of the National Forest" (Fire History-Sheepmen Fires by Thomas West 1932). Areas close to the mining towns were used for both cattle and sheep, although this use was not extensive.

The 1900-1930 period: By 1910, fires set by sheepherders were being curtailed but intensive grazing use continued. "Early historical accounts of the range in the Sierra foothills report that the land had been overgrazed to the point of being badly abused. The reason for this being the accessibility to local ranches and the closeness of the Yosemite National Park back country to livestock grazing. With the loss of their summer range in Yosemite, the local ranches of Mariposa County freely made use of the Forest Service land west of the Park" (Chowchilla Allotment Management Plan, Sierra National Forest). This high use was true throughout the western foothills of the Sierra. Livestock use peaked in most cases in the early 1920s. After this time there were some efforts to reduce use, and in the southern forests sheep use declined and some areas were not re-stocked with cattle.

The 1930-1950 period: While there was an increase in use from 1939 to 1944 due to World War II, many reductions occurred after that time. Allotments were combined, dropped and boundaries changed in order to make the allotments economical units, and most sheep allotments by 1945 changed to cattle allotments. With the suppression of fire since 1920, many areas were reverting to brush and timber and were deemed uneconomical. Even though closures took place and stocking was reduced, the area was often stocked above the carrying capacity: "This area was not excepted from the heavy use common in the Sierra early in the century. As recently as the 1960s, sheep were brought through this area enroute to higher elevation sheep allotments... No matter which period of the grazing history we discuss we will find the area was overstocked" (Chiquito Allotment Management Plan, Sierra National Forest). It was in the 1950s that many vegetation 'type-conversion' projects were proposed, but most did not take place until later.

The 1950-1970 period: It was during this time that many vegetation 'type conversion' projects took place. These involved burning, mechanical clearing, and herbicide spraying of brush then reseeding with annual or perennial grasses. There was also much reseeding on burned areas, and following reseeding areas were often heavily stocked by either cattle or sheep. This practice was significant since the burned acreage was extensive. The following quote is indicative of this vegetation management practice: "... steadily decreased use due to brush encroachment and diversion of livestock to the other units. In 1920-30 there were several large fires that opened up previously timbered or brush covered land. From 1960-64, 274 acres of land were 'cleared and converted' to perennial and annual grassland, clearing and reseeding again occurred in 1979" (Hyde Mill Allotment Management Plan, Sequoia National Forest). Even with these projects most allotments were becoming uneconomical not only due to reversion to brush and timber, but also due to encroaching housing development and resultant impacts: "... 1944-because of mining and agricultural settlement, this is just a place to put small herds of cattle for a short period. It is my opinion that this area will not be grazable much longer as people are the disturbing factor" (Otter Creek Allotment Management Plan, Eldorado National Forest).

The 1970-1990 period: As previously stated it was not until the late 1970s and early 1980s that resource protection became a greater emphasis relative to forage resource production. At this time many Sierra transitory range-based allotments were already closed. Those that were open were often put in rest-rotation systems of grazing thus decreasing their use. In areas where fire destabilized soil, revegetation projects were implemented. Where gully erosion occurred from grazing, fire or logging, check dams were installed. The overall trend in use was toward shorter seasons and lower numbers. It became accepted policy that these more marginal transitory ranges were not suitable as permanent range.

Central and Southern Sierra

The Central and Southern Sierra area includes the upper montane areas of the Lake Tahoe Basin, Eldorado, Stanislaus, Sierra, and Sequoia National Forests, and parts of Yosemite and Sequoia National Parks before they were closed to grazing. This area includes the Mother Lode Gold Rush area, is highly accessible, and has extensive water sources. These factors contributed to higher early use by both cattle and sheep than many areas of the Sierra. Access and location relative to valley urban areas later contributed to a reduction in grazing due to increased recreational use and development. Highest use occurred before the National Forests were established in 1908: "Use was heavy in the 1920s, decreased during the drought years of the 1930s, increased greatly during the 1940-1946 war years, decreased slightly from 1948-1952, and has remained constant to date (1960)" (Haskell Allotment Management Plan, Sierra National Forest).

The 1870-1900 period: There were several areas that received particularly high use by transient sheep grazing during this period, both the Lake Tahoe Basin and Sonora Pass area of the Stanislaus National Forest. By 1900 the number of transient sheep bands were significantly reduced throughout the Sierra.

The 1908-1930 period: Once the National Forest took over management, transient sheep use was gradually brought under control, and it was further reduced by a disease outbreak. In 1925, there was an outbreak of foot-and-mouth disease on the Stanislaus National Forest which resulted in all of the livestock being slaughtered. After this time numbers were reduced to 66% of previous stocking, which also forced some sheep operations to change to cattle. Movement of sheep over the Sonora Pass onto the eastern Sierra ranges effectively stopped thus eliminating the driveway use on the Stanislaus National Forest. Permitted use on the allotments was still high, but there was an awareness of degraded and deteriorating conditions: "It can safely be stated that all grasslands in the Forest are decreasing in food value annually. This circumstance is due to several causes. First, consumption of the grass before it re-seeds. Second, trampling of cattle on the wet meadows. Third, the general practice which is now being remedied, the over-stocking of the range. Fourth, improper handling of cattle on the range" (1910 Annual Grazing Report, Eldorado National Forest). Improvements were recommended but few reductions in numbers or season of use were made: "The only remedy in any case, seems to be a large reduction of stock and, after determining by experiments the character of grasses that will grow the best in certain localities, reseed the areas and exterminate the marmots by poison" (1910 Annual Grazing Report, Eldorado National Forest).

Use began to decline by the mid 1920s: "Livestock numbers and total animal months during the early years of record, 1912-1916, must have undoubtedly been partially responsible for conditions existing on the range today. During this period numbers exceeded 14,000 AUMs. This stocking rate is 3-4 times the amount permitted under present management. By 1930, use had declined by 66% ... Over 90% of the primary and more than 75% of total suitable range is in poor condition. The present management, though not the best, has shown some improvement over past years" (1970s Breckenridge Allotment Management Plan, Sequoia National Forest).

The 1930-1950 period: As the previous quote indicates use began to decline in the 1930s. During World War II permitted use again went up, but only to a fraction of the pre-1920 use. In some cases the actual use did not go up: "In 1942 through the World War II period use dropped approximately 1,000 head. Stockmen were receiving good prices and they concentrated on feedlot management where possible. The lack of man-power for range riding and cost of transportation was high" (Letter to Tuolumne County Supervisor from Stanislaus Forest Supervisor, 1965). The montane areas and foothill ranges were rapidly reverting to brush and timber types due to fire suppression. The previous practice of using a lower elevation allotment in conjunction with a higher elevation allotment became less feasible with the decrease in productivity of transitory ranges, and with the lack of man power after World War II many permittees dropped out all together.

An effort was made to make ranching on Forest Service land economical by combining the less economical allotments, splitting of the large community allotments and clearing of brush and reseeding. This practice met with little success as timbered areas closed in with thickening timber stands, and there was less burned area and shrub browse for livestock. "The timbered type is not good range, and will be less in demand when the present old-time users drop out of business" (Functional Inspection, Stanislaus National Forest, 1949). By 1950, use was significantly lower over the region.

The 1950-1970 period: Reductions in livestock numbers continued through the 1970s, again due to uneconomical operations: "1953--a sizable number of larger operations dropped out voluntarily ... From 1948-1963, 32 permits representing 7,217 cattle were voluntarily dropped. 5 permittees dropped their numbers ... Also during this time the Forest Service administratively reduced the carrying capacity on 8 ranges" (Letter to Tuolumne County Supervisor from Stanislaus Forest Supervisor, 1965). There are some references to increased use on the central and southern Sierra Forests due to loss of adjacent ranges to development, overgrazing, and allotment closures. This augmented stocking of livestock does not appear to have been long lasting, however. Again during this time many resource enhancement projects were undertaken in an effort to increase productivity of rangeland: "In 1963, brush was cleared and burned and grasses were seeded, and later spraying of brush occurred. Through 1965, 434 acres were cleared" (Sugarloaf Allotment Management Plan, Sierra National Forest).

The 1970-1990 period: Though poor range condition was recognized prior to this time, it was not until the late 1970s and 1980s that management began to focus on resource protection: "This range sustained a high rate of grazing use under National Forest administration for at least 45 years and unrestricted use for several decades before that, due to accessibility. Since much of the range is in a depleted state, the ultimate objective should be to retire it completely from grazing use. Important key areas will be of prime importance for recreation ..." (1963 Stanislaus Meadow Allotment Management Plan, Stanislaus National Forest). Most actual reductions in use were made in the 1980s and 1990s. Also due to the focus on riparian areas in the 1980s, projects were applied to these areas including willow plantings, riparian pastures, exclosures, and in-stream structures (Meadow Inventory Study, Eldorado National Forest, 1994). Most plantings used native willow and dogwood species. In most cases reduction in livestock use was made in project areas, at least on a temporary basis.

High Sierra

According to all accounts the high elevations received the greatest grazing abuse by bands of sheep than any area of the Sierra or Modoc Plateau (Kinney report). After establishment of National Forests, use decreased immediately but was still high until the 1920s. From the 1920s until the mid 1940s use decreased and fluctuated. By 1946, most of the highest elevation areas were ungrazed by cattle and sheep. Recreational packstock impacts have increased since that time. Other areas of the high Sierra have reduced numbers and have gradually converted to cattle.

The 1870-1908 period: High Sierran meadows were the destination point for summer sheep grazing during this time period. While forage and water were abundant, there were also extremely sensitive areas which were degraded rapidly given the granitic parent material and young geologic age of the Sierra Mountain Range. The entire high Sierra range appears to have been intensely overgrazed for decades, beginning in the early 1860s (Vankat 1970, Ratliff 1985). When the National Forests and National Parks were established, sheep grazing was greatly curtailed: "About 1900, sheep grazing was practically banned from the Forests because of heavy damage in high meadows. In 1958, we had 3 sheep permittees with a total of approximately 4,600 sheep. One of these dropped out because of economics. Another has taken 5 years non-use. Active sheep are now 2,550 in number" (Letter to Tuolumne County Supervisor from Forest Supervisor, Stanislaus National Forest 1965).

The 1908-1946 period: During this period grazing was allowed in the high Sierra on National Forest land, but only by local ranchers or ranchers holding 'base property' according to the Taylor Grazing Act. Controls on transient use greatly reduced the numbers of sheep. Use was still high and did not allow regeneration of many of the meadow areas. In the National Parks, packstock replaced livestock use as soon as the Parks were created. In Yosemite National Park packstock immediately had significant impacts; in Sequoia National Park use was low until the 1940s.

The 1946-1970 period: Packstock use increased everywhere after World War II due to increased road access and the public having more leisure time and money for recreation. Many more allotments became vacated due to conflict with recreation and range productivity declines with packstock use: "Recovery will be slow at such elevations (9,000-10,000 ft.), in fact it may be 10-20 years ... The Forest officers propose to remove all cattle and sheep from the high country, as soon as practicable ... to allow nature to heal..." (Functional Inspection, Stanislaus National Forest, 1949). This pattern of closure of livestock allotments continued; some sheep were still stocked on some of the higher allotments but cattle replaced sheep on most allotments that still allowed livestock.

Many areas still received high use and were not brought into accordance to their carrying capacity. Management of the Mulkey Allotment, Inyo National Forest, typifies this: "A large % of this allotment is in the Golden Trout Wilderness. Few records were kept before 1906. For the whole Kern Plateau 200,000 sheep were trailed across. Mulkey Meadows was used as a staging area in the fall. By 1900, cattle were becoming the dominant livestock. From 1906 to 1961, the Templeton common area (which was composed of Templeton and Mulkey Allotments) sustained 6,000 animal months (AMs). In 1962, Mulkey was separated out and stocked with 450 AMs. In 1967, range analysis was done and the acres were calculated to be 1,051 suitable acres and deemed capable of supporting 318 AMs. But it was still stocked with 450 AMs until 1971. In 1971, though carrying capacity was estimated to be 335 AMs, stocking rate was still at 450 AMs, also in 1975, 255 AMs were added. In 1981, 701 AMs were permitted. Pack stock use in 1983 was 1,175 stock nights, it was increased in 1988 to 4,401 stock nights" (Mulkey Allotment Management Plan, Inyo National Forest).

The 1970-1990 period: Reductions continued through the 1970s and no doubt the degraded range conditions influenced management decisions: "Permitted grazing continued in the Pecks-Dillon areas somewhat longer, 40 head were grazed until 1970, after that it was closed to commercial grazing. Several factors led to the reduction and eventual elimination of the permit. Conflicts with recreation, wildlife, and the National Park Service, plus deteriorating range condition, led to its closure" (Kern Allotment Management Plan, 1970s, Sequoia National Forest). It was not until the 1980s and 1990s that a serious movement towards resource protection was taken. This change was prompted by the writing of wilderness management plans. Very little monitoring of range impacts due to packstock use has been done. Monitoring is increasingly important since packstock use is now the primary impact of the high Sierra.

Eastern Sierra

This area includes the east slope of the Inyo National Forest and the Bridgeport and Carson Ranger Districts of the Toiyabe National Forest. The area was settled somewhat later than the west slope of the Sierra. It also received high use by sheep but not until 1880, when the sheep, being banned from some areas on the western Sierra, came over Sonora Pass to the east. After 1908, when the National Forests were established, transient sheep grazing was curtailed and in 1924, with the outbreak of foot-and-mouth disease, sheep were not allowed over Sonora Pass again. Sheep, however, still continued to be driven in by way of the Mojave Desert until the 1940s. Cattle and sheep use was high through the 1920s and 1930s. In the late 1940s, use was reduced through shorter seasons and fewer numbers when many of the large community allotments were split and converted to cattle. Livestock use declined gradually in the 1970s, especially on the higher elevation allotments as mentioned above in the High Sierra section. In the 1980s and 1990s, use was further reduced.

The 1880-1912 period: It was during this time that large bands of sheep grazed this area: "In the 1880s, the 'California' sheep began to come in large numbers and were able to go in and clean up uncontrolled range so thoroughly that there would be no feed left for cattle. This forced many small cattle ranches into the sheep business ... The California sheep came in by two routes. One route, part of which is still used, was from Bakersfield, California in the spring, through the Mojave Desert and along the foothills of the Sierra. They traveled north and reached the higher elevations of the Walker River, Mono Basin and Owens River for the summer and continued back to the west side of the Sierra via Sonora Pass by fall. The second route went over the Sonora Pass very early in the spring, into the Walker Range. 200,000 sheep are estimated to have grazed in the E & W Walker country, including the Bodie Hills ... The sheep migration still continued to some extent through the Mojave Desert (1946)" (Ranger District Management Plan (1947), Bridgeport Ranger District, Toiyabe National Forest).

Since the Carson City community supported many people, there were many small local ranches there. The following is a description of the early livestock use in the Carson City area: "During 1865-1895 due to the mining and logging populations, the meadows in the Carson Valley area were used for dairy herds. In 1893 the first large herds of sheep started coming in from southern California. It is said that the migration was due to the West side grazing ranges being included in the National Forests so that their grazing there was curtailed and they turned to the East side. Local ranchers were pleased when the National Forest was established in 1912. In 1915-1931 there was a gradual decrease in the numbers of cattle and a corresponding increase in the numbers of sheep. After 1931, the trend was reversed" (Alpine (Carson) Ranger District Report (1947), Toiyabe National Forest). Some sheep were also brought into the area through the Tahoe Basin, but this is not well documented.

The 1912-1945 period: With the elimination of large roaming sheep bands on National Forest Lands actual use went down considerably, but many small operators converted to sheep in the early 1900s. Increases again occurred in the 1930s and 1940s. Sheep use tended to deplete the slopes more than cattle since sheep could access and thus use more areas. Few changes were made during this time to reduce use. Use was extremely high during the World War I years: "the main concern was to use all 'available forage' ... 1918, most of the ranges appeared grazed to their full capacity. Any material increase would, in many cases, force the permittee to leave for want of forage" (Alpine (Carson) Ranger District Report (1947), Toiyabe National Forest). Use was reduced somewhat after that, more due to economics than a conscious conservation effort. Also during this time, many changes were made to make allotments more economically feasible, these changes included splitting large community allotments, initiation of resource enhancement projects, dual use of rangeland by cattle and sheep etc. The following quote represents the general management of rangelands during this time: "Shortly after the formation of the National Forests the numbers of livestock were sharply reduced and until very recently, there has not been a major change... In 1930-35 sheep ranges were increased by allowing the sheep to go to the cattle ranges in the fall after cattle were removed ... In general, management by the National Forest Service has consisted of the following: Setting allotment lines, setting opening and closing dates, and setting permitted numbers. Allotment lines have often been overlapped between sheep and cattle allotments, opening dates have in general been from one to two weeks too early, closing dates as much as a month too late, and numbers often above safe capacity" (Ranger District Management Plan (1947), Bridgeport Ranger District, Toiyabe National Forest). Use during World War II was in most cases increased but never as high as pre-1920.

The 1946-1970 period: During this time, local livestock economics were changing, operations were smaller and most were converting to cattle. There was concern over depleted range conditions because of this and many changes in management occurred. Marginal allotments were closed, many larger allotments were split, most were converted to cattle with a reduction in use, and much attention was given to resource enhancement projects: "From 1941-46 there has been a significant trend from sheep to cattle. Although this trend has given some relief to the range it was not until the last 2 years that a change from sheep to cattle actually brought stocking to what appears to be true grazing capacity" (Ranger District Management Plan (1947), Bridgeport Ranger District, Toiyabe National Forest). Though the dates here are 1941-46, most of the actual conversions were later. The following is typical of the changes in allotment management: "Until 1947, this was part of Clover Patch, it then became the Wilfred Allotment and was converted to cattle. In 1967 half the allotment was sprayed and in 1969 the other half was sprayed. In 1968 the Cashbaugh unit was separated out into the Glass Mtn. Allotment" (Wilfred Allotment Management Plan (1970s), Inyo National Forest). The aforementioned spraying was to reduce sagebrush encroachment in drying meadows, many areas were then reseeded with wheatgrasses, timothy, bromegrasses and other species. "In 1948 reseeding occurred on Dry Lake. In 1951 the south end of Sweetwater was reseeded. In 1958, 59 and 60 the rest of Sweetwater was reseeded" (Sweetwater Allotment Management Plan, Bridgeport Ranger District, Toiyabe National Forest). There was also reference made to water-spreading or irrigation projects: "Great possibilities exist for water spreading on many ranges" (Ranger District Management Plan (1947), Bridgeport Ranger District, Toiyabe National Forest).

The 1970-present period: Many more allotments were combined and split in the 1970s in order to make them more economical and facilitate management. Beginning in the 1980s, management concentrated on resource protection. At this time numbers and perhaps more importantly seasons of use were reduced significantly. On the Toiyabe National Forest, especially, major new vegetation inventory projects were conducted leading to a more 'ecological' approach to livestock management. Again, riparian rehabilitation projects took place with reduced use on riparian areas, riparian exclosures, riparian pastures, and rest-rotation grazing systems were begun.

PLANT INDICATORS OF LIVESTOCK GRAZING EFFECTS

Plant species composition and bare soil exposure in wet and dry meadows and upland sagebrush-steppe and other shrublands on National Forests have been monitored periodically for up to 5 decades on permanently located Parker 3-Step transects by the U.S. Forest Service. These data are the only long-term, widespread range vegetation information available in the Sierra and Modoc Plateau. Thus analysis of these data is one key element to interpreting the sustainability of livestock grazing programs on rangelands in the Sierra Nevada Ecosystem Project study area. Given the history of reported overgrazing of the region from 1865 to the early 1900s and the time needed for recovery with improved management since that time, these data should show improving range conditions if sustainable stewardship has been occurring over the last 50 years.

A large literature exists justifying plant community composition and bare soil exposure changes as indicators of grazing impacts (NRC 1994 and Ratliff 1985). We will not review that literature here except to say that excessive defoliation and trampling, both temporally and spatially, can selectively reduce growth capacity of individual plant species thereby reducing their fitness and survival leading to plant community composition change. On the other hand, lack of herbivore (wildlife and livestock) grazing in grazing-adapted ecosystems such as grasslands, including meadows, can lead to unnatural plant compositions especially those subjected to exotic plant invasion or high litter accumulation. Over time the plant community composition reflects grazing effects. Since soil is the ultimate resource supporting terrestrial biota, changes in soil exposure to erosion indicates potential risk for soil loss and therefore sustainability. Thus reduction in bare soil on Parker transects is a second important indicator of good stewardship.

The potential underlying causal mechanisms for plant community changes are numerous, including 1) reduced rooting depth and water uptake by native plants in excessively trampled and closely grazed meadows or sagebrush-steppe, 2) shading out of small plants by large tall plants and their litter accumulation with little or no grazing in highly productive meadows and grassland, 3) lowering of water tables due to gullying thereby shifting composition to species suited to drier soil conditions, 4) inadequate reproductive success due to frequent seedhead removal, and aggressive weed competition, etc.

Permanent Parker 3-step transects are typically 100 feet in length where plant species or other soil coverage (litter, rock, moss, bare, etc.) categories are read and recorded at 1 foot intervals using a 3/4 inch loop reference area immediately above the soil surface. The method was developed to assess range condition and trend and is in all older Forest Service Range Handbooks. For the purposes of this SNEP analysis, only the raw species composition, bare ground, litter and other soil coverage information was used. There is an extensive literature criticizing range condition and trend rating systems so we chose to only use the raw data and not any of the past value-laden condition ratings (NRC 1994). We realize that many species identification problems exist in the data, but by correcting known misidentifications, and by using a lumped species to genus or other family or life-form categories many of the limitations are reduced. All data (numerous species codes and their synonyms) were entered into an Oracle database for data summarization. These databases and the Oracle programs will be made available to Forest Service Districts and others who desire them.

Since one of the potential primary negative impacts of overgrazing is to alter the water holding capacity of soils due to soil compaction or lowering of water tables due to stream downcutting, the relative abundance of grasslike and true grass species is an important indicator of this change. A large group of grasslike species are wet-site related (see below). In Sierran wet meadows, sedges (Carex spp.) are by far the most important genus of grasslike plants. Identification of Carex spp. to the species level was not common in the Parker transects which limits other more site specific interpretations, but not the major one of soil water relations change. Certain Carex species indicate alpine communities, bogs/fens, springs/seeps, streambanks, wet/moist meadows or dry meadow edges/uplands and are therefore useful indicator species for plant community classification, which is not the task here. Distinct environmental conditions and restrictions largely determine the composition and structure of these plant communities. The following sections discuss plant indicators in general for rangelands in the Sierra Nevada Mountains and Modoc Plateau. Specific findings on changes observed in the Parker transects will follow this background material.

Grasslike Plant Indicators

Much is known about some grasslike species such as Carex nebrascensis, C. scopulorum, C. aquatilis, and C. rostrata which indicate quite different environmental and grazing impacted conditions. Much of this species-specific information was developed from the collective experience of range scientists, specialists and ecologists, and from reference material including the Range Plant Handbook (USDA Forest Service 1937). A discussion of a limited number of Carices follows.

Carex nebrascensis is one of the most easily identified grasslike species and is a very widespread rhizomatous plant which can survive frequent trampling and a degree of dewatering with lowering of a water table (it was usually identified to species). This capability is supported by the fact that it is still found in grazed dry meadows. Throughout its range Nebraska sedge occurs exclusively in such wet sites as along slow streams, near springs, in shallow swampy areas, and wet meadows. In the wet meadows of the Sierra it is frequently one of the dominant plants. Its strongly developed rootstocks, from which new plants arise, make it particularly well adapted to withstand abusive grazing. An important fact is that C. nebrascensis is the wet meadow site Carex species least affected by livestock disturbance (trampling and defoliation). Another genus of grasslikes, the Scirpus species (bullrushes), are not as palatable to livestock as many Carices and also have very well established roots and survive well under grazing.

Carex scopulorum is very similar in appearance to Nebraska sedge but is often found at higher elevations mostly where a good source of cold water is present, such as in seeps and wet meadows. It is more susceptible to grazing and trampling disturbances, and when very abundant it indicates later seral ecological conditions (less grazing impacted).

Carex aquatilis is also very similar to the previous two species in appearance, but it is most likely to be found at stream edges with its roots always in running water or saturated soils. However, it is not found in bogs, fens or seeps. Some taxonomists/ecologists have thought that this species is just an ecotype of C. nebrascensis.

Carex rostrata is a large robust sedge occurring on low gradient landforms ranging from permanently flooded basins to floodplains and wet meadows, and not in stagnant water such as bogs, fens or seeps. It is moderately palatable to cattle in late summer. In Oregon, Kovalchik (1987) has observed that beaked sedge is replaced by Nebraska sedge or is lost to streambank erosion or streambed downcutting with continued overuse

Carex athrostachya is a dry to moist meadow species often found at the edges of wet meadows. It grows in a bunch form that withstands grazing. It is a lower elevation species, not normally found in alpine meadows. It is perhaps the most common Carex species which increases in abundance with grazing in wet meadows. Carex microptera indicates similar conditions, but it is more susceptible to intense grazing and thus its abundance indicates later seral moist meadow conditions at low-moderate elevations. Carex praegracilis again is similar to the previous two, but occurs at lower elevations and seems to be more common in the northern Sierra. It tolerates livestock grazing. Carex jonesii indicates much wetter conditions and is often found in seeps, or around springs and wetter meadows at low-moderate elevations, and is more sensitive to dewatering than defoliation. Carex abrupta is very similar in appearance to C. athrostachya, but it grows in montane subalpine and alpine moist/wet meadows and can withstand moderate grazing. Carex integra is very similar to C. praegracilis in appearance but grows at higher elevations and is mostly found in the southern Sierra.

Carex simulata indicates wet to very wet conditions such as seeps, springs, fens and wet meadows. It does not withstand heavy grazing or the subsequent dewatering if abusive grazing and trampling continue, thus it indicates plentiful water and good soil structure conditions. Carex echinata or ormantha are primarily higher elevation sensitive species and when present indicate a good cold water source and later seral conditions.

Carex douglasii is a classic invader species and often indicates severely disturbed, dry, denuded areas, meadow borders and other semi-moist soils, and frequently forms a distinct zone between dry upland vegetation and wet meadow or other moist-soil types.

924

Carex filifolia was often a misidentification of several other sedges on Parker transects, including C. exserta, C. breweri, C. subnigricans, C. nigricans, C. capitata, C. geyeri, C. rossii, and Eleocharis species. Again these are distinct species with distinct indications. Carex filifolia is a dry/moist montane to alpine species which tolerates a moderate amount of grazing and indicates mid to late seral upland conditions. C. exserta is similar but occurs mostly on drier sites. C. breweri is an alpine meadow species and indicates relatively high species diversity and late seral conditions. C. subnigricans and nigricans are similar to C. breweri but they grow on slightly wetter sites. C. capitata is found at montane to alpine elevations in bogs, seeps and around areas of snowmelt, and indicates relatively high species diversity and late seral conditions. C. geyeri and rossii are upland species.

Other common grasslike plant genera on Sierran rangeland are Juncus, Luzula, Eleocharis, Eriophorum and Scirpus. The rushes (Juncus) are the most common of these and most often identified on Parker transects. J. orthophyllus, J. ensifolius, J. nevadensis, Luzula and Scirpus species were often lumped because of their high palatability to livestock. J. orthophyllus was often misidentified as a Carex, Luzula or Scirpus, and is as palatable as most Carex spp. but not very resistant to overgrazing. It is commonly found along streambanks and in wet meadows. It responds to lowered water tables and when present it indicates late seral conditions and high diversity montane meadows and riparian areas. J. ensifolius grows in habitat very similar J. orthophyllus but grows in wetter areas and does not survive under overgrazing or excessive trampling. J. ensifolius has a very distinct appearance thus was usually identified correctly. Species most commonly misidentified as J. ensifolius are Iris missouriensis, J. drummondii, J. orthophyllus, and Sisyrinchium species. J. nevadensis is a moderately palatable species that grows in moist to wet montane meadows and along streambanks and ephemeral lakes. It was often misidentified as J. balticus, but it does not survive in dry areas like J. balticus, and does not survive heavy grazing. Other Juncus species of moderate palatability to livestock are J. saximontanus, J. occidentalis, J. oxymeris, and J. xiphoides.

J. balticus was the catchall code for all narrow stemmed/leafless grasslike plants. It is by far the most widespread of the Juncus species and is a poor forage value species growing in dry, dewatered areas, and not favored by livestock. It does not hold soil as well as other higher value species and does not provide much ground cover. J. confusus looks like J. balticus but grows at higher elevations and indicates later seral, high diversity wet meadow or riparian conditions. It does not withstand dewatering or trampling well but when abundant it holds soil fairly well. J. drummondii is an upland species that has been extensively misidentified as J. balticus, Eleocharis species, or J. nevadensis. This mistake is misleading since J. drummondii grows only on uplands and is not associated with wet meadows. It should not appear in this SNEP dataset.

J. buffonius is a diminutive species and is often overlooked or misidentified as Eleocharis acicularis. It is found from low to moderate elevations in vernal pools, thermal mud holes, trampled streambanks, open areas in wet meadows and drier areas. It indicates denuded overused wet to seasonally wet areas. Eleocharis acicularis, varieties bella and acicularis, were often misidentified as J. buffonius, J. drummondii and as annual grasses of the genus Agrostis. These are quite distinct indicator species that grow in moist to saturated soil areas, but not bogs with their highly organic soils. They do not seem to grow above 8,000 feet. They are affected by trampling and do not survive in large numbers in overgrazed areas and provide moderately good soil protection.

The Eleocharis species are indicators of very wet conditions and do not withstand trampling and grazing well. Eleocharis pauciflora was mostly misidentified as J. drummondii through the 1970's and even the 1980's, with only the most recent transect data consistently identify it correctly. This misidentification is extremely important since E. pauciflora is a wetland species in contrast with its common misnomer, J. drummondii, an upland species. E. pauciflora grows from low-alpine elevations in wet meadows, seeps, springs, thermal mud holes, snowmelt areas, and streambanks, but not bogs. It is the most common Eleocharis and the only one reported in alpine meadows. E. pauciflora does not withstand a lot of grazing, it is palatable and sensitive to trampling and dewatering. It provides moderately good soil stability. E. palustris (formerly macrostachys) is a low to mid elevation species that is not as commonly reported and tends to grow along streambanks and in some wet meadows. It is similar in grazing sensitivity to E. pauciflora. E. montevidensis occurs on the Sierra National Forest and possibly other western slope forests. It is similar in habitat requirements and growth form to E. pauciflora.

Luzula comosa, L. subcongesta, and L. orestra are the most commonly recorded Luzulas in the Sierra on Parker transects. These are often misidentified as Carex species, J. orthophyllus and Scirpus species, or were simply recorded as members of the family Cyperaceae. They occur on moist soils in meadows and also in adjacent lodgepole pine forests. L. comosa is a montane species and is found in moist/wet montane meadows and wooded riparian areas. L. subcongesta and L. orestra are found in subalpine to alpine meadows and along streambanks; they are susceptible to grazing and trampling and indicate relatively high species diversity and later seral conditions. Other Luzula species are L. divaricata, L. parviflora, and L. spicata and are mostly forest to alpine upland species.

There are two commonly identified Scirpus species in the Sierra Nevada, S. congdonii and S. microcarpus. These were often recorded as the family Cyperaceae, the genus Carex or Juncus orthophyllus. Scirpus species are a rough leaved species and are not very palatable to livestock. This characteristic and their strong root systems allow them to endure grazing and trampling but not dewatering. They bind and protect soil on streambanks. S. microcarpus is a montane species that grows in wet meadows and along streambanks. S. congdonii is a higher elevation species more common in wet meadows and along streambanks, and is not as robust or resistant to grazing as S. microcarpus.

Eriophorum species common in the Sierra are E. criniger (formerly Scirpus criniger), and E. gracilis. Fimbristylis species are low elevation vernal pool and thermal pool species, and only rarely occur in the Sierran Parker transects. Until 1969 that recorded as Fimbristylis was most commonly E. criniger at moderate to high elevations and E. gracilis at high elevations. Both species of Eriophorum are commonly misidentified as Carex species, Luzula species or Juncus orthophyllus. They are very different particularly in that they are generally subalpine to alpine species and only seem to grow in late seral, high species diversity wet meadows, seeps, bogs and snowmelt areas. They do not withstand dewatering or heavy grazing.

<u>Grass Plant Indicators</u>

This section would be much too long if we were to mention all the grasses that occur in the transect data. We concentrate the discussion on those species that indicate specific conditions or were extensively misidentified. The most important wet/moist meadow and riparian grass genera are <u>Agrostis</u>, <u>Calamagrostis</u>, <u>Danthonia</u>, <u>Deschampsia</u>, <u>Glyceria</u>, <u>Muhlenbergia</u>, <u>Phleum</u>, and <u>Poa</u>. We will discuss separately (see below) the grasses important in the perennial bunchgrass, sagebrush-steppe ranges of the Modoc Plateau and eastside Great Basin influenced areas, and upland areas at high elevations.

<u>Agrostis</u> species until about 1968 were lumped into primary and secondary categories on Parker transects. The primary species were <u>Agrostis</u> <u>alba</u> (now <u>stolonifera</u>) (a non-native) and <u>exarata</u>, occurring mainly in the northern Sierra Nevada in larger moist montane meadows. They survive grazing fairly well and indicate mid to late seral conditions. They also occur along streambanks but usually above the waterline. Secondary <u>Agrostis</u> species are annuals including <u>A</u>. <u>scabra</u> (formerly <u>hiemenodies</u>), <u>A</u>. <u>variablis</u>, <u>A</u>. <u>idahoensis</u>, and <u>A</u>. <u>humilis</u>. Of these <u>A</u>. <u>scabra</u> is by far the most common, occurring in moist to wet meadows, seeps, and snowmelt areas at moderate to high elevations. This species indicates late seral conditions when it occurs in low abundance as an understory species in highly diverse wet meadows. When very abundant it indicates early seral conditions. The annual <u>Agrostis</u> species do not hold soil well and cannot be depended upon for protection from soil erosion.

The primary <u>Agrostis</u> species have been confused sometimes with <u>Deschampsia</u> and <u>Calamagrostis</u> species. Only one species of <u>Calamagrostis</u> is reported with any regularity on the Parker transects, that being <u>C</u>. <u>breweri</u>, a subalpine to alpine species which indicates relatively high diversity moist sites. Together with <u>Carex</u> <u>exserta</u> this makes up the 'shorthair' sedge type of the high Sierra Nevada. Like many alpine species, it does not sustain heavy grazing and trampling.

<u>Deschampsia</u> or the hairgrasses are very important in montane and subalpine meadows. <u>D</u>. <u>caespitosa</u> is the most widespread grass in meadows, is a very good livestock and wildlife forage, and provides good soil holding capacity. It is a very sturdy bunchgrass which resists trampling and grazing effects but needs moist to wet conditions. It has been overrated as the classic livestock 'ice cream' plant of meadows, that is, as the most palatable grass of meadows. It is sometimes misidentified as <u>Agrostis</u>, <u>Calamagrostis</u> or <u>Poa</u>, but usually is identified correctly. <u>Deschampsia</u> <u>elongata</u> is most commonly found along streambanks or at low density in wet to moist montane meadows. It is a delicate species and is susceptible to grazing and trampling. It usually indicates good conditions and high diversity. It is also often misidentified as an <u>Agrostis</u> species. <u>Deschampsia</u> <u>danthonioides</u> is a native annual invader species that occurs throughout the Sierra and indicates disturbance. It occurs mostly in moist to dry meadows, or in annual grasslands at lower elevations.

Three species of oatgrasses (<u>Danthonia</u> spp.) occur in the Sierra including <u>D</u>. <u>californica</u>, <u>D</u>. <u>intermedia</u> and <u>D</u>. <u>unispicata</u>. <u>D</u>. <u>californica</u> and <u>intermedia</u> occur in dry to moist meadows and tend to indicate disturbance conditions when found in wet meadows. D. intermedia tends to grow at higher elevations in or near forested areas, while D. californica occurs more often in foothill areas. D. unispicata is a low to mid elevation species, most common in the Modoc Plateau, Great Basin and eastside areas of the Sierra. It is a dry meadow, sagebrush-steppe and gravel bar colonizing species, and indicates early seral conditions in meadows. All Danthonia species tend to increase in abundance with moderate to heavy grazing, and since they are usually identified correctly, they are good indicator species.

The mannagrasses (Glyceria spp.) are most commonly G. elata or striata. All occur in later seral condition wet/moist meadows and along streambanks. They do not grow in alpine areas or in bogs or fens. They do not survive overgrazing, excessive trampling or dewatering. They are rarely misidentified so are a potentially good indicator species, however they are quite uncommon.

The two most common muhly grasses (Muhlenbergia spp.), M. filiformis and M. richardsonis, are very similar mat-like appearing plants and are often confused. M. filiformis is restricted to moist to wet areas, meadows, streams, marshes, bogs/fens, seeps, etc. and thus indicates wetter, later seral conditions. It is an annual, however, and does not provide good soil protection. It indicates later seral conditions when present as an understory species in an otherwise highly diverse meadow. If dominant, it indicates declining soil stability conditions. M. richardsonis can grow in wet, moist and dry areas, so as a generalist it has little value as an indicator species. The muhlys therefore are marginal indicator species except when they increase in abundance over time in formerly wet meadows that once had a greater component of taller statured native grasslike plants or grasses.

Two distinct timothy species (Phleum spp.), P. alpinum and P. pratensis occur in the Sierra. Alpine timothy (P. alpinum) is a native species that occurs in montane, subalpine and alpine wet to moist meadows. It also occurs in bogs/fens, seeps and along streambanks and is a late seral meadow species. P. alpinum is often confused with Alopecurus species which also indicate good wet conditions but tends to grow in lower elevation bogs/fens. Common timothy (P. pratensis), a non-native grass, has been seeded in many montane meadows. Its abundance typically indicates drier sites with a history of overgrazing and a rehabilitation project, but currently may indicate recovered mid seral condition moist meadows. Common timothy does not pose any risk to meadow sustainability and is not invasive.

Many bluegrass (Poa) species occur in the Sierra and Modoc Plateau. They typically are rhizomatous in wet to moist meadows, and bunchgrasses in drier upland sites. Only very common or indicator species are discussed here. Poa pratensis is the most common rhizomatous Poa species complex (several subspecies exist) occurring in livestock grazed dry to wet meadows, stream margins, etc. One subspecies (ssp. pratensis) is introduced, one is probably introduced (ssp. angustifolia) and one is possibly native (ssp. agassizensis) according to Hickman (1993). All have stout rhizomes, provide excellent soil stability, and are excellent forage for wildlife and livestock. There is concern because P. pratensis can replace other natives and is rather invasive. Poa palustris (also introduced) is usually misidentified as P. pratensis but grows at lower elevations and is more susceptible to grazing and trampling. Poa compressa is often confused with P. pratensis and grows on denuded streambanks and moist to dry meadows at lower elevations only and indicates early seral conditions. P. compressa does, however, provide good soil protection when other species are eliminated.

Poa nevadensis, P. secunda and P. scabrella are sagebrush-steppe, perennial bunchgrasses occurring primarily on the eastside of the Sierra and Modoc Plateau. When present in wet meadow areas they indicate disturbance, dewatering and early seral conditions. They tolerate grazing very well. Poa cusickii has a bunchgrass growth form and occurs in drier areas, meadow edges and uplands and indicates disturbance when present in meadows. Poa bolanderi (native annual) occurs at meadow edges adjacent to forest communities, is usually not identified correctly, and again indicates low soil water when present in otherwise wet to moist sites. Poa bulbosa and Poa annua are non-native annuals that are two of the most widespread grass species in the World. They indicate very early seral conditions and disturbance, but both are good forage species for all herbivores and granivores although productivity is low.

From 1940 through the 1960s various range improvement projects were implemented on the eastern slope, Great Basin and Modoc Plateau ranges. These were designed to decrease big sagebrush, western juniper and other shrub densities, and increase the perennial bunchgrass component of sagebrush-steppe communities which formerly had more perennial grasses. Improvement areas were variously burned, mechanically manipulated, sprayed, and seeded.

All Agropyron (currently Pseudoroegneria or Elytrigia) species except the native bluebunch wheatgrass (A. spicatum) were perennials introduced in reseeding projects and include: A. cristatum, A. desertorum, A. intermedium, A. dasytachyum, A. smithii, and A. trachycaulum. Since all these introduced wheatgrass are lower palatability, coarser-leaved grasses, they do not fill the same role as bluebunch wheatgrass. However, all are of moderate palatability when managed for forage production and all provide excellent soil protection in otherwise low soil coverage upland communities. Bluebunch wheatgrass was the primary native perennial grass of upland sagebrush-steppe plant communities. It is very poorly adapted to continuous grazing and was largely grazed out during the historical overgrazing period. Remnant populations are present almost everywhere, but large vigorous stands are rare.

The native perennial grasses California brome (B. carinatus) and introduced smooth brome (B. inermis) indicate mid seral upland conditions typically in large moist to dry meadows and forest openings. Seed of many local ecotypes of B. carinatus are now commercially available for restoration projects. All of the annual bromegrasses are invaders and include B. brizaformis, B. japonicus, and B. tectorum (cheatgrass) on the eastern side of the Sierra, the Great Basin and Modoc plateau, and B. hordeaceus (formerly mollis), B. diandrus, and B. rubens on the western slope of the Sierra in foothills below 3,000 ft. elevation. All annuals in the first group are invaders of montane meadows and sagebrush-steppe ranges and indicate varying degrees of disturbance. Given the rather complete transformation of the herbaceous component of foothill grassland/oak woodland communities on the western slope, the annual bromes listed above in the second group are now considered 'resident annuals' and permanent members of what is now named the California annual grassland. The greatest threat to sustainability of these western slope grasslands is exotic weed invasion, especially yellow star-thistle (Centaurea solstitialis).

Three wildrye species include <u>Leymus</u> <u>cinereus</u>, <u>Elymus</u> <u>glaucus</u> and <u>Leymus</u> <u>triticoides</u> are common in the SNEP study area. The two <u>Leymus</u> species were previously classified in the <u>Elymus</u> genus. Great Basin wildrye (<u>L</u>. <u>cinereus</u>) grows in a bunchgrass form or with short rhizomes and indicates deep soils and lack of grazing abuse when abundant. Much of it was hayed in sagebrush-steppe meadow floodplains and was lost due to too frequent haying, grazing and burning following European settlement of the West. Blue wildrye (<u>E</u>. <u>glaucus</u>) is an incredibly variable species with a wide range of habitats throughout the Sierra. It commonly grows in conifer forest openings, edges of moist meadows, and in the understory of oak woodlands and savannas. Sites with a substantial component of blue wildrye indicate low grazing intensity. Seed of many local ecotypes of blue wildrye are now commercially available for restoration projects. Creeping wildrye (<u>L</u>. <u>triticoides</u>) is a rhizomatous species often growing in saline environments of the Great Basin, but occurs in many other habitats. Invasion of blue or creeping wildrye into formerly wet meadows indicate disturbance.

Idaho fescue (<u>F</u>. <u>idahoensis</u>) bunchgrass habitat is typically eastside pine understory and gaps in conifer forest/sagebrush-steppe complexes. When present in meadows it indicates early to mid seral conditions. Green fescue (<u>F</u>. <u>viridula</u>) is an alpine species and indicates late seral upland conditions. <u>Koeleria</u> <u>macrantha</u> (formerly <u>cristata</u>) is a widespread perennial bunchgrass and indicates later seral conditions; it is never a dominant grass over a large area. The bunchgrass Indian ricegrass, <u>Achnatherum</u> (formerly <u>Oryzopsis</u>) <u>hymenoides</u>, indicates less severe livestock disturbance conditions at low to moderate elevations east of the Sierran crest and on the Modoc Plateau. <u>Ptilagrostis</u> (formerly <u>Oryzopsis</u>) <u>kingii</u> occurs in subalpine to alpine streambanks and meadows and indicates mid to late seral upland conditions. Like many alpine species it is quite sensitive to heavy grazing.

Finally, saltgrass (<u>Distichlis</u> <u>spicata</u>) occurs on the Modoc Plateau and in the Great Basin and is indicative of alkali flats, vernal pool margins, early to mid seral dry meadows, thermal mudholes and generally disturbed, dry open areas especially on alkaline soils. It is a distinctive species and not usually misidentified.

Forb Plant Indicators

Many forbs encountered on Parker transects were either recorded as annual or perennial weeds with the exception of several common and easily identified species. Misidentification is a problem since many forbs are very good indicators of species diversity, meadow seral stage, and soil water status. Some small perennial forbs were consistently classified as annual. Almost all the common forbs discussed below are native, those that are exotic and/or introduced are noted. In addition to Hickman (1993) two other forb references were used (Dayton 1960 and Hermann 1966) in putting this section of the assessment together.

The common native perennial forb <u>Epilobium</u> <u>glaberrimum</u> is indicative of seeps, springs and wet meadows, and begins to decline in abundance with drying or denuded conditions. It occurs from low elevations to subalpine meadows. It is usually not observed until the overstory species are thinned by grazing, but is usually present in small numbers in late seral meadows. Hypericum anagalloides can be annual or perennial and is an elevation generalist native forb restricted to moist meadows that are not too wet or too dry. Polygonum douglasii is a meadow invader annual (native) that colonizes open ground and thus indicates disturbance and early seral conditions. Yarrow (Achillea millifolium) is a very common native annual forb that was usually identified correctly and indicates drier conditions and disturbance, often by small mammals to begin with. It readily invades sites with overgrazing and makes colonization difficult for later seral, less grazing resistant, palatable species.

Other native weed species, Stellaria longipes (perennial), Veronica perigrina (annual), Collomia linearis (annual), Claytonia perfoliata (annual--miner's lettuce) and Collinsia parviflora (annual--blue-eyed Mary), are common in moist meadows and indicate moderately disturbed, early seral conditions. Rorippa curvisiliqua is a native annual or biennial forb that often roots in water and requires wet areas, streambanks, seeps, springs but not bogs and fens. It indicates mid to late seral conditions with some seasonal flowing water. The perennial exotic forb sheep sorrel (Rumex acetosella) is very common in disturbed moist areas of all kinds of habitats. Gayophytum diffusum is a common annual forb in open forest and sagebrush-steppe. Lotus purshianus is a native annual legume occurring in dry, disturbed areas, and bird's-foot trefoil (Lotus corniculatus) is an introduced perennial legume used in irrigated pastures and has likely been introduced to meadows by seed passing the gut of ruminant animals.

The native monkeyflowers Mimulus primuloides (mat-forming perennial) and Mimulus guttatus (annual or rhizomed perennial) both indicate mid to late seral wet meadow conditions near seeps, springs, or streambanks. M. primuloides also grows in bogs, alpine meadows and around snowmelt. M. guttatus can survive better under drying conditions but only grows to moderate elevations; both species are susceptible to grazing impacts. Several of the native annual Navarretia species are indicative of seasonally wet and dry upland conditions such as on the Modoc Plateau and the foothills of the Sierra in vernal pools.

The following native forbs were typically recorded as perennial weeds on Parker transects even though some were annuals (as noted): Ranunculus alismifolius, R. cymbalaria, Gentianopsis simplex (annual), and Veronica americana. All these are found in wet places, streambanks and meadows at moderate to high elevations and indicate later seral conditions; they do not withstand heavy grazing. Penstemon rydbergii, Sidalcea species, Perideridia gairdneri, P. parishii, Iris missouriensis, Achillea millifolium, Potentilla gracilis, P. glandulosa, P. millefolia, Ranunculus occidentalis, Aster occidentalis, A. adscendens, Arnica chamissonis, Geum macrophyllum, and Dodecatheon jeffreyi are found in moist to drying meadows, vernally wet meadows or low slopes and indicate disturbance conditions if present in large numbers in moist meadows. Note that I. missouriensis is classified as a noxious weed because its leaves are unpalatably bitter, it spreads with heavy grazing, and once established, greatly retards the regeneration of palatable species. It was either identified correctly or as Juncus ensifolius on the Parker transects; this is a very misleading mistake since I. missouriensis often indicates overgrazed conditions where J. ensifolius does not.

931

Dodecatheon alpinum, Potentilla drummondii ssp. breweri, Aster alpigenus, Lewisia species, Veronica wormskjoldii, Gentiana newberryi, and Gentianopsis holopetala are perennial subalpine to alpine species that grow in wet meadows. They indicate later seral conditions and high plant species diversity when present in small numbers. Note that Aster and Erigeron species were often confused on the Parker transects. Most of the species that were identified as Erigeron were Aster species. The most common Aster species is A. occidentalis followed by A. alpigenus, and A. adscendens. Erigeron foliosus and E. peregrinus occur in Sierran meadows, E. foliosus at moderate elevations in moist shaded areas, E. peregrinus in subalpine to alpine meadows.

Horkelia species, Phalacroseris bolanderi, Antennaria media, and A. pulchella (note both Antennaria spp. were formerly A. alpina) are subalpine to alpine species that grow in moist to dry meadows and upland areas and do not necessarily indicate meadow conditions; they do, however, indicate good ground cover for uplands and are affected by grazing.

Sibbaldia procumbens grows mainly in areas of snowmelt. Antennaria rosea is an upland or meadow edge species that when present in dry meadows indicates disturbance. Antennaria species are found to a greater or lesser extent on nearly all western rangeland; on severely overgrazed sites they are sometimes very abundant or dominant. The annual forb Gnaphalium palustre may be mistaken for Antennaria species. It grows in wet areas and is not necessarily an indication of overgrazing, but does seem to occur on basic, somewhat saline, ephemerally wet sites.

Trifolium species are mentioned separately because of their abundance in meadows, and like all clovers, grazing of taller, competitive grasses can favor these legumes. The most common indicative species are: T. cyathiferum (annual), T. longipes, T. wormskioldii, T. variegatum (annual or possibly short-lived perennial), and T. monanthum. T. cyathiferum is a low to moderately high elevation species occurring on drier meadow sites and indicates disturbance conditions. T. longipes and wormskioldii occur from low to subalpine elevations in wet to moist areas, streambanks and springs. These species indicate early to mid seral conditions and moderate grazing and trampling tolerance. T. variegatum occurs in subalpine to alpine wet meadows, seeps, springs, and streambanks, and with decreasing abundance at lower elevations. It is a small prostrate plant of little forage importance but indicates good diversity and wet conditions. All these clovers are native species. Their role in nitrogen fixation should not be overlooked because of the typical nitrogen limitation to plant growth in meadows and the important agricultural role these systems have today.

Other forbs often recorded on the Parker transects are the native perennials western bistort (Polygonum bistortoides) and corn lily or false hellebore (Veratrum californicum), the biennial, woolly mullein (Verbascum thapsus), the perennial, common dandelion (Taraxacum officinale), and the usually perennial, common plantain (Plantago major). Polygonum bistortoides grows in wet meadows, seeps and streambanks from moderate to high elevations. It indicates fair to good conditions, but when very abundant it indicates overgrazing, especially historical overgrazing by sheep in higher elevation meadows. Veratrum californicum provides similar indications when found in meadows, but it does not grow as high in elevation or in such wet areas. Verbascum thapsus, Taraxacum officinale, and Plantago major are all exotic weeds. A typical habitat for dandelion (T. officinale) is the gully-drained soils of eroded meadows. All these exotics indicate poor to very poor conditions and possibly previously denuded areas. Another group of large forb species, mules ears (Wyethia spp.), are all natives and have increased with overgrazing by sheep.

SAGEBRUSH-STEPPE RANGELAND ASSESSMENT

The highly altered state of sagebrush-steppe rangelands in the West is clearly articulated in a recent symposium proceedings (Monsen and Kitchen 1994) where management of these lands as 'annual rangelands' is discussed. Heavy livestock grazing coupled with Quaternary climate change (Tausch et al. 1993) and little herbivore adaptive evolutionary background in these communities has led to a rangeland system that has been highly modified since European settlement (Young et al. 1988). The primary alteration has been the loss of native perennial grasses, an increase in sagebrush and alien annual grasses, especially cheatgrass (Bromus tectorum), and an increase in fire frequency. The significant characteristic of these altered sagebrush-cheatgrass systems is that they are stable systems from many perspectives (Laycock 1991). Livestock exclosures established by Professor Ed Tisdale more than 6 decades ago and followed by Tueller (1973) and others, including Menke's personal observations over 25 years, have shown that these systems don't recover to what scientists suspect were pre-disturbance states of the sagebrush-steppe.

From two other perspectives, sagebrush-steppe communities are not stable systems. They continue to be invaded by new weed species, and with increased ignition sources from human habitation, fire tends to remove sagebrush (Artemisia spp.), further exacerbating ecosystem function. Fire is a natural disturbance process in sagebrush-steppe, but when it occurs too frequently the shrub component can become inadequate for maintanance of critical elements of the ecosystem. For example, sagegrouse and pronghorn antelope habitat must include a sagebrush component and a substantial component of forbs is highly desirable. The tendency for replacement of understory forbs by cheatgrass is a definite negative for ground-nesting birds. The question is, with continued livestock grazing are sagebrush shrubs and native perennial grasses declining and are these systems becoming more weedy and unstable.

Seven attributes (% composition) were analyzed from Parker C&T transect data for the 7 National Forests with significant acreage of sagebrush-steppe:

> Big sagebrush composition
> Native perennial grass composition
> Forb composition
> Non-native species composition
> Litter cover
> Bare soil exposure
> Erosion pavement

933

The Parker loop sampling frame is not very sensitive to plant composition changes in desert communities where plant cover is low and many readings are on bare ground. The loop method is particularly insensitive to annual grass change since these plants have little basal area, and with summer sampling, much annual material is lumped in the litter category making it indistinguishable from other shrub and forb litter. Sagebrush-steppe communities naturally have always had a very high level of bare ground exposed because they are cold desert systems.

In all cases 2-4 repeated readings of the same transects were used in the analysis and averaged within the decade for which they were read. We always used the first and latest readings of each transect to get the longest term trend indications possible. The following findings are trends and have not been subjected to statistical testing. We realize that results can be affected by weather pattens in the year of sampling. By averaging response variables over decades, some of the annual weather effect is removed. One very positive aspect of the Parker loop method is that it measures plant occurrence at the ground surface level, thereby not being affected by foliar canopy which changes during the growing season.

Big sagebrush cover (%) appears to have declined based upon the weighted average over all 7 Forests (Table 3). Four out of 7 Forests had less sagebrush during the last decade than at least two of the previous 4 decades, and two others not sampled in the most recent decade showed declines in the 1976-85 decade compared to at least one previous decade. Limited samples for the seventh Forest (Plumas) did not allow any trend detection. Using averages from those decades with at least 8 transects of data indicate that native perennial grass composition increased at least by one third on the Modoc, Lassen, Toiyabe and Inyo National Forests (Table 3). Trends for native perennial grasses on the other three Forests appear to be static or downward. Overall forb composition has been remarkably stable with a tendency for a small downward decline in abundance on most Forests (Table 3).

Cheatgrass is the most common non-native component of the monitored sagebrush-steppe communities (Table 4). While cheatgrass cover in all cases was low relative to native perennial grasses, competitive effects reducing native perennial grass and forb seedling recruitment could be important. The Modoc, Tahoe and Inyo National Forests had the highest composition of cheatgrass but sample sizes are so small that it is impossible to detect trends. Further discussion of cheatgrass and other annual grasses is given below in the litter discussion. No other non-natives except wheatgrasses on a few transects on the Plumas were of significance. Medusahead (Taeniatherum caput-medusae) is known to be a major problem on many sagebrush-grass ranges but it was not an important component of any of these transects. Overall, weeds other than cheatgrass were not detected as a problem. General knowledge of resource managers indicates that medusahead has become a much more important invader in the 1980s and 90s, so some of its increase has likely been missed due to lack of repeat readings of transects.

Litter cover (%), and bare soil and erosion pavement exposure (%) indicate soil surface processes and protection or lack there-of from wind and water erosion (Table 5). All three measures showed no clear overall trend based upon weighted average values, but individual Forests showed important changes and the canceling effects of bare soil and litter parameters. Litter cover on the Modoc and Lassen Forests has increased by more than a third and that on the

934

Inyo is upward but to a lesser degree. We suspect this is primarily due to the increasing abundance of cheatgrass. The trend in litter cover appears to be downward on the Toiyabe and static on the other 3 Forests.

While sample sizes are small, bare soil appeared to decline on the Modoc and Lassen Forests and increase on the Stanislaus and Inyo Forests. The other 3 Forests exhibited more static bare soil exposure when small samples were discounted. Most if not all of the reduced bare soil exposed on the Modoc and Lassen Forests was likely due to cheatgrass litter. Cheatgrass litter is a much less effective agent protecting against surface soil erosion than bases of perennial bunchgrasses or sagebrush canopy cover protecting against raindrop impact. Since litter cover has increased and bare soil has also increased on the Inyo Forest, some serious concerns arise on these upland sagebrush-steppe communities. Given that most of the Inyo sagebrush-steppe communities have strong rainshadow influences and are relative dry systems, they need particularly well managed livestock grazing programs. The same can be said for the Toiyabe Forest.

Based on our historical review of livestock grazing on what is now National Forest land, the Modoc Forest was the most disturbed in the sagebrush-steppe and the Lassen, Inyo and Toiyabe were probably not far behind. While the Modoc and other Forests are showing declines in sagebrush and increases in cheatgrass, the increase in native perennial grasses is a very favorable change. Similarly, increases in native perennial grasses on the Lassen, Toiyabe and Inyo National Forests is a very favorable indicator of improving ecosystem biodiversity. The general reduction in sagebrush cover is desirable so long as it remains as a major component of the sagebrush-steppe. Promiscuous prescribed burning of sagebrush-steppe must be avoided where additional spreading of cheatgrass is the likely result (Rasmussen 1994). Some reduction in sagebrush will be required to free up water resources for maintenance of a larger composition of perennial grasses. The slowly declining forb composition will likely contribute to poorer ground nesting bird diets in the future. The high and increasing cheatgrass component on many of the Forests is alarming especially as California becomes more populated and even remote areas have greater probability of fire ignitions.

While this assessment spans 5 decades of monitoring, it is important to reiterate that although substantial reductions in livestock grazing intensity have occurred, most ranges were stocked above carrying capacity for decades until very recently. A key indicator of improved condition that we have observed is an increase in native perennial grass composition on some of these upland rangelands. A key indicator of declining condition is the continued cheatgrass invasion. We agree with Young (1994) that sagebrush-steppe managers should continue to seek to improve the native perennial grass component of these systems on public land. Use of livestock as a management tool appears to be limited (Valentine and Stevens 1994), although some Holistic Resource Managers (HRM) may have new alternatives which should be scrutinized. We were unable to locate relevant long-term HRM results for this assessment. Close monitoring data on the perennial component of sagebrush-steppe communities should direct management so long as perennial grasses continue to increase in abundance.

MOUNTAIN MEADOW RANGELAND ASSESSMENT

In highly productive wet and mesic meadows grazed by livestock, change in plant community species composition is the primary way to assess a complex of direct and indirect impacts and responses to management of livestock grazing. Temporal information on bare soil exposure complements the interpretation of species composition and successional processes since open patches are colonization sites for weeds as well as late successional grasses and forbs. As described in the plant indicator section of this assessment, much is known about many individual species' responses to grazing. Ratliff (1985) has compiled an extensive list of species responses to grazing in Sierran meadows.

Moderate livestock grazing usually increases native plant species' diversity in wet and mesic meadows, but can depress diversity in dry meadows (Ratliff 1985). Particularly in grasslike plant (Carex spp. especially) dominated wet parts of meadows, livestock grazing can reduce dominance and litter accumulations and allow more species to inhabit a site. These species are usually native. Heavy grazing usually reduces foliage density and increases bare ground in the community thereby making sites available to invasion of exotic species if they are present on a grazing unit. Many of the so-called 'increasers' on mountain meadow rangelands are native forbs which can be substantially increased in abundance with frequent grazing (Ratliff 1985).

Trampling impacts can also indirectly affect plant species diversity. Trampling reduces soil porosity especially when soils are wet and of high clay content (D. Zamudio, Toiyabe National Forest, pers. comm.). Repeatedly trampled wet or mesic meadows tend to become drier and of lower productivity due to lowered water infiltration and water holding capacity, and increased runoff. Reduced rooting depth and plant vigor, lowered productivity of aboveground biomass of grasses, grasslike plants and forbs, and bare ground exposure, promote colonization of exotic species (weeds). All these processes indirectly affect microhabitat conditions (water, light and nutrient regimes) and competitive conditions for native plant species. From an agricultural perspective the decline in productivity of these sites tends to shift the burden of grazing to uplands which can lead to unsustainable capacity for a grazing permit and needed reductions. It is imperative that meadows be managed carefully since they often provide the bulk of an allotment's forage productivity.

In the 1990's impairment of riparian ecosystem function has become a primary issue in range management (NRC 1994). For example, stream reaches that pass directly through meadows without adequate meanders tend to produce dry meadow water regimes since the passing of each unit of water through the meadow happens rapidly. Natural meandering keeps water on meadows longer thereby creating or maintaining water tables and more mesic or wet meadow conditions. A common meadow riparian problem is one where meanders have been lost, streams have become straighter with steeper gradients, and have downcut due to faster moving water. One primary livestock-related cause of loss of meanders is overgrazing and loss of woody plants which provide armoring of bends in meanders. The result is that much of the undercut bank structure and therefore fish habitat functionality is lost. Likewise, meadow productivity is depressed due to lowered water tables. Enhanced fish and forage production are shared meadow restoration goals.

The rate of streambank and in-stream recovery is highly site specific. Recovery to a former meandering structure may require increased stream protection from bank disturbance so that over time banks can rebuild, meandering can increase, meadows can become wetter, and fish and other aquatic habitat functionality can return. On the other hand, upstream water quantity and water quality changes could prevent streambank-based approaches from ever working; extreme flood events are a serious risk. Many streams have become degraded due to a combination of grazing disturbance and flood events, especially before land management agencies were established and before humans knew about important riparian ecosystem dynamics. Little information exists on time frames needed for such full functionality to return. One can expect the vegetative functionality to recover most rapidly, followed by the erosion deposition processes, and finally the hydrologic and aquatic habitat functions. Too often in riparian demonstration projects, vegetative recovery is equated with a return of functionality when, in fact, it is the undercut banks and clean gravel deposits which are limiting fish habitat-- both physical attributes which take longer to develop.

Resource experts are able to interpret species composition indicators and riparian ecosystem functionality impairment. Teasing out the ultimate causal mechanism, i.e. separating historic effects of extreme flood events from excessive overgrazing periods or their interaction, which is in the history of many meadow/riparian ecosystems, is difficult or impossible in most situations. 'Reading the system functionality', however, and determination of trend in a recovering system is readily possible in most situations with an adequate set of temporal monitoring data. Functionality parameters include such factors as healthy recent recruitment of seral willow vegetation which tends to armor streambanks if the site has the potential for willow; abundance of large woody debris in larger stream systems, and where the adjacent riparian forest contains decadent trees and snags, assurance of a source of woody material into the foreseeable future; lack of excessive erosion or sediment deposition even in relative high precipitation years; adequate herbaceous vegetative cover along streambanks at the end of each grazing season; etc.

What is the target level of protection of riparian ecosystem functionality, how much protection is enough, and how do you tell it is enough? Meadow and riparian ecosystems have greater potential for response to management and recovery than any other range ecosystem type. By their very nature they are well watered systems, plant growth is rapid, and species composition is diverse. There exists many plant community successional pathways and possible future conditions so long as the primary soil resource has not been lost. Trampling compaction effects will naturally reverse themselves with natural freeze/thaw and wetting/drying annual cycles if sites are protected from grazing during wet periods for 5-10 years. Tap roots of abundant forbs in overgrazed meadows will decompose providing routes for improved water infiltration so that it again reaches subsoil layers. Fibrous rooted grasses will become more deeply rooted during meadow/riparian restoration stages. Productivity will increase. Temporally controlled livestock grazing can be a part of this restoration process because grazing stimulates nutrient availability and plant growth if managed strategically.

The key level of protection is where local meadow and riparian disturbance mechanisms cease to happen with any regularity. For example, periodic and locally excessive grazing and trampling on wet meadows prior to normal range readiness, virtually never is allowed to happen. Herding and salting practices are frequent and ongoing management tools, and visual monitoring by knowledgeable permittees with modifications of livestock distribution occurring with regularity (permittees apply principles of 'adaptive management' at the allotment and grazing subunit scale). Acute stream head cuts, where possible, are dealt with in a timely fashion by erosion control experts from the responsible land management agency or landowner. Where plant species diversity problems are apparent, grazing monitoring and management options, i.e., alternative grazing rotations, numbers and distributions are used in an adaptive way to determine the suitable solution. When necessary, special aquatic resources, for example, fens, bogs, or critical riparian habitat may need to be protected for a recovery period or permanently using electric or 'let-down' fencing to exclude livestock.

Six plant community composition attributes were analyzed from Parker C&T transect data on mountain meadows for 10 National Forests of the Sierra Nevada and Modoc Plateau including grass, legume, sedge and rush species composition, non-native species composition, and bare soil exposed. The Parker loop sampling frame reading of basal cover of plants or bare soil is most appropriately used in these thick-sward herbaceous plant communities. Sample sizes are indicated in the three tables of results and emphasis is given to values based upon larger numbers of transects and allotments.

The first complex of indices we used to indicate meadow functionality is grass, legume, sedge and rush relative composition and trends. Wet and mesic meadow ecosystems should not show a trend of grass and legume composition increase at the expense of sedge and rush composition. Such trends usually result from those mechanisms discussed above which ultimately result in drier site conditions and lowered productivity. The opposite trend, however, typically indicates restoration of a water table, reduced runoff and increased infiltration, gully repair, etc. Given that livestock numbers have been reduced and many grazing systems and restoration projects have occurred during the 5 decade monitoring period, we should expect some reversal of dewatering indicators i.e., increases in grasslike plant composition.

Two Forests, the Modoc and Toiyabe, showed the apparent unfavorable meadow water regime response of a reduction in sedges and an increase in grasses as an aggregate response. The trend was strong for the Modoc and weak for the Toiyabe (Table 6). In both cases rushes (Juncus spp.) did not compensate for the sedge reduction. On the Eldorado Forest grasses increased through the third decade (ending 1975) at the expense of sedges, but rushes compensated in the grasslike plant category. Grasses increased on Lassen meadows over the past 4 decades with a relatively stable component of grasslike plants. Grasses have tended to decline on the Plumas, Tahoe and Stanislaus meadows with upward compensation by sedges, and together with rushes appear to be a stable grasslike component. Sedges are dominating meadows on the Sierra and Sequoia Forests, and grasses continue to decline on the Sierra Forest. Grass relative to grasslike composition trends have been relatively stable for the Sequoia but appears somewhat cyclical on the Inyo meadows with recent changes leading to about the same relative composition as 30 years ago. Native legume (Trifolium spp. almost exclusively) composition has tended to increase on the Modoc, Lassen, Plumas, Tahoe, and Toiyabe Forests and show no obvious trend on the other forests.

The non-native species, Kentucky bluegrass, is the primary invader of mountain meadows on all 10 Forests, especially in the north and also the Inyo (Table 7). Generally, bluegrass appears to be increasing on mountain meadows, especially on the Modoc, Lassen and Tahoe Forests. Redtop grasses are the second most common non-native component of meadows with greatest composition on the Plumas through the Stanislaus Forests (Table 7). Increases in composition of redtop are occurring but to a lesser degree than for bluegrass. Common dandelion is the third most common non-native species occurring on mountain meadows, and while being the most common non-native forb its abundance is substantially less than for bluegrass and redtop (Table 7). Cheatgrass was the next most common invader on drier parts of meadows especially from the Tahoe Forest northward, and except for the Modoc Forest its abundance is usually very low (Table 7). Other non-native species encountered on the Parker transects include medusahead, wheatgrasses, orchardgrass, Alopecurus sp., timothy, silver hairgrass, clovers, tumble mustard, buttercup, Klamathweed, velvet grass, dock and Borago officinalis. None of these latter species appear to be increasing in abundance.

Weighted average bare soil exposure in mountain meadows on 10 National Forests appears to have stabilized at between 4 and 5% more than 30 years ago (Table 8). Trends toward reduced bare soil exposure are most apparent on the Modoc, Lassen, Tahoe, Stanislaus, Sierra, and Sequoia Forests. Bare soil exposed on the Plumas and Eldorado may be increasing, while that on the Inyo appears static and for the Toiyabe, cyclical or indeterminant. The very high bare soil exposure on the Eldorado of 25% for the 1986-95 decade was an average of only three sites, 0%, 31% and 44%, which indicates some severe local disturbance problems in need attention.

Based on the historical evidence of abuse of California mountain meadows during the post-Gold Rush Era (Kinney's and our reports above), the recolonization by native plants, low abundance of non-native weeds, and the soil protection being provided by herbaceous vegetation as indicated by 4-5 decades of range monitoring data is significant. Considering past heavy grazing (see above) in northeastern California, the eastern Sierra in the Carson City and Tahoe environs, and lands of the Mother Lode nearest Sacramento, it is not surprising that the Modoc, Plumas, Tahoe, Eldorado and Toiyabe Forests are continuing to lag a bit in recovery since their meadows were probably most impacted during the early days following settlement. The declining abundance of grass species on the Sierra National Forest and the low abundance of grass species on the Sequoia National Forest during the 4-5 decade monitoring period is a biodiversity concern. The status of grasses and sedges on these two forests may be due to grazing use standards too closely tied to Nebraska sedge which may underestimate forage utilization by livestock on drier components of monitored meadows.

CORRELATION OF MEADOW AND RIPARIAN CONDITION--A CASE STUDY

During summer 1995, 24 Parker transects were re-read on 7 National Forests from the Lassen through the Inyo (see Appendix 1 for summarized data from 1995 and previous readings). The nearest stream/riparian segment to the transect was evaluated using the riparian system functionality 'standard checklist' of 17 parameters developed by the Bureau of Land Management (USDI-BLM 1993). Six other parameters: elevation, width/depth ratio, BLM checklist-predicted functionality and trend in functionality, whether the stream/riparian system previously had a specific restoration project, and whether the allotment has been vacant (non-use for 3 or more years) in the last decade not including 1995, were recorded (Table 9). Functionality and trend in functionality ratings were based on finding several corroborating parameters not in conflict with other parameters to make a determination (see classes of responses in Table 9). Trend was not estimated for those riparian systems determined to be fully functioning.

This exercise was done to determine whether meadow status from Parker transect information, as evaluated using such parameters described above in the plant indicator and meadow assessment sections of this report, could predict nearby stream/riparian system condition. The 24 transects were chosen pseudo-randomly to cover the southern Cascade and Sierra Mountain range wet and mesic meadows, including transects which had been read several times over the last 5 decades, and ones that had a perennial stream in the meadow within 100 meters of the transect location (Table 10). In addition to testing for meadow and riparian status relationships, this exercise was invaluable in that it got us out in the field with experienced range professionals on many sites, and we got up to date transect readings which were used in the regional meadow assessments as well. During this field project many ideas, issues, problems and opportunities for improved range management were discussed with each agency person.

Individual hydrologic, vegetative, erosion deposition and other ratings are presented in Table 11, where sample numbers cross-reference each of the transects (Table 10 and Appendix Table 1). Restoration projects (RP) included fenced riparian exclosures, in-stream structures to reduce stream velocity and to dissipate energy, and planting of vegetation, usually willow cuttings. Animal management (AM) ratings include allotment vacancy in all but one case where substantial changes in animal distribution occurred. The projects and management changes are described below by Forest, District and allotment:

Lassen/Almanor/Butte Meadows: In-stream structures

Lassen/Almanor/Soldier Meadows: In-stream structures within the segment surveyed and exclosures placed upstream. Rewetting of the meadow has occurred where it was previously dry and dominated by bluegrass. High human impact (camping) and an old railroad grade also impact the site.

Lassen/Almanor/Feather River: Electric fence that shocked cattle if in stream. Aspen regeneration project upstream in 1984 because of lack of recruitment.

Plumas/Milford/Ridenour: Two mile livestock exclosure along stream with off-site watering. This site has had extensive logging in the watershed throughout the 1960's and more recently some clear cutting.

Tahoe/Sierraville/Bear Valley: Upper reaches of stream had considerable problems with erosion of streambanks and stream widening so a fence was constructed to exclude cattle. Rock material was placed in the channel to dissipate energy. The site is within the Cottonwood Fire of 1994.

Tahoe/Sierraville/Perazzo: Ongoing stream restoration includes in-stream log structures, bank stabilization with willow, logs placed vertically against steep banks, and split rail fencing not to exclude livestock but to minimize impacts to steeply incised segments of the stream. The site has had extensive logging including clear cuts in the watershed.

Eldorado/Placerville/Little Round Top: Limited restoration project. Rock material has been placed in the channel to dissipate energy. The high elevation watershed with south facing aspect is considered potentially flashy.

Inyo/Mt. Whitney/Monache: Sediment dam far upstream erected in 1980s for blockage of brown trout predation on golden trout. Extensive riparian pasture fencing, streambank log and branch in-stream structures, and rock placements in stream at crossings. High elevation, very large meadow system with deeply incised stream which occurred prior to 1905. Area impacted by high recreation including ORVs.

Animal management and allotment vacancies include the following:

Lassen/Almanor/Butte Meadows: 70% reduction in numbers of cattle and one month shorter season.

Lassen/Almanor/Soldier Meadows: change in animal distribution management by permittee.

Plumas/Beckwourth/Mapes: 3 years vacancy
Plumas/Milford/Doyle: 8 years vacancy
Tahoe/Sierraville/Haypress: 5 years vacancy
Tahoe/Sierraville/Lincoln allotments: 5 years vacancy
Eldorado/Amador/Indian Valley: vacancy for some time but length unknown

Other possible contributing factors leading to meadow and riparian degradation on the 24 sites include logging of uplands, wildfire, historical homesteads, and recreation. Recent high intensity logging in the watersheds above Lincoln and Perazzo (including clear cuts) on the Tahoe, and Ridenour, Jenkins and Doyle on the Plumas. All sites visited have had at least some moderate selective logging in the past. Fire-affected areas include Ridenour, Jenkins, and Doyle on the Plumas and Bear Valley on the Tahoe. The combination of heavy logging and intense fires make watershed conditions potentially flashy and may have contributed significantly to poor riparian conditions seen on many of the Plumas Forest allotments we evaluated. High human impacts due to homestead and/or recreational activities have affected Soldier Meadows (combination of close proximity to major road, camp site, and old railroad grade) on the Lassen. The Mattley (C2) site in Pumpkin Valley, formerly part of the Stanislaus Forest, has remnants of an old homestead, a developed spring, and currently is in private ownership. The complexity and diversity of site specific disturbance elements which interact with the primary focus here, livestock impacts, can make accurate interpretation of causal mechanisms difficult.

Results

Eight of the 24 riparian systems in this case study had restoration projects done on them in the last decade, two of which also had reductions in animal use for the allotment in general, including the meadows where the Parker transects are located (Table 11). Six additional allotments had reductions in use for 3-8 years of the last decade. This finding is indicative of the increased management attention riparian areas and meadows are receiving today.

Seven of the 24 riparian systems were rated as fully functioning, 13 were functioning but at risk, and 4 were not functioning (Table 11). For the functioning-at-risk group of 13, 6 showed upward trend in functioning, 4 showed static trend, and 3 downward trend. Functioning and not functioning riparian systems in the study were not rated for trend. It is the functioning-at-risk riparian systems that we are interested in determining whether we can predict their status and trend from the nearby permanent Parker transect condition and trend plant composition and bare soil exposure database (Appendix Table 1) for the meadow. It is the functioning-at-risk riparian systems that managers have the greatest likelihood of restoration in the foreseeable future and so they are of greatest interest. If prediction were possible, more of this kind of detailed analysis could be done with exisiting data to evaluate many mountain meadow riparian systems in the Sierra without having to do riparian surveys. Such analysis is also an outstanding training exercise for learning how to interpret meadow/riparian system dynamics for improved management in the future.

The canonical correspondence analysis (CANOCO) helped in two important ways. First it identified riparian/stream condition variables (Table 11) not contributing to the separation of conditions along species gradients in the ordination space, and also that cause inflation in variance of the predictive model or have undue influence on the model coefficients. Hydrologic variables 2 and 4, vegetative variables 2 and 5, and erosion deposition variable 2 were thus eliminated from the analysis (see Table 9). On further consideration of these variables, their lack of application or subjectivity became apparent. Beaver dams and their rarity (HYD2), apparent widening of riparian zones which is difficult to judge with one visit (HYD4), diverse composition in largely herb dominated meadows (VEG2), the subjective evaluation of plant vigor in herbs (VEG5), and revegetation of usually non-existent point bars for these sites (ED2) made elimination of these variables an easy decision. The AM variable was not included in the analysis because of the variable effects of different periods of vacany or reductions in numbers of livestock. The BLM checklist obviously was designed for a wide range of riparian systems, and our narrow application to Sierran montane meadows made some of the variables less applicable or redundant (multicollinear) with others.

Secondly and most important, it became apparent from the model that if a site had had a riparian restoration project performed on it, or if the riparian system showed a downward trend (or both), the system had some functionality deficiencies. Functionality and performance of a restoration project were most closely correlated with the first canonical axis but in opposite directions (Appendix Table 2). The FU correlation with Axis 1 equals -.29 and the restoration project (RP) correlation with Axis 1 equals +.33. Trend was close in ordination space to RP with an Axis 1 correlation of +.21. What this means is that in the dual ordination of Parker species and bare soil exposure variables on the riparian/stream site data and vice versa in CANOCO, there were variables in both datasets which successfully separated the species and sites along a common axis, in this case Axis 1. With all the variables involved, the Parker species and bare soil exposure and the riparian stream environment had an overall correlation of 0.99 and an explained variance (eigenvalue for Axis 1) of 72%. This result indicates that prediction should be possible.

Using the aggregated Parker transect data to the genus level, the lifeform categories of grasses, legumes, sedges, rushes, and forbs, and the raw data of bare soil exposure, litter and non-native species (Appendix Table 1) present currently and over the last 5 decades, we were able to predict 11-12 of the 13 functioning-at-risk riparian/stream trend directions correctly. As used in the assessments above, variable dynamics indicating sedge to grass ratio changes without compensation of rushes, invasion or retreat of weedy forbs, reductions in abundance of late seral grasses such as <u>Deschampsia</u> and <u>Glyceria</u> species, radical fluctuation in clovers, and 'red-flag indicators like more than 7-10% bare soil exposure sometime in the meadow's 40-50 year history, was adequate to make the predictions. Using the typical Forest Service allotment folder information on changes in grazing management and site-specific restoration project history would improve this predictive power. This finding should stimulate further testing of these approaches for more diverse meadow/riparian and sagebrush-steppe rangeland plant communities in the future.

REFERENCES

Dayton, W. A. 1960. Notes on western range forbs: Equisetaceae through Fumariaceae. U.S. Dept. of Agriculture, Forest Service, Agric. Handbk. No. 161. U.S. Gov't. Printing Office, Wash., D.C.

Hermann, F. J. 1966. Notes on western range forbs: cruciferae through compositae. U.S. Dept. of Agriculture, Forest Service, Agric. Handbk. No. 293. U.S. Gov't. Printing Office, Wash., D.C.

Hickman, J. C.,ed. 1993. *The Jepson manual: Higher plants of California.* Berkeley and Los Angeles: University of California Press.

Jongman, R. H. G., C. J. F. ter Braak, and O. F. R. Van Tongeren. 1987. *Data analysis in community and landscape ecology.* Pudoc, Wageningen, The Netherlands.

Kovalchik, B. L. 1987. Riparian zone associations. Deshutes, Ochoco, Fremont, and Winema National Forests. U.S. Dept. of Agriculture, Forest Service, R6 ECOL TP-279-87. Pacific Northwest Region, Portland, Oregon.

Laycock, W. A. 1991. Stable states and thresholds of range condition on North American rangelands: a viewpoint. *Journal of Range Management* 44:427-433.

Monsen, S. B. and S. G. Kitchen, comps. 1994. *Proceedings--Ecology and management of annual rangelands.* Gen. Tech. Rep. INT-GTR-313. Ogden, UT: U.S. Department of Agriculture, Forest Service, Intermountain Researh Station.

NRC. 1994. *Rangeland Health: New Methods to Classify, Inventory and Monitor Rangelands.* Committee on Rangeland Classification, Board on Agriculture, National Research Council. National Academic Press, Wash., D.C.

Rasmussen, G. A. 1994. Prescribed burning considerations in sagebrush annual grassland communities. *In: Proceedings--ecology and management of annual rangelands*, compiled by S. B. Monsen and S. G. Kitchen, 69-70. Gen. Tech. Rep. INT-GTR-313. Ogden, UT: U.S. Department of Agriculture, Forest Service, Intermountain Research Station.

Ratliff, R. D. 1985. Meadows in the Sierra Nevada of California: state of knowledge. U.S. Dept. of Agriculture, Forest Service, Gen. Tech. Rep. PSW-84. Pacific Southwest Forest and Range Expt. Sta., Berkeley, California.

Tausch, R. J., P. E. Wigand, and J. W. Burkhardt. 1993. Viewpoint: Plant community thresholds, multiple steady states, and multiple successional pathways: legacy of the Quaternary? *Journal of Range Management* 46:439-447.

Tueller, P. T. 1973. Secondary succession, disclimax, and range condition standards in desert shrub vegetation. *In: Arid shrublands*, edited by D. N. Hyder, 57-65. Society for Range Management, Denver, Colo.

USDI-BLM. 1993. Riparian Area Management. Tech. Ref. 1737-9. USDI-BLM Service Center, Denver, Colorado.

Vallentine, J. F. and A. R. Stevens. 1994. Use of livestock to control cheatgrass--a review. *In: Proceedings--ecology and management of annual rangelands*, compiled by S. B. Monsen and S. G. Kitchen, 202-206. Gen. Tech. Rep. INT-GTR-313. Ogden, UT: U.S. Department of Agriculture, Forest Service, Intermountain Researh Station.

Vankat, J. L. 1970. *Vegetation change in Sequoia National Park, California.* Ph.D. Diss., University of California, Davis.

Young, J. A. 1994. History and use of semiarid plant communities--changes in vegetation. *In: Proceedings--ecology and management of annual rangelands*, compiled by S. B. Monsen and S. G. Kitchen, 5-8. Gen. Tech. Rep. INT-GTR-313. Ogden, UT: U.S. Department of Agriculture, Forest Service, Intermountain Researh Station.

Young, J. A., R. A. Evans, and J. Major. 1988. Sagebrush steppe. *In: Terrestrial vegetation of California*, edited by M. G. Barbour and J. Major, 763-796. California Native Plant Society Special Publication No. 9.

Table 1. Approximate number of Forest Service condition and trend (Parker C&T) transects read or re-read per decade by National Forest for the Sierra Nevada and Modoc Plateau.

National Forest	1950	1960	1970	1980	1990
Modoc	84	190	99	38	2
Lassen	107	323	107	25	50
Plumas	42	153	127	62	21
Tahoe	43	107	77	0	18
Lake Tahoe Basin	3	6	2	0	0
Eldorado	10	50	12	0	3
Toiyabe	3	20	20	11	1
Stanislaus	17	65	70	9	2
Sierra	73	150	80	3	6
Sequoia	41	182	71	5	0
Inyo	29	101	45	52	38
Total	452	1347	710	205	141

Table 2. Approximate number of Forest Service condition and trend (Parker C&T) transects by range type in the Sierra Nevada and Modoc Plateau[1].

Range type	Number of C&T transects
Perennial grassland	47
Meadow	504
Perennial forb	22
Sagebrush	171
Browse-mountain shrub and chaparral	23
Conifer	114
Waste	0
Barren	0
Pinyon-juniper	22
Woodland-annual grass	55
Annual grassland	18
Cultivated	0
Transitory	27

Total number of allotments = 467

[1]Does not include all the Toiyabe NF allotment data since that Forest has adopted nested frequency methods as part of the Forest Service Region 4 policy.

Table 3. Big sagebrush, native perennial grass and forb composition (%) in sagebrush-steppe communities on 7 National Forests over 5 decades from Parker transect (n = no. of 100-loop transects) data.

Forest	before 1956	1956-65	1966-75	1976-85	1986-95
Modoc (n)	(9)	(3)	(0)	(1)	(11)
Big sagebrush	15.4	22.0	-	15.0	14.8
Perennial grasses	7.3	3.0	-	6.0	10.5
Forbs	21.7	24.3	-	27.0	18.2
Lassen (n)	(0)	(12)	(2)	(0)	(8)
Big sagebrush	-	12.8	17.0	-	11.2
Perennial grasses	-	6.5	6.5	-	8.4
Forbs	-	19.8	20.0	-	22.1
Plumas (n)	(0)	(11)	(3)	(3)	(3)
Big sagebrush	-	23.7	9.7	17.7	30.0
Perennial grasses	-	2.9	5.0	5.3	3.0
Forbs	-	35.0	19.7	22.3	38.0
Tahoe (n)	(3)	(5)	(11)	(3)	(0)
Big sagebrush	1.7	20.8	14.3	16.7	-
Perennial grasses	1.7	2.8	3.0	1.7	-
Forbs	8.7	29.6	21.7	19.3	-
Stanislaus (n)	(0)	(0)	(7)	(5)	(0)
Big sagebrush	-	-	31.7	19.0	-
Perennial grasses	-	-	7.1	4.2	-
Forbs	-	-	41.7	25.6	-
Toiyabe (n)	(0)	(10)	(2)	(10)	(2)
Big sagebrush	-	24.4	32.0	20.4	21.0
Perennial grasses	-	2.8	2.0	5.2	0.5
Forbs	-	29.3	25.3	28.1	43.0
Inyo (n)	(0)	(8)	(2)	(0)	(10)
Big sagebrush	-	16.9	14.0	-	13.4
Perennial grasses	-	0.4	0.0	-	3.3
Forbs	-	24.8	25.5	-	23.7
Weighted Average (n)	(12)	(49)	(27)	(22)	(34)
Big sagebrush	12.0	19.7	19.8	19.0	15.2
Perennial grasses	5.9	3.3	4.2	4.5	6.6
Forbs	18.4	27.2	27.1	25.5	23.9

Table 4. Non-native species[1] composition (%) in sagebrush-steppe communities on 7 National Forests over 5 decades from Parker transect (n = no. of 100-loop transects) data.

Forest	before 1956	1956-65	1966-75	1976-85	1986-95
Modoc (n)	(9)	(3)	(0)	(1)	(11)
Cheatgrass	0.8	3.7	-	0	2.5
Medusahead	0	0	-	0	0.6
Filaree	0.1	0	-	0	0
Dandelion	0.1	0	-	0	0
Lassen (n)	(0)	(12)	(2)	(0)	(8)
Cheatgrass	-	0	2.0	-	0.1
Filaree	-	0.4	0	-	0
Plumas (n)	(0)	(11)	(3)	(3)	(3)
Cheatgrass	-	0.2	0.3	0	0
Filaree	-	0.6	0	0	0
Wheatgrass	-	0	0	9.0	0
Tahoe (n)	(3)	(5)	(11)	(3)	(0)
Cheatgrass	2.3	0.2	5.5	0.3	-
Wheatgrass	0	0	0.3	0	-
Plantain	1.3	0	0	0	-
Stanislaus (n)	(0)	(0)	(7)	(5)	(0)
Filaree	-	-	0.4	0	-
Toiyabe (n)	(0)	(10)	(2)	(10)	(2)
Bull thistle	-	0	0	0.2	0
Inyo (n)	(0)	(8)	(2)	(0)	(10)
Cheatgrass	-	0.9	0.5	-	4.8

[1]Cheatgrass (Bromus tectorum), medusahead (Taeniatherum caput-medusae), filaree (Erodium spp.), dandelion (Taraxacum officinale), wheatgrass (Agropyron spp.), plantain (Plantago spp.), and bull thistle (Cirsium spp.)

Table 5. Litter (%), bare soil (%), and erosion pavement (%) in sagebrush-steppe communities on 7 National Forests over 5 decades from Parker transect (n = no. of 100-loop transects) data.

Forest	before 1956	1956-65	1966-75	1976-85	1986-95
Modoc (n)	(9)	(3)	(0)	(1)	(11)
Litter	29.6	20.3	-	28.0	40.1
Bare soil	33.3	41.7	-	27.0	20.3
Erosion pavement	1.6	0.7	-	4.0	3.3
Lassen (n)	(0)	(12)	(2)	(0)	(8)
Litter	-	24.4	16.0	-	38.9
Bare soil	-	18.2	2.0	-	9.6
Erosion pavement	-	12.3	0.0	-	10.5
Plumas (n)	(0)	(11)	(3)	(3)	(3)
Litter	-	34.5	36.3	38.7	34.0
Bare soil	-	14.5	17.3	18.0	17.0
Erosion pavement	-	10.5	23.0	0.0	2.7
Tahoe (n)	(3)	(5)	(11)	(3)	(0)
Litter	36.3	33.0	36.9	44.0	-
Bare soil	47.0	25.4	23.9	29.3	-
Erosion pavement	3.7	8.4	5.4	5.7	-
Stanislaus (n)	(0)	(0)	(7)	(5)	(0)
Litter	-	-	16.1	14.2	-
Bare soil	-	-	9.0	19.4	-
Erosion pavement	-	-	24.7	34.4	-
Toiyabe (n)	(0)	(10)	(2)	(10)	(2)
Litter	-	35.3	21.5	30.2	23.5
Bare soil	-	18.5	20.0	24.8	10.5
Erosion pavement	-	8.5	18.5	6.4	19.0
Inyo (n)	(0)	(8)	(2)	(0)	(10)
Litter	-	19.9	29.5	-	23.5
Bare soil	-	19.2	23.5	-	26.5
Erosion pavement	-	32.9	20.5	-	17.4
Weighted average (n)	(12)	(49)	(27)	(22)	(34)
Litter	31.3	28.8	28.2	29.5	33.4
Bare soil	36.7	19.8	17.4	23.4	18.7
Erosion pavement	2.1	13.4	14.0	11.7	10.0

Table 6. Grass, legume, sedge and rush species[1] composition in wet and mesic meadows on 10
National Forests over 5 decades from Parker transect (n = no. of 100-loop transects) data.

Forest	before 1956	1956-65	1966-75	1976-85	1986-95
Modoc (n)	(2)	(9)	(9)	(0)	(10)
Grasses	7.5	10.6	26.1	-	25.0
Legumes	5.0	7.0	10.3	-	9.0
Sedges	14.5	16.3	17.2	-	7.7
Rushes	4.5	5.0	6.1	-	2.5
Lassen (n)	(0)	(13)	(13)	(1)	(15)
Grasses	-	22.6	19.9	31.0	29.4
Legumes	-	2.8	4.8	1.0	7.2
Sedges	-	20.4	22.0	26.0	19.6
Rushes	-	12.5	9.2	4.0	10.2
Plumas (n)	(0)	(14)	(13)	(5)	(13)
Grasses	-	25.1	18.4	14.0	20.5
Legumes	-	6.6	3.4	4.0	13.0
Sedges	-	20.6	21.1	22.8	23.2
Rushes	-	13.1	16.1	9.6	11.1
Tahoe (n)	(1)	(16)	(12)	(11)	(7)
Grasses	13.0	32.9	31.9	28.6	20.3
Legumes	0.0	10.1	4.8	3.9	15.0
Sedges	25.0	18.6	22.2	22.3	24.4
Rushes	19.0	2.9	11.8	10.1	11.0
Eldorado (n)	(5)	(12)	(13)	(0)	(3)
Grasses	24.4	22.6	46.7	-	16.7
Legumes	4.6	6.0	8.0	-	4.0
Sedges	20.6	13.1	12.9	-	1.0
Rushes	0.4	9.1	12.2	-	0.0
Stanislaus (n)	(1)	(8)	(14)	(10)	(2)
Grasses	10.0	27.4	20.3	19.1	7.5
Legumes	0.0	18.0	6.4	11.0	2.0
Sedges	2.0	28.8	35.6	31.7	30.5
Rushes	0.0	0.6	1.9	0.8	3.5

Table 6. (continued)

Sierra (n)	(6)	(13)	(15)	(0)	(4)
Grasses	29.2	19.3	18.6	-	6.2
Legumes	10.3	3.6	4.3	-	4.5
Sedges	19.7	40.8	34.3	-	47.0
Rushes	1.7	4.6	6.1	-	9.0
Forest	before 1956	1956-65	1966-75	1976-85	1986-95
Sequoia (n)	(0)	(10)	(8)	(4)	(0)
Grasses	-	12.5	8.5	11.8	-
Legumes	-	8.0	8.8	8.0	-
Sedges	-	41.9	50.4	41.2	-
Rushes	-	10.8	6.1	6.2	-
Toiyabe (n)	(0)	(10)	(1)	(10)	(0)
Grasses	-	16.3	17.0	24.8	-
Legumes	-	6.7	0.0	8.7	-
Sedges	-	26.4	44.0	22.4	-
Rushes	-	6.2	14.0	7.4	-
Inyo (n)	(0)	(20)	(3)	(15)	(11)
Grasses	-	12.5	13.0	9.6	18.0
Legumes	-	6.9	5.0	10.2	2.5
Sedges	-	37.8	25.5	53.8	35.3
Rushes	-	8.6	33.5	3.4	8.1

[1] Grasses (Poaceae), legumes (Fabaceae, primarily Trifolium spp.), sedges (Cyperaceae, primarily Carex, Scirpus and Eleocharis), and rushes (Juncaceae, primarily Juncus).

Table 7. Non-native species[1] composition (%) in wet and mesic meadows on 10 National Forests over 5 decades from Parker transect (n = no. of 100-loop transects) data.

Forest	before 1956	1956-65	1966-75	1976-85	1986-95
Modoc (n)	(2)	(9)	(9)	(0)	(10)
Bluegrass	0	0.6	3.4	-	10.5
Redtop	0	0.4	0.8	-	0.6
Dandelion	0	0	0.1	-	0.5
Cheatgrass	0	2.7	0.1	-	1.0
Medusahead	0	0	0.3	-	0.3
Wheatgrass	0	0	0.1	-	1.2
Orchardgrass	0	0	0	-	0.1
Alopecurus sp.	0	0	0	-	0.1
Lassen (n)	(0)	(13)	(13)	(1)	(15)
Bluegrass	-	2.4	4.1	0	6.7
Redtop	-	0.2	0.1	0	0.7
Dandelion	-	0.5	0.1	0	1.3
Timothy	-	0	0	0	0.3
Silver hairgrass	-	0.1	0	0	0
Clover	-	0	0	0	0.3
Tumble mustard	-	0	0	0	0.2
Plumas (n)	(0)	(14)	(13)	(5)	(13)
Bluegrass	-	2.0	4.6	1.8	1.8
Redtop	-	0	3.0	0.4	2.6
Dandelion	-	0.2	0.5	0.4	0.1
Cheatgrass	-	0	0	0.2	0.1
Wheatgrass	-	0	0	0.4	0
Buttercup	-	0	0	0	0.1
Tahoe (n)	(1)	(16)	(12)	(11)	(7)
Bluegrass	0	2.0	1.0	3.6	5.7
Redtop	0	0.4	0.2	0.5	1.6
Dandelion	0	0	0	0	1.6
Cheatgrass	0	0	0.2	0	0
Eldorado (n)	(5)	(12)	(13)	(0)	(3)
Bluegrass	0	0	0.8	-	1.7
Redtop	0	0.6	1.1	-	0
Stanislaus (n)	(1)	(8)	(14)	(10)	(2)
Bluegrass	1.0	0.4	0.3	0.1	2.5
Redtop	0	0.2	0.6	1.6	1.5
Dandelion	1.0	0.1	0.1	0.4	0

Table 7. (continued)

Forest	before 1956	1956-65	1966-75	1976-85	1986-95
Sierra (n)	(6)	(13)	(15)	(0)	(4)
Bluegrass	0	0.8	0.1	-	0.2
Redtop	0	0.6	0	-	0
Cheatgrass	0	0	0.1	-	0
Klamathweed	0	0	0.9	-	0
Velvet grass	0	0	0	-	2.2
Dock	0.3	0	0	-	0
Sequoia (n)	(0)	(10)	(8)	(4)	(0)
Bluegrass	-	2.1	0.2	0	-
Redtop	-	0	0.1	0	-
Dock	-	0	0	2.0	-
Toiyabe (n)	(0)	(10)	(1)	(10)	(0)
Bluegrass	-	0	0	3.3	-
Dandelion	-	1.4	0	2.4	-
Wheatgrass	-	0	0	0.5	-
Borago officinalis	-	0	0	0.3	-
Inyo (n)	(0)	(10)	(2)	(5)	(11)
Bluegrass	-	2.8	5.5	0.6	0.3
Dandelion	-	0.7	2.0	0	0.5
Dock	-	0.1	0	0	0

[1]Bluegrass (Poa pratensis), redtop (Agrostis stolonifera), dandelion (Taraxacum officinale), cheatgrass (Bromus tectorum), medusahead (Taeniatherum caput-medusae), wheatgrass (Agropyron spp.), orchardgrass (Dactylis glomerata), timothy (Phleum pratense), silver hairgrass (Aira caryophyllea), tumble mustard (Sisymbrium sp.), buttercup (Ranunculus sp.), Klamathweed (Hypericum perforatum), velvet grass (Holcus lanatus), and dock (Rumex spp.).

Table 8. Bare soil (%) in wet and mesic meadows on 10 National Forests over 5 decades from Parker transect (n = no. of 100-loop transects) data.

Forest	before 1956	1956-65	1966-75	1976-85	1986-95
Modoc	23.0	16.0	5.3	-	7.3
Lassen	-	3.9	5.0	0.0	2.3
Plumas	-	3.2	2.5	9.4	3.8
Average	23.0	6.7	4.1	7.8	4.1
n	2	35	35	6	38
Tahoe	16.0	2.1	2.5	5.5	1.9
Eldorado	16.2	9.6	5.3	-	25.0
Stanislaus	10.0	1.9	6.8	2.2	3.5
Average	15.3	4.6	5.0	3.9	7.9
n	7	36	40	21	12
Sierra	1.5	2.2	2.1	-	0.5
Sequoia	-	2.5	1.5	0.0	-
Average	1.5	2.3	1.9	0.0	0.5
n	6	23	22	4	4
Toiyabe	-	7.4	2.0	7.2	-
Inyo	-	3.6	0.0	4.2	4.1
Average	-	5.5	0.7	6.2	4.1
n	0	20	3	15	11
Weighted average	10.8	4.9	3.9	4.8	4.6
n	15	114	100	46	65

Table 9. Checklist for rating riparian system functionality[1].

Variable[2]	Description
Hydrologic	
HYD1	Floodplain inundated in 'relatively frequent' events (1-3 years)
HYD2	Active/stable beaver dams
HYD3	Sinuosity, width/depth ratio, and gradient are in balance with landscape setting (i.e., landform, geology, and bioclimatic region)
HYD4	Riparian zone is widening
HYD5	Upland watershed not contributing to riparian degradation
Vegetative	
VEG1	Diverse age structure of vegetation
VEG2	Diverse composition of vegetation
VEG3	Species present indicate maintenance of riparian soil moisture characteristics
VEG4	Streambank vegetation is comprised of those plants or plant communities that have root masses capable of withstanding high streamflow events
VEG5	Riparian plants exhibit high vigor
VEG6	Adequate vegetative cover present to protect banks and dissipate energy during high flows
VEG7	Plant communities in the riparian area are an adequate source of coarse and/or large woody debris
Erosion Deposition	
ED1	Floodplain and channel characteristics (i.e., rocks, coarse and/or large woody debris) adequate to dissipate energy
ED2	Point bars are revegetating
ED3	Lateral stream movement is associated with natural sinuosity
ED4	System is vertically stable
ED5	Stream is in balance with the water and sediment being supplied by the watershed (i.e., no excessive erosion or deposition)
Other	
EL	Elevation in feet: 1=4,000-4,999, 2=5,000-5,999, 3=6,000-6,999, 4=7,000-7,999, 5=8,000+
WD	Width/depth ratio: 1=<1, 2=1, 3=>1, 4=>>1
FU	Functionality: 1=proper, 2=functioning at risk, 3=not functioning
TR	Trend in functionality: 1=up, 2=not apparent, 3=down, 5=not rated
RP	Restoration project: 1=yes, 2=no
AM	Allotment vacant for a period or change in grazing use: 1=yes, 2=no

[1] Taken from USDI-BLM. 1993. Riparian Area Management. Tech. Ref. 1737-9. USDI-BLM Serv. Cntr., Denver, CO. 51 pp. except for variables EL, WD and RP.

[2]Hydrologic, vegetative and erosion deposition variables: 1=yes, 2=intermediate, possibly or somewhat, 3=no or not the case, 5=not rated.

Table 10. Forest, sample number, distict, allotment, cluster and SNEP code for 24 meadow condition and trend transects re-read in summer 1995 to test correlation with stream functionality[1].

Forest	Sample No.	District	Allotment, Cluster	Code
Lassen	1	Almanor	Butte Mdws., 115	LBM19519
	2		Soldier Mdws., 36	LSM39520
	3		Feather River, 9A	LFR99521
Plumas	4	Beckwourth	Mapes Canyon, 1	PMA19307
	5		Grizzly Vly., 1	PGV19508
	6	Milford	Ridenour, 2	PRI29509
	7		Jenkins, 3	PJE39510
	8		Doyle, 4	PDO49511
Tahoe	9	Sierraville	Lincoln, 2	TLI29501
	10		Bear Valley, 1	TBE19502
	11		Perazzo, 1	TPE19503
	12		Bickford, 1	TBI19504
	13		Haypress, 2	THA29505
	14		Independence, 2	TIN29506
Eldorado	15	Placerville	Ltl. Round Top, 1	ERT19522
	16	Amador	Silver Lake, 1	ESL19523
	17		Indian Valley, 1	EIV29524
Stanislaus	18	Calaveras	Mattley, 2	STM29516
	19		Mattley, 3	STM39517
Sierra	20	Minarets	Chiquito, 1	SCH19512
	21	Pineridge	Mt. Tom, 1	SMT19513
	22		Mt. Tom, 2	SMT29514
	23		Mt. Tom, 3	SMT39515
Inyo	24	Mt. Whitney	Monache, 3	IMO39118

[1]Color photographs of the transects and stream segments taken in summer 1995 are available in the SNEP database for these transects.

Table 11. Hydrologic, vegetative, erosion deposition and other stream/riparian system functionality ratings[1] for 24 stream segments on 7 National Forests read in summer 1995.

Forest	Sample No.	Hydrologic 1 2 3 4 5	Vegetative 1 2 3 4 5 6 7	Erosion Dep. 1 2 3 4 5	EL	WD	FU	TR	RP	AM
Lassen	1	3 3 3 3 1	1 1 1 3 1 3 3	3 1 1 1 1	4	1	2	1	1	1
	2	3 3 1 3 3	1 1 1 1 1 1 3	1 2 3 3 3	3	2	2	1	1	1
	3	1 1 3 1 3	1 1 3 1 1 3 3	3 1 1 1 3	3	4	3	5	1	2
Plumas	4	3 3 1 3 1	1 1 1 3 1 1 3	1 1 1 1 1	3	3	2	2	2	1
	5	3 3 1 3 1	1 1 1 1 1 1 1	1 1 1 1 1	3	2	1	5	2	2
	6	3 3 1 3 1	1 1 1 3 3 3 3	3 1 1 1 1	3	4	2	2	1	2
	7	1 3 1 3 3	5 1 1 1 1 1 3	1 1 1 1 1	2	1	2	1	2	2
	8	1 3 1 3 1	1 1 1 1 1 1 3	1 1 1 1 1	3	3	1	5	2	1
Tahoe	9	1 3 3 3 1	1 1 3 3 1 3 3	3 1 3 3 3	2	4	3	5	2	1
	10	1 3 3 2 3	3 3 3 3 1 3 3	3 3 3 3 3	2	3	3	5	1	2
	11	1 1 3 3 3	1 1 2 1 1 3 3	3 1 3 1 3	2	3	2	3	1	2
	12	3 3 1 3 1	5 1 1 1 1 1 3	1 1 1 1 1	1	3	1	5	2	2
	13	1 3 1 2 1	3 1 1 1 1 1 3	1 1 1 1 1	4	2	2	2	2	1
	14	3 3 3 1 3	1 1 1 1 1 3 1	3 3 3 1 3	5	4	2	3	2	2
Eldoorado	15	1 3 1 3 1	5 1 1 1 1 1 3	1 1 1 1 1	5	1	1	5	1	2
	16	3 3 1 3 1	1 1 1 1 1 1 1	1 1 1 1 1	3	3	1	5	2	2
	17	1 3 1 3 1	1 1 1 1 1 1 3	1 1 1 1 1	4	3	2	1	2	1
Stanislaus	18	3 3 3 3 3	3 3 3 3 1 3 3	3 1 3 3 3	5	4	3	5	2	2
	19	3 3 3 3 3	1 1 1 3 1 3 1	3 1 3 1 3	2	4	2	3	2	2
Sierra	20	1 3 1 3 3	1 1 1 1 1 1 3	1 1 3 1 1	1	3	2	1	2	2
	21	1 3 1 3 1	1 1 1 1 1 1 1	1 1 1 1 1	2	3	1	5	2	2
	22	1 3 1 3 1	1 1 1 1 1 3 3	3 1 1 1 1	5	3	2	2	2	2
	23	1 3 1 3 1	3 1 1 1 1 1 1	1 1 1 1 1	5	3	1	5	2	2
Inyo	24	3 3 1 3 1	3 3 1 3 3 1 3	3 1 1 3 1	5	3	2	1	1	2

[1]See Table 9 for explanation of functionality ratings.

Appendix Table 1. Condition and trend transect bare soil (%), litter (%), non-native species (%), and plant species[1] composition (%) for 24 meadow transects on 7 National Forests read in 1995[2] and over the previous 5 decades. Transect sample numbers cross-reference Tables 10 and 11, and year and month for each transect reading are given.

Forest/Allotment Year-Month	Management and Transect Summary

Lassen

Butte Meadow   Sample no. 1

1995-8

Bare soil 1 Litter 4 Non-native species 30
Danthonia 17 Deschampsia 2   POPR 29
Carex 3 (CANE 3)   Juncus 13   (JUBA 13)
Trifolium 17
Cirsium 1
Grasses 48   Legumes 17   Sedges 3   Rushes 13   Forbs 31

1986-7

Bare soil 0 Litter 0 Non-native species 8
Danthonia 25 Deschampsia 3   Muhlenbergia 1   POPR 8
Carex 17 (CANE 7) Juncus 3 (JUBA 3)   Eleocharis 7
Trifolium 34
Grasses 37   Legumes 34   Sedges 24 Rushes 3   Forbs 36

1970-9

Bare soil 0 Litter 15 Non-native species 20
Danthonia 13 POPR 20
Carex 9 Juncus 28 (JUBA 26)
Trifolium 5
Grasses 33   Legumes 5   Sedges 9   Rushes 28   Forbs 15

1965-7

Bare soil 1 Litter 5 Non-native species 5
Danthonia 9 Deschampsia 2   Muhlenbergia 1   POPR 3
Carex 14 (CANE 1)   Juncus 38 (JUBA 30)
Eleocharis 2

Trifolium 5
Taraxacum 2
Grasses 15   Legumes 5   Sedges 17 Rushes 38   Forbs 22

1960-7

Bare soil 1 Litter 15 Non-native species 6
Danthonia 5 Deschampsia 5   Muhlenbergia 1   POPR 6
Carex 27 (CANE 4)   Juncus 21 (JUBA 21)
Eleocharis 4

Trifolium 1
Grasses 17   Legumes 1   Sedges 32 Rushes 21   Forbs 1

959

Appendix Table 1 (continued):

Soldier Meadow   Sample no. 2

        1995-8   Bare soil 0 Litter 0 Non-native species 12
Danthonia 10 Deschampsia 12 Phleum 4   Poa 14 (POPR 1)
  AGST 1 Carex 13 (CANE 11)   Juncus 14 (JUBA 14)
  Eleocharis 6
Trifolium 6
Taraxacum 3 Sisymbrium 3
Grasses 41   Legumes 6   Sedges 19 Rushes 14   Forbs 26

        1986-7   Bare soil 0 Litter 4 Non-native species 25
Danthonia 1 Deschampsia 2 Muhlenbergia 3 POPR 5
  AGST 2
Carex 25 (CANE 7) Juncus 17 (JUBA 17)
Eleocharis 7
Trifolium 3 (all non-native)
Taraxacum 15
Grasses 13   Legumes 3   Sedges 32 Rushes 17   Forbs 33

        1964-5   Bare soil 0 Litter 7 Non-native species 12
Danthonia 22 Deschampsia 2 Muhlenbergia 4 POPR 8
Agrostis 2
Carex 15 Juncus 4 (JUBA 3)
Trifolium 4
Taraxacum 4
Grasses 38   Legumes 4   Sedges 19 Rushes 4   Forbs 28

Feather River   Sample no. 3

        1995-9   Bare soil 0 Litter 9 Non-native species 15
Danthonia 2 Deschampsia 8 Hordeum 3 AGST 1 POPR 13
Carex 32 (CANE 32) Juncus 5 (JUBA 1)
Trifolium 5
Taraxacum 1
Salix 15
Grasses 27   Legumes 5   Sedges 32 Rushes 5   Forbs 26

        1969-7   Bare soil 0 Litter 12 Non-native species 3
Glyceria 5 POPR 3
Carex 37 Cyperus 5 Juncus 0
Salix 6
Grasses 8   Legumes 0   Sedges 42 Rushes 0   Forbs 34

Appendix Table 1 (continued):

        1967-8

Bare soil 1 Litter 12 Non-native species 8
Danthonia 1 Deschampsia 2 Hordeum 1 Agrostis 3
(AGST 1) POPR 6
Carex 33 Eleocharis 1
Trifolium 1
Taraxacum 1
Salix 21
Grasses 13   Legumes 1   Sedges 34 Rushes 0   Forbs 32

Plumas
 Mapes Canyon   Sample no. 4
        1993-9

Bare soil 0 Litter 2 Non-native species 2
Agrostis 8   Poa 6 (POPR 2)   Hordeum 6 Deschampsia 1
Agropyron 1
Carex 23 Juncus 18 (JUBA 16)
Trifolium 2
Grasses 22   Legumes 2   Sedges 23 Rushes 18   Forbs 35

        1975-7

Bare soil 1 Litter 16 Non-native species 6
POPR 5 Hordeum 3   Muhlenbergia 1
Carex 18 (CANE 11)   Juncus 16 (JUBA 16) Eleocharis 1
Trifolium 4
Grasses 9   Legumes 4   Sedges 19 Rushes 16   Forbs 16

        1963-6

Bare soil 7 Litter 3 Non-native species 4
Poa 14 (POPR 4) Hordeum 1 Muhlenbergia 1 Agrostis 6
Carex 11 (CANE 11) Juncus 22 (JUBA 22)
Trifolium 2
Grasses 22   Legumes 2   Sedges 11 Rushes 22   Forbs 23

 Grizzly Valley   Sample no. 5
        1995-6

Bare soil 4 Litter 1 Non-native species 8
Poa 13 (POPR 6)   BRTE 1
Carex 9 (CANE 8) Juncus 14
Trifolium 5
Taraxacum 1
Grasses 14   Legumes 5   Sedges 9   Rushes 14   Forbs 58

        1979-7

Bare soil 1 Litter 41 Non-native species 0
Poa 17
Carex 23 (CANE 23) Juncus 8 (JUBA 8)
Trifolium 1
Grasses 17   Legumes 1   Sedges 23 Rushes 8   Forbs 10

961

Appendix Table 1 (continued):

                1959-9   Bare soil 7 Litter 24 Non-native species 0
                                        Poa 38
                                        <u>Carex</u> 12 JUBA 18
                                        Grasses 38   Legumes 0   Sedges 12 Rushes 18   Forbs 0

Ridenour   Sample no. 6
                1995-8   Bare soil 0 Litter 4 Non-native species 14
                                        <u>Danthonia</u> 1 <u>Deschampsia</u> 7 <u>Muhlenbergia</u> 10 <u>Agrostis</u> 1
                                         <u>Hordeum</u> 5 POPR 14
                                        <u>Carex</u> 26 (CANE 26)   <u>Juncus</u> 10 (JUBA 0) <u>Eleocharis</u> 1
                                        <u>Trifolium</u> 6
                                        Grasses 38   Legumes 6   Sedges 27 Rushes 10   Forbs 15

                1970-7   Bare soil 4 Litter 30 Non-native species 0
                                        <u>Deschampsia</u> 16 <u>Muhlenbergia</u> 1 Poa 6
                                        <u>Carex</u> 35 (CANE 35)   <u>Juncus</u> 4 (JUBA 4)
                                        <u>Trifolium</u> 1
                                        Grasses 23   Legumes 1   Sedges 35 Rushes 4   Forbs 3

                1959-7   Bare soil 0 Litter 28 Non-native species 6
                                        <u>Deschampsia</u> 10 POPR 6 <u>Hordeum</u> 2
                                        <u>Carex</u> 32 (CANE 32)   <u>Juncus</u> 9 (JUBA 8)
                                        <u>Trifolium</u> 5
                                        Grasses 18   Legumes 5   Sedges 32 Rushes 9   Forbs 9

Jenkins   Sample no. 7
                1995-8   Bare soil 0 Litter 6 Non-native species 14
                                        Poa 30 (POPR 2) <u>Hordeum</u> 2 <u>Muhlenbergia</u> 2 AGST 12
                                         <u>Agropyron</u> 8
                                        <u>Carex</u> 20 (CANE 14)   <u>Juncus</u> 6 (JUBA 2)
                                        <u>Trifolium</u> 2
                                        Grasses 54   Legumes 2   Sedges 20 Rushes 6   Forbs 14

                1975-7   Bare soil 6 Litter 29 Non-native species 9
                                        Poa 9 (POPR 0) <u>Hordeum</u> 1 AGST 9 <u>Agropyron</u> 2
                                        <u>Carex</u> 11 (CANE 4)   <u>Juncus</u> 13 (JUBA 7)
                                        Grasses 21   Legumes 0   Sedges 11 Rushes 13   Forbs 17

                1957-7   Bare soil 5 Litter 38 Non-native species 0
                                        <u>Agrostis</u> 10 <u>Agropyron</u> 1 <u>Festuca</u> 15
                                        <u>Carex</u> 7 (CANE 3)   <u>Juncus</u> 9 (JUBA 9)
                                        Grasses 26   Legumes 0   Sedges 7 Rushes 9   Forbs 12

Appendix Table 1 (continued):

Doyle   Sample no. 8

       1995-8   Bare soil 0 Litter 6 Non-native species 22
                           Agrostis 24 (22 AGST) Poa 3
                           Carex 5 (CANE 1) Juncus 59 (JUBA 38) Luzula 2
                           Grasses 27   Legumes 0   Sedges 5   Rushes 61   Forbs 1

       1973-7   Bare soil 0 Litter 23 Non-native species 6
                           AGST 5 POPR 1
                           Carex 12 (CANE 4) Juncus 43 (JUBA 26)
                           Trifolium 0
                           Grasses 6   Legumes 0   Sedges 12 Rushes 43   Forbs 14

       1968-7   Bare soil 1 Litter 27 Non-native species 7
                           AGST 7
                           Carex 42 (CANE 42) Juncus 14 (JUBA 14)
                           Trifolium 1
                           Grasses 7   Legumes 1   Sedges 42 Rushes 14   Forbs 9

Tahoe
Lincoln   Sample no. 9

       1995-8   Bare soil 1 Litter 0 Non-native species 0
                           Hordeum 7 Muhlenbergia 3
                           Carex 21 (CANE 10) JUBA 3
                           Trifolium 35
                           Grasses 10   Legumes 35   Sedges 21 Rushes 3   Forbs 65

       1977-8   Bare soil 1 Litter 19 Non-native species 0
                           Deschampsia 22 Muhlenbergia 18
                           Carex 17 (CANE 11)
                           Trifolium 20
                           Grasses 40   Legumes 20   Sedges 17 Rushes 0   Forbs 23

       1958-10   Bare soil 2 Litter 10 Non-native species 0
                           Poa 18 Muhlenbergia 13
                           Carex 24 (CANE 0) JUBA 1
                           Trifolium 31
                           Grasses 31   Legumes 31   Sedges 24 Rushes 1   Forbs 31

Appendix Table 1 (continued):

Bear Valley   Sample no. 10
     1995-8   Bare soil 0 Litter 5 Non-native species 0
                                Agrostis 5 Poa 2 Muhlenbergia 1 Hordeum 1
                                Carex 47 (CANE 43) JUBA 6
                                Trifolium 1
                                Grasses 9   Legumes 1   Sedges 47 Rushes 6   Forbs 33

     1974-7   Bare soil 1 Litter 14 Non-native species 0
                                Poa 3 Muhlenbergia 5 Hordeum 3
                                Carex 29 (CANE 27) JUBA 7
                                Grasses 11   Legumes 0   Sedges 29 Rushes 7   Forbs 14

     1954-6   Bare soil 16 Litter 12 Non-native species 0
                                Poa 12 Sitanion 1
                                Carex 16 (CANE 16) JUBA 19 Eleocharis 1   Fimbristylis 8
                                Grasses 13   Legumes 0   Sedges 25 Rushes 19   Forbs 6

Perazzo   Sample no. 11
     1995-8   Bare soil 1 Litter 0 Non-native species 34
                                Poa 28 (POPR 27) Agrostis 1 Hordeum 1
                                Carex 1 (CANE 1) Eleocharis 5
                                Trifolium 23
                                Taraxacum 7
                                Grasses 30 Legumes 23   Sedges 6   Rushes 0   Forbs 62

     1976-9   Bare soil 5 Litter 14 Non-native species 40
                                POPR 35 AGST 5
                                Carex 5 (CANE 5) Juncus 31
                                Grasses 40 Legumes 0   Sedges 5   Rushes 31   Forbs 5

     1965-8   Bare soil 0 Litter 14 Non-native species 31
                                POPR 16 AGST 6 Deschampsia 2
                                Carex 29 (CANE 28) Juncus 1
                                Trifolium 11
                                Taraxacum 9
                                Grasses 24   Legumes 11   Sedges 29 Rushes 1   Forbs 32

Bickford   Sample no. 12
     1995-8   Bare soil 0 Litter 0 Non-native species 11
                                POPR 8 Deschampsia 14
                                Carex 36 (CANE 27) JUBA 1
                                Trifolium 24
                                Taraxacum 3
                                Grasses 22   Legumes 24   Sedges 36 Rushes 1   Forbs 41

Appendix Table 1 (continued):

        1977-8

Bare soil 0 Litter 16 Non-native species 5
POPR 5 <u>Deschampsia</u> 31 <u>Muhlenbergia</u> 4
<u>Carex</u> 29 (CANE 29)
Grasses 40 Legumes 0 Sedges 29 Rushes 0 Forbs 7

        1965-8

Bare soil 0 Litter 11 Non-native species 0
<u>Deschampsia</u> 35 <u>Muhlenbergia</u> 6 <u>Danthonia</u> 1
<u>Carex</u> 13 (CANE 13) <u>Eleocharis</u> 23
<u>Trifolium</u> 1
Grasses 42 Legumes 1 Sedges 36 Rushes 0 Forbs 9

Haypress   Sample no. 13

        1995-8

Bare soil 10 Litter 0 Non-native species 3
POPR 3 <u>Deschampsia</u> 12 <u>Hordeum</u> 17 <u>Agrostis</u> 1
<u>Carex</u> 10 (CANE 5) JUBA 1 <u>Eleocharis</u> 1 <u>Scirpus</u> 1
<u>Trifolium</u> 9
Veratrum 7
Grasses 33 Legumes 9 Sedges 12 Rushes 1 Forbs 44

        1972-9

Bare soil 5 Litter 14 Non-native species 6
POPR 6 <u>Deschampsia</u> 25 <u>Hordeum</u> 13 <u>Muhlenbergia</u> 13
<u>Carex</u> 2 (CANE 2) <u>Juncus</u> 10
<u>Trifolium</u> 10
Grasses 57 Legumes 10 Sedges 2 Rushes 10 Forbs 12

        1958-10

Bare soil 1 Litter 6 Non-native species 0
Poa 24 <u>Deschampsia</u> 23 <u>Hordeum</u> 5 <u>Muhlenbergia</u> 4
<u>Carex</u> 8 (CANE 6) <u>Juncus</u> 0
<u>Trifolium</u> 19
Grasses 56 Legumes 19 Sedges 8 Rushes 0 Forbs 27

Independence   Sample no. 14

        1995-8

Bare soil 0 Litter 0 Non-native species 3
POPR 2 <u>Deschampsia</u> 6
<u>Carex</u> 45 (CANE 32) JUBA 19 <u>Eleocharis</u> 1
<u>Trifolium</u> 13
<u>Taraxacum</u> 1
Grasses 8 Legumes 13 Sedges 46 Rushes 19 Forbs 27

Appendix Table 1 (continued):

            1979-8   Bare soil 0 Litter 5 Non-native species 1
                                       Deschampsia 12 Muhlenbergia 8
                                       Carex 26 (CANE 17) JUBA 14
                                       Trifolium 4
                                       Hypericum 1
                                       Grasses 20 Legumes 4   Sedges 26 Rushes 14 Forbs 14

            1964-9   Bare soil 1 Litter 3 Non-native species 0
                                         Deschampsia 26 Muhlenbergia 12
                                       Carex 9 (CANE 0) JUBA 11
                                       Trifolium 2
                                       Grasses 38 Legumes 2   Sedges 9 Rushes 11 Forbs 13

Eldorado
  Ltl. Roundtop   Sample no. 15
            1995-8   Bare soil 31 Litter 16 Non-native species 5
                                         Muhlenbergia 10   Hordeum 2   POPR 5
                                       Carex 0
                                       Trifolium 12
                                       Grasses 17 Legumes 12 Sedges 0 Rushes 0   Forbs 36

            1972-7   Bare soil 1 Litter 3 Non-native species 8
                                         Muhlenbergia 65   Hordeum 2   POPR 8
                                       Carex 4
                                       Trifolium 9
                                       Grasses 75 Legumes 9   Sedges 4 Rushes 0   Forbs 17

            1969-7   Bare soil 11 Litter 2 Non-native species 3
                                         Muhlenbergia 54   Poa 5 (POPR 3)
                                       Carex 1
                                       Trifolium 6
                                       Grasses 59 Legumes 6   Sedges 1 Rushes 0   Forbs 26

Silver Lake   Sample no. 16
            1995-8   Bare soil 44 Litter 1 Non-native species 0
                                       Grasses 0 Legumes 0   Sedges 0 Rushes 0   Forbs 55

            1972-7   Bare soil 10 Litter 9 Non-native species 0
                                       Deschampsia 5
                                       Juncus 47 Eleocharis 5
                                       Trifolium 10
                                       Grasses 5 Legumes 10 Sedges 5 Rushes 47 Forbs 24

Appendix Table 1 (continued):

1962-8   Bare soil 19 Litter 18 Non-native species 0
                  Muhlenbergia 2
                  Carex 14   Juncus 29
                  Trifolium 10
                  Grasses 2   Legumes 10   Sedges 14 Rushes 29   Forbs 13

Indian Valley   Sample no. 17
1995-8   Bare soil 12 Litter 24 Non-native species 0
                  Deschampsia 22   Muhlenbergia 6
                  Danthonia 5
                  Carex 3
                  Grasses 33   Legumes 0   Sedges 3   Rushes 0   Forbs 24

1967-8   Bare soil 0 Litter 0 Non-native species 0
                  Deschampsia 10   Muhlenbergia 3
                  Danthonia 41 Poa 17
                  Carex 11 Juncus 5
                  Trifolium 6
                  Grasses 71   Legumes 6   Sedges 11 Rushes 5   Forbs 12

1955-10   Bare soil 19 Litter 15 Non-native species 0
                  Deschampsia 1 Danthonia 4 Poa 27
                  CANE 13
                  Trifolium 1
                  Grasses 32   Legumes 1   Sedges 22 Rushes 0   Forbs 7

Stanislaus
Mattley 2   Sample no. 18
1995-8   Bare soil 7 Litter 5 Non-native species 8
                  POPR 5 AGST 3 Danthonia 7
                  Carex 16 Juncus 7 Eleocharis 2
                  Trifolium 2
                  Veratrum 1
                  Grasses 15   Legumes 2   Sedges 18 Rushes 7   Forbs 26

1975-8   Bare soil 2 Litter 9 Non-native species 1
                  AGST 1 Muhlenbergia 1
                  Carex 42 Juncus 12 Scirpus 5
                  Trifolium 2
                  Veratrum 3
                  Grasses 2   Legumes 2   Sedges 47 Rushes 12   Forbs 28

Appendix Table 1 (continued):

                    1958-8   Bare soil 2 Litter 12 Non-native species 10
                                              POPR 3 Muhlenbergia 9
                                              Carex 50 Juncus 0
                                              Trifolium 2
                                              Taraxacum 1 Hypericum 6
                                              Grasses 12 Legumes 2   Sedges 50 Rushes 0   Forbs 19

Mattley 3   Sample no. 19
                    1995-8   Bare soil 0 Litter 5 Non-native species 11
                                              Carex 24 Juncus 0 Eleocharis 12 Scirpus 7
                                              Trifolium 2
                                              Hypericum 11
                                              Grasses 0   Legumes 2   Sedges 43 Rushes 0   Forbs 51

                    1977-6   Bare soil 0 Litter 10 Non-native species 3
                                              Muhlenbergia 11 Danthonia 1
                                              Carex 58 Juncus 0 Eleocharis 8 Scirpus 2
                                              Hypericum 3
                                              Grasses 12 Legumes 0   Sedges 68 Rushes 0   Forbs 9

                    1967-8   Bare soil 0 Litter 0 Non-native species 0
                                              Muhlenbergia 1
                                              Carex 73 Juncus 0 Eleocharis 24
                                              Grasses 1   Legumes 0   Sedges 97 Rushes 0   Forbs 2

Sierra
 Chiquito   Sample no. 20
                    1995-9   Bare soil 1 Litter 3 Non-native species 12
                                              HOLA 9
                                              Carex 6 Juncus 21 (JUBA 1) Eleocharis 23
                                              Trifolium 16
                                              Cirsium 1 Hypericum 2
                                              Grasses 9   Legumes 16   Sedges 29 Rushes 21   Forbs 36

                    1971-8   Bare soil 4 Litter 6 Non-native species 13
                                              Danthonia 6 Muhlenbergia 29
                                              Carex 21 (CANE 10) Juncus 5 (JUBA 0) Eleocharis 5
                                              Trifolium 5
                                              Hypericum 13 Veratrum 1
                                              Grasses 35 Legumes 5   Sedges 26 Rushes 5   Forbs 22

Appendix Table 1 (continued):

1959-8   Bare soil 3 Litter 8 Non-native species 10
                      POPR 10 Danthonia 5
                      Carex 13 (CANE 6) Juncus 0 Eleocharis 45
                      Trifolium 3
                      Grasses 15   Legumes 3   Sedges 58 Rushes 0   Forbs 16

Mt. Tom 1   Sample no. 21
1995-9   Bare soil 1 Litter 7 Non-native species 1
                      POPR 1
                      Carex 28 Juncus 14 Eleocharis 5 Scirpus 4
                      Trifolium 2
                      Grasses 1   Legumes 2   Sedges 37 Rushes 14   Forbs 31

1975-8   Bare soil 0 Litter 0 Non-native species 6
                      POPR 2 Muhlenbergia 12 Agrostis 6 Danthonia 1
                      Carex 21 Juncus 21 Eleocharis 6
                      Hypericum 4
                      Grasses 21   Legumes 0   Sedges 27 Rushes 21   Forbs 16

1960-8   Bare soil 4 Litter 5 Non-native species 1
                      POPR 1 Muhlenbergia 25 Danthonia 1
                      Carex 36 (CANE 1) Juncus 3 (JUBA 3) Eleocharis 4
                      Grasses 27   Legumes 0   Sedges 40 Rushes 3   Forbs 11

Mt. Tom 2   Sample no. 22
1995-9   Bare soil 0 Litter 12 Non-native species 0
                      Muhlenbergia 2 Poa 1
                      Carex 47 (CANE 1) Juncus 1 Eleocharis 20
                      Grasses 3   Legumes 0   Sedges 67 Rushes 1   Forbs 5

1975-8   Bare soil 1 Litter 20 Non-native species 0
                      Muhlenbergia 3
                      Carex 27 Juncus 19 Eleocharis 26
                      Grasses 3   Legumes 0   Sedges 53 Rushes 19   Forbs 4

1960-8   Bare soil 3 Litter 14 Non-native species 5
                      Muhlenbergia 4 AGST 3
                      Carex 22 (CANE 3) Juncus 2 Eleocharis 37
                      Hypericum 2
                      Grasses 7   Legumes 0   Sedges 59 Rushes 2   Forbs 10

Appendix Table 1 (continued):

Mt. Tom 3   Sample no. 23

         1995-9   Bare soil 0 Litter 4 Non-native species 1
                         Muhlenbergia 8 Agrostis 4
                         Carex 26 (CANE 17) Juncus 0 Eleocharis 29
                         Hypericum 1
                         Grasses 12 Legumes 0   Sedges 55 Rushes 0 Forbs 17

         1975-8   Bare soil 2 Litter 0 Non-native species 1
                         Muhlenbergia 4
                         Carex 11 (CANE 5) Juncus 4 Eleocharis 65
                         Hypericum 1
                         Grasses 4   Legumes 0   Sedges 76 Rushes 4 Forbs 12

         1960-8   Bare soil 0 Litter 2 Non-native species 5
                         Muhlenbergia 10 AGST 5
                         Carex 1 (CANE 0) Juncus 1 Eleocharis 59
                         Grasses 15 Legumes 0   Sedges 60 Rushes 1 Forbs 21

Inyo
Monache   Sample no. 24

         1991-7   Bare soil 14 Litter 51 Non-native species 0
                         Muhlenbergia 18
                         Carex 7   Juncus 4
                         Trifolium 1
                         Artemisia 2
                         Grasses 18 Legumes 1   Sedges 7 Rushes 4   Forbs 6

         1980-8   Bare soil 10 Litter 7 Non-native species 0
                       Muhlenbergia 4
                         Carex 56 (CANE 25)   Juncus 1
                         Trifolium 10
                         Grasses 4   Legumes 10 Sedges 56 Rushes 1 Forbs 22

         1963-7   Bare soil 0 Litter 16 Non-native species 3
                       POPR 3 Muhlenbergia 16 Hordeum 1
                       Carex 25 Juncus 5 (JUBA 4)
                       Trifolium 10
                       Grasses 4   Legumes 10 Sedges 56 Rushes 1   Forbs 34

[1]Species codes are POPR (Poa pratensis), AGST (Agrostis stolonifera), HOLA (Holcus lanatus), CANE (Carex nebrascensis), JUBA (Juncus balticus), and BRTE (Bromus tectorum). Plant abundances in parentheses are included in the previous genus abundances.

[2]In a few cases transects had been read recently so were not re-read in 1995.

Appendix Table 2. Canonical correspondence analysis results from CANOCO program computer output. Environmental variable[1] names are described in Table 9.

Program CANOCO Version 3.12 April 1991 - written by Cajo J.F. Ter Braak
Copyright (c) 1988-1991 Agricultural Mathematics Group DLO
Box 100, 6700 AC Wageningen, the Netherlands.
For explanation of the input/output see the manual or
Ter Braak, C.J.F. (1987) Ordination. Chapter 5 in:
Data Analysis in Community and Landscape Ecology
(Jongman, R.H.G., Ter Braak, C.J.F. and Van Tongeren, O.F.R., Eds), Pudoc,
Wageningen.

No samples omitted	0
Number of samples	24
Number of species	99
Number of occurrences	326
No interaction terms defined	
No transformation of species data	
No species-weights specified	
No sample-weights specified	
No downweighting of rare species	
No. of active samples:	24
No. of passive samples:	0
No. of active species:	99

Weighted correlation matrix:

	SP-AX1	SP-AX2	SP-AX3	SP-AX4	EV-AX1	EV-AX2	EV-AX3	EV-AX4
SP-AX1	1.0000							
SP-AX2	-.0075	1.0000						
SP-AX3	-.0226	.0088	1.0000					
SP-AX4	.0057	.0011	-.0030	1.0000				
EV-AX1	.9902	.0000	.0000	.0000	1.0000			
EV-AX2	.0000	.9875	.0000	.0000	.0000	1.0000		
EV-AX3	.0000	.0000	.9832	.0000	.0000	.0000	1.0000	
EV-AX4	.0000	.0000	.0000	.9826	.0000	.0000	.0000	1.0000
HYD1	.1565	.0446	-.2145	-.2629	.1580	.0452	-.2182	-.2676
HYD3	-.1534	-.1497	-.0225	.2485	-.1549	-.1516	-.0229	.2529
HYD5	-.2509	-.1864	-.2492	.3595	-.2533	-.1888	-.2534	.3658
VEG1	.5044	.0197	-.1758	.0598	.5094	.0200	-.1788	.0608
VEG3	-.2143	-.0938	.0779	.1686	-.2164	-.0950	.0792	.1716
VEG4	-.2941	.0269	.0266	-.1068	-.2970	.0272	.0270	-.1087
VEG6	-.1891	-.0552	-.0157	.2257	-.1910	-.0559	-.0160	.2297
VEG7	-.0506	-.3163	-.1051	-.0149	-.0511	-.3203	-.1069	-.0152
ED1	-.1841	.0541	.0011	.2041	-.1859	.0548	.0011	.2078

971

ED3	-.1932	-.1020	-.1836	.5077	-.1951	-.1033	-.1867	.5167
ED4	-.1564	.1448	.1074	.0884	-.1579	.1467	.1092	.0899
ED5	-.1594	-.1435	-.0563	.3397	-.1610	-.1454	-.0573	.3457
EL	.2547	.6718	.3839	-.0012	.2572	.6803	.3905	-.0012
WD	-.0157	.0626	.1431	.2089	-.0158	.0634	.1455	.2126
FU	-.2859	.0071	-.0827	.0419	-.2887	.0071	-.0841	.0426
TR	.2068	-.1240	.3535	.1045	.2089	-.1255	.3595	.1063
RP	.3269	-.0520	.0333	.2655	.3302	-.0526	.0339	.2702

Summary:

Axes	1	2	3	4	Total
Eigenvalues	.720	.590	.537	.506	7.332
Species-environment correlations	.990	.988	.983	.983	
Cumulative percentage variance					
of species data	9.8	17.9	25.2	32.1	
of species-environment relation:	12.9	23.4	33.0	42.1	

Sum of all unconstrained eigenvalues	7.332
Sum of all canonical eigenvalues	5.591

No transformation
Biplot scores of environmental variables:

N	NAME	AX1	AX2	AX3	AX4
	R(SPEC,ENV)	.9902	.9875	.9832	.9826
1	HYD1	.1580	.0452	-.2182	-.2676
3	HYD3	-.1549	-.1516	-.0229	.2529
5	HYD5	-.2533	-.1888	-.2534	.3658
6	VEG1	.5094	.0200	-.1788	.0608
8	VEG3	-.2164	-.0950	.0792	.1716
9	VEG4	-.2970	.0272	.0270	-.1087
11	VEG6	-.1910	-.0559	-.0160	.2297
12	VEG7	-.0511	-.3203	-.1069	-.0152
13	ED1	-.1859	.0548	.0011	.2078
15	ED3	-.1951	-.1033	-.1867	.5167
16	ED4	-.1579	.1467	.1092	.0899
17	ED5	-.1610	-.1453	-.0573	.3457
18	EL	.2572	.6803	.3904	-.0012
19	WD	-.0158	.0634	.1455	.2126
20	FU	-.2887	.0071	-.0841	.0426
21	TR	.2089	-.1255	.3595	.1063
22	RP	.3302	-.0526	.0339	.2702

[1] Environmental variables eliminated from analysis were HYD2, HYD4, VEG2, VEG5, ED2 and AM.

WILLIAM C. STEWART
Pacific Institute for Studies in Development,
  Environment, and Security
Oakland, California

23

Economic Assessment of the Ecosystem

Sierra Nevada Ecosystem Project: Final report to Congress, vol. III, *Assessments, Commissioned Reports, and Background Information*. Davis: University of California, Centers for Water and Wildland Resources, 1996.

ABSTRACT

The Sierra Nevada region has supported a wide range of economic activities for more than 150 years. Timber harvesting, grazing, irrigated agriculture, and mineral extraction have occurred continuously since the Gold Rush of 1849. And even more significant from an economic viewpoint than these, is the extensive development of the streams and rivers of the Sierra Nevada—for hydropower, large irrigation project, and municipal water uses. Every human activity in the Sierra Nevada entails some degree of environmental alteration in the course of utilizing resources for individuals and business enterprises. The following economic assessment uses two complementary approaches to assess the human utilization of the Sierra Nevada ecosystem. The first assesses the status of the regional economy based on employment and business enterprises. The second assesses the major resource-based sectors that directly impact the ecosystem.

The distribution of Sierran jobs (between commodity-producing jobs and service-producing jobs) is the same now as it was in 1970. Diversification has occurred within each sector, the number of jobs has more than doubled, but the relative proportion of commodity and service jobs stayed constant. Recreation, timber, and agriculture are the three largest types of employment sectors directly dependent on the ecosystem. From the perspective of gross revenues generated from natural resources, water is the most valuable commodity, followed by timber, livestock, and other agricultural products. Based on estimates of direct resource values as one input (not the total revenue produced by resource dependent activities), the Sierra Nevada ecosystem produces approximately $2.2 billion worth of commodities and services annually. Water accounts for more than 60% of that total value. Other commodities account for 20% as do services.

Public timber and private recreation are the largest net contributors of funds to county governments both in total dollars and as a percentage of their total value. Around 2% of all resource values are presently captured and reinvested into the ecosystem or local communities through taxation or revenue sharing arrangements. The declining status of some aspects of the Sierra Nevada ecosystem suggests that this level of reinvestment is insufficient to ensure sustainable utilization of the ecosystem.

The patterns of employment, commodity production, and services directly dependent on the Sierra Nevada ecosystem vary greatly across the range. Regions defined either by economic linkages or major vegetative types exhibit unique economic-ecosystem linkages. These variations complicate the application of many range-wide strategies but also create the basis for future opportunities involving the many stakeholders. The flow of economic values from the Sierra Nevada provides an empirical basis for assessing how different levels of government; producers and consumers; and employers and employees could be involved in new approaches.

Keywords (Economic Development; Federal lands; Forests and forestlands; Hydropower; Labor; Recreation; Resource Economics; Water Runoff; Wood and wood products)

CHAPTER 1: INTRODUCTION TO THE ECONOMIC ASSESSMENT

The Sierra Nevada region has supported a wide range of economic activities for more than 150 years. Timber harvesting, grazing, irrigated agriculture, and mineral extraction have occurred continuously since the Gold Rush of 1849. And even more significant from an economic viewpoint than these, is the extensive development of the streams and rivers of the Sierra Nevada—for hydropower, large irrigation projects, and municipal water uses. The Sierra Nevada also supports an enormous amount of recreational activities ranging from developed recreational sites such as downhill ski resorts to millions of acres of wilderness. Over the past twenty five years, a considerable portion of the private land in the region has been converted from forests and ranches into residential areas for the roughly 300,000 people who have moved into the Sierra Nevada.

Every human activity in the Sierra Nevada entails some degree of environmental alteration in the course of utilizing resources for individuals and business enterprises. Many aspects of the ecosystem have exhibited considerable resiliency and recovery throughout the century and a half of widespread and often intensive resource use. Other aspects, however, have exhibited significant decline with minimal recovery. The goal of this assessment is to provide a common framework for assessing the major economic benefits and costs of existing uses of the Sierra Nevada. This allows for a more informed basis upon which future policies can be made.

The following economic assessment uses two complementary approaches to assess the human utilization of the Sierra Nevada ecosystem. The first assesses the status of the regional economy based on employment and business enterprises. The second assesses the major resource-based sectors that directly impacts the ecosystem.

The regional economic analysis (Chapter 2) is based on Census, employment, and business activity data sources collected at federal and state levels. The data are typically disaggregated to county and sometimes sub-county levels. Chapters 3 , 4 and 5 are devoted to assessing the major commodities and services directly based on the Sierra Nevada ecosystem. The major commodities are water, timber, forage, and other irrigated agriculture. In addition, estimates of the economic value of the ecosystem to the recreation industry and to local residences are presented. These two sectors are dealt with in greater detail elsewhere in the SNEP report (Duane 1996-a and 1996-b), but their inclusion here allows for direct comparison to the resource-based economic sectors. Many of the financial implications of resource use show up at the county level through a range of taxation and revenue sharing arrangements. These effects are the subject of Chapter 6. The concluding chapter provides an overview of the economic and financial trends of the various resource sectors.

Wherever possible we have tried to differentiate the direct value of an individual resource from the larger industry in which it is used. Timber stumpage values, forage values and the estimated value of the right to divert water are all lower than the final value of the wood products, livestock and agricultural crops to which they contribute. For recreational and residential-open space services, a 'rent' to the ecosystem of ten percent of total revenue was used.

For some resources such as timber stumpage, the value of the right to harvest specific commodities is set through open market bidding and accurately monitored for tax collection purposes. For resources such as private forage that are often used inside of integrated operations or bundled with other values, the value is based on the available rental rates or government estimates of value. The value of water rights are the most difficult to value because so few water rights are sold separately in California. Estimates are based on prices paid for alternative supplies such as pumped ground water for agriculture and municipal uses, and other sources of wholesale electricity for hydroelectric production. The value of non-consumptive uses accruing to recreationists, tourists, and new residents are always bundled with other benefits and have few direct market equivalencies. The lack of Sierra Nevada-specific willingness to pay (WTP) or contingent valuation methodology (CVM) studies required us to estimate the values of these non-market uses as a fraction of total revenues, wages or taxes. No attempt was made to place a monetary value on the preservation and protection of ecosystems, species or any other aspect of biodiversity.

Resource Ownership and Management in the Sierra Nevada

The land base of the SNEP region is roughly two thirds federal and one third private. The total asset value of the Sierra Nevada is considerably less biased towards federal control than land ownership would suggest. For one, water rights are primarily controlled by private interests and all ownerships (including federal) are governed by state water law. Additionally, most improvements to residential, commercial, and agricultural lands are privately financed.

In addition to different rationales for setting prices and fees for different resources, the state and federal government take very different approaches to achieve similar goals. The state of California owns very little land within the Sierra Nevada. In most cases the state uses a regulatory framework while the federal government uses a planning framework to implement essentially comparable sets of laws developed to address social concerns and ensure long term ecological health of ecosystems. The two approaches have very different costs and levels of assurance that the overall goals will be met. In most cases the impact of state and federal approaches overlap because ecosystems rarely follow jurisdictional boundaries.

Aggregate analysis for the 20 million acre study area, or even the one to five million acre regions masks variations in local asset values of the Sierra Nevada. In many cases, 50% of a single resource value occurs on 10% or less of the total area. Broad scale resource based policies may be too strong in many areas but too weak in the most important 10% of the cases. Aggregate economic analysis can mask many of the public/private, state/federal, and regional/local variations that occur in a region the size of the Sierra Nevada. Regional assessments based on county groupings or ecological regions are presented where possible to allow for region-specific analyses of conditions and trends.

CHAPTER 2: REGIONAL ECONOMY OF THE SIERRA NEVADA

The following analysis of the regional economy of the Sierra Nevada and the diverse character of regions is based primarily on analyses of personal income, employment, and the types of firms operating within the Sierra Nevada. Long term trends are addressed through economic data aggregated at the county level. More detailed analyses of regions are based on community-level aggregations developed from economic data in the 1990 Census.

Many counties in the Sierra Nevada stretch from the Central Valley to the Sierra crest. Population in most counties is concentrated along the western foothills and in a few towns on the east side of the Sierra Nevada crest. National Forest and National Parks dominate land ownership in all parts of the Sierra Nevada except the western foothill region. Large cities such as Sacramento, Reno, and Fresno provide employment opportunities for Sierra Nevada residents willing to commute out of the region. The population of the Sierra Nevada has been grouped into 180 community aggregations for the SNEP assessment (Doak and Kusel 1996). These aggregations closely conform to the 160 unique ZIP codes used by the US Postal Service. Relatively long work commutes throughout the Sierra Nevada (average travel time ranges between 20 and 29 minutes most regions) and relatively high rates of residential mobility (more than one third of residents in 1990 have arrived in their county within the last five years) suggest that the many residents look beyond their local community for employment. The 180 community groupings are then combined in two complementary types of regions. The first is based on county boundaries, transportation networks and major urban centers. The second is based on three major vegetation zones—woodlands (foothill), conifer forests (Western Sierra Nevada), and the drier east side forests and shrublands (Eastern Sierra Nevada). Regional groupings of communities provide a more realistic view of the range of economic opportunities than individual community analyses. The major geographic attributes and the regional groupings are illustrated in the three maps below.

Total personal income rather than money income is used to address the growth non-wage income sources that now constitute more than half of all of personal income in the Sierra Nevada. The money income data reported by the Census significantly undercounts non-wage income as calculated by the Bureau of Economic Analysis (CCSCE 1996). In this analysis, the undercounting is corrected by allocating non-wage income to community level aggregations based on a linear transformation of the Census data. Most of the differences involves how non-interest based financial income and government-supplied health care are addressed. The Census methodology excludes these types of personal income such as Medicare because they do not involve direct cash payments. The Bureau of Economic Analysis reports personal income at a greater levels of aggregation and uses actual financial records and the full costs of government programs to calculate total personal income. The use of county level relationships on community aggregations may create errors for communities with very low and very high incomes. Employment data from the Census is used along with monthly employment data aggregated at the county level. Census employment data will overestimate the relative importance of part-time and seasonal employment because no correction is made for the number of hours per week or months per year the person is employed.

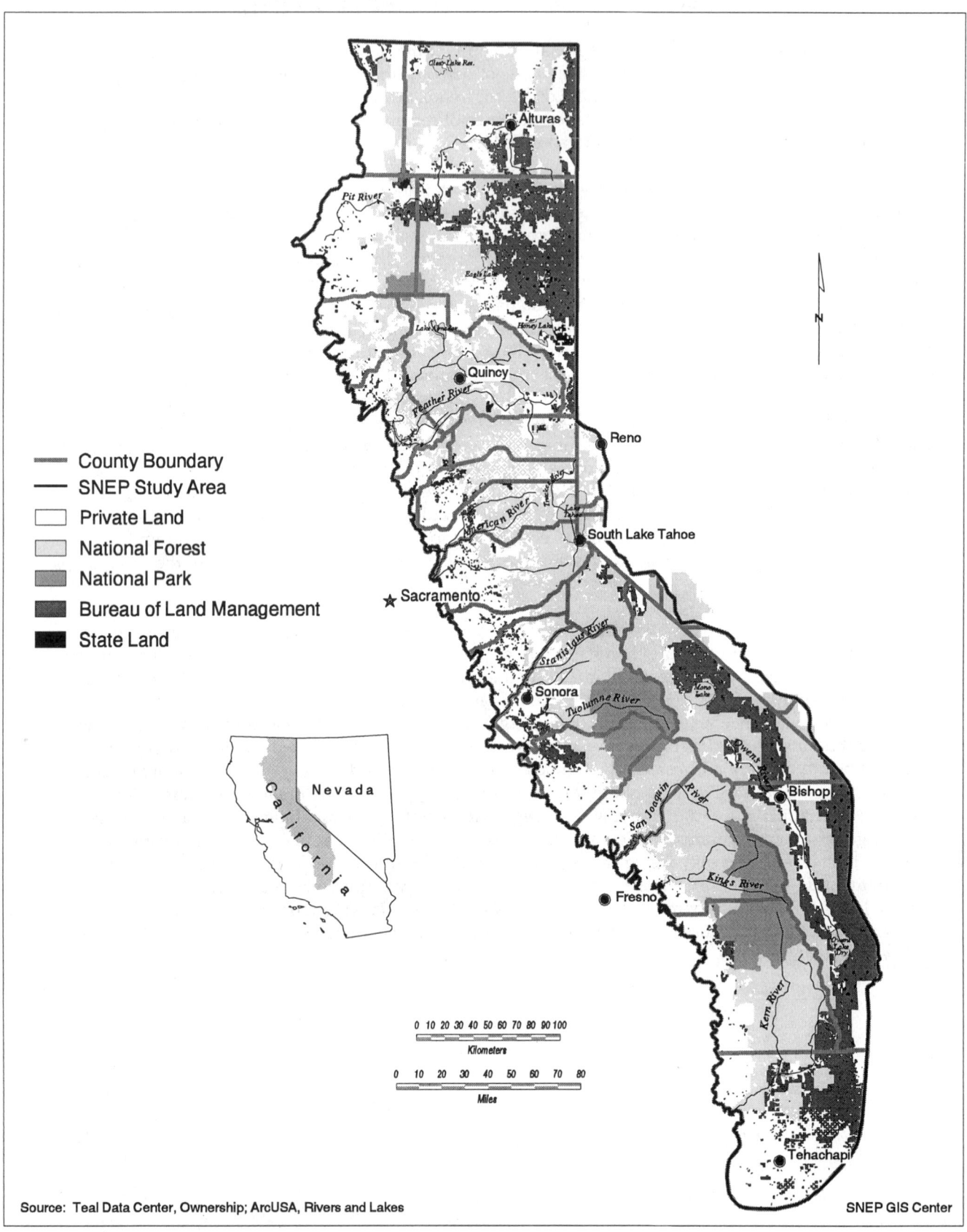

Legend:
- County Boundary
- SNEP Study Area
- Private Land
- National Forest
- National Park
- Bureau of Land Management
- State Land

Source: Teal Data Center, Ownership; ArcUSA, Rivers and Lakes

SNEP GIS Center

Figure 2.1

978

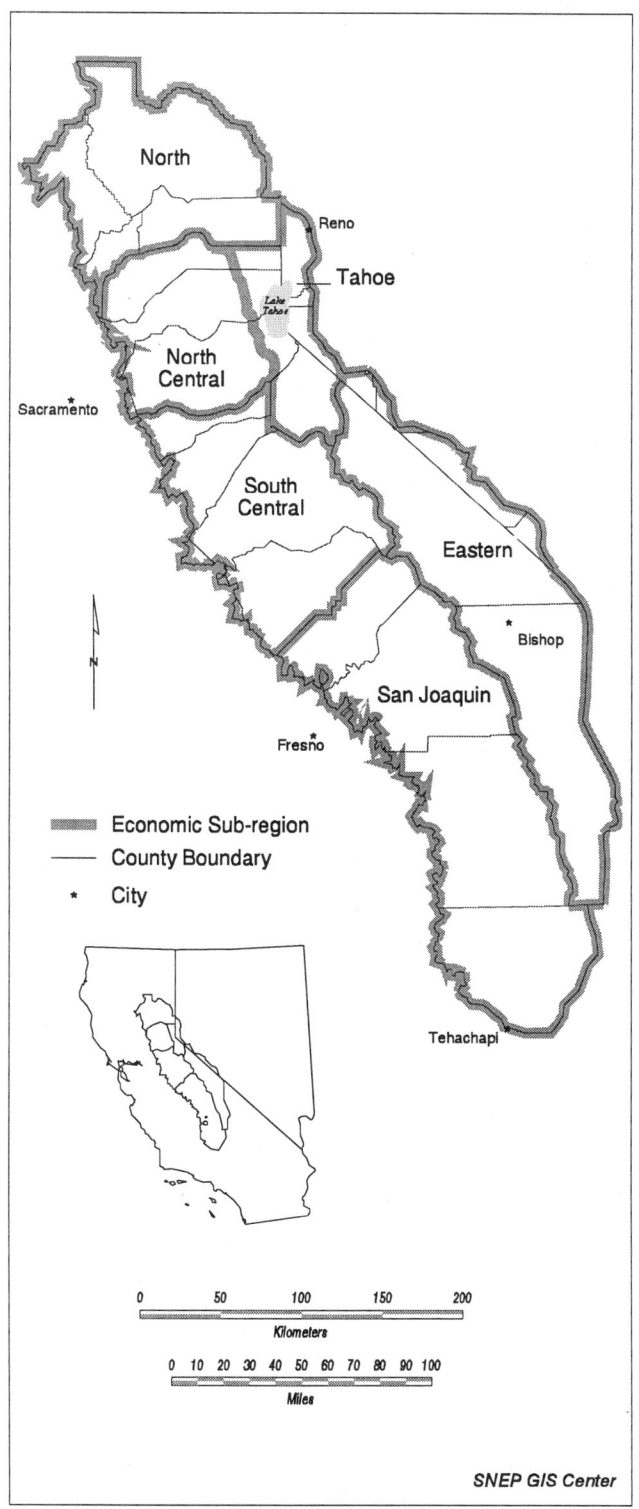

North

Reno

Tahoe

Lake
Tahoe

North
Central

Sacramento

South
Central

Eastern

Bishop

San Joaquin

Fresno

Economic Sub-region
County Boundary
City

N

Tehachapi

| 0 | 50 | 100 | 150 | 200 |
Kilometers

0 10 20 30 40 50 60 70 80 90 100
Miles

SNEP GIS Center

Figure 2.2

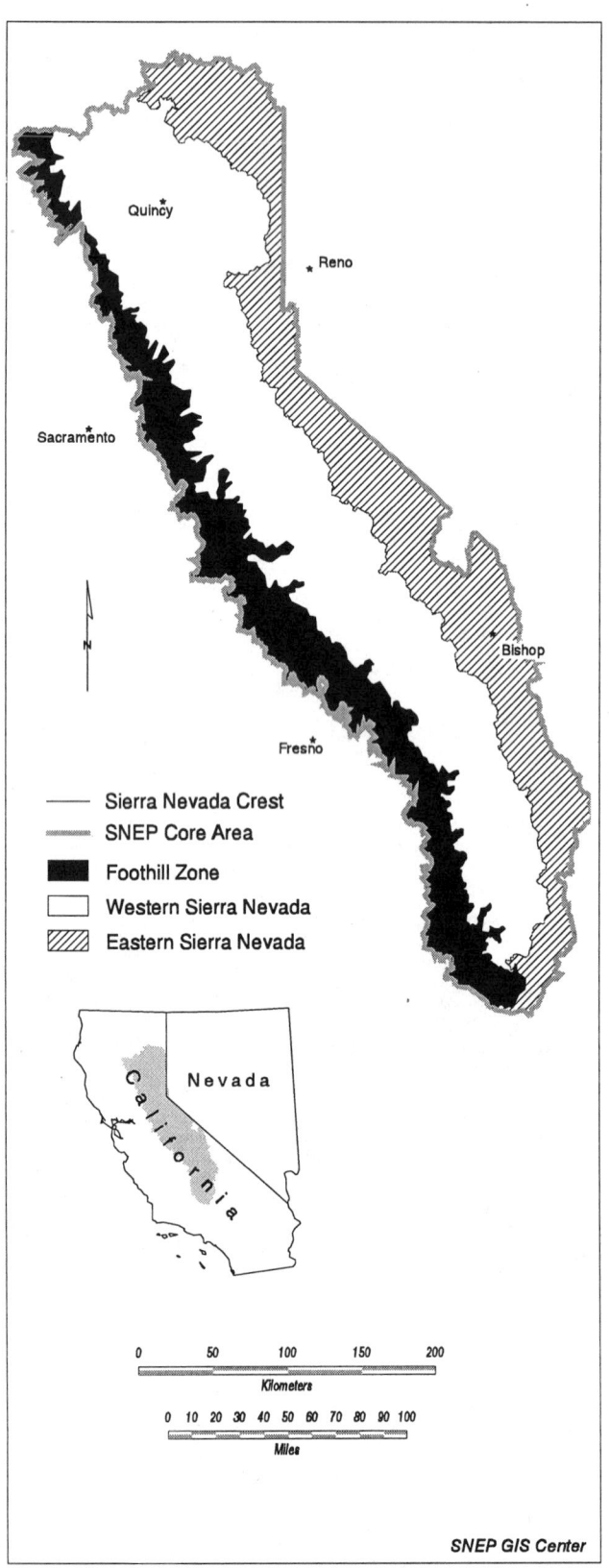

Quincy

Reno

Sacramento

Bishop

Fresno

— Sierra Nevada Crest
— SNEP Core Area
■ Foothill Zone
□ Western Sierra Nevada
▨ Eastern Sierra Nevada

N

California

Nevada

| 0 | 50 | 100 | 150 | 200 |
Kilometers

0 10 20 30 40 50 60 70 80 90 100
Miles

SNEP GIS Center

Figure 2.3

Employment Patterns in Regions of the Sierra Nevada

The size and diversity of the Sierra Nevada requires regional analyses to complement Sierra-wide analysis. Six economic regions and three vegetative regions are when Census data are available. When county level data are used, the regional analysis must follow slightly different boundaries. The following table summarizes which counties are in economic regions.

Table 2.1: Counties and Economic Regions for Census-Based Analyses

Economic Region	Counties Fully Within Region	Counties Mainly Within Region	Counties Partly Within Region
North	Plumas, Sierra		Lassen, Butte, Yuba
North Central	Nevada, El Dorado	Placer	
Greater Tahoe	Alpine		Nevada, Placer, El Dorado, Douglas, Washoe
South Central	Amador, Calaveras, Tuolumne, Mariposa		
San Joaquin			Madera, Fresno, Tulare, Kern
East Side	Mono	Inyo	

The Greater Tahoe region is used when the community level data from the 1990 Census is available. Greater Tahoe includes portions of counties in the Tahoe Basin and Truckee River watershed, the Lake Tahoe shoreline communities in Nevada, and sparsely populated Alpine county. This region is separated because of the overwhelming influence of recreation and tourism and its difference from the western portions of the counties. When only county level data is available, the Nevada, Placer, and El Dorado county portions of the Greater Tahoe region are included in the North Central group. The South Central region includes Amador, Calaveras, Tuolumne and Mariposa counties. The San Joaquin region includes the Sierra Nevada portion of four populous counties—Madera, Fresno, Tulare, and Kern—that all have county seats in the San Joaquin Valley. These four counties are excluded when county level data analysis is conducted because 95% of the total population of these counties live in the San Joaquin Valley. All of Mono county and the Owens Valley portion of Inyo county make up the Eastern region. Alpine county is included in the East Side when only county level data is available.

In addition to the county based analysis, another analysis was conducted by grouping communities into three major vegetative regions. This allows for a more detailed analysis of the link between the ecosystems and economic condition. The foothill region includes communities from the Central Valley up to the start of the mixed conifer forests around the 3,000 foot elevation. The forest region includes all the communities within the mixed conifer and higher altitude forests on the west side of the Sierra Nevada. The thinly populated east side of the Plumas county is also included in the forest region. This is the largest region in size but has few residents because most of the land is federally owned. Finally, the Greater Tahoe region is combined with the East Side to form the Eastern vegetative region.

The following table summarizes the population distribution among the different regions based on the community aggregations. In every western region, most people live in the foothill rather than the forest region. This is even true in the North economic region because where the population in communities in the foothill portions of Yuba and Butte county outnumber the total population of the much larger Plumas and Sierra counties. This decreases the relative importance of forest related ecosystem employment and revenue compared to the larger economy of the Sacramento and San Joaquin Valleys.

Table 2.2: Population of Total SNEP Area by Economic and Vegetative Regions

Region	Foothill	Forest	Eastern	Total	Pct of Total
North	84,000	44,000		128,000	20%
North Central	193,000	29,000		222,000	34%
South Central	98,000	30,000		128,000	20%
San Joaquin	68,000	9,000		77,000	12%
Greater Lake Tahoe			63,000	63,000	10%
East			28,000	28,000	4%
Total	443,000	112,000	91,000	646,000	
Pct. of Total	69%	17%	14%		

In many cases, data are only available on a county basis. In these circumstances, the regions include only the twelve counties where all or nearly all the population lives in the geographically defined Sierra Nevada region. Portions of Lassen, Butte, Yuba, Madera, Fresno, Tulare, and Kern counties in California; and Washoe and Douglas counties in Nevada are left out because more than 90% of the population lives outside of the SNEP region. The total population and counties within each county-based region are shown in Table 2.3.

Table 2.3: Population and Counties within County-Based Regions

County-based Region	1990 Population	Counties
North	23,300	Plumas, Sierra
North Central	383,400	Nevada, Placer, El Dorado
South Central	126,600	Amador, Calaveras, Tuolumne, Mariposa
East	29,700	Alpine, Mono, Inyo
Total	563,000	

Trends in Personal Income

Personal income levels across the Sierra Nevada have been far below state levels for decades. Over the past fifteen years personal incomes in the Sierra Nevada have followed two different patterns. Per capita income in the North Central region have rapidly approached the state levels while all other regions have remained at 80% of state levels. Placer county is now the only inland county in the state where personal income levels are above state levels (CCSCE 1996).

Table 2.4: Per Capita Incomes in Constant 1995 Dollars

Region	1980	1990	1995
California	$21,524	$23,675	$23,058
North	$17,166	$18,629	$18,767
North Central	$19,374	$22,932	$22,675
South Central	$16,870	$18,035	$17,751
East	$18,773	$19,978	$19,886

Source: CCSCE (1996); 1980 and 1990 are from Bureau of Economic Analysis; 1995 is CCSCE projection from 1993 data.

The composition of personal income in all counties has shifted away from local wage income because of relatively faster growth of commute wages, interest and dividends, and government transfer payments. The overall share of total personal income from local wages dropped from 67% in 1972 to 49% in 1992. A significant implication of this trend is that the local economic conditions are now less related to local economic conditions and more related to national and state economic conditions than they were twenty years ago. This shift has provided economic stability to the region where local employment sectors such as seasonal recreation and commodity production are highly variable. The major difference at a regional level is the importance of commute-based wages in the North Central region compared to the rest of the Sierra Nevada. In the early 1990s, commute-based wages constitute more than 30% of all wages in the North Central counties but less than 5% of all wages elsewhere in the Sierra Nevada.

Figure 2.4: Composition of Personal Income in the Sierra Nevada 1972 and 1992

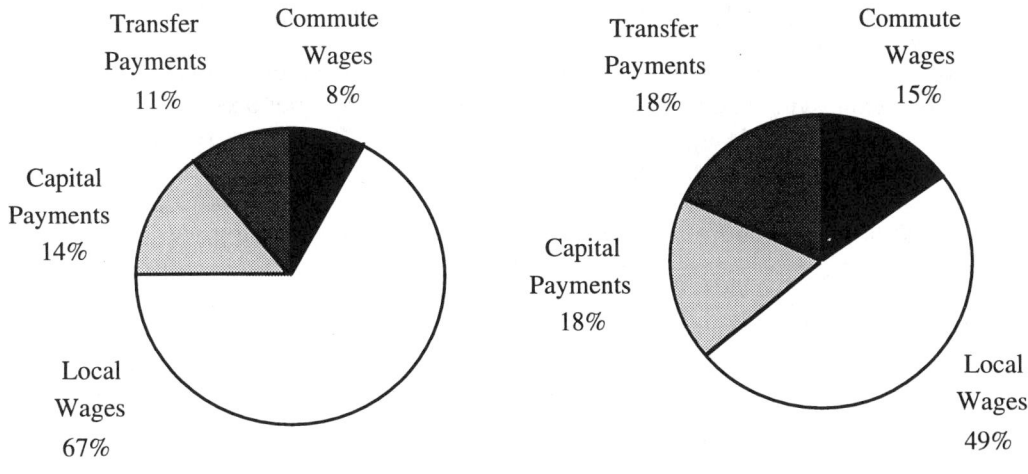

In addition to the changes in the overall sources of personal income, the types of jobs have also changed. The following table compares employment patterns from the 1970 and 1990 Census for the twelve counties fully within the SNEP boundary. The relative proportion of goods-producing and service-producing jobs remained constant over twenty years for the Sierra Nevada as a whole. Within the goods-producing sectors, agricultural and mining employment dropped and manufacturing employment increased. The most noticeable change in service-producing employment was a reduction in public administration employment (law enforcement, land management, environmental and programs) and an increase in high-wage service jobs in areas such as health, business, and legal services.

Table 2.5: Relative Size of Goods-Producing And Service-Producing Sectors
Remained Constant for Past 20 Years, 1970-1990

	Goods Producing				Service Producing			
Region 1970	Agr. & Mining	Manu-facturing	Const-ruction	Total Goods Producing	High Wage	Low Wage	Public Admin.	Total Service Producing
North	8%	19%	5%	32%	39%	24%	5%	68%
North Central	5%	9%	8%	22%	34%	34%	10%	78%
South Central	8%	13%	10%	31%	30%	28%	10%	68%
East	13%	4%	11%	28%	29%	36%	7%	72%
Total	7%	10%	9%	26%	33%	32%	10%	75%
	Goods Producing				Service Producing			
Region 1990	Agr. & Mining	Manu-facturing	Const-ruction	Total Goods Producing	High. Wage	Low Wage	Public Admin.	Total Service Producing
North	8%	14%	10%	32%	36%	27%	4%	67%
North Central	3%	13%	9%	25%	37%	32%	6%	75%
South Central	6%	11%	11%	27%	33%	31%	7%	71%
East	7%	3%	10%	20%	32%	37%	9%	78%
Total	4%	12%	10%	26%	36%	32%	6%	75%

Source: 1970 and 1990 Census.
Notes: Percentages may not add to 100 due to rounding. Census defined occupations are not adjusted for seasonal employment and will overstate the percentage of jobs in seasonal occupations.
Definition of Service Jobs: High Wage Service Jobs: Health, education, legal, finance, professional business services, transportation, communications. Low Wage Service Jobs: Retail, lodging, entertainment, business repairs.
Public Administration: Justice, police, prisons, environmental quality, housing.

The following table present the employment patterns for the whole SNEP region rather than just the counties mainly within the Sierra Nevada. Timber industry employment is separated out of total manufacturing employment with the use of county employment data. The local service sector includes many different job types with few jobs directly related to the ecosystem.

Table 2.6 : Major employment sectors - 1990

	Number of Workers	Local Services	Timber	Agr. & Mining	Travel	Public Admin.	Non timber Manuf.	Construction
Total	260,000	59%	4%	5%	8%	7%	6%	11%
North	44,000	61%	4%	6%	5%	8%	7%	9%
North Central	93,000	61%	3%	3%	5%	7%	9%	12%
South Central	46,000	57%	3%	6%	7%	8%	9%	11%
San Joaquin	29,000	58%	9%	7%	6%	9%	0%	10%
Greater Tahoe	35,000	51%	0%	2%	31%	4%	4%	9%
East Side	13,000	59%	0%	8%	13%	7%	3%	10%
Foothill	169,000	59%	3%	6%	5%	7%	8%	12%
Conifer	44,000	56%	8%	8%	8%	9%	2%	9%
Tahoe & East Side	48,000	53%	0%	6%	21%	6%	3%	11%

Source: 1990 Census and Employment Development Department.

Notes: Local Services - health, education, professional services, wholesale and retail trade, transportation, communications and public utilities; Timber - private sector employment in logging, sawmilling and remanufacturing. Private foresters and tree planters can not be separated from the larger agricultural category. USFS employees working on timber programs are included under Public Administration; Agriculture & Mining - agriculture is dominated by ranching, followed by irrigated agriculture and mining; Travel- hotels, motels, and recreational establishments; Public Administration: justice, police, prisons, environmental quality, housing; Non-timber manufacturing - electronics, metal fabrication, printing, food processing; Construction - residential and commercial construction.

Basic Income Analysis of Local and Regional Economies

One of the methods used to assess local economies is the economic base model based on the concept that economies can be understood by analyzing the amount of revenue coming into a region and how often it is spent and respent locally. The central assumption of the economic base model is tha all local income depends directly on basic money brought in via three sources. The first is wages associated with selling goods or services to residents or businesses outside the local economy. Basic wages account for less than a third of all local wages in Sierra Nevada communities. The second is the transfer of capital payments such as interest and dividends from the national economy to local households. And the third is the various types of government transfer payments including social security, medicare, and welfare. While economic base models can not produce the industry specific analyses available with IMPLAN or other regional input-output models, they can produce analyses for areas smaller than counties with publicly available data on personal income and employment. Many economic base models use only employment data and neglect the large and fast growing sources on income from capital payments (interest, dividends and rental income) as well as transfer payments (both cash payments and services). The difference between the money income of the Census and the total personal income used by the Bureau of Economic Analysis produces an even larger difference in the estimate of basic income because a significant portion of both capital payments and transfer payments are not recorded as money income. The following table illustrates the difference in the composition of basic income according to the more comprehensive BEA accounting methodolgy and the method used for the 1990 Census. The Department of Commerce will use the BEA methodolgy for the next Census to address the present inaccuracies. The more inclusive personal income method is used in this economic assessment and accentuates the relative importance of capital and transfer payments. The more detailed analysis of basic wages complements the total personal income analysis and should not be used as an alternative method of assessing the driving economic forces for local economies.

Table 2.7: Percentage of Basic Income by Bureau of Economic Analysis and Census Methodologies

Income Source	BEA	Census
Wages	23%	40%
Capital Payments	64%	46%
Transfer Payments	13%	14%
Basic Income/Total Income	71%	58%

Regional Variations in Personal Income and Local Respending

Capital payments and transfer payments are correlated with the demographic make-up of the population and are relatively independent of local employment patterns. Capital payments in the form of interest, dividends, rental payments, and appreciation of other financial assets, go primarily to wealthier households and retirees with private pensions. Transfer payments are dominated by social security payments and associated health benefits. Welfare, Aid to Families with Dependent Children (AFDC), disability payments, and unemployment insurance constitute a small fraction of total transfer payments.

Basic wages are the most variable type of basic income and are closely related to the types of businesses in a region. The sources of personal income do not have a strong statistical relationship with local respending patterns. The average dollar brought into local economies led to a total spending of $1.45 — the original dollar plus 45 cents of additional respending within the local economy. While there is considerable variation in the local income multiplier among communities, there is no strong statistical relationship between the size of the income multiplier and the sources of basic income, regions, total income, or relative importance of resource-based employment. The only communities with much higher income multipliers were those along the major trans-Sierra highways and proximal to year round recreation centers. The average income multiplier of 1.45 is equivalent to a average employment multiplier of 1.6-2.0, due to the higher wages of 'basic' jobs compared to most local service jobs. This overall basic job multiplier is within the range of employment multipliers for Sierra counties calculated from the 1987 IMPLAN model (e.g. 1.65 for lumber and wood products, 1.47 for construction, 1.26 for hotels for Nevada county) (California Trade and Commerce Agency 1992). Not surprisingly, they are lower than the 1995 employment multipliers that cover state -wide rather than county-wide employment impacts (U. S. Department of Commerce 1995).

Figure 2.5: Local Income Multipliers for 180 SNEP Communities

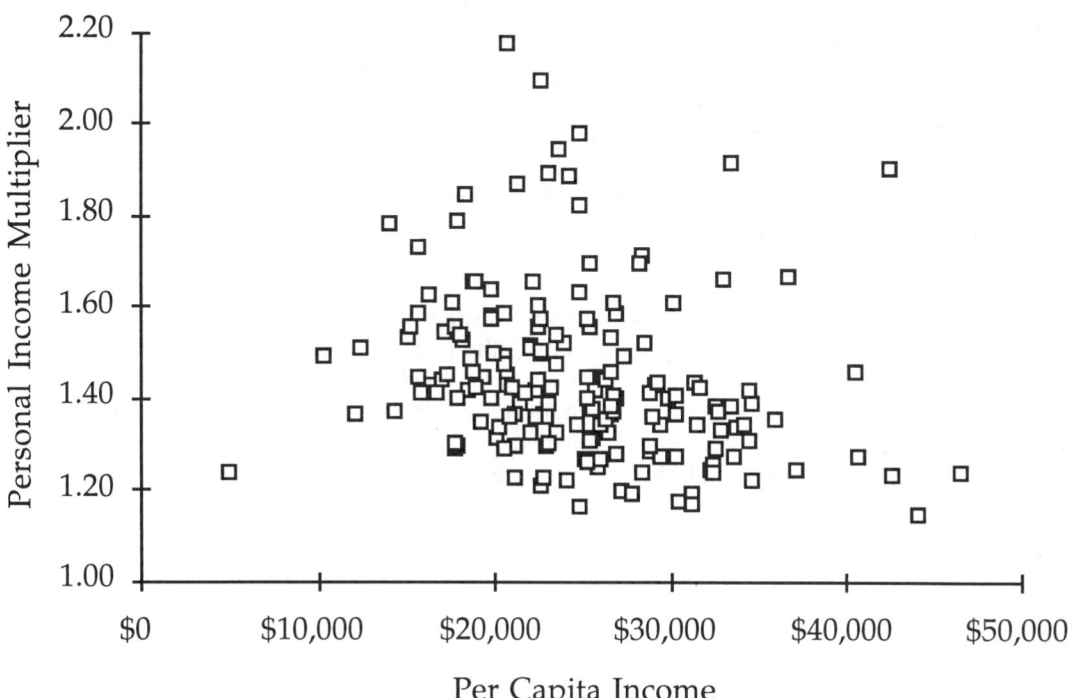

Source: Author's calculation from 1990 Census money income corrected by Bureau of Economic Analysis personal income data.

The relationship between local economies and direct economic benefits of the ecosystem is apparent in basic wages. Even though all community economies are buffered from sector specific downturns through the increasingly diversified sources of personal income, the pattern of local jobs the most visible expression of local economic diversification. Basic jobs are those involved in producing goods or services for sale to non-local customers. Basic wages are only a portion of total wages but are a major source of the basic income that supports local or non-basic employment. The type and size of basic wages varies considerably between communities and tracks major employment changes. The following table is based on 1990 Census employment with wage corrections from employment and wage data in the County Business Patterns (1992).

Table 2.8: Sectoral Composition of Basic Wages in Economic and Vegetative Regions

	Pct of Total Pop- ulation	Timber	Agr.	Mining	Recreation	Fed Land Agencies	Const- ruction	Hi Wage Services	Other Manuf.	Other Public Admin.
Total	100%	11%	8%	3%	16%	4%	14%	15%	20%	10%
Economic Regions										
North	20%	13%	12%	2%	9%	7%	7%	20%	20%	10%
North Central	34%	9%	6%	1%	7%	4%	18%	15%	29%	10%
South Central	20%	11%	9%	7%	13%	4%	14%	10%	23%	10%
San Joaquin	13%	27%	11%	3%	8%	8%	11%	18%	0%	13%
Greater Tahoe	10%	0%	4%	1%	58%	1%	12%	11%	12%	1%
East	4%	0%	11%	8%	33%	5%	11%	12%	11%	8%
Vegetative Regions										
Foothill	68%	11%	8%	3%	8%	5%	15%	15%	26%	10%
Conifer	17%	24%	10%	3%	12%	5%	10%	18%	5%	13%
East & Tahoe	14%	0%	6%	3%	51%	1%	12%	12%	12%	4%

Source: 1990 Census.
Note: Census-based job classifications do not differentiate part-time from full time jobs.

Role of the Ecosystem in Local Employment

When the discrete sectors are grouped according to their linkage to the ecosystem, clear patterns emerge. The role of the ecosystem in stimulating the local economy has grown and diversified over decades. The growth of developed recreation and tourism sector has expanded the non-commodity based stimulus to the Sierra Nevada economy. The majority of basic wage income comes from jobs related to the metropolitan nature of the region. Basic wages (but not all basic income since the large captial and transfer payments are not included) are grouped into four different categories in the following table.

Table 2.9: Basic Wages by Direct and Indirect Links to Ecosystem

	Direct Ecosystem		Metropolitan or Indirect Ecosystem	
	Commodity	Services	Residents	Regional
Total	22%	20%	28%	30%
Economic Regions				
North	27%	16%	27%	30%
North Central	16%	11%	33%	39%
South Central	26%	17%	23%	34%
San Joaquin	42%	16%	29%	13%
Greater Tahoe	5%	59%	23%	13%
East	19%	38%	23%	19%
Vegetative Regions				
Foothill	22%	13%	30%	36%
Conifer	37%	17%	28%	18%
East & Tahoe	9%	52%	24%	16%

Commodity - Timber, agriculture and mining; Services - Recreation and tourism above location quotient; Residents - High wage services and new construction for residents above location quotient estimate of local population requirements; Regional - Non-timber manufacturing and federal and state employment not associated with land management agencies.

For the region as a whole, ecosystem-related wages constituted over 40% of all basic wages, split relatively equally between commodities and services. When the wage-based data is analyzed by economic or vegetative regions, each region exhibits its own unique pattern with no region following the Sierra-wide pattern. Commodity based wage income is greater than service based wage income in four of the six economic regions and two of the three vegetative regions.

At a Sierra Nevada wide scale, basic wages are well distributed among diverse sectors. The possibility of the whole region being sent into recession because of major changes in any one industry are minimal. When the analysis is conducted according to vegetative regions, the dominance of the metropolitan related manufacturing and construction sectors can be separated from the timber sector that dominates the conifer dominated landscapes of all the west-facing economic regions. The timber industry dominance is due to the lack of alternative basic sectors in the conifer region. Over 60% of timber related employment is in the foothills where the relative impact is less because of the larger absolute size of other sectors. Although recreation is the second most important sector on a Sierra wide basis, and the most important wage source outside of the foothills, its dominance at a regional level is limited to the Lake Tahoe and East Side communities.

Employment and Unemployment Patterns

Over the past twenty years the number of jobs in the Sierra Nevada has grown faster than the overall population. Even with increasing rates of adult participation in the workforce, overall unemployment rates have dropped from what had been some of the highest rates in the state. However, with the exception of the three counties in the North Central region, unemployment rates within the SNEP region are still consistently above those of the state as whole. All the counties followed California into the recession of 1992 and 1993 and have since participated in an economic upswing.

The most significant aspect of the unemployment patterns within the Sierra Nevada is the marked seasonal unemployment patterns for all regions except the North Central region.

Diversification through the growth of less seasonal industries appears to be crucial for reducing unemployment throughout the region. Agriculture, timber, and tourism employment will remain major components of total employment, all seasonal in nature, but the regional patterns to date suggest that lower overall unemployment rates will only come with greater diversification of employment opportunities.

Figure 2.6 : Regional Unemployment Rates 1990-1995

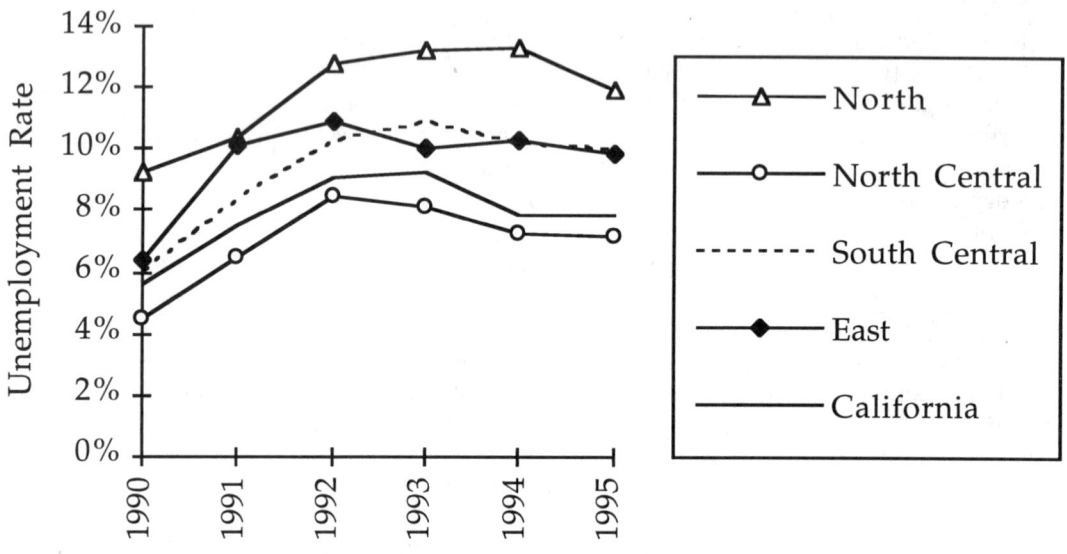

Figure 2.7: Average Monthly Unemployment Rates 1990-1995

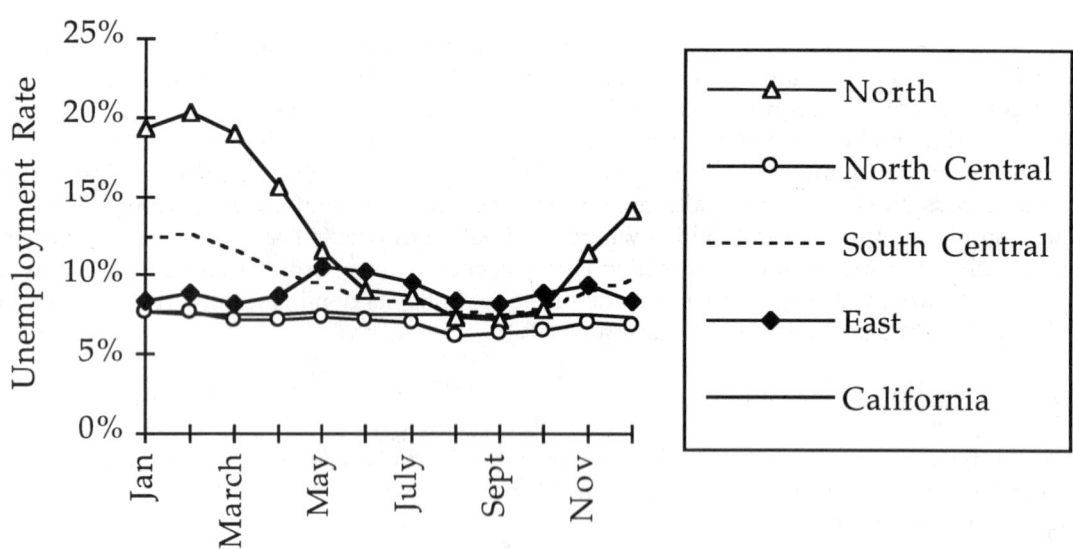

Conclusion

Ecosystems are linked to the regional economy in two primary ways. Direct linkages exist through jobs and firms that use commodities harvested from the ecosystem or provide services that require the unique ecosystem of the Sierra Nevada. Indirect linkages occur where the desirable environmental attributes attract commuters and retirees who choose to live in region when they could live elsewhere. Economic growth has occurred primarily in sectors indirectly linked to the ecosystem.

A significant change in the Sierra Nevada economy over the past twenty years has been the rapid expansion of personal income from sources other than local employment. Personal income from commuting, interest and dividends, and government transfer payments constituted 51% of total personal income in 1992 compared to 32% in 1972. Driven primarily by the movement of new residents into the Sierra Nevada, this change buffers the large variations in employment directly related to ecosystem commodities and services.

Over the past twenty years, the timber, ranching, agriculture, and mining sectors remained relatively stable while the rest of the economy doubled. Changes in commodity prices and governmental policies have had a relatively greater impact than the physical availability of natural resource for timber, agricultural, mining, and water diversion activities. Direct ecosystem commodity and service sectors remain large components of the Sierra Nevada and differentiate the Sierra Nevada from the rest of the state. Sustaining these sectors in a manner that does not reduce the overall value of the ecosystem to the regional economy requires considerations of tradeoffs between different sectors.

The number of local jobs is now than twice as large as it was when the integrated land management planning efforts were begun for the National Forests after the passage of the National Forests Management Act in 1976. This growth alone has substantially reduced the relative importance of natural resource based activities in local economies. Within the Sierra Nevada, major regional differences are large and no two regions have similar mixes of economic linkages to the ecosystem. This is true for regions based on county boundaries and adjacency to nearest metropolitan area and for regions following major vegetative boundaries.

CHAPTER 3: THE USE AND VALUE OF WATER FLOWS

The diversion of water for irrigation, residential, industrial, and power generation constitutes one of the most significant alterations of the Sierra Nevada ecosystem. Unlike gold mining, sheep grazing, and timber harvesting which have declined or stabilized during recent decades, the extent of water diversions has never declined and is greater now than at any time in history. Many ecological indicators related to water dependent resources are declining and show no sign of stabilizing. The ecological roles of water in different ecological systems are addressed in numerous other sections of the SNEP report.

The purpose of this chapter is to assess the economic benefits of different types of water diversions so that they can be considered alongside ecological and hydrologic assessments. The largest single revenue-generating use of water involves running water through turbines for hydropower. Of the water that is diverted from Sierra Nevada rivers and streams for consumptive uses, most goes to irrigated agriculture, with smaller volumes going to municipal uses and wetlands outside of the Sierra Nevada region. Estimates of economic values of water diverted for irrigation, municipal, and hydropower, suggest that water diversions represent the largest single commodity produced from the Sierra Nevada ecosystem. Additionally, economic values complementary to in-stream uses accrue through water dependent recreation activities such as fishing, white water rafting and wetland related uses. Declines in water quality and in-stream water quantity will have significant economic costs on these sectors.

Water's high value for diverted uses is predicated on its continued availability at its area of origin. History is replete with efforts to protect the headwaters of Sierra Nevada rivers and increase or alter their water yield. While the value of securing these source areas is accepted without contest, resource protection has been addressed through a reliance on legislative approaches rather than on market forces or economic policy. For example, the Sequoia National Forest was originally reserved from the public domain as part of the four million-acre Sierra Forest Reserve in 1893, in part because of heavy lobbying efforts by San Joaquin Valley agricultural interests concerned with threats to their water supply posed by upstream mining, grazing, and lumbering (Dilsaver and Tweed 1990). While the forest reserve strategy for protection of water resource was once politically viable, contemporary efforts are focused on preserving water quality for all of its beneficial uses through regulatory approaches. This approach is embodied in the Federal Water Pollution Control Act of 1972, amended 1977, and the Clean Water Act of 1987.

California's population is expected to double over the next forty years and will require considerable new water deliveries to urban areas. The development of the State Water Bank in the 1980s as well as other efforts of Southern California's urban water agencies to buy water rights elsewhere in the state suggest that existing water allocation patterns may change substantially. The possible expansion of the public trust doctrine to water resources outside of the Mono Lake basin is another potential change. These potential changes increase the need to assess existing patterns use for Sierra Nevada water resources.

Major Water Uses

Water diversions have been central to the economic development of the Sierra Nevada and California as a whole since the discovery of gold at Sutter's water-powered grain mill in 1848. The extensive infrastructure now controlling the distribution of water flowing from the Sierra Nevada includes two of the world's largest irrigation projects, nearly 500 reservoirs, and over one hundred hydroelectric generation facilities. The enormous investments in water moving infrastructure made over the past one hundred and fifty years highlight western water's peculiar distinction of having its greatest value at considerable distances from its area of occurrence. Water diversions have allowed for the residential and industrial growth in California's distant urban centers and made the Central

Valley the most productive agricultural region in the world. Coinciding with these investments in the reallocation of water, has been an enormous reduction in in-stream flows which support aquatic ecosystems, riparian plant communities and offer recreational and aesthetic opportunities on streams and rivers throughout the Sierra Nevada. Many of the ecological assessments in this report suggest that present land and water uses are responsible for the continued decline of many water-dependent ecosystems.

The annual unimpaired flow from the Sierra Nevada's nineteen major drainages is estimated by the Department of Water Resources at 20.8 million acre feet over the past 50 years. The following table presents the 50 year average of unimpaired runoff for the major river systems in the Sierra Nevada.

Table 3.1: Annual Unimpaired Flows for Major Sierra Nevada Rivers

Hydrologic Regions and Rivers	Unimpaired Flow Thousand Acre Feet (50 year average)
Sacramento Region (Sierra Portion)	
Feather	4,617
Yuba	2,389
American	2,736
San Joaquin Region	
Consumes	385
Mokelumne	747
Stanislaus	1,149
Tuolumne	1,882
Merced	966
San Joaquin	1,776
Tulare Lake Region	
Kings	1,669
Kaweah	444
Tule	145
Kern	716
South Lahontan Region	
Owens/Mono Basin	149
North Lahontan Region	
Truckee	409
Carson River, West Fork	75
Carson River, East Fork	264
West Walker River	185
East Walker River	115
Total	20,818

Based on Hydrologic Regions as defined by the
California Department of Water Resources.

Water flowing from the Sierra Nevada is put to many uses across both California and Nevada. Based on water use and inter-regional transport data from the Department of Water Resources (Department of Water Resources 1994) , estimates of end uses were developed for all water running off the Sierra Nevada. Water use estimates include ground water basins that must ultimately be recharged by Sierra Nevada water as well as inter-basin transfers. Since the Department of Water Resources publishes water use estimates for regional basins rather than individual river basins, exact estimates by river system were not completed. Within each of the six hydrologic regions covering parts of the Sierra Nevada, we estimated flows and use within the Sierra and non-Sierra portions. Inter-basin transfers from one region to another are referred to as exports and were calculated from the most recent California Water Plan Update (Department of Water Resources 1994). Net, rather than gross volumes were used in the calculations. The figures are based on what are referred to as 1990 corrected water volumes and include corrections to address missing data.

The three major uses of water are irrigated agriculture, municipal and industrial uses in urban areas, and environmental uses as defined by DWR. A relatively small amount of water referred to as 'other' that is lost through evaporation or can not otherwise be accounted for are excluded in the following calculations. Environmental water use refers to "water demand based on water needs of managed fresh water wetlands, environmental in-stream flow needs, Delta outflow and Wild and Scenic rivers" (Department of Water Resources 1994). Environmental water use may all not be consumptive and may cover some amount of ground water recharge. Most of the environmental water use refers to flows of the Wild and Scenic section of the Feather River which ends up in Lake Oroville and can be diverted from there. Since some of this water may recharge wetlands that do not have legal water rights, the environmental water use ascribed to the Wild and Scenic portion of the Feather River may be more accurately considered to be used consumptively outside the Sierra Nevada region. For consistency, the volumes used here are reported as they are published by DWR. The calculated volume of water used is nearly identical to the unimpaired flow estimates for the major rivers. The three major geographic areas of use are: within the Sierra (SN); within the drainage of the river systems (IR); and exported (EX). Export water includes inter-basin water projects such as the State Water Project, Central Valley Project, Hetch Hetchy Aqueduct, and the Owens Valley Aqueduct.

Table 3.2: Water Use for DWR Hydrologic Regions in Sierra Nevada in Thousand Acre Feet

DWR Region	Agriculture			Municipal			Environment		Total
	SN	IR	EX	SN	IR	EX	SN	IR	
Sacramento	373	2,791	953	79	289	1,589	1,420	999	8,495
San Joaquin	21	3,552	983	43	181	575	554		5,909
Tulare Lake	20	3,585		5	95		34		3,739
S. Lahontan	147	16		15	12	437	128		755
N. Lahontan	460		580	31	3	40	17	550	1,681
Total	1,021	9,945	2,517	173	581	2,641	2,153	1,549	20,580

Note: SN - within Sierra Nevada; IR - within hydrologic region; EX - export across major watersheds. Sacramento Region excludes most of the Sacramento River and western tributaries.

Table 3.3: Water Use for DWR Hydrologic Regions in Sierra Nevada as a Percent of Total Flow

DWR Region	Agriculture			Municipal			Environment		Total
	SN	IR	EX	SN	IR	EX	SN	IR	
Sacramento	4%	33%	11%	1%	3%	19%	17%	12%	100%
San Joaquin	0%	60%	17%	1%	3%	10%	9%		100%
Tulare Lake	1%	96%		0%	3%		1%		100%
S. Lahontan	19%	2%		2%	2%	58%	17%		100%
N. Lahontan	27%		34%	2%	0%	2%	1%	33%	100%
Total	5%	48%	12%	1%	3%	13%	10%	8%	100%

Note: SN - within Sierra Nevada; IR - within hydrologic region; EX - export across major watersheds. Sacramento Region excludes most of the Sacramento River and western tributaries.

Water rights to Sierra Nevada water are predominantly controlled by downstream agricultural and urban users. In terms of total water use, agriculture accounts for 65% of the total use. Urban use is supplied mainly through inter-regional transfers to large coastal cities and accounts for 17% of total use. Environmental uses such as wetlands and riparian areas along Wild and Scenic Rivers accounts for the final 18%. Water use patterns vary considerably among hydrologic regions. West-facing rivers draining the central and southern portions of the Sierra Nevada are dominated by agricultural uses in the Central Valley. Rivers draining the northern and eastern portions of the Sierra Nevada provide considerably more water to distant urban users, wetlands, and local agricultural uses.

Although 100% of the water flows through the SNEP region, only 6% of total consumptive agricultural and urban uses is consumed within the region. On a region wide level, most water use in the Sierra also goes to agriculture but in many individual river basins, municipal use is greater. Nearly all agricultural water use in the Sierra Nevada occurs in the sparsely populated watersheds east of the Sierra Nevada crest.

Dams, Reservoirs and Other Diversions

The seasonal pattern of precipitation and runoff in the Sierra Nevada requires major diversions for uses that do not occur when runoff is highest. Water diversions in the Sierra Nevada range from stock ponds on small streams to the massive reservoirs just above the floor of the Central Valley. Most downstream water use is based on diversions from the 490 dams monitored by Department of Water Resources. Smaller diversions such as stock ponds and other structures storing less than 50 acre feet of water or less than 25 feet tall, are not monitored by the DWR.

Although thousands of reservoirs and miles of flumes criss-crossed the Sierra Nevada during the Nineteenth century (Beesley 1996 and Larson 1996) most of these structures no longer exist. Structures built in the twentieth century are much larger and alter much more of the total water flow. The present capacity of all the reservoirs in the Sierra Nevada is roughly equal to the total unimpaired flow of 20 million acre feet. The following figure illustrates the cumulative capacity of upstream and foothill reservoirs built during this century. Foothill reservoirs are defined as sites below an altitude of 3,000 feet. Sites for upstream reservoirs were selected earlier and primarily constructed between 1920 and 1960. They supply water for hydropower generation, municipal water uses, and smaller irrigation districts. In contrast, most of the large foothill reservoirs were built after 1950 with large public investments.

The construction of a series of large reservoirs in the foothills during the 1960s and 1970s more than doubled total reservoir capacity and altered the water flow patterns on a much larger scale than the previous systems of reservoirs. Very large reservoirs now account for more than 80% of total storage capacity. The ecological impacts of these reservoirs extend through the major river systems and the Bay-Delta ecosystems.

Figure 3.1: Cumulative Major Reservoir Capacity in the Sierra Nevada

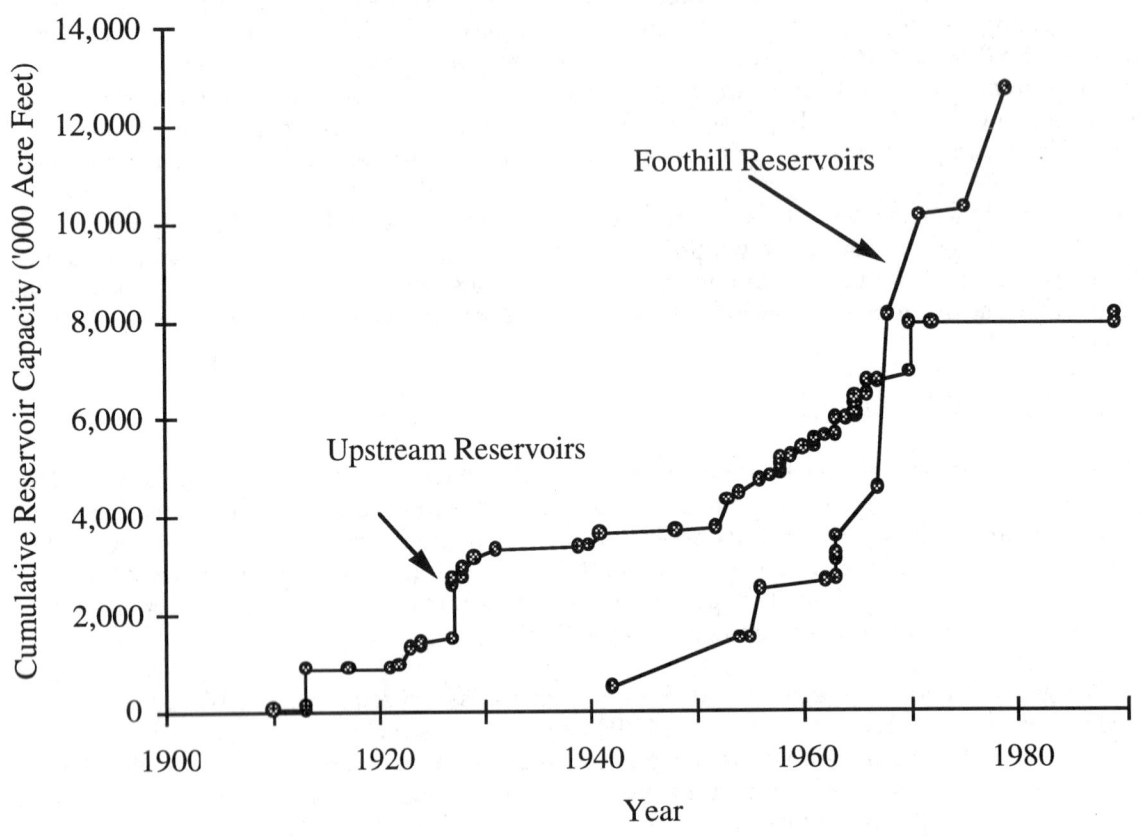

Table 3.4: Reservoir Capacity Relative to Annual Flow from West-Flowing Sierra Nevada Rivers

Hydrologic Region	Unimpaired flow in TAF	Reservoir Capacity Thousand Acre Feet (TAF)			Reservoir Capacity as Percent of Unimpaired Flow		
		Total	Upstream	Foothill	Total	Upstream	Foothill
Sacramento (Sierra only)	9,742	8,663	3,978	4,685	89%	41%	48%
San Joaquin	6,905	7,841	1,810	6,878	114%	26%	100%
Tulare Lake	2,974	2,044	901	1,143	69%	30%	38%
Total	19,621	18,548	6,689	12,706	95%	34%	65%

Note: The Sacramento-Sierra only region excludes the Sacramento River above Shasta Dam and all streams draining the west side of the Sacramento Valley. The South Lahontan and North Lahontan data are less accurate due to flows outside of the main river gauging stations and flow into Nevada.

The major ecological impacts of the foothill reservoirs have been the blockage of nearly every river and the retention of an enormous fraction of annual flow. Nearly all salmon and steelhead migration into the Sierra Nevada is blocked and downstream river flows in the Central Valley are significantly altered. Upstream reservoirs constitute less than half of the total reservoir capacity and have a different set of ecological impacts. In addition to flooding areas behind the dams, impeding fish and amphibian movement up the water course, they also drastically modify in-stream flows within

996

the Sierra Nevada itself. Approximately one third of total reservoir storage is not used on an annual basis so that it is available for flood storage.

Table 3.5: Reservoir Capacity by Year Constructed

Period	Number of Dams	Percent of Total Capacity
1850 -1900	57	<1%
1901-1950	198	22%
1951-1965	130	27%
1965-1993	105	50%

Source: DWR, Dam Safety Jurisdiction Data Base.

Table 3.6: Reservoir Capacity by Size Class

Dam Rank from Largest to Smallest	Size of Reservoirs in Acre Feet	Percent of Total Capacity
#1-#25	135,000 - 3,538,000	84%
#26-#50	48,000 - 135,000	10%
#51-#75	16,000 - 48,000	3%
remaining 425	20 - 16,000	3%

Source: DWR, Dam Safety Jurisdiction Data Base.

Foothill reservoirs exist on every river flowing from the Sierra Nevada except the Cosumnes. These reservoirs can store anywhere from 38% to 100% of total runoff of the river systems and have significantly reduced flows into downstream aquatic ecosystems. The main ecological impacts of foothill reservoirs within the region are that they stop nearly all salmon migration upstream, flood large areas of what was foothill riparian vegetation, and break the continuity of terrestrial riparian vegetation and habitats. Upstream reservoirs are more numerous, smaller, and are not on every tributary. Overall, they withhold a much smaller fraction of total runoff than the foothill reservoirs. Their ecological impacts within the region show up in both the reduced and seasonally altered downstream flows, and in the site specific flooding of upstream areas.

Any changes in reservoir management to improve the status of aquatic and riparian systems dependent on water flow will have to be implemented by the reservoir operators. Ownership of Sierra Nevada reservoirs is split among five major sets of organizations. Nearly all of the large foothill reservoirs are operated by federal, state, and local public agencies for the main purpose of irrigation. In contrast 67% of the volume of upstream reservoirs is operated by municipal water districts and power companies. The beneficiaries of the foothill reservoirs are primarily agricultural water users in the Central Valley while the beneficiaries of upstream reservoirs are primarily urban consumers of water and electric power. The institutional participants who must be involved in any plans to change water flows to address the serious declines in aquatic and riparian ecosystems will vary depending on the elevation and river system.

Table 3.7: Operators of Major Reservoirs

Operator	Whole Region		Foothill		Upstream	
	Acre Feet	Pct of Total	Acre Feet	Pct of Total	Acre Feet	Pct of Total
DWR	3,701	18%	3,538	28%	163	2%
Federal Agencies	7,317	35%	5,536	44%	1,781	22%
Irrigation Districts	3,816	18%	3,111	24%	705	9%
Municipal Water Districts	3,718	18%	521	4%	3,197	39%
Power Companies	2,276	11%	0	0%	2,276	28%
Total	20,828	100%	12,706	100%	8,122	100%

Source: DWR, Dam Safety Jurisdiction Data Base.

Hydropower Generation in the Sierra Nevada

Hydropower generation varies with California's precipitation and has constituted from 9 to 21% of total electric power generated in the state over the last decade. Precipitation and minimum in-stream flow requirements on natural water courses determine the maximum amount of water that can be diverted through turbines to generate electricity. The physical size of the turbines and the structures to store and release the spring runoff permitting year-round operation determine how much of this potential flow can be used to generate electricity.

The majority of hydropower plants in the Sierra Nevada were constructed in three distinct periods. The early projects were designed and built during the 1920s by engineers for private power companies. New construction technologies as well as increased public financing led to a enormous increase in hydroelectric capacity throughout the 1950s and 1960s. Finally, high energy prices and streamlined federal regulatory approval processes led to the applications for hundreds and the actual construction of 63 smaller hydroelectric projects since 1979. Relatively few plants have been completed since 1990 and the projected size of future plants is relatively small (California Energy Commission, 1992). The following figure illustrates the trend in hydroelectric capacity over this century.

Figure 3.2: Hydropower Capacity in the Sierra Nevada

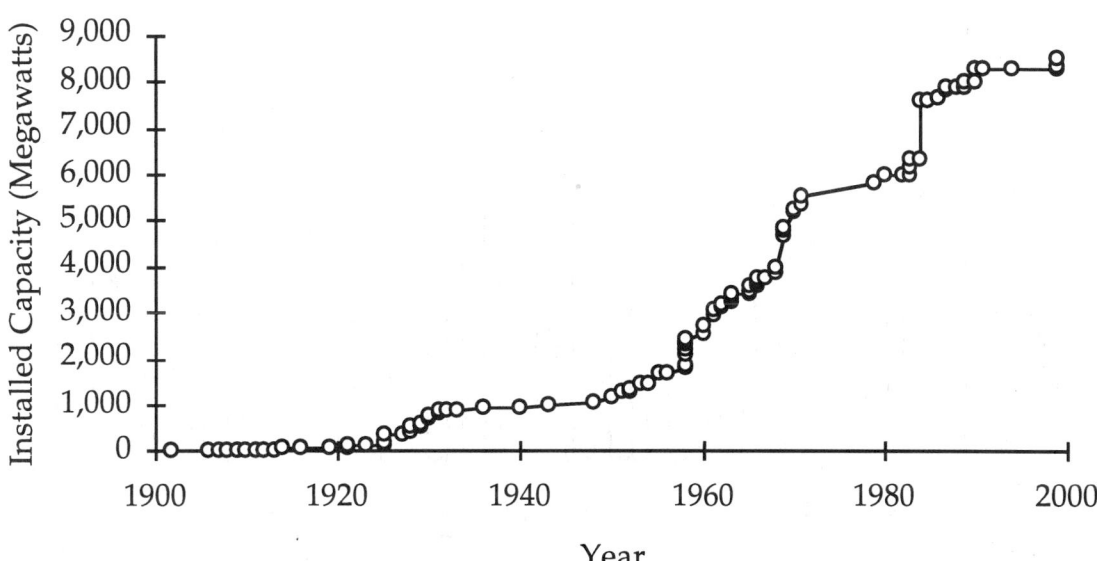

Sources: DWR 1994 and CEC 1992.
Note: the 1,000 MW Helms Canyon pump-storage facility (1984) is not dependent on diverting natural water flows.

Hydropower production trends over the past 24 years (1970-1994) illustrate the dominant importance of precipitation in overall production. In "wet" years such as 1975 and 1983, hydroelectric production reached 54.6 and 42 billion kWh respectively. During the most recent drought however, hydroelectric production fell, averaging less than 15 billion kWh per year between 1987 and 1992. This drop in production represents a decline in overall capacity utilization, since generating capacity had increased with the 63 new projects installed since 1979.

Figure 3.3: Hydropower Generation in the Sierra Nevada

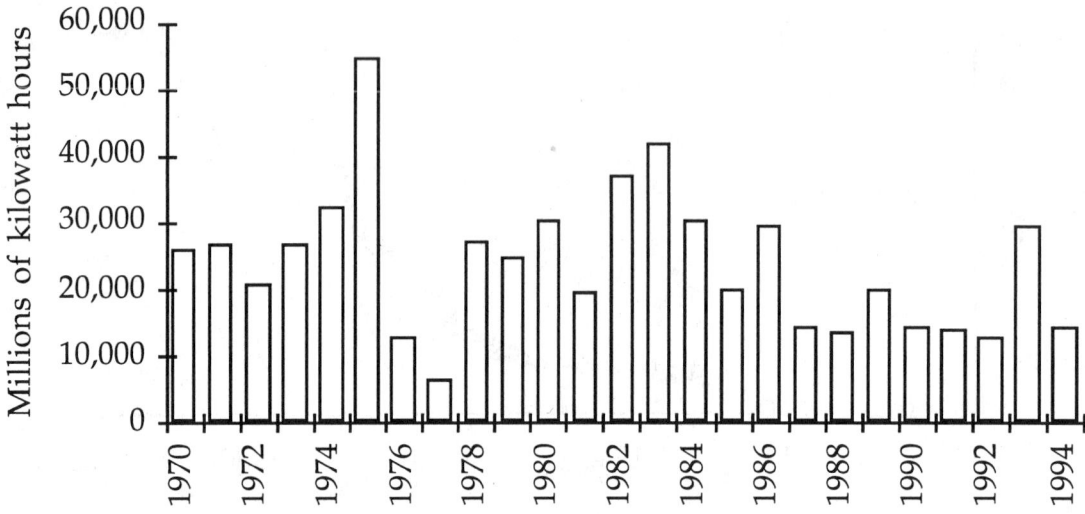

Source: Federal Energy Regulatory Commission records

The location of the hydropower sites in the Sierra Nevada are identified in Figure 3.4. In addition, Table 3.8 lists the name, watershed, and other relevant information on the 124 hydropower sites identified within the SNEP boundary. The sources of original data and the methods used for the calculated values are described immediately after the table.

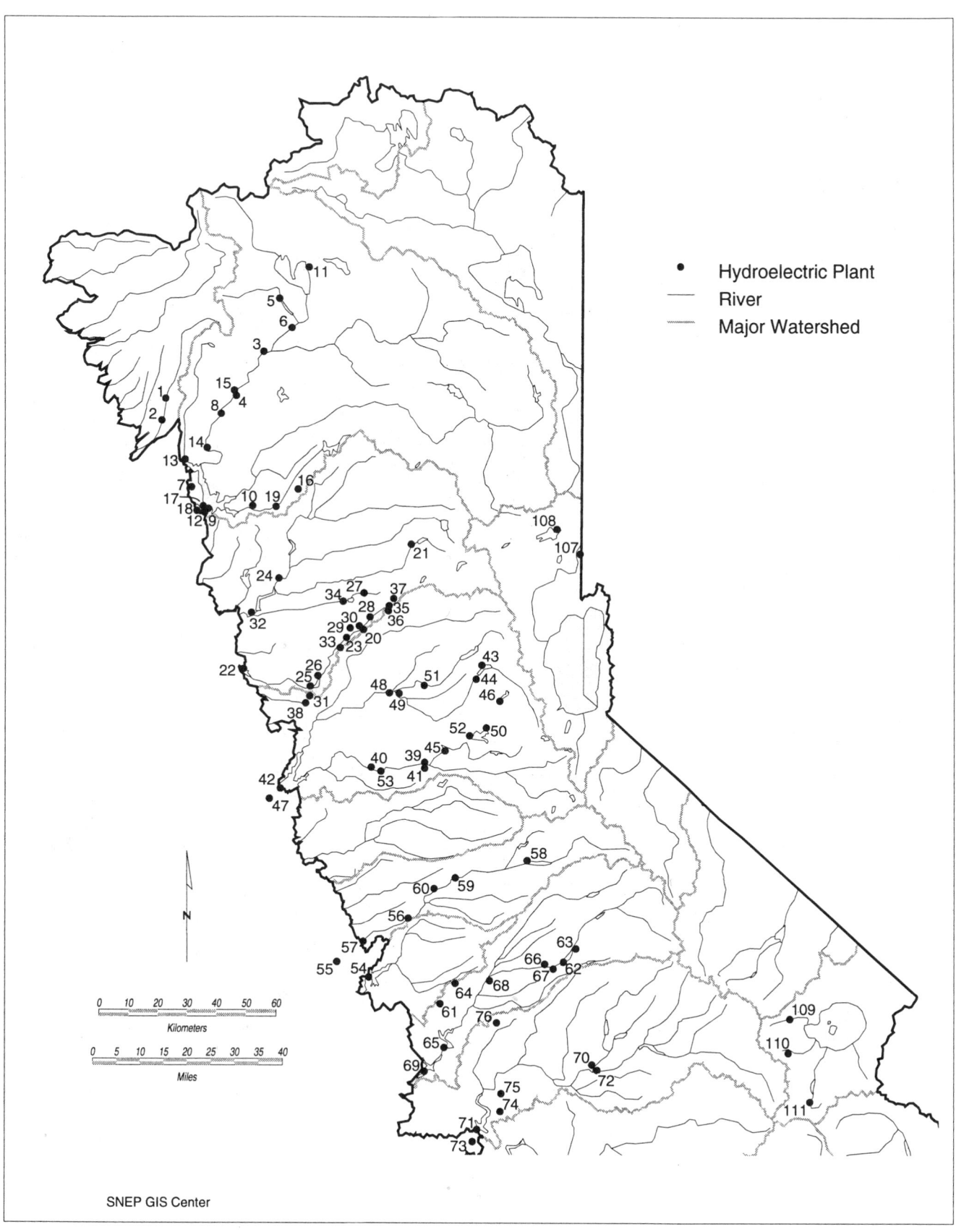

SNEP GIS Center

Figure: 3.4

1001

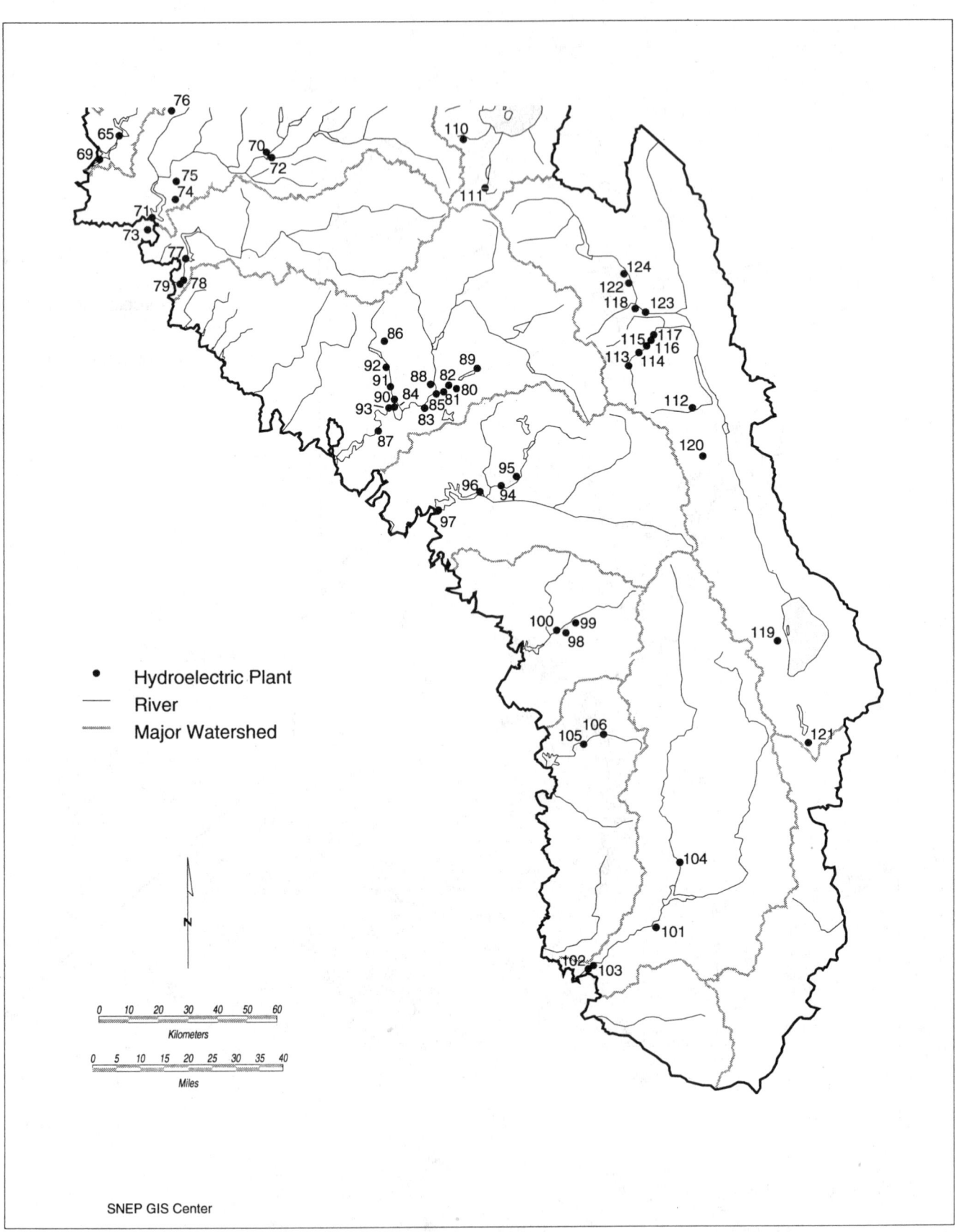

Hydroelectric Plant
River
Major Watershed

SNEP GIS Center

Figure: 3.4

Table 3.8 Hydropower Plants

Map Ref. # (a)	Powerplant Name	Watershed Name	Owner (b)	Completion Date (c)	Capacity MW	Yearly MWh Production (d)	Head (in feet)	Kwh per AF Water (e)	Value per AF (f)	Cumulative AF Value (g)
1	Centerville	Butte Creek	PG&E	1900	6.4	41,273	557	473	$12	$12
2	De Sabla	Butte Creek	PG&E	1963	18.5	125,825	1,545	1,313	$33	$45
3	Belden	Feather	PG&E	1969	125	408,545	770	655	$16	$102
4	Bucks Creek	Feather	PG&E	1928	77.8	245,915	2,558	2,174	$54	$129
5	Butt Valley	Feather	PG&E	1958	39.1	168,395	358	304	$8	$134
6	Caribou 2 (&1)	Feather	PG&E	1958	195	652,038	1,149	977	$24	$127
7	Coal Canyon	Feather	PG&E	1969	125	6,765	770	655	$16	$26
8	Cresta	Feather	PG&E	1928	77.8	358,218	2,558	2,174	$54	$75
9	Edward Hyatt	Feather	California	1958	39.1	1,875,552	358	304	$8	$10
10	Forbestown	Feather	OWID	1958	195	159,933	1,149	977	$24	$34
11	Hamilton Branch	Feather	PG&E	1921	2.4	24,522	410	349	$9	$143
12	Kelly Ridge	Feather	OWID	1963	10	69,751	668	568	$14	$17
13	Lime Saddle	Feather	PG&E	1906	1.6	10,322	462	393	$10	$20
14	Poe	Feather	PG&E	1958	142.8	628,760	477	405	$10	$20
15	Rock Creek	Feather	PG&E	1950	113.4	554,103	535	455	$11	$86
16	Sly Creek	Feather	OWID	1984	13	25,229	225	191	$5	$71
17	Thermalito	Feather	California	1968	115.1	267,354	102	87	$2	$2
18	Thermalito Div.	Feather	California	1987	3	18,333	74	63	$2	$2
19	Woodleaf	Feather	OWID	1963	55	263,091	1,495	1,271	$32	$66
20	Alta	Yuba-Bear	PG&E	1902	1	5,814	648	551	$14	$29
21	Bowman	Yuba-Bear	Nevada ID	1986	3.6	9,107	162	138	$3	$9
22	Camp Far West	Yuba-Bear	SMUD	1985	6.8	14,048	165	140	$4	$4
23	Chicago Park	Yuba-Bear	Nevada ID	1966	41.5	164,959	481	409	$10	$16
24	Colgate (New)	Yuba-Bear	Yuba CWA	1970	341	1,245,871	1,390	1,182	$30	$35
25	Combie Lake*	Yuba-Bear	Nevada ID	1984	1.5	3,479	70	60	$1	$5
26	Combie North	Yuba-Bear	Nevada ID	1988	0.33	592	40	34	$1	$6
27	Deer Creek	Yuba-Bear	PG&E	1908	4.6	25,242	837	711	$18	$21
28	Drum 1 & 2	Yuba-Bear	PG&E	1965	103.5	414,585	1,370	1,165	$29	$58
29	Dutch Flat 1	Yuba-Bear	PG&E	1943	23	83,784	643	547	$14	$29
30	Dutch Flat 2	Yuba-Bear	Nevada ID	1966	26	111,041	591	502	$13	$29
31	Halsey	Yuba-Bear	PG&E	1916	11	70,208	327	278	$7	$17

1003

Table 3.8 Hydropower Plants

Map Ref. # (a)	Powerplant Name	Watershed Name	Owner (b)	Completion Date (c)	Capacity MW	Yearly MWh Production (d)	Head (in feet)	Kwh per AF Water (e)	Value per A Water (f)	Cumulative AF Value (g)
32	Narrows	Yuba-Bear	PG&E	1970	64.9	271,271	240	204	$5	$5
33	Rollins	Yuba-Bear	Nevada ID	1980	11	61,596	215	183	$5	$10
34	Scott Flat	Yuba-Bear	Nevada ID	1984	0.9	2,839	140	119	$3	$3
35	Spaulding 1	Yuba-Bear	PG&E	1929	7	32,484	197	167	$4	$62
36	Spaulding 2	Yuba-Bear	PG&E	1929	4.4	13,228	344	292	$7	$28
37	Spaulding 3	Yuba-Bear	PG&E	1929	5.8	39,418	318	270	$7	$61
38	Wise	Yuba-Bear	PG&E	1970	14.7	98,999	519	441	$11	$28
39	Camino	American	SMUD	1968	150	381,757	1,061	902	$23	$50
40	Chili Bar	American	PG&E	1965	2.3	34,156	60	51	$1	$9
41	El Dorado	American	PG&E	1924	21	103,641	1,910	1,624	$41	$68
42	Folsom	American	USBR	1955	198.7	620,655	333	283	$7	$8
43	French Meadows	American	Placer CWA	1966	15.3	62,884	654	556	$14	$95
44	Hell Hole	American	Placer CWA	1983	0.5	2,316	359	305	$8	$18
45	Jaybird	American	SMUD	1961	139	539,510	1,530	1,301	$33	$82
46	Loon Lake	American	SMUD	1971	78	98,183	1,140	969	$24	$124
47	Nimbus	American	USBR	1955	13.5	63,937	43	37	$1	$1
48	Oxbow	American	Placer CWA	1966	6.57	31,124	89	76	$2	$10
49	Ralston	American	Placer CWA	1966	85	374,471	1,250	1,063	$27	$36
50	Robbs Peak	American	SMUD	1965	22	47,416	400	340	$9	$100
51	Stephenson LJ*	American	Placer CWA	1930	120	517,330	2,101	1,786	$45	$81
52	Union Valley	American	SMUD	1963	37	115,505	430	366	$9	$92
53	Whiterock	American	SMUD	1961	223	580,352	852	724	$18	$27
54	New Hogan	Calaveras	Modesto ID	1986	3.3	3,081	195	166	$4	$4
55	Camanche	Mokelumne	EDMUD	1983	11	20,192	107	91	$2	$2
56	Electra	Mokelumne	PG&E	1948	89.1	444,191	1,272	1,081	$27	$36
57	Pardee	Mokelumne	EDMUD	1930	29	89,232	327	278	$7	$9
58	Salt Springs	Mokelumne	PG&E	1931	44	220,283	2113	1796.05	$45	$114
59	Tiger Creek	Mokelumne	PG&E	1931	51	325,397	1,219	1,036	$26	$69
60	West Point	Mokelumne	PG&E	1931	13.6	95,888	312	265	$7	$43
61	Angels Camp	Stanislaus	PG&E	1940	1.4	7,013	444	377	$9	$25
62	Beardsley	Stanislaus	OSSJ	1958	11	59,775	264	224	$6	$21

Table 3.8 Hydropower Plants

Map Ref. # (a)	Powerplant Name	Watershed Name	Owner (b)	Completion Date (c)	Capacity MW	Yearly MWh Production (d)	Head (in feet)	Kwh per AF Water (e)	Value per AF Water (f)	Cumulative AF Value (g)
63	Donnels	Stanislaus	OSSJ	1958	67.5	317,865	1,484	1,261	$32	$70
64	Murphy's	Stanislaus	PG&E	1954	3.6	22,089	684	581	$15	$40
65	New Melones	Stanislaus	USBR	1979	300	393,829	583	496	$12	$16
66	Sand Bar	Stanislaus	TDP	1986	16.2	57,200	389	331	$8	$56
67	Spring Gap	Stanislaus	PG&E	1921	6	41,381	1,865	1,585	$40	$55
68	Stanislaus	Stanislaus	PG&E	1963	81.9	397,766	1,525	1,296	$32	$48
69	Tulloch	Stanislaus	OSSJ	1958	4.5	96,838	157	133	$3	$3
70	D R Holm	Tuolumne	HHWD	1960	135.9	739,491	2,481	2,109	$53	$67
71	Don Pedro	Tuolumne	Turlock ID	1970	179	545,833	530	451	$11	$14
72	Kirkwood R C	Tuolumne	HHWD	1936	50.3	568,117	1,450	1,233	$31	$71
73	La Grange	Tuolumne	Turlock ID	1924	3.9	15,728	119	101	$3	$3
74	Moccasin	Tuolumne	HHWD	1969	88	496,040	1,257	1,068	$27	$41
75	Moccasin L H	Tuolumne	HHWD	1987	3	7,579	76	65	$2	
76	Phoenix	Tuolumne	PG&E	1940	1.6	11,810	1,190	1,012	$25	$39
77	Exchequer	Merced	Merced ID	1970	89	289,581	464	394	$10	$12
78	McSwain	Merced	Merced ID	1967	10	36,623	56	48	$1	$2
79	Merced Falls	Merced	PG&E	1930	3.5	15,558	26	22	$1	$1
80	Big Creek 1	San Joaquin	SCE	1925	70	521,430	2,131	1,811	$45	$144
81	Big Creek 2	San Joaquin	SCE	1925	158	454,419	1,875	1,594	$40	$98
82	Big Creek 2A	San Joaquin	SCE	1928	95	390,537	2,418	2,055	$51	$110
83	Big Creek 3	San Joaquin	SCE	1970	147	844,733	827	703	$18	$43
84	Big Creek 4	San Joaquin	SCE	1951	92	450,573	416	354	$9	$26
85	Big Creek 8	San Joaquin	SCE	1929	58	327,943	713	606	$15	$58
86	Crane Valley	San Joaquin	PG&E	1919	1.1	3,345	128	109	$3	$66
87	Kerchoff 2	San Joaquin	PG&E	1983	173.7	409,058	792	673	$17	$17
88	Mammoth	San Joaquin	SCE	1960	149	610,219	1,100	935	$23	$67
89	Portal	San Joaquin	SCE	1956	10	51,608	230	196	$5	$148
90	San Joaquin 1A	San Joaquin	PG&E	1923	0.4	1,433	42	36	$1	$48
91	San Joaquin 2	San Joaquin	PG&E	1923	3.2	12,328	307	261	$7	$54
92	San Joaquin 3	San Joaquin	PG&E	1923	4.2	15,172	405	344	$9	$63
93	Wishon	San Joaquin	PG&E	1910	12.8	64,737	1,412	1,200	$30	$47

Table 3.8 Hydropower Plants

Map Ref. # (a)	Powerplant Name	Watershed Name	Owner (b)	Completion Date (c)	Capacity MW	Yearly MWh Production (d)	Head (in feet)	Kwh per AF Water (e)	Value per AF Water (f)	Cumulative AF Value (g)
94	Balch 1 & 2	Kings	PG&E	1958	139	603,190	2,389	2,031	$51	$76
95	Haas	Kings	PG&E	1958	135	492,366	2,444	2,077	$52	$128
96	Kings River	Kings	PG&E	1962	44.1	194,072	798	678	$17	$25
97	Pine Flat	Kings	KRCD	1983	165	197,499	386	328	$8	$8
98	Kaweah 1	Kaweah	SCE	1929	2.3	13,471	1,326	1,127	$28	$28
99	Kaweah 2	Kaweah	SCE	1929	1.8	12,462	367	312	$8	$24
100	Kaweah 3	Kaweah	SCE	1913	2.8	25,633	775	659	$16	$16
101	Borel	Kern	SCE	1932	12	65,869	261	222	$6	$30
102	Kern Canyon	Kern	PG&E	1921	8.5	68,144	264	224	$6	$6
103	Kern River	Kern	SCE	1930	24.8	184,629	877	745	$19	$24
104	Kern River 3	Kern	SCE	1921	32	174,132	821	698	$17	$47
105	Tule (lower)	Tule	SCE	1909	2	18,152	1,140	969	$24	$24
106	Tule River	Tule	PG&E	1914	6.4	25,362	1,544	1,312	$33	$57
107	Farad	Truckee	SPPC	1933	2.8	10,340	82	70	$2	$2
108	Stampede	Truckee	USBR	1987	3	6,683	183	156	$4	$4
109	Lundy	Mono Lake	SCE	1912	3	10,103	785	667	$17	$17
110	Poole	Mono Lake	SCE	1963	10	30,052	1,671	1,420	$36	$36
111	Rush Creek	Mono Lake	SCE	1916	8.4	49,081	1,807	1,536	$38	$38
112	Big Pine	Owens River	Los Angeles	1925	3.2	15,796	1,243	1,057	$26	$26
113	Bishop Cr. 2	Owens River	SCE	1911	2.3	43,739	953	810	$20	$76
114	Bishop Cr. 3	Owens River	SCE	1913	7.2	40,724	809	688	$17	$55
115	Bishop Cr. 4	Owens River	SCE	1909	7.4	52,951	1,112	945	$24	$38
116	Bishop Cr. 5	Owens River	SCE	1970	3.5	23,428	420	357	$9	$14
117	Bishop Cr. 6	Owens River	SCE	1913	1.6	12,865	260	221	$6	$6
118	Control Gorge	Owens River	Los Angeles	1952	37.5	151,812	780	663	$17	$18
119	Cottonwood 3	Owens River	Los Angeles	1909	1.5	6,252	1,267	1,077	$27	$27
120	Division Creek	Owens River	Los Angeles	1909	0.6	5,221	1,250	1,063	$27	$27
121	Haiwee	Owens River	Los Angeles	1927	5.6	27,791	193	164	$4	$4
122	Middle Gorge	Owens River	Los Angeles	1952	37.5	154,089	795	676	$17	$35
123	Pleasant Valley	Owens River	Los Angeles	1958	3.2	12,333	76	65	$2	$2
124	Upper Gorge	Owens River	Los Angeles	1953	110	142,012	872	741	$19	$54

Sources and Footnotes for Table 3.8: Hydropower Plants in the Sierra Nevada

Sources: DWR bulletin 160-93, Pp. 304-319; FERC 1970-94 unpublished yearly production data; and authors' calculations.

(a) These reference numbers are located on Figure 3.4 .

(b) These hydroelectric power plants account for 98 percent of hydroelectric power production in the Sierra Nevada based on natural flow. Helms Canyon power plant has been excluded since, despite its size, it is a net consumer of energy (by FERC accounts it has consumed on average 156,028 megawatt hours (mWh) of energy per year between 1984 and 1994. Helms Canyon is primarily a pump storage facility and does not rely on the normal flow of the river for power generation.

(c)   SCE = Southern California Edison Co.
        PG&E = Pacific Gas and Electric Co.
        ID = Irrigation District
        OWID = Oroville Wyondotte ID
        SMUD = Sacramento Municipal Utility District
        USBR = US Bureau of Reclamation -- Mid Pacific Region
        CWA = County Water Agency
        TDP = Tri-Dam Project
        OSSJ = Oakdale South San Joaquin
        EBMUD = East Bay Municipal Water District
        SPPC = Sierra Pacific Power Co.
        KRCD = Kings River Conservation District
        HHWD = Hetch Hetchy Water District

(d) Year Installed are taken from Bulletin 160 of DWR except when FERC recorded production previous to those dates.

(e) Average yearly energy production for each plant is calculated from 1970-1994 FERC data. Where plants have been operating for less than that entire time, the average is calculated over the observed dates. The average yearly net value of energy generated is calculated by multiplying the energy generated at each plant (from the previous column) by $25 per megawatt hour (mWh). The net value of $25 per MWh of electricity was calculated as follows. In 1992, the value of a kilowatt hour (KWh) of electricity averaged around 3 cents (source: Public Utilities Commission, *Summary of Utilities Avoided Energy Prices*), from which 0.5 cents were subtracted per kWh for estimated average operating and maintenance costs (source: Energy Information Administration, 1992, *Electric Plant Cost and Power Production Expenses 1991*), to get a net value of 2.5 cents per kWh generated, or $25 per mWh.

(f) The kWh generated per acre foot (AF) of water diverted through turbines is calculated as follows. The engineering formula for measuring hydroelectric power generation is

$$Power(KWh) = \left(Flow(cfs) \times Head(feet) \times Efficiency \right) / 11.8$$

According to Dr. Calvin Warnick, (professor at the University of Idaho and author of "Hydropower Engineering"), the average efficiency of turbines in hydroelectric power plants in California is approximately 82-83 percent. Using the above formula yields a multiplier of 0.846 KWh of energy generated for every foot of head (drop).

(g) The net value of hydroelectric production per AF of diverted flow is calculated by multiplying the KWh generated (in the previous column, see footnote (g)) by 2.5 cents per KWh (see footnote (f)).

(h) The cumulative net value of hydroelectric power generated per AF of diverted water gives the value of diverting the water not only at the hydroelectric power plant listed, but also of diverting it at all hydroelectric power plants below that point along the tributary. This value can be translated as the potential hydroelectric value of runoff water originating from, or above, the given power plant (see Figure 3.8).

Actual Costs, Market Values and Estimated Economic Values of Water Diversions

The most explicit valuation of water flowing from Sierra Nevada rivers is for its non-consumptive use to generate electricity. Since there is a large market with many buyers and sellers for wholesale electric power, as well as an accepted methodology for comparing the opportunity costs of different types of electric power, the economic value of water used to produce hydropower can be calculated. The economic value of water diverted and consumed for agricultural and municipal uses is more difficult to estimate, since these uses are based on water rights that are not actively traded or independently valued. The following estimates are based on the limited market valuations and estimates of the total revenue benefits of using the water. The rapidly evolving area of inter-regional water marketing in California that began in earnest with the State Water Bank during the past drought will clarify economic values of water in California. In-stream water flows also create direct and indirect economic benefits to many recreational users. Fishing and white water rafting are the two most identifiable activities that directly benefit from in-stream water flows. In addition, a large fraction of boating, camping, hiking, and other dispersed recreational activity takes place near rivers and streams and indirectly benefits from in-stream water flows.

The high value of water diverted from its Sierra Nevada origin, is enshrined in the legal doctrine that has evolved to facilitate the transfer of use rights. The doctrine of prior appropriation—a system often described with the phrase "first in time, first in right"—allows acquisition of a water right simply by diverting it from its natural stream and applying it to a "beneficial use." The application of appropriative rights brought some semblance of order to the unprecedented manipulation of west side streams and rivers during the gold mining era of the mid-1800s. The extension of the appropriation doctrine into the 20th century reinforced the primacy of diverted water over in-stream water as a valued commodity. The enormous public investments in irrigation works and municipal supply lines throughout this century, formalized a system that values water if it can be moved out of the stream or river.

Values of Water for Hydropower Generation

The economic value of water used to generate hydropower is unique in many respects. First, the total value of the output is only weakly correlated with the capital investment in hydropower plants because of highly variable rainfall, and fluctuations in region-wide wholesale electricity prices. Even with relatively low electricity prices and rainfall, significant revenues are produced. For example, the profit made by the City of San Francisco from the power generated as their drinking water exits Hetch Hetchy reservoir was over $30 million dollars in 1994 (Lucas 1995).

Nearly all the value goes to public utilities or corporations based in distant cities that own the hydropower plants. Property taxes paid to counties on hydropower facilities return a small fraction of the surplus value generated. With the exception of some small watershed restoration projects in the Feather River drainage, there is little reinvestment of hydropower revenues to restore or mitigate the environmental impacts. Even though water used for hydropower production is still available downstream and produces considerable revenue, hydropower water rights are often junior to irrigation rights. Water diversion schedules are rarely optimized to achieve the highest level of total hydropower and irrigation benefits.

Since most hydropower is produced by companies that also distribute it, a specific market price for hydropower does not exist. The California Energy Commission (CEC) estimates the value of hydropower by comparing it to the cost avoided by not having to use the next most expensive fuel—gas or oil-fired power plants. This essentially represents what electric utility providers are willing to pay for electricity on the open market. Avoided costs have ranged from as low as 1.4 cents per kWh in the early 1970's, to almost 8 cents per kWh in 1981, based on constant 1992 values (Figure 3.5). The present availability of inexpensive power generated with natural gas suggests that the wholesale value of electrical power will not return to the levels of the early 1980s in the near future.

Figure 3.5: Avoided Costs of Not Having To Use Fossil Fuels

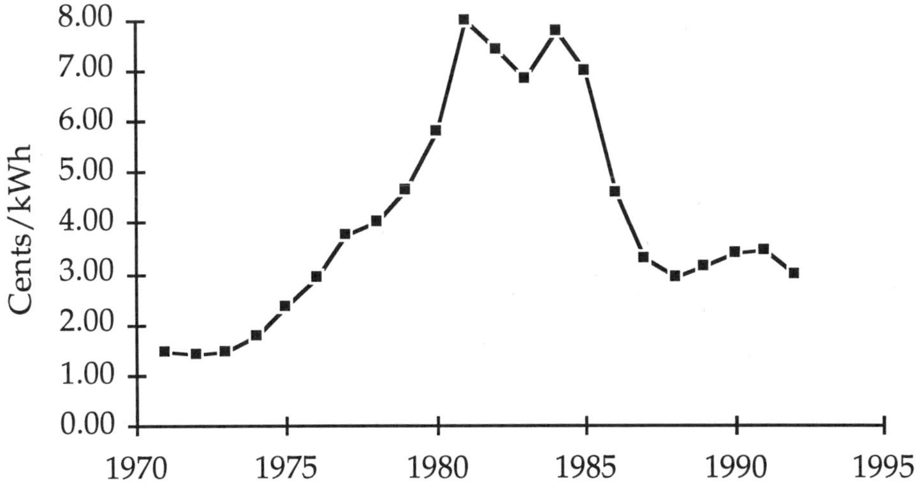

Sources: American Petroleum Institute before 1980, PUC from 1980. 1992 Dollars

The increased costs of oil and gas made hydropower production increasingly attractive up through 1983. The California Energy Commission and the Department of Water Resources promoted the development of new power plants, forecasting a doubling of energy prices in real terms by the year 2000 (CEC 1981; DWR 1979; DWR 1981). Such predictions encouraged the industry to develop sites that may otherwise have remained undeveloped at then prevailing energy rates. Contrary to projections, energy prices fell after 1984 and many plants whose feasibility was based on the optimism of these forecasts may be unable to recover their initial investment costs.

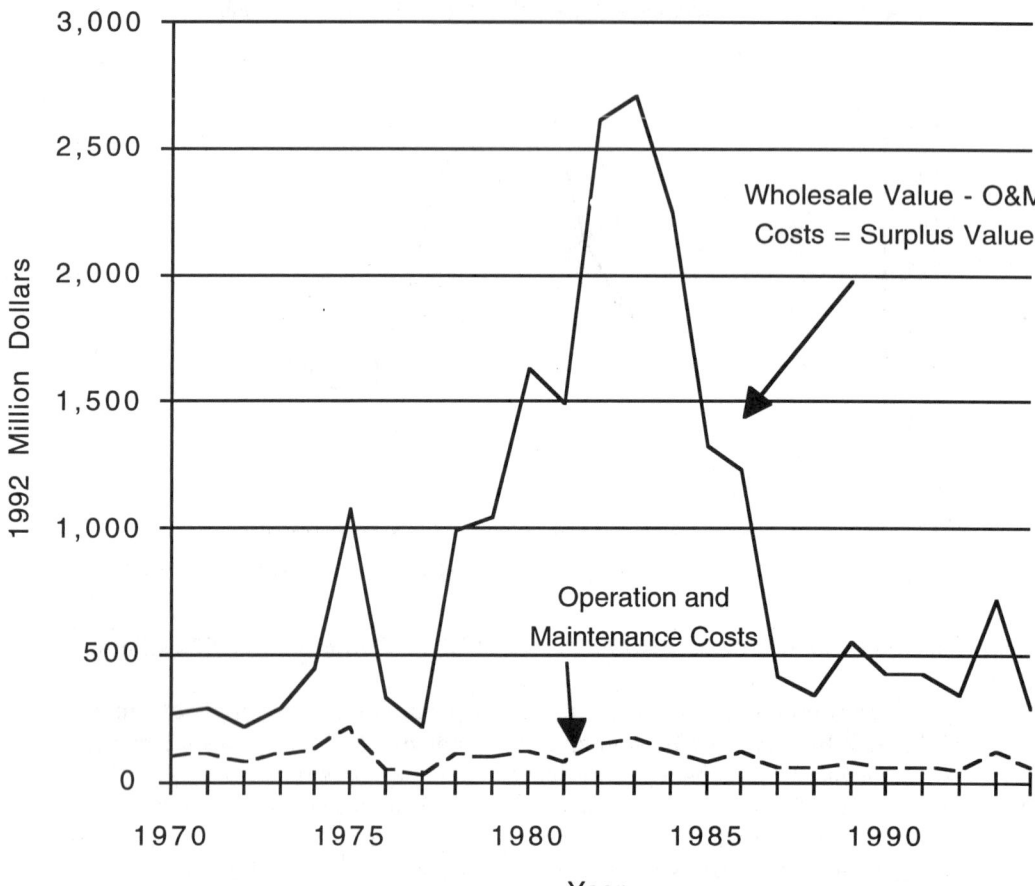

Figure 3.6: Surplus Value from Hydropower Generation in the Sierra Nevada

Source: operating and maintenance costs derived from California Energy Commission data.
Note: 1973 value extrapolated from 1972 and 1974 values.

The surplus value of Sierra Nevada water from generating hydropower is large and highly variable (Figure 3.6). It has ranged from a low of $217 million in 1972 to a high of $2.7 billion in 1983 (all values in constant 1992 dollars). The average surplus value $914 million per year over the past 24-year period is considerably higher than the more conservative projection of $600 million per year based on present low wholesale electricity prices.

With essentially free water and very low operation and maintenance costs, hydropower is relatively inexpensive to produce once facilities have been built. Operating and maintenance costs for producing energy average around 0.5 cents per kWh (Energy Information Administration 1992). Surplus value is calculated as the revenues from sales of hydropower, minus operating and maintenance costs. Investment costs are not accounted for since these sunk costs have usually been written off during the early years of production.

<u>Distribution of Hydropower Generation by River, Watersheds, and Power Plants</u>

Within the Sierra Nevada and within each river basin, hydropower plants are not spread evenly. Based on the average power output per acre foot of total flow, the most developed river systems are the tributaries of the Owens River on the east side and the San Joaquin River in the south. The degree of hydropower development is consistently high on most of the rivers in the central and northern Sierra Nevada. Figure 3.7 illustrates the power output pattern of sites with dots sized to plant output. Even for the most productive river basins such as the San Joaquin and Feather , most output is concentrated on a few reaches, or 'power tributaries.'

Table 3.10: Hydropower Value by River Basin

River Basin	Million Kilowatt Hours (1970-1994 average)	Million Dollars at 2.5¢/kWh	Unimpaired Flow in TAF	Power Value Per Acre foot
Butte Creek	167,098	$4.18	NA	NA
Feather	5,736,826	$143.42	4,617	$31
Yuba-Bear	2,668,565	$66.71	2,389	$28
American	3,573,237	$89.33	2,736	$33
Mokelumne	1,195,183	$29.88	747	$40
Calaveras	3,081	$0.08	NA	NA
Stanislaus	1,393,756	$34.84	1,149	$30
Tuolumne	2,384,598	$59.61	1,882	$32
Merced	341,762	$8.54	966	$9
San Joaquin	4,157,535	$103.94	1,776	$59
Kings	1,487,127	$37.18	1,669	$22
Kaweah	51,566	$1.29	444	$3
Tule	43,514	$1.09	145	$8
Kern	492,774	$12.32	716	$17
North Lahontan	17,023	$0.43	409	$1
South Lahontan	778,249	$19.46	149	$131
Total	24,491,894	$612.30	19,794	$31

Source: Hydropower production - FERC; Unimpaired Flow - DWR.
Notes: NA - not available.

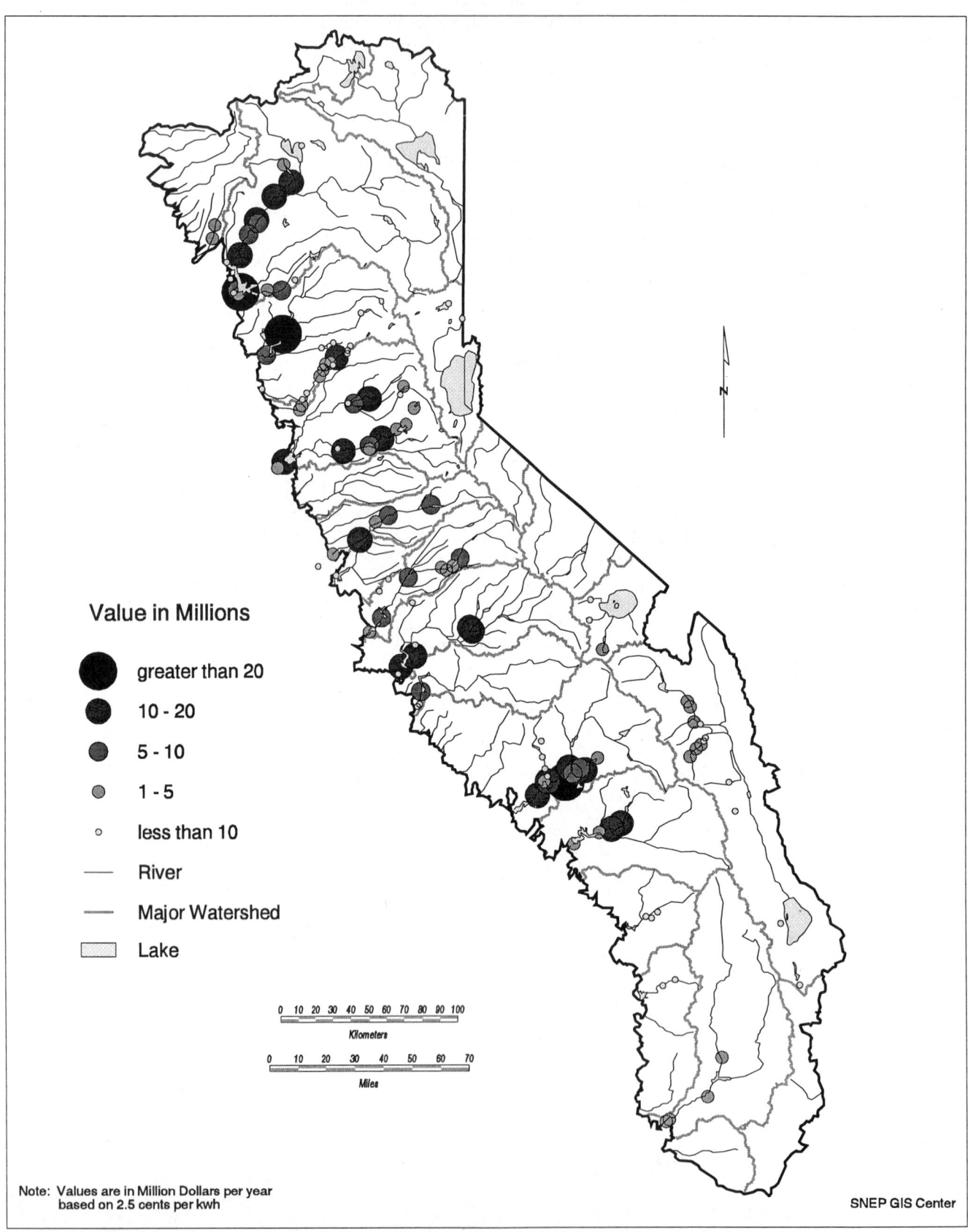

Value in Millions

- greater than 20
- 10 - 20
- 5 - 10
- 1 - 5
- less than 10
- —— River
- —— Major Watershed
- Lake

0 10 20 30 40 50 60 70 80 90 100
Kilometers

0 10 20 30 40 50 60 70
Miles

Note: Values are in Million Dollars per year
based on 2.5 cents per kwh

SNEP GIS Center

Figure 3.7

1012

The possibility of increasing runoff to supply downstream hydropower turbines has been the focus of considerable research. Cloud seeding to increase precipitation, specific forest canopy patterns to delay the snowmelt, and vegetation removal to reduce evapo-transpiration from trees and other vegetation have all been suggested as means to increase the value of Sierra Nevada runoff (Romm et. al. 1988; Marvin 1996). Based on a methodology similar to that used by Romm and Ewing (1987), Figure 3.7 illustrates the potential hydropower value of one additional acre foot of runoff from each planning watershed in the Sierra Nevada study region. Watersheds immediately upstream of long vertical drop hydropower sites would produce very large revenues per acre foot while watersheds flowing directly into the foothill reservoirs would produce very little additional value.

The variation in the economic value derived from hydropower production is also apparent at the level of individual power plants. Across the whole Sierra Nevada, 40 million acre feet of water go through hydropower turbines in an average year. This is twice the total annual flow, since a considerable amount of water goes through a sequence of turbines. Overall, each acre foot diverted through turbines produces $15 of electric power valued at a wholesale power rate of 2.5 cents/kWh. Hydropower facilities typically associated with the large multipurpose dams in the Sierra Nevada produce nearly half the power because so much water is diverted through their turbines. Of the remaining 99 hydropower facilities, the half with large vertical drops divert the same amount of water as the sites with smaller vertical drops but produce more than five times as much power. The financial benefits for the less efficient sites are relatively small relative to the amount of water they divert from Sierra Nevada rivers. Figures3.8 and 3.9 illustrate the substantial variation in hydropower production in terms of location and plants.

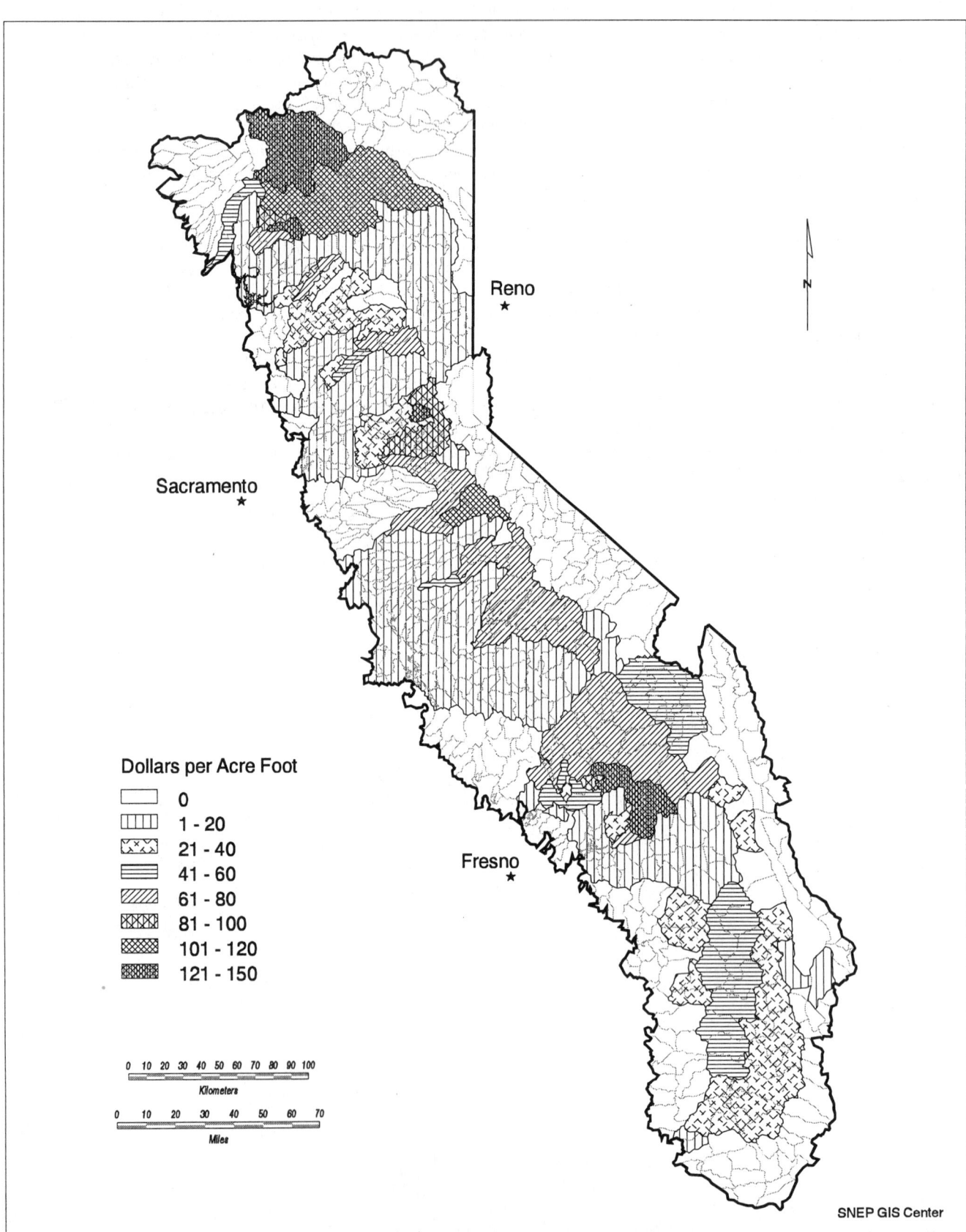

Dollars per Acre Foot

☐	0
▥	1 - 20
▨	21 - 40
▤	41 - 60
▨	61 - 80
▦	81 - 100
▦	101 - 120
▦	121 - 150

Reno

Sacramento

Fresno

0 10 20 30 40 50 60 70 80 90 100
Kilometers

0 10 20 30 40 50 60 70
Miles

SNEP GIS Center

1014

Figure 3.8

Table 3.11: Hydropower Facility Typology

Figure 3.9 Reference	Type of Facility	Number of Facilities	Percent of total diversions	Percent of total power	Average $/AF	Total Value Million Dollars
1	Large multi-purpose	25	66%	47%	$11	$289
2	More efficient	49	18%	45%	$38	$276
· 3	Less efficient	50	16%	8%	$7	$47

Figure 3.9 : Volumes and Financial Efficiency of Hydropower plants

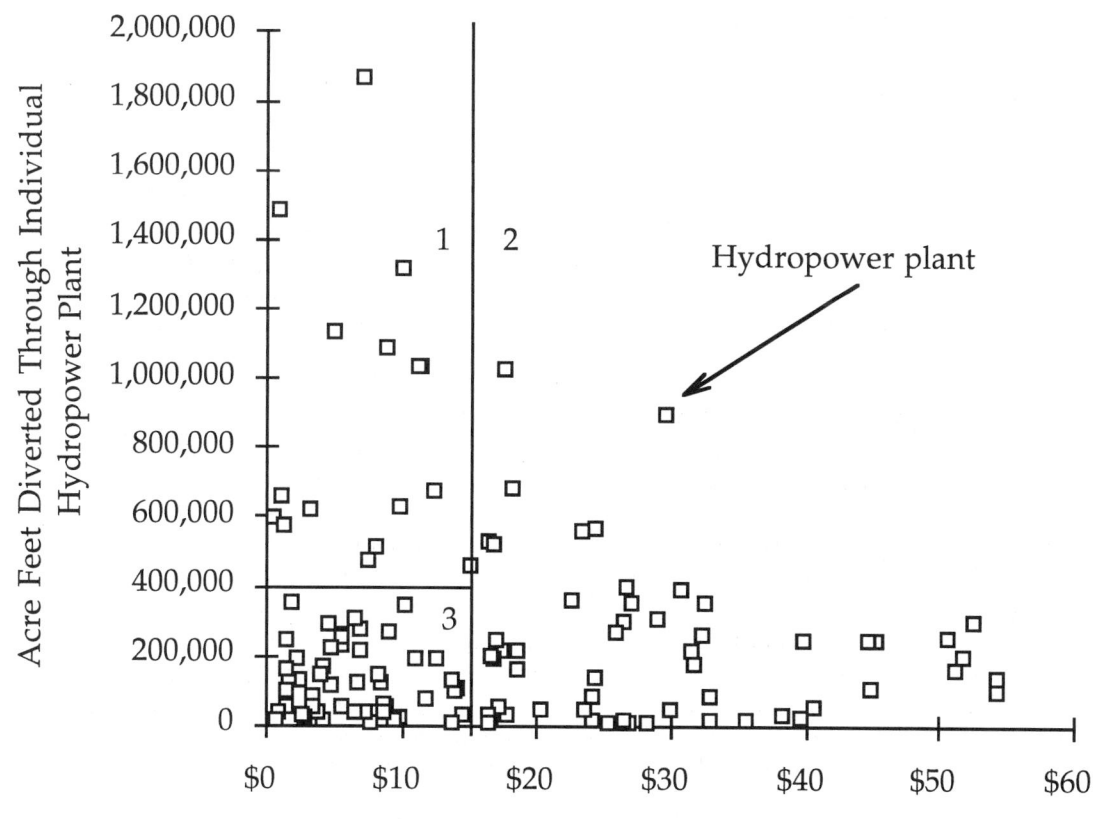

Note: the two large dams of the State Water Project (Oroville Dam and Thermalito) are not shown in the figure but are included in the calculations.

Hydropower in the Sierra Nevada is produced by both public entities and private corporations. Pacific Gas & Electric generates the most power of any single producer in the region (Table 3.3). Irrigation districts serving various communities in the Central Valley and the Sierra Nevada combine to make up the second largest type of institutional owner. Of the more distant urban water rights holders, Sacramento and San Francisco receive large hydropower benefits compared to the Los Angeles Department of Water and Power and the East Bay Municipal Utility District.

Table 3.12: Power Production by Institution

Institution	Pct of Total Power Production
Pacific Gas & Electric Co.	32%
Irrigation Districts	20%
Southern Calif. Edison Co.	18%
State Of California	9%
Hetch Hetchy Water and Power	8%
Sacramento MUD	7%
U.S. Bureau of Reclamation	4%
Los Angeles Dept. of Water and Power	2%
East Bay MUD	0.4%

calculated from FERC records

Values of Water for Direct Recreational Use and Indirect Recreational uses

The recreational value of in-stream water is difficult to measure because few direct fees are collected and the availability of the water is only one component of many recreational experiences. A large fraction of recreation in the Sierra Nevada is closely associated with lakes, rivers, and streams but it is difficult to assign a dollar value to the in-stream value. Based on estimates of the consumer value or willingness to pay for just two related activities—recreational fishing and white water rafting, the annual value is in excess of $250 million. Using the travel cost method, the Forest Service estimated the value of a day of fishing at $18.96 (McCollum 1990). Based on the total number of fishing days estimated by the Forest Service on National Forests within the Sierra Nevada, the total economic value of recreational fishing in the Sierra Nevada is $146 million (Tripp and Rockland 1988). The estimate of recreational fishing at reservoirs, lakes and rivers outside of National Forests could increase the overall economic value to over $200 million.

White water rafting is the second most significant recreational use of Sierra Nevada water with an estimated 849,000 visitor days per year on rivers within the Sierra Nevada (Department of Water Resources 1994). Based on an average cost of commercial trips of $80/day and two thirds of the trips being commercial (George Wendt 1995), the recreational value is over 50 million dollars annually. Fishing and white water rafting are just two activities dependent on maintaining high quantities and high quality of the water bodies which comprise a critical component of the large recreational industry in the Sierra Nevada. The millions of dollars spent to maintain high water quality in the Lake Tahoe Basin is additional evidence of the importance of in-lake and in-stream flows.

Total Economic Benefits of Agricultural, Municipal, Hydropower and Recreation-related Water Uses

The lack of an active market among different users of diverted or in-stream water uses makes it impossible to place a single dollar value on water use for all sectors. A variety of alternative approaches are used to develop dollar values for different water uses. The marginal value of water for different uses is estimated using approaches similar to those reviewed in Boggess et. al. (1993). The primary approach uses a value based on the cost of alternative supplies purchased in the limited water markets. The value for environmental uses is based on the price paid in 1995 for water purchased under the CVPIA for use in wetlands throughout the region. Municipal water values are based on current costs for water supplies being purchased by growing metropolitan regions.

Different levels of subsidies for agricultural water supplies limits the usefulness of current delivery prices to estimate the value of water used for different crops. The values assigned to water used in agriculture in different agricultural regions are based on regional shadow values of ground water calculated in different regions as calculated by the Department of Water Resources (Farnam 1994), and as a fraction of the total revenue per acre foot of water applied to the most common crops grown in different regions. A recent analysis of the crop-specific and region-specific revenues per acre foot of irrigation water (Sunding et. al. 1995) illustrates a range from $15 to $1,000 per acre foot for different crops grown with water diverted from Sierra Nevada rivers. The estimated values of water rights for different uses in different agriculutral regions are summarized in table 3.13.

Table 3.13 Farm Revenue per Acre Foot of Irrigation Water

Crop	Revenue per acre foot (AF) of water
Pasture	$15-$19
Rice	$44-$65
Field crops	$60-$140
Row crops	$176-$259
Vegetables	$451-$843
Orchards, Vineyards	$337-$940

Source : (Sunding et. al. 1995)

Table 3.14: Estimated Economic Value of Water Rights for Different Uses

Use and Location	$/acre foot	Rationale
Agriculture		
Sierra Nevada (SN)	$10	Irrigated pasture and hay make up 90% of irrigated acreage (Agricultural Commissioners Reports)
River Basin (IR)	$25	Earlier irrigation projects along Sacramento River and on east side grow medium value crops. Cost of ground water pumping vary from $30 to $100 depending on ground water basin (Farnam 1994)
Inter-basin export (EX)	$100	High value cotton and orchard crops are major consumers (Sunding et. al. 1995).
Municipal		
Sierra Nevada and River Basin (SN and IR)	$50	Urban suppliers charge from $400 to $700 per acre foot in these areas (Black + Veatch 1995)
Inter-basin export to coastal cities (EX)	$100	Southern California's Metropolitan Water District is purchasing new water rights of $150 to $175 per acre foot. Average urban water rates vary from $700 to $1,000 per acre foot in major coastal metropolitan areas (Black + Veatch 1995).
Environment		
Riparian areas and wetlands (SN and IR)	$25	CVPIA and FWS purchase water at $25/AF for wetlands in Sacramento Valley (USBR 1995).

Based on the estimates in table 3.13, the water use volumes in table 3.14 can be converted into economic value of the water rights for different end users. Future evidence from direct water marketing or more detailed pricing analyses should be used to improve these initial estimates.

Table 3.15: Water Use in Thousand Acre Feet by Hydrologic Region and End Use

Region	Agriculture			Municipal			Environment		Hydro-power	Total Water Use
	SN	IR	EX	SN	IR	EX	SN	IR	see Note	
Sacramento	373	2,791	953	79	289	1,589	1,420	999	24,159	8,495
San Joaquin	21	3,552	983	43	181	575	554		12,641	5,909
Tulare Lake	20	3,585		5	95		34		2,251	3,739
S. Lahontan	147	16		15	12	437	128	550	1,186	755
N. Lahontan	460		580	31	3	40	17		163	1,681
Totals	1,021	9,945	2,517	173	581	2,641	2,153	1,549	40,400	20,580

Note: Water used for hydropower is temporarily diverted through turbines and is not a consumptive use as are the agriculture, municipal, and environmental end uses.

Table 3.16: Estimated Economic Water Value by Hydrologic Region and End Use

	Agriculture			Municipal			Environment		Hydro-power	Total Water Value
Est. Value /AF	$10	$25	$100	$50	$50	$100	$25	$25	NA	
Region	SN	IR	EX	SN	IR	EX	SN	IR	SN	
Sacramento	$4	$70	$95	$4	$14	$159	$36	$25	$299	$706
San Joaquin	<$1	$89	$98	$2	$9	$58	$14		$237	$507
Tulare Lake	<$1	$90		<$1	$5		$1		$52	$148
S. Lahontan	$1	<$1		$1	$1	$44	$3		$19	$70
N. Lahontan	$5		$58	$2	<$1	$4	<$1		$5	$73
Totals	$10	$249	$252	$9	$29	$264	$54	$25	$612	$1,503

Legend : SN - within Sierra Nevada; IR - within hydrologic region; EX - inter-basin transfers.
Source: (California Department of Water Resources, 1994).
Note: The Sacramento region excludes the main Sacramento River and all western tributaries.

When the different economic value of water to various users is accounted for, the economic benefits are dominated by hydropower users (40%) and irrigated agriculture (34%). The economic value of municipal water use (20%) is proportionally greater than the volume used because of the high value to large metropolitan areas of a steady supply of high quality water. The extensive infrastructure to move water through hydropower turbines and out of natural drainage basins leads to three quarters of the economic value going to users who are not in the natural drainage basins of the rivers. Water uses allocated to environmental uses in Wild and Scenic rivers and in wetlands (including a small share for the Bay-Delta) accounts for a relatively small share of total water volume or value.

Conclusion

Large scale water diversions are the source of a considerable portion of the value produced by the Sierra Nevada ecosystem. Major reservoir capacity in the Sierra Nevada is now equal to the unimpaired flow of all the major rivers. In an average year, 40 million acre feet, double the unimpaired flow, is taken out of streams , run through hydropower turbines and returned. Nearly two thirds of the water diverted from Sierra Nevada rivers and streams goes to irrigated agricultural in the Central Valley. The remaining water diverted out of the rivers goes to municipal users and wetland habitats in the Central Valley.

Water diversions are both a major source of economic value to the eventual users and the cause of much of the decline in fish populations and other water dependent populations and habitats. The estimated annual value of the right to divert water from the Sierra Nevada is approximately $1.5 billion. Hydropower, followed by irrigated agriculture and municipal uses in distant cities, are the three largest sources of economic value. Recreation associated with in-stream flows is also a major source of economic value.

The large economic benefits of water diversions and in-stream flows produce few direct payments, user fees, or taxes. The value of both diverted and in-stream water flows are not uniform across the Sierra Nevada. The non-random patterns of economic value and aquatic value suggests considerable scope for potential approaches to improve aquatic conditions dependent on more natural flows with limited reductions in the total economic value derived from Sierra Nevada water.

CHAPTER 4: FEDERAL AND PRIVATE TIMBER IN THE SIERRA NEVADA

Timber harvesting and management have been central facets of land use in the Sierra Nevada since 1850. The present timber resource base of the Sierra Nevada includes 2.4 million acres of private timber lands and 4.6 million acres of federal land on which commercial timber harvesting is allowed. In general, private timber lands are at lower elevations, have higher site quality, and have been harvested continuously since the Nineteenth Century. Much of the federal timberland is at higher altitude, often of lower site quality, and was not harvested, if at all, until after World War II. Since 1948 records of private and public timber harvests have followed two distinct patterns. Private harvests peaked in 1952 and have only recently begun to increase since a harvest nadir around 1970. Federal harvests climbed rapidly after World War II and stabilized at a plateau of 800 million board feet from 1966 until 1979. Large fluctuations in timber markets in the 1980s and the 1990s affected both public and private harvest levels. Policy changes for both federal and private lands during the 1990s has increased the variability in harvest levels and uncertainty over future harvest levels.

Figure 4.1: Private and Public Timber Harvests 1948-1994

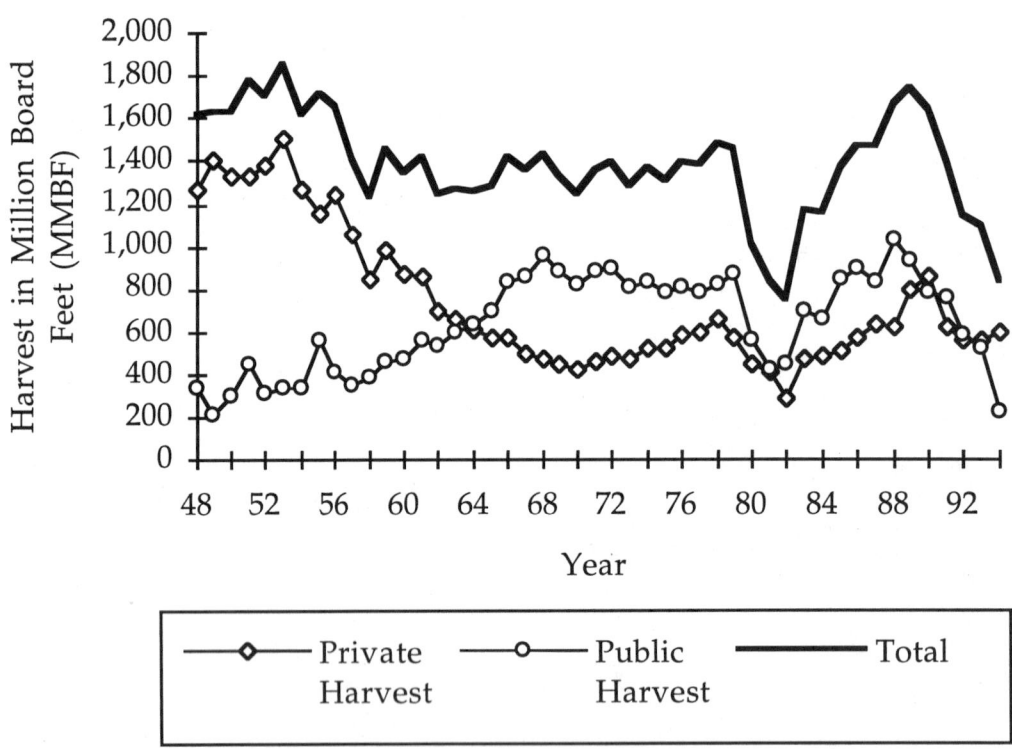

Sources: USFS PNW and Zivnuska et. al. (1965) for 1948-1978, California State Board of Equalization 1978-1994.

Regional Forest Productivity

Two types of site productivity measurements are used for taxation of private lands and forest planning on federal lands respectively. Region-wide comparisons of site productivity are difficult because neither measurement is available for all forested acres within each county. If harvest levels are assumed to be proportional to site productivity, then the long term harvest averages provides a measurement of forest productivity in the Sierra Nevada. The most productive forests in the Sierra

Nevada are those in the central Sierra Nevada. Forests in both the northern and southern ends of the Sierra Nevada have lower site quality and considerably lower harvests per total commercial forest acre levels. A comparison of average harvest levels from 1948 to 1977 and 1978 to 1994 shows a slight drop in the average harvest per acre as the harvest pattern shifted from old growth to young growth stands.

Table 4.1: Total County Harvest per Acre of Total Commercial Forests 1948-1977 and 78-94

Major Timber Producing Counties	Board Feet/Acre 1948-1977	Board Feet/Acre 1978-1994
Lassen	221	147
Plumas	200	175
Sierra	202	206
Butte	246	209
Yuba	508	276
Nevada	223	152
Placer	252	222
El Dorado	391	351
Amador	358	461
Calaveras	433	346
Tuolumne	296	244
Mariposa	80	163
Madera	236	201
Fresno	237	210

Source: harvest - USFS PNW and California Board of Equalization; commercial forest acreage (1985) - USFS PNW.

Harvest Composition

From an economic perspective , the two most significant changes in timber harvests in the Sierra Nevada over the past two decades have been the increase in the harvest of young or second growth timber and the increasing prices for what had traditionally been considered lower grade timber. After 1982, the level of young growth harvests more than doubled while old growth harvests have steadily declined. Most of the timber harvest from private land now consists of young growth trees. Restrictions on old growth harvests on federal lands have also increased the relative importance of young growth harvests. Compared to other regions of California, the Sierra Nevada is less dependent on old growth harvests and has more acres of mature young growth forests which can produce sustainable harvests.

Figure 4.2: Young and Old Growth Harvests in the Sierra Nevada, 1968-1992

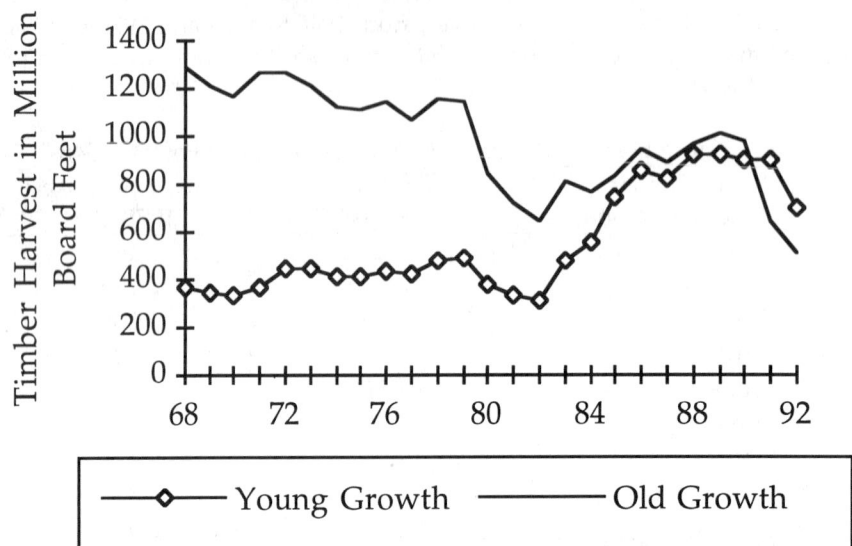

Source: USFS PNW.

Young growth, fire and disease salvage, and firs have consistently receive lower prices than old growth, green trees, and pines but the gap has narrowed. These relative values have changed in recent years as producers and consumers have responded to constraints on the supply of higher quality stumpage. Lower quality stumpage received 43% of the value of higher quality stumpage on average between 1978 and 1988 . Since 1995, lower quality stumpage has received an average of 61% of higher quality stumpage (California State Board of Equalization Various Years-a). This increase in the relative value of lower value trees may have significant impacts on the priorities for timber management. In particular, many types of multi-product sales that previously had been considered as uneconomical may be viable if the lower value products receive higher prices.

Revenue Flows from Timber

Total revenue from timber harvests have not been proportional to harvests due to the pattern of stumpage prices over the past ten years. Since the California State Board of Equalization began publishing summaries of stumpage prices by county and species, average Sierra Nevada stumpage rates rose steadily from 1985 to 1992 and then escalated very rapidly between 1992 and 1994. California State Board of Equalization values for 1995 and 1996 as well as long term price trends used by some timber industry consultants (Rinehart 1995) suggest that prices are dropping and will return to the price trajectory of the 1985-1992 period. Projections of revenue based on the high stumpage prices received in the early 1990s will significantly overstate probable revenues over the next decade if these prices follow the projected path suggested by recent stumpage prices.

Figure 4.3 : Price Trend and Projections for Sierra Stumpage, 1984-2010

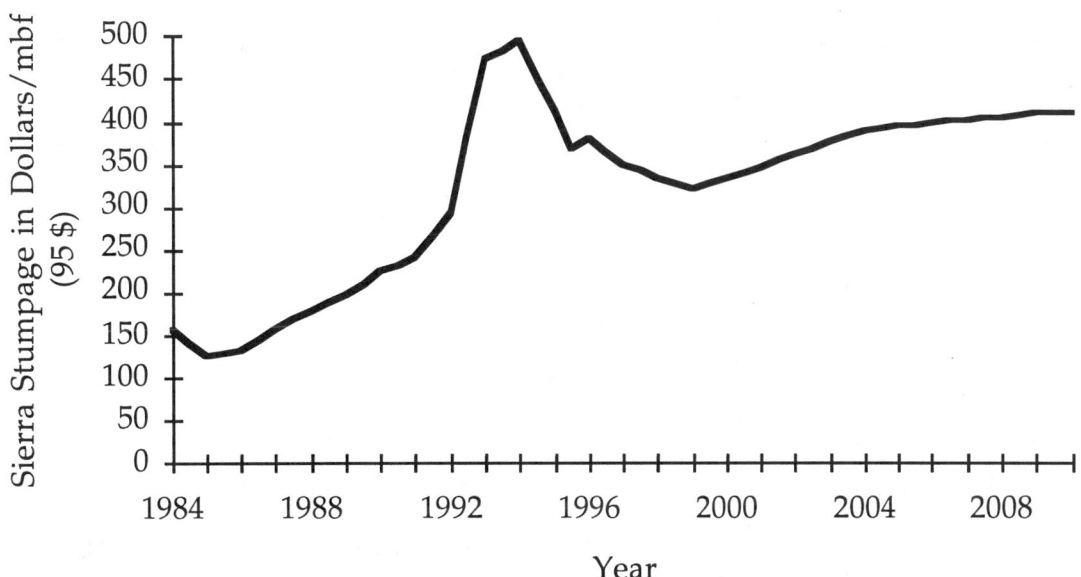

Sources: California State Board of Equalization 1984-1996 and Rinehart and Associates for timber price projections 1996-2010. Prices in constant 1995 dollars.

Total Harvest Value

The doubling of stumpage prices from the 1980s to the 1990s led to a large increase in the total harvest value from the Sierra Nevada over the past decade. In the 1990s, the value of private timber harvests surpassed the value of public timber harvests for the first time in more than three decades . County revenues from the Forest Service revenue sharing stayed relatively stable until 1994 when very low volumes and lower prices combined to reduce overall public harvest value to its lowest level in a decade. The average value of all public and private stumpage over 1984 to 1994 period was 318 million dollars (1995 dollars).

Table 4.2: Stumpage Value in Million 1995 Dollars

Year	Public Harvests	Private Harvests	Total Harvests
1984	109	77	185
1985	104	69	173
1986	128	83	211
1987	158	105	263
1988	186	135	322
1989	171	178	349
1990	167	212	379
1991	186	177	362
1992	146	193	339
1993	186	326	513
1994	96	310	406

Source: California State Board of Equalization

Employment

Direct employment in timber management and harvesting in the Sierra Nevada reflects a combination of changing harvest levels, increases in labor productivity, and changes in the types of wood products produced in the Sierra Nevada region. Since the low point of harvests and employment in 1982, overall employment rose rapidly until 1990 and has since declined. Most of the employment growth has occurred in the remanufacturing sector. Increased labor productivity in the logging and sawmill sectors slowed the increase in job creation during the increasing harvest levels during the latter half of the 1980s.

Figure 4.4: Total public and private sector jobs in timber industry

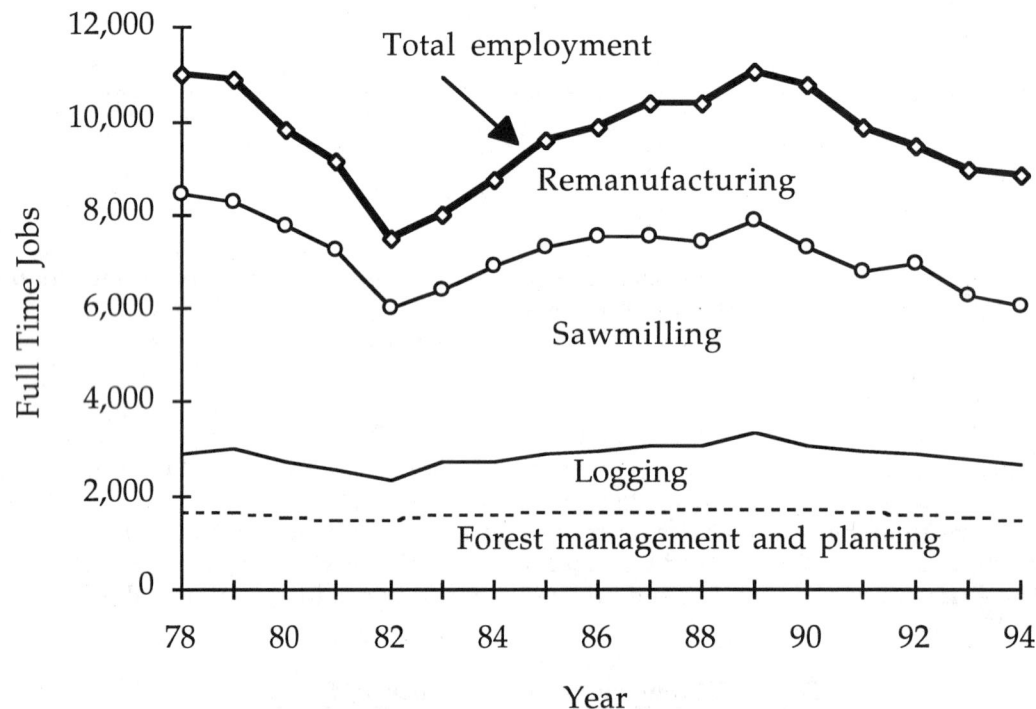

Source: Employment Development Department. Forest management and employment estimated from U.S. Forest Service employment records and timber industry case studies.

During the 1990s, sawmills went through a period of consolidation similar to that which occurred after the 1982 recession. Sawmills constructed on optimistic projections of continuing high Forest Service harvests of the late 1980s increased capacity above actual harvest levels and led to the closure of a number of older mills. From 1987 to 1992, milling capacity dropped by 7% while the number of mills dropped by 43% (from 38 to 22). Since 1992 there has been further consolidation owing to declining federal harvests as well as technological change in sawmilling. Employment associated with timber harvesting has historically been a large portion of total Sierra Nevada manufacturing employment. Employment derived from Sierra Nevada timber resources is of two principal types: employment directly tied to resource extraction, mainly logging and sawmilling, and employment tied to wood products remanufacturing. The first type is by necessity based in the region where the trees grow; the second is often located closer to transportation networks and final demand.

Timber employment in the SNEP region accounts for less than 5% of total employment in all but three counties—Amador, Plumas and Sierra. Regionally, timber employment as a percentage of all employment decreased from 3.4% to 2.6% for the counties totally within the Sierra Nevada during the 1978 to 1994 period. For the twelve counties fully within the SNEP region, timber employment dropped from 63% of all manufacturing employment in the Sierra Nevada in 1978 to only 29% in 1993 (U. S. Bureau of the Census 1980; U. S. Bureau of the Census 1995).

Contrary to standard assumptions, timber industry employment has not varied linearly with timber harvest levels. An analysis of data covering the past fifteen years suggests three reasons for the differences. First, labor productivity is increasing due to new technology and smaller logs. Second, short term rigidities in sawmill staffing reduce layoffs as long as sawmills stay open. And finally, market-led rather than raw material-led changes in wood remanufacturing employment represent the majority of the net changes in timber industry employment.

The following figure illustrates a long term decline in labor requirements and an inverse relationship of labor requirements and harvest levels in the Sierra Nevada. Over time, 1 to 1.5 loggers are required per million board feet of timber harvest in the Sierra Nevada. The number of sawmillers pre million board feet dropped to 2.5 in 1990 and climbed to over 5 during periods of very low harvest levels. Industry wide adoption of more efficient sawmilling technology and consolidation within the industry will most probably drive long term labor requirements towards the level achieved during 1989 and 1990.

Figure 4.5: Labor Requirements and Timber Harvest Levels in the Sierra Nevada

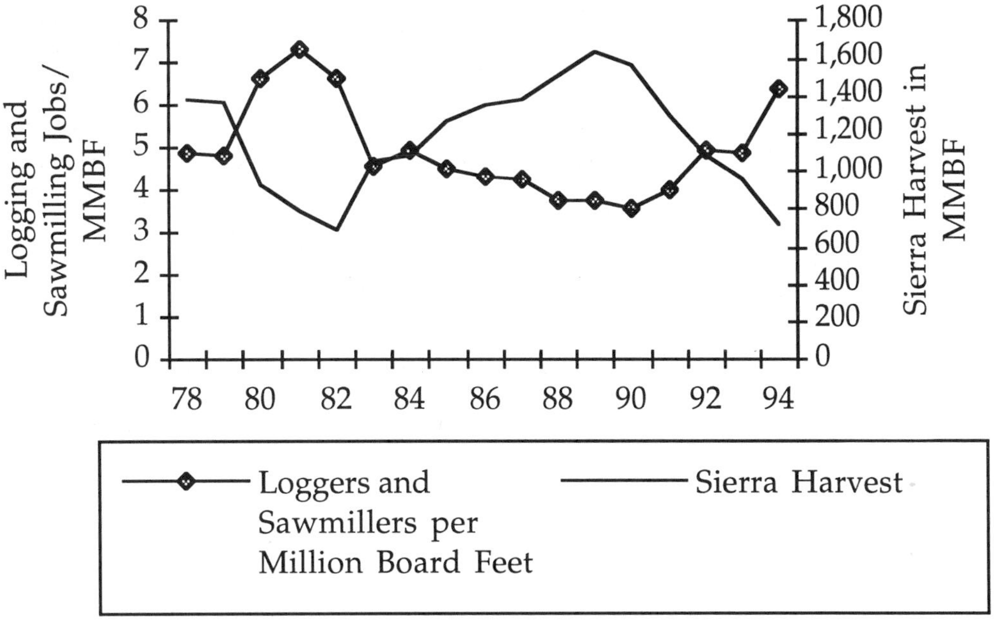

Sources: Employment - Employment Development Department; Harvest - California State Board of Equalization.

Employment in the wood remanufacturing sector has grown consistently over the past fifteen years and now employs more workers in the Sierra Nevada and Central Valley than logging and sawmilling combined. Many of these jobs are in counties outside the Sierra Nevada and the operations are not dependent on raw material from the Sierra Nevada and can purchase supplies from across the western United States and Canada. In 1992, approximately 50% of lumber arriving at remanufacturing facilities in the Central Valley was from California, 40% from Oregon, and the balance came from other regions (Stewart 1993). As timber harvests dropped in the 1990s, wood remanufacturing employment was buoyed up by overall market demand and did not shrink as much as employment in logging and sawmilling.

Regional Employment Patterns

The following tables present timber related employment in four regions of the Sierra Nevada. Logging and sawmilling employment is relatively evenly spread among the four regions while remanufacturing employment is concentrated in only two regions. The lack of employment diversification within the timber sectors in the North and South Central regions will limit the potential to maintain or increase the number of jobs in the timber industry.

Table 4.3: Logging and Sawmilling Employment in the Sierra Nevada, 1978-1994

Year	North	North Central	South Central	San Joaquin	Total
78	1,701	1,631	1,503	1,976	6,811
79	1,518	1,575	1,560	1,970	6,623
80	1,578	1,509	1,314	1,844	6,245
81	1,383	1,514	1,095	1,783	5,775
82	1,243	1,129	933	1,256	4,561
83	1,547	1,046	932	1,326	4,851
84	1,618	1,279	1,127	1,308	5,332
85	1,499	1,435	1,240	1,547	5,721
86	1,641	1,446	1,444	1,344	5,875
87	1,692	1,594	1,369	1,243	5,898
88	1,692	1,626	1,256	1,167	5,741
89	1,802	1,734	1,411	1,246	6,193
90	1,715	1,667	1,171	1,059	5,612
91	1,424	1,394	1,320	1,069	5,207
92	1,439	1,384	1,359	1,213	5,395
93	1,414	1,248	1,300	770	4,732
94	1,424	1,109	1,438	601	4,572

Source: Employment Development Department. North includes Plumas, Sierra and Lasssen.

Table 4.4: Remanufacturing Employment in the Sierra Nevada, 1978-1994

Year	North	North Central	South Central	San Joaquin	Total
78	225	578	52	1,677	2,532
79	194	647	85	1,710	2,636
80	182	416	39	1,398	2,035
81	147	374	29	1,325	1,875
82	104	284	34	1,039	1,461
83	117	362	46	1,066	1,591
84	130	447	55	1,204	1,836
85	110	513	69	1,538	2,230
86	110	546	60	1,631	2,347
87	120	716	113	1,912	2,861
88	100	766	131	1,973	2,970
89	86	904	186	1,988	3,164
90	80	1,180	238	2,001	3,499
91	71	1,033	86	1,826	3,016
92	67	686	78	1,692	2,523
93	39	689	69	1,913	2,710
94	37	732	54	1,952	2,775

Source: Employment Development Department. North includes Plumas, Sierra and Lasssen.

Employment Projections

Employment in the timber industry will depends on total harvest levels as well as the business decisions of individual businesses regarding consolidation, new investment, and product diversification. If capacity utilization returns to high levels achieved during 1989 and 1990, the logging and sawmilling jobs per million board feet of harvest will probably decline to less than four jobs per million board feet, rather than six or seven jobs per million board feet experienced during the low harvests of 1993 and 1994. Employment in the remanufacturing sector is concentrated in the regions closer to transportation networks and final markets. An expansion in remanufacturing employment in regions and communities that have been more dependent on logging and sawmilling jobs requires new investment in retooling sawmills or adding new production facilities.

Public and Private Harvest Projections

Recent published projection of future harvest levels vary widely because they use slightly different forest growth computer models and very different policy assumptions. The figure below compares three sets of projections with historic harvest levels. The historic harvests cover the counties from Lassen to Kern. The federal harvest projections are from the 1995 draft California Spotted Owl Environmental Impact Statement (EIS) (USDA Forest Service 1995). The final EIS will be published in 1996 and was not available for this analysis. The different Forest Service harvest levels are primarily a function of how much land is taken out of the existing timber base and managed for non-commodity values. The CATS projections were made by Krumland and McKillop (1990) for private forest lands in the California. They assume nearly all non-industrial owners would harvest their inventory based on a price response function common to larger industrial owners. Their estimate is the top of the white triangle. The bottom side of the white triangle is simply a constant harvest level from the baseline. The Forest and Rangelands Resources Assessment Program (FRRAP) estimate was based on a forest growth model that was more conservative than the one used by Krumland and McKillop as well as an analysis of actual harvest rates by ownership class. A major difference is their assumption that non-industrial owners will continue to harvest at the low rates they documented during the 1970s and 1980s.

The lower edge of the black triangle is the harvest estimate and the upper edge is the growth estimate. The lower estimate would be more realistic if private timber land owners increasingly valued forest for their non-timber values as opposed to their harvest value. It is apparent that all the estimates are strongly influenced by institutional assumptions regarding the timber and non-timber values to the decision making institutions. Different assumptions result in estimates of plus or minus 50% over the median estimates for both public and private timber harvests.

Figure 4.6: Historic and Projected Sierra Nevada Timber Harvests

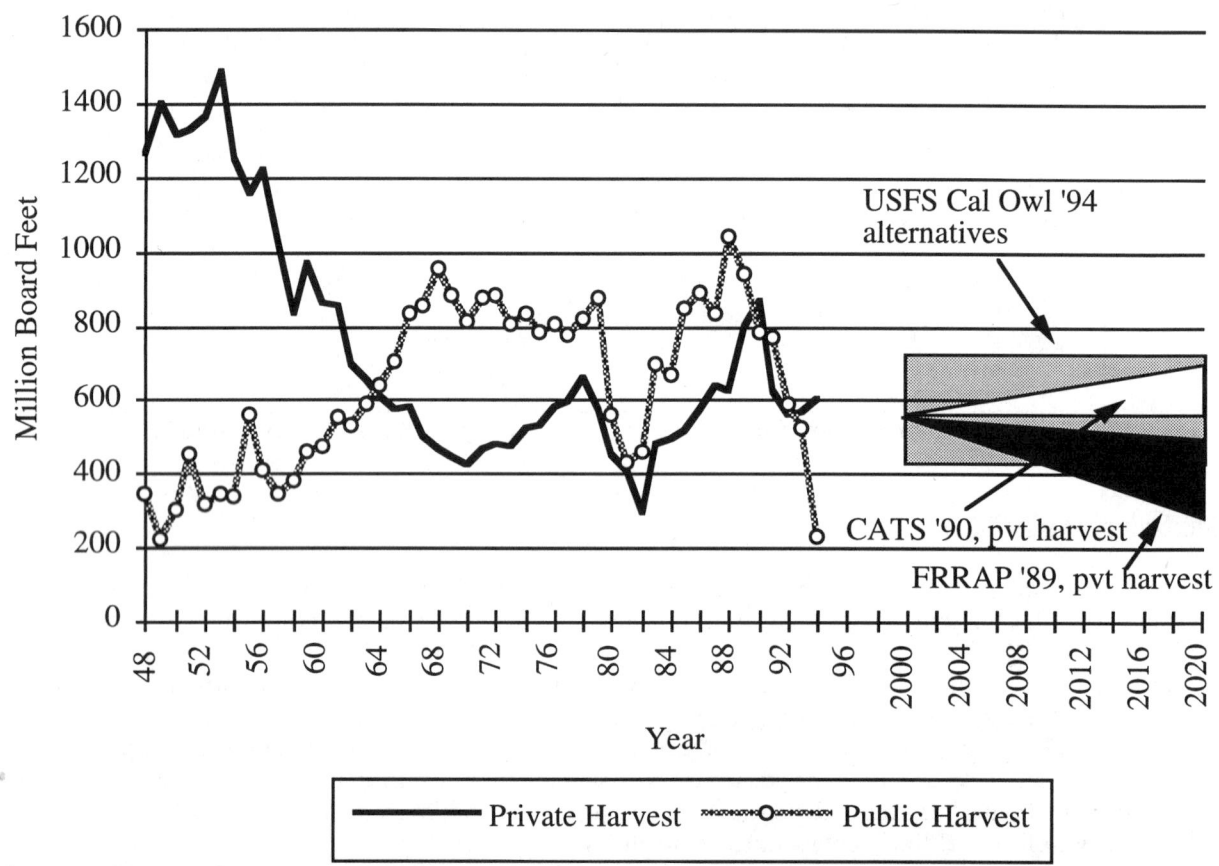

Sources: Historic harvests - USFS PNW, Zivnuska et. al., California State Board of Equalization; Projected harvests - Krumland and McKillop (1990), Forest and Rangeland Resources Assessment Program (CDF 1988), and USFS (1995).

Costs of Forest Service Ecosystem Management

Since 1991, the Forest Service shifted towards methods of forest management designed to provide more attention to non-timber attributes of the forests such as wildlife habitat, riparian zones, and old growth stands. Overall employment for the National Forests in the Sierra Nevada increased slightly even though timber harvests declined. Based on Forest Service employment classifications, the most significant employment shifts have been the reduction in new road building (civil works) and reduction in the timber operations staff within the broader forestry and fire protection category. Staffing levels are now more closely tied to the total land area that is managed than timber output. The Plumas National Forest, for example has historically been the major timber producing forest in the Sierra Nevada and is the lowest staffing per forested acre or timber output. It was the only National Forest to have a significant decline in total staff between 1986 and 1994.

Table 4.5: Forest Service Staffing Patterns by National Forest

National Forest	1986	1994
Eldorado	274	339
Inyo	166	170
Plumas	415	350
Sequoia	275	274
Sierra	329	341
Stanislaus	307	338
Tahoe	318	321
LTBMU	86	94
Region Office	412	514
Sierra Forests	2,170	2,227
Sierra share of Regional Office staff	171	231
All Sierra	2,341	2,458
Total Region	5,635	5,478

Table 4.6: Forest Service Staffing Patterns by Job Type

Staffing	1986	1994
Total Region 5 Employees	5,635	5,478
Ecosystem Scientists	5%	7%
Forestry and Fire Protection	50%	49%
Range	1%	1%
Civil Works	11%	7%
Organizational (includes recreation)	34%	36%

Source: Region 5 Employment Records, USDA Forest Service.

Cost Accounting for Federal Timber Programs

The combination of reduced harvest levels and more intensive planning and in-forest management has led to significant increases in unit costs according the accounting methodology used in the Timber Sale Program Information Reporting Systems (TSPIRS) methodology. Unit costs for the Sierran forests have increased at a rate considerably less than the National Forests covered by northern spotted owl requirements but at a rate faster than the Lassen and Modoc National Forests where there are no new planning requirements.

Table 4.7: Timber Program Expenses per Thousand Board Feet for
Selected National Forests in California

Year	Northern Spotted Owl National Forests	Sierra Nevada National Forests	Lassen and Modoc National Forests
1988	$78	$61	$57
1989	$93	$69	$58
1990	$104	$73	$61
1991	$112	$83	$61
1992	$154	$107	$74
1993	$201	$124	$87
1994	$225	$142	$86

Source: TSPIRS various years. Values in constant 1995 dollars.

Table 4.8: Cost Breakdown of Timber Management in Northern California Forests
(Average costs per mbf between 1991-94 in 1994 dollars)

Cost Categories	Northern Spotted Owl National Forests		Sierra Nevada National Forests		Lassen and Modoc National Forests	
Fixed Costs	$77		$51		$33	
Variable costs	$83		$55		$38	
(planning)		$33		$26		$17
(ecosystem analysis)		$17		$14		$8
(reforestation)		$29		$12		$9
(silviculture)		$5		$4		$4
Total	$161		$106		$71	

Source: TSPIRS various years. Values in constant 1995 dollars.

The cost differentials between different national forests can not be ascribed to any specific activity as similar differences were reported for all fixed and variable costs (Table 4.7 and 4.8). Costs associated with additional ecosystem analysis averaged $14 per million board feet for the 1991-1994 period. Ecosystem analysis costs account for only 10 to 13% of the total costs in the National Forests in the Sierra Nevada.

Trends in Costs and Revenues from Federal Timber Harvesting

Even with increasing costs, the Sierran Forests have continued to produce a significant financial surplus after accounting for the 25% share of gross receipts given to the counties. With the exception of the Sequoia National Forest, no National Forest in the Sierra Nevada was close to becoming a below cost forest according to the TSPIRS accounting system for the period 1991 to 1994. The implication for the upcoming decade is that revenues per board foot may drop while harvest costs will increase.

Table 4.9: Estimated Net Revenue per Thousand Board Feet after TSPIRS Costs and
County Revenue Sharing, 1988-94

Year	Northern Spotted Owl National Forests	Sierra Nevada National Forests	Lassen and Modoc National Forests
1988	$35	$48	$128
1989	$36	$39	$139
1990	$35	$32	$147
1991	$23	$28	$119
1992	$33	$20	$122
1993	$5	$43	$95
1994	-$8	$38	$141

Source: TSPIRS various years. Values in constant 1995 dollars.

Since 1993 timber harvests have been classified as forest stewardship (based on ecosystem management principles) or timber commodity (designed to help meet the demands of US citizens for wood products) (USDA Forest Service 1993). Although the revenue per million board feet was higher for timber commodity sales because of larger diameter and higher quality stumpage, the cost per million board feet for the forest stewardship program was 10% lower on every forest that produced a significant volume of timber in 1993 and 1994.

Conclusion

Timber harvesting on both private and public land is increasingly dominated by second growth or young growth trees. Sustainable timber harvesting policies that maintain the desired ecological viability of forests at a landscape level are under review for all types of land ownerships in the Sierra Nevada. Projections of future timber harvests vary widely because of different policy assumptions and forest growth models. It appears probable that private harvests may equal or exceed public harvests over the next few decades.

Timber industry output and employment have exhibited strongly cyclical patterns over the past fifteen years. Consolidation in logging and sawmilling sectors and expansion of remanufacturing sector have shifted activity towards the Central Valley and away from sites within the forest. The total number of mills has dropped considerably but employment has fluctuated around 10,000 workers over past fifteen years. Long term employment will depend on technological innovation; whether value-added remanufacturing is done in the Sierra Nevada or elsewhere ; and the total of public and private harvest levels.

Both public and private forestry are striving towards more realistic accounting of full costs and benefits of forest management costs so that addresses both timber and ecosystem values. Two preliminary conclusions come out of an analysis of the costs of federal forest management in the 1990s as reported in the TSPIRS accounting system. The direct costs of ecosystem management as measured by the forest stewardship programs and additional ecosystem analysis costs are minimal and appears to increase in-forest costs less than 15%.

CHAPTER 5: PRIVATE ECONOMIC SECTORS - AGRICULTURE, COMMERCIAL RECREATION, AND RESIDENTIAL DEVELOPMENT

Ranching on private lands and on public leases is the most extensive land use in terms of area in the Sierra Nevada. Irrigated agriculture is also prevalent throughout the region where water resources have been developed. Commercial recreation complements the extensive area of public land where recreation is promoted and produces the greatest amount of revenue from direct use of land and water resources. Finally, residential development is expanding rapidly and represents the largest change in total value of all natural and human assets in the Sierra Nevada. Each of these sectors is dealt with in greater depth elsewhere in the SNEP Assessment. The primary purpose of this section is to integrate the economic impacts of these sectors with the more traditional timber and water sectors.

Ranching

Private ranches cover approximately four million acres of the 20 million-acre SNEP region. In addition, grazing permits and leases cover most Forest Service, Bureau of Land Management, and most large private industrial timber lands. Grazing on both private and public lands is therefore the most extensive type of land use in the Sierra Nevada. The ecological aspects of grazing are covered in Menke (1996) and Kinney (1996). This section summarizes some of the major economic aspects of the ranching industry in the Sierra Nevada. Close links between ranching activities in the Sierra Nevada and the larger livestock industry of the Central Valley of California, as well as the western portions of Nevada, make it difficult to fully separate Sierra Nevada dependent activities from pasture- and feed lot-based activities. In a number of instances we excluded counties where most of the livestock industry is outside of the SNEP region.

Grazing by Ecological Types

Of National Forest lands available for grazing, only 75% of the actual Animal Unit Months (AUMs) are used by the lessees (USDA Forest Service 1993-b). The following tables summarize grazing in the Sierra Nevada region (including parts of Shasta and Tehama counties) by land owner and vegetation cover type. Based on a study of California's livestock industry done for the California Department of Forestry and Fire Protection (CH2M Hill 1989), most of the forage value comes from the oak woodlands on the western side of the Sierra Nevada. Conifer land is the single largest vegetation type grazed but produces only 8% of the revenues and 10% of the total forage. The market value calculations are proportional to the forage value of the lands and do not include any differences for water supplies, fencing or other services that may be included in market based AUM rates. Much of the grazed land is owned by the Forest Service or the Bureau of Land Management. Based on AUM and fee estimates, federal lands account for 34% of the acres, 15% of the forage, and only 3% of the total revenue.

Table 5.1: Grazing by Vegetation Cover Type in Sierra Nevada and Portions of Modoc Plateau

Vegetation Type	Grazed Acres	Revenue in 1995 Dollars	Full Market Value of Forage
Chaparral	772,964	1,716,494	1,958,774
Conifer	4,004,815	3,542,229	5,532,470
Desert	1,186,396	729,409	882,014
Juniper	583,251	854,007	1,469,139
Oak Woodlands	2,470,022	28,873,207	30,234,514
Sagebrush	2,168,238	6,094,819	8,243,960
Wetlands	310,530	5,257,570	5,643,368
Total Area in Study	11,496,216	$47,067,737	$53,964,239
	Percent of Acres	Percent of Revenue	Percent of Full Market Value
Chaparral	7%	4%	4%
Conifer	35%	8%	10%
Desert	10%	2%	2%
Juniper	5%	2%	3%
Oak Woodlands	21%	61%	56%
Sagebrush	19%	13%	15%
Wetlands	3%	11%	10%

Source: Adapted from CH2M Hill (1989).

Table 5.2: Grazing by Land Owner

	Grazed Acres	Revenue in 1995 dollars	Full Market Value of Forage
BLM	1,172,411	374,524	2,752,402
Forest Service	2,743,916	711,699	5,230,322
Other Public	182,938	544,755	544,755
Private	7,396,951	45,436,759	45,436,759
Total	11,496,216	$47,067,737	$53,964,239
	Percent of Acres	Percent of Revenue	Percent of Full Market Value
BLM	10%	1%	5%
Forest Service	24%	2%	10%
Other Public	2%	1%	1%
Private	64%	97%	84%

Source: Adapted from CH2M Hill (1989).

Trends in the Sierra Nevada Livestock Industry

According to County Agricultural Reports, more than two million acres of private rangeland and 150,000 acres of irrigated pasture are in the counties that are fully or mainly within the Sierra Nevada. The four southern counties of Madera, Fresno, Tulare, and Kern have more than 1.7 million acres of private non-forest land in the Sierra Nevada region. Much of this land is probably in ranches but sub-county breakdowns of acreage and revenue could not be calculated due to the dominating influence of imported feed-based livestock operations in the Valley. The following tables compare the changes in the Sierra Nevada livestock industry over the past decade.

Table 5.3: Cattle Numbers, Range Acres and Irrigated Pasture Acres, 1985 and 1994

Region 1985	Cattle Numbers	Private Range	Irrigated Pasture
North	24,700	87,150	41,500
North Central	89,763	578,000	46,050
South Central	92,415	1,233,300	5,905
East Side	48,553	256,000	70,000
Total w/o San Joaquin	255,431	2,154,450	163,455
Region 1994	Cattle Numbers	Private Range	Irrigated Pasture
North	43,700	88,200	41,800
North Central	69,882	539,500	36,180
South Central	76,077	1,240,200	5,950
East Side	45,418	312,000	64,000
Total w/o San Joaquin	235,077	2,179,900	147,930

Source: County Agricultural Commissioners Reports.

Over the past decade, the number of cattle and acres of irrigated pasture decreased by more than 8%. Although private rangeland acres did not show any decline, it appears that the overall livestock industry in the Sierra Nevada is declining.

Other Agriculture

In addition to scattered irrigated pasture throughout the region, other irrigated agriculture is concentrated along the western fringe of the SNEP region. In the 1990 Census 4,835 households reported some farm income. The total reported farm proprietor income was $56 million. With the exception of areas dominated by ranching, the low average household income suggests that most of these operations are only part time. Throughout the early part of this century, agriculture was the major occupation throughout the Sierra Nevada (Weeks et. al. 1943). Although irrigated acreage in 1985 was nearly identical to the 219,000 acres mapped in 1922 (U. S. Bureau of Public Roads 1922), much more of the acreage is now on the western rather than the eastern side of the Sierra Nevada. The purchase of water rights in the Owens Valley by Los Angeles and the development of pump-based irrigation on the western side have been the two major reasons for the shift. The following tables summarize the reported agricultural acreage for the twelve counties fully within the SNEP region. Counties that extend into the Sacramento and San Joaquin Valleys are excluded because of the overwhelming influence of agricultural acreage in the valleys.

Table 5.4: Sierra Nevada Crop Acreage, 1985 and 1994

Region 1985	Field Crops	Orchards and Vineyards	Row Crops	Total Crop Acreage
North	23,820	0	0	23,820
North Central	21,700	5,106	0	26,806
South Central	8,995	4,022	47	13,064
East Side	14,715	15	136	14,866
Total w/o San Joaquin	69,230	9,143	183	78,556
Region 1994	Field Crops	Orchards and Vineyards	Row Crops	Total Crop Acreage
North	16,480	0	0	16,480
North Central	24,010	5,064	0	29,074
South Central	4,738	4,722	47	9,507
East Side	11,750	25	1,715	13,490
Total w/o San Joaquin	56,978	9,811	1,762	68,551

Table 5.5: Sierra Nevada Total Agricultural Revenue, 1985 and 1994
in Million Dollars (Constant 1994 dollars)

Region 1985	Field Crops	Orchards and Vineyards	Vegetable Crops	Livestock Related	Major Crops and All Livestock Revenue
North	$5	$0	$0	$15	$20
North Central	$13	$16	$0	$31	$9
South Central	$2	$4	$0.43	$34	$41
East Side	$9	$0	$0.28	$12	$22
Total w/o San Joaquin	$29	$20	$0.70	$92	$141
Region 1994	Field Crops	Orchards and Vineyards	Vegetable Crops	Livestock Related	Major Crops and All Livestock Revenue
North	$3	$0	$0	$15	$18
North Central	$15	$16	$0	$23	$53
South Central	$1	$7	$0.31	$30	$39
East Side	$6	$0	$3.43	$12	$22
Total w/o San Joaquin	$25	$23	$3.74	$79	$131

Table 5.6 Sierra Nevada Gross Revenue per Acre for Major Agricultural Uses, 1985 and 1994

Region 1985	Field Crops	Orchards and Vineyards	Vegetable Crops	Irrigated Pasture	Private Rangeland
North	$208	NA	NA	$42	$3
North Central	$581	$3,041	NA	$132	$8
South Central	$228	$1,089	$9,139	$154	$10
East	$619	$1,969	$2,024	$22	$1
All Sierra	$415	$2,180	$3,851	$63	$8
Region 1994	Field Crops	Orchards and Vineyards	Vegetable Crops	Irrigated Pasture	Private Rangeland
North	$185	NA	NA	$34	$4
North Central	$606	$3,151	NA	$103	$8
South Central	$289	$1,518	$6,574	$120	$9
East	$530	$6,000	$2,000	$18	$1
All Sierra	$442	$2,372	$2,122	$47	$7

Note: Regions with small acreages in certain uses may have unusually high
or low gross revenue per acre.

Table 5.7: Livestock and Major Crop Percentage of Total Agriculture Revenue
by Region, 1985 and 1994

Region 1985	Livestock Related	Major Crops
North	75%	25%
North Central	52%	48%
South Central	83%	17%
East Side	56%	44%
Total	65%	35%
Region 1994	Livestock Related	Major Crops
North	83%	17%
North Central	42%	58%
South Central	77%	23%
East Side	54%	46%
Total	60%	40%

Ranching represents more than 96% of the acreage of the agricultural sector in terms of private acreage, but only 60% of total revenue in the region for which county level data can be used. Field crops such as wheat, barley and oats produce the remaining 20% of total agricultural revenue but declined by over 10% in the past decade. More intensively cultivated crops such as orchards, vineyards, and vegetables bring in revenue of over $2,000 per acre and produce more than 20% of total revenue from less than 0.5% of private agricultural land. Smaller farms that grow and sell fresh vegetables are typically not included in the County Agricultural Commissioner reports and would increase the reported farm-based acreage and revenue in many counties.

The overall trend in Sierra Nevada agriculture over the last decade has been a shrinking of the livestock based sector and an expansion of high value agricultural operations such as orchards, vineyards, and vegetable farms. In addition to the reported orchards and vegetable farms, small wineries based on the grape acreage add considerable revenue to the agricultural sector. If the acreage in the Sierra portions of the San Joaquin Valley is used in a similar fashion to the land in the South

1036

Central region, the estimate of total agricultural revenue in the SNEP region in 1994 would be $170 million. In addition to this revenue, agriculture is valued throughout the region to maintain open space and the rural character.

Recreation and Tourism

Provision of recreational opportunities within the Sierra Nevada has been considered a major social benefit ever since the development of Yosemite Valley more than a century ago. In addition to the extensive area of federal forests, parks, and water bodies developed for recreational use, a large private sector recreation and tourism industry provides a growing range of services to visitors and local residents. In addition to lodging, restaurants, and retail stores, private firms provide a broad range of recreation oriented services. Numerous ski resorts, white water rafting operations, private campgrounds, and recreational guides provide services on lands and water bodies throughout the region.

Ninety-five percent of the population in the western United States describes participation in outdoor sports as a great idea and are more likely than others to participate in activities which take advantage of natural resources such as hiking, backpacking, camping of all kinds and rock climbing (Roper-Starch Worldwide 1995). In a recent survey of Americans' outdoor recreational habits, 68% said the main reason for such habits was for 'family togetherness', followed at 64% by 'appreciation of nature' (Roper-Starch Worldwide 1995).

Employment in recreation and tourism is focused on more developed recreational opportunities and is only part of the total value of the Sierra Nevada for recreational opportunities that do not always involve the purchase of private services. The large social value of dispersed recreation occurring in national forests, national parks, and state parks is addressed by Duane (1996-b). The private recreational and tourism sector is the single largest employer in the Sierra Nevada. Based on the 1990 Census as well as business surveys, we estimated that more than 23,000 employees work in 3,000 different enterprises associated with recreation and tourism.

Recreation and Tourism Related Businesses and Employment in the Sierra Nevada

Employment in the private businesses involved in recreation and tourism is spread among lodging, restaurants, and retail, as well as in firms supplying direct recreational services such as ski resorts, rafting companies, sports equipment suppliers, and guide services. A study of the county level travel impacts (Damon Runyan Associates 1995) was commissioned by the California Trade and Commerce Agency. Travel expenditures include many business expenses as well as expenses by local residents and will be considerably larger than recreation and tourism related revenues. After accounting for the split counties that are only partly in the SNEP study region, an estimated $2.4 billion of travel-related expenditures were spent in the Sierra Region in 1993. Our independent assessment of travel and recreation related workers from the 1990 Census data, suggests that approximately one-third of the employees and expenditures are derived from local residents, with the remaining two-thirds come from visitors to the region.

A count of all businesses listed in telephone directories involved in recreation industry (identified by four-digit Standard Industrial Codes (SIC)) provides another estimate of firms and total revenue within the California portion of the SNEP region. The large gaming industry on the Nevada side of Lake Tahoe was not included but is a major draw for visitors on the California side also. Using a 1994 CD-ROM directory of business telephone listings, firms with SIC codes clearly dominated by recreation and tourism were inventoried. This method under counts the many retail stores, groceries, bakeries, and gas stations that may get a large share of their business from visitors. In addition to the more than 2,400 motels and hotels, also more than 500 businesses provide specific outdoor activity related equipment or services. California averages for 1992 revenue for these business types were reduced by half to account for local use and assumed smaller business sizes.

Table 5.8: Major Recreational Businesses in the Sierra Nevada by Area Code

Business	Tahoe Region	Other Northern Sierra	Central Sierra	Eastern Sierra	Total
Area Code	(916)	(916)	(209)	(619)	
Motels	758	222	142	40	1,162
Restaurants	305	573	360	40	1,278
Sporting Goods	100	43	18	7	168
Campgrounds	81	156	32	0	269
Outdoor Recreation Services	51	6	3	4	64
Total	1,295	1,000	555	91	2,941
	44%	34%	19%	3%	

Source: ProPhone (1995)

Based on the businesses listings, estimates of total business, payroll, and employment estimates were developed by using the 1992 Census of Retail Trade and 1992 Census of Service Industries averages for California. Statewide averages were reduced by 50% to account for non-tourism related activity as well as smaller business size. Even with these conservative estimates, the recreation and tourism sector has an overall business revenue of nearly $1.4 billion. This estimate is very close to the $1.6 billion (two thirds of the $2.4 billion travel expenditures) estimated from the Damyon Runyan Associates study.

Table 5.9: Estimated Recreational Business Revenues in Millions

	Tahoe Region	North Sierra	Central Sierra	East Sierra	Total
Motels	$590	$173	$110	$31	$904
Restaurants	$77	$144	$91	$10	$322
Sporting Goods	$40	$17	$7	$3	$67
Campgrounds	$16	$31	$6	$0	$54
Outdoor Recreation Services	$18	$2	$1	$1	$23
Total	$741	$368	$216	$45	$1,370

Source: ProPhone (1995), Census of Service Industries (1994), Census of Retail Trade (1994).

1990 Travel and Recreation and Tourism Employment

Employment in the 3,000 firms in the travel and recreation sectors can be derived from 1990 Census data. Based on employment data from the 1990 Census supplemented with employment estimates for restaurants, the travel industry employed more than 35,000 people in the SNEP region in 1990. Based on a national estimate that a local economy will have around three percent of its workforce involved in lodging and recreation related jobs simply to serve local needs, an estimated 23,000 of these employees are serving tourists from outside the region. This estimate excludes the hundreds of employees in federal and state agencies that provide recreational opportunities. With nearly 3,000 businesses and over 23,000 employees the recreation and tourism industry is the largest employer within the region. Revenue data on local motel and hotel taxes (Transient Occupancy Taxes (TOT)) presented in the following section suggest that the recreation and tourism sector has grown at a significant rate throughout the 1990s.

Table 5.10: Travel and Tourism Related Employment

Region	Travel, Recreation and Tourism			Recreation and Tourism Only		Total
	Lodging, Recreation	Restaurants	Total	Lodging, Recreation	Restaurants	
North	2,397	1,027	3,424	932	399	1,331
North Central	4,427	1,897	6,324	1,258	539	1,797
South Central	3,625	1,554	5,179	2,054	880	2,934
San Joaquin	1,639	702	2,341	658	282	940
Tahoe	10,955	4,695	15,650	9,772	4,188	13,960
East Side	1,885	808	2,693	1,444	619	2,063
Foothill	8,714	3,735	12,449	2,998	1,285	4,283
Conifer	3,374	1,446	4,820	1,905	816	2,721
Greater East	12,840	5,503	18,343	11,216	4,807	16,023
Total	24,928	10,683	35,611	16,118	6,908	23,026

Sources: Lodging and recreation employment - 1990 Census; Restaurants - ProPhone (1995), and Census of Retail Trade (1994).

Regional data illustrate that more than half of the recreation and tourism related employment is in the greater Lake Tahoe region. Communities on the east side and in the areas adjacent to the National Parks in the South Central region also have large travel and tourism components. Most of the travel related employment in the foothill region is associated with local residents.

Conclusion for Recreation and Tourism Industry

The recreation and tourism industry is the single largest employment sector in the Sierra Nevada with more than 23,000 employees in more than 3,000 firms. Although many of these jobs are not full time, the total number of jobs is considerably larger than employment in the timber and similar to the large construction sector. With an annual revenue of $1.4 billion spread across more than 3,000 businesses, the recreation and tourism industry is a major component of the regional economy. Like many of the commodity based sectors, the distribution of these jobs and businesses is not uniform across the region. Nearly half of the private sector employment is centered around Lake Tahoe and the nearby ski resorts. In comparison, recreation and tourism related employment is a relatively minor portion of employment in the foothill and conifer forest regions.

Residential Development

The most significant economic changes in the Sierra Nevada over the past two decades have been driven by the large inflow of new residents attracted by the environmental and social amenities available in the region. A detailed analysis of these trends is provided in Duane (1996-a). The economic impact of human settlement is addressed here for two reasons. First, the new residential and commercial construction is by far the largest change in the total financial assets of the Sierra Nevada region. New construction has substantially increased the amount of property tax collected by county governments. And second, the increase in the number of new residents has also increased the total value of environmental benefits accruing to full time residents in a manner similar to an expansion in the number of tourists.

Since 1980 over $16 billion (1995 dollars) of new residential and commercial construction have been built in the twelve counties fully within the Sierra Nevada. The total construction value is split

1039

with around 80% residential and 20% commercial. In 1995, these properties generated an estimated 160 million dollars in property tax revenue (at the rate of one percent of assessed value). Although most of this money is used to finance infrastructure and social services for the residents, if the benefits of living in the Sierra Nevada are proportional to property values, then millions of dollars of ecosystem-based benefits accrue to the new residents of the Sierra Nevada. If ten percent of all these property value and property taxes were ascribed to environmental attributes, the annual resource value and reinvestment value from these new residents would be $110 million and $11 million respectively. The following table summarizes the value of new residential and commercial construction for the counties within the SNEP region.

Table 5.11: Value of New Residential and Commercial Construction in the Sierra Nevada, 1980-1995 in Million Dollars (Constant 1995 Dollars)

Year	North	North Central	South Central	East	All Sierra Counties
1980	$45	$583	$240	$67	$935
1981	$39	$475	$187	$117	$818
1982	$26	$378	$146	$48	$598
1983	$33	$445	$181	$17	$676
1984	$29	$540	$182	$15	$765
1985	$23	$546	$243	$21	$832
1986	$28	$734	$238	$19	$1,019
1987	$27	$949	$248	$22	$1,245
1988	$36	$1,200	$244	$34	$1,514
1989	$28	$1,377	$278	$64	$1,746
1990	$32	$1,193	$285	$105	$1,616
1991	$27	$809	$242	$33	$1,111
1992	$38	$674	$226	$40	$979
1993	$15	$588	$142	$37	$783
1994	$33	$709	$114	$36	$892
1995	$20	$667	$101	$35	$824
1980-1995 Total	$478	$11,866	$3,297	$710	$16,352

Source: California Department of Finance.

Conclusion

Private sector uses of the Sierra Nevada ecosystem are more significant than the percentage of private land would suggest. At the Sierra Nevada wide level, the economic output of every private sector except ranching grew over the past decade. The mix of ranching, irrigated agriculture, commercial recreation and tourism, and new residential development varies tremendously from region to region.

Private animals graze more acres of the Sierra Nevada than are used for timber management, recreational use, or residential development. Most forage comes from private ranches in western foothills and from irrigated pastures. The overall size of the livestock sector is highly variable but declined by nearly 10% over the past decade. For agriculture as a whole, land uses with low revenue per acre have been declining in acreage while high value orchards, vineyards and vegetable farms are increasing in size and revenues.

In contrast to the patterns within the overall agricultural sector, commercial recreation and residential development continue to grow. Commercial recreation and tourism is the largest single employment sector in the Sierra Nevada and now contributes an increasing share of county revenues. Commercial recreation occupies relatively little land and complements the recreational opportunities provided on federal and state lands. Residential development continues to expand and dominates the financial character of the Sierra Nevada. Investments in new residential and commercial development averaged more than $ 1 billion per year over the past fifteen years. Most of this residential growth is concentrated between Sacramento and Lake Tahoe.

CHAPTER 6: GOVERNMENT FINANCE

Federal, state and local governments have different responsibilities for monitoring resource use and management , distributing benefits, and enforcing environmental standards. An assessment of the streams of government revenues and expenditures derived from, and directed toward, the region's natural resources highlights these patterns. This chapter's assessment of government finance provides insight into how the ecosystem generates revenue for a wide spectrum of public services. The analysis focuses on county level financing for three reasons. The first is that county level analysis illustrates the different regional patterns across the Sierra Nevada. Second, county budgets reflect the myriad responsibility and revenue sharing arrangements between federal, state, and local governments more realistically than an analysis of the small fraction of much larger federal and state budgets. And finally, county budgets integrate the traditional natural resource sectors with the other private use sectors commonly not considered in broader ecosystem analyses.

A complex pattern of land and water rights creates a situation where government jurisdictions are rarely aligned with unique ecosystems or settlement patterns. Various explicit and implicit patterns of revenue sharing and cost sharing exist among the three levels of government. In addition to the revenue sharing arrangements between national forests,school districts and the county public works, other revenue and reinvestment programs are operated by the federal, state, and county governments. Federal expenditures in the region include the operational expenditures of the land management agencies as well as numerous cost-sharing arrangements for social services, transportation, planning, and other public administration activities. Federal government expenditures on national parks, developed recreational areas, and wilderness areas provide the backdrop for a large recreation and tourism industry in the Sierra Nevada. Recreation and tourism oriented businesses then generate millions of dollars of county tax revenue through Transient Occupancy Tax (TOT) and sales tax. Expenditures by the state of California on parks, water quality programs, and land acquisition are other examples of reinvestment into the Sierra Nevada ecosystem. County governments implement programs to reduce the property tax burden on private forest and agricultural landowners to discourage dispersed residential conversion and its associated public service cost. These programs are all examples of government financing programs that address both ecosystem health and economic well-being.

In addition to financing responsibility for most education, the state provides over half the funds for all programs administered by counties. Fire protection and transportation are two of the most significant financial responsibilities of the state of California within the SNEP region. The state of California also provides financing for a wide variety of ecosystem related activities in spite of the fact that the state owns relatively little land in the Sierra Nevada. The California Resources Agency is responsible for a wide range of programs including state parks, fish and game management, land conservation, forestry and fire protection, and water quality monitoring and enforcement. Most of these programs are funded through the legislature and do not have the local revenue impacts of other financing mechanisms such as Forest Services Revenue Sharing, Williamson Act and Timber Production Zone tax programs, and the Transient Occupancy Tax. One area where state financing related to ecosystem health issues are state bond measures concerning the development and expansion of state parks and state regulations on rural land use. A measure of the public's willingness to finance recreation, wildlife protection and preservation oriented activities, is the voting pattern on these types of state bonds. The following figure summarizes regional voting trends on four sequential bonds to fund increases in the state park system.

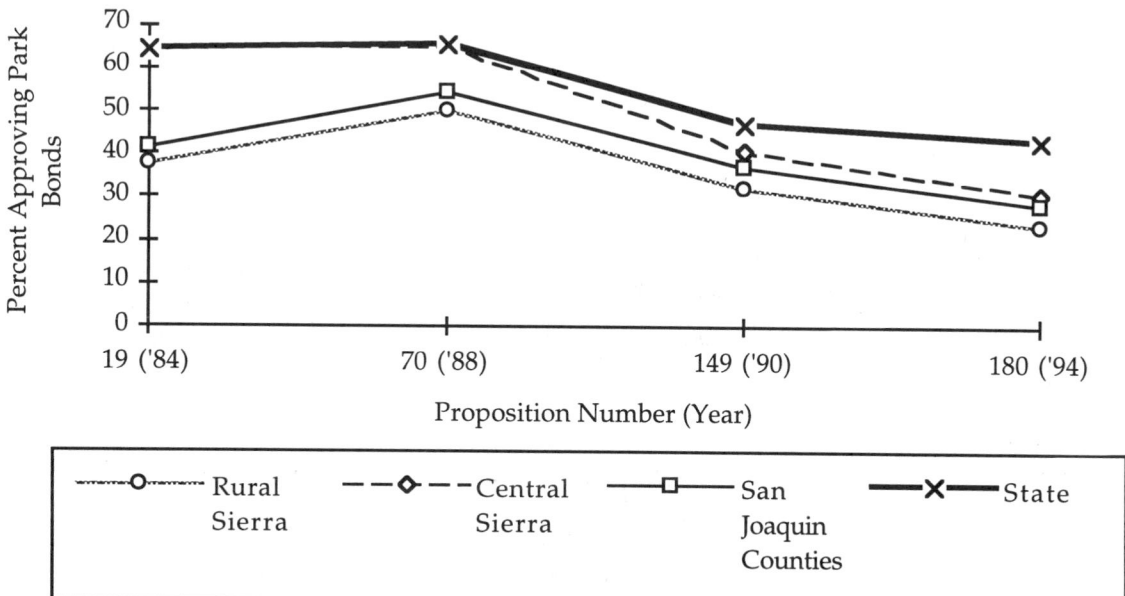

Figure 6.1: Regional support for state park bonds

Source: Secretary of State. Statement of the Vote.

The results of these bond votes suggests that many residents in or adjacent to the Sierra Nevada see less need for more land purchase or programs to provide more parks and protected areas in the Sierra Nevada. One explanation for the results is that most of the residents experience no shortage of outdoor recreational opportunities because so much of the Forest Service lands is available for local recreation with no extra fees or taxes. Votes on state bonds involve choices on both the goals and the means by which they are to be accomplished and can not be interpreted based on only one characteristic. For example, in Contra Costa county in the San Francisco Bay Area, Proposition 180 was also voted down in 1994 . Two years earlier, residents agreed to create a special assessment district to support expanded activities of the East Bay Regional Park District (EBRPD). The EBRPD measure costs considerably more per household than the state bond, but local residents had more say in how the money would be collected and on what it would be spent (Mikkelsen 1995).

Timber-based Revenues for County Governments

Although public and private timber harvests have been similar over the past decade, the revenue implications for county governments are very different. Private timber harvests are taxed through the state yield tax set at approximately 2.9% of the stumpage value. In addition, an equal amount of revenue is collected through property taxes on the timber land. Revenues to counties from the National Forests, include a) forest revenue sharing (25% of stumpage), b) Payments In-Lieu of Taxes (PILT), and c) the State timber yield tax that is assessed on all timber harvested in the state. PILT funds from Forest Service lands follow a complex formula that consider alternative revenue sharing receipts, land zoning, and year to year fluctuations. The following figure illustrates the large differences in the county revenue per million board feet of public and private timber harvests over the past decade.

Figure 6.2: Effective County Revenue per Thousand Board Feet of Public and Private Timber

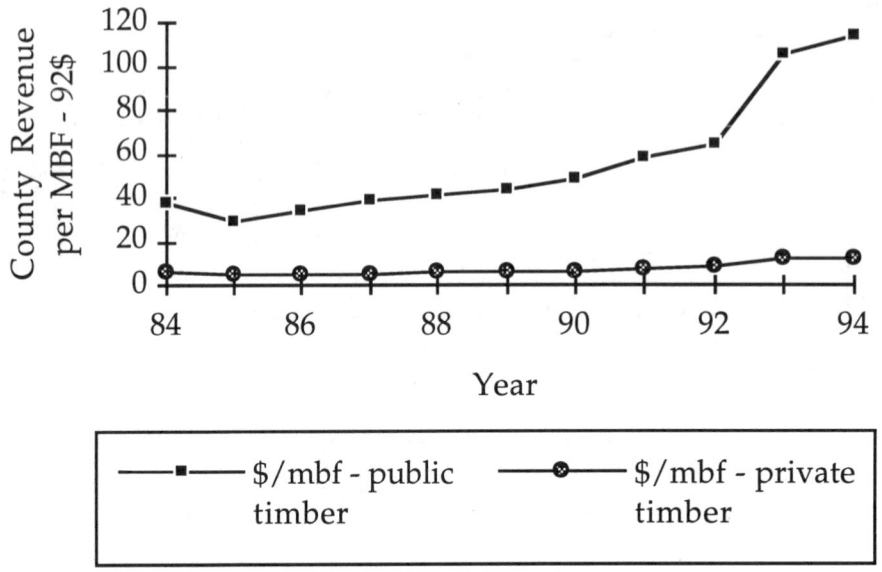

Source: California State Board of Equalization.

The proportion of total county revenues derived from National Forests has declined throughout the Sierra Nevada over the period examined. Federal timber revenue sharing makes up less than 2% of total county revenues across the SNEP study area but is substantially greater in some of the regions. From FY 1980-81 to FY 1992-93, the North region (including Lassen) showed the greatest reliance on federal timber revenues for financing county budgets. The county governments of this region received $7.6 million from federal timber revenue sharing in FY 1992-93, comprising 10.8% of total revenues. The North Central region received $3.3 million, (1% of total county revenues), and the South Central region received $2.6 million (2%) for the same period.

The net effect for Sierra Nevada counties is that increases in private harvests do not make up for reductions in public harvests in terms of taxes. However, reduced supplies can drive up prices so much that the reduction in federal receipts is far smaller than the reduction in federal harvests.

Property Tax and Transient Occupancy Tax

New residential and commercial construction produces far more revenue than any other land use (Table 6.1). As developing areas demand services and infrastructure, the costs of expansion rise along with the revenues from the expanding tax base. County land use policies regarding residential expansion result in far greater impacts on revenues than tax policies on private timber land and federal harvest levels in all regions except the far northern counties. Increasing human settlement of the North Central and South Central regions has resulted in a growing property tax base and a reduced reliance on commodity based sources of revenue. In the northern Sierra, no comparable demographic shifts have occurred and these counties and school districts have greater vulnerability to decreasing revenues from National Forests. The Transient Occupancy Tax (TOT) is collected on lodging and tracks overall expenditures in recreation. In every region except the North, TOT revenues exceed timber revenues from both public and private harvests.

Overall County Revenue from Ecosystem Related Activities

The following figures illustrate the trends in four major revenue sources for all counties in the Sierra Nevada region. Of the different revenue sources, property taxes from new residential homes are associated with the largest expenditures for new roads and other infrastructure, police protection and fire protection. Revenues from public and private forest lands and from Transient Occupancy Tax (TOT), on the other hand, far outweigh county expenditures on those enterprises. The following table summarizes the amount of revenue from local taxes and revenue sharing going to the counties in the Sierra Nevada region.

Table 6.1: Sierra Wide County Tax Revenues from Timber, Residential and Commercial Development, and Motel Taxes in Millions of Dollars, 1980-1992

Year	Federal Timber	Private Timber	Post-1980 Homes	Transient Occupancy Tax	Commercial Development
1980	$12.68	$1.97	$4.94	$7.37	$2.43
1981	$13.97	$2.13	$9.15	$7.59	$4.52
1982	$7.44	$1.03	$11.99	$7.67	$6.25
1983	$12.91	$0.81	$15.14	$8.77	$8.40
1984	$13.31	$0.87	$18.14	$8.20	$11.25
1985	$8.98	$0.91	$21.67	$8.53	$14.27
1986	$14.32	$0.95	$27.02	$9.37	$17.48
1987	$14.83	$1.17	$32.96	$10.80	$21.47
1988	$17.53	$1.82	$39.01	$11.75	$27.19
1989	$17.19	$2.35	$45.21	$12.06	$34.22
1990	$16.07	$2.28	$50.83	$12.21	$40.89
1991	$12.16	$1.78	$55.80	$14.47	$44.74
1992	$14.81	$2.82	$60.05	$15.20	$48.28

Sources: Financial Transactions of Counties, State Controller; Department of Finance; California State Board of Equalization.
Note: All figures are expressed in Nominal dollars. Federal forest revenue includes timber based revenue sharing, PILT, and the state yield tax paid on federal timber. Private forest revenue comes from similar proportions of the timber yield tax and property taxes. Residential and commercial construction values exclude Placer and the four counties in the San Joaquin region. Residential and commercial property taxes on construction since 1980 are based on 1% of assessed value increasing at the Proposition 13-allowed 2% per year. TOT revenue is based on tax rates set by each county.

The following analysis of the regions focuses on the three main sources of county revenue from forested land and its uses in the Sierra Nevada: federal timber, private timber, and TOT. Residential property taxes are much larger than these revenue sources but are left out because a substantial portion of the houses are built on the far western edge or outside of the SNEP boundary. PILT payments associated with land rather than commodity production, remain low throughout the region.

Table 6.2: Timber-related and Recreation-related County Revenue in Million Dollars
SNEP Region, 1980-1993
(Nominal Dollars)

Fiscal Year	Federal Timber Revenues	Payment in Lieu of Taxes	Private Timber Revenues	Transient Occupancy Tax
1980-81	$7.46	$1.88	$1.16	$3.99
1981-82	$9.07	$2.35	$1.38	$4.87
1982-83	$5.13	$3.62	$0.71	$5.23
1983-84	$9.16	$2.80	$0.57	$6.16
1984-85	$9.86	$4.02	$0.65	$6.02
1985-86	$6.91	$2.62	$0.70	$6.51
1986-87	$11.19	$3.21	$0.74	$7.27
1987-88	$11.96	$2.96	$0.95	$8.65
1988-89	$14.73	$2.77	$1.53	$9.81
1989-90	$15.22	$2.84	$2.08	$10.61
1990-91	$15.02	$2.61	$2.14	$11.32
1991-92	$11.81	$2.68	$1.73	$13.97
1992-93	$14.81	$2.94	$2.82	$15.08

Table 6.3: Timber-related and Recreation-related County Revenue in Million Dollars
North Region, 1980-1993
(Nominal Dollars)

Fiscal Year	Federal Timber Revenues	Payment in Lieu of Taxes	Private Timber Revenues	Transient Occupancy Tax
1980-81	$3.03	$0.11	$0.27	$0.15
1981-82	$2.63	$0.16	$0.30	$0.16
1982-83	$1.44	$0.15	$0.17	$0.18
1983-84	$2.83	$0.15	$0.16	$0.18
1984-85	$4.47	$0.15	$0.18	$0.21
1985-86	$2.53	$0.15	$0.16	$0.23
1986-87	$4.68	$0.15	$0.20	$0.26
1987-88	$4.17	$0.16	$0.28	$0.31
1988-89	$5.82	$0.16	$0.43	$0.34
1989-90	$5.20	$0.16	$0.42	$0.37
1990-91	$5.12	$0.16	$0.40	$0.41
1991-92	$4.87	$0.16	$0.49	$0.67
1992-93	$5.53	$0.16	$0.83	$0.70

Table 6.4: Timber-related and Recreation-related County Revenue in Million Dollars
North Central Region, 1980-1993
(Nominal Dollars)

Fiscal Year	Federal Timber Revenues	Payment in Lieu of Taxes	Private Timber Revenues	Transient Occupancy Tax
1980-81	$1.72	$0.05	$0.65	$0.92
1981-82	$2.42	$0.05	$0.84	$1.16
1982-83	$1.52	$0.41	$0.34	$1.19
1983-84	$2.03	$0.09	$0.22	$1.31
1984-85	$2.27	$0.04	$0.20	$1.79
1985-86	$1.53	$0.05	$0.22	$2.10
1986-87	$2.41	$0.06	$0.25	$2.06
1987-88	$2.97	$0.12	$0.44	$2.62
1988-89	$3.29	$0.15	$0.61	$3.02
1989-90	$3.53	$0.15	$0.73	$3.16
1990-91	$3.77	$0.12	$0.92	$3.19
1991-92	$3.00	$0.16	$0.77	$4.05
1992-93	$3.13	$0.16	$1.17	$4.43

Table 6.5: Timber-related and Recreation-related County Revenue in Million Dollars
South Central Region, 1980-1993
(Nominal Dollars)

Fiscal Year	Federal Timber Revenues	Payment in Lieu of Taxes	Private Timber Revenues	Transient Occupancy Tax
1980-81	$0.91	$0.06	$0.14	$0.98
1981-82	$1.73	$0.22	$0.17	$1.16
1982-83	$0.62	$0.49	$0.14	$1.38
1983-84	$1.53	$0.27	$0.14	$1.64
1984-85	$1.23	$0.88	$0.15	$1.65
1985-86	$1.15	$0.28	$0.12	$1.82
1986-87	$1.22	$0.33	$0.24	$2.33
1987-88	$2.14	$0.22	$0.20	$2.65
1988-89	$2.58	$0.43	$0.45	$2.92
1989-90	$2.46	$0.26	$0.82	$3.28
1990-91	$2.00	$0.17	$0.67	$3.74
1991-92	$1.36	$0.16	$0.43	$5.08
1992-93	$2.42	$0.16	$0.72	$5.21

Table 6.6: Timber-related and Recreation-related County Revenue in Million Dollars
San Joaquin Region, 1980-1993
(Nominal Dollars)

Fiscal Year	Federal Timber Revenues	Payment in Lieu of Taxes	Private Timber Revenues	Transient Occupancy Tax
1980-81	$1.27	$0.85	$0.09	$0.63
1981-82	$1.69	$1.16	$0.05	$0.75
1982-83	$1.10	$1.91	$0.07	$0.86
1983-84	$1.96	$1.61	$0.04	$1.08
1984-85	$1.31	$2.25	$0.08	$1.25
1985-86	$1.09	$1.42	$0.18	$1.39
1986-87	$2.22	$1.96	$0.05	$1.55
1987-88	$1.97	$1.73	$0.03	$1.86
1988-89	$2.19	$1.31	$0.03	$2.17
1989-90	$3.11	$1.55	$0.10	$2.32
1990-91	$3.42	$1.42	$0.14	$2.38
1991-92	$2.06	$1.46	$0.05	$2.35
1992-93	$2.68	$1.63	$0.10	$2.73

Table 6.7: Timber-related and Recreation-related County Revenue in Million Dollars
East Region, 1980-1993
(Nominal Dollars)

Fiscal Year	Federal Timber Revenues	Payment in Lieu of Taxes	Private Timber Revenues	Transient Occupancy Tax
1980-81	$0.52	$0.80	$0.00	$1.31
1981-82	$0.59	$0.75	$0.02	$1.64
1982-83	$0.45	$0.67	$0.00	$1.63
1983-84	$0.80	$0.68	$0.01	$1.94
1984-85	$0.59	$0.70	$0.03	$1.11
1985-86	$0.61	$0.70	$0.02	$0.98
1986-87	$0.66	$0.70	$0.00	$1.08
1987-88	$0.71	$0.72	$0.01	$1.22
1988-89	$0.86	$0.73	$0.01	$1.35
1989-90	$0.93	$0.73	$0.01	$1.47
1990-91	$0.72	$0.74	$0.00	$1.60
1991-92	$0.52	$0.74	$0.00	$1.81
1992-93	$1.07	$0.83	$0.00	$2.00

Source: Counties of California, Financial Transactions. Annual Report, State Controller, various years.

During the period from 1980 to 1993, county revenues from the Transient Occupancy Tax (TOT) surpassed the sum of all revenue from federal and private timber in every region except the North region comprised on Plumas and Sierra. For the SNEP region as a whole, TOT was roughly comparable to all timber revenue by the 1992-1993 fiscal year. Since then, drops in federal timber harvests and timber prices have reduced timber related revenue while recreation-related revenue has continued to climb.

Summary of Ecosystem-based Revenues for County Governments

County taxes on private ranchland, farmland, and forest land are kept low to discourage undesired conversion of these lands to residential and commercial development. High infrastructure costs and loss of rural quality of the landscape are major reasons why many county governments have tried to reduce the spatial extent of residential development.

Commodity based revenues represent more than two percent of total county and school budgets in three counties in Sierra Nevada region, Plumas, Sierra, and Lassen. More important is the economic stimulus provided through the federal lands that are a backdrop to $1.4 billion dollar recreation and tourism industry. The positive impact of the federal-state compact for Lake Tahoe as well as the negative impacts of the 1995 Christmas season temporary government shutdown on Mariposa County where Yosemite National Park is located, illustrate the importance of this ecosystem-dependent economic stimulus. The unequal distribution of recreational and commodity revenues, however, can create inequitable situations at the county level for policies that are revenue positive for the region as a whole.

County Expenditures

The original revenue sharing arrangements for federal lands in rural counties were developed to account for the fact that federal land would never produce property tax revenues needed to finance local services. Over time, state-county financing arrangements, as well as the types of public services desired by counties, have changed dramatically. In California, the state ensures a basic level of school financing and takes responsibility for much of transportation infrastructure. Combined 1993 expenditures on protection services (mainly police and fire), public assistance, roads, and health and sanitation account for between 80% and 91% of total county expenditures in the three regions examined. This represents a modest increase from Fiscal Year (FY) 1980-81 for the North region (plus Lassen) and North Central region (3%), but a marked increase in the South Central region (19%), due in large part to a four-fold increase in the cost of protection services in Amador and Calaveras counties. All three regions saw the portion of their budgets dedicated to protection services increase by no less than 22%.

The North region (plus Lassen) stands out from the other regions in the proportion of the counties' budgets spent on public assistance, health and sanitation, and roads (Figure 6.3). This same region spends approximately two times what other regions spend on road maintenance, as a percentage of total expenditures. And, it is the only region where spending on public assistance increased over the period examined. Over the past decade, relative county expenditures in the northern counties are increasingly similar to those of other regions.

Figure 6.3: Major Programs as a Percent of Total County Expenditures, 1981 and 1993.

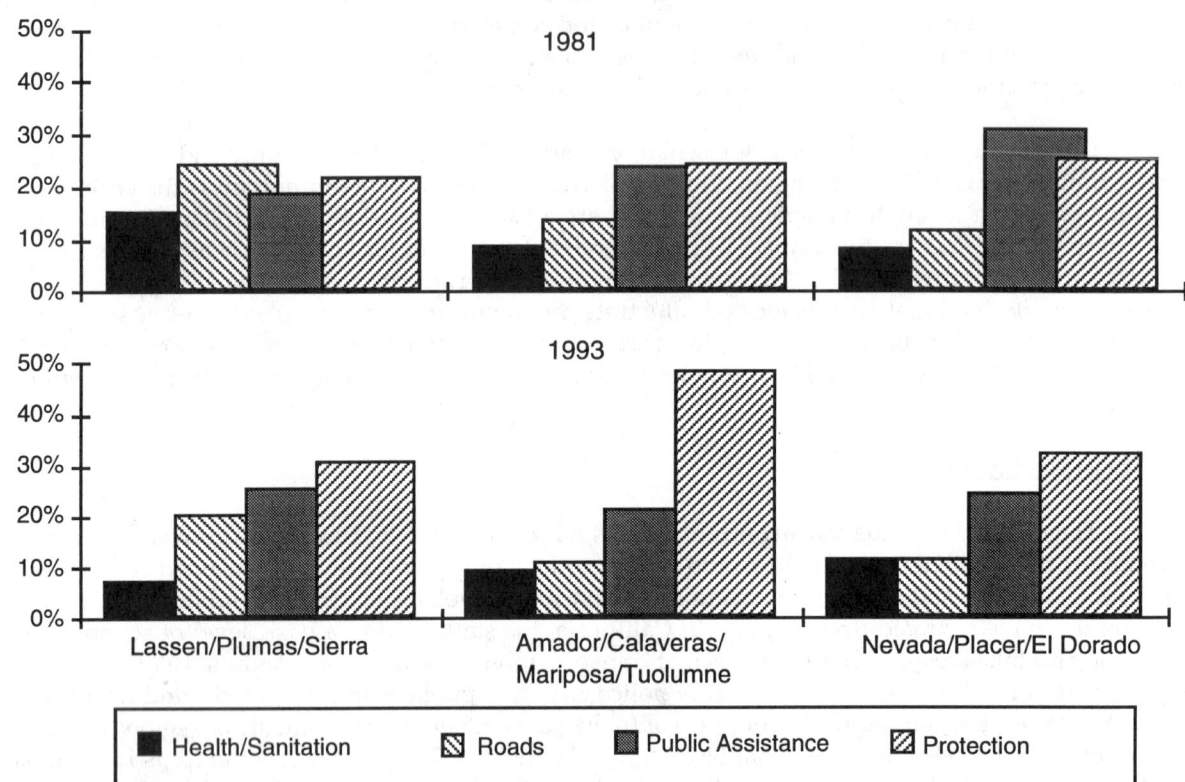

Source: Counties of California, Financial Transactions. Annual Reports 1980-81 and 1992-1993. State Controller.

Educational Revenues

Rapid escalation in stumpage prices from 1990 to 1993 mitigated the impact of dropping harvest levels for the counties receiving Forest Service revenue sharing funds. Decreasing stumpage prices and further declines in federal harvests in 1994 and 1995 reduced fiscal resources of many timber-producing counties. Table 6.8 illustrates the role of revenue sharing for the counties in the Sierra Nevada in 1991-1992.

Table 6.8: U.S. Forest Service Revenue Sharing and County Budgets, Fiscal Year 1991-92

County	Population 1992	County Budget (Million $)	School Budget (Million $)	USFS Revenue Sharing (Million $)	USFS Revenue as Percent of County Budget	USFS Revenue as Percent of School Budget
Alpine	1,195	5.58	2.27	0.71	15.54%	6.32%
Amador	32,142	25.43	18.82	0.61	1.59%	1.18%
Butte	191,207	149.37	151.54	0.90	0.29%	0.30%
Calaveras	35,712	38.87	99.58	0.19	0.09%	0.24%
El Dorado	137,241	106.14	117.33	3.81	1.62%	1.79%
Fresno	713,719	697.22	697.56	2.11	0.15%	0.15%
Kern	584,086	556.50	590.26	0.25	0.02%	0.02%
Lassen	28,718	29.12	28.35	3.33	5.85%	5.70%
Madera	97,155	72.32	97.34	0.87	0.44%	0.59%
Mariposa	15,620	21.10	13.73	0.42	1.48%	0.96%
Nevada	83,562	66.89	54.26	0.57	0.52%	0.42%
Placer	186,861	151.52	156.90	1.25	0.39%	0.41%
Plumas	20,735	25.80	21.39	7.71	17.99%	14.92%
Shasta	157,716	139.53	138.47	3.30	1.19%	1.18%
Sierra	3,362	8.43	6.68	1.44	10.74%	8.51%
Tehama	52,734	48.48	51.00	2.06	2.01%	2.12%
Tulare	329,999	315.42	208.84	0.60	0.14%	0.09%
Tuolumne	51,681	48.58	40.39	1.41	1.73%	1.44%
Yuba	61,113	62.92	58.43	0.24	0.20%	0.18%
Total	2,784,558	2569.22	2553.14	31.76	0.62%	0.62%

Source: Conserving the California Spotted Owl (Wildland Resource Center 1994).

Basic school funding provided by the State of California is equalized across the state to reduce local differences based on property taxes. The 12.5 % of Forest Service revenue (one half of the 25% revenue share split between education and roads) going to local school districts places timber-producing counties' revenue on top of the basic statewide expenditures per pupil (Table 6.9). Where the ratio of Forest Service revenue share to students is high, average expenditures per student are far above those in Los Angeles—home to California's most populous school districts and representative of the state average for urban districts. The pattern of school expenditures for 1992-93, when there was considerable Forest Service revenue sharing, suggests that without the extra Forest Service revenue, rural school districts spend far less than the state average.

Table 6.9: School Expenditures for Unified School Districts, 1992-93.

County	Average Expenditure/Pupil	Compared to Los Angeles
Alpine	$9,838	215%
Amador	$3,968	87%
Butte	$3,833	84%
Calaveras	$3,797	83%
El Dorado	$4,262	93%
Fresno	$4,371	96%
Inyo	$9,842	215%
Kern	$4,404	96%
Lassen	$5,619	123%
Madera	$4,037	88%
Mariposa	$4,731	103%
Modoc	$6,394	140%
Mono	$5,235	115%
Nevada	$4,217	92%
Placer	$4,171	91%
Plumas	$4,875	107%
Sierra	$6,168	135%
Tulare	$4,023	88%
Tuolumne	$4,912	107%
Yuba	$4,111	90%
Los Angeles	$4,572	100%

Source: Financial Transactions of School Districts, State Superintendent of Public Education, 1993.

Overall Trends in County Revenues and Expenditures

County finances provide important insights into the various streams of revenue derived from the production of goods and services from the Sierra Nevada ecosystem. They illustrate the unique patterns in different parts of the Sierra Nevada as well as the changes which have occurred over the past few decades. The historic importance of revenue based on timber harvests from the national forests has declined in most counties as other economic sectors have grown. The fiscal impact of changing public timber harvest is small relative to the large extent of federal ownership in the Sierra Nevada. Except for the three northern counties, tax and revenue sharing from timber yields represent less than 0.4% of county or school revenues. Conversion of wildlands into residential property and commercial recreational development have much greater revenue and expenditure implications. County tax revenues from overnight visitors is now equal to all federal forest revenue sharing and has grown consistently over the last decade.

Lassen, Plumas, and Sierra counties are very different from the rest of the Sierra Nevada and have a much greater dependence of federal revenue sharing for county and school revenues. The fiscal impact of overall declines in revenue from reduced federal timber harvesting will be concentrated in these counties. The sparsely populated counties of Modoc, Alpine, Mono, and Inyo also receive a considerable portion of their revenues from National Forest revenue sharing. The relative importance of commodity based revenue in these counties has dropped because of the rapid growth in tax revenue from the recreation and tourism sector.

1052

For most of the Sierra Nevada, the most significant financial impact related to the use of Sierra Nevada ecosystems is the rapid development of new residential properties throughout the region. Residential development produces a large and growing stream of property tax revenue at the same time that it places new demands for a bigger and more extensive road network, higher levels of fire protection, and water and sewage infrastructure. These ecosystem impacts may be greater than those associated with the direct conversion of land for house sites and accompanying yards.

CHAPTER 7: OVERVIEW OF THE ECONOMIC ASPECTS OF THE SIERRA NEVADA ECOSYSTEM

The economic value of the Sierra Nevada has been and will continue to be a major force in setting overall goals for the ecosystem as a whole. The ecosystem continues to have a large and direct role in the economy through revenue-generating commodity and services, employment, government revenues, and a wide array of non-market benefits to residents and visitors. The economic assessment identified the major stakeholders and beneficiaries who benefit from existing patterns of resource use in the Sierra Nevada. From the perspective of employment and local businesses, commodities and services directly related to uses of the ecosystem account for approximately one quarter of jobs (Table 7.1). From the perspective of the natural resources, water is the basis for most of the economic value. Timber, animal forage, other agricultural crops, and a range of recreational and residential services directly dependent of the ecosystem comprise the rest of the natural resource value. At the Sierra-wide level, a majority of the economic benefits from the use of the natural resource accrue to beneficiaries outside the region. Regional accounting of employment patterns and different natural resources highlights both the differences and commonalties among regions.

The size of local economies have more than doubled over the past twenty years. Sources of personal income in the Sierra Nevada are now considerably less dominated by wages earned locally than they were twenty years ago. Personal income in the form of interest payments, dividends, social security, and government financed health services have grown considerably throughout the Sierra Nevada. In addition, a large increase in the number of workers commuting into Sacramento and other metropolitan areas have substantially broadened the sources of personal income. The net effects have been to buffer local economies from the cyclical nature of many resource dependent sectors and to tie local economies to state and national economic trends.

The distribution of Sierran jobs (between commodity-producing jobs and service-producing jobs) is the same now as it was in 1970. Diversification has occurred within each sector, the number of jobs has more than doubled, but the relative proportion of commodity and service jobs stayed constant. Recreation, timber, and agriculture are the three largest types of employment sectors directly dependent on the ecosystem. The most significant growth has been in non-timber manufacturing and high-wage service sectors. Both of these sectors are less dependent on the direct use of natural resources than the historically large agriculture, timber and mining sectors. The distribution of employment provides a clear portrait of the relative importance of different sectors across the Sierra Nevada. The patterns of employment, commodity production, and services directly dependent on the Sierra Nevada ecosystem are inconsistent across the range. Regions defined either by economic linkages or major vegetative types exhibit unique economic-ecosystem linkages. These variations complicate the application of many range-wide strategies but also are the basis for future opportunities. The major implication of this is that effective strategies for the Sierra Nevada will not be uniform across the range.

Table 7.1: Major Employment Sectors, 1990

	Number of workers in 1990	Local Services	Timber	Agr. & Mining	Travel	Public Admin.	Non-timber Manuf.	Cons-truction
Total	260,000	59%	4%	5%	8%	7%	6%	11%
North	44,000	61%	4%	6%	5%	8%	7%	9%
North Central	93,000	61%	3%	3%	5%	7%	9%	12%
South Central	46,000	57%	3%	6%	7%	8%	9%	11%
San Joaquin	29,000	58%	9%	7%	6%	9%	0%	10%
Greater Tahoe	35,000	51%	0%	2%	31%	4%	4%	9%
East Side	13,000	59%	0%	8%	13%	7%	3%	10%
Foothills	169,000	59%	3%	6%	5%	7%	8%	12%
Conifer Belt	44,000	56%	8%	8%	8%	9%	2%	9%
Tahoe & East Side	48,000	53%	0%	6%	21%	6%	3%	11%

Source: 1990 Census.

From the complementary perspective of natural resources, water is the most valuable commodity, followed by timber, livestock and other agricultural products. The Sierra Nevada ecosystem also provides the setting for a large recreation and tourism industry as well as new residences built for the large influx of people who enjoy living within the Sierra Nevada ecosystem. Based on estimates of direct resource values as one input (not the total revenue produced by resource dependent activities), the Sierra Nevada ecosystem produces approximately $2.2 billion worth of commodities and services annually. Water accounts for more than 60% of that total value. Other commodities account for 20% as do services. Most of the water value accrues to water rights holders and beneficiaries outside of the region. Although the infrastructure to hold, divert, and channel the water is very valuable, relatively little direct employment is needed to operate and maintain these facilities. The other resource-based sectors involve many more employees and firms and are hence have greater visibility in the local economies.

In addition to supporting businesses and employment, the different economic uses of the Sierra Nevada ecosystem also generate revenue for ecosystem and community reinvestment. Ecosystem reinvestment is part of overall resource management costs and involves expenditures within individual agencies and private ownerships. While reinvestment is required to sustain economic uses of the ecosystem, actual levels of reinvestment are hard to track across different resource-controlling institutions. Reinvestment that benefit local communities is more tractable when funds are transferred between different parties through revenue sharing, fees, taxes or subsidies. Under existing institutional relationships, the rate of reinvestment varies considerably among different commodities and services. Public timber and private recreation are the largest net contributors both in total dollars and as a percentage of their total value. The following table presents an overview of the major resource-based commodity and service sectors that are directly or indirectly dependent on the Sierra Nevada ecosystem.

Table 7.2: Estimated Annual Resource Values and Reinvestment for Major Ecosystem Commodities and Services

Ecosystem Commodities and Services	Resource Value (Million $)	Percent of Sierra Resources	Economic Sectors Benefiting from Sierra Nevada Resources	Direct Reinvestment (Million $)
Downstream Irrigation Water (1)	450	20%	Central Valley Agriculture	(a)
Downstream Municipal Water (1)	290	13%	Metropolitan Areas	(a)
Hydroelectric Power (1)	610	27%	All Users of Electricity	(b)
Water Total		61%		
Private Recreation & Tourism (2)	140	6%	Overall Recreation and Tourist Sector	10
Public Recreation in parks and forests (3)	225	10%	Users of Public Recreation Facilities (45 Million Visitor Days per Year)	(c)
New Residential ecosystem values (4)	110	5%	Total Residential Sectors within Sierra Nevada	10
Recreation/Resid. Total		21%		
Public Timber (5)	150	7%	Timber Industry	23
Private Timber (5)	170	8%	Timber Industry	3
Timber Total		14%		
Public Grazing (6)	8	<1%	Livestock Industry	-7 (d)
Private Grazing (6)	16	1%	Livestock Industry	<1
Private Pasture (6)	8	<1%	Livestock Industry	<1
Other Irrigated Agriculture (6)	50	2%	Local Agricultural Processing, Wineries, etc.	<1
Agriculture Total		4%		
Total	2,227	100%		39

Source: Resource value estimates:
(1) Derived value of water rights (Stewart, this volume)
(2) 10% of 1995 total revenue estimate (Stewart, this volume)
(3) $5/day for estimated 45 million annual visitor days (Duane 1996-b)
(4) 10% of annual new construction value
(5) California State Board of Equalization, 1985-1994
(6) County Agricultural Commissioners, 1985,1994
Direct re-investment estimates:
(a) Water rights are not taxed as property and hence return no value to area of origin.
(b) Hydroelectric power plants are taxed as commercial property but the assessments are very low in comparison to revenue generation.
(c) Public recreation in National Forests, National Parks, State Parks, and other facilities is funded primarily from general funds rather than user fees.
(d) Public grazing fees are far below those charged by private or other public land owners

The estimates are based on the average for the past decade and flatten out growth trends and cyclical patterns. The values are considerably less than the full value of the output of the business sectors that use the resources. For example, the total output value of the timber and livestock industries are considerable greater than the values of the stumpage or forage values. Similarly the estimates for private recreation and new construction attribute only 10% of the total revenue directly to the ecosystem. The ecosystem 'rent' of public recreation of $5 per day is far below charges at developed private recreation facilities and survey data on the consumer value ascribed to the full recreational experiences. It was chosen to approximate the daily entrance fees charged for many state parks and charges and simple private campgrounds. Most of the private charges or consumer's willingness to pay are more accurately ascribed to other services provided by the recreational facility operators. The estimates of the water value are based only on the value of the water right (or wholesale product in the case of electric power) and not the final delivery price.

Direct reinvestment estimates are ten year averages of specific revenue sharing or taxation applied to different commodities and services. Public timber produces most of the total revenue going to counties through the 25 percent share of gross revenues allotted to counties as well as the timber yield tax that applies to both public and private stumpage. Taxes are relatively low on private timber and agricultural lands to sustain private management and prevent undesirable fragmentation and conversion to residential uses. Most of the reinvestment on these private lands is provided directly by the land owners and does not show up in this accounting framework. The transient occupancy tax (TOT) levied on the overnight visitor component of the recreation and tourism industry is the fastest growing source of ecosystem-derived funding. Property taxes on new residential development grow rapidly because they are paid every year and not just for the year the house was built. Currently, most property taxes go for infrastructure and services rather than ecosystem management. Explicit ecosystem management funding based on private residential property values are typically financed through state park bonds or parcel taxes for local park or open space districts.

In terms of funds that could potentially be reinvested into the ecosystem and communities, around 2% of all resource values are presently captured through federal, state, and county governments. Although this tally does not account for private reinvestments or other federal or state appropriations, it does suggest that additional mechanisms to promote reinvestment are necessary to maintain and enhance the Sierra Nevada ecosystem so that it can continue to provide the socially desired outputs. The status of many components of the Sierra Nevada ecosystem suggests that this level of funding is insufficient to assure long term production at current rates.

The core of the under investment problem is straightforward. The ecological and community assessments in this report suggest that sustaining and enhancing the Sierra Nevada ecosystem will require massive and directed investment of time and money. Compared to the size of the local economies and the value of the natural assets the cost is small. The investment is currently not forthcoming for four primary reasons:

1. Many attributes of the ecosystem are not valued in a manner that motivates investment.
2. Restrictions on exchange prevent value formation for aspects of the ecosystem that generate economic benefit.
3. Barriers between agencies and governments prevent efficient responses to economic values where these are known.
4. Localities lack the capacity to capture economic surpluses they generate and to then invest these surpluses for ecosystem health and social well-being.

These problems can be addressed with different kinds of institutional resolutions. Where the attributes are not valued in a manner that motivates investment, new boundaries can create the constituencies so that potential exchanges will yield their full value. Where restrictions on exchange restrict economic value formation, arrangements can be created to open opportunities for trade. Where barriers within and among governments prevent efficient responses to economic values, cooperative agreements can be formed to lessen these barriers. Where localities lack capacity to capture and invest economic surpluses, new local organizations can provide the necessary structure.

The actual configuration of possibilities vary tremendously among conditions, but certain aspects display features that benefit from common attention at higher scales of governance. In general, institutions that are oriented primarily toward the mobilization of people and synthesis of activity operate best at local levels. Those that require specialized technical, financial and legal capacities operate better at higher levels. Programs to address reinvestment needs can be more effective if they explicitly address the full range of opportunities.

ACKNOWLEDGMENTS

This report could not have been completed without the extensive research assistance of Bruce McWilliams, Dominic Roques, George Woodward, and Kacy Collons. We are all indebted to the scores of local, state, and federal employees who unfailingly assisted us in finding and collecting the data used in this report. Finally, the report gained from the insightful comments and criticisms of the numerous reviewers.

REFERENCES

Agricultural Commissioner. 1986. Agricultural Crop Reports: 1985, Various Counties.

Agricultural Commissioner. 1995. Agricultural Crop Reports: 1994, Various Counties.

Barrette, Brian R., Donald R. Gedney, Daniel D. Oswald. 1968. California Timber Industries, 1968, Mill Characteristics and Wood Supply: State of California, Division of Forestry.

Beesley, David. 1996. Reconstructing the Landscape: An Environmental History, 1820-1960. In Sierra Nevada Ecosystem Project: Final report to Congress, vol. II, chap 1. Davis: University of California, Centers for Water and Wildland Resources.

Boggess, William, Ronald Lacewell and David Zilberman. 1993. Economics of Water Use in Agriculture. In *Agricultural And Environmental Resource Economics*, edited by Gerald A. Carlson, David Zilberman, and John A. Miranowski. New York. Oxford University Press.

Black + Veatch. 1995. *California Water Charge Survey*. Irvine, CA.

Bureau of Economic Analysis. 1995. Regional Economic Information System: U.S. Department of Commerce.

California Department of Finance. Various Years. *California State Abstract*.

California Energy Commission. 1981. Small Hydroelectric Systems: A Guide to Development in California: California Energy Commission.

California Energy Commission. 1992. California Power Plant Maps: California Energy Commission.

California Energy Commission. 1981. Small Hydroelectric Systems: A Guide to Development in California: California Energy Commission.

California State Board of Equalization. Various Years-a. Harvest Value Schedules.

California State Board of Equalization. Various Years-b. Timber Volumes and Values by County and Species.

California Trade and Commerce Agency. 1992. Impact of New Jobs: Using Multipliers to Measure Benefits. Office of Economic Research.

Center for the Continuing Study of the California Economy. 1996. *California County Projections 1995/1996 Edition*.

CH2M Hill. 1989. California Livestock Industry Economic Model.

Colclasure, Perry, Joel Moen, and Charles Bolsinger. 1986b. Timber Resource Statistics for the Northern Interior Resource Area of California: U.S.D.A. Forest Service.

Damon Runyan Associates. 1995. California Travel Impacts by County: 1993: California Trade and Commerce Agency; Division of Tourism.

Department of Water Resources. 1979. A Survey of Small Hydroelectric Potential at Existing Sites in California: State of California Resources Agency.

Dilsaver, Larry M., and William C. Tweed. 1990. *Challenge of the Big Trees: A Resource History of Sequoia and Kings Canyon National Parks*. Three Rivers, California: Sequoia Natural History Association.

Department of Water Resources. 1981. Small Hydroelectric Potential at Existing Hydraulic Structures in California: State of California Resources Agency.

Department of Water Resources. 1993. Dams within Jurisdiction of the State of California. Division of Safety of Dams Statistical File.

Department of Water Resources. 1994. California Water Plan Update.

Department of Water Resources. 1995. California Water Supply Outlook: Division of Flood Management, Department of Water Resources.

Doak, S. C. and J. Kusel. 1996. Well-Being in Forest-Dependent Communities, Part II: A Social Assessment Focus. In Sierra Nevada Ecosystem Project: Final report to Congress, vol. II, chap 13. Davis: University of California, Centers for Water and Wildland Resources.

Duane, T. P. 1996-a. Human Settlement, 1850-2040. In Sierra Nevada Ecosystem Project: Final report to Congress, vol. II, chap 11. Davis: University of California, Centers for Water and Wildland Resources.

Duane, Tim. 1996-b. Recreation in the Sierra. In Sierra Nevada Ecosystem Project: Final report to Congress, vol. II, chap 19. Davis: University of California, Centers for Water and Wildland Resources.

Employment Development Department. 1996. Labor Market Information On-line: State of California.

Energy Information Administration. 1992. *Electric Plant Cost and Power Production Expenses 1991*.

Farhad, Farnam. 1994. California Department of Water Resources (DWR) economist. Letter describing ground water pumping costs.

Federal Energy Regulatory Commission. Unpublished. 1970 - 1994 Yearly Production Statistics for FERC Licensed Power Plants.

Forest and Rangeland Resources Assessment Program. 1988. *California's Forests and Rangelands: Growing Conflict Over Changing Uses*. Sacramento, CA: California Department of Forestry and Fire Protection.

Hiserote, Bruce A., and James O. Howard. 1978. California's Forest Products Industry: 1976: U. S. Department of Agriculture, Forest Service, Pacific Northwest Forest and Range Experiment Research Station.

Hiserote, Bruce, Joel Moen, and Charles Bolsinger. 1986. Timber Resource Statistics for the San Joaquin and Southern California Resource Area of California: USDA Forest Service.

Howard, James O. 1974. California's Forest Products Industry: Wood Consumption and Characteristics 1972: U. S. Department of Agriculture, Forest Service, Pacific Northwest Research Station.

Howard, James O. 1984. California's Forest Products Industry: 1982: U. S. Department of Agriculture, Forest Service, Pacific Northwest Research Station.

Howard, James O., and Franklin R. Ward. 1986. California's Forest Products Industry: 1985: U. S. Department of Agriculture, Forest Service, Pacific Northwest Research Station.

Howard, James O., and Franklin R. Ward. 1991. California's Forest Products Industry: 1988: U. S. Department of Agriculture, Forest Service, Pacific Northwest Research Station.

Kinney, William C. 1996. Conditions of Rangelands before 1905. In Sierra Nevada Ecosystem Project: Final report to Congress, vol. II, chap 3. Davis: University of California, Centers for Water and Wildland Resources.

Krumland, Bruce, and William McKillop. 1990. Prospects for Supply of Private Timber in California: University of California, Berkeley.

Larson, D. J. 1996. Historical Water Use Priorities and Public Policies. In Sierra Nevada Ecosystem Project: Final report to Congress, vol. II, chap 8. Davis: University of California, Centers for Water and Wildland Resources.

Lloyd Jr., J.D., Joel Moen, and Charles Bolsinger. 1986b. Timber Resource Statistics for the Sacramento Resource Area of California: USDA. Forest Service.

Lucas, Greg. 1995. Local Lawmakers' Ploy Saves S.F. $30 Million. San Francisco Chronicle, June 3,1995, A15.

Marvin. S. 1996. Possible Changes in Water Yield and Peak Flows in Response to Forest Management. In Sierra Nevada Ecosystem Project: Final report to Congress, vol. III. Davis: University of California, Centers for Water and Wildland Resources.

McCollum W. 1990. Fishery Resources of the National Forests: USDA Forest Service.

McWilliams, Bruce, and George Goldman. 1994. The Forest Products Industries in California: Their Impact on the State Economy: University of California Division of Agricultural and Natural Resources.

Menke, John. 1996. Rangeland Conditions. In Sierra Nevada Ecosystem Project: Final report to Congress, vol. III. Davis: University of California, Centers for Water and Wildland Resources.

Mikkelsen, Tom. 1995. East Bay Regional Parks Planner. Personal Communication.

ProPHONE 1.0. 1995. Select Phone Book:U.S. Business and Residential Listings. CD-ROM. Danvers, Mass.

Public Utilities Commission. Various Years. Summary of Utilities Avoided Energy Prices.

Rinehart, James. 1995. Rinehart and Associates. Personal Communication.

Romm, Jeff, Robert Z. Callaham, and Richard C. Kattleman. 1988. Toward Managing Sierra Nevada Forests for Water Supply: Wildland Resources Center.

Romm, Jeffrey M., and Amy Ewing. 1987. The Economic Value of Water in National Forest Management. Paper read at California Watershed Management Conference, at West Sacramento, California.

Roper-Starch Worldwide. 1995. Outdoor Recreation in America Survey: Recreation Roundtable.

Secretary of State, California. Various Years. Statement of the Vote.

State of California. Various Years. *California Statistical Abstract.*

State Controller of California. Various Years. Counties of California, Financial Transactions, Annual Report.

State Superintendent of Public Education, California. Various Years-b. Financial Transactions of School Districts, Annual Report.

Stewart, William. 1993. Predicting Employment Impacts of Changing Forest Management in California. Ph.D., University of California at Berkeley.

Sunding, David, David Zilberman and Neal MacDougall. 1995. Water Markets and the Cost of Improving Water Quality in the San Francisco Bay Delta Estuary. *Hastings West Northwest Journal of Environmental Law and Policy* 2:159-166.

Tripp R., and M. Rockland. 1988. The Net Economic Value of Recreation on the National Forests: Twelve Types of Primary Activity Trips Across Nine Forest Service Regions: USDA Forest Service.

U. S. Bureau of Public Roads. 1922. Irrigation Map of Central/Northern California. Washington, D.C.: U. S. Bureau of Public Roads: Irrigation Investigation.

U.S. Bureau of Reclamation. 1995. Progress Report: CVPIA Programmatic Environmental Impact Statement.

U. S. Department of Commerce. 1980. *County Business Patterns, California 1978.* Washington, D. C.: U. S. Government Printing Office.

U. S. Department of Commerce. 1983. *County Business Patterns, California 1981* Washington, D. C.: U. S. Government Printing Office.

U. S. Department of Commerce. 1987. *County Business Patterns, California 1985* Washington, D. C.: U. S. Government Printing Office.

U. S. Department of Commerce. 1990. *County Business Patterns, California 1988.* Washington, D. C.: U. S. Government Printing Office.

U. S. Department of Commerce. 1995. *County Business Patterns, California 1993.* Washington, D. C.: U. S. Government Printing Office.

U. S. Department of Commerce. 1994a. *1992 Census of Retail Trade: California*: U.S. Government Printing Office.

U. S. Department of Commerce. 1994b. *1992 Census of Service Industries: California*: U.S. Government Printing Office.

U. S. Department of Commerce, Bureau of the Census. 1971. California 1970: Summary Social, Economic, and Housing Characteristics.

U. S. Department of Commerce, Bureau of the Census. 1991. California 1990: Tape 3A .

U. S. Department of Commerce, Bureau of Economic Analysis. Various Years. *Local Area Personal Income*: U. S. Government Printing Office.

U. S. Department of Commerce, Bureau of Economic Analysis. 1995. California: Total Multipliers, by Industry Aggregation, for Output, Earnings, and Employment.

USDA Forest Service. 1995. Draft Environmental Impact Statement: Managing California Spotted Owl Habitat in the Sierra Nevada National Forests of California: An Ecosystem Approach: USDA Forest Service.

USDA Forest Service. 1989. Timber Sale Program Annual TSPIRS Report, Pacific Southwest Region, Fiscal Year 1989.

USDA Forest Service. 1990. Timber Sale Program Annual TSPIRS Report, Pacific Southwest Region, Fiscal Year 1990.

USDA Forest Service. 1991. Timber Sale Program Annual TSPIRS Report, Pacific Southwest Region, Fiscal Year 1991.

USDA Forest Service. 1992. Timber Sale Program Annual TSPIRS Report, Pacific Southwest Region, Fiscal Year 1992.

USDA Forest Service. 1993-a. Timber Sale Program Annual TSPIRS Report, Pacific Southwest Region, Fiscal Year 1993.

USDA Forest Service. 1994. Timber Sale Program Annual TSPIRS Report, Pacific Southwest Region, Fiscal Year 1994.

USDA Forest Service. 1993-b. Grazing Statistical Summary FY 1992: USDA Forest Service Range Management.

Warnick, Calvin. 1995. Professor at the University of Idaho and author of "Hydropower Engineering". Personal Communication.

Weeks, David, A. E. Wieslander, H. R. Josephson, and C. L. Hill. 1943. *Land Utilization in the Northern Sierra Nevada*. Berkeley, California: University of California Agricultural Experiment Station.

Wendt, George .1995. President O.A.R.S. Personal Communication.

Zivnuska, John A., Paul Cox, Adon Poli, and David Pesonen. 1965. The Commercial Forest Resources and Forest Products Industries of California: University of California Division of Agricultural Sciences.

JONATHAN KUSEL
Forest Community Research
Westwood, California

24

Coordinated
Resource Management

Sierra Nevada Ecosystem Project: Final report to Congress, vol. III, *Assessments, Commissioned Reports, and Background Information.* Davis: University of California, Centers for Water and Wildland Resources, 1996.

INTRODUCTION

Coordinated Resource Management Planning is an innovative, and in the last five years, an increasingly utilized approach to resource planning involving multiple agencies and a diversity of public and private land owners. The longest running Coordinated Resource Management (CRM) group and one of the most successful in California is the Feather River CRM. Located in the Northern Sierra County of Plumas, the Feather River CRM encourages local initiative and participation in resource management on public and private land. The group is active on 763,600 square acres of the North and Middle Forks of the Feather River watershed, the headwaters of the California State Water Project and one of the most productive water and power rivers in the Sierra. The purpose of this paper is to identify factors which gave rise to the Feather River CRM, briefly discuss a CRM project, and describe how the group has succeeded as both an institution and process (see Anderson and Baum 1987, for a more general discussion of the Coordinated Resource Management framework). Information for this study was collected primarily through interviews of key Feather River CRM participants and others knowledgeable about the process. Their names are listed in the references.

THE BIRTH OF COORDINATED RESOURCE MANAGEMENT IN THE HEADWATERS OF THE FEATHER RIVER

Fierce polarization around natural resource use and management characterized Plumas County during the 1980's. Like many other areas in the Sierra, anger and distrust fostered a gridlock in which no one party or interest group could fully prevail. Among some residents, however, there was growing recognition that continued battles would only further local anguish as the changing timber industry--important to many local economies--would never be the same, regardless of whether one viewed the changes as driven by environmental restrictions, industry restructuring, or both. These residents also realized that the loss of local control resulting from these battles did not serve any party's interest and that a new mode of cooperative interaction was needed to maintain local representation in the resource management process. They also viewed cooperation as necessary to encourage the considerable creativity needed to develop new economic opportunities in the County.

At the same time, federal and state agencies began to seriously examine the cumulative effects of over a century of logging, mining and grazing, on fisheries, water quality, and rangelands of the watershed. Agency personnel also perceived that social conflicts, as well as inter-agency conflicts over resource management approaches were interfering with the achievement of their institutional mandates.

Similarly, Pacific Gas and Electric (PG&E) recognized the costly, long-term effects of upstream soil erosion which drastically reduced the life-span of its reservoirs and other components of its hydropower infrastructure. For example, accumulated sediment had reduced the capacity Rock Creek and Cresta Reservoirs, two upstream reservoirs, 46 and 56 percent, respectively (Harrison and Lindquist 1995). Because the utility was prohibited by law from flushing accumulated sediments downstream, PG&E proposed to dredge the reservoirs. The cost of dredging was estimated at seven million dollars.

In early 1985, upon hearing of plans for massive investment in dredging that would be paid to out-of-county firms, Leah Wills, from the Plumas County economic development agency, the Plumas Corporation, approached newly elected County Supervisor John Schramel with an alternative plan. She proposed that PG&E's long-term strategy directly address the sedimentation problem by financing upstream restoration projects as opposed to after-the-fact dredging. By emphasizing erosion prevention, this strategy would not only save the utility money but would direct funds into the local economy and create jobs. It would also provide the basis for initiating environmental restoration projects on a watershed scale throughout the county.

These goals were in accordance with Supervisor John Schramel's agenda of job creation for the county and also attracted the interest of Terrie Benoit of the USDA Forest Service (USFS) and Richard Flint of the California Department of Fish and Game (CDF&G). Benoit and Flint had both grown interested in local restoration projects in the Feather River watershed but were unable to move forward due to agency inertia and inter-agency conflicts. With the addition of John Sheehan, then of the County's Housing and Community Development Department, Ray Stine of California Department of Forestry, and Mike Kossow, a local environmentalist, the nucleus around which the Feather River CRM, referred to as the "gang of seven," was formed. This group met for many long hours around John Schramel's kitchen table and at the Quincy office of the U.S. Forest Service to outline a stream restoration and erosion control proposal for PG&E.

The first steps in the development of the CRM group were two meetings, the first called by John Schramel in April 1985 with key local players to create a more detailed watershed erosion-control plan. The second, organized by John Sheehan one month later, set up a formal Memorandum of Understanding (MOU) to establish roles and responsibilities for cooperating parties. Twelve federal, state, regional, and local entities signed onto the MOU which included the following objectives: identify erosion sources across the watershed; develop a cooperative regional erosion control plan; design, fund, and implement cost effective erosion control measures; and work with both public and private landowners. In the MOU, signatories agreed to a series of goals and objectives (see Clifton 1993 for additional discussion). These included:

1) Optimize all beneficial uses of water;
2) Emphasize education and prevention over regulation: appeal to "enlightened self-interest;"
3) Resolve participants' concerns through proactive involvement in a consensus-based planning process.

These goals were to be met by the following objectives:

1) Improve high quality mid-summer to late-fall stream flows through restoring ground water recharge potential in meadows and uplands;
2) Reduce erosive power of winter and spring storms and flatten storm run off peaks by stabilizing stream banks and upland soils;
3) Prioritize water quality and quantity improvements on lands yielding the highest multiple returns to landowner and other participants;
4) Reduce potential conflicts on more marginal lands by increasing productivity on prime lands.

Virtually all CRM members interviewed agreed, that without the willingness of several organizations to commit money to as yet an unproved process, the Feather River CRM may never have gotten off the ground. PG&E agreed the erosion control strategy would cost less in the long run and serve to leverage the organization's funds and benefit local communities, and therefore provided financial support for the proposed plan. Additional organizations which provided financial support included California Department of Forestry, Soil Conservation Service (SCS) and the Plumas County Housing and Community Development Department. The Plumas Corporation was chosen to coordinate the process because it was widely supported and viewed as a neutral party due to its organizational mandate to attract jobs and economic development to the County. A portion of the funds were used to hire Leah Wills of the Plumas Corporation as erosion control coordinator.

EVOLUTION OF THE FEATHER RIVER CRM

The first project initiated by the MOU signatories was the Red Clover Creek Demonstration Project. Like most later CRM efforts, this project resulted from the convergence of many contributing factors: PG&E was interested in funding a demonstration site to test the erosion prevention approach; CDF&G which had been conducting a cattle exclusion study on a reach of the creek managed by the USFS suggested the same site as a first project; SCS identified an adjacent privately owned portion of the creek as an ideal location; and the private landowner decided that given the historic damage, a restoration project was worth the risk. The Red Clover Creek Demonstration Project had two characteristics which were critical factors for the emergence of the CRM: speed--it took only six months to design and install the erosion control structures-- and durability--the structures withstood the fury of the 1986 floods. According to Coordinator Leah Wills, by setting a precedent of efficient and effective actions, the Red Clover Creek Project energized the process and proved that continued participation in the CRM was worth member financial and time commitments. It also helped convince local land owners and managers of the potential benefits of a CRM project on their land.

After undertaking several projects similar to the Red Clover Creek Demonstration Project in the late 1980's, signatories to the MOU were presented with the idea of becoming an official CRM group. Up until this point, the group had been operating under the framework of the original MOU. A representative from the SCS suggested the Coordinated Resource Management Planning (CRMP) federal enabling framework (established by the USFS, BLM, Co-operative Extension Service, and the SCS) as a means to foster better coordination among resource management agencies and to gain increased access to federal programs and grants for work on public and private land. Importantly, the CRMP framework would allow existing group processes to continue without constraint while conferring additional advantages including increased legitimacy among federal agencies and expansion of membership. As Mike Kossow, one of the gang of seven, stated, "We were a CRMP but just didn't know it yet." While formation of a CRMP led to a new institutional structure for the group, members did not hesitate to modify this structure to meet its specific needs and values. The commitment of the group to maintaining a results-focused process and an emphasis on projects as opposed to planning, led the group to drop the "P" (for planning) in the CRMP name and call itself the Feather River CRM.

The Feather River CRM's role subsequently evolved towards the remediation of cumulative watershed damage. The group developed criteria to select projects based on whether proposed projects would address Cumulative Watershed Effects (CWEs). CWEs are a prominent factor in the CRM management area, and are defined as situations in which all or most of the following ecological and institutional characteristics are present:

- Land ownership is intermingled with multiple public and private owners;
- Conflicts over management are likely or occurring;
- Resource benefits extend beyond individual, political, and agency boundaries and jurisdictions;
- Multiple resource uses coexist in beneficial and detrimental ways;
- Causes of degradation are multiple, complex and/or historical in character;
- Resource problems cannot be solved by rest or management changes alone within a reasonable investment period;
- Lasting solutions require comprehensive, long-range strategies.

AN ANALYSIS OF THE CRM PROCESS

The Feather River CRM has achieved considerable success by crafting a process that reflects the particular ecological, institutional and social contexts of the CRM area, and links a range of ecological, institutional and social goals. This section describes components of the Feather River CRM that have been important components of its success.

Involvement

One of the most significant potential barriers to CRM involvement is landowner fears of coercion, loss of control, or being forced to compromise fundamental values. The CRM group addresses these concerns in at least three ways. First, all projects are initiated on a voluntary basis: a private landowner or public land manager approaches the CRM with a project proposal. Private landowners work first with the Feather River Resource Conservation District to provide an initial analysis of the problem and set project goals prior to working directly with the CRM. Second, early in the process landowners or managers are asked to identify their "worst fears" or "worst case scenarios" that might result from CRM involvement. Once identified, the CRM is able to address these fears directly. Third, the CRM makes sure it pairs agencies with individuals that landowners tend to trust.

It is important to point out, however, that project initiation on strictly a voluntary basis does have drawbacks. Relying on landowner initiative makes it difficult to create long-term and comprehensive restoration strategies and can leave the overall process vulnerable to changes in the political climate. The process is also less able to accommodate the prescriptions of a comprehensive watershed management framework. In fact, at an early 1996 CRM meeting, the group called for a refocusing of the group's emphasis from discrete projects to a broader watershed management approach. It is too early to tell, however, how this change will affect landowner volunteerism and involvement, and how landowner involvement and project planning will be linked.

Coordination

Julie Spezia, Executive Director of the California Association of Resource Conservation Districts, indicated that based on her first hand knowledge of CRMP groups across the state, behind successful groups is a catalyzing coordinator who keeps participants working together and focused on moving forward. The Feather River CRM coordinator, Leah Wills, describes her role as keeping the process "alive and vital," thereby maintaining the active commitment of the CRM members. According to Wills, because of the pervasive cynicism about the possibilities for change in resource management, commitment to and faith in the CRM process can only be maintained by making successes visible and innovation continual. While this requirement for constant action has contributed to a lack of program stability within the CRM, Wills recognizes that paradoxically, the "mobile anarchy" of constant adaptation to changing circumstances has led to the CRM's longevity and vitality. Wills views her role as a guide rather than a controller of this ever-shifting process. She does not pretend to be "neutral," but rather is explicit about her personal and professional commitment to a vision of economic and ecological sustainability, a vision embraced by most if not all CRM members.

Group Process

CRM members have identified the following qualities which keep the process dynamic and for which the coordinator has responsibility to ensure.

* Maintaining and honoring a diversity of opinions and perspectives.

* Prohibiting the group from attacking an individual or point of view and maintaining an experimental atmosphere in which the group remains open to new ideas and approaches. This experimental atmosphere is matched to both the ecological context of complexity and uncertainty, and to the social context of diverse interests and expertise of the CRM participants.

* Members must believe that "win-win" solutions can be derived from consensus, and that at the same time, expressing differences in a constructive fashion can lead to enriched ideas for everybody.

* CRM project goals and action are determined through a broad consensus decision-making process. Approval by a several CRM committees is required for any CRM project to reach the implementation stage.

* Group adoption of a "no blame" policy. Instead of fixing blame on one individual or entity for environmental damage, which is often impossible given the large spatial and temporal scales of the problems which the CRM group addresses, the group attempts to enlist all party support to solve the problem at hand. By not tagging any one individual or entity as the culprit, defensiveness and hostility is avoided, and feelings of responsibility for the land (which many local landowners and public agency managers do have) can emerge. As Wills noted, "No one wants to shoulder all the burden, but almost everyone is willing to shoulder some of it."

- The group focuses on long-term solutions rather than quick fixes and short-term investment horizons.

Approach to Knowledge and Learning

For each project a Technical Advisory Committee is established to develop and oversee the project design.. This committee includes resource specialists, landowners, and other interested members of the public. CRM resource agency personnel conduct a stringent assessment of a project site and project proposal, and evaluate both its ecological impact and consistency with the CRM's ecological and institutional goals.

An historical baseline is established for each project site. This is developed from available scientific information and landowner knowledge. Development of this baseline yields vital ecological information and, equally important, develops a shared social identity for a project.

Historical baseline information is coupled with agency technical knowledge to determine appropriate interventions. As described by Wills, "The landowners know what happened [to the site] but may not know what to do about it; the agency people know what to do, but they don't really know what happened." On projects which include a large number of landowners, public meetings are held to gather input. These meetings are important not only for information collection, but are important forums for obtaining needed public involvement and support. One land owner involved in the Wolf Creek project in Greenville commented, "We looked forward to the meetings because they told us, 'We need your ideas, we can't do it without you.'"

Monitoring of implemented projects is conducted to track project performance relative to the goals of individual projects and the overall CRM framework. Monitoring allows CRM agreements to be revisited if project goals are not being achieved as predicted. Monitoring of CRM projects has also generated considerable direct benefits to the local high school and community college students. The Plumas County Unified School District and the Feather River Community College, both CRM signatories, have had students actively involved in collecting data for CRM projects. Both the School District and the Feather River College have ongoing monitoring training programs. Some CRM members note that the caring attitude fostered in these youth toward the local environment is one of the most satisfying accomplishments of the CRM.

Harrison and Lindquist (1995) estimated that CRM projects over the long-term may reduce waterborne sediment to upstream reservoirs by 50 percent, but, to date, there has been inadequate monitoring to verify this estimate. Most CRM project monitoring has focused on bank and channel stabilization on individual projects. Monitoring is needed that isolates and quantifies aggregate erosion control benefits from CRM projects in the Feather River headwaters. Limited funding and the individual project focus of the CRM group have contributed to this lack of comprehensive data. Obtaining funding for monitoring has been problematic because monitoring is extremely costly and offers little in the way of visible returns. The lack of a comprehensive monitoring program has contributed to unresolved divisions within the CRM about how to evaluate successes and failures of projects and project methodologies, and makes it more difficult for organizations like PG&E to justify continued investment.

The CRM group places a priority on actions over issues. This is based in the larger conception of the CRM as "implementors" as opposed to decision-makers. The CRM takes on projects around which general community and agency consensus either already exists or is probable. The CRM, then, is used as a forum by which local consensus can be "put on the ground" to begin reaping both social and environmental benefits. Paralleling this pragmatic stance is an experimental approach to projects in which mistakes are not feared, but drawn upon for lessons on future improvement. In this dynamic and ground-based approach to learning ideas from all CRM members are welcomed. This has been especially important in facilitating the participation of landowners in the CRM projects by reducing the divisions between "expert" and "non-expert" knowledge and the associated resentment caused by perceptions of "expert arrogance." Finally, in addition to the diffusion of specific erosion control and stream restoration techniques both within and beyond the CRM group, the CRM has created a general climate of inquiry in which agency personnel and area residents develop watershed protection projects matched to local ecological and social conditions.

CONCLUSION

The ability of a wide range of individuals representing such varied (and often historically conflicting) institutions to come together around a common goal has been deemed the most important success of the CRM. One observer noted that the CRM group represents an important evolutionary phase of bringing communities together around the practice of sustainable development, that is not theoretical, but concrete and grounded. In the roughly ten years of operation, specific accomplishments of the Feather River CRM include: initiation of 38 watershed restoration projects on 4100 acres, rehabilitation of 14.5 stream miles, and four million dollars contributed to the Plumas County economy, most of it through the creation of local jobs.

A fundamental quality of the CRM process has been that members have been able to subjugate their individual differences to the larger mutual goal of healthy communities in a healthy watershed. By uniting diverse interests around common goals, the Feather River CRM has reduced tensions and increased cooperation both between public agencies and private landowners, and between agencies themselves. By demonstrating the benefits of cooperation, the CRM has created an atmosphere in the community for increased trust which catalyzes other community building activities and allows other consensus-based initiatives such as the Quincy Library Group to grow and flourish. CRM members recommend that the practice-derived knowledge and social learning generated through the CRM's projects should now be allowed to "trickle up" to better shape state and federal policy to local social and ecological conditions.

REFERENCES

Anderson, W. E. and R. C. Baum. 1987. Coordinated Resource Management Planning: Does it Work? *Journal of Soil and Water Conservation* 42(3):161-166.

Harrison, L. and D. Lindquist. 1995. Hydro Power Benefits of Cooperative Watershed Management. Paper prepared for the 1995 Waterpower Conference (July), San Francisco, California.

Clifton, C. 1993. East Branch North Fork Feather River Erosion Control Strategy. Unpublished file report, U.S. Forest Service, Quincy, California.

List of Individuals Interviewed

Terrie Benoit, USDA Forest Service, Plumas National Forest. 8/17/95

Michael De Lasaux, U.C. Cooperative Extension Service. 9/15/95

Robert Farnworth, Landowner; Director, Feather River Resource Conservation District. 8/16/95

Richard Flint, California Department of Fish and Game. 8/18/95

Louise Gallagher, Landowner, Greenville. 8/16/95

Dennis Heiman, Regional Water Quality Control Board. 8/18/95

Mike Kossow, Meadowbrook Conservation Associates. 9/5/95

Donna Lindquist, Pacific Gas & Electric, 9/13/95

Robert Meacher, Plumas County Board of Supervisors. 8/15/95

John Schramel, former Plumas County Board Supervisor. 8/16/95

Cindy Wallach, California Department of Parks and Recreation. 8/18/95

Reyna Weyrauch. Natural Resource Conservation Service. 8/23/95

Ray Whitely, Soper-Wheeler. 8/23/95

Leah Wills, CRM Erosion Control Coordinator, The Plumas Corporation. 8/15/95

Jura Young, The Nature Conservancy. 9/5/95

ERIN FLEMING
Centers for Water and Wildland Resources
University of California
Davis, California

25

Compilation of Workshops Contributing to Sierra Nevada Assessments

Acting on the charge from Congress, the Sierra Nevada Ecosystem Project Science Team assessed the status of various Sierra Nevada ecosystem components. Assessments represent the best available information. Experts throughout the Sierra Nevada contributed to the collection of information by giving of their time and knowledge. Accordingly workshops were held throughout the Sierra Nevada to gather this expert knowledge.

This chapter is a compilation of participant lists, agendas, and descriptions of workshops. This is not an exhaustive list of the working groups and individuals who participated, however, we include this information as acknowledgment of the valuable contributions of those whose expertise added so much to many of the assessments. Additional acknowledgments are found in chapters of volumes II and III.

Late Successional/Old Growth Mapping
March, 1994
Sacramento, CA

Amedee Brickey	Sierra National Forest, Pineridge Ranger District
Ramiro Rojas	Sierra National Forest, Pineridge Ranger District
Artie Colson	Sequoia National Forest, Cannell Meadow Ranger District
Ed Armenta	Sequoia National Forest, Cannell Meadow Ranger District
Frank Brassell	Sequoia National Forest, Cannell Meadow Ranger District
Al Vazquez	Plumas National Forest, Milford/Laufman Ranger District
Dominic Cesmat	Plumas National Forest, Milford/Laufman Ranger District
Genny Wilson	Plumas National Forest, Milford/Laufman Ranger District
Beth Corbin	Lassen National Forest
Mike Jablonski	Lassen National Forest
Russ Volke	Lassen National Forest
Boyd Turner	Lassen National Forest
Rod Vineyard	Lassen National Forest
Judy Welles	Lassen National Forest
Chris Click	Modoc National Forest, Big Valley Ranger District
Julie Rechtin	Modoc National Forest, Big Valley Ranger District
Dale Evans	Modoc National Forest, Warner Mountain Ranger District
Mike Brown	Stanislaus National Forest
Ginnelle O'Connor	Plumas National Forest, Oroville/Laporte Ranger District
Neil Sugihara	Stanislaus National Forest
Mike Mateyka	Plumas National Forest, Oroville/Laporte Ranger District
George Stundinski	Modoc National Forest, Devil's Garden Ranger District
John Bradford	Tahoe National Forest
Kathy Van Zuuk	Tahoe National Forest
Pat Farrell	Tahoe National Forest
Stephanie Sager	Tahoe National Forest
Ann Carlson	Tahoe National Forest
Karen Hayden	Tahoe National Forest
Bob Cary	Tahoe National Forest
Jerry Kent	Tahoe National Forest, Truckee Ranger District
Joe Sherlock	Stanislaus National Forest, Mi-Wok Ranger
Liz Fisher	Modoc National Forest, Doublehead Ranger District
Dave Sinclear	Modoc National Forest, Doublehead Ranger District
Pat Stygar	Sierra National Forest, Minarets Ranger District
Dave Smith	Sierra National Forest, Minarets Ranger District
Ron Keil	Inyo National Forest
Brian Miller	Inyo National Forest
Dale Johnson	Inyo National Forest
Kathy Noland	Inyo National Forest
Terry Hicks	Inyo National Forest
Sydney Smith	Modoc National Forest
Chuck Bredesen	Sierra National Forest, Mariposa Ranger District
Bea Olson	Sierra National Forest, Mariposa Ranger District
Teri Drivas	Sierra National Forest, Mariposa Ranger District
John Sweetman	Eldorado National Forest, Amador Ranger District
Chuck Loffland	Eldorado National Forest, Amador Ranger District
Don Errington	Eldorado National
Marie Kennedy	Eldorado National Forest
Linda Tatum	Eldorado National Forest
Bob Carroll	Eldorado National Forest

Charis Genter	Eldorado National Forest
Dennis Haas	Eldorado National Forest
Jo Ann Fites	Eldorado National Forest
Erich Fischer	Eldorado National Forest, Placerville Ranger District
Joe Oden	Lake Tahoe Basin
Lori Allessio	Lake Tahoe Basin
Jim Schmidt	Stanislaus National Forest
Andy Aldrich	Stanislaus National Forest, Summit Ranger District
Bart Bloom	Stanislaus National Forest, Summit Ranger District
Dan Leedy	Stanislaus National Forest, Caleveras Ranger District
Larry Ford	Tahoe National Forest, Sierraville Ranger District
Steve Weaver	Tahoe National Forest, Sierraville Ranger District
Mike Newman	Tahoe National Forest, Foresthill Ranger District
Slim Stout	Tahoe National Forest, Foresthill Ranger District
Andy Hosford	Sierra National Forest, Kings River Ranger District
Dick Castaldini	Plumas National Forest
Dennis Clemens	Plumas National Forest, Quincy/Greenville Ranger District
Erik Ostly	Sequoia National Forest
Gary Rotta	Plumas National Forest, Quincy/Greenville Ranger District
Mike Martini	Plumas National Forest, Beckwourth/Mohawk Ranger District
Ron O'Hanlon	Plumas National Forest, Oroville/Laporte Ranger District
Tom,Higley	Inyo National Forest, Mono Lake Ranger District
Richard Perloff	Inyo National Forest, Mammoth Ranger District
Rich Coakley	Lassen National
Lew Jump	Sequoia National Forest
Steve Anderson	Sequoia National Forest
Paul Miller	Sequoia National Forest, Tule River Ranger District
Dan,Marlatt	Bureau of Land Management
Peggy Cranston	Bureau of Land Management
Jim Barry	California State Parks and Recreation, Natural Heritage
Elizabeth Bergstrom	Toiyabe National Forest, Carson Ranger District
Bob Jennings	Toiyabe National Forest, Carson Ranger District
Roland Shaw	Toiyabe National Forest, Carson Ranger District
Gerald Grevstad	Toiyabe National Forest
Tina Mark	Toiyabe National Forest
Dan Duriscoe	Sequoia and Kings Canyon National Parks
Tom Warner	Sequoia and Kings Canyon National Parks
Sylvia Haultain	Sequoia and Kings Canyon National Parks, National Biological Survey
Nate Stephenson	Sequoia and Kings Canyon National Parks, National Biological Survey
Peggy Moore	Yosemite National Park
Jan van Wagtendonk	National Biological Survey, Yosemite Field Station
Wayne,Harrison	Califonia State Parks and Recreation
Jerry Westfall	Tahoe National Forest
Lisa Acree	Yosemite National Park
Steve Underwood	Tahoe National Forest

Staff and Science Team Support:
Jo Ann Fites, Mary Cunha, Doug Leisz, Dave Graber, Norm Johnson, Debbie Elliott-Fisk, John Sessions, Karen Gabriel, Karen Beardsley, Joan Brenchley Jackson, John Gabriel, Russ Jones, Kay Gibbs, Minghua Zhang, Steve Greco, Chris Riper, Dana Murphy, Erin Fleming

The workshop was a step in the Late Successional/Old Growth assessment by Jerry Franklin.

Genetic Workshop Participants and Report Reviewers
Fall, 1994
Institute of Forest Genetics, Placerville

Workshop Participants

Diane Elam, Natural Heritage Division
Deborah L. Elliott-Fisk, Natural Reserve System, University of California
Gary M. Fellers, National Biological Service
George Ferrell, USDA Forest Service, Silvicultural Laboratory
Matteo Garbelotto, Department of Envionmental Science, Policy and Management
Graham A.E. Gall, Department of Animal Science
Jay H. Kitzmiller, USDA Forest Service, Chico Genetic Resource Center
Eric E. Knapp, Department of Agronomy and Range Science
Bohun B. Kinloch, Institute of Forest Genetics, USDA Forest Service
F. Thomas Ledig, Institute of Forest Genetics, USDA Forest Service
William Z. Lidicker, Museum of Vertebrate Zoology, University of California, Berkeley
Marjorie Matocq, Department of Biology, University of California, Los Angeles
Constance I. Millar, Institute of Forest Genetics, USDA Forest Service
Chris Nice, Section of Evolution and Ecology, University of California, Davis
James L. Patton, Museum of Vertebrate Zoology, University of California, Berkeley
Calvin O. Qualset, Genetic Resources Conservation Program
Kevin Rice, Department of Agronomy and Range Science, University of California, Davis
Larry Riggs, Biosphere Genetics, Inc.
Deborah L. Rogers, Institute of Forest Genetics, USDA Forest Service
H. Bradley Shaffer, Section of Evolution and Ecology, University of California, Davis
Arthur M. Shapiro, Section of Evolution and Ecology, University of California, Davis
Thomas B. Smith, Department of Biology, San Francisco State University
David B. Wake, Museum of Vertebrate Zoology, University of California, Berkeley
Robert D. Westfall, Institute of Forest Genetics, USDA Forest Service
Randy Zebell, Department of Biology, San Francisco State University

Report Reviews

Don Bluth, Department of Biology, University of California, Los Angeles
David Bradford, U.S. Environmental Protection Agency
Diane Elam, Natural Heritage Division
Norm Ellstrand, Department of Botany and Plant Sciences, University of California, Riverside
Gary Fellers, National Biological Service, U.S.D.I, Pt. Reyes National Seashore
John Helms, Department of ESPM, University of California, Berkeley
Ned Johnson, Museum of Vertebrate Zoology, University of California, Berkeley
Eric Knapp, Department of Agronomy and Range, University of California, Davis
Bohun Kinloch, Institute of Forest Genetics, USDA Forest Service, PSW Research Station
Bill Lasley, Institute of Toxicology and Environmental Health, University of California, Davis
Bill Libby
Jennifer Neilsen, Hopkins Marine Station, Stanford University
James Patton, Museum of Vertebrate Zoology, University of California, Berkeley
Kevin Rice, Department of Agronomy and Range Science, University of California, Davis
Arthur M. Shapiro, Section of Evolution and Ecology, University of California, Davis
David Wake, Museum of Vertebrate Zoology, University of California, Berkeley
Philip Ward, Entomology Department, University of California, Davis
John Hopkins, Range Watch

"History of Sierra Nevada Ecosystems"
Fall, 1994
Institute of Forest Genetics, Placerville

Workshop Planners and Staff

Deborah Elliot Fisk, Natural Reserve System
Connie Millar, Pacific Southwest Research Station, USDA Forest Service
Wally Woolfenden, Inyo National Forest, Mono Lake Ranger District
Deborah Rogers, Pacific Southwest Research Station, USDA Forest Service
Erin Fleming, SNEP Center
Molly Pohl, Dept. of Geography, Arizona State University

Workshop Participants

David Adam, U.S. Geological Survey, Branch of Paleontology and Stratigraphy
Scott Anderson, Environmental Sciences Project
Andy Bach, Department of Geography, Arizona State University
Patrick Bartlein, Department of Geography, University of Oregon
Bob Bettinger, Department of Anthropology, University of California, Davis
Bud Burke, Geology Department, Humbolt State University
Roger Byrne, Geography Department, University of California, Berkeley
Dan, Cayan, Climate Research Division, Scripps Institution of Oceanography
Malcolm Clark, U.S. Geological Survey
Doug Clark, Department of Geological Sciences, University of Washington
Ken Cole, National Biological Survey, Department of Forest Resources, University of Minnesota
Owen Davis, Department of Geosciences, University of Arizona
Alan, Gillespie, Department of GeologicalSciences, University of Washington
Lisa Graumlich, Institute for the Study of Planet Earth, University of Arizona
Malcolm Hughes, Tree Ring Laboratory, University of Arizona
Tom Jackson, Pacific Legacy
Steven Jennings, Department of Geography, Texas A&M University
Susan Lindstrom
Michael Moratto, INFOTEC
George I. Smith, U.S. Geological Survey
Nate Stephenson, Sequoia-Kings Canyon National Parks, National Biological Survey
Scott Stine, California State University, Hayward
Tom Swetnam, Laboratory of Tree Ring Research, University of Arizona
Jim West, Bureau of Reclamation
Peter Wigand, Desert Research Institute, University of Nevada

SNEP Participants (Science Team and Affiliates)

Don Erman, SNEP Team Leader and Director, Centers for Water and Wildlands Resources, UC Davis
Mike Diggles, US Geological Survey, Western Mineral Resources
Don Fullmer, USDA Forest Service, Sequoia Natinal Forest
Dave Graber, National Biological Survey, Sequoia and Kings Canyon National Parks
Rick Kattelmann, Sierra Nevada Aquatic Research Laboratory, University of California
Bill Kinney
David Parsons, Aldo Leopold Wilderness Research Institute
Carl Skinner, Pacific Southwest Research Station, USDA Forest Service
Rowan Rowntree, Pacific Southwest Research Station, USDA Forest Service
Joy Schaber, SNEP Center, University of California, Davis
Phil Weatherspoon, Pacific Southwest Research Station, USDA Forest Service
Bob Westfall, Pacific Southwest Research Station, USDA Forest Service

Reconstructing an 1800's Sierran Landscape
December 10 and 11, 1994
Sewell Hall, Room S 110, Sierra College

Saturday, December 10, 1994

8:00 • Introductions
      • Logistics
      • Objectives of this Workshop Within the SNEP Context

8:30 First Session:
      • *Human Populations and Impacts, 1750–1840 (Stine)*

10:00 Break

10:15 First Session Continued

11:30 Lunch

12:30 Second Session:
       • *Climate, Vegetation, and Hydrology, 1750–1840 (Anderson/Morotto)*

1:45 Break

2:00 Second Session Continued

3:30 Break
4:00 Third Session
      • *Spatial Patterns of Sierran Landscape Change, 1826–1900 (Beesley)*

5:15 Break

5:30 Third Session Continued

Sunday, December 11, 1994

8:00 Review and Consolidation

9:30 Research Priorities

10:00 Break

10:15 Discuss process of writing summary of plans and deadlines.

11:30 Lunch and Workshop Conclusion (Conclusion of Workshop expected at 2:00 pm)

Reconstructing an 1800's Sierran Landscape
December 10 and 11, 1994
Sewell Hall, Room S 110, Sierra College

Attendance List:

* Barbara Balen, USDA Forest Service, Stanislaus National, Sonora, CA
* Bern Kreissman, 926 Plum Lane, Davis, CA
* Bill   Laudenslayer, Forestry Sciences Lab, Fresno, CA
* Bill Tweed, Sequoia and Kings Canyon National Parks, Three Rivers, CA
* Bob Rogers, US Forest Service, Porterville, CA
* Bruce Perieni, Sacramento, CA
* C. Kristina Roper, INFOTEC, Fresno
* Carl Skinner, Pacific Southwest Research Station, Redding, CA
* Carmel Barry-Meisenbach, Tahoe National Forest, Nevada City, CA
* Chiru Chang, School of Environment, Duke University
* Chris Baisan, Laboratory of Tree-Ring Research, University of Arizona, Tucson, AZ
* Dan Cayan, Climate Research Division, Scripps Institute of Oceanography, La Jolla, CA
* David Beesley, Sierra College, Rocklin, CA
* David Comstock, Grass Valley, CA
* Denise McLemore, USDA Forest Service, Eldorado National Forest, Placerville, CA
* Doug Miller, State Lands Commission, Sacramento, CA
* Edwyn Tyson, Nevada City, CA
* Frances Williams, Sacramento, CA
* Fred Velasquez, Valley Springs, CA
* Gail, Firebaugh, Stanislaus National Forest, Sonora, CA
* George, Gruell, Carson City, NV
* Hank Meals, Tahoe National Forest, Downieville Ranger District, Camptonville, CA
* Harold Basey, Groveland, CA
* Jan van Wagtendonk, National Biological Survey, Yosemite Field Station, El Portal, CA
* Jane LaBoa , Auburn, CA
* Jeff Mount, Department of Geology, University of California, Davis, CA
* Jerry Miller, Quaternary Sciences Center, Desert Research Institute, Reno, NV
* Jim Barry, CA State Parks and Recreation, Sacramento, CA
* Jim Johnston, Lassen National Forest, Susanville, CA
* Jim West, Bureau of Reclamation, Sacramento, CA
* Joe Medeiros, Department of Biological Sciences, Sierra CollegeRocklin, CA
* John Holson, Pacific Legacy Co., Albany, CA
* Kat Anderson, University of Kansas, St. Lawrence, KS
* Kevin McKelvey, Redwood Sciences Lab, Arcata, CA
* Liana Smith, Nevada City, CA
* Linda Lux, USDA Forest Service, San Francisco, CA
* Michael Moratto, INFOTEC Research Inc.,Fresno, CA
* Michelle Stevens, Davis, CA
* Norm Wilson, Auburn, CA
* Owen Davis, Department of Geosciences, University of Arizona, Tucson, AZ
* Richard Garcia, Redding, CA
* Richard Minnich, Earth Sciences Department, University of California, Riverside, CA
* Robert, Jackson, Woodland, CA
* Roger Poff, Nevada City, CA
* Ron Goode, Clovis, CA
* Ross Trotter, Camptonville, CA
* Scott Kruse, Fresno, CA
* Scott Stephens, University of California, Berkeley, CA

* Scott Stine, California State University, Hayward, CA
* Susan Lindstrom, Trukee, CA
*Dana Supernowicz, Eldorado National Forest, Placerville, CA

List of Invited Guests and Contributors

Bob Cermack, Oroville, CA
Craig Bates, Yosemite National Park, CA
David Perry
David Dulitz, Mountain Home State Forest, Springville, CA
Dennis Martinez, Eagle Point, OR
Dick Markley, USDA Forest Service, Nevada City, CA
Douglas Strong, San Diego
Frank Fisher CA Dept Fish and Game, Redbluff, CA
Fred Wagner, Utah State University, College of Natural Resources, Logan, UT
Glenn Ferris, Davis, CA
Hector Franco, Visalia, CA
Helen McCarthy, Davis, CA
Jared Verner, Forestry Sciences Lab, Fresno, CA
Jay Johnson, Yosemite, CA
Jim Parsons, University of California, Berkeley, CA
John Foster, California State Parks and Recreation, Sacramento, CA
Kent Lightfoot, Anthropology Department, University of California, Berkeley, CA
Kevin Starr, State Library, Sacramento, CA
Lary Dilsaver, Department of Geography, University of South Alabama, Mobile, AL
Laurie Planis, Fresno, CA
Linda Reynolds
Lynn Hunziker, ESPM, University of California, Berkeley, CA
Marty Rose, Desert Research Inst., Reno, NV
Michael Claytor, Department of Anthropology, Sierra College, Rocklin, CA
Michael Singer, LAWR, University of California, Davis, CA
Michael Smith, Oakland, CA
Nate Stephenson, Sequoia and Kings Canyon National Parks, Three Rivers, CA
Paul Starrs, University of Nevada, Reno, NV
Peter Lindert, Agricultural History, University of California, Davis, CA
Phil McDonald, Redding Silvicultural Lab, Pacific Southwest Research , Redding, CA
Philip Wilkie, Anthropology Department, University of California, Riverside, CA
Rick Fielitz, Sacramento, CA
Roger Byrne, Department of Geography, University of California, Berkeley, CA
Scott Anderson, Center for Environmental Science and Ed., Northern Arizona University
Tom Jackson, Pacific Legacy, Aptos, CA
Tom Swetnam, Lab of Tree Ring Research, University of Arizona, Tucson, AZ
Tom Vale, Dept of Geography, University of Wisconsin, Madison, WI
Wally Woolfenden, USDA Forest Service, Inyo National Forest, Lee Vining, CA

Insects & Pathogens And Their Influence On Sierra Nevada Forests
January 19-20, 1994
3201 Hart Hall, U.C. Davis

Sierra Nevada Ecosystem Project Objectives:

1. Assess existing condition of Sierra Nevada ecosystems.
2. Describe historical (paleo- and recent) conditions of Sierra Nevada ecosystems.
3. Assess status and trends of Sierra Nevada ecosystems under current management.
4. Develop options for sustainable management of Sierra Nevada ecosystems.
5. Evaluate implications for ecological conditions under each option.

Insects and Pathogens Workshop Objectives:

1) Summarize available information on the historic, current, and predicted impacts of insects and pathogens on forest structure and function by forest type. Where possible, impact assessments will be made beyond the forest system into other vegetation types.

2) Develop conceptual models which relate drought, fire, air pollution, and stand composition and structure to insect and pathogen impacts. Where sufficient data exists, quantitative linkages will be made to the policy analysis modeling effort.

3) Identify and prioritize essential research needs for the next decade.

4) Predict future impacts of insects and pathogens under various management scenarios.

Invitation list for SNEP Insect and Pathogens Workshop Jan 19th and 20th

Fields Cobb, Don Dahlsten, John Dale, Don Fullmer, Gregg DeNitto, George Ferrell, Connie Gill, Jane LaBoa, Bro Kinloch, John Kliejunas, Phil McDonald, Don Owen, Bill Otrosina, Dick Parmeter, John Pronos, Bruce Roettgering, Dave Schultz, Bob Scharpf, Pat Shea, Carl Skinner, Dick Smith, Mark Smith, Sheri Smith, Phil Weatherspoon, John Wenz, Dave Wood, Mike Yost

And SNEP Science Team Members, Special Consultants, and Associates

Insects & Pathogens And Their Influence On Sierra Nevada Forests
January 19-20, 1994

THURSDAY JANUARY 19, 1994

9:30   Coffee/Participant Arrival

10:00   Introduction to Workshop
        Welcome (George/Joan), Logistics (Joan)
        Role facilitator (Connie)
        Introduction of participants (Connie)
                Name, affiliation, expertise
        Background on SNEP (Joan)
        Goals/Scope of Workshop (George)
        Role of participants in assessment (George)

10:30   **Identify Key Insects and Pathogens and Develop Conceptual
        Models to Describe Effects on Sierra Nevada Forests**
        - What linkages are there with other environmental factors such as droughts, fire,
          logging, air pollution, etc.?
        - What are the resulting temporal and spatial patterns?
        - What are the effects on vegetative composition and structure?
        - What effective mitigation treatments are available?
        - What are the major information gaps? Are there problems with data quality?
        - What are important research needs?

12:00   LUNCH

1:00   Develop Conceptual Models (cont'd)+

3:00   **Assess Risk of Invasion by Exotic Insects and Pathogens**
        - What are the important factors affecting risk?
        - Increased trade with Mexico, Chile, Canada (NAFTA), or Siberia, New Zealand
          (GATTI)?
        - Asian Gypsy Moth, European Pine Shoot Moth?
        - Increased migration from coastal cities to Sierra Nevada foothills?
        - Pitch Canker?
        - What mitigation treatments are available?
        - What are the major information gaps, research needs?

5:00   Adjourn

FRIDAY JANUARY 20

9:00   Coffee/Participant Arrival

9:30   **Attempt to Predict Future Under Various Management
        Scenarios**
        - What will be trends in ecosystem effects if present practices, influences, continue?
        - What will be trends under "best practices" mitigation?
        - What will be trends if widespread treatments to reduce fire hazard (prescribed burning,
          understory thinning) are applied?

12:00   Lunch

1:00   Continue discussions if necessary or adjourn

Mediated Settlement Agreement/Giant Sequoia Workshop
February 3, 1995
Porterville, CA

Mike Ahrens	California Association of 4-Wheel Drive Clubs
Jane Baxter	Range Watch
Carla Cloer	Sierra Club
Jim Craine	California Forestry Association
Jim Crates	Retired United States Forest Service
Glen Duysen	Sierra Forest Products
Larry Duysen	Sierra Forest Products
Kent Duysen	Sierra Forest Products
Patrick Emmert	Sequoia Forest Industries
Joe Fontaine	Sierra Club
Bob Jasperson	Save-the-Redwoods League
Jeff Lilley	Hume Lake Christian Camps
Bret Matzke	California Trout
Leonard Manuel (JR)	Tule River Indian Reservation
Frank Price	
John Rasmussen	Sierra Club
Brian Rueger	Forester for Tule River Indian Reservation
Ron Schiller	High Desert Multiple Use Coalition
Dan	Tule River Conservancy
Ray West	Tule River Conservancy
Dwight Willard	
Steve Worthley	Sequoia Forest Industries
Jip Woudstra	Tule River Indian Reservation
Judith Ewing	Montecito-Sequoia Lodge

Sequoia National Forest:
Julie Allen
Mary Bradley
Mary Chislock-Bethke
Don Fullmer
Sandra Key
Bob Rogers
Bruce Waldron

SNEP:
Debbie Elliott-Fisk
Rick Kattelmann
Nate Stephenson
John Aubert
Dana Murphy
Joy Schaber
Scott Stephens

Mediated Settlement Agreement/Giant Sequoia
Public Workshop
February 4, 1995
Porterville, CA

Gary Rogers	Dinuba, CA
Claude Rouch	Springville, CA
Burl Wood	Lindsay, CA
Jim Crates	Porterville, CA
David Dulitz	Springville, CA
Larry Otter	Springville, CA
Dick Phillips	Springville, CA
Gary Hohnstein	Bakersfield, CA
Kathleen &	Terra Bella, CA
Larry Duysen	
Mike Ahrens	Hemet, CA
Janet Fanning	Three Rivers, CA
Malinee Crapsey	Three Rivers, CA
Annie Esperanza	Three Rivers, CA
Barbara Brydolf	Camp Nelson, CA
Byron Miksch	Three Rivers, CA
Larry Bancroft	Three Rivers, CA
Ruth Dyer	Lafayette, CA
Rick Elstow	
Bill Anderson	Porterville, CA
Skip Primo	Camp Nelson, CA
Dave Johnston	Kingsburg, CA
Dave Pengilly	Porterville, CA
Jeff Gletne	Terra Bella, CA
Gay &	
Jim VerSteeg	Porterville, CA
Jose Medina	Springville, CA
Jim Warner	Kings Canyon NP, CA
Jim Maples	Tulare Co. 5th Dist. Supervisor
Ed Wristen	Visalia, CA
Lindell Yostimura	Visalia, CA
Charles Morgan	Springville, CA
Kent Duysen	Porterville, CA
Glen Duysen	Porterville, CA
Lloyd	California Hot Springs, CA
James Burger	Porterville Recorder
Gerald Davis	Bakersfield, CA
Bob Styles	Porterville, CA
Doug Hanson	Porterville, CA
Linda & Dan Utt	Camp Nelson, CA
Phil Sexton	Foresthill, CA
Loren Ross	Lake Isabella, CA
Gary Aoest	Camp Nelson, CA

SNEP Workshop with
Coalition for Unified Recreation in the Eastern Sierra
and the Eastern Public
February 8 and 9, 1995
Bishop, California

February 8, 1995
Pre-workshop session to discuss/display SNEP GIS data
(The focus of this session is on SNEP's geographic database and few SNEP sceintists will be in attendance.)

6:30-6:45   Brief introduction to SNEP

6:45-9:00   SNEP data display and general discussion

February 9, 1995

10:00-10:30   Introduction to SNEP and the workshop
                Jonathan Kusel and others

10-30-11:00   Recreation and Development
                Tim Duane

11:00-11:30   Community Well-being
                Jonathan Kusel and Sam Doak

11:30-12:00   Riparian Areas
                Rick Kattleman

12:00-12:45   Lunch

12:45-1:15   Rangeland Assessment
                John Menke

1:15-1:45   Mammoth-June/Significant Areas
                Connie Millar

1:45-2:00   Break

2:00-4:00   Open discussion between SNEP scientists and workshop participants

4:00-4:15   Closing comments

4:15-4:30   Workshop evaluations

Sierra Nevada Ecosystem Project
Public Meeting With Steering Committee And Science Team
Freeborn Hall, U.C. Davis
February 21, 1995

8:00 - 8:15
I. AGENDA, GOALS, AND INTRODUCTIONS - Jim Space, Chair, SNEP
    Steering Committee.

II. REPORTS TO THE PUBLIC - Moderated by Don Erman, SNEP ScienceTeam Leader.

8:15   A. Jerry Franklin - Late successional/old growth forests update.

8:40   B. John Sessions - Vegetation modeling of the Sierra Nevada.

PANEL SESSION I.

9:05   C. John Menke - Grazing and rangeland assessments.

9:25   D. Rick Kattelmann - Water resources, riparian and watershed
            conditions.

9:45   E. Peter Moyle - Status and trends of fish, amphibians, and
            aquatic habitats.

10:05   DISCUSSION on topics by Menke, Kattelmann, Moyle.

10:25   BREAK

PANEL SESSION II.

10:45   F. Dave Graber - Wildlife habitat relationships.

11:05   G. Bill Stewart - Economic assessments.

11:25   H. Norm Johnson - Policy scenarios.

11:45   DISCUSSION on topics by Graber, Stewart, Johnson.

12:05   LUNCH

1:30   ROUND ROBIN TABLE DISCUSSIONS

4:00   RECONVENE FOR DISCUSSION AND FEEDBACK SESSION

4:45   ADJOURN

SNEP Human Settlements Workshop
April 6, 1995
Institute for Forest Genetics, Placerville

The workshop was called by the Coordinating Committee in order to promote better integration of human settlement issues into all SNEP assessments and the policy analysis efforts. Tim Duane chaired the meeting and it was attended by the following guests:

Stafford Lehr	California Department of Fish and Game
Daniel Hinz	California Department of Fish and Game
Bob Mapes	California Department of Fish and Game
Jim Smith	California Department of Forestry and Fire Protection
Greg Greenwood	California Department of Forestry and Fire Protection

SNEP Science Team and Special Consultant and Associate attendees included:

Tim Duane
Dave Graber
Mike Oliver
Larry Costick
Scott Martens
Don Erman
John Sessions
Doug Leisz
Rowan Rowntree
Joan Brenchley-Jackson
Joe McBride
Jonathan Kusel
Sam Doak.

SNEP Workshop
with the Quincy Library Group
and the Northern Sierra Public
April 11, 1995
Quincy Library

April 11, 1995

10:00 a.m.- 4:30 p.m., GIS demonstration/discussion of SNEP data layers 4:30-6:00 p.m., at the Quincy Library

10:00--10:15	Introduction to SNEP, workshop format, questions	Jonathan Kusel
10:15--10:35	LS/OG	Jerry Franklin & Jo Ann Fites
10:35--10:55	Fire	Joan Brenchley-Jackson, Jan van Wagtendonk & Berni Bahro
10:55--11:10	Modeling	John Sessions
11:10--11:50	Questions & Discussion: interplay of models and LS/OG polygons, etc.	Jerry Franklin, Joan Brenchley-Jackson, Jan van Wagtendonk, John Sessions & Berni Bahro
11:50--1:00	LUNCH	
1:00--1:20	Riparian Areas	Rick Kattelmann
1:20--1:40	Rangeland	John Menke
1:40--2:00	Questions & Discussions: interplay between riparian and range issues	Rick Kattelmann & John Menke
2:00--2:10	Break	
2:10--2:30	Introduction to Policy Scenarios	Norm Johnson & Bill Stewart
2:30--4:15	Open Discussion: development of policy scenarios and associated interdisciplinary dynamics	All SNEP members and participants
4:15	End main workshop	Jonathan Kusel
4:15--4:30	Break	
4:30--6:00	GIS data workshop	Sam Doak, Jonathan Kusel, Jerry Franklin, Jo Ann Fites & others

SNEP Fuels Strategies Workshop
March 16-17, 1995.
Cabernet Room, Silo Building, UC Davis

THURSDAY MARCH 16, 1995

8:30   Participant Arrival/Coffee

9:00   Introduction to Workshop
        Welcome (Phil Weatherspoon, Joan Brenchley-Jackson)
        Logistics (Joan Brenchley-Jackson)
        Introduction of Participants--name, affiliation, expertise (all)
        Background on SNEP (Joan Brenchley-Jackson)
        Workshop Objectives and Approach (Phil Weatherspoon)

9:30   Presentations (representing a cross-section of perspecti es and experiences related to
        fuels managemant strategies and decisionmaking; each time slot will allow 5
        minutes for Q&As--time for more extensive discussion will be available following
        all the presentations)

11:55   Lunch

1:00   Presentations--continued
        1300   JoAnn Fites, USFS/University of Washington
        1320   Ray Hermit/JaneLaBoa, USFS/CASPO EIS Team
        1405   John Sessions, Oregon State University

2:25   General Discussion
        Focus will be on followup from presentations, sharingof additional relevant
        activities, and workshop objectives 1 and 2.

5:00   Adjourn

FRIDAY MARCH 17

8:00   Continue Discussion
        Incorporate all workshop objectives, as the group considers appropriate, with a
        focus on accomplishing objective 5.

12:00   Lunch

1:00   Continue Discussion

2:40   Wrapup
        Assessment of workshop; discussion of followup, next steps (if any)

3:00   Adjourn (or earlier if group agrees)

SNEP Fuels Strategies Workshop
March 16-17, 1995.
Cabernet Room, Silo Building, UC Davis

Participant list:

Steve Arney	Tahoe National Forest
Bernie Bahro	Eldorado National Forest
Gary Biehl,	Stanislaus National Forest
Joan Brenchley-Jackson	University of California at Davis, SNEP
Jim Carter	VMP/California Department of Forestry
Ken Castro	Lassen Volcanic National Park
Gary Cones	Stanislaus National Forest
Norm Cook	California Department of Forestry
Gary Fildes	Tahoe National Forest
JoAnn Fites	US Forest Service/University of Washington
Don Fullmer	Sequoia National Forest
Aaron Gelobter	Sequoia National Forest
Connie Gill	PSW Research Station
Greg Greenwood	California Department of Forestry
Ray Hermit	CASPO EIS Team, US Forest Service
Jerry Hurley	Plumas National Forest
Sue Husari	Region 5, US Forest Service
Russ Jones	SNEP
Jane LaBoa	CASPO EIS Team, US Forest Service
Mike Landram	R-5, US Forest Service
Louise Larson	Sierra National Forest
Jeff Manly	Sequoia-Kings Canyon National Park
Kevin McKelvey	Pacific Southwest Research Station
Ed Murphy	Sierra Pacific Industries
Christie Neill	Eldorado National Forest
Jay Perkins	Klamath National Forest
John Sessions	Oregon State University, SNEP
Carl Skinner	Pacific Southwest Research Station
Scott Stephens	SNEP/Pacific Southwest Research Station
Phil Weatherspoon	Pacific Southwest Research Station
Joe Wood	Plumas National Forest

Community Capacity Workshops
Spring, 1995

Community capacity was assessed for the community aggregations based on local expert knowledge. A series of local workshops were held in 19 different locations across the Sierra. All but one workshop focused on aggregations falling primarily within a single county. This workshop covered aggregations in the Greater Lake Tahoe Basin, which included aggregations in six separate counties.

The number of participants in each workshop ranged from three to 18, depending on the area and the number of aggregations to be addressed. To ensure a diversity of perspectives in workshop discussions, participants were selected from a variety of backgrounds. Included were those individuals who--by nature of their profession, local involvement, or history of residence-- are knowledgeable about the physical, human, and social capital of most of the communities within each workshop's area of focus. Participants included but were not limited to, planners and planning commissioners, community development professionals, current and former county supervisors, education administrators, business people, health and human service providers, and long-term residents with diverse backgrounds and experiences.

To ensure consistency in the information gathered, the following process was used in each workshop.

1. The creation, composition and general charge of SNEP is introduced to the group.
2. The role of the social assessment component within the SNEP process is discussed and the entire social assessment methodology is reviewed, including a brief introduction to the analysis units and the concepts of well-being and community capacity.
3. The process for determining the capacity of community aggregations within the workshop's area of interest is outlined .
4. The community aggregations for the area of interest are reviewed by the group for appropriateness. In some cases, alterations are made to the aggregations.
5. The concept of community capacity is reintroduced and defined in more detail.
6. Participants are asked to indicate the various community aggregations with which they are most knowledgeable and most familiar. Based on the responses, assignments are made to individual participants to ensure that each aggregation is assessed by two different people (though limited expert knowledge and limited number of experts occasionally led to one assessment). Participants are asked to complete a separate community capacity worksheet (see Appendix) for each aggregation including: a narrative assessment of capacity and a rating of capacity on a seven point scale ranging from very low to very high. In assessing capacity, participants are asked to consider the level of physical, human, and social capital in the communities within each aggregation.
7. The individual capacity rankings for each aggregation are summarized and anonymously presented to the group for their review. During a facilitated group discussion, the capacity ratings for each aggregation are discussed; there is further elaboration of issues relating to capacity for each aggregation; and a final capacity ranking is determined by the group for each aggregation.

Information gathered from each workshop includes individual community aggregation narratives and capacity rankings, final group capacity rankings, and notes from the facilitated discussion of all aggregations.

The results of each workshop were reviewed to ensure the capacity rankings and related discussions were consistent with other workshops. If a group did not adequately grasp the concept of capacity or if numerical ratings generated by the experts appeared significantly different from those of other groups, a second panel was convened. Two additional panels were convened for these reasons. In these instances, the narratives of both groups were incorporated into the assessment, but the capacity ratings were selected from the group that appeared to have the best understanding of capacity and that were consistent with ratings employed in other workshops.

In most workshops experts proved reluctant to apply the highest and lowest capacity ratings on the seven point capacity scale, and very few aggregations actually received either a 1 or a 7. To ensure greater consistency in the analysis across the study, the scale was collapsed to a 5 point range with scores of 1 and 2 forming the lowest capacity score and scores of 6 and 7 forming the highest.

Case Study of Capacity Assessments in Plumas County

A case study of community capacity was conducted to examine the congruence of expert capacity assessment with community self-assessments. Study of individual communities also allowed in-depth exploration of local issues. Plumas County was chosen as the case study because of the varying types of forest dependence (e.g., commodity production, service industry associated with recreation and a growing number of retirement communities and other communities in which the forest was important as a backdrop) and because it is the home of the Plumas Children's Network. The Plumas Children's Network, working with a grant from the Sierra Health Foundation, was conducting community assessments to develop strategies to improve the health and well-being of children and families in Plumas County. They agreed to work with the SNEP researchers because of an interest in community capacity assessment. Working with the Plumas Children's Network provided SNEP social assessment researchers access to local networks and individuals who were able to help organize community workshops and ensure higher local participation. In addition, the Plumas Children's Network was able to immediately use SNEP research for their community assessment and to help secure additional funding for a second phase of a grant. As a result, local communities benefited not only by learning about themselves, but from the advancement of the Plumas Children's Network projects.

Involving local residents to assess community capacity required development of a community "self-assessment" workshop, one quite different from the process used for the expert assessment of capacity for the aggregates. Evening workshops, which averaged two hours in length, were conducted in the towns of Chester, Graeagle, Greenville, Portola, Quincy, and Sierra Valley. Workshops followed the format below.

1. Participants are introduced to researchers, to SNEP and to the Plumas Children's Network. This is followed by a brief description of workshop objectives, and a discussion of meeting ground rules. The meeting objectives are to identify key issues that affect local capacity and to numerically rate community capacity on a seven point scale (1-very low, 2-low, 3-medium-low, 4- medium, 5-medium-high, 6-high, 7-very high).
2. SNEP researchers describe the concept of capacity and its application to communities.
3. SNEP researchers discuss issues that define and determine community capacity.
4. Working individually, participants are asked to write the most important items/issues on cards that affect their community's capacity and to numerically rate their community's capacity.
5. Participants are individually asked to identify the three most important issues that determine capacity.
6. Working in small groups, participants share and discuss their lists of most important items/issues with each other and determine the five or six most important to the small group.
7. The five or six most important items/issues from each group are posted in front of the full group.
8. Items/issues are organized into categories.
9. The large group re-examines the list, discusses it, and adds any important items/issues that are missing.
10. In several workshops participants voted on the most important issues and are allotted five votes to distribute among issues they feel are most important;
11. Individually, participants rate the capacity of the community a second time; and a SNEP researcher and the Plumas Children's Network coordinator briefly recap the meeting, review group determinations, and thank participants.

SNEP Policy Assessment Workshop
Garrison Room, Memorial Union UCD
May 17, 1995

Presentations made to the SNEP Science Team

8:00 a.m.   Welcome and Introductions

8:20 a.m.   Presentation - David Beesley, Sierra College

9:00 a.m.   Comments - Linda Lux, U.S. Forest Service

9:15 a.m.   Discussion

9:45 a.m.   Break

10:00 a.m.   Presentation - Paul F. Starrs, University of Nevada, Reno

10:40 a.m.   Comments: Bob Twiss, UC Berkeley
                              David Robertson, UC Davis
                              Gene Rose, journalist (Fresno Bee) and historian

11:25 a.m.   Discussion

Noon   Lunch

12:45 p.m.   Presentation - David J. Larson, CSU Hayward

1:25 p.m.   Discussion

2:00 p.m.   Presentation - Larry Ruth, UC Berkeley

2:40 p.m.   Comments - Mark Nechodom, UC Davis

2:55 p.m.   Discussion

3:30 p.m.   Break

3:45 p.m.   Review and synthesis - Jeff Romm, UC Berkeley

4:15 p.m.   Discussion

5:00 p.m.   Adjourn

This workshop focused on policy assessment and used David Beesley's SNEP-commissioned work on environmental history as a point of departure. Thereafter, the focus was on three policy studies commissioned by SNEP, in each of which the author had been asked to address this question: "Which public policies have been most significant in shaping the ecosystems of the Sierra Nevada as they exist today?"

Cumulative Watershed Effects Workshops

June 1995
Pacific Southwest Research Station, Albany

    Participants:

    John Sessions
    Larry Costick
    Brude McGurk
    Neil Berg
    John Chatoian.

June 27, 1995
UC Davis

    Participants:

    Larry Costick
    Bruce McGurk
    Neil Berg
    John Chatoian
    Christine Christiansen
    Terry Henry
    Jerry DeGraff
    Mike Lowry

Fall 1994, Winter 1995 and Fall 1995
UC Davis

    Participants:

    California Rivers Assessment Team at UC Davis

Sierra Nevada Ecosystem Project (SNEP)

Institutions/Organizations Workshop

July 24, 1995
9:00 am to 3:30 pm

Garrison Room, Memorial Union
University of California, Davis

Objectives:

1. Articulate institutional challenges confronting organizations that will bear the responsibility to address and implement SNEP findings and recommendations.

2. Discuss how an understanding of the institutional/organizational challenges can be used to organize the SNEP Report and to inform the development of findings and recommendations.

3. Develop guidelines for consideration of institutional/organizational requirements by SNEP.

Problem Statement:

Science-based assessments of environmental and/or natural resource systems have a tendency to be silent on the organizational means required to address the problems they identify. This occurs because of the convenient myths we all hold that separate the natural and social sciences, thought from action, and "establishment" from "vernacular" views of nature. These distinctions may help in the process of discovery, but they are problematic if social organization is required to implement environmental or economic policies. Recent examples of the downside of not adequately addressing organizational issues are the Forest Ecosystem Management Assessment Team (FEMAT) effort and the attempt to institutionalize a national biological survey/service.

SNEP has an opportunity to face up to the practice requirements of the recommendations or insights it will preach. By focusing on certain organizational, capital, and cultural realities now, SNEP can improve the likelihood that assessment findings and policy options will be heard and that individuals, agencies and legislative bodies will be motivated to act.

Rich examples of new approaches to understanding organizational dynamics are evident in the organizational theory, public administration, and business literature and in the experience of many policy practitioners. This workshop will try to contribute to SNEP learning largely by providing a forum for practitioners to speak and respond to questions, and by allowing all the participants to contribute to the development of guidelines.

Sierra Nevada Ecosystem Project (SNEP)
Institutions/Organizations Workshop
July 24, 1995 -- 9:00 am to 3:30 pm

Garrison Room, Memorial Union
University of California, Davis

Agenda:

9:00 to 9:15 am
Introductions and Statement of Purpose
Bob Ewing
SNEP Special Consultant

9:15 to 10:45 am
Variations in the Response of Agencies to "Outside" Advice
Bob Wolf
Congressional Research Service (retired)

Paul Sabatier
University of California, Davis

Roger Clark *(invited)*
Pacific Northwest Forest and Range Experiment Station

10:45 to 11:00 am
Break

11:00 am to 12:00 noon
The Art and Requirements of Agency Leadership

Michael Mantell
Resources Agency of California

Ed Hastey *(invited)*
Bureau of Land Management

Noon
Lunch Provided

1:00 to 2:00 p.m.
Cultural and Capital Resources for Commitment and Change
Margaret Shannon
Maxwell School, Syracuse University

Bill Stewart
Pacific Institute

2:00 to 2:30 pm
Open Discussion and Break

2:30 to 3:30 pm
Facilitated Session to Develop Guidelines for Consideration of Institutional and Organizational Requirements

Mark Nechodom
University of California Extension

3:30 p.m.
Close
Bob Ewing

Participants:

Mike Diggles, Sam Doak, Hap Dunning, Bob Ewing, Greg Greenwood, Russ Henly, Rick Kattelmann, Jonathan Kusel, Dennis Machida, Mike Oliver, Rowan Rowntree, Larry Ruth, Margaret Shannon, Jim Shevock, Vicki Sturtevant, Bob Wolf

SIERRA NEVADA ECOSYSTEM PROJECT
Science Team Workshop with Key Contacts
June 22, 1995
Cabernet Room, UC Davis

1:00 • Welcome, Explanation of the Purpose and Agenda for the Session, and Participant Introduction
(Jim Space and Don Erman)

• SNEP Update: State of Assessments and Public Involvement Activities
(Don Erman)

• Explanation of SNEP Development of Policy Scenarios and Modeling Framework
(Norm Johnson and John Sessions)

• Review of Public Comment on Scenario Development
(Norm Johnson and John Sessions)

• Questions of Clarification

1:45 Small Group Discussions
(Key Contacts with Science Team)

• What general concerns and suggestions do the key contacts have regarding the development of policy scenarios?

• What elements or components should be included in policy scenarios?

3:30 Return to Whole Group

3:40 Reports from Small Groups

4:05 Next Steps for the Policy Scenario Development Process and Future SNEP Public Involvement Activities
(Don Erman)

4:15 Post-SNEP Activities
(Don Erman)

4:30 Adjourn

SNEP Fire Modeling Workshop
July 25, 1995
2124 Wickson Hall
University of California, Davis

Objectives:

1. To gain a complete understanding of the methodology, assumptions and results of all SNEP fire modeling efforts. Are results consistent? Why or why not? What are we overlooking?

2. To begin the development of the "big picture" implications of fire modeling results for the Sierra Nevada, and to discuss how model results impact SNEP scenario development of policy decisions in general.

Directions for Speakers:

Please plan your presentation for twenty minutes based on the following outline. Answers to key Questions should form the body of your presentation. A slide projector and overhead will be availible.

- Briefly describe your project - how does it contribute to our overall SNEP objectives?
- What are the key assumptions? What is the spatial and temporal scale?
- What data are you using and what are their limitations?
- KEY QUESTION: How does your project results impact SNEP scenario developement?
- KEY QUESTION: How does your project link to other projects in SNEP? How will these links be made?
- What procedures are necessary to validate and confirm the rigor of your modeling effort?

What still needs to be done withing the SNEP time frame? What are the future, post-SNEP applications of the model?

Directions for Invited Guests:

As the agenda depicts, we would like to provide an opportunity for outside experts to briefly and informally respond to the material being presented. What concerns do you have? How can we improve our effort in the short time remaining? Where are gaps and overlaps? These comments are simply impromptu statements that will help to focus our discussions.

Participants:

Joan Brenchley-Jackson, Kevin McKelvey, Greg Greenwood, Sue Husari, Neil Sugahara, Dave Sapsis, Russ Jones, Jan van Wagtendonk, David Weise, Scott Stephens, Rick Kattelmann, Jim Shevock, Jo Ann Fites, Ray Hermit, John MacMillian, Bernie Barho, Tom Nichols, John Sessions, Martin Ritchie, Phil Weatherspoon, Connie Gill, Carol Miller

SNEP Fire Modeling Workshop
July 25, 1995

8:00   Coffee, Teas

8:30   Welcome, Introductions - Joan Brenchley-Jackson,
            Statement of Purpose and meeting logistics - Kevin McKelvey

8:50   Presentation: A statistical evaluation of 20th century fire patterns on forest
            service lands in the Sierra Nevada - Kevin McKelvey

9:10   Brief Discussion

9:20   Presentation: Estimation of Fire Risk and Fire Hazard - Greg Greenwood

9:40   Brief Discussion

9:50   Presentation; Use of a deterministic fire growth model to test fuel
            treatments - Jan van Wagtendonk

10:10   Brief Discussion

10:30   Response: David Weise
            Overview Discussion

11:10   Presentation: Giant Sequoia Fire Modeling - Scott Stephens

11:30   Brief Discussion

12:10   Lunch

1:00   Presentation: Camp Creek Fire Modeling Case Study - Bernie Barho

1:20   Brief Discussion

1:30   Response; Tom Nichols
            Overview Discussion

2:10   Break

2:20   Presentation: The Fire Subroutine of the SNEP Scenario Analysis Model -
            John Sessions

2:30   Response: Martin Ritchie
            Overview Discussion

3:00   Presentation: QELIG - Current status, capabilities and prospectus - Carol
            Miller

3:20   Summary Discussion:
            What issues and concerns have emerged from this workshop? comments
            from invited guests and participants.

4:00   Close - Kevin McKelvey

Key Contacts Work Group Meeting
July 25, 1995
2140 Hart Hall, UC Davis

Purpose

Begin planning the September SNEP Public Meeting
- Clarify Outcomes
- Develop Agenda
- Discuss Logistics

Agenda

1:00 Welcome, Introductions
Purpose, Agenda Review

1:15 Updates
- Assessments
- Scenarios
- SNEP Report

1:30 Outcomes/Purpose of September Meeting

1:45 Agenda Components

2:30 Structure & Activities

3:30 Logistics
- Publicity
- Materials
- Other Advice

3:55 Summary
Evaluation

4:00 Adjourn

SNEP Public Meeting
September 26, 1995
The Grand
1215 J Street
Sacramento

Participants:

Andrea Lawrence
Nancy Rosasco
Jeanne Adams
Rebecca Bendick
Susan Carpenter
Jonathan Kusel

Laurel Ames
Joan Reiss
Rose Comstock
Sam Doak
Vicki Sturtevant
Erin Fleming